HANDBOOK OF SEXOLOGY

This book is dedicated to the millions who still suffer from sexual prejudices and to our parents, Frank Money, Ruth Mary (Read) Money, Max Musaph and Marianne (Sanders) Musaph, who taught us to love.

Excerpta Medica ISBN: 90 2192104 9

PUBLISHED BY:

Elsevier/North-Holland Biomedical Press,
335 Jan van Galenstraat, P.O. Box 211,
Amsterdam, The Netherlands

SOLE DISTRIBUTORS FOR THE U.S.A. AND CANADA:

Elsevier/North-Holland Inc.,
52 Vanderbilt Avenue,
New York, N.Y. 10017

Library of Congress Cataloging in Publication Data

Main entry under title:

Handbook of sexology.

Includes bibliographies and index.
1. Sex (Biology) 2. Sex (psychology)
3. Sex. I. Money, John. II. Musaph, Herman.
III. Title: Sexology.
QP251.H24 616.6 76-42449
ISBN 90-219-2104-9

Printed in Great Britain

HANDBOOK OF SEXOLOGY

Edited by

JOHN MONEY, Ph.D.

Professor of Medical Psychology and Associate Professor of Pediatrics, The Johns Hopkins University, Baltimore, Md. 21205, U.S.A.

and

HERMAN MUSAPH, M.D., Ph.D., F.R.C. Psych.

Head, Department of Medical Sexology, Academisch Ziekenhuis, University of Utrecht, Utrecht, The Netherlands

1977

EXCERPTA MEDICA — AMSTERDAM · LONDON · NEW YORK

Introduction

Sexology does not yet have a conventional definition of the extent or scope of its subject matter. This Handbook will undoubtedly take the science and medicine of sexology a giant step forward in formulating that definition. In so doing, it may give the impetus to a medical school, probably one becoming newly inaugurated, to establish a department of sexology. In all of the New World, and the Old, there is not one medical school that has a department of sexology. The first and only department of sexology in all the universities of North and South America is nonmedical, and it was officially established as recently as 1975. It is at the French-speaking Université du Québec à Montréal, in Canada.

In Europe, the celebrated Sexuological Institute at Charles University, Prague, survived Hitler's ravages which destroyed Magnus Hirschfeld's Institute in Berlin. The Institute in Prague provides contemporary sexology with its closest, continuous historical link with its 19th and early 20th century origins. Though linked with the medical school, it has quasi-autonomous status and does not function as would a full department of sexology in a medical school.

In the post-war era, German sexology regenerated itself with the establishment of the Institute for Sex Research at the University of Hamburg. This Institute functions within the department of psychiatry, and is not the equivalent of a department of sexology. In the early 1970s, a special unit in sexual medicine was established at the University of Frankfurt; it also does not function as a full department of sexology. Elsewhere, European medical schools are as impoverished as are those in America with respect to sexology as a health science and practice with full departmental status.

In America there are two sex-research institutes of world renown, neither of which is closely affiliated with a medical school. One is Kinsey's famous Institute of Sex Research at Indiana University. The other is the Reproductive Biology Research Foundation of Masters and Johnson, an autonomous organization. Elsewhere in America, human sex research and sex therapy are conducted under the aegis of nonsexological departments. Psychology departments deal with those aspects of sex that can safely be investigated with the clothes on. Psychiatry departments do the same, except that they have referral facilities for nude physical examinations, and that they are more likely to be concerned with anomalies of erotic practice. When the primary complaint is presented as either a copulatory or fertility deficiency, then the male goes to urology. The female goes to gynecology, as she does also with problems of pregnancy. Should a problem be construed as one of impaired postpubertal masculinization or feminization, in either body or mind, then the referral most likely will be to endocrinology.

Today, sexology is a haphazard merry-go-round: psychology, sociology, anthropology, psychiatry, urology, gynecology, endocrinology, venereology, and perhaps plastic surgery, neurology or neurosurgery. Logistically, it is self-evident that problems of sexuality should be the province of one specialist, the sexologist, who knows how to integrate all the multiple components of human sexuality.

There are some sexological complaints, including those of fertility as well as those of impaired ability to establish a love relationship, that apply to the male or the female alone. The majority of sexological complaints, however, pertain not to the lone individual, but to the erotic partnership. Sexology is a science of couples. Even in the case of V.D., the proper therapy is not of one, but two (or more) people. Sexology as a branch of medicine is, par excellence, one in which treatment means treatment not only of the patient as a person, but of the partnership. Treatment of the diseased organ system is not enough; and treatment of the laboratory results — a method allowable in the anonymous urgency of an epidemic — is never adequate for the sexological syndromes, excepting possibly epidemic V.D.

In all the systems of the body, the only analogue of sexual dimorphism is age dimorphism. The sexual system is unique in being dimorphic from conception to death. Sexology is the discipline that pertains to every aspect of the dimorphism of men and women in their sexual lives together. Inevitably it must be its own science and its own medical specialty. Otherwise, the science and health-care of mankind will be incomplete, and so will the happiness and sense of well-being of us all.

The taboo on sex in the very society that produced this Handbook is so pervasive that it has created for some people a problem concerning the dignity of the term, sexology. Sexuology came up for consideration as being perhaps less vulgar. In the end, the editors decided in favor of the simpler spelling. Call a spade a spade: sex is sex, and sexology is sexology.

The history of this Handbook dates from 1969 when the publisher approached Herman Musaph with a proposal for a text in sexology. Herman Musaph in turn approached John Money. The next step was to work out a synoptic table of contents, and a list of potential contributors and section coordinators. It was decided to make the book as international in scope as possible. Inevitably some of the well known people in sexology were unable to accept yet a new responsibility, and so their names regrettably are not included. Conversely, there are many younger sexologists whose careers are still formative who should have been included, but are not, because of constraints of space. Space constraints are responsible for those various detailed aspects of sexology that are not treated in full, or are not included.

It was the policy of the editors to give section coordinators a fair degree of autonomy to modify the suggested contents of their sections, and to select contributors. In consequence, each section reflects not only the scientific dimensions of knowledge regarding its topic, but also the intellectual vantage point of the section coordinator. The result is to give the Handbook a diversity and variety that it would not have, had it been written by a single author. Ranging as it does from basic, hard science to applied science, and from descriptive phenomenology to historical and ideological doctrine, the Handbook accurately achieves unity by representing sexology as it is actually developing and being practised in the world today. There are many references to animal sexological research throughout the Handbook, but always because of the inferences that may be drawn from them, now or in the future, with respect to human sexology. It is the purpose of this Handbook to lay a firm foundation for the sexology of human beings.

John MONEY
Herman MUSAPH

List of contributors

George Abraham, M.D.
13, Avenue Frieg, 1208 Genève, Switzerland

John Bancroft, M.D., M.R.C.P., F.R.C. Psych
MRC Unit in Reproductive Biology, 2 Forrest Road, Edinburgh, U.K.

Geoffrey N. Bianchi
Senior Lecturer, University of Otago, Christchurch Clinical School, Department of Psychological Medicine, Christchurch, New Zealand. Mailing address: Christchurch Hospital, Christchurch 1, New Zealand

Edward M. Brecher, M.A.
Yelping Hill, West Cornwall, Conn. 06796, U.S.A.

Donn Byrne, Ph.D.
Professor of Psychological Sciences, Purdue University, West Lafayette, Ind. 47907, U.S.A.

John E. Cawte, M.D., Ph.D.
Associate Professor, School of Psychiatry, University of New South Wales, Kensington, N.S.W., Australia 2033

S.T.H. Chan, Ph.D.
Department of Zoology, University of Hong Kong, Hong Kong

Heleen Crul, Journalist
Oude Kleefsebaan 74, Berg en Dal, The Netherlands

Jean Daléry, M.D.
Hôpital Neurologique, U. 502, 59 Boulevard Pinel, Lyon 69003, France

Bengt E. Danielsson, Ph.D.
Box 558, Papeete, Tahiti, French Polynesia

Henry P. David, Ph.D.
Director, Transnational Family Research Institute, 8307 Whitman Drive, Bethesda, Md. 20037, U.S.A.

Myriam de Senarclens, M.D.
Privat-docent, Lecturer and Consultant in Psychosomatic Gynecology, Medical School, University of Geneva, Geneva, Switzerland

Günter Dörner, M.D.
Director, Institute of Experimental Endocrinology, Humboldt-University, Schumannstr. 20/21, 104 Berlin, G.D.R.

Anke A. Ehrhardt, Ph.D.
Associate Professor, Department of Psychiatry and Pediatrics, State University of New York, Children's Hospital, 219 Bryant Street, Buffalo, N.Y. 14222, U.S.A.

Stephen G. Eisele
Research Assistant, Wisconsin Regional Primate Research Center, 1220 Capital Court, Madison, Wisc. 53706, U.S.A.

Elemer Endröczi, M.D., D.Sc.
Professor, Postgraduate Medical School, P.O. Box 112, 1389 Budapest, Hungary

Barry J. Everitt, Ph.D.
Department of Anatomy, University of Cambridge, Downing Street, Cambridge CB2 3DY, U.K.

Harvey H. Feder, Ph.D.
Professor, Institute of Animal Behavior, Department of Psychology, Rutgers University, Newark, N.J. 02102, U.S.A.

Dennis Friedman, M.R.C. Psych.
Psychiatrist in charge, Sexual Dysfunction Clinic, Department of Psychological Medicine, St. Bartholomew's Hospital, London. Present address: 52 Harley Street, London W1N 1DE, U.K.

Herbert L. Friedman, Ph.D.
American Institutes for Research, 3 rue du Port, 1204 Geneva, Switzerland

Elisabeth Frijling-Schreuder, Ph.D.
Emeritus Professor of Child Psychiatry, University of Amsterdam, Amsterdam, The Netherlands

Elise Gaulin-Krener, Ph.D.
Department of Biobehavioral Sciences, University of Connecticut, Storrs, Conn. 06268, U.S.A.

Paul H. Gebhard, Ph.D.
Director, Institute for Sex Research and Professor, Department of Anthropology, Indiana University, Bloomington, Ind. 47401, U.S.A.

Robert W. Goy, Ph.D.
Professor of Psychology, University of Wisconsin at Madison; Director, Wisconsin Regional Primate Research Center, 1220 Capitol Court, Madison, Wisc. 53706, U.S.A.

Richard Green, M.D.
Professor of Psychiatry and Psychology, Department of Psychiatry and Behavioral Science, State University of New York, Stony Brook, N.Y. 11794, U.S.A.

Ann Gregory
Staff Member, International Health Foundation, Cours des Bastions, 4, 1205 Geneva, Switzerland

Edward W. Gresik, Ph.D.
Department of Anatomy, Downstate Medical School, State University of New York, Brooklyn. Present address: Department of Anatomy, Mount Sinai School of Medicine, Fifth Avenue at 100th Street, New York, N.Y. 10029, U.S.A.

Béla Halász, M.D., D.Sc.
Professor of Anatomy, Second Department of Anatomy, Semmelweis University Medical School, Tüzoltó utca 58, H-1094 Budapest, Hungary

Hendrika C. Halberstadt-Freud, Ph.D., M.I.P.A.
Van Breestraat 131, Amsterdam, The Netherlands

James B. Hamilton, Ph.D.
Department of Anatomy, Downstate Medical School, State University of New York, Brooklyn, N.Y., U.S.A.

J.P. Hanby
Subdepartment of Animal Behavior, University of Cambridge, Downing Street, Cambridge CB2 3DY, U.K. Present address: Serengeti Research Institute, P.O. Seronera via Arusha, Tanzania

John R.W. Harris, M.R.C.P., D.T.M. & H.
Consultant Venereologist, Praed Street Clinic, St. Mary's Hospital, London W2, U.K.

Ary A. Haspels, M.D., Ph.D., F. Neth, C.O.G.
Full Professor of Obstetrics and Gynecology, Academic Hospital, University of Utrecht, Catharijnesingel 101, Utrecht, The Netherlands

Joseph Herbert, M.B., Ph.D.
Fellow of Gonville and Caius Colleges, and Lecturer, Department of Anatomy, University of Cambridge, Downing Street, Cambridge CB2 3DY, U.K.

Preben Hertoft, M.D.
Associate Professor in Psychiatry, and Head, Psychiatric Out-Patient Clinic and the Sexological Research Unit, University Clinic of Psychiatry, Rigshopitalet, Blegdamsvej 9, DK-2100 Copenhagen Ø, Denmark

K. Heslinga
Molenweg 7, Eelde, The Netherlands

John Hoenig, M.D., F.R.C.P., D.P.M.
Professor and Chairman in Psychiatry, Memorial University of Newfoundland, St. John's, Newfoundland, Canada, A1C 5S7

Murray E. Jarvik, M.D., Ph.D.
Professor of Psychiatry and Pharmacology, University of California at Los Angeles, School of Medicine, The Center for Health Sciences; and Chief, Psychopharmacology Research Unit, Brentwood Veterans Administration Hospital, Los Angeles, Calif. 90037, U.S.A.

Raymond L. Johnson
Programicon, Inc., 907 6th Street S.W., no. 901, Washington, D.C. 20024, U.S.A.

Warren R. Johnson, Ed.D.
Professor of Health Education and Director, Children's Health and Developmental Clinic, University of Maryland, College Park, Md. 20742, U.S.A.

John H. Kennell, M.D.
Professor of Pediatrics, Case Western Reserve University, Medical School, Cleveland, Ohio 44106, U.S.A.

Eric B. Keverne, Ph.D.
Department of Anatomy, University of Cambridge, Downing Street, Cambridge CB2 3DY, U.K.

Marshall H. Klaus, M.D.
Professor of Pediatrics, Case Western Reserve University, Medical School, Cleveland, Ohio 44106, U.S.A.

Janet S. Knight, Ph.D.
Assistant Professor of Anatomy, Medical University of South Carolina, 80 Barro Street, Charleston, S.C. 29401, U.S.A.

J. Kremer, M.D.
Gynecologist, University of Utrecht, Utrecht. Present address: Parklaan 16, Groningen, The Netherlands

C. Lauritzen, M.D.
Chairman, Department of Gynecology and Obstetrics of the University, Prittwitzstr. 43, D-7900 Ulm, G.F.R.

Arye Lev-Ran, M.D., Ph.D.
Chief, Endocrine Laboratory of the Sick Fund, Tel-Aviv, and Diabetic Clinic, Beilinson Medical Center, Petah-Tikva; Senior Lecturer in Endocrinology, Tel-Aviv University Medical School, Israel. Formerly Senior Investigator, Department of General Endocrinology, Institute of Obstetrics and Gynecology of the Academy of Medical Sciences of the U.S.S.R., Leningrad, U.S.S.R. Present address: Department of Endocrinology and Metabolism, The City of Hope National Medical Center, 1500 East Duarte Road, Duarte, Calif. 91010, U.S.A.

Roger W. Libby, Ph.D.
Institute for Family Research and Education, Syracuse University, 760 Ostrom Avenua, Syracuse, N.Y. 13210, U.S.A.

Joseph LoPiccolo, Ph.D.
Associate Professor of Psychiatry, School of Medicine, State University of New York, Stony Brook, N.Y. 11794, U.S.A.

Tina Mandel
Practicing Psychotherapist, Member of the Psychology Faculty, Richmond College and City University of New York; Supervising Psychotherapist at Identity House, New York. Present address: 106½ Douglas Street, Brooklyn, N.Y. 11231, U.S.A.

Terry Maple, Ph.D.
Assistant Professor, Department of Psychology, Emory University, Atlanta, Ga. 30322, U.S.A.

Judd Marmor, M.D.

Franz Alexander Professor of Psychiatry, University of Southern California School of Medicine, Los Angeles, Calif. 90033, U.S.A.

Clyde E. Martin, Ph.D.

Sociologist, Gerontology Research Center, National Institute on Aging, National Institutes of Health, Baltimore City Hospitals, Baltimore, Md. 21224, U.S.A.

Tom Mazur, Psy.D.

Instructor in Medical Psychology, Department of Psychiatry and Behavioral Sciences, The Johns Hopkins University and Hospital, Baltimore, Md. 21205, U.S.A.

E. Patricia McCormick, M.S.N., Ph.D.

Research Scientist, American Institutes for Research, Washington, D.C. Present address: 4977 Battery Lane, Bethesda, Md. 20014, U.S.A.

Margaret Mead, Ph.D.

Curator Emeritus of Ethnology, The American Museum of Natural History, 15 West 77th Street, New York, N.Y. 10024, U.S.A.

Heino F.L. Meyer-Bahlburg, Dr. rer. nat.

Research Associate Professor of Psychology in Psychiatry and Pediatrics, School of Medicine, State University of New York, Buffalo. Present address: Office of Psychoendocrinology, Children's Hospital of Buffalo, 219 Bryant Street, Buffalo, N.Y. 14222, U.S.A.

G. Mitchell,

Professor of Psychology, University of California, Davis, Calif. 95616, U.S.A.

John Money, Ph.D.

Professor of Medical Psychology, Department of Psychiatry and Behavioral Sciences and Associate Professor of Pediatrics, The Johns Hopkins University and Hospital, Baltimore, Md. 21205, U.S.A.

Emily C. Moore, Ph.D., Ex. Dir., PPMW

International Institute for the Study of Human Reproduction, Columbia University, New York, Present address: 30 Seitz Avenue, Hempstead, N.Y. 11550, U.S.A.

R.S. Morton, F.R.C.P. (Ed.)

Consultant Venereologist, Royal Infirmary and Lecturer in Venereal Disease, University of Sheffield, 11 Cortworth Road, Sheffield S11 9LN, U.K.

P. Müller, M.D.

Department of Gynecology and Obstetrics of the University, Prittwitzstr. 43, D-7900 Ulm, G.F.R.

Rudolf Müller, M.D.

Vorstandsmitglied der Deutchen Gesellschaft für Sexualforschung, Bismarckstr. 115, 2 Hamburg 20, G.F.R.

Herman Musaph, M.D., F.R.C. Psych.

Head of Department for Medical Sexology, Academisch Ziekenhuis, University of Utrecht, The Netherlands

Lucile F. Newman, Ph.D.

Assistant Professor of Anthropology, Section of Community Health, Division of Biomedical Sciences, Brown University, Providence, R.I. 02912, U.S.A.

Niles Newton, Ph.D.

Professor, Department of Psychiatry, Northwestern University Medical School, 303 East Chicago Ave., Chicago, Il. 60611, U.S.A.

Barry Nurcombe, M.D.

Associate Professor of Child Psychiatry, The Avoca Clinic, Division of Family and Child Psychiatry, University of New South Wales, Kensington, N.S.W., Australia 2033. Present address: University of Vermont Medical School, Burlington, Ver., U.S.A.

Pamela Oline, M.S.

Psychotherapist in Private Practice and Psychotherapist at Identity House, New York and Co-director of Urban Counseling Service, New York. Present address: 100 Riverside Drive, New York, N.Y. 10024, U.S.A.

Willy Pasini, M.D.
Director, Unit of Psychosomatic Gynecology and Sexology, Medical School of Geneva, 1205 Geneva, Switzerland

Roland A. Pierloot, M.D.
Professor of Psychiatry and Medical Psychology, University of Leuven, Leuvenbaan 100, 3070 Kortenberg, Belgium

Gloria Pruce, M.ed., C.A.S.E.
6702 Darwood Drive, Baltimore, Md. 21209, U.S.A.

Ira L. Reiss, Ph.D.
Professor, Department of Sociology and the Family, Study Center, University of Minnesota, Minneapolis Minn. 55453, U.S.A.

I. Rosen, Ph.D.
Paddington Centre for Psychotherapy, 217–221 Harrow Road, London W2, U.K.

Jay S. Rosenblatt, Ph.D.
Director, Institute of Animal Behavior and Professor of Psychology, Rutgers State University, Newark, N.J. 07102, U.S.A.

Eliyahu Rosenheim, Ph.D.
Senior Lecturer, Department of Psychology, Bar-Ilan University, Ramat-Gan, Israel

Alice S. Rossi, Ph.D.
Professor, Department of Sociology, University of Massachusetts, Amherst, Mass. 01002, U.S.A.

S. Bruce Schearer, Ph.D.
Assistant Director, Biomedical Division, The Population Council, Rockefeller University, New York, N.Y. 10021, U.S.A.

Gunter Schmidt, Ph.D.
Institut für Sexualforschung, Universitätskliniken Eppendorf, Martinstr. 52, 2000 Hamburg 20, G.F.R.

Helmuth Schmidt, M.D.
Professor Deutsch Klinik für Diagnostik, Aukammallee 160, 6200 Wiesbaden, G.F.R.

C.B.S. Schofield, M.D., F.R.C.P.E. & G.
Consultant, Department of Sexually Transmitted Diseases, 67 Black Street, Glasgow G4 0EF, U.K.

Robert V. Sherwin, J.D.
Practicing Attorney and Author. Formerly Adjunct Lecturer, Borough of Manhattan Community College, Brooklyn College, Iona College, New York University, and others. Present address: 12 East 41st Street, New York, N.Y. 10017, U.S.A.

Lynn G. Smith, Ph.D.
Research Psychologist, 550 Canal Street, San Rafael, Calif. 94901, U.S.A.

James R. Smith, M.A.
Director, Self-Actualization Laboratory, P.O. Box 7135, Berkeley, Calif. 94707, U.S.A.

Paul Sporken, Ph.D.
Professor in Medical Ethics, Rijks Universiteit Limburg, Maastricht, The Netherlands

Martha L. Stein, M.S.W.
Practicing Psychotherapist, c/o Brandt and Brandt, 101 Park Avenue, New York, N.Y. 10017, U.S.A.

Elsie Taber, Ph.D.
Professor of Anatomy, Medical University of South Carolina, 80 Barre Street, Charleston, S.C. 29401, U.S.A.

Antony J.W. Taylor, Ph.D., F.B.Ps.S.
Professor of Clinical Psychology and Chairman, Psychology Department, Victoria University of Wellington, Private Bag, Wellington, New Zealand

Gyula Telegdy, M.D., D.Sc.
Institute of Pathophysiology, University Medical School, Szeged, Hungary

Evelyn B. Thoman
Associate Professor, Department of Biobehavioral Science, University of Connecticut, Storrs, Conn. 06268, U.S.A.

Christopher Tietze, M.D.

Senior Consultant, The Population Council, 245 Park Avenue, New York, N.Y. 10017, U.S.A.

Mary Anne Trause, Ph.D.

Instructor of Psychology, Department of Pediatrics, Case Western Reserve University, Medical School, 2103 Adelbert Road, Cleveland, Ohio 44106, U.S.A.

F.O. van Gennep

Rector, Theologisch Seminarium, Nederlands Hervormde Kerk, Hydeparklaan 8, Driebergen, The Netherlands

Pieter A. van Keep, M.D.

Director, International Health Foundation, 8 Avenue Don Bosco, 1150 Brussels, Belgium

A. Verkuyl, M.D.

Specialist in Rehabilitation and Medical Superintendent, Revalidatiecentrum "De Hoogstraat", Leersum, The Netherlands

Klaus-Dieter Voigt, M.D.

Professor, Department of Clinical Chemistry, Medical Clinic, University of Hamburg, Martinstr. 52, 2000 Hamburg 20, G.F.R.

Nathaniel N. Wagner, Ph.D.

Professor, Department of Psychology, University of Washington, Seattle, Wash. 98105, U.S.A.

Paul A. Walker, Ph.D.

Director of the Gender Clinic, Assistant Professor of Psychiatry, University of Texas Medical Branch, Galveston, Tex. 77550, U.S.A.

Stanley Walzer, M.D.

Assistant Professor of Psychiatry, Harvard Medical School and Senior Associate in Genetics and Psychiatry, Children's Hospital Medical Center, 295 Longwood Avenue, Boston, Mass. 02115, U.S.A.

Ingeborg L. Ward, Ph.D.

Associate Professor, Department of Psychology, Villanova University, Villanova, Penn. 19085, U.S.A.

Bradford Wilson, M.A.

Practicing Psychotherapist and Supervisor of Peer Counselors at Identity House, New York, and Faculty Workshop Institution for Living Learning, New York. Mailing Address: 333 Central Park West, New York, N.Y. 10025, U.S.A.

John E. Wolf

Project Specialist, Wisconsin Regional Primate Research Center, 1220 Capitol Court, Madison, Wisc. 53706, U.S.A.

Sherwyn, M. Woods, M.D.

Director, Graduate Education in Psychiatry; Director, Student Psychiatric Services; and Professor, Department of Psychiatry, University of Southern California School of Medicine, Los Angeles County and University of Southern California Medical Center, 1237 North Mission Road, Los Angeles, Calif. 90033, U.S.A.

The index was prepared by:
Russell Jobaris, B.A.

Research Assistant, Psychohormonal Research Unit, Johns Hopkins University and Hospital, Baltimore, Md. 21205, U.S.A.

Contents

SECTION I   History and theory of sexology
Section coordinator: Herman Musaph

SECTION II   Genetics, cytogenetics, sex reversal and behavior

Section coordinator: S. Walzer

xviii

SECTION III Prenatal hormones and the central nervous system

Section coordinator: E. Endröczi

SECTION V   Youth and Sex

Section coordinator: Gunter Schmidt

SECTION V   Hormones and sexual behavior in adulthood

Section coordinator: J. Herbert

SECTION VI   Customs of family formation and marriage

Section coordinator: Preben Hertoft

xxiv

SECTION VII   Regulation of procreation

Section coordinator: Christopher Tietze

SECTION VIII   Pregnancy and childbirth

Section coordinator: Ary A. Haspels

SECTION IX   On parenthood

Section coordinator: Niles Newton

SECTION X   Geriatric sexual relationships

Section coordinator: Pieter A. van Keep

SECTION XI Psychosexual impairment

Section coordinator: Dennis Friedman

SECTION XII   Sexual problems of the chronically impaired: selected syndromes

Section coordinator: John Money

SECTION XIII   Personal and social implications of diseases of the genital tract

Section coordinator: C.B.S. Schofield

SECTION XIV   Special issues: social

Section coordinator: A.J.W. Taylor

Chapter 89   Sex education in medical schools, by Sherwyn M. Woods   *1107*

Chapter 90   Law and sex, by Robert Veit Sherwin   *1121*

SECTION XV   Special issues: personal

Section coordinator: Herman Musaph

Chapter 91   Introduction, by Herman Musaph   *1137*

Chapter 92   On masturbation, by Elisabeth Frijling-Schreuder   *1139*

SECTION XVI   Treatment and counseling for sexual problems

Section coordinator: John Bancroft

SECTION XVII   Religion, ideology and sex

Section coordinater: Paul Sporken

SECTION I

History and theory of sexology

Section coordinator: Herman Musaph

CHAPTER 1

Introduction

HERMAN MUSAPH

Sexology is a science which had its beginning at the end of the 19th century and mainly came into being at the turn of the century in Europe. It was almost exclusively physicians who laid the foundation for the study of normal and deviant behavior in men.

At that time, despite the intimacy of the circle of the officium nobile and despite the inaccessibility of its members, one could still perform science. However, it is a mistake to think that those medical doctors — although protected by their professional laws — could work in freedom. At that time it was particularly courageous to break through the taboo on sexual topics. All the investigators who will be considered in this section were in this sense courageous. I think that we can show our gratitude to them in applying strict scientific criteria to their work, in the light of subsequent discoveries.

The significance of this opinion lies in the attitude which is taken in several circles towards psychoanalysis. The work of Freud is evaluated mainly in two ways: either one denies its significance or one denies the value of any critic. Both attitudes are to the same extent pernicious for sexology as a science.

One can ask oneself whether psychoanalysis belongs more in the history or the theory of sexology. It is no denigration or devaluation of psychoanalysis to label it history as well as theory. In the last decades no essential discoveries have taken place. This is not too surprising. In the past fifty years, in the well organised International Psychoanalytic Association and its local branches a great number of psychoanalysts have been trained as practitioners rather than researchers. Their scientific contribution to human psychology in general, and sexology in particular, has remained marginal.

I am of the opinion that the cause of this phenomenon lies in the fact that every science expands mainly through the introduction of new techniques, and in psychoanalysis technique has remained unchanged. Besides this, the inability to compete with Freud's genius certainly plays a role.

In this section Dr. Halberstadt-Freud describes in a clear way the dis-

Handbook of Sexology, edited by J. Money and H. Musaph
© *Elsevier/North-Holland Biomedical Press, 1977*

4

coveries of psychoanalysis which are still valid. Dr. Hoenig deals with the
development of pre-Freudian sexology during the second half of the 19th
century, and adds flesh and blood to its non-Freudian bones by giving selected short biographies. At this time sexologists were concerned chiefly
with symptomatology and nosology. Theoretically they drew on simple constructs and principles of etiology, for example hereditary and environmental,
constitutional and acquired factors, such as were then in vogue in medicine
and psychiatry. A genuine developmental theory of sexology began with
Freud. Its more recent advances and multidisciplinary connections are dealt
with in the two concluding chapters of the section.

CHAPTER 2

The development of sexology during the second half of the 19th century

J. HOENIG

1. INTRODUCTION

The study of the abnormal, and later of the normal, in sexual behavior became a separate yet integrated discipline of the medical sciences in the last quarter of the 19th century with Krafft-Ebing's epoch-making work which was first published in 1886 under the title of 'Psychopathia Sexualis'. By the end of the century and in the beginning of the 20th century many important contributions had been made and the discipline had reached a certain maturity in the sense that the foundations on which modern sexology is based had been laid. The culmination of the development is represented particularly by the work of Iwan Bloch who in fact created the term 'Sexualwissenschaft' or sexology, establishing it as a discipline with its own methodology. The new discipline continued to draw on the medical and psychological disciplines introduced during the era of Krafft-Ebing's Psychopathia Sexualis, but stripped it of its inhibiting philosophical—religious explicit or implicit concepts and ideas, and carried it further by making use of the methodology of other disciplines, mainly of cultural anthropology. In order to understand the work of the outstanding men who had contributed to this subject during the second half of the 19th century, one must recall some of the prevailing ideas at the time they began their work. Very little serious historical work on this subject is available, and what does exist consists of either popular cliché-ridden superficial accounts, or school-oriented interpretations. In 1959 Wettley and Leibbrand wrote a very scholarly survey which they called (in translation) 'From Psychopathia Sexualis to Sexology', and on which this chapter largely draws.

2. THE FRENCH ORIGINS

The men who contributed to the development of sexology belonged mainly to the German-speaking part of Europe, namely, Krafft-Ebing, Moll,

Handbook of Sexology, edited by J. Money and H. Musaph,
© *Elsevier/North-Holland Biomedical Press, 1977*

Steinach, Eulenberg, Hirschfeld, Freud and Bloch. Even the Swiss—French Forel, or the English Ellis were closely linked with that circle. Forel was the director of the Burghölzli Hospital in German-speaking Zürich; Ellis had to publish some of his writings in Germany where the atmosphere was more free than in his native England. There he constantly risked persecution, and actually had some of his books before the courts on obscenity charges. Both Forel and Ellis had very close contacts with German-speaking psychiatry and sexology. But although these men and their work are mainly a part of the history of Teutonic psychiatry of the second half of the 19th century, their basic ideas are nevertheless, as we shall try to show, very much of French origin.

In particular two concepts dominated medical thinking of the day. One was the theory of 'dégénérescense', or degeneration, associated with the names of Morel (1809—1873) and Magnan (1835—1912). The other was the prevailing view of the serious danger and pathogenic effect of masturbation, which had been strongly stated by Tissot in his 'L'Onanisme, un Dissertation Physique sur les Maladies Produites par la Masturbation', and which survived the publication of this popular science book in 1760. Both these ideas did in fact, at least partly, survive right into the 20th century. Tissot's influence up to the present has been partly reviewed recently by Hare (1962). One need only remember Kretschmer's (1918) 'Masturbantenwahn', a variety of his sensitive delusions of reference, which was not an uncommon condition in the 1920s, to remind us of the grip these ideas of the harmfulness of masturbation had on the popular imagination. We still find a faint echo of them in medical views expressed even today on the supposed harmfulness of 'excessive' masturbation. Certainly during the 19th century masturbation was believed to be traumatic to health and a possible cause of dégénérescense.

3. DÉGÉNÉRESCENSE

The concept of 'degeneration' was not expressed for the first time by Morel, but he gave it a meaning which was new. Although born in Vienna in 1809, Benedict A. Morel was French. When he was six years old his father and the entire family returned to France where he later studied theology. He soon dropped theology and took up the study of medicine. He worked for many years at the Salpetrière, in Paris until he died in 1873 of diabetes. In his 'Traité des Dégénérescences Physiques, Intellectuelles et Morales de l'Espèce Humaine et de ses Causes qui Produisent ces Variétés Maladives' which appeared in 1857, he developed his ideas about the nature of the morbid variations which afflict humanity. His concepts were religious and refer to the book of Genesis. In short, the degenerative types are conceived as deviations from the 'type primitif' (Adam) who was created in the image of God, but through his fall became exposed to factors in the environment which caused him to change — to change also into illness, physical and mental.

Valentin Magnan accepted Morel's concept of dégénérescense but secularised it by dismissing the 'type primitif' as inconceivable to have stood as a perfect specimen at the beginning of our species. Magnan was born in 1835 in Perpignan, studied medicine in Lyon and Paris and became an assistant of Beillarger at the Salpetrière. He was an experimentalist. Magnan's thinking was strongly influenced by Darwin's 'Origin of the Species' which appeared in 1859. According to Magnan healthy humanity is set on a course of progressive evolution, but individuals can be affected in such a way that their ascending evolution is stopped and they then embark on a degenerative course, eventually leading to their extinction. The degeneration is passed on by heredity, becoming more severe with each generation leading to sterility until the line becomes extinct. This applies to mental disorders no less than to all kinds of physical illnesses.

Magnan's degeneration theory was taken up in Germany amongst others by Schüle. He was born in 1840 in Freiburg im Breisgau. He was on the staff of the famous Illenau Hospital, a mental hospital which was referred to as a 'school' of psychiatry. Krafft-Ebing was a distinguished member of it. The scientific concepts of heredity and the much more nebulous concept of degeneration were not always carefully kept separate by Schüle and Krafft-Ebing. It was held that degeneration could be brought on by a variety of traumata such as, to name but a few, alcohol, phthisis, epilepsy — and masturbation.

4. PSYCHOPATHIA SEXUALIS

These were the prevailing ideas around the middle of the 19th century when Krafft-Ebing began to turn his attention to the sexual disorders. He had already published a very influential textbook on forensic psychiatry, 'Lehrbuch der Gerichtlichen Psychopathologie' (1875), having been stimulated earlier by his family background to take an interest in medicolegal matters. In 1886 while in Graz he published his 'Psychopathia Sexualis' with the subtitle 'A Clinical—Forensic Study'. With this work Krafft-Ebing became the actual founder of what was later to become Sexology. His approach to the sexual disorders was fundamentally the same as that used for psychiatric disorders in general; he thus drew the study of sexual disorders entirely into psychiatry, and with that into the discipline of medicine. Yet he was the first to present the sexual disorders and anomalies in a separate publication, which first appeared as a slim volume but grew during twelve successive editions to an extensive work. It was the first work presenting a comprehensive classification, and a summary of contemporary knowledge of these disorders, and he did this at a time when his entire subject was still a matter for disdain. Bräutigam (1962) in a historical sketch says, "We have to thank Krafft-Ebing for the first many-sided description of the sexual perversions and for an attempt at a comprehensive appreciation of all their manifestations which he undertook in 1886. This first great and distinguished complete presentation and inventory of that field has the character of a large catalogue of perversions. In a picture-book-like series are offered the most monstrous cases of his time and of history, particularly cases collected by Krafft-Ebing himself as a widely sought medicolegal consultant. The perversions are described in their most extreme forms. This collection of brutal necrophiliacs, anthropophages, sexual murderers and sodomites, of cunning and cultured sadists, masochists and transvestites has in its degree of deviation never been surpassed. By this extreme presentation, Krafft-Ebing has removed the sexual disorders far away from general sexuality." In the first edition of 'Psychopathia Sexualis' he felt obliged, by way of introduction, to apologize as it were, stating that is 'the sad privilege of medicine and of psychiatry in particular to see the shadow side of life, the human weakness and poverty'. It is noteworthy, however, how the tone changed in subsequent editions, obviously under the influence of experiences gained also outside the courtroom. In a foreword to 'Psychopathia Sexualis' in 1902, Krafft-Ebing says that there are a large number of unhappy people who read his book hoping for "explanations and solace for the puzzling aspects of their own vita sexualis, and who find them there. Innumerable letters from all countries to the author from such stepchildren of nature are proof of the correctness of this assumption. The reading of these letters, the authors of which are in their majority spiritually and socially of the highest quality and often very sensitive, arouses the deepest sympathy". Thus has Krafft-Ebing rehabilitated the sexual abnormalities as a task for medicine, a task to make them its concern and to bring help to those afflicted by them.

5. CASE HISTORIES

Krafft-Ebing drew on yet another great tradition of French Psychiatry. Since Esquirol, French psychiatric literature provided some of the finest examples of clinical case histories. Krafft-Ebing followed that example. His detailed and classical case histories have done more than anything else to lay the foundations of medical scientific sexology. The lucidity and courage with which the details of abnormal sexual behavior are described, followed through and illuminated by the life history of the patient or offender, and sometimes enriched by descriptions of his family background, are admirable. These histories have stood the test of time and still make profitable reading for the modern sexologist. Many of the case histories in his books were not his own, but collected from journals, archives and court records. Many were supplied by Moll and other sexologists, but Krafft-Ebing edited them so skillfully that they set new standards for that type of pathography often written by patients themselves.

The early development of sexology can never be understood unless seen against the background of its time. That time was the reign of Queen Victoria in England, and of Kaiser Wilhelm in Germany. The moral code had banished the topic of sex, and even in medical circles the subject was treated with nothing but disdain, or ignored altogether. Those who took it up, did so often at their personal peril. They were threatened with prosecution in court on charges of lewdness or pornography. As late as 1891 in a book review of the 5th edition of 'Psychopathia Sexualis' in the Journal of Mental Science, the leading psychiatric journal in Great Britain, the reviewer felt that much of the sordid detail in the numerous case histories could have been omitted, and that the medical profession 'is in danger of pandering to morbid tastes' and of 'increasing the coil it is intended to loosen'. Johnson (1973), reviewing this event recently, also tells us that the same criticism had, at the time, led to a suggestion that Krafft-Ebing's honorary membership of the Medico-Psychological Association of Britain should be terminated.

It is strange that these brilliant case histories should give offence to certain popularisers of sexology even today. Brecher (1970) accuses Krafft-Ebing of moralising, of lacking in sympathy, and of being an apostle of doom. It is true, the descriptions of the sexual perversions and activities are often accompanied by such adjectives as ghastly, despicable or disgusting, but these sentiments are for the deed, not for the perpetrator. The perversions are afflictions, the afflicted are ill. They are in need of help and of treatment. Krafft-Ebing in writing the book is anxious to provide the judiciary with scientific information, and he made many efforts to bring about reforms of laws on homosexuality, and of criminal responsibility of sexual offenders. He pleaded for medical assessments of sexual offenders in every case to assist the court. The object was to prevent harsh, primitive verdicts when the cause of the criminal offence is a pathological state.

6. THE IDEA OF DEGENERATION AND THE SEXUAL DISORDERS

Krafft-Ebing's concept of 'degeneration' came as mentioned earlier from France, from Morel and Magnan, and strongly influenced medical thinking of the 2nd half of the 19th century. It was applied to medical sexology by Krafft-Ebing as well as by Moll, Forel, Ellis, Freud and many others. Jaspers (1962) says "Morel and Magnan grasped, not so much conceptually as intuitively, the significance of heredity and degeneration; they recognised the types of degenerative mental disorders and with that the fundamental distinction between the endogenous and exogenous psychoses". Krafft-Ebing explains his concept as follows: "it is well known that various pathogenic aspects can affect individuals and bring about quite specific changes, which as they are passed on by heredity from generation to generation show increasingly strong characteristics, until the power of procreation is lost and the line becomes extinct." These pathogenic agents are numerous and varied. They include alcohol, drugs, mineral poisons; also illnesses such as pellagra, malaria or venereal infections; and they can include social and psychological stresses; in the case of the sexual perversions which are conditions of degeneration, they certainly included masturbation. Degeneration declared itself by a variety of disorders in members of the patient's family. The belief in the progression of the degenerative process from generation to generation leading finally to the extinction of the line shows influences coming from Darwin, and indeed Darwin's 'Origin of Species' is often mentioned by Krafft-Ebing as a profound formative influence.

Degeneration as an etiological factor is firmly adhered to by Krafft-Ebing in his classification of psychiatric disorders. He divides them into 'psychoneuroses' in which the disorder develops as a psychic disturbance on the basis of a 'fit' brain, and the 'psychic degenerations' which develop on the basis of an 'invalid' brain, damaged by hereditary and unfavourable environmental influences. The sexual perversions are regarded as belonging to the second category. Even fetishism, brilliantly described by Binet (1887) as the result of associative learning, was accepted as such by Krafft-Ebing, but with the modification that the learning of perversity can only take place if degeneration had prepared the ground.

Alfred Binet (1857—1911) was born in Nice just before that city was incorporated into France. He was descended from a long line of distinguished physicians, but had not studied medicine himself. He had in fact studied law, but changed his interests and became a psychologist. He was strongly influenced by Ribot and Charcot with whom he worked at the Salpetrière. Later he became director of the Laboratory for Experimental Psychology at the Sorbonne, but full academic recognition in his field of abnormal psychology eluded him, mainly because he had never received the doctorate in medicine. This unfortunately frustrated him but did not impair his genius to which psychology, psychiatry and sexology owe so much. He died young at 54, probably of a cerebral tumor.

The distinction between normal and morbid fetishistic tendencies had already been made by Binet. Krafft-Ebing stressed the transitional forms between the two and regarded the pathological to be characterised by the exclusiveness. "The abnormality consists only if a partial aspect of the person of the opposite sex will attract the entire sexual interest, so that all other aspects pale beside it more or less into indifference. Therefore the body-part fetishist is not a monstrum per excessum as is, for example, the sadist or masochist, but rather a monstrum per defectum". The differentiating criterion for pathological fetishism is the need of the presence of the fetish as a sine qua none for coitus. A sharp distinction, he emphasises, is not possible. He wrote: "One can agree with Binet that in the life of every fetishist there can be assumed to have been an event which determined that the particular stimulus is coloured by sexual pleasure.

This event will have taken place in early youth, as a rule, at the time of sexual awakening. This awakening will have coincided with a sexual partial stimulus (because the fetish is always a thing which is somehow related to women) and stamped it the main object of sexual interest for the entire life. The occasion when this association occurred is as a rule forgotten. Only the result remains conscious". He continues: "Basic here is only the characteristic which generally predisposes to psychopathy, the sexual hyperaesthesia of such individuals". Krafft-Ebing makes a difference between perverse acts, which are not pathological and perversions which "are a sign of a usually hereditary pathological disposition of the central nervous system", that is, of a functional degeneration, and are an expression of cerebral anomaly.

The concept of degeneration served as an intellectual tool to discover and deal with the role heredity obviously plays in mental disorder in general. It became undermined and finally discarded with the growth of knowledge in neuropathology and genetics. As specific scientific knowledge grew such portmanteau concepts lost their usefulness. It remained in use, nevertheless, throughout the 19th and well into the 20th century by Forel and Moll, and lingered with Ellis and Freud until disposed of finally by Bumke in his 'Lehrbuch der Geisteskrankheiten', in 1924, salvaging for modern genetics what was useful, and discarding what had become obsolete, but had more or less uncritically been carried along. The author who had opposed the concept most strongly in the realm of sexology was Iwan Bloch; he achieved a breakthrough by overcoming the predominantly biological approach altogether and introducing anthropological—ethnological methods to this field.

7. HISTORICAL PERSPECTIVE

Two developments in the history of ideas which have taken place in the course of the 19th and beginning of the 20th centuries should not be confused. One is the development of the concept of degeneration — purifying it and thereby gradually discarding it — towards the specific scientific concepts which belong to modern neuropathology and human genetics. One aspect of this development is the progressive limitation of the biological concept of degeneration, demarcating more and more precisely the field of its application, and thus creating the space for the study of psychological factors as etiological influence for all or some disorders. This development applies to the entire field of psychiatry and concerns sexology as a part of it.

The second great development is specific to sexology and consists in coming to understand the relationship between the sexual disorders, in particular the perversions, to normal sexuality. Here the prevailing taboo which covered normal sexuality by impenetrable silence was the main obstacle to overcome. It is in particular for this reason — this taboo of silence — that the medical and general anthropological interest in normal sexuality has arrived via the perversions.

Various sexologists have taken different approaches to these two problems and unless these two historical trends are studied separately, the individual contributors and their work cannot be justly evaluated.

8. DEGENERATION AND SOCIAL INFLUENCES

As regards the development of etiological theories, on the basis of the French ideas of degeneration, we have seen their embryonic beginnings in the work of Krafft-Ebing. While remaining rooted in biological theories of etiology, he also drew attention to the social aspects of sexuality. In the forword to the first edition of his 'Psychopathia Sexualis' he says, "Very few are fully aware what powerful influences sexual life has on the feeling, thinking and acting, both in the individual existence and in society in general". But he deliberately refrains from contributing to a psychology of the sexual life. "The object of this work is to gain knowledge of the psycho-pathological phenomena of sexual life, and an attempt to trace them to the underlying conditions to which scientific laws apply. This can only be achieved with the help of the natural, and in particular the medical sciences." "Perhaps" he hopes "it will succeed in this way to establish the philosophical knowledge in a mediating position equidistant from the pessimistic philosophies of Schopenhauer or Hartman on the one hand, and the serenely naive one of the poets on the other". In the first chapter he approvingly quotes Maudsley (Deutsche Klinik 1873,2,3): "If man was bereft of the sexual drive and of all which springs from it, practically all poetry and perhaps also all moral sentiment would be torn out of his life". The development of civilisation has in its turn an influence on the sexual life. Krafft-Ebing, as was mentioned earlier, was already concerned with a differentiation between perversion and perversity. Successive writers like Moll, Ellis, Freud and Hirschfeld were concerned with a narrowing of the field of application of the concept of degeneration. Moll, however, still adhered to it strongly but accepted that there were a small residue of cases where neither illness nor degeneration were the cause. He referred, for instance to the homosexuality of the ancient Greeks. In general Moll saw the cause of homosexuality and perversions as a change in the libido brought about by cultural influences which replace natural stimuli by artificial ones, thus weakening it. The sine qua none, however, is the degeneration which makes the individual vulnerable and exposes him to these deleterious cultural influences.

9. DEGENERATION, PSYCHOTHERAPY AND HEALTH EDUCATION

Moll, who had studied under Charcot and also in Nancy, was an enthusiast of hypnosis, which he introduced to Germany and fostered as a treatment of sexual disorders. By hypnosis he tried to reverse the environmental effects which had impinged on the defective constitution, and also to prevent future damage by inducing aversion to such traumatic inclinations and habits. His methods of psychotherapy are clearly advanced forerunners of behavior modification therapy based on learning theory.

Forel's position is similar to that of Krafft-Ebing's whose classification of the sexual disorders he accepted and retained throughout successive editions of his book 'The Sexual Question'. He was primarily concerned with sexual hygiene in the sense of public health education. Believing as he did that various sexual abuses such as prostitution, excessive masturbation, or unprincipled sexual indulgence could have adverse effects on the constitution which could thus acquire hereditary traits or habits in the sense of degeneration, he considered sex education a method of primary prevention. Sex education has in our time become widely accepted although its aims have to a certain extent been lost sight of. At its best it seems to have acquired a slightly hollow ring, although of course not entirely so; at its worst, in its search for self-justification, it appears to have found it in entertainment. Forel or Ellis might have been more than a little shocked at the spectacle of the latest fruits which have grown of the tree they so carefully nurtured and protected in their day.

10. DEGENERATION AND EROTIC SYMBOLISM

Havelock Ellis modified Krafft-Ebing's concept of degeneration considerably but still held the view that most sexual perversions are inherited. However, he opposed too loose a useage and emphasised that before degeneration can be diagnosed a number of definite signs must be established. Like Moll, he believed there can be a small number of persons who have sexual perversions but are otherwise healthy. Ellis did not hold inheritance to be identical with degeneration, that is to say with progressive inheritance. He believed that the average homosexual is not necessarily mentally ill nor is he showing degeneracy, although he does usually have a number of relatives who show neuropathic traits. In his interpretation of the perversions he used the concept of 'erotic symbolism', taking the work of Binet as a starting point, and he regarded them as 'sexual equivalents' of the normal sexual act. Wettley (1959) traces that concept back to Iwan Bloch (1906) who wrote (before Ellis and Freud) "that there are psychic sexual equivalents into which the potential energy of the sexual drive can be transformed". He includes here not only perversions but also other affects, poetry, religion and generally the contents of fantasy life in the widest sense.

Ellis divides abnormalities into those which are caused by special occasional incidences in the patient's life giving rise to faulty associations on the basis of an already labile brain, and those which are due to physical causes and degeneration. Ellis distinguishes three groups of erotic symbolism.

The first includes those where the symbol is a part of the body (from foot fetishism to necrophilia); the second where it is an inanimate object (from garments to pygmalionism); and the third includes events or poses (like flagellation, smells etc.). The symbolism comes about by placing the other into oneself, a kind of conscious introjection. Therefore the symbolism is a personal unique experience rather than a generic or public event. Besides this however, Ellis also sees a relationship to ethnological evolutionary developments. He reminds us that all these symbols which strike us now as perversions have once been sanctioned as revered rituals. And yet, in spite of these psychological and anthropological references, Ellis remains within biological concepts. Wettley sharply exposes this unresolved inner contradiction in Ellis's work, a contradiction which had to await the work of Bloch for its solution.

What was said about Ellis also applies to a certain degree to Freud. Quoting Ellis, Freud draws attention to the vagueness of the concept of degeneration and even questions its usefulness. Nevertheless he does not dismiss it but enumerates a number of signs without which it should not be invoked. He points out how rarely these signs are found in inverts or perverts. The explanation of the perversions — and their negatives, the neuroses — being the results of an abnormal development of the partial instincts of the libido, retains a constitutional component. The constitutional aspect is modified to "something which is inborn in everyone, which as an anlage may vary in intensity and awaits emphasis through life experiences. We are speaking of inborn, in the constitution-resting roots of the sexual drive, which in one series of cases develop to actual carriers of sexual activity (perverts), and in another series receive insufficient repression, so that they can, in a roundabout way, attract as symptoms a good deal of sexual energy . . .". "We shall say further that the assumed constitution which contains the seeds of all perversions can only be demonstrated in the child, although in him all drives only appear with a modest intensity". The contradiction between this etiological theory, and the psychological theories are an essential aspect of psychoanalysis in general. While Krafft-Ebing has brought the sexual disorders into the orbit of medical science, Freud sexualized the medical sciences themselves, by ascribing first the neuroses, then the psychoses and lastly, in psychosomatic medicine, the entirity of pathology to disorders of the libido and its development.

11. DEGENERATION AND THE INTERSEX THEORY

Hirschfeld's work is important in this context mainly because of his theories on homosexuality. In his 'Zwischenstufentheorie', or theory of the intersexes, he postulated that the bisexual anlage could give rise to diverse developments of morphology and direction of drive. He saw the cause of these variations in the genetic laws of latent and alternating heredity which variably passes male or female characteristics, including sexual propensity, from the male and female forebears on to the offspring. Nevertheless, the concept of degeneration is not entirely put aside. He wrote of a "degeneration substitute", whereby "nature uses homosexuality as a means to prevent degeneration". He thus concluded that genuine homosexuality is always inborn. The inborn state consists in a specific homosexual characteristic of the brain, which shows a special mixture of male and female hereditary substance. Affected persons, he claimed, often show a greater general lability of the brain, and this and tho homosexual constitution are causally related. External factors are only effective in the presence of the homosexual constitution. Hirschfeld did not view homosexuality as an illness but rather as a variation of nature.

12. THE INTERSEX THEORY AND ENDOCRINOLOGY

Hirschfeld used advances in the endocrinology of his day to underpin his theory. Certain aspects of the theory also required modification in the light of further developments in endocrinology. The stimulus came from Steinach in Vienna who, at the suggestion of Hirschfeld, experimented on animals by implanting testicles or ovaries into animals of both sexes. He contended that these organs had an endocrine function as well as the excretory one of producing germ cells. This endocrine function he ascribed to the 'Pubertätsdrüse'. He noticed that the sexual or gender behavior of the animal changed under the influence of the Pubertätsdrüse. He wrote: "By these experiments a new physiological fact has been established, namely that the nervous system reacts very sharply to variations in sex-hormone levels, in getting eroticised into male or female directions in quick succession depending on the increase in the particular hormone". Hirschfeld accepted this conclusion unreservedly, and also claims by others that men and women had been found who had cross-sexual Pubertätsdrüsen cells in their testes or ovaries. These conclusions and the observation that there are males and females who show cross-gender characteristics of various degrees led him to the conclusion that homosexuality and transvestitism (which would today include transsexualism), first described and named by Hirschfeld, can be explained by consideration of the various combinations of sex hormones circulating in the blood.

13. THE ESTABLISHMENT OF MODERN SEXOLOGY

Historically there has been a progressive modification of the concept of degeneration in sexology and a gradual limitation of its application to etiological theories. However, so long as the approach to the understanding of sexual abnormalities remained mainly based on the biological sciences, the confinement of theory which stems from this could not be overcome. The decisive breakthrough was achieved by Iwan Bloch. He brought to the study of sexual disorders the methods of other disciplines, in particular those of ethnology and anthropology. By the extension of methodology, he widened the studies to a new discipline which he called 'Sexualwissenschaft' or 'Sexology' (1906). He defined it as follows: "So as to fully appreciate the entire significance of the love life for the individual and for society, as well as for the entire cultural development of humanity, its study has to be arranged with the study (Wissenschaft) of man as such, in which and towards which all disciplines combine; general biology, anthropology, ethnology, philosophy, psychology, medicine, and the histories of literature and of culture in their entirety". Sexual pathology as a medical science herewith finds a new framework within which to unfold.

Bloch was influenced by the ethnologist Bastian, who taught that all humanity shared certain 'elementary ideas' which manifest themselves in all cultures and at all times. The particular form these ideas take will be determined by a number of geographic, economic and historic circumstances. Under such specific conditions certain elementary ideas become common property and manifest themselves as 'Völkergedanken' (tribal or national ideas). These concepts were used by Bloch to theorise about sexual perversions. The perversions in that light are neither illnesses nor are they the results of degeneration, but general human, ubiquitous phenomena, which recur in different populations at all times without essential qualitative differences. In his 'Beitrage zur Aetiologie der Psychopathia Sexualis' (Contributions to the etiology of psychopathia sexualis) which appeared in 1902 and 1903 he attempted for the first time to study these disorders from the viewpoint of the anthropologist and ethnologist. "Up to now, the clinical, purely medical concepts have dominated the study of the sexual abnormalities ... which thereby come to fall entirely within the domain of the physician and are understood to be the results of degeneration." " ... Richard von Krafft-Ebing brought modern sexual pathology into a comprehensive scientific system which stands or falls with the concept of degeneration". He continues, "Let us leave the sick ward and the doctor's office, let us travel around the world, let us look at the sexual activities of genus homo in all their diversity, not as physicians but just as ordinary observers, let us compare the sexuality of cultured man with that of primitives; then we shall realise how infinitely wider the horizons are for the assessment of the sexual abnormalities, how the cultural and timebound phenomenon recedes behind the general human one which in its basic characteristics is everywhere the same. Psychopathia Sexualis can be found everywhere and in all ages. Culture, civilisations, illness, degeneration only play the role of predisposing, modifying, intensifying factors".

The underlying sexual drive was conceived of as purely physical, untouched by time, place or culture. Its refinements and differentiation, however, have evolved with the development of sensuality in the relationship between men and women. The so called deviations like fetishism, sadism, masochism and exhibitionism, can appear at all times, in the same way, dependent on such conditions as climate, race and nationality, to bring them into being. The study of the varied manifestations of the vita sexualis at all times and in all races would enable men to see what they have in common, and what are their specific basic traits.

Bloch did not believe, as did Freud, that the tendency to perversions is the original general anlage of the human sexual instinct, which undergoes suppression in the course of individual development. He did write however, that "humanity as such, besides the normal manifestations of sex, also possesses perversions as one of its characteristics, and these are independent of culture; and their incidence among cultured and primitive races exceeds by far the number of the 'degenerates' . . . . The mass of sexual anomalies and aberrations is linked to mental and physical health and is not due in any way to pathological causes".

The main result of this approach was the total refutation of degeneration as a cause of sexual perversions, and an explanation of them in all deviations in terms of the sexual drive itself and its peculiar structure. This structure has two characteristics which provide the most general explanation for the diversity of sexual life. They are the 'need for variation' and the 'hunger for sexual stimulation'. Besides these there is also the ease with which the sexual drive can be modified by including the manifold external stimuli into sexual sensitivity; Bloch called this the 'synaesthetic stimuli in the love life of man'. The need for variation will account for most perversions arising in adults, whereas the synaesthetic stimuli will cause often permanent deviations in childhood. Here we see an acceptance of Binet's theories. The repetition of the deviant sexual behavior will help to fixate it as a habit. Suggestion and imitation can play a role in bringing about widespread deviations.

14. HOMOSEXUALITY

Although undertaking the exploration of anthropological factors, Bloch did not lose sight of the limitations of that approach. Fetishism, masochism and sadism are subsumed with relative ease into the general scheme resulting from Bloch's basic approach. At first he also included homosexuality. In fact, Krafft-Ebing and Moll had difficulties in explaining the homosexuality of ancient Greece in terms of 'degeneration', and Bloch's views on the need for variation seemed singularly suitable to 'explain' this phenomenon. However, Bloch's friend Hirschfeld, himself homosexual, introduced a number of homosexuals to Bloch, men and women who were intelligent and articulate, and who presented a picture of their condition which eventually led Bloch to modify his views. He still held to the view that homosexuality can be the result of the need for variation, and he believed that the classical epoch of Greece manifested this, but he called this 'pseudohomosexuality'. Also homosexuality found in prison, in boarding schools, in the armed services was called 'pseudohomosexuality', and was understood to be due to the hunger for stimulation. But he came to the conclusion that 'true or genuine' homosexuality was of a different origin.

"In the years 1905 and 1906 I have concerned myself almost exclusively with the problem of homosexuality. I had occasion to see a large number of genuine homosexual men and women, to examine them and to observe them over long periods in their homes and in their public lives, to see their ways, their habits, their views, all their activities including their relations to nonhomosexual persons of the same or of the opposite sex. I realised without doubt that the frequency of genuine homosexuality as an inborn phenomenon was much higher than I formerly thought, so that I am forced to regard the other category, the acquired, apparent, occasional homosexuality of the existence of which I am still firmly convinced, as 'pseudohomosexuality', and to separate it from the former". In the case of homosexuality of the type which manifests itself in early childhood, and also of some other abnormalities, Bloch decided that he was probably dealing with an inborn defect. He noted that it occurs in healthy individuals, independent of degeneration or adverse cultural influences all over the world. He regarded this as essentially unexplained, but offered a theory. He postulated a physiological factor, not originating from the reproductive organs which are normal, which decisively and early in life, changes the direction of the sexual drive. The nature of this factor he conceived to be chemical and operative during fetal life. He did not conceive it as hereditary. This genuine homosexuality which manifests itself in earliest childhood and persists without deflection is not due to degeneration, but occurs in most cases in otherwise healthy persons. Bloch not only dismissed degeneracy as a cause of homosexuality, but also had reservations about Hirschfeld's theory of the intersexes. To him, that theory explained more easily the case of bisexuality than the case of virile male homosexuals or effeminate female homosexuals. Bloch was not entirely satisfied with his theory.

He regarded homosexuality a variation which had no relevance to the development of humanity; at the same time he defended the rights of homosexuals to be the same as those of heterosexuals. The sexual drive is powerful and can temporarily overshadow reason, and even lead to a 'crime passionel'. Bloch, emphasising this, pleaded for the adoption of the judicial concept of diminished responsibility, but only in sexual crimes, not yet for all crimes committed under the influences of strong affects of any kind.

15. FIN DE SIECLE

Bloch's work has links to the post-Freudian schools, which in America are leaning mostly on the behavioral sciences, sociology and anthropology, and in Europe on philosophy or the humanities.

Bloch's work can be seen as a historical culmination of the development of the idea of degeneration. He overcame the problem of the dichotomy of etiological theories which forced a choice between organic versus psychogenic. His work is also a culmination of the second great historical theme of bringing the study of perversions into the general area of the study of sexual life as a whole.

16. THE SEXUAL DISORDERS AND THE PSYCHOLOGY OF SEX

Krafft-Ebing perhaps had to refrain from attempting to integrate sex and its disorders into a single theory, in order to bring medicine to concern itself with the grossest and largely forensic material of sex. Moll did not abandon that position of seeing these disorders as something apart, although he concerned himself with a wider spectrum of abnormalities, having collected his cases in private practice where he saw the milder forms of these disorders. Moll also systematically studied the normal and abnormal sexual life of children, and wrote the first comprehensive account of this hitherto taboo subject. In the forward to his book he wrote: "By all these considerations I have been induced to study the problem of the sexuality of children from the most widely different points of view. Although other writers, such as Freud, Bell and Kötscher, have contributed certain data towards the solution of these questions, no comprehensive study of the subject has hitherto been attempted" (Moll, 1912). Hirschfeld's theoretical position classified the perversions as psychologically apart from normality, namely as intersexes, but as a homosexual he was deeply involved in attempts to help such people as himself to a place in the sun. The history of medicine counts many who have come to study sexuality because of their personal biography. By their self-sacrificing and often hazardous efforts they have done much to dispel prejudice and remove harsh and unjust laws which are the tragic fate of so many of our patients.

Havelock Ellis was presumably led to sexology partly by the anguish of urophilia which haunted his younger years. His work as a public educator, like that of Forel, brought enlightenment regarding normal sexuality to a very wide public, and removed much fear about the minor sexual anomalies. Ellis in particular did much to dispel misconceptions concerning masturbation, and he did more than others of his time to change the prevalent patriarchal attitude toward women. Nevertheless, his theoretical position, like that of the majority of his sexological contemporaries, was in essence similar to that of Krafft-Ebing, although much modified.

Freud was very much a 19th century figure as regards his attitude to women, but he achieved perhaps more in this respect than any of his contemporaries because of his ingenious new theories, and because, although still working with concepts of constitutional determinism, he was too great a psychologist to remain confined by them. This led him to an unresolved theoretical dilemma, but in practice did much to relate psychopathia sexualis to sexual life in general.

BIBLIOGRAPHY

Binet, A. (1887) *Du Fetischisme dans l'amour.* (Revue philosophique, Paris.)

Bloch, I. (1907) *Das Sexualleben unserer Zeit.* Transl. by M.E. Paul (Berlin).

Bloch, I. (1908) *The Sexual Life of our Time.* (London.)

Bräutigam, W. (1962) Die ärztliche Beurteilung. In: (H. Giese, Ed.) *Psychopathologie der Sexualität.* (Ferdinand Enke, Stutgart.)

Brecher, E.M. (1970) *The Sex Researchers.* (Andre Deutsch, London.)

Hare, E.H. (1962) Masturbatory insanity: the history of an idea. *J. Ment. Sci.* 108: 2—25.

Jaspers, K. (1962) *General Psychopathology.* Transl. by J. Hoenig and M.W. Hamilton, (Univ. Press, Toronto).

Johnson, J. (1973) Psychopathia Sexualis, *Br. J. Psychiatr.* 122: 211—218.

Krafft-Ebing, v.R. (1894) *Psychopathia Sexualis.* (Ferd. Enke, Stuttgart.)

Kretschmer, E. (1918) *Der sensitive Beziehungswahn: Ein Beitrag zur Paranoiafrage und zur psychiatrischen Characterlehre.* (Berlin.)

Krich, A.M. (1964) *The Sexual Revolution, Pioneer writings on Sex: Krafft-Ebing, Ellis, Freud.* Vol. 1 (Deltabook, New York).

Moll, A. (1912) *The Sexual Life of the Child.* Transl. by E. Paul (MacMillan, New York).

Pichot, P. (1963) Alfred Binet, 1857—1911. In: (Ed. K. Kolle) *Grosse Nervenärzte,* Vol. 3, (Stuttgart, Thieme).

Tissots, S. (1766) *L'Onanisme on Dissertation Physique sur les Maladies Produites par la Masturbation.* Paris, 1760, transl. by A. Hume (London).

Wettley, A. and Leibbrand, W. (1959) Von der 'psychopathia sexualis' zur Sexualwissenschaft. *Beitr. Sexualforsch.* 17 (F. Enke, Stuttgart).

Wettley, A. (1959) Zur Problemgeschichte der "dégénérescence". *Südhoff's Arch.* 43(3) 193—212.

CHAPTER 3

Dramatis personae: selected biographical sketches of 19th century pioneers in sexology

J. HOENIG

1. RICHARD VON KRAFFT-EBING, 1840—1902

Introduction

Jaspers presents Krafft-Ebing as one of the great descriptive psychiatrists, a careful clinical observer and able to convey a vivid picture, yet remaining sober without losing elegance. He places him in line with Esquirol who started that tradition with greatness. Like Esquirol, Krafft-Ebing lived with his patients and knew them intimately, working as he did in one of the great mental hospitals in Germany, in Illenau.

Biography

Krafft-Ebing was born in Mannheim in Germany on August 14, 1840. His father, a distinguished civil servant, lived in that city which had great cultural traditions. His mother came from a family with several lawyers and her father, H.J.A. Mittermaier, was well known for his distinguished work in prison reform. While engaged in his medical studies Richard stayed at his maternal grandfather's house, and his interest in forensic medicine was awakened at this early stage. He studied medicine, as was usual, at various universities including Zurich, Vienna, Prague and Heidelberg. He graduated from Heidelberg in 1863, and in 1864 joined the staff of Illenau Mental Hospital. That hospital which is often referred to as the Illenau School had a number of doctors on its staff who made notable contributions to psychiatry, among them the well known H. Schüle who had published a textbook, and whose views were largely shared by Krafft-Ebing. They were of approximately the same age. Both came from southern Germany and they remained friends for life. When Krafft-Ebing published his textbook of psychiatry he dedicated it to Schüle.

Handbook of Sexology, edited by J. Money and H. Musaph
© *Elsevier/North-Holland Biomedical Press, 1977*

Medical studies

In 1868 Krafft-Ebing settled in Baden—Baden in southern Germany, building his private practice as Nervenarzt (neuropsychiatrist). He took part as a military physician in the Franco—German war of 1870/71, and at the end of the war he rehabilitated himself as a specialist in Leipzig, under Wunderlich. In 1870 the German medical schools began to create chairs in psychiatry, and in 1872 by mediation of Bismarck, Krafft-Ebing was called to the new university department at Strassburg as Docent. That city had just been annexed by Germany after the war and it was here that he established his new teaching unit. His clinical teaching facilities comprised the bare minimum. He was given one 2-bedded room for male patients, and another one of equal size for women. Besides this he had a cell for violent patients which could accommodate one patient at a time. He stayed in that post for only one year, and in 1873 he accepted a call to the University of Graz in Carinthia, a city he was to grow very fond of. The appointment as Professor of Psychiatry included the directorship of the mental hospital in Feldhof where, of course, he had a large number of patients under his care. He had difficulties, however, in using them for his teaching purposes because the hospital was an hour's walk away from Graz, too far for the staff and students to travel. He was also frustrated because the patients treated there were mostly sufferers of GPI (syphilitic General Paralysis of the Insane), epilepsy and alcoholic dementia. The range of disorders was limited and certainly did not include the types he felt were important to prepare his students for their practice, such as the functional psychoses and the acute toxic states. He wrote many memoranda making suggestions as to how this situation might be remedied. It was not, however, until 1886 that his frustrations came to an end. In that year he opened his own sanatorium, called Mariagrün, where he treated neurological as well as acute psychiatric conditions. The only other clinic where such innovations had succeeded was in Vienna under Meynert.

Vienna

In 1889 he moved to Vienna to succeed Leidesdorf as director of the first psychiatric clinic, and in 1892 he received a call to the senior chair in psychiatry at Vienna where he succeeded Theodor Meynert. Krafft-Ebing's lectures were famous and attracted many eminent students. His efforts went in the direction of bringing psychiatry firmly into medicine, but he also concerned himself with reforming the mental hospitals. Shortly after arriving in Vienna in 1889 he published his paper on 'The Development of Psychiatry into a Clinical Science'. In this he stressed the importance of the clinical approach to the subject, describing neuroanatomy and physiology as ancillary sciences to psychiatry. According to Wagner-Jauregg there was a fundamental disagreement in these matters between Krafft-Ebing and his predecessor Meynert. Meynert had developed neuroanatomy to a great height and was working on the task of finding the pathological changes underlying the psychiatric disorders. He did not place great hope in the clinical approach.

Krafft-Ebing's merit was to rehabilitate psychiatry as a clinical science by showing the importance of, careful bedside observation. His productivity was astonishing. He had a total of 400 publications including several large textbooks. Krafft-Ebing on his retirement, when he was succeeded by Wagner-Jauregg, had brought further fame to that chair. His successor later won the Nobel prize for his discovery of the malaria therapy of GPI. Krafft-Ebing made strenuous efforts to have psychiatry firmly integrated into the general medical education, and was pressing for it to be made a special subject of the final examination. Success, however, came only after his death. The last few years of his life were marred by painful illness as he was suffering from trigeminal neuralgia and also from arteriosclerosis and renal disease. In 1901, at 61, he had to retire. He returned to his beloved Graz where he died in 1902. When he left Vienna with his wife, his two sons and daughter, he was not preparing for a quiet retirement, very ill though he was. He took 20,000 case histories with him which he intended to exploit for clinical research.

Krafft-Ebing's importance for Austrian psychiatry was recognised by the Association of Viennese neurologists and psychiatrists who in 1908 unveiled a statue of him. Wagner-Jauregg was the speaker on that occasion.

Publications
Krafft-Ebing had published a good deal already around the time of the Franco—German war on such diverse clinical topics as compulsive states, neuras thenia, hallucinations, moral insanity and much else. In 1875, shortly after his arrival in Graz, he published his 'Lehrbuch der Gerichtlichen Psychopathologie mit Berücksichtigung der Gesetzgebungen von Österreich, Deutschland und Frankreich' (Textbook of Forensic Psychopathology with special reference to the Law in Austria, Germany and France). The book went into its sixth edition at the time of his death. It had a considerable impact on contemporary medicine. In 1879/80, he published his 'Lehrbuch der Psychiatrie auf Klinischer Grundlage' (Textbook of Psychiatry, on a Clinical Basis), which became one of the most influential textbooks.

Of particular interest here is his work on the sexual disorders. He had already published various papers on this topic when, in 1886, his 'Psychopathia Sexualis mit besonderer Berücksichtigung der Conträren Sexual Empfindung' (with special reference to the contrary sexual feeling), was published, which he subtitled 'A Clinical Forensic Study'. Krafft-Ebing's lasting fame is based more on this book than on any of his other by no means small achievements. The book appeared first as a slim volume but had grown in size by the time it reached its 12th and last edition. The main achievement of this book is that by treating the sexual disorders as a distinct area within the discipline of psychiatry, he had laid the foundation of what was later to become the discipline of sexology. His approach to the study of the sexual disorders was that of psychiatry itself. The prevailing general contemporary theories of the medical sciences were being applied to the study of this group of disorders.

Humanitarian attitudes

While studying the sexual disorders Krafft-Ebing did not disregard the patients as sufferers. He defended them against the prejudice of his time. For him they were the 'stepchildren of nature', people in need of sympathy and help. The sexual perversions were illnesses, not sins. He was concerned with law reform and presented with emphasis his plea for the abolition of the harsh laws dealing with homosexuality. He was fully aware of the social force which emanated from sexuality, and he was not afraid to face the consequences of these views, as theoretician on the one hand and as a consultant to many courts where he dealt with individual cases on the other. His book 'Psychopathia Sexualis', although written for doctors and lawyers — the crucial passages were written in Latin to make them less accessible to the lay public — was nevertheless widely read, often by sufferers who found consolation in its pages. Moll tells us that Krafft-Ebing received a vast mailbag from sufferers from all parts of the world, and replied to these letters, offering advice where he could.

The 19th century was a century of prudery, and to take up the study of sexual disorders and write about them required great courage. Even as late as 1891 the 5th edition of the 'Psychopathia Sexualis' drew hostile criticism in the Review section of the Journal of Mental Science. Johnson (1973) tells us that the cancellation of his Honorary membership of the Royal Medicopsychological Association was called for by a medical member of that association. Krafft-Ebing's work on the sexual disorders cannot be fully appreciated without taking into account the prude climate of opinion of his age.

2. ALBERT MOLL, 1862—1939

Biography

Albert Moll was born on May 4th, 1862 in Lissa in Germany, the son of a Jewish businessman. We have very little information about his life, mainly perhaps because a few years before his death the Germans persecuted him for racial reasons and, as they did with all Jewish doctors, in September 1938 revoked his license to practice. He died, sick and alone on September 23, 1939. After a life of eminence and patriotic devotion, no newspaper and no learned or professional journal even as much as announced his death. There are no obituaries and no evaluations of his work. Biographical information is gleaned mostly from his review of his life's interests and endeavours, presented in a discursive and loose style (Moll, 1936).

Medical studies

He studied medicine at the Universities of Breslau, Freiburg i.B. Jena and Berlin, and passed his state examination in 1884. After working under

Rudolf Virchov he obtained his 'Promotion' in 1885. After completion of his undergraduate studies he visited a number of centres to study neurology, neuropathology and psychiatry. He first went to Vienna in Austria to study under Meynert who was aiming to create a neurotopological diagnostic schema of psychiatric disorders. While in Vienna he was working with, among others, Wagner-Jauregg, Moritz Benedikt and Krafft-Ebing. Later he went to London, England where he was working with Hughlings Jackson, Gowers, Bastian, Ferrier and Horsley. He gained psychiatric experience in the Bethlem Royal Hospital and was working with Daniel Hack Tuke. What he most enjoyed was the proximity of his London residence to the British Museum, which he visited frequently.

The most formative influence came from Paris where he stayed for some time after leaving London in 1885. In Paris he was working under the great Charcot whom he admired immensely. While in Paris he met the assistants of Charcot, including Babinski, Binet, Marie, Gilles de la Tourette and others. Charcot at that time was most interested in hysteria and hypnosis. Believing hysteria to be due to a cerebral lesion, Charcot also considered hypnosis to be a physiological rather than a psychic phenomenon. Later Moll became more interested in the work of Bernheim in Nancy who was of the opinion that hypnosis was the result of suggestion. Moll visited Nancy, but returned once more to Paris to consider the matter carefully before shifting his allegiance, as he saw it, from Charcot to the school of Nancy. The disagreement between Paris and the Nancy school was the topic of fierce public controversy which was fought by Charcot with vigor, sarcasm for his opponents, and much feeling.

Return to Berlin

After three years of travel and study Moll returned to Berlin. He had acquired an excellent experience in neurology and psychiatry, and felt he was ready to make his mark at home. The latest developments concerning hypnosis, in particular the views of the Nancy school, were hardly known in Germany, and Moll made this the topic of his first lecture in October 1887 read to the Berliner Medizinischen Gesellschaft. The lecture was severely attacked by Ewald who considered hypnosis as something "which can be done by any shoemaker or shepherd", which did not require any skill or knowledge, and should not be the concern of doctors. Moll, who had placed such importance on this lecture was discouraged and downhearted about this fiasco; nevertheless, he persevered with his work, and when he came in 1889 to present a second lecture on the topic the reception by the meeting under the chairmanship of Virchov was markedly better. Even Ewald gave qualified approval.

Medical associations and political views

Moll, although he wrote extensively, was never associated with a particular University or other academic institution, but was a private practitioner of psychiatry. At the same time he was very active in a number of associations. He wrote: "My memories of the Berlin medical professional organisations are not altogether pleasant . . . there never was a good relationship among the colleagues as one might have excepted . . . . In general there existed, even then, already a division between Christian and Jewish doctors which had caused a rift within the professional organisations". Moll, however, did not remain an unconstructive critic. He took the initiative in unifying the profession, and the fact that he was elected to high office would appear proof that his efforts found recognition. He had the confidence of the Ministers of Government with whom he negotiated on behalf of the medical profession, particularly during the 1914/18 war, and was even asked during the stormy days following the German defeat to represent the doctors on the Berlin Sowjet of Workers and Soldiers. He was acceptable to them, it appears, although he frankly declared right at the outset that his political sympathies were not with them, but rather against them.

Moll had always been very patriotic, militaristic and loyal to the monarchy. Even as a boy he had been fascinated by the military, and although he did not serve with the armed forces during the war, he was deeply involved in the war effort. He regarded pacifists and social democrats as despicable enemies of the fatherland and deplored their activities during and after the war. The German defeat affected him deeply, and after the war he would decline invitations to parties where there were French soldiers in uniform. Strange as such patriotic fervor may be, this behavior is perhaps still more understandable than the fact that in 1936, after the National Socialists had come to power he went out of his way in his 'Reminiscences' to make positive comments about that government. It was all the more tragic that he himself had to become their victim later on.

Besides the professional associations, Moll also supported or even founded a number of learned societies. In 1888 he founded the 'Society for Experimental Psychology', later renamed the 'Berlin Society for Psychology and Characterology'. He became its president in 1903. In 1913 he founded the 'International Society for Sex Research' and organized the first international congress on sexology in the years after the first World War. He was a member of the 'German Society for Population Policy' and of a number of other such organizations.

Fields of interest
Besides his interests in hypnosis he also developed another form of psychotherapy which he called 'association therapy' and which was a forerunner of modern behavior modification therapy. He considered the sexual disorders the prime indications for that treatment. He had recognized the reinforcement effect of pleasurable fantasies on the perpetuation of perversions, and devised elaborate modes of conduct for his patients to avoid such reinforcement.

He also showed interest in what would now be called psychometrics but which was referred to at the time as 'psychotechnique', in particular its application to vocational guidance, personnel selection and other fields.

An odd trend was his passionate interest in the occult. Like Houdini he studied the claims of the practitioners of that art to prove that the astonishing effects are not due to supernatural forces. He maintained an intense interest in this right to the end of his very full life.

3. AUGUSTE HENRI FOREL, 1848—1931

Introduction

Forel, like Ellis, has not done a great deal of original research in sexology, and his role in this field is that of an important populariser and educator. Unlike Ellis, however, he remained firmly rooted in medicine and did not only carry out original research in neuropsychiatry which brought him lasting recognition, but taught on the medical faculty, administered a large psychiatric hospital, and practised clinical psychiatry. His greatest successes were achieved in his work as entomologist; he was and is an authority on ants. This work was probably closest to his heart and he devoted himself to it throughout his life no matter how busy he may have been in other important matters. On the one hand a highly critical and careful investigator, he was at the same time deeply involved in various social and political movements such as pacifism, socialism, women's rights, anti-alcoholism, and his publications on the sexual question have the character of these activities rather than that of his scientific or professional work. It was because of his stature as physician, medical scientist and entomologist that his social and political activities, including his efforts in sex education, carried the weight they did.

Biography

The outward diversity of his interests and activities had a natural internal cohesion, which is understandable in the light of his life experiences. He came from French stock; his father was French Swiss from the Canton Vaud on Lake Geneva, his mother came from the South of France. He was brought up in the Calvinist religion and his mother's strict religion and the father's remoteness made the boy rebel very soon against the hellfire teaching and the church itself, which he considered hypocritical and oppressive. Having turned against organised religion already at the age of 15 he nevertheless retained a strict adherence to the high principles which came from his mother's influence, an inexorable love for the truth and a never faltering readiness to help.

Until much later in life, perhaps in his thirties, when he managed to overcome this, he was very shy, having been a timid boy who was afraid of his school companions and their rough games, so much so that his mother at first arranged private tuition at home. This lonely child turned his interests to small insects, particularly ants, which he observed intensely and, against his grandmother's protests, collected and brought home. He was saved by his uncle who managed to appease grandmother, and who gave him Pierre Huber's work on the 'Behaviour of Ants'. Already at the age of 12 or 13 he started systematically to record his observations filling some thirty copy books with them. At 17, while at the gymnasium in Lausanne, a friend who shared his interests in entomology gave him Charles Darwin's 'Origin of Species'. The two authors had an immediate and lasting effect on Auguste. "If the animals are descended each from the others, then this must also apply to man; and then the brain must be the organ of the soul in all animals, including the ants; I absolutely must study and compare the brain and its functions", he wrote in his autobiography. "I kept my word to the end; my life had received its direction; ants and the brain, both were to become my religion".

Entomology

His first publication on ants appeared when he was 20 and reported an original observation made when he was eleven years old. He pursued these studies throughout his life traveling all over the world to collect insects. He would start his field work right in the hotel garden but would also collect in the desert of North Africa or in the jungle of South America. He would later travel extensively in connection with his pacifist and anti-alcoholic activities, but he would take every opportunity, wherever he was, to collect local insects. At 24 he published a large volume on 'The Ants of Switzerland' for which he received a prize. This work brought him into correspondence with Charles Darwin who presented him with a book. His last work on ants appeared in 1923 at the age of 75; 'Le Monde Social des Fourmis' (The social world of the ants) in 5 volumes. Of the approximately 7000 known ants Forel had described in detail 3500. He actually himself found and described 70 species, 49 races and 120 types. He discovered many of the inner organs of ants such as the poison apparatus, the pump-stomach, the olfactory organs, the topochemical smell and much else, and he made innumerable discoveries about their behavior. His work on ants alone would have secured for him a permanent place in the history of science.

Medical studies

At 18 Forel went to Zurich to study medicine. His plans to study the brain were fostered by Gudden's lectures on anatomy and he decided very early to become a psychiatrist, a 'Nervenarzt' or neuropsychiatrist. In 1871 he failed part of his examination. The disappointment was oil on the fire of his self doubts and insecurity, and he became very depressed. He found solace in a study tour on ants in southern Switzerland, and later went to Meynert in Vienna to write his doctoral dissertation. Meynert, it will be remembered was also later a teacher of Freud. He chose a comparative anatomical topic on the thalamus opticus. He was disappointed by Meynert's "leaps of the imagination which were ten times as bold as mine. The longer I remained" he wrote, "the more I lost faith in his encephalogical schemata . . . which he perceived in the brain". He finished his work successfully, however, although Meynert was not pleased when he disagreed with him. "In Meynert's ward the greatest disorder prevailed, and the greatest uncleanliness, so that it did not in the least tempt me to prolong my stay". On his return to Lausanne he obtained his final degree after this time comfortably passing his examination; and after a short stay in Paris ("to get some notion of the state of medicine there" but which was mostly spent in the zoo) he went to Munich in Germany, to work under Gudden for five years. He was at first mostly in the laboratory where he developed what later came to be known as 'Gudden's microtome'. He learned and substantially developed Gudden's method of nerve extirpation, and with it discovered the origins of the olfactory and acoustic nerves. Later he took charge of the disturbed ward and obtained a good grounding in clinical work. Later, while already back in Switzerland he used Golgi's new method of staining nervous tissue and showed that the accepted theory of anastomoses of nerve fibers was wrong. However, no notice was taken of this fundamental discovery on which the neuron theory is based, so named by Waldeyer in Berlin, until in 1889 Ramon y Cajal in Barcclona had confirmed Forel's findings, quoting him briefly. Forel left Munich, his post being taken by Kraepelin and, after a short journey to Columbia to study insects, he accepted the assistant director post of the Burghölzli hospital in Zurich.

The Burghölzli
Forel soon became director and by thoroughly reorganising the hospital much plagued by corruption, drinking, licentious behavior and violence amongst the staff, he laid the foundations of this famous hospital which has made so many great contributions to the advancement of psychiatry. Many of the things he introduced have a modern ring. He saw the importance of segregation of patients, of observation wards, of work therapy, of studying the patients' social and economic background and much more. The post carried with it the chair in psychiatry, and Forel introduced psychiatry as a major subject into the final oral examination for the whole of Switzerland. While there he collected many famous students and assistants such as Adolf Meyer, Eugen Bleuler, Oskar Vogt and others. At the age of 50 he retired, to be succeeded by E. Bleuler. His clinical approach was what would now be called a holistic one. He did not accept the syndromatic descriptions and classifications, believing them to introduce unwarranted divisions — there are only symptoms; disease entities are superficial. He opposed the schizophrenia concept and courageously tackled the soul—brain problem, regarding them as one and opposing any kind of mind—brain parallelism. His philosophical views were characteristic for the 19th century and represented

a kind of philosophical materialism or rationalism. One of his main clinical interests was hypnosis which he had studied in Nancy under Bernheim, and he was an accomplished hypnotist, having recognized the phenomenon to be the product of suggestion.

Other interests
Forel was very active in the world movement for anti-alcoholism. He lectured all over the world and took part in international congresses. His pacificism for which he felt strongly since the Franco—German war of 1870/71 gradually brought him in contact with international political figures and he became a socialist. In 1918 he was elected to the Academy of Soviet Russia but declined the appointment "unless the deeds of violence of which I spoke cease immediately".

The testament
At 35 he married Emma, the daughter of his friend Steinhill, whom he had met during his Munich years. At the time of her marriage Emma was 18 years old. They were very happy although they were not spared tragedy when some of their six children or, later, their spouses died.

The indomitability of the man was shown when he suffered a stroke in his dominant hemisphere in 1911 at the age of 63. He learned to write with his left hand, struggled with his dysphasia and never allowed himself to drop out of his whirlwind of congresses, Good Templer meetings, or pacifist work, while also pursuing his writings. Before he died he asked not to have a clergyman at his graveside. Instead he wrote his own 'testament' to be read there. This is the credo of a great Victorian — an outstanding scientist in the fields of entomology and of the neurosciences, and a rationalist and populariser of social, political, legal and other views, not least, on the sexual problem.

4. HENRY HAVELOCK ELLIS, 1858—1939

Havelock Ellis had an influence on the cultural and social climate of our age which is comparable to that of Marx or Freud. This is true at least for the English-speaking world. He led an unceasing struggle against Victorian views, in particular against the puritanical views on sex and against the attitude towards women who had been "assigned their proper place". Although involved with the contemporary movements for women's rights, sex education and tolerance towards sexual deviants, he managed to avoid taking extreme positions. His contributions were not in the field of sexological research; even the writings on sexology are not primarily based on his own clinical observation, but on case histories collected from elsewhere. He exercised his influence as a publicist who wrote well and brought to his essays an uncommon erudition. Sexual problems of his time were re-examined by him in the light of the many writings on cultural and social anthropology with which he was familiar, and which were well suited to break through the narrow confines of Victorian prejudice.

Biography

Havelock Ellis was born in Croydon, which is now a suburb of London, England. His interest in tracing his ancestors included an anxious search for traces of an hereditary trait. Having obtained some family papers from his father, he embarked on his search and pursued his ancestry as far back as the 16th century. Both his maternal and paternal ancestors (in fact the paternal grandfather and the maternal grandmother were first cousins) came from puritan families who lived in the east country around Suffolk. Both parents came from seafaring families and his father spent half a century at sea. Although this gave Havelock the opportunity for long sea voyages when he was allowed to accompany his father, it also caused the home to be dominated by his mother, not only during the long absences of his father, but even when he spent some time at home between voyages "When my father returned from his long sea-voyages she instinctively remained the mistress of the house and he instinctively fell into the position of guest . . . . He felt, rightly enough, . . . that at home she was the captain".

Havelock goes on, "throughout life I have possessed an instinctive and unreasoned faith in women, a natural and easy acceptance of the belief that they are entitled to play a large part in many fields of activity". The mother is said to have experienced a religious 'conversion' and to have followed strictly 'evangelical' principles and practices, with an avoidance of all 'worldliness'. No doubt this exerted a formative influence on the psychosexual development of Havelock and his four sisters, none of whom ever married.

At the conclusion of his search among his forebears he wrote: "When I survey my ancestral stocks as a whole from the eugenic standpoint, I can find little that seems in the slightest degree unbalanced or unsound . . . . As regards mental soundness, I see no definitely weak point . . . . In my mother there was a latent nervousness which I have inherited in a heightened degree; it renders me in some ways an abnormal person, though scarcely morbid . . . it is never likely to be degraded into insanity".

His psychosexual development was unusual, even for an English boy of his time. Although possessed of a passion for a slightly older girl cousin, which lasted for four years, his feelings for her were never sexual. A few kind attempts by slightly older boys to introduce him to masturbation as a means to develop the genital organs, although the motive was fully approved by him, remained unsuccessful. As he grew older there seem to have been many opportunities for him to have sexual relations with women, but he ignored or even scorned them.

His first intimate woman friend was Olive Schreiner, the South African novelist. He was in his late twenties when they met. She was four years older. Their friendship endured for a lifetime, but he married another when he was 32 and their sexual relationship such as it was, ceased. In his autobiography he states "We were not what can be technically or even ordinarily called lovers". He had other mistresses later, but coitus apparently was not possible, probably because of premature ejaculation. As a boy he had been very worried about nocturnal emissions, which at the time were regarded by doctors to be an illness which tended to lead to general deterioration.

His difficulties were not overcome until he was 58 when he had a happy relationship with Francois Delisle, a young French divorcee of about 30 who adored him, and with whom there seemed to have been complete understanding. Ellis's relationship to Edith Lee, his wife, was complex. After the first year of their marriage all sexual relations which had never been satisfactory, ceased. They both had affairs with the other's knowledge and tolerance, Havelock with a number of ladies, Edith with a succession of women. She was a lesbian. Havelock was entirely tolerant, and they treated each other with consideration. Indeed their relationship remained close, affectionate and warm, as the many letters from Edith to him show.

Edith was herself active in women's movements, and in the Legitimation League "for the advocacy of unconventional ideas on marriage and parenthood, upholding a formal acknowledgement of union in preference to legal marriage and seeking to raise the position of the illegitimate child". She knew many of the great women leaders of the suffragette movement such as Emily Pethic and Eleanor Marx; she gave lectures and toured the USA repeatedly as a lecturer. She published a number of novels, short stories and plays.

Edith's health was fragile, however, and in addition to physical illnesses she suffered from recurrent manic and depressive swings which appear to have grown more severe with advancing years. Ellis never wavered in his dedicated attention to her and helped her through her many difficulties. She believed in spiritualism and was convinced of contacts with the world of spirits, in particular with Lily, one of her lovers who died suddenly while still young. Later she became interested in sufism, at the time inspired by Inayat Khan. ". . . it is not clear to me how far its leader was a charlatan . . ." writes Ellis. The often fine line of demarcation between avant-guardism and crankiness easily blurred.

Besides the various psychosexual difficulties already mentioned, Havelock Ellis also described another slight erotic deviation. He derived sexual pleasure from watching women urinate, preferably in the standing position. He traced this interest back to an early experience when first his nursemaid and later his mother indulged in this habit in his presence — not uncommon at the time of the long wide skirts of the period. This interest may have been a source of worry to the young Havelock, but was not later when he found that most ladies were pleased to oblige his taste.

Choice of career
It is likely, but not certain, that his own psychosexual experiences influ-

enced his decision when he was just under twenty to give up his work as teacher to become sexologist. He was in Australia at the time. Back in England he took up the study of medicine, not for the purpose of practice, but as background to the studies in his real field of interest. He became a Licentiate of the Society of Apothecaries (LMSSA) in 1889. He had been a good if somewhat perfunctory student, much more interested at the time in his literary activities, than in his medical studies.

For a short time he practiced medicine mostly as locum tenens in country practices but soon gave that up for good. In fact it is difficult to ascertain whether he had any kind of practice where he saw sexological conditions. The origin of the elegantly written case histories included in his sexological writings are never stated. Were they obtained by him from patients? Were they taken by others and placed at his disposal? He spent his time in the reading rooms of the British Museum when he was not traveling or in the country. No mention is made in his autobiography of any kind of clinical practice. He did not seem to have studied clinical psychiatry in any depth. When writing of his wife's illness he says ". . . in what later might have been termed her schizoid temperament — from morbid apathy to morbid energy".

His publications soon ran into difficulties. His writings were courageous and the age was far from tolerant in Britain, even less tolerant than elsewhere in Europe. His major writings had to be published abroad. Not even the medical press gave him quarter. When in 1898 he submitted a paper on homosexuality, the publishers gave the manuscript to Dr. Hack Tuke for judgement. Hack Tuke was a leading psychiatrist and editor of the 'Journal of Mental Science'. He advised against publication. "There are always", he said, "the compositers," for whose souls the Quaker Tuke showed such concern lest they should become corrupted. In 1939 after the British Medical Journal published an obituary on Ellis, Dr. Eric Gardner from Weybridge wrote in a letter to the editor (August 5, 1939, p. 320), "Your sympathetic obituary notice on the late Dr. Havelock Ellis reminds me that not only did his work meet with disapproval in the law courts, but it is not so long ago that the open discussion of sexual matters was frowned on even in the columns of the British Medical Journal. I can well remember reading a review of Krafft-Ebing's 'Psychopathia Sexualis', published between 1896 and 1900 when I was at Cambridge. Your reviewer deplored the publication of such a work and in vitriolic phrases pilloried author, translator, publisher, and printer, but this concluding sentence has always remained in my mind. It was to this effect: 'Finally with regard to the paper on which this book is printed, we only hope it may be put to the basest use to which paper can be applied'."

At one time one of Ellis's books came to trial and he himself was threatened with arrest, ". . . not a single prominent scientific or medical person came publicly forward for the defence (of the book) . . . and though I received . . . the most handsome testimonials from the leading authorities in the medico-psychological sphere . . . the writers were not prepared to go into the witness box on behalf of the book." Part of the difficulty no doubt arose because the entire affair had somehow become linked with the Legitimation League.

Self-evaluation

Havelock Ellis had to endure much hostility. Recognition eluded him until his later years. He never achieved affluence. We know what the world feels about his work. How did he feel about his life's work? Nothing could be more illuminating than this passage in his autobiography. "I had not ... achieved an immortal work of scientific art. My work, I knew, must in the nature of it be always crumbling and every day grow a little more out of date ... I had not created a great work of art. But I had done mankind a service which mankind needed, and which, it seemed, I alone was fitted to do. I had helped to make the world better ... by liberating the human spirit. The gratitude of men, and of women, has made me humble. I have sometimes felt that the taunt might be flung at me which was flung at Jesus: 'He saved others, himself he could not save'. Yet I am well assured with as little truth in the one case as in the other, for I have never sought any salvation for myself. I have been well content to be a Knight of the Holy Ghost. As I write these words I recall that Edith's pet euphemism for the male sex organ was 'the Holy Ghost'. Well, be it so!"

5. MAGNUS HIRSCHFELD, 1868—1935

Introduction

Although in some ways still rooted in the general theories which formed the basis of the sexology of the 19th century, Hirschfeld succeeded in advancing these studies significantly, taking them in many respects beyond the limits set by the earlier workers. While not abandoning the theory of dégénérescence completely, he severely limited its application. Instead he proposed his 'Zwischenstufentheorie', the theory of intersexes, and he recognized the importance of endocrinology. He had also completely overcome the 18th century views on the pathogenic effect of masturbation.

Biography

Magnus Hirschfeld was born on May 14, 1868 in a small German spa on the Baltic sea called Kolberg. His father Hermann, who came from a poor Jewish family, was a respected general practitioner in Kolberg, and the town honored him after his death by a statue, which the Germans destroyed when the National Socialist government came to power. His mother Frederika, née Mann, succeeded in making the home for her husband and seven children a happy one. Magnus was the second youngest. His father was in the habit of taking his sons as they grew older with him on his rounds and discussing his work with them. Magnus felt that his flare for detailed clinical observation came from these 'lessons' of his childhood. However, at the time he did not intend to take up medicine but had literary ambitions. He wanted to become a writer. After completing high school he inscribed at Breslau University for philosophy and comparative literature. He did not complete his studies, but switched to science and medicine. His later writings show that his literary ambition was backed by considerable talent. His medical books and papers are exceptionally well written, far above what one can usually expect in such publications. His style is lucid and elegant and the reading of his work provides esthetic pleasure as well as dramatic interest.

Medical studies
He studied medicine at Strassburg, Munich, Heidelberg and Berlin where he graduated in 1892 at the age of 24. He received his 'Promotion' one year later on a thesis on 'The Nervous Sequelae of Influenza'. Professionally established at 25, he did not want to settle down but traveled, first to the USA and later to Africa. On his return he opened a general practice first in Magdeburg, and shortly afterwards in Charlottenburg. Already at this early stage in his career he had become interested in the problem of homosexuality. One of his patients had commited suicide, as it turned out later, because he was a homosexual. This experience prompted Magnus to write a book called 'Sappho und Sokrates' with the subtitle 'How can one explain the love of men or women to persons of the same sex'. Sensing the danger of writing on the topic of sex he published the book in 1896 under the pseudonym Th. Ramien. The book met with success. In the same year the young doctor went before the public again, this time and from then on always, under his own name. He wrote a book called '§175. Die Homosexuelle Frage im Urteil der Zeitgenossen' (§175, (from the German criminal law dealing with homosexuality) The question of homosexuality in the judgement of contemporaries). At the same time he submitted a petition to the Reichstag for the removal of this law from the statute book. He had formed in 1897 together with a number of eminent men, the 'Wissenschaftlich Humanitäre Komitee' (Scientific-Humanitarian Committee) which was to lead the fight for equal rights for sexual minorities. In 1899 he founded the 'Jahrbücher für sexuelle Zwischenstufen' (Yearbooks for Intersexes) which was the official organ of the 'Komitee', and of which there are 22 volumes. They contain a series of very important articles by many authors. The first volume contained a paper by Hirschfeld on "the objective diagnosis of homosexuality" in which he presents for the first time his intersex theory.

Scientific work
This combination of excellent, original and very extensive scientific research and social commitment with a courageous fight against injustice and for social and legal reform was characteristic of his entire life's work. His courage can only be fully appreciated if one takes into account that Hirschfeld

was himself a homosexual, who cultivated his friendship with many well known homosexuals, stood by them and helped where he could, privately and publicly, when this was necessary. This involvement brought him enemies as well as friends. One of his fierce adversaries was Albert Moll, himself an outstanding figure in the field of sexology. The controversy began in 1907 during a famous court case of an alleged sex offence in which Hirschfeld acted as an expert witness, and drew fire from Moll who disagreed with his report. Hirschfeld, at about the same time, however, did become very friendly with the dermatologist Iwan Bloch with whom he collaborated for many years to come.

Transvestism and transexualism

In 1908 Hirschfeld founded the 'Zeitschrift für Sexualwissenschaft', a name introduced by Bloch, which published articles by the most eminent sexologists such as Forel, Freud, Bloch, Juliusburger, Kronfeld, Lombroso, Stekel and many others. He conducted a busy practice, and in 1910 he had in his possession already about 10,000 case histories. In that year he published his book on 'Die Transvestiten' (Berlin, Pulvermacher) which was really the first systematic account of the syndrome now known as 'transexualism'. The year 1912 brought the 'Kasuistik des Verkleidungstriebes' (Case histories of transvestitism) in the Neurologisches Zentralblatt, and also an article on 'Geschlechtsumwandlungen' (sex change). This topic was pursued in a number of other publications in 1913 and 1918. It was after Hirschfeld's publications that Ellis wrote on what he called Eonism. Before Hirschfeld the 'Konträre Sexualempfindung', as Westphal had called it, was not clearly distinguished from homosexuality. Hirschfeld pointed out that most or at least many transvestites (a name introduced by him) are heterosexual.

In 1912 he published 'Naturgesetze der Liebe' (Natural laws of love) — (Berlin, Pulvermacher) and 'Kastratenstudien. Untersuchungen über sexuellen Chemismus'. (Studies on castrates. Investigations on sexual chemism). In these papers he discussed his views of biochemical aspects of the sexual drive which seem to be based on his studies of castrates which he examined during a visit to Bucharest in Roumania and Constantinople in Turkey. He surmised hypothetical endocrine substances being produced by tissues in the testes (Andrin) and the ovaries (gynacin) which, he thought, exercised a decisive influence on the sex drive.

Homosexuality

In 1913 he returned to his main topic in a paper on 'Male Prostitution' in which he clarified Bloch's concept of 'pseudohomosexuality' and in 1914 in an exhaustive account of 'Die Homosexualität des Mannes und des Weibes' (Homosexuality of men and women) which appeared as Vol. 3 of the 'Handbuch der Gesamten Sexualwissenschaft in Einzeldarstellungen' (Handbook of all sexology in special presentations) edited by Iwan Bloch.

In that volume of over 1000 pages he summarised all that was known on homosexuality from the earliest ages of recorded history, to the latest transplant experiments by Steinach which he had accepted without reservations. The frame of this masterful presentation is his intersex theory which he supported with his extensive evidence. He also dealt extensively with the medicolegal aspects of homosexuality.

The World War

The war in 1914 found him a member of the 'Bund Neues Deutschland', an organisation which was working for democracy and internationalism. During the war years his democratic and socialist convictions grew and at the end of the war he strongly supported the democratic revolution in Germany. One of the progressive political suggestions of Hirschfeld at the end of the war was the institution of a Ministry of Health.

During the war he had been publishing his 'Sexualpathologie' in 3 volumes and a paper on 'Metatropismus (1918)' by which are meant the perversions of sadism and masochism, integrating them in his system of intersexes. In 1919 he founded his 'Institute für Sexualwissenschaft', which served as a research centre, a sex education center, and a service center — it contained for instance, consulting facilities and a marriage advice bureau. The center was often open to the public. Consultations were free of charge. Hirschfeld had bought the house, a palatial building, with his own means, had renovated it to suit his purposes, and had later donated it to the German nation. The latter closed it and destroyed his collections and publicly burned his books when the National Socialist government was elected. Until then, however, the institute was extremely active. The case archives at his disposal for research numbered nearly 20,000 records after the first year and was growing fast. The institute attracted a number of outstanding sexologists who advanced the studies further.

The interwar years

In 1921 Hirschfeld took part in the organisation of the 'International Congress for Sex Reform' in Berlin, which was followed in later years by similar Congresses in Copenhagen and London. In 1928 he published his opus magnum called 'Geschlechtskunde', a comprehensive presentation of the entire field of sexology in 5 volumes.

Hirschfeld was not only a daring researcher but a social and political fighter. His work has all along drawn many attacks. During the late 1920s and early 1930s, however, with the growth of intolerance in Germany, his position became gradually untenable. It became increasingly difficult and eventually impossible for him to appear in public at home, so he accepted invitations for lecture tours abroad. He again visited the U.S., and also Japan, China, Java, Ceylon, India, Egypt and Palestine, using his time to collect material and information.

Luckily, when the German holocaust broke and his Institute was ransacked, Hirschfeld was abroad in France. He lived mostly in Nice where he shared a house with Alfred Neumann and Theodore Wolff. He continued to cultivate his literary interests both before and after he left Germany. His sister was the writer Franciska Mann, and with her he frequented literary salons. On his birthday in 1935 Magnus Hirschfeld collapsed in the street just as he was about to enter his house, and died.

6. IWAN BLOCH, 1872—1922

Introduction

Bloch's work represents the culmination of the 19th century development of the study of the sexual abnormalities which had started with Krafft-Ebing's 'Psychopathia Sexualis', and which had received powerful stimulus and contributions by such men as Forel, Moll, Eulenburg, Steinach, Hirschfeld, Ellis and Freud, but had remained essentially a biological science. Bloch's contribution was the introduction of the social sciences to this field, in particular anthropology and ethnology, thereby breaking the too-narrow biological confines and laying the foundation of modern sexology. It fell to the so-called post-Freudian schools to build on these foundations, and to the contemporary experimentalists, epidemiologists and geneticists, to harvest the fruits of it. As an inspired student of Virchow and of the natural philosopher Ernst Haeckel, Bloch never abandoned the biological approach. This multidisciplinary but coordinated approach he called 'Sexualwissenschaft', or 'Sexology'. We even have to thank him for the very name of our subject. Bloch's contribution, like all leaps in the history of ideas, was essentially a methodological one, although the details of its execution, the collection and survey of new information, the evaluation of it, and the elegance of presentation were all masterly and brilliant in their own right.

Biography

His work was achieved in all too short a life. He died on November 19, 1922 in Berlin, Germany, after a long and painful illness. As a result of vascular disease he had to undergo amputation, first of one leg and then of the other. Already confined to his bed he saw and greatly enjoyed the celebrations of his fiftieth birthday, with many scientists from all over the world expressing their congratulations and appreciation of his achievements. A few months later he died.

Iwan Bloch was born on April 8, 1872 in Delmenhorst, Oldenburg, in North Germany. His father was a Jewish merchant who passed to his son his passion for literature, in particular the classics. Already during his high school years Iwan was an avid reader of philosophy, a love which he never lost. He studied medicine in Bonn, Heidelberg and Berlin but did not confine himself to medicine alone. In 1896 he obtained his doctorate in Würzburg after submission of a thesis on 'The Influence of Iodine, Thyroidin and Thyrades on Metabolism'. His postgraduate studies were in dermatology which then always included venereology, and he became a specialist in 1897. He settled in Berlin practising dermatology and venereology, but his practice did not seem to have made too great a demand on him, as he was able to leave for long periods to pursue his studies. He went to Hamburg to study under the great dermatologist Unna. Very soon Unna, who had recognised Bloch's gifts, placed his records at his disposal, and asked him to evaluate and publish the material. From that period came 'Die Praxis der Hautkrankheiten' (The practice of dermatology) with the subtitle (in translation) 'Unna's teaching for students and practitioners' which appeared in 1908. The book has become a classic. At the same time he also pursued his studies in anthropology, cultural history and ethnology which took him well outside the normal confines of the medical sciences. To equip himself to use original sources he learned modern and ancient languages — he even tried himself on Sanskrit — for which he had special gifts. He spoke several languages fluently and was able for instance, to have books published which were written by him in English. He wrote "Since my earliest youth I grew up in the most colourful of all worlds, in the world of books." He was a passionate bibliophile and had an intimate knowledge of the literature of all times and all cultures. He had a valuable collection of 80,000 volumes in his private library. He soon acquired a high reputation for his erudition and astonished his listeners when debating at professional meetings by his vast knowledge and by the way he always seemed to have his facts at his fingertips.

Literary activities and social reform
In 1910 he began editing a series of monographs called 'Sexual-psychologische Bibliothek'. The work which was published in that series was greatly enriched by the extensive and erudite bibliographies he supplied. In 1912 he began editing his 'Handbuch der Gesamten Sexualwissenschaft.' The work consists of contributions from various authors each on a particular subject. In 1914 he founded, together with Eulenburg, the 'Zeitschrift für Sexualwissenschaft'.

In addition to these literary activities he took an active part, together with a number of contemporaries including Hirschfeld and Moll, in the struggle for sex reform which included sex education and law reform.

International recognition for this extraordinarily creative and active life was signified in 1913 when he was elected a corresponding member of The Royal Society of London, and in 1920 when he was elected an honorary member of the British Society for Sex Psychology in London.

Areas of interest
Bloch's main areas of interest fell into Dermatology and Venereology, History of Medicine and Sexology. In each of these he had major achievements. In dermatology he published the already mentioned 'Praxis der Hautkrank-

heiten' in 1908. Earlier, in 1898, he had published several polemical papers against the bactericidal treatment of gonorrhea. His attention soon focused, however, on historical and ethnological questions of dermatology and venereology. He wrote on such diverse subjects as 'Historical Aspects of the Treatment of Burns' (1898), 'The 19,000 Leprosaria in the 13th century' (1899), 'The Prehistory of Leprosy' (1899), 'The Shipdoctors in the Byzantium' (1902), 'Official prison Doctors in Italian Cities' (1903) and on many others.

His outstanding work in the field of medical history brought him an invitation by Pagel, a medical historian, to write a number of chapters in Pagel's 'Handbuch der Geschichte der Medicine' (Handbook of the history of medicine). Bloch wrote the sections on Indian Medicine, Ancient Roman Medicine, Greek Physicians of the 3rd and 4th Post-Christian Centuries, Byzantine Medicine and others. The best known work on historical aspects of venereology in his 'Ursprung der Syphilis' (Origin of Syphilis) which appeared in 1901 (Vol. 1), and in 1912 (Vol. II). He argued that the disease was brought to Europe from America, and although that thesis was not universally accepted, the erudition with which he had supported his case found recognition, and, in Sudhof's words, gives it lasting value.

Sexology
Without detracting from his achievements in those areas, his contributions to sexology are probably the most important of all his work. As already mentioned, the concept of sexology as we know it today and its very name are his creations. When Bloch entered his field, matters concerning sex were not talked or written about freely, even in medical circles, and writers risked severe disapprobation. It was perhaps partly because of this that Bloch published his early work under the pseudonym Eugen Dühren. He explained, however, "When I chose a pseudonym I wanted merely to express that as a physician I had entered an area which is alien to the purely medical, namely that of cultural history." Whatever the explanation, the early work of Dühren attracted much attention, and for a long time it was not known who the young author really was. The books were 'Der Marquis de Sade und unsere Zeit' (1900) (The Marquis de Sade and our time), and 'Rétif de la Bretonne, der Mensch, der Schriftsteller, der Reformer' (1906) (Rétif de la Bretonne, the man, the writer, the reformer). With the study of these two strange men Bloch already outlined his new concepts of the nature and cultural significance of sexual abnormalities. In 1901, 1902 and 1903 he published, still under the name of Dühren, the 3 volumes of 'Das Geschlechtsleben in England' (Sexual life in England). Subsequent works were all published under his real name.

In 1907 appeared the 'Sexualleben unserer Zeit' translated into English the following year by E. Paul as 'The Sexual Life of our Time in its Relations to Modern Civilisation'. In that book and in his two volumes of 'Beiträge zur Aetiologie der Psychopathia Sexualis' (Contributions to the etiology of psychopathia sexualis) which appeared in 1902 he gave a systematic account of his views on the etiology and nature of sexual abnormalities. They were further elaborated in his work on 'Prostitution' which was to appear in several volumes but remained a fragment. Volume I appeared in 1912 but the work was interrupted by the war.

The war years

Bloch had to serve in the armed forces during the war. To him the life as a soldier was destruction itself. He suffered horribly while in the service, and was never able to adapt to that way of life. Bloch was described a very sensitive person, who felt hurt very easily and who recoiled when attacked rather than fight back. His friends knew this and their relationship towards him was always protective. The general tone of army life was anathema to him. A few years after the war a group of young American psychoanalysts who were interested in sexology visited Bloch in Berlin. Iago Galdston gives a charming account of the visit. Bloch complained to them about the war. For 4 years he had had to work in a hospital as internist. Galdston writes, "He was one of those few German savants who protested against the war, and who pleaded with the men of science for a world fraternity of learning, against an unholy alliance of imperialism, greed, bigotry, and that most vicious pseudohumanism that threw the cloak of democracy over the most colossal crime in the history of the world". He complained bitterly about the interruption of his work on the second volume of his 'Prostitution' which could not be completed before he was called up.

He was afraid that it would take him a long time to regain command over his material, and indeed it took him years after the war to read himself once more into the extensive and diverse source-literature. However, his fate would not permit him to complete the book. His illness made it impossible. Bernstein wrote "The book on prostitution is the culmination of the life work of Bloch. Indeed, in it we can see the great wealth of his spirit and his heart, the combination of all which in Roman times formed the concept of 'humanitas', of the freedom and dignity of a true humanity".

Bloch always defended those inflicted, if this is the right word, with sexual abnormalities against persecution and injustice. He drew attention to the power of the sexual drive to induce a state of "monomania", temporarily brushing aside the principles of character and sound judgement, and rendering the person "irresponsible". He pointed to the medicolegal consequences of this and advocated the adoption into the legal code of the concept of diminished responsibility in the 'crime passionel'. Although homosexuality was regarded as an abnormality and, as regards the cultural development, as nondialectical and sterile, he never failed to stress the rights of the homosexual in society.

ACKNOWLEDGEMENT

I do not wish to conclude this chapter without expressing my gratitude to Ms. Faye Cammaert who gave valuable assistance in the library searches, the typing of the manuscripts and the proofreading.

BIBLIOGRAPHY

Richard von Krafft-Ebing

Biographisches Lexicon Hervorragender Arzte aller Zeiten und Völker. Ed., A. Hirsch (Wien, 1886) Vol. 3, p. 539.

Eulenburg, A. (1903) Nekrologe Krafft-Ebing. *Dtsche Med. Wochenschr.* V. 29, 39.

Jaspers, K. (1966) *General Psychopathology.* Transl. J. Hoenig and M. Hamilton (Toronto University Press, Toronto).

Johnson, J. (1973) Psychopathia Sexualis. *Br. J. Psychiatr.* 122: 211—218.

Karplus, J.P. (1903) Krafft-Ebing. *Wien. Klin. Wochenschr.* 16: 21—23.

Kenez, J. (1968) Richard v. Krafft-Ebing. *Orv. Hetil.* 109: 317—319.

Krafft-Ebing, R. (1965) *Psychopathia Sexualis, a Medico-forensic Study.* Transl. H.E. Wedeck (Putmann, New York).

Krich, A.M. (1964) *The Sexual Revolution. Krafft-Ebing, Ellis, Freud.* (Deltabooks, New York.)

Niedermayer, A. (1957) Krafft-Ebing. In: *Osterreichische Arzte als Helfer der Menschneit.* (Notring Joahrbuch, Wien) p. 89.

Wagner-Jauregg, v. R. (1902) Festrede aus Anlass des 30 Jährigen Professoren Jubiläums von Hofrath v. Krafft-Ebing, *Wien. Klin. Wochenschr.* 12: 318—319.

Wettley, A. and Leibbrand, W. (1959) *Von der 'Psychopathia Sexualis' sur Sexualwissenschaft.* (Ferd. Enke, Stuttgart.)

Albert Moll

Moll, A. (1913) *The Sexual Life of the Child.* Transl. E. Paul (McMillan Co., New York).

Moll, A. (1936) *Das Leben als Arzt der Seele, Erinnerungen.* (Dresden.)

Winkelmann, O. (1965) Albert Moll (1862—1939) als Wegbereiter der Schule von Nancy in Deutschland. *Praxis Psychother.* 10: 1—7.

Auguste Henri Forel

Darwin, F. (1887) *Leben und Briefe Charles Darwin.* Vol. III, (Stuttgart).

Forel, A. (1924) *The Sexual Question.* Transl. C.F. Marshall (Physicians and Surgeons Book Co., New York).

Forel, A. (1927) Auguste Forel. In: (L.R. Grote, Ed.) *Die Medizin in Selbstdarstellungen.* (Felix Meiner, Leipzig) pp. 53—87.

Forel, A. (1937) *Out of My Life and Work.* Transl. B. Miall (Allen and Unwin, London).

Forel, A. (1968) *Auguste Forel, Brief Correspondance 1864—1927.* H.H. Walser, Ed. (Huber, Bern).

Kuhlenbeck, H. (1970) Auguste Forel (1848—1931). In: (W. Haymaker and F. Schiller, Eds.) *Founders of Neurology.* 2nd edn (Thomas, Springfield, Illinois).

Muralt, A.v. (1929) Auguste Forel. *Schweiz. Med. Jahrbuch.* 6—17.

Henri Havelock Ellis

Cox, C. (1966) *The Enigma of the Age*. (Longmans, Green and Co., London.)
Delisle, F. (1946) *Odyssey of a Friendship*. (Heineman, London.)
Ellis, H. (1923) *The Dance of Life*. (Riverside Press, Boston.)
Ellis, H. (1930) *Fountain of Life*. (Riverside Press, Boston.)
Ellis, H. (1934) *My Confessional*. (Carlton House, New York.)
Ellis, H. (1936) *Studies in the Psychology of Sex*. (Random House, New York.)
Ellis, H. (1940) *My Life*. (Heineman, London.)
Goldberg, I. (1926) *Havelock Ellis*. (Simon and Schuster, New York.)
Obituary, Henry Havelock Ellis. LSA, FRCP (1939) *Lancet* II, 164—165.
Obituary, Havelock Ellis FRCP (1939), *Br. Med. J.* II, 203—204.

Magnus Hirschfeld

Hirschfeld, M. (1913) Die Homosexualität des Mannes und des Weibes. In: *Handbuch der Sexualwissenschaft in Einzeldarstellungen*. Vol. IIIv. Ed., Iwan Bloch (Louise Marcus, Berlin).
Hirschfeld, M. (1917) *Sexualpathologie*. (Bonn).
Hirschfeld, M. (1925) *Die Travestiten, Verl. Wahrheit*. (F. Spohr, Leipzig.)
Praetorius, N. (1918) Magnus Hirschfelds wissenschaftliches Werk. *Jahrb. Sexuelle Zwischenstufen*, 18: 19—35.
Seidel, R. (1968) Sexuelle Zwischenstufen als Anthropologische Varietäten. Zum 100. Geburtstag von Magnus Hirschfeld. *Med. Klin.*, 63: 812—815.
Steinach, E. (1913) Feminisierung von Männchen und Maskulinisierung von Weibchen. *Zentralbl. Physiol.*, 27.
Wettley, A. and Leibbrand, W. (1959) *Von der Psychopathia Sexualis zur Sexualwissenschaft*. (F. Enke, Stuttgart.)

Iwan Bloch

Bastian, A. (1868) *Das Beständige in den Menschenrassen und die Speilweite ihrer Veränderlichkeit*.
Bernstein, A. (1923) Iwan Bloch. *Zschr. Sexualwiss.* 9: 265—267.
Bloch, I. (1902) Zur Genesis sexueller Anomalien *Med Blätter 25*: No. 5 3(41—42), 4(60—62), 6(96—98), 8(127—129).
Bloch, I. (1907) *Das Sexualleben unserer Zeit in seinen Beziehungen zur Modernen Kultur*. Berlin.
Bloch, I. (1908) *The Sexual Life of our Time in its Relations to Modern Civilization*. transl. from 6th Ed. E. Paul (London).
Ebstein, E. (1923) In Memoriam: Iwan Bloch. *Med. Life*. 30: 57—70.
Galdston, I. (1923) Impressions of Iwan Bloch. *Med. Life*. 30: 169—173.
Hirsch, M. (1923) Iwan Bloch. *Arch. Frauenheilkunde*.9: 1.
Pinkus, F. (1923) Iwan Bloch. *Dermatol. Wochenschr*. 76: 13—15.
Wettley, A. and Leibbrand, W. (1959) *Von der Psychopathia Sexualis zur Sexualwissenschaft*. (F. Enke, Stuttgart.)

CHAPTER 4

Freud's libido theory

HENDRIKA C. HALBERSTADT-FREUD

'The mind is a world'

Saul Bellow

1. INTRODUCTION

The change Freud caused in the perception of man's inner world can be compared to the change brought about by Galileo and Marx in man's view of the universe and of society. In connection with Freud, two other scientists who also influenced the ascent of man, deserve mentioning. Darwin, who greatly inspired Freud, and Einstein, whom he befriended.

The ideas of relativity and evolution could easily make man feel like a grain of sand, moved by the tides and the sea: not withstanding the stormy development of the natural sciences in the 19th century.

Freud can be seen as a counterforce, extolling the individual by making him a unique and meaningful entity, worthwhile of thorough analysis. He discovered a method which made the meaning of mental phenomena accessible to science. Until then this had been the realm of mystics, artists and novelists. Mental illness, neurosis, dreams and the happenings of daily life like slips of the tongue, henceforth could be understood, deciphered and translated into understandable language.

In Freud's lifetime the natural sciences enjoyed great prestige. A scientific model, adapted to the study of human behavior, such as communication theory, social psychology's systems theory, or modern semantics, did not exist. Freud was trained in medicine, especially in physiology and neurology, not in psychology. He tried to incorporate his empirical findings, which were in essence of a psychological nature, into the mechanistic language of the physics of his age. Consequently concepts like conservation of energy, the constancy principle, quantity, tension, discharge and excitation were

Handbook of Sexology, edited by J. Money and H. Musaph
© *Elsevier/North-Holland Biomedical Press, 1977*

familiar to him. Freud endeavored to found a scientific psychology, with the same prestige as the natural sciences and resistant to their constant reproaches and ridicule. He formulated a psychoanalytic theory, his metapsychology, in causal deterministic and materialistic terms. Its inherent reductionistic abstractions can hardly do justice to Freud's greatest findings. Besides it he formulated a clinical theory close to empirical facts and couched in psychological language. Freud founded a semantic theory that enabled him to make common sense out of seemingly chaotic communications.

The theoretical formulations of the various scientists mentioned, including Freud, might be dated and become outdated; the impact of their ideas will hardly be affected thereby. Even if Freud's so-called metapsychology might become replaced by modern concepts or forgotten altogether, his mode of thinking has pervaded all aspects of human life from the arts to child rearing. Freud was not a writing-desk scientist. He observed his patients, and while working with them in a relationship, he discovered a new method of treating mental disorders. From this starting point he was able to formulate general psychological principles.

2. FREUD'S MAIN DISCOVERIES

Freud was born in Moravia in 1856; he worked most of his life in Vienna, and died in London in 1939. The peak of his creativity lies around 1900, the year in which he published his 'Interpretation of Dreams'. Dreams form the royal road to the unconscious, and the major role of unconscious processes in mental life became firmly established. Connected with this discovery was the discovery of different modes of thinking. The primary process is not only typical for dreams and neurotic symptoms, but for unconscious mental processes in general. Primary process thinking aims at immediate satisfaction by any means, regardless of time or reality. Thinking takes place in images and symbols instead of words. Much use is made of condensation and displacement: one person can stand for another, one image can be connected with many different ideas. Abstract ideas like love and hate are translated into imagery.

The secondary process is the realistic time- and logic- bound, conscious mode of thought.

Freud published his ideas about infantile sexuality in 1905 in his 'Three Essays on the Theory of Sexuality'. In this book Freud put forward his ideas on the development of psychosexuality from early childhood into adulthood. A genetic or developmental point of view was established which sees man in the perspective of his own history. Freud's studies on hysteria had led him to both discoveries, namely of mental life being for a large part unconscious and of the development of infantile into adult sexuality. Hitherto hysteria and other mental disorders had been explained solely by heredity and other physical causes, without any psychic coherence or meaning.

To speak of his sexual theories is to speak of Freud, but to speak of Freud is not to deal exclusively with sexuality. There sometimes arises a semantic difficulty based on the superficial view that Freud interpreted everything as sexual.

The so-called libido, the sexual drive * in all its ramifications, develops throughout the course of life, beginning at birth. The libido undergoes many vicissitudes, changing either aim or object or both through the various developmental phases. Development can come to a standstill called fixation or move backwards to a fixation point, called regression. The main source of satisfaction in each phase of infantile development is called an erotogenic zone.

Besides libido, aggression passes through several developmental phases also. At birth and throughout the first year there is the oral phase, characterized by primacy of the mouth region, for both food intake and satisfaction. Biting is considered to be part of oral sadistic satisfaction.

In the next phase the child discovers and widens his world. He controls his muscles better, and with his sphincter he can control his bladder as well. Cleanliness training is started as a beginning of socialization. This is a source of ambivalent feelings, that is of love and hate alternating. Part of the super-ego (see below) is already formed at this time. In accordance with the many feelings, sensations and satisfactions centered around the anal region, this is called the anal phase. Witholding and letting go become pleasurable body functions, besides eliciting general pleasure in functioning.

Fixation to anal satisfaction especially to anal sadism, can lead to a sado-masochistic perversion, to an obsessional neurosis, or to anal character traits such as stubbornness, stingyness, and over-meticulousness. This is an example of the connection between libidinal development and mental disorders.

Gradually, as the sexual organs become better represented in the psyche of the child he enters the phallic phase. Pleasure in masturbation, seeing other's and showing one's own genitals and being proud of them, and comparison between boys and girls come to the fore. The complicated relationships in the family circle which now become possible, accompanied by feelings of love, hate and jealousy are labelled the oedipal phase. In terms of object relations the child has passed from mainly autoerotic to mainly alloerotic experience, and from need-satisfying objects to objects with an identity of their own.

Freud's phase theory laid more stress on biological development than on object relations. Klein (1934) amended Freud's theory in 1934. She did not define development in terms of libidinal phases any more, but in terms of

---

* The concepts 'drive' and 'instinct' are used as alternatives. Freud spoke mostly of 'Triebe' in the original German text. In the Standard Edition of his complete works the concept of 'instinct' is used. In most instances the word 'drive' would be more appropriate, as Freud seldom spoke of instincts (Instinkte) which denote inborn and inherited traits of questionable applicability to man.

'positions' and the object relations during them. For example, the depressive position takes place during the oral phase, while object relations are already of an oedipal character, with oral characteristics. Her theory was mostly derived from the analysis of young and sometimes psychotic children. Later findings, however, have born out her idea that the oedipal phase and other developments take place much earlier than Freud assumed. The child has an awareness of both male and female genitals from quite early on. He does not discover this in the phallic oedipal phase with the castration complex as a consequence according to Melanie Klein. Further, she holds that the phallic phase in women is not an authentic development, but a defensive structure. The superego and the defenses develop much earlier than had been assumed by Freud, namely even before repression is organized.

Just as Freud widened the concept of mental life to encompass both conscious and unconscious phenomena, so he widened the concept of sexuality to the seeking of pleasure in general. The concept of sexuality has a much wider meaning than the functioning of the mature sexual apparatus and its concomitant satisfactions. Remote branches can take root in the same tree. On the one hand one has neurosis as an outgrowth of stultified sexual development, but there is also sublimation, to account for man's higher achievements. Gratification can be achieved with a change of aim and object, called sublimation. For example, the sexual curiosity of the small child is said to become sublimated into the intellectual curiosity of the latency child. Jealousy can become sublimated into a need for justice and morality derives from the need to control the drives. In Freud's theory of motivation, the higher order cultural and intellectual achievements and interests can be considered canalizations of more primary motives. Man is born with a tendency to seek satisfaction, called the pleasure principle, notwithstanding barriers and obstacles from the outside world and from within (conscience). Satisfaction has to take place according to the reality principle, that means the maximum obtainable without anxiety (loss of love or self-esteem, or superego anxiety).

Man's sexual development is biphasic, the first phase being formed by infantile sexuality, then follows a period of so-called latency (during elementary school age), a phase of mental and physical immaturity, whereupon the revival of sexuality in puberty forms the second phase.

The passing through several phases, the differential psychosexual development of the male and the female child, and the necessity of acculturation and socialization present very many pitfalls in the form of possible fixations and regressions. On the one hand there is the impoverished personality where too much repression of wishes and feelings has taken place, or which develops too many and too rigid defense mechanisms: neurosis. On the other hand there is the impulse-ridden psychopathic or perverse personality. Freud had a picture of man as having to escape the Scylla of too much socialization against the Charibdis of letting the libido get the upper hand.

In speaking of Freud's libido theory one has to envisage the whole of psychic functioning, normal and pathological. In Dora (Fragment of an Analysis of a Case of Hysteria, 1905), Freud combined his ideas about the unconscious, the two modes of mental functioning, and infantile sexuality. He showed how the psychoneuroses are linked up with repression of sexuality and lack of satisfaction. He demonstrated how symptoms are formed as a compromise formation between a wish and a defense; how condensation and displacement and reversal of affect are at work in determining or over-determining the symptom, which has to be translated back into the original wish to eliminate the symptom. Transformation of unconscious processes into conscious experiences is what psychotherapy is about.

3. FREUD'S THEORY

In his long scientific career Freud adapted his theory several times to incorporate new findings. He developed two models of the mind, to be used thereafter side by side. First came the topographical model, according to which the psychic apparatus consists of different regions, the unconscious, the preconscious and the conscious. The unconscious is the site of primitive wishes and ideas, dynamically striving for gratification. This tendency is opposed by a contrary one: the repression of undesirable wishes and ideas barring them from consciousness. Later Freud discovered that not only undesirable wishes or drives remain unconscious. In fact many habitual ways of solving conflicts remain unconscious, and defenses as well; internal perception becomes distorted in neurosis. In 1923 Freud put forward his second model of the mind, the structural theory. The mental apparatus was now assumed to consist of different structures, namely the id, the ego and the super-ego, to each of which the attribute of consciousness can be applicable.

The id is mostly synonymous with being unconscious, though consciousness can be arrived at for deep-rooted and primitive wishes and ideas as well. Sexual needs are normally conscious, death wishes are not. The ego is a regulatory system that takes care of adaptation. Part of it is conscious secondary process thinking, but many defense mechanisms remain unconscious. The super-ego, containing the ideals of a person as well as his moral imperatives is only partially conscious. The ego and the super-ego lend themselves very well to the therapeutic aim of enlarging the realm of consciousness. For example, a patient can gradually come to understand that he denies his aggressive tendencies, projects them onto others, and is not allowed by his conscience ever to be angry.

Psychoanalysis went through an evolution already during Freud's lifetime. Gradually the ego, as a mediator between wishes and reality, began to play a greater role. Other mechanisms of defense besides repression were discovered and described in greater detail by Freud's daughter Anna Freud in 1936. Today we know that there exist more than the ten defense mechanisms she described. In fact every person has his idiosyncratic forms of adaptation and defense, so that they become literally countless. They form the character of the person and in a neurotic person are his shield against the world. Psychoanalysis or psychotherapy on analytic lines has become ego analysis or character analysis. Along with the shifting of emphasis from the unconscious (the drives) to the ego, unconscious ego functioning has become the main target of treatment.

After Freud's death, psychoanalysis, aiming at becoming a general psychology, developed a complete ego psychology as an integral part of its theory. Autonomous, non-instinctual ego functions and learned modes of behavior became better understood, and reduction to primary needs was no longer necessary.

Freud adapted his libido theory as well to new discoveries. He always remained a dualist in contrast to Jung (1875—1961) and Adler (1870—1937), but redefined the conflicting forces several times. Freud began, as in biology, by making a division between sexual and self-preservative instincts. The treatment of paranoid and homosexual patients made Freud more sensitive to the role of object relations, and the conflict between love for oneself and love for the object. Being able to maintain object relations presupposes a healthy love for oneself, or self-esteem. Under pathological circumstances the love for the object can be retracted and the patient becomes difficult to approach: he has regressed to a narcissistic position taking himself as an object. Narcissism as described is a normal state in early infancy (primary narcissism), and a pathological one in schizophrenia. The neurotic difficulty in establishing satisfying object relations lies between the two extremes. Accordingly, in 1914 Freud came to a change in his theory, now distinguishing between object-libido and libido of the narcissistic type.

Still later, after the first world war, and after his most beloved daughter and dearest grandchild had died, while he himself was affected by cancer of the jaw, he again changed his theory to account more for aggression. In 1920, in 'Beyond the Pleasure Principle', Freud put forward a new dualism namely the conflict between libido, a life and sexual instinct, and a death instinct, also designated as Eros and Thanatos. By way of complicated biological and metapsychological, abstract theorizing, aggression became an inborn drive instead of a reaction against frustration. It is true that sadism had always been considered as part of the component instincts of orality and anality, but now the aim of destruction and finally of self-destruction was hypothesized. This turn of the theory was not generally followed by psychoanalysts, and has stirred up much controversy, till the present day. Nevertheless, the idea inspired philosophers such as Herbert Marcuse, and psychiatrists such as Karl Menninger and Melanie Klein, who held the view that aggression plays a much greater part in development from the beginning, than libido.

Freud's theory remained a conflict theory throughout. Once the libido, the seeking of satisfaction, was opposed by the need for survival of the individual and the species, for example, the toll demanded by reality. Later it was aggression opposing the libido.

4. FREUD'S PHILOSOPHY

Freud saw life as an eternal struggle, in which complete satisfaction is precluded. Even psychoanalysis can only change neurotic suffering into normal everyday unhappiness. Freud's cultural philosophy is put forward in 'Civilization and its Discontents' (1930) where he stresses the giving up of personal needs and bypassing satisfaction as the raw material culture is made of. Sublimated perversions provide the energy for a great number of our cultural achievements. Marcuse (1955) has continued the discussion of this problem in 'Eros and Civilization', trying to place Freud's insights in a modern perspective. Marcuse, who calls Freud a revolutionary in contrast to the neo-Freudians who repudiated infantile sexuality and promise happiness instead, thinks that more gratification might be possible after all, but only through a radical change of society. Freud was a revolutionary thinker striving for inner freedom, but not a social reformer. He regarded the end of envy as alien to the nature of man. He was a realist, not an utopian.

Besides being a conflict theory, Freud's is a dynamic theory of personality. Opposing forces are at work, either in the direction of repression or of liberation. "Where id was ego shall be" was his credo for psychoanalytic treatment. The structure of the personality can be changed and repression lifted. The past is not an irrevocable fate, doom can be averted by treatment, through insight. In this sense Freud is not a pessimist but optimistic and full of faith in man.

5. FREUD'S METHOD

The core of the psychoanalytic treatment situation is the transference. The use of transference was Freud's great discovery of a method making cure possible through the patient—therapist relationship. The patient transfers his feelings, especially his infantile misperceptions, mostly grown in relation towards the parents, onto the analyst. The analyst, who asks the patient to tell everything that comes to his mind, regardless of importance or triviality, follows the free associations of his patient. He often remains silent until he has formed a clear hypothesis of what the patient tries to tell him, and then he can make an interpretation. Ideally interpretation should lead to more affect, the availability of feelings hitherto defended, and to more insight. The private language of the patient is interpreted back into the communal language of consciousness. Though the past of the patient is important, the feelings actualized can pertain to the present as well, and to happenings in and outside the transference relationship. The core of the transference relationship is formed by the oedipal conflicts.

6. THE OEDIPAL CONFLICT: MALE AND FEMALE SEXUALITY

In Freud's conception the central challenge deciding between mental health or neurosis occurs in the oedipal phase. Freud called the oedipus complex the nuclear complex of neurosis, originating in unresolved oedipal feelings. The child between three and five years of age is not only a very sensitive tabula rasa, but he also is mature enough to organize his world in terms of object relations. The central figures in the life of the small child are the parents, and the oedipal triangle an inescapable source of conflict to be solved. Conflict solving can stimulate maturation if there is no developmental interference in the form of stress or trauma impinging on the child. Freud's libido was in essence of a masculine nature and his conception of development mostly follows the male model. The little boy, firmly attached to and dependent on his mother in the pre-oedipal period, comes gradually to perceive her as his love object. Though adult ideas of sexual intercourse and marriage are not clear cut aims to him, he feels sexual genital excitation, he tends to court his mother and play the little lord in the household, and he fantasies about sole possession of the mother. The father, as far as he stands in the little boy's way, is felt as a rival, though in other ambivalent respects he might be of help and support. Agression and even death wishes or fantasies towards the father may develop in this period. Ambivalent feeling towards the parent of the other sex also exists, of course, though is spoken of less. The resolution of this love—hate conflict, in which anxiety over loss of love and loss of the cherished organ (castration fear) play a part, requires giving up the aim of replacing the father. Identification with the father and his aims, other than possessing the mother, is the healthy solution which helps the boy to postpone the gratification of his wishes till his mental and physical development make him ready for a psychosexual identity of his own, and a relationship of his own choice in accordance with it. Freud considered the superego, which is mostly formed in this period, as the heir of the oedipal conflict. The superego regulates behavior as the ego does, but not by interposing reality, secondary process thought and postponement of gratification, but by interiorizing the ideals and commandments of the culture through the parents, especially the father.

The little girl is supposed to go through an analogous development, only more complicated and hazardous than that of the boy. The girl discovers she has no penis like the little boy to be proud of, and this makes her jealous of him. During the phallic phase she also wants to court her mother, her prime and pre-oedipal love object. Her lack of a penis robs her of the fantasy that she can be successful in her endeavor to replace the father. She develops a grudge against the mother who did not supply the wished-for organ. At first she may fantasy she has a penis some place, that she had it once, or that she will still get it, but finally she has to acknowledge the fact she is a girl and resign herself to it. Her clitoris makes her feel inferior, and she will give it up in the end as a source of masturbatory satisfaction and fantasy. According to

Freud, she remains attached to her mother longer than the boy does. Her oedipal phase lasts longer and leaves behind more traces in her later development and object choice. Disillusionment with her mother finally influences the girl to turn to her father as a love object instead. The girl's oedipal choice is second best as it were. Her father, like mother, is unable to give her a penis, neither does he give her the wished for child as a substitute; nor does he love and court her as he does her mother. The little girl is bound to become jealous of men and women both. The 'ideal' solution is resignation to her lot in life. In the boy the castration complex ends the oedipal phase. In the girl it only initiates it. She feels herself a castrated boy and desires the father as someone who, unlike mother, has a penis. The girl has no real reason ever to outgrow her oedipal phase completely, or to give up her father as a love object. Later she might choose a man like her father as a husband. The long attachment to the mother often makes itself felt in an object choice reminding her of mother as well. During puberty the oedipal conflicts are revived once more, until emancipation from the family circle is established. Incestuous wishes have to be replaced by exogamous ones. The masculine and the feminine psychosexual characteristics and identity have to become firmly founded. The girl has to relinquish what still remains of her masculine position. To become a real woman she has to give up clitoral satisfaction through masturbation and during coitus. She has to attain sexual gratification culminating in orgasm through the vagina, the clitoris henceforth only transmitting excitation. The contradiction in the last two sentences is representative of Freud's ambiguity on the subject.

Freud's doctrine means that woman has to change her leading zone of sexual gratification: that is, she has to repress feelings around the clitoris, which is considered a pseudo-male organ, and with it her masculine tendencies. Her frequent failures in solving the complicated demands of feminity make woman more prone than man to neurosis, especially hysteria. In general, women have more problems in life than men. First there is every mother's ambivalence towards her female baby, then the lack of a penis and ensuing jealousy problems, the change of object, and finally, in puberty the change of erotogenic zone as well, namely from clitoris to vagina. Women tend to have problems with their femininity; they often have a difficult relationship with their mothers, and they enjoy less sexual and general gratification in life.

All this is according to Freud's view of femininity. He might have been biased by Victorian prejudices and by his own life history. Freud married late in life after a long betrothal and abstinence. His scientific career made him outgrow his wife's horizon. Even if married life did not bring Freud complete satisfaction, he remained a faithful family man and father. He himself had the feeling that he could not solve the riddle of femininity. He did have very satisfying intellectual relationships with women, like Lou Andreas Salomé, but on the very intimate level, probably less so. Freud once exclaimed "What does woman want?" (Was will das Weib?). He felt this was a question he had not answered satisfactorily.

Already during Freud's lifetime there came a reaction against his ideas on femininity. Psychoanalysts like Karen Horney, Ernest Jones and Melanie Klein considered the girl as feminine from the start. They assumed the vagina to be a sensitive organ from early childhood onwards. Authentic feminine feelings must have existed in women from the very beginning. Woman is not made but born. Oedipal feelings towards the father are a natural and early choice for her. It is unbiological and hence unprobable to consider feminine development as stunted masculine development. After Masters and Johnson, the tenets of the critics of Freud and modern commonsense can be considered as proven, namely, that the clitoris and the vagina are an integrated complex of organs both essential for femininity and sexual gratification. It is not a question of the clitoris being given up in favor of the vagina. The clitoris appears rather to be an authentic feminine organ instead of a penis that has not come to development.

Freud's view of feminine development is not wrong, but more representative of a neurotic or less-than-ideal state of affairs. Though this neuroticism might often occur, it should not therefore be called normal or even desirable.

The oedipal phase might fall short of mental health in two other ways, perversions and homosexuality. Primacy of the genital zones might not be obtained, the component instincts remaining the prime source of satisfaction. Perverse wishes and tendencies belong to normal adult sexuality, where they take the form of forepleasure. The child is even called polymorphous perverse by Freud, mainly in his pre-oedipal period, but continuing until latency. Playing with each other's genitals, looking, kissing, and (mutual) oral stimulation of the genitals, biting, playful fighting and stimulation of the anal region are examples of this. Freud also held the view that all neurotic problems go back to sexual aberrations, but sexual aberrations can exist without neurotic problems. When orgasm is not habitually reached through coitus, but exclusively through substitute activities, like sadism, masochism, exhibitionism, fetishism, and so on, the activity is called a perversion. The preparatory and partial aims of sexuality have become ends in themselves. Freud thought of perversion as the negative of neurosis. What is repressed in the first is acted out in the latter. Nowadays it is said that perversions as a pathological state also have something to do with problems in the realm of narcissism, with primitive object relations, with problems of identity, and with ego defects. Perverse syndromes are often closer to borderline psychotic than to neurotic states, or to the consequence of inadequacy in sexual interaction between partners. The oedipal phase has not been sufficiently reached, which in itself has pathological consequences. There is more to a perversion than living out otherwise suppressed wishes. Nevertheless, one must admit that Freud was right in comparing the perverse fantasies of an obsessional neurosis, as in his case history of the "Rat Man", to perverse sadistic acts carried out in reality.

Another outcome of the oedipus complex short of the normal is said to be homosexuality. The negative oedipus complex means the choice of the parent of the same sex as a love object, instead of the other sex as is the case in the positive oedipus complex. If the negative oedipal choice remains dominant, then homosexuality might follow. Homosexuality, as Freud discovered, is also closely linked up with problems of narcissism. The choice of a partner with a likeness to oneself often plays an important part. The male homosexual might choose a boy as a partner with whom he can play mother and child or father and child. There are many different varieties of object choice in homosexuality. The level of object relations reached is the decisive criterion for normality or pathology. Freud thought of homosexuality mostly in the form of a sexual aberration and devoted many articles to it, describing its special characteristics. It is now recognised that a mature form of object choice, where the partner is an individual in his or her own right, with whom a reciprocal relationship is possible (instead of a part of oneself or a necessary source of satisfaction only) can exist in homosexuality as well as in heterosexuality. In general, pathological developments can be defined in terms of the level of object relations reached. This can be according to a more infantile or mature model. The theory of object relations was not worked out thoroughly by Freud, though he used the ample knowledge he had of them in his consulting room.

7. CONCLUSION

Freud might have been led astray sometimes by his tendency towards biological instead of psychological thinking. His theory may have become outdated in parts. This does not hold for the way he worked and the discoveries he made through his observations of patients. To this his beautiful case histories bear witness. Freud gave more attention, at least in his theorizing, to energy concepts, developmental phases, the division of instincts, the mental apparatus and the different models of the mind he built, than to affects and object relations. His case histories abound, though, with evidence of his theories falling short. It is still very rewarding and worthwhile to read Freud himself. Freud's clinical acuity and insight still provide one of the richest sources of psychotherapeutic knowledge.

ACKNOWLEDGEMENT

The author wishes to express her gratitude to Dr. Herman Musaph, for his stimulating suggestions and to Dr. G.R. van den Berg for help in the conceptualization of this paper.

BIBLIOGRAPHY

Fenichel, O. (1946) *The Psychoanalytic Theory of Neurosis*. (Routledge & Kegan Paul Ltd., London.)

Fliegel, O.Z. (1973) Feminine psychosexual development in Freudian theory; a historical reconstruction. *Psychoanal. Quart.* Vol. XLII (3) 385—408.

Freud, A. (1937) *The Ego and the Mechanisms of Defence.* (Hogarth Press, London.)

Freud, S. (1900) The Interpretation of Dreams. *The Standard Edition of the Complete Psychological Works of Sigmund Freud,* Vol. IV. (Hogarth Press, London, 1953).

Freud, S. (1905) Fragment of an analysis of a case of hysteria. *S.E.* Vol. VII.

Freud, S. (1905) Three essays on the theory of sexuality. *S.E.* Vol. VII.

Freud, S. (1909) Notes upon a case of obsessional neurosis, (the "Rat Man"), *S.E.* Vol. X.

Freud, S. (1915) Instincts and their vicissitudes. *S.E.* Vol. XIV.

Freud, S. (1920) Beyond the pleasure principle. *S.E.* Vol. XVIII.

Freud, S. (1923) The ego and the id. *S.E.* Vol. XIX.

Freud, S. (1930) Civilization and its discontents, *S.E.* Vol. XXI.

Freud, S. (1933) New introductory lectures on psycho-analysis. *S.E.* Vol. XXII.

Gillespie, W.H. (1975) Women and her discontents. A re-assessment of Freud's views on female sexuality. *Int. Rev. Psychoanal.* 2.

Marcuse, H. (1955) *Eros and Civilization.* (Becon Press, Boston.)

Nagera, H. (1966) Early childhood disturbances, the infantile neurosis, and the adulthood disturbances. Problems of a developmental psychoanalytic psychology. *Monogr. Ser. Psychoanal. Study Child,* 2. (International Universities Press, Inc., New York.)

Nagera, H., Ed. (1970) Basic psychoanalytic concepts on the theory of instincts. *Hampstead Clinic Psychoanalytic Library,* Vol. III. (George Allen and Unwin, Ltd., London.)

Rycroft, C. (1966) Introduction: Causes and meaning. In: (C. Rycroft, Ed.) *Psychoanalysis Observed,* (Constable, London.)

Sandler, J. (1968) Psychoanalysis: An introductory survey. In: (Walter G. Joffe, Ed.) *What is Psychoanalysis.* Published for the Institute of Psychoanalysis (Baillière, Tindall & Cassell Ltd., London).

Segal, H. (1973) *Introduction to the Work of Melanie Klein.* (Hogarth Press, London.)

CHAPTER 5

Determinants of human gender identity/role

JOHN MONEY

1. PRINCIPLE OF DIFFERENTIATION AND DEVELOPMENT

Sexual behavior in man, like the sexual anatomy itself, is by reason of man's place in the phyletic scale, dimorphic. That is to say, its growth from its inception onward is simultaneously a process of differentiation as well as of development. This fact tends to have been overlooked historically in psychiatry which has spoken mainly of psychosexual development. Sexual theory has been impoverished thereby.

Reduced to its barest essentials, traditional sexual theory in psychiatry is built on two constructs: libido and identification. Libido, the instinctual sexual force, has not been conceived of as sexually dimorphic, per se, though possibly as bisexual. Manifest difference in behavior between the sexes has been regarded conceptually as secondary to libido and mainly as the developmental product of identification: to somewhat oversimplify, little girls identify with their mothers, little boys with their fathers. It is possible, though by no means justified, to account for identification exclusively in terms of stimulus-response and reward-reinforcement theory. Thus, there has been grown up a strong current tradition of explaining differences in behavior between the sexes — or deviations therefrom — as socioenvironmental or cultural in origin.

A theory in which the totality of dimorphism in sexual behavior is attributed exclusively to postnatal social and cultural determinants, is, a priori, open to the charge of being too narrow and simple. Moreover, notwithstanding the cogent evidence of the power of postnatal events in shaping gender identity and gender role in human beings, one would be hard-pressed to defend an exclusively cultural theory against the newly accumulating evidence of animal sexology on the fetal influence of hormones on the governance of sexual behavior by way of the central nervous system.

Supported in research by Grant HD00325, U.S.P.H.S. and by funds from the Grant Foundation, New York.

Handbook of Sexology, edited by J. Money and H. Musaph
© *Elsevier/North-Holland Biomedical Press, 1977*

2. PRINCIPLE OF SEQUENTIAL DIFFERENTIATION

The antecedents of sexual dimorphism of behavior in human development are typically sequential, beginning with the genetic dimorphism of the sex chromosomes, XY for the male and XX for the female. Then follows the differentiation of the gonads and their differentiated fetal hormonal functioning, differentiation of the internal reproductive anatomy, external genital morphology, sex assignment at birth, rearing as a boy or girl, differentiation of a gender role and identity, of hormonal puberty, and differential response to falling in love, courtship, mating and parenthood.

3. CRITICAL-PERIOD PRINCIPLE

Differentiation of the embryonic gonads is normally governed by the sex chromosomes, but only if the genetic code written into the chromosomes is permitted to express itself normally (the genetic norm of reaction) without interference or disruption at a critical period from an environment liable to produce distortions. The most dramatic distortion of the genetic code of the sex chromosomes is one in which their role as sex determinants is completely reversed. Yamamoto (1962) was able to bring about such a complete reversal in the killifish, *Oryzias latipes*, by exposing larvae to sex hormone. Exposed to estrogen, the female sex hormone, an XY larva destined to have differentiated into a male, thereupon differentiated into a female. Amazingly enough, this XY female was able to breed with a normal XY male and produce young. Twenty-five percent of the second generation larvae were then chromosomally XX (female), fifty percent XY (male) and twenty-five percent YY, which, if left untreated, would differentiate as males, but if treated with estrogen, would become YY females. In the succeeding generation, it was then possible to breed YY females with YY males, the resultant progeny all being YY and differentiating as males, if left unexposed to experimental hormone treatment. Yamamoto was also able to produce XX males by treating XX eggs with male sex hormone. The strongly and competitively masculine mating behavior of YY males has been studied by Hamilton et al. (1969).

Yamamoto's experiment is not the first in which the germ cells have been reversed to produce ova instead of sperms, or vice versa, while still retaining their reproductive fertility. Many years ago, Witschi demonstrated that overripe toad eggs all developed as morphologic males. Not only the genetic males, but also the genetic females had the appearance of males and produced sperms, but without the male sex chromosome present in them (Witschi, 1956, 1965). Witschi and his co-workers (Chang and Witschi, 1955, 1956; Mikamo and Witschi, 1963) also succeeded in producing a similar reversal of genetic sex in toads by implanting sex hormones into the developing larvae. In 1964, Turner and Asakawa made a first step toward achieving the same result in a mammal by transplanting the gonads of fetal mice into a host animal, so that the fetal testis turned the fetal ovary into an ovotestis in which spermatogenesis progressed to the point of secondary spermatocytes. Burns (1961) had in 1956 used estradiol in the fetal opossum to convert a would-be testis into an ovotestis producing ovocytes.

It has not yet been reported experimentally possible to reverse the sex differentiation completely from that of the genetic sex of the fertilized egg in mammals. Nonetheless the fish and amphibian experiments demonstrate how profound can be the reversal of everything pertaining to genetic sex: morphology, behavior and fertility. These experiments require that one keep an open mind with regard to possible partial reversals of the expression of the genetic sex in human beings, perhaps of direct relevance to sexual psychopathology, from causes as yet unknown.

The fish and amphibian experiments also point out a profoundly important principle in the theory of heredity versus environment (perhaps more appropriately designated as genetics versus environmentics). It is a principle that transcends the old dichotomy between nature and nurture by introducing the concept of the critical period. There is only a limited period during which a fertilized egg may be tampered with and forced to reverse the program for which it is genetically coded. After this limited, or critical period, the die is cast and the program cannot be changed or, having been changed, cannot revert.

The die is cast regarding the differentiation of the gonads in the human species at around the sixth week after conception. In the XY embryo, the core of the undifferentiated gonad proliferates to form into a testis, and the rind becomes vestigial; whereas in the XX embryo, the rind proliferates, while the core becomes vestigial, to form an ovary.

4. PRINCIPLES OF DIFFERENTIATION: VESTIGIATION VERSUS HOMOLOGUES

The principle of commencing with the anlagen for both sexes, then allowing one to proliferate while the other vestigiates, is one which nature extends from the differentiation of the gonads to the differentiation of the internal reproductive structures from the Müllerian and Wolffian ducts, both of which are initially laid down in parallel. Here another principle first becomes evident, namely this: for the differentiation of a male, something extra must occur—something must be added. In the total absence of gonads, whether by experimental castration of the fetus in utero, or by reason of a cytogenetic defect as in Turner's syndrome (typically 44 + X = 45 chromosomes), the fetus will develop as a female. There is no doubt about it that nature's first disposition is to make a female. Morphologically, for a female to be differentiated, it is not necessary to have fetal gonads able to release hormonal substances; whereas, for the differentiation of a male, it is absolutely necessary to have them and they must be testes. These fetal testes must release the so-called Müllerian-inhibiting substance which causes the homolateral Müllerian duct to regress, thus preventing the formation of the uterus and Fallopian tube on that side. The fetal testes must also release an androgenic or male-hormonal substance which prevents regression of the Wolffian ducts, thus ensuring the differentiation of the male internal sexual structures. When the Müllerian-inhibiting substance fails, it is possible to have a male born with fully differentiated uterus and tubes. So far as is known, this rather extraordinary anomaly does not have any subsequent primary influence on sexual behavior. In the case of uni-lateral failure of the Müllerian-inhibiting substance, only a half uterus and one tube is formed; subsequent external sexual development is liable to be hermaphroditic, with attendant risks of anomalously affecting sexual behavior.

Differentiation of the external sexual organs comes after that of the internal organs and proceeds on the basis of an entirely different principal—the principal of homologues. Here nature begins with the same anlagen and uses them for sexually different purposes: the genital tubercle becomes either the clitoris or the penis; the genital folds become either the hood of the clitoris and the labia minora or the foreskin and the wrap-around of the penis which forms the penile urethra; and the genital swellings become either the labia majora or the scrotal sac, joined by the same median raphe that fuses the penile urethra. It is between the second and third month of fetal life in the human species that external-organ differentiation takes place.

5. MASCULINE DIFFERENTIATION: ADDITIVE PRINCIPLE

The differentiating principle at this stage of embryonic development is once again: add something to obtain a male. The something added is androgen. In the absence of androgen, a fetus will differentiate externally as a female, regardless of chromosomal sex; and in the partial absence of androgen, differentiation will be as an unfinished male, that is with incomplete fusion of the penile and scrotal skin, the penis being diminished in size and the testes possibly being undescended. Conversely, in the presence of a sufficient quantity of androgen even an XX fetus will differentiate externally as a male.

Brain differentiation

At around the same time as the external genitalia differentiate (6 weeks after conception), fetal androgens exert an influence also on the developing central nervous system. In the lower, estrous species, androgen administered to the fetus at the appropriate critical development period counteracts its primary disposition to develop, subsequently, the cyclic estrous function of the female. The findings of different investigators using different techniques (reviewed by Harris, 1964; Money, 1965; Money and Ehrhardt, 1972) converge on the hypothalamus as the responsible area of the brain. Nuclei in the hypothalamus govern, by way of their neural releaser-hormones, the pituitary gland's activity. The pituitary, in turn, by cyclically or noncyclically releasing its gonad-stimulating hormones, the gonadotropins, regulates the production of sex hormones from the ovaries or testicles.

The overall principle emerging from the foregoing neurohormonal (or neurohumoral) research is once again the familiar one: add something, androgen, to obtain a male. Whether the differentiation regulated by androgen follows the homologous pattern of the external genitals, or the vestigiation pattern of the gonads and internal organs, remains to be ascertained. One piece of evidence in favor of the vestigiation hypothesis is that of Fisher (1956, 1966) who was able to elicit simultaneous female (maternal) and male (mating) behavior in a male rat by injecting minute amounts of testosterone directly into the preoptic area of the hypothalamus. The schema of female behavior is dormant, of course, or vestigial in the male, under ordinary circumstances.

Masculinized female monkeys

The experiments that have so far been performed on primates, as contrasted with subprimates, have not shown a direct effect on hormonal cycling as manifested in the menstrual cycle. There is some evidence, however, to indicate a fetal effect on the central nervous system that will eventually influence sexual behavior. For example, investigators at the Regional Primate Research Center, Beaverton, Oregon (Young et al., 1965; Phoenix, 1966) have produced genetic female rhesus monkeys so effectively virilized in utero by androgen injections of the mother that they were born with a normal male-appearing penis and empty scrotum instead of a clitoris and vaginal orifice. In the juvenile years, these animals gained behavior scores for initiating play, engaging in rough-and-tumble play, making threatening gestures, and adopting the position in sexual play, that were closer to the scores of normal control males than to normal control females. As they approached puberty and adolescence, these anatomically masculinized females tended to lose the masculine trend in their behavioral scores, but the complete story has not yet been ascertained, and the complete repertory of appropriate tests remains to be performed.

Masculinized human females

In human beings, there are two clinical syndromes that are the counterpart of fetal monkey androgenization. One is the syndrome of progestin-induced hermaphroditism in females. The other is the female adrenogenital syndrome of hermaphroditism, specifically in cases where masculinization is restricted to fetal life, its continuance after birth being prevented by treatment with cortisone. It is superfluous to the needs of this chapter to digress into a full clinical description of these two syndromes and their differential etiology, prognosis and therapy; see instead Wilkins (1965) and Money (1968a). It is sufficient for present purposes to note that, regardless of etiology, one has here examples of females subjected to masculinization in fetal life sufficient to enlarge the clitoris and partially fuse the labia, so as to create the appearance of hypospadias in the male. This anatomical abnormality is surgically corrected soon after birth, so that the appearance looks correctly female, in agreement with the rearing. Hormonal function, either spontaneously or by regulation, is female, and puberty is normal in onset. What then of behavior?

The evidence to data (Ehrhardt and Money, 1967; Ehrhardt et al., 1968) is that fetal androgenization in the above two syndromes does indeed influence the subsequent development of behavior, though only to a limited extent. It does not induce a complete reversal of gender role and gender identity in the sense that a girl feels she ought to be a boy or would like to change her sex. Nor does it automatically steer her in the direction of lesbianism. But it does tend to make her a tomboy, as judged by self-declaration and confirmed by parents and friends. Her tomboyism is defined, perhaps above all else, by vigorous, muscular energy expenditure and an intense interest in athletic sports and outdoor activities in competition with boys. It is not especially associated with aggression and fighting. It is accompanied by scorn for fussy and frilly feminine clothes and hair-dos in favor of utility styles. It is incompatible with a strong interest in maternalism as revealed in the rehearsals of childhood doll play or in future ambitions for the care of tiny babies. It does not exclude the anticipation of romance, marriage and pregnancy, but these are regarded in a somewhat perfunctory way as secondary to a career. Career ambitions are consistent with high academic achievement and with the high IQ, which tends to be a characteristic of girls with fetal androgenization.

Antiandrogenism: rats

The experimental opposite of fetal androgenization of the female is nonandrogenization or antiandrogenization of the male. The former can be achieved by means of fetal castration, a technically difficult operation even in a species like the rat in which the young are delivered fetally immature. Neonatal castration of the rat does indeed preserve cyclic functioning of the pituitary, as in the female (Harris, 1964). The use of antiandrogen is even more dramatic in its effect. When such a hormone is injected, with the proper timing, into the pregnant mother, then the fetal testes of the genetic males become dormant and fail to supply androgen to the anlagen of the external genitalia. In consequence, the animal, to be specific a rat (Neumann and Elger, 1965), is born with completely normal-appearing female genitals. By castrating the animal to eliminate all further influence of its own testes and giving replacement doses of female hormones at puberty, it is possible to obtain normal female mating behavior from these genetic males (Neumann and Elger, 1966). The stud males of the colony do not distinguish them from normal females. The sex-behavior reversal is complete.

Androgen insensitivity: human

In human beings, two clinical syndromes are close counterparts of experimental antiandrogenism in animals, namely Turner's syndrome and the testicular-feminizing or androgen-insensitivity syndrome (Wilkins, 1965; Money, 1968a). In both instances, fetal androgenization of the external genitals fails so that the baby is born with normal-appearing female external genitals. In Turner's syndrome, there are neither ovaries nor testes as a result of the chromosomal error responsible for the syndrome, so that fetal androgenization is an impossibility. In the androgen-insensitivity syndrome, the testes are present and the chromosomal sex is 44 + XY = male. The testes produce male sex hormone in an amount normal for a male; and at puberty, they produce also female sex hormone in an amount normal for a male. It is not the testes that are at fault in this condition, but all the cells of the body which manifest a genetic inability to respond to male sex hormone. The body therefore responds to the testes output of female hormone; it develops a normal female appearance, including breasts at puberty. There is no uterus, however, since the testes produced their Müllerian-inhibiting substance early in embryonic life, thus causing its vestigiation.

The behavior of girls and women with either Turner's syndrome (Money and Mittenthal, 1970) or the androgen-insensitivity syndrome (Money et al., 1968; Masica et al., 1969) is indisputably feminine. They are not tomboys. In childhood their interest is in traditionally feminine play and activities. They show strong maternalistic interests in doll play from an early age, generally like to take care of children as they grow through childhood, and rehearse fantasies of romance, marriage and motherhood as their primary ambition for the future. They are bitterly disappointed when their case is diagnosed and they learn the prognosis of sterility and motherhood by adoption. When eventually they do adopt children, they make good mothers. Their sex-lives in marriage are the same as for anatomically normal wives selected at random and subject to the same vicissitudes—except for the probability of needing long-term hormonal therapy and, in some cases of androgen insensitivity, surgical lengthening of the vagina for ease in sexual intercourse.

6. CORE GENDER IDENTITY: PRINCIPLE OF DISSOCIATION

Babies who will in future be diagnosed as having the androgen-insensitivity syndrome are almost never diagnosed at birth or in early childhood, for the obvious reason that they look normally female. The same is true for Turner's syndrome, except that various of the possible congenital defects of this syndrome may bring the child to earlier medical attention. In therefore happens that the differentiation of gender identity in these female-appearing people cannot be studied except under the reinforcement of a rearing that is female, like their appearance. The real test of the influence of sex of assignment and rearing on psychosexual differentiation is better studied in cases of sexual anomaly where the visible appearance is hermaphroditically ambiguous so that people of the same diagnosis can be found, differing only in that some have been assigned, reared, and surgically and hormonally treated as boys, the others as girls.

This condition, though rare, is met often enough to demonstrate the extraordinary power of postnatal events on the differentiation of gender role and identity. The typical finding is that gender role and identity differentiate in conformity with the sex of assignment and rearing. This conformity can withstand various partial contradictions which include: 1) even the extreme contradictory hormonal puberty such that a person raised as a girl virilizes like a boy or, being raised as a boy begins to grow breasts and pass menstrual blood through the urethra; 2) tomboyism of energy expenditure in a person raised as a girl; 3) imperfect pubertal virilization with a nonerectile stub of a penis in a person raised as a boy; and 4) a masculine type of threshold, in a person living as a woman, for erotic arousal in response to visual and narrative material as contrasted with the more feminine dependence on tactile stimulation.

There are exceptions, nonetheless, when gender identity does not differentiate in conformity with sex assignment. Disparity between the two is most likely to arise when the assignment itself is ambivalent. The parents may be given no medical conviction about their infant's sexual diagnosis, or even may be told to half expect that a sex change might be necessary later. Parental ambivalence can be further reinforced if the genitalia are left surgically uncorrected during childhood so that they not only are a reproach to the child, when he or she looks at them, but also may be the source of teasing by siblings, cousins or friends. Under such circumstances the child, sensing and then knowing full well that something is wrong, does not tolerate the cognitive dissonance of his ambiguity. It is very rarely that an hermaphrodite settles for an ambiguous or hermaphroditic gender identity. A resolution of ambiguity is achieved instead by the simple expedient of repudiating the attributed status, so obviously wrong and unsatisfactory, in favor of its opposite, which at least has the virtue of not having yet been proved wrong and unsatisfactory.

This process of reassignment, when it occurs, usually takes place early during an hermaphrodite's childhood; for the resolution of an ambiguous gender identity cannot feasibly be postponed. To achieve formal recognition of the change then becomes something of a cause célèbre and a real driving force in life.

The question of whether or not the influence of fetal hormones on sex differentiation of nuclei of the hypothalamus may have any bearing on an hermaphrodite's conviction of the need for sex reassignment cannot at present be answered. One can simply note (Money, 1969) that the decision seems to be arrived at more frequently by male than female hermaphrodites, and is more likely to require a female-to-male change of status than vice versa—which may have more to do with ambiguity of anatomy and of diagnosis of hermaphroditism than with assigned sexual status, per se.

The fact that some few hermaphrodites do not consolidate their gender identity from infancy onward, but reach a point of self-reassignment, contrasts strongly with those who do, and for whom a sex reassignment by edict would be a disaster. In the sex assignment of hermaphrodites, it is still relatively common for an on-the-spot decision to be made at the time of birth and then to have to be changed later, after completion of a full diagnostic work-up. As a result, a reannouncement of the baby's sex has to be made. Provided the parents are correctly guided through this dilemma, it need have no adverse effect, then or subsequently, on the differentiation of the child's gender identity.

It is somewhere between the ages of twelve and eighteen months, dependent on a baby's facility in the understanding and use of language, that a sex reannouncement becomes more than an adjustment problem for the parents alone, and one for the child as well. By the time he has command of names, nouns and pronouns differentiating the sexes, a boy has a clear concept of himself as a boy, and a girl of herself as a girl. There is now no such simple thing as a sex reannouncement: it will be a sex reassignment involving the child as a person. Psychologically, it is very serious business, for the child already has a self-identity as boy or girl; the core gender identity, to use a term increasingly in vogue, is already on the way to being firmly established. This is an aspect of psychosexual differentiation not accounted for in the traditional Freudian scheme of the oral, anal and genital stages of psychosexual development.

The differentiation of a core gender identity probably follows the same principle as the differentiation of the gonads and the internal reproductive organs. In other words, two systems are present to begin with, only one of which becomes finally functional. In the case of gender identity, however, the nonfunctional system or schema does not become vestigal, in the true sense, but is dissociated — coded as not to be manifested by oneself, but to be expected from members of the other sex, and responded to reciprocally. Thus a boy grows up to know how to do all the boy things, because he knows also how to expect a girl to do all the girl things, to which he himself responds. The brain coding involved resembles that in bilingualism, especially that kind of bilingualism found in an immigrant child who knows how to listen to the old people's language, though he himself declines to speak it.

7. PRINCIPLE OF IDENTIFICATION AND COMPLEMENTATION

The two gender schemas which become coded in one's brain, one as suitable for one's personal gender identity/role, and the other, to use in predicting and responding to the gender-dimorphic, or gender-coded role of the other sex, are differentiated according to the principles of identification and complementation.

Identification, a long-familiar principle, refers to learning that takes place by direct copying or imitation of a model. Complementation, not so familiar, refers to learning the behavior of another, so that one's own behavior complements or reciprocates it in response. Identification and complementation both take place according to the ordinary contingencies of reinforcement and avoidance learning. Each may involve either overt instruction and indoctrination, or covert assimilation from experience.

In the usual nuclear family, identification is primarily with the parent of the same sex, and complementation with the parent of the other sex. Other members of the household may, however, augment or substitute for the parents. A missing identification figure, say a parent, may also be represented in absentia by a complementation figure at the same time as he/she plays the role of complementatee.

With advancing age, a child's identification and complementation models extend beyond the household to include playmates, older children, and heros and heroines of folklore, sports and television.

Identification figures in absentia do not require responsive reaction from oneself except, maybe, in fantasy. When present in person, an identification figure is not simply a model to copy, but also a person whose behavior needs to be reciprocated or complemented, regardless of sex. This kind of complementarity is age-coded, as between parent and child, siblings of different age, and members of the same age/peer group. It may also be coded according to social, racial, or health status, and so on.

Sexually dimorphic roles which become incorporated into one's own gender identity/role are of two types. Sex roles, in the strict sense, pertain to eroticism and the function of the sex organs. Sex-coded roles are those that by custom and tradition are differentially assigned on the basis of genital status. They pertain to work, play, dress, cosmetics and manners, and are not specifically related to eroticism and the functioning of the sex organs.

Under special circumstances in a developing child, the complementary and the identification schemas may become transposed. Such a transposition occasionally occurs in an hermaphrodite child, with a resultant decision in favor of sex reassignment. Some anatomically normal children reach the same transsexual decision, on the basis of an etiology chiefly unknown. Transvestism and the extreme manifestations of effeminate homosexuality in males and virilistic lesbianism in females represent other, less complete forms of transposition of gender identification and complementation (see Table I). Gender transposition may occur under circumstances of severe personality

Table I
Transpositions of gender role/identity in 3 × 2 classification of intensity and duration
(with permission, from Money, 1975).

	Total	Partial	Trivial
Chronic	Transexualism	Effeminate male and virilistic female homo-sexuality	Sex-coded work and legal status
Episodic	Transvestism	Bisexuality	Sex-coded play, grooming, and manners

disorganization associated with adolescent psychosis. A behavioral sex
change may emerge still later in life, in certain rare cases of temporal lobe
epilepsy, or as a consequence of senile brain deterioration, and may be
manifest in the form of personality changes, among others, toward transvestism or homosexuality.

8. PRINCIPLE OF MASCULINE VULNERABILITY

Except for hyposexual syndromes, it is widely acknowledged that the incidence of psychosexual disorders is higher in males than females. The variety
of psychosexual disorders is also greater in males than females; some of the
more bizarre and exotic anomalies simply are not recorded in the female.
It is quite likely that one has here a by-product of yet one more manifestation of the principle of sexual differentiation, namely that something must
be added to differentiate a male. The something added that makes the
difference between female and male in psychosexual erotic functioning
might well, once again, be androgen. Its site of action, or absence thereof,
would undoubtedly be the brain. Its mechanism of action would most likely
pertain to threshold sensitivity for erotic arousal from a visual stimulus or,
perhaps, its evocation in imagery from a narrative stimulus. After puberty,
it is males who are girl watchers, not females who are boy watchers. Teenaged boys use nude pictures as masturbation stimuli, but girls do not. At puberty, the boy is self-presented with realistic erotic images in dreams accompanied by orgasm; the girl is not. The very sexual performance of the boy is
categorically different from that of the girl, in that his penis must be aroused
to erection before he can begin; and it must ejaculate in orgasm if reproduction is to be effected. In the girl, by contrast, it is possible for conception
to occur without either arousal or orgasm. It is possible for the male to be
erotically aroused by touch alone, a fact to which many long-married husbands can attest. But it is typically the visual image that lends an element of
excitement and, above all, incites the male to be the one who takes erotic
initiative. This principle of male initiative is widespread in the animal king-

dom, and in many species is dependent on visual stimulation, the closest competitor being smell.

If nature seems always to need to add something to make a male, then she seems also more likely to fail in her effort. The birth ratio, 106:100, in favor of males, allows for the more rapid wastage of the male, and the conception ratio, estimated at as high as 140:100 shows even more dramatically how easy it is for a male to fail. There are no definite figures available, but the vulnerability of the male is again demonstrated at puberty, when, in the clinic, partial or complete failure of hormonal puberty is more common than in the female (excluding the postpubertal problems of ovulatory and menstrual irregularity). In the matter of psychosexual arousal, nature's difficulty in differentiating a male again manifests itself in the greater number of males than females who are "turned on" by a wrong stimulus, that is, one that has positive arousal value when it should be either neutral, negative or partial. All the anomalies in a textbook of sexual psychopathology can be interpreted in terms of being aroused by the wrong stimulus. Sometimes it is almost possible to glimpse how the wrong connections between behavioral components can be established by reason of their proximity of representation in the nervous system, as MacLean (1965) has pointed out with respect to oral-anal representations in the limbic system.

Vulnerability to errors of psychosexual functioning has no single source of origin. In some few cases gentics can definitely be implicated, as in the case of the XXY (Klinefelter's) syndrome or the XYY syndrome. Men with either of these cytogenetic anomalies are likely to have some or other peculiarity of sexual behavior. XXY men are also very weak in libido, as well as sterile.

Whether events in intrauterine life may predispose human beings to psychosexual errors later in life is uncertain. In animal experiments it has been found that androgenization of the female fetus can be blocked by barbiturates (Gorski, 1968). One wonders what effect, if any, sleeping pills taken by a pregnant mother may have on the unborn fetus.

The bulk of today's evidence points unquestionably to events in early post-natal life and infancy as of prime importance in relation to eventual psychosexual normalcy. Harlow's (1965) work with rhesus monkeys raised on dummy mothers and in isolation from playmates is too well known to need retelling here. It points to the hitherto unsuspected importance of clinging and the sense of touch in primate development. It points also to the need to be able to play at the appropriate critical period — sexual play included — if normal reproductive behavior and parenthood is subsequently to be achieved. A report from the chimpanzee colony in New Mexico (Kollar et al., 1968) shows that, like the rhesus monkey, these primates also are very vulnerable to errors of psychosexual function when captured from their normal jungle troop and imprisoned in captivity. In fact, their sex-behavior problems are uncannily human.

As for human beings themselves, there is no highly systematic body of knowledge concerning the contingencies between rearing and subsequent sexual behavior, though there is a store of clinical knowledge and hypothesis, too vast to be reviewed here. It is perhaps a safe generalization to say that almost any major disruption of a child's developmental experience, regardless of its origin or type, is a potential source of disturbance in subsequent psychosexual development — the more so the younger the child. The vulnerability of the psychosexual system to disturbance may simply reflect the fact that its differentiation is actively in progress during early childhood. It may also be a reflection of the fact that, in many societies, our own included, psychosexual development is subject to an excess of taboos, such as the taboo on sexual play in childhood. If one judges from the evidence of the other primates, then childhood sexual play is a neccessary and normal rehearsal, in preparation for adolescence and adulthood. Perhaps we would do well to reexamine our policies on childhood sexual play as a determinant of adult sexual behavior.

9. PRINCIPLE OF LOVE AS AN IMPRINT

After the advent of hormonal puberty, a new milestone in psychosexual development is reached, namely the capacity to experience falling in love. Children in kindergarten have play romances, and children in the so-called latency period (not so very latent, either!) may play at copulation games, but they do not fall in love, unless precocious falling in love may itself be a specific sign of psychosexual maldevelopment. The capacity to be aroused and possessed by the stimulus of the love object is not simultaneous with puberty. It does not occur, for instance, in children with precocious puberty of infantile onset until they become older — twelve is probably about the youngest. By contrast, in children, most notably boys, with long-delayed puberty, it is possible though not routine to observe the experience of falling in love sometime from middle to late teenage, even when complete hormonal infantilism still persists (Money and Alexander, 1967). One suspects, therefore, that whereas one neurohumoral mechanism (or biological clock) in the hypothalamus turns on puberty by way of activating the pituitary, another mechanism, site unknown, activates the capacity to fall in love.

Falling in love resembles imprinting, in that a releaser mechanism from within must encounter a stimulus from without before the event happens. Then that event has remarkable longevity, sometimes for a lifetime. The kind of stimulus that, whether it be acceptable or pathological, will be the effective one for a given individual will have been written into his psychosexual program, so to speak, in the years prior to puberty and dating back to infancy. Especially in the case of psychopathology, a boy or girl may be shocked and guilty to be 'turned on' by an abnormal stimulus, while at the same time secretly fascinated and obsessed with it because of the sexual feeling it releases. The effective erotic stimulus may not initially be revealed in full, so that there is some element of discovery and expansion to erotic experience with the passage of time. By and large, however, human beings stay remarkably stable in their erotic preferences. Thus, it is not possible to teach a man or even a teenager to be, say, a masochist or a peeping-Tom; and a few teenaged exposures to homosexuality do not create an appetite for more. The appetite has to be there in the first place. Earlier in childhood, the power of exposure and experience is probably far more impressive and lasting. However, a great deal more work needs to be done on the after-effects of childhood sexual experiences. There seem to be distinct personality types so far as falling in love is concerned, and they may correspond to the augmenters and diminishers of sensation as described by Petrie (1967). At one extreme are people of (psychopathic or) sociopathic personality disposition, the Don Juan and nymphomaniac types who are the experts at one night stands. These are perhaps diminisher-people whose experiences fade quickly and stand in need of constant repetition and novelty.

By contrast, at the other extreme are the augmenter-people who cannot let an experience go. It reverberates and enlarges in their memories, and haunts them. The love affairs of many schizoid and schizophrenic people have this quality. They may have an anguished love affair without ever declaring themselves to the partner; or even possibly conduct the whole love affair with an imaginary partner by way of a photograph.

The majority of mankind, of course, falls somewhere between these two extremes. Each tends to judge the other from within the solipsism of his own "egg shell" as being like himself. But the fact is that we are quite differently determined so far as sexual behavior goes.

10. ANDROGEN-LIBIDO PRINCIPLE

When a teenager who has a syndrome of sexual infantilism nonetheless has a falling in love experience, it is not as intense and full-bodied as it will be once he is given effective hormone replacement therapy. The sex hormones do not in any way govern the cognitional content of eroticism — they do not cause homosexuality, for example — but they do affect the intensity and frequency of its expression, though without exercising total responsibility in this respect. Androgen is probably the libido hormone for both sexes (Money, 1961a; Herbert, 1967; Trimble and Herbert, 1968) though some women, notably those with androgen insensitivity, seem to be able to function adequately without it. Normal women tend to report a more receptive attitude of wanting to be possessed at around the time of ovulation, which is when the estrogenic phase of the menstrual cycle is in the ascendant. Estrogen tends to be an inhibitor of androgen. At the menstrual phase, when progesterone levels are higher, and androgen may be less inhibited, women are more likely to take an initiating role of inducing the male. The birth control pill may change this cycle, but in a way that seems to depend on the formulae of the different brands (Grant and Pryse-Davies, 1968). According to newly accumulating evidence from Hamburg and from Johns Hopkins (Money, 1968b), antiandrogens may prove to be very beneficial in enabling certain sex criminals to gain a measure of control over their otherwise ungovernable sexual behavior. The effect is reversible when the medication is stopped, without adverse side effects. The same medication promises also to be helpful in the regulation of violent temper outbursts in some temporal lobe epileptics (D. Blumer, personal communication).

The hormonal changes of pregnancy have no routinely systematic effect on woman's sex life. The mechanics of carrying a baby affect different women differently, as does the psychologic effect of the meaning of pregnancy and parenthood. Being a parent affects husband and wife equally and may have a profound effect, it goes without saying, on their opportunities for sexual behavior.

As with the hormonal changes of pregnancy, those of the menopause have no systematic effect on woman's sex life, except insofar as the vaginal mucosa may become atrophic and too dry, with an adverse effect on sexual intercourse. This effect can be be reversed by the judicious prescription of estrogen (which also will serve as a protection against osteoporosis). The direct effect of the hormonal changes of the menopause on mood and temperament varies widely, as does the effect of the psychologic meaning of having reached the end of childbearing, consequently, both of these effects themselves bear no systematic relationship to postmenopausal sexual behavior. It is important for many couples to know that the menopause does not mark the end of woman's sexual desire and ability. Her sexual life may continue, and even be improved, far into old age.

The male's sex life also may continue far into old age, unmarked by any such dramatic hormonal event as the menopause of the female. The refractory interval between erections and between orgasms lengthens as age increases, but with great individual variation. Failing potency can generally be improved in older men whose own androgen levels have declined by the judicious prescription of testosterone. Impotence not associated with a falling-off in androgen production is not improved by treatment with hormones, and the same holds true for frigidity in women.

Apart from the aging effect, deficit or impairment of sexual behavior and its frequency has many different etiologies, requiring considerable astuteness to establish a diagnosis. It is necessary to consider that the symptom of deficient or impaired sexual activity may be a sequel to: a genetic defect; an error of metabolism; an endocrine error; a mechanical, neurological or circulatory defect; a traumatic injury; an adverse psychologic reaction to illness (for example, after a heart attack); a primary psychiatric disorder (especially depression); a disturbance of personality and the interpersonal relationship of sex; or a lack of sufficient timing, variety or novelty of stimulation.

An excess of sexual activity is more often regarded boastfully as an asset rather than as a symptom. Yet it may be a symptom, especially when it represents a change from a former lesser level, together with a change in the type of behavior. The most likely diagnostic considerations then are: an endocrine error; a neurological error (particularly a trauma, tumor, or senile atrophy of the brain); a primary psychiatric disorder (especially mania or hypomania); or a disturbance of personality and the interpersonal relationship of sex.

11. PRINCIPLE OF GENITOPELVIC SENSATION

It all but belabors the obvious to say that one of the determinants of sexual behavior is the integrity of the sexual organs with which coitus is performed. Yet the fact of the matter is that large amounts of sexual tissue can be removed without destroying the capacity for erotic response (Money, 1961b). Following amputation of the penis, whether by accident or because of malignancy, orgasm is retained. Sexual desire remains as before, sometimes creating a serious problem of morale in being unable to satisfy the partner.

A more complete loss of penile tissue is entailed in sex-reassignment surgery for male transexualism, for the corpora are extirpated and only the skin retained as a lining for the new vagina (Jones et al., 1968). Postoperatively and living as females, transexuals claim they experience erotic satisfaction in the female sexual role, and some report a climatic feeling of orgasm which, if different than they formerly experienced as males, satisfies them more because they are able to be in the female role.

Penile tissue is not lost but the corpora are, in many cases, functionally destroyed as a sequel to priapism. Erection is impossible. Here again orgasm and desire for intercourse are retained, while the morale may be seriously injured.

The morale problem is, by contrast, quite different in cases of paraplegia (Money, 1960) where the loss is not of genital tissue, but of all spinal cord connection with the brain. The genitalia are able to respond reflexly to local tactile stimulation, but the patient has no feeling and awareness of what has happened. A paraplegic male has no erection in response to erotic thoughts and imagery. The nearest he gets to an orgasm is by dreaming one, and even sexual dreams disappear as the years pass after the paraplegic injury occurred. The paraplegic knows that he has lost his sex life and would elect, if he could, to have it returned, but there is none of the quality of urgency and frustration found in men whose genitals can perform only a part of their sexual function without completing it. Signals from the genitals are obviously a principal component or determinant of sexual behavior.

In women as in men, ablation of genital tissue is compatible with the retention of erotic sensation and orgasm. The evidence comes from women who undergo radical resection of the vulva for epidermoid cancer, and from hermaphroditic females whose hypertrophied clitoris is resected or extirpated. According to the evidence of genital ablation, an orgasm is an orgasm regardless of the stimulation that triggers it—which is precisely the verdict of the Masters and Johnson (1966) research into the human sexual response. These authors effectively put to rest the ghost of the old controversy of the clitoral versus the vaginal orgasm as a determinant of mature sexual behavior in the female.

12. PRINCIPLE OF DIMORPHIC SIGNALS

Over and beyond the specifics of genitopelvic sexual behavior, there is a vast amount of human behavior that is sexual in the sense that it is dimorphic in relation to gender: what men do one way, women do another. This kind of gender-related behavior ranges from fashions of dress to conventions of work and earning a living, from rules of etiquette and ceremony to labor-sharing in the home. Though these various stereotypes of what is masculine and what is feminine may ultimately derive from such fundamental sex differences as urinary posture, menstruation, childbearing, lactation, stature, weight, and muscular power, the conventions themselves are defined by custom and may be arbitrary and subject to sudden changes of fashion or slow changes in the cultural pattern. It does not matter that they change. It is the fact that they exist in any given time and place that counts, for we human beings are sensitively dependent on our cognition of the signals and cues emanating from others—they are determinants of our own sexual behavior, just as are plumage differences in birds. We differ from birds in being able to adapt and change the signals historically, but we cannot obliterate them altogether. There is no more convincing evidence in support of this principle than the fact that the average man or woman tends to accept the impersonation put forth by a transvestite or a transexual—provided of course, that it is a perfect or near-perfect impersonation. It is then possible to accept the impersonation, even after the truth is known, as being more genuine than the sex of the sex organs. It is even possible for a psychosexually normal person to fall in love with a transexual impersonator. Resolution of the incongruity between impersonation and the sex organs is then achieved by responding to the impersonator as someone beset by misfortune who is deserving or needing medical or surgical help. There is no more cogent illustration of how compelling is the influence of the senses over that of judgment in determining human sexual behavior!

13. PRINCIPLE OF CULTURAL DETERMINANTS

Cultural tradition determines not only the criteria of sexually dimorphic behavior, but also various criteria of sexual interaction. The variety of possibilities is extensive but not limitless, although the limits have not yet been catalogued. Variability can be classified as pertaining to the following characteristics of partnerships:

a) age: same or disparate
b) physique: juvenile, adolescent or adult
c) sex: same or opposite
d) kinship: related or not related by blood, clan or race
e) caste or class: same or different
f) number: unity or plurality of partnerships
g) time: sequential or contemporaneous partnerships, or one partnership only
h) span: transient or constant partnerships
i) privacy: public or concealed
j) accessories: plain or modified by material artifacts, e.g., personal ornament, contraceptive device, etc.

To illustrate: the people of the lake region of northern Sumatra live in a cultural tradition that permits an age difference in a sexual partnership, ranging over the entire spectrum of physique, but only in homosexual and not heterosexual partnerships. In late childhood, it is not decent for children to stay sleeping in their parent's single-roomed house. A girl takes her sleeping mat to the home of a widow or old woman who accommodates about half a dozen girls who range in age from prepuberty to late adolescence. A boy joins a group of a dozen to fifteen males, his own age or older, who sleep in a boy's house specially constructed for them. There he learns from the adolescents and young men how to participate in paired homosexual play with them or older boys *: primarily mutual masturbation of penis held against penis, maybe anal coitus, but never fellatio. All members of the group may become one member's partner, in rotation. Relationships are not necessarily unobserved, but they are always in pairs, not in larger groups. Partnerships among group members do not involve falling in love, but they are constant up to the point where a young man opts to leave the group by marrying. No man is permitted to remain a bachelor.

When he is ready to marry, a young man asks his close friends to join him in a prescribed etiquette of approaching the chosen girl and his own family, to see if they have the wealth to pay the bride price and put on a wedding festival.

The young man in search of a wife narrates the procedure of his courtship to his companions in the boys' house. Once married, he discloses details about sexual intercourse. In this way information is transmitted down the generations, and a young adolescent is prepared to anticipate his graduation from the era of homosexual experience to heterosexual falling-in-love and marriage.

---

*Information about homosexuality among females is conjectural among males, as talk about sexual activities, except between husband and wife, is taboo between the sexes.

The homosexual era in adolescence, by sequestering the sexes, ensures that young women will be virgins until married. The sanctions against premarital sex are stringent, so that a girl who is discovered in transgression probably commits suicide. Once a marriage is effected, the parties discontinue homosexuality, though men away on working parties in the jungle may temporarily resume them.

By contrast with the allowable age disparities in homosexual partnerships, the heterosexual partnership is formed between people of like age in young adulthood, or else the girl may be younger, in her teens, than the man, in his twenties. The relationship between the pair may be as close as cousins, but there is no special kinship obligation in the choice of a partner. There is a preference for partnerships within the racial—linguistic group. Marriage is the first and only heterosexual partnership, except for remarriage after the early death of one of the spouses. A marriage cannot otherwise be broken. Being married is, of course, publicly announced. The coital relationship of marriage is, by convention private and unobserved, except that young children may awaken when the parents are copulating. They then must not disclose their observation, but ignore it. According to the formalities of the culture, they learn about sex not at home, but from their adolescent and young adult friends.

Changing sexual traditions in our society

The cultural traditions of a lakeside village in Sumatra have been able to survive intact for an unspecified number of generations, but now, under the impact of cultural contact through education and broadcasting, these traditions are yielding to change. Change is a hallmark of the cultural traditions of our own society in the present age of instantaneous broadcast communication, nuclear-space technology and, in matters sexual, effective contraception. Whereas to some, the change in sexual traditions is anathema, to others it is utopia, but to none is it very clear, what, exactly, is happening. In terms of the seven schematic categories above-listed, one may suggest the following. There has been no change of tradition with respect to a preference for pairing couples of similar age, with continuing toleration of a few exceptions of disparity within the adult years. There is still a rigid rule against juvenile sexual play, though the age of "sex education" is subject to radical downward revision, amidst sometimes acrimonious social controversy. There is no issue more heated than that of the rights of adolescents and young adults to have sexual and love affairs premaritally, with or without intention to marry and/or have children. The trend is toward greater freedom. Sanctions against homosexuality are being examined and eased, though ambivalently, in favor of consensual agreements between adults. Problems of kinship in mating continue to be singularly unimportant, so long as the incest taboo is respected. The issue of miscegenation is so explosive that it can scarcely be mentioned in public and political discussion, perhaps because it is a foregone conclusion that black-white intermarriage will become routine. Class and caste preferences and distinctions in sexual pairing remain otherwise about the same as ever.

The leading pressure point of change in our society's sexual traditions would seem to be toward a greater plurality of sexual relationships, for females as well as males, on a basis of mutual reciprocity. This change is registered in sequential more often than contemporaneous plurality of relationships, before or after marriage. Even contemporaneous relationships are constant, over a period of time, rather than transient. Availability of effective contraception is undoubtedly the material artifact that underlies this cultural change, though in the case of serial marriage and divorce, with children to be supported, the economic and legal emancipation of women is also a major factor. Despite the plurality of partnerships, the preference is still for episodic monogamy or fidelity, rather than running more than one affair contemporaneously. However, a new institution, its future still uncertain, is the "swinging scene" of partner exchanging and group sex, coexistent and compatible with contractual marriage and long-term loyalty and emotional allegiance to one partner.

Participation in any sexual relationship outside of marriage is still subject to at least a partial need for concealment, though increasing freedom is accorded to young adults to be frank and open about their non-marital sexual liaisons and living together. Coitus itself is still subject to the rule of privacy, though some group sex participants are indifferent to being observed or to engaging in activities with more than one partner simultaneously.

Whether or not these changes in sexual tradition constitute a sexual revolution or are simply variations of basic primate behavior has become a subject for rhetoric and politics as well as for science and medicine. The reader must formulate his own conclusions.

14. PRINCIPLE OF NATIVISM VERSUS CULTURALISM

The juxtaposition of nature versus nurture has long been a favorite topic of argument pertaining to the behavior of human beings. Fascination with the topic stems ultimately from the issue of free will versus determinism. Nature is cast in the deterministic role of imperatively governing an inevitable and inexorable destiny variously named as biological, hereditary, constitutional, instinctual, and innate or inborn. Nurture by contrast is cast in the probabalistic role of optionally governing a modifiable and reversible fate, variously named as social, environmental, acquired, learned and developmental.

Irrespective of terminology, the conceptual problem lurking in the nature—nurture dichotomy is that the two interact. They are not independent variables. Table II presents a different conceptualization of how to differentiate the inevitable from the optional in a $2 \times 2 \times 2$ scheme which simultaneously differentiates the phylographic from the idiographic, and the

Table II
Nativism and culturalism as determinants of gender identity/role, classified simultaneously with phylographic versus idiographic, and imperative versus optional determinants
(with permission, from Money, 1975).

		Nativistic	Culturistic
Phylographic (species shared)	Imperative	Menstruation, gestation, lactation (women) vs. impregnation (men)	Social models for identifi-cation and complementa-tion in gender-identity dif-ferentiation
	Optional	Population size, fertility rate and sex ratio	Population birth/death ratio. Diminishing age of puberty
Idiographic (individual-ly unique)	Imperative	Chromosome anomalies, e.g., 45,X; 47,XXY; 47,XYY. Vestigal penis. Vestigal uterus. Vaginal atresia.	Sex announcement and rearing as male, female, or ambiguous.
	Optional	Getting pregnant. Breast feeding. Anorectic amenor-rhea. Castration.	Gender-divergent work, law, cosmetics and grooming, child care.

nativistic from the culturistic. That which is phylographic is species shared,
whereas the idiographic is personally unique. Both may be either nativistic
or cultural in origin, and, either way, may exist as imperatives or options.
    The cells of Table II may be filled in for a variable other than that of
gender identity/role *, the variable which is here appropriate.

BIBLIOGRAPHY

Burns, R.K. (1961) Role of hormones in the differentiation of sex. In: (W.C. Young, Ed.)
    Sex and Internal Secretions, (Williams and Wilkins, Baltimore).
Chang, C.Y. and Witschi, E. (1955) Breeding of sex-reversed males of Xenopus laevis Dau-
    din. Proc. Soc. Exp. Biol. Med. 89: 150—152.
Chang, C.Y. and Witschi, E. (1956) Genic control and hormonal reversal of sex differen-
    tiation on Xenopus. Proc. Soc. Exp. Biol. Med. 93: 140—144.
Ehrhardt, A.A., and Money, J. (1967) Progestin-induced hermaphroditism: IQ and psy-
    chosexual identity in a study of ten girls. J. Sex. Res. 3: 83—100.

* The two-word term, identity/role is actually redundant, since identity and role are opposite sides of the same coin. The self perceives its own identity, whereas others can only
infer it from its role manifestation, which is both verbal and nonverbal. People tend to
dichotomize identity and role, instead of keeping them a unity.

78

Ehrhardt, A.A., Epstein, R. and Money, J. (1968) Fetal androgens and female gender identity in the early-treated adrenogenital syndrome. *Johns Hopkins Med. J.* 122: 165—167.

Fisher, A.E. (1956) Maternal and sexual behavior induced by intracranial chemical stimulation. *Science* 124: 228—229.

Fisher, A.E. (1966) Chemical and electrical stimulation of the brain in the male rat. In: (P.A. Gorski and R.E. Whalen, Eds) *The Brain and Gonadal Function.* Vol. III of *Brain and Behavior.* (University of California Press, Berkeley.)

Gorski, R. (1971) Sexual differentiation of the hypothalamus. In: (H.C. Mack and A.I. Sherman, Eds) *The Neuroendocrinology of Human Reproduction.* (Charles C. Thomas, Springfield, Illinois.)

Grant, E.C.G. and Pryse-Davies, J. (1968) Effect of oral contraceptives on depressive mood changes and on endometrial monoamine oxidase and phosphatases. *Br. Med. J.* 3: 777—780.

Hamilton, J.B., Walter, R.O., Daniel, R.M. and Mestler, G.E. (1969) Competition for mating between ordinary and supermale Japanese medaka fish. *Anim. Behav.* 17: 168—176.

Harlow, H.F. and Harlow, M.K. (1965) The effect of rearing conditions on behavior. In: (J. Money, Ed.) *Sex Research, New Developments.* (Holt, Rinehart and Winston, New York.)

Harris, G.W. (1964) Sex hormones, brain development and brain function. *Endocrinology* 75: 627—648.

Herbert, J. (1967) The social modification of sexual and other behavior in the rhesus monkey. In: (D. Starck, R. Schneider and H.-J. Kuh, Eds) *Progress in Primatology.* (Gustav Fisher, Stuttgart) pp. 222—246.

Jones, H.W., Schirmer, H.K.A. and Hoopes, J.E. (1968) A sex conversion operation for males with transsexualism. *Am. J. Obstet. Gynecol.* 100: 101—109.

Kollar, E.J., Beckwith, W.C. and Edgerton, R.B. (1968) Sexual behavior of the ARL colony chimpanzees. *J. Nerv. Ment. Dis.* 147: 444—459.

MacLean, P.D. (1965) New findings relevant to the evolution of psychosexual functions of the brain. In: (J. Money, Ed.) *Sex Research, New Developments.* (Holt, Rinehart and Winston, New York.)

Masica, D.N., Money, J., Ehrhardt, A.A. and Lewis, V.G. (1969) IQ, fetal sex hormones and cognitive patterns: Studies in the testicular feminizing syndrome of androgen insensitivity. *Johns Hopkins Med. J.* 124: 34—43.

Masters, W.H. and Johnson, V.E. (1966) *Human Sexual Response.* (Little, Brown, Boston.)

Mikamo, K. and Witchi, E. (1963) Functional sex-reversal in genetic females of *Xenopus laevis,* induced by implanted testes. *Genetics* 48: 1411—1421.

Money, J. (1960) Phantom orgasm in the dreams of paraplegic men and women. *Arch. Gen. Psychiat.* 3: 373—382.

Money, J. (1961a) Components of eroticism in man. I: The hormones in relation to sexual morphology and sexual desire. *J. Nerv. Ment. Dis.* 132: 239—248.

Money, J. (1961b) Components of eroticism in man. II: The orgasm and genital somethesia. *J. Nerv. Ment. Dis.* 132: 289—297.

Money, J. (1965) Influence of hormones on sexual behavior. In: (A.C. Degraff, Ed.) *Annu. Rev. Med.* Vol. 16 (Annual Reviews, Inc., Palo Alto) pp. 67—82.

Money, J. (1968a) Hermaphroditism and pseudohermaphroditism. In: (J.J. Gold, Ed.) *Textbook of Gynecologic Endocrinology.* 2nd edn, 1975 (Harper and Row, New York).

Money, J. (1968b) Discussion: Clinical effects of agents affecting fertility. (Antiandrogen to control behavior.) In: (R.P. Michael, Ed.) *Endrocrinology and Human Behaviour.* (Oxford University Press, London.)

Money, J. (1969) Sex reassignment as related to hermaphroditism and transsexualism. In: (R. Green and J. Money, Eds) *Transsexualism and Sex Reassignment.* (Johns Hopkins Press, Baltimore.)

Money, J. (1975) Nativism versus culturalism in gender-identity differentiation.In: (E. Adelson, Ed.) *Sexuality and Psychoanalysis.* (Brunner/Mazel, New York.)

Money, J. and Alexander, D. (1967) Eroticism and sexual function in developmental anorchia and hyporchia with pubertal failure. *J. Sex Res.* 3: 31—47.

Money, J. and Ehrhardt, A.A. (1972) *Man and Woman, Boy and Girl: The Differentiation and Dimorphism of Gender Identity from Conception to Maturity.* (Johns Hopkins Press, Baltimore.)

Money, J., Ehrhardt, A.A. and Masica, D.M. (1068) Fetal femininization induced by androgen insensitivity in the testicular femininizing syndrome: Effect on marriage and maternalism. *Johns Hopkins Med. J.* 123: 105—114.

Money, J. and Mittenthal, S. (1970) Lack of personality pathology in Turner's Syndrome: Relation to cytogenetics, hormones and physique. *Behav. Genet.* 1: 43—56.

Neumann, F. and Elger, W. (1965) Proof of the activity of androgenic agents on the differentiation of the external genitalia, the mammary gland and the hypothalamic-pituitary system in rats. *Excerpta Medica, Int. Congr. Ser. 101: Androgens in Normal and Pathological Conditions,* pp. 169—185.

Neumann, F. and Elger, W. (1966) Permanent changes in gonadal function and sexual behavior as a result of early feminization of male rats by treatment with an anti-androgenic steroid. *Endokrinologie,* 50: 209—225.

Petrie, A. (1967) *Individuality in Pain and Suffering.* (University of Chicago Press, Chicago).

Phoenix, C. (1966) *Psychosexual Organization in Nonhuman Primates.* Paper delivered at the Conference on Endocrine and Neural Control of Sex and Related Behavior. (Puerto Rico, Dorado Beach).

Trimble, M.R. and Herbert, J. (1968) The effect of testosterone or oestradiol upon the sexual and associated behavior of the adult female rhesus monkey. *J. Endocrinol.,* 42: 171—185.

Turner, C.D. and Asakawa, H. (1964) Experimental reversal of germ cells in ovaries of fetal mice. *Science* 143: 1344—1345.

Wilkins, L. (1965) *The Diagnosis and Treatment of Endocrine Disorders in Childhood and Adolescence,* Third edn. (Charles C. Thomas, Springfield, Ill.)

Witsche, E. (1956) Etiology of gonadal agenesis and sex reversal. In: (C.A. Villee, Ed.) *Transactions of the Third Conference,* (Princeton).

Witsche, E. (1965) Hormones and embryonic induction. *Arch. Anat. Microsc. Morphol. Exp.* 51: 601—611.

Yamamoto, T. (1962) Harmonic factors affecting gonadal differentiation in fish. *Gen. Comp. Endocrinol,* 1, 311—345.

Young, W.C., Goy, R.W. and Phoenix, C.H. (1965) Hormones and sexual behavior. In: (J. Money, Ed.) *Sex Research, New Developments,* (Holt, Rinehart and Winston, New York).

CHAPTER 6

Sexology: a multidisciplinary science

HERMAN MUSAPH

1. MORPHOLOGY AND PSYCHOLOGY

If one considers sexology as a science, which has as its objective the study of patterns of behavior and feelings which in some way concern sex, one has made an attempt at delimination. In this respect, a great number of disciplines can be seen to have a tangential plane with sexology. If we limit ourselves to the realm of mammals, it is clear that each individual is male or female.

Very rarely does morphology present us with difficulties. A male individual produces only spermatozoa and a female individual only ova. The very rare exceptions to this rule were already known in the past century. It goes without saying that, as far as male and female morphology is concerned, only the pattern of behavior linked to reproductive fertility is rigidly sex differentiated.

In the last decades it has become clear that reality is not as simple as here presumed. Sexual behavior patterns are not only determined by the sex organs. Moreover, gender identity does not necessarily coincide with anatomy. The increase of our knowledge in this field mainly came from the study of psychology.

2. CULTURAL ANTHROPOLOGY

Cultural anthropology has increased knowledge of the influence of the many patterns of culture on the sexual patterns of behavior. This science has taught us that one needs to refrain from absolute values in judging sex patterns. The concepts of good and evil, adequate and inadequate, normal and abnormal have only relative values, which have to be judged within the framework of a certain pattern of standards. This pattern is liable to alterations.

Handbook of Sexology, edited by J. Money and H. Musaph
© *Elsevier/North-Holland Biomedical Press, 1977*

A layman in the field of sexology can permit himself to express an absolute value judgment on sex behavior applicable to all human beings. It is an objective of science to describe and study why this layman has such a dogmatic opinion. Since Freud, one can no longer speak of human sex behavior as an absolute. Sexology is in a process of development of which probably only the coarser features are presently known. It is the merit of psychoanalysis to have given more insight into mature sexual life in physical adulthood. Nevertheless, knowledge of dynamic development of sex is rather poor. One knows that general emotional patterns vary considerably individually in intensity and equality, and this variability also applies to sexual emotional patterns.

Behaviorists in particular have tried to get around the complex problems of scientifically approaching emotions by judging only the behavior of emotions. The enormous advantage of this approach lies in the fact that behavior can be made accessible for quantification. The judgment of results of measurement in an experimental situation in which, for example, sexual excitement is defined exclusively in terms of behavior, reveals more about the present sexual status, than of the history that led up to it. Despite the enormous advantage of this approach, there is a danger of oversimplification and overgeneralization. Behaviorism gives us more insight into the laws of human and animal behavior in a given situation. This certainly is an enrichment if one has an open eye for the immense diversity of human motivation.

3. PSYCHOPHYSIOLOGY

The great contribution of psychophysiology lies in the description of the autonomous response patterns such as pulse rate, respiration, galvanic skin response and blood flow in certain emotions, such as sexual excitement. The work of Masters and Johnson and their co-workers particularly increased the body of knowledge in this field. But again one must take care to register and describe the accompanying appearance of emotion. In an scientific approach to studying sexuality one cannot afford to miss registering personal and general expressions in preference for physiological parameters. And not only this: it is desirable to encourage every attempt to study sexual emotions and behavior in an experimental situation. There still exists much in animal and human behavior which has only become available for scientific exploration very recently.

4. ETHOLOGY

Ethology set a basis for the elaboration of sexual knowledge. Here one thinks in particular of the work of ethologists in the jungles of Africa, studying sexual behavior patterns in primates not made neurotic by captivity in a zoo. Ethological investigations in human beings in various culture patterns is still complicated by taboos of our own making. A clear example is the difficulty one finds in studying sexual behavior patterns in children before puberty, for example by a hidden camera.

Empirical investigation of masturbation patterns in children which is necessary to test psychoanalytical hypotheses, still meets with great objection. This applies to Anglo—Saxon countries as well as Latin. In this field much work has still to be done.

5. PSYCHOPATHOLOGY

Until recently psychopathology and clinical psychiatry were above all preoccupied with deviant behavior in sexual matters. Scientific workers in this field have introduced during the past century terms such as: sexual perversion, exhibitionism, homosexuality, fetishism, pedophilia and voyeurism. Opinion with reference to these concepts has changed in a revolutionary way in the course of the years. Today's doctors, when in medical school, were taught that these inadequate patterns of behavior had to be considered as expressions of a disordered or psychopathic personality structure. European sexology in particular has been characterized by this approach since before World War II. This concept was criticized not only by psychiatrists, but also by medical—psychological and clinical—psychological investigations, which showed that the link between sexual deviant or variant behavior and human psychopathology was dictated too strongly by unscientific, moral prejudices. In a modern Handbook of Sexology the concept of sexual perversion as synonymous with socially deviant or stigmatized behavior belongs to the chapter "History of Sexology".

6. FUNCTIONAL APPROACH

In modern sexological investigations the tendency to disengage deviant behavior from psychopathology is getting stronger. Modern psychiatry is developing more and more in a relational and situational direction. Here, a sexual emotional and behavioral pattern has to be studied more in interaction with one's fellow man, within the framework of complementarity. In this way a functional approach to sex is growing. It is necessary to know which role sex plays within the framework of other emotions, which can be studied longitudinally and situationally — the role of emotions such as anxiety, hostility, resentment and sorrow, and the experience and disappearance of sexual patterns of feeling and behavior. What function has sex, as a phase of mental growth, with respect to fight and flight patterns in interaction between individuals? What function has sex in a relationship and especially in a love relationship? In this way sex is placed in a complicated profile. Everyone knows that in a love relationship, many emotions play a role, in which sex takes an important place but not a monopolistic one.

7. SOCIOLOGY

Sociology teaches that the place of sex is also determined by social learning, social rules and role playing. In general, these are rigid patterns, determined by traditions and institutions of industrialization, acculturation, religion, and generation conflicts. And so it is that sex has many faces. Consequently a complete operational definition is not quite possible. One could say that sex in and of itself cannot exist.

It is a living human being who experiences his sexuality in interaction with another person, in fantasies and reality. His sexuality is determined by his social environment, his culture pattern, his conflict situation and his mental and physical health. These points of view cannot be neglected if one tries to operationalize the concept of sex. It has a 'surplus meaning', that is to say it contains more than can be found by the empirical approach alone. The same can be said of such concepts as health, illness, aggression and social adaptation. A modern Handbook of Sexology has to start from the empirical approach and should be followed by a consideration of the surplus meaning. It goes without saying that this needs a multidisciplinary approach.

SECTION II

Genetics, cytogenetics, sex reversal and behavior

Section coordinator: S. Walzer

CHAPTER 7

Introduction

S. WALZER

Medicine has passed through an era in which molecular biology dominated the scientific arena. Scientists have looked for the ultimate in cause—effect relationships and have tended to focus down on the unitary factors behind processes. There was a tendency to apply a reductionistic schema to all scientific investigations. If one could only identify the appropriate ultimate unitary principle or process, one could understand its natural outcome or elaboration.

The field of genetics appeared to be a most fertile ground for such an orientation. After all, it was based on three primary laws: segregation, independent assortment and the Hardy—Weinberg law of population equilibria. Any science that is accountable by law for its organization must be reducible to clearly defined unitary principles. Searching for a clear dichotomy between what was nature and what was nurture became the vogue.

During this period of time, human psychological development was viewed almost solely in terms of experiential and environmental determinants. Individual uniqueness was related almost solely to environmental factors, with little or no attention being given to any prior biological roots. Psychological development did follow sequential patterns ontogenetically but was the result of environmental influences. Thus, psychological sex differentiation was explained in terms of modeling and reinforcement — not denying the impact of biology, but not attempting to include it meaningfully in any dynamic way. Developmental psychology was, in a sense, an ultimate social science.

Over the last decade, however, certain clear-cut principles, laws and dichotomies have been shown to demonstrate a degree of variability previously unappreciated. For example, as the clinical syndromes of 45,X, XXY, and XYY were defined, it became obvious that there were, indeed, limitations on the Mendelian law of segregation. As psychological investigations became increasingly prospective and systematic — reaching back to early infancy — a large number of studies demonstrated important individual differences that

Handbook of Sexology, edited by J. Money and H. Musaph
© *Elsevier/North-Holland Biomedical Press, 1977*

did exist at birth and could not be explained on an experiential basis. Furthermore, it became increasingly evident that a considerable organization of behavior already existed at birth, suggesting that some innate properties of the nervous system were relevant contributants to subsequent behavioral development.

It is obvious, then, that a handbook such as this — one that is committed to studying such a complex science as sexology, with all of its bio-, psycho-, social parameters — must examine critically the biological roots, bringing them into line with modern day concepts of interactionalism. We must consider the limitations imposed on the genetic determiners by the environment and the limitations imposed on the environment by the genotype. Throughout this chapter it will become increasingly clear that the genotype must be viewed as a biological potential, unfolding in interaction with the environment at all levels (cellular, fetal and postnatal) and that the phenotypic outcome is the result of this bioenvironmental mutuality.

The concept of interactionalism can be more clearly studied in animals where various manipulation experiments can be performed and specific outcomes studied. Human studies do not allow for this and, therefore, interactionalism is less easy to see.

If we begin our investigations at a basic morphological level, that is, at the level of the sex chromosomes and their relationship to sex-specific physical development, we would expect some degree of reductionistic simplicity. For after all, the sex of an individual is a biological variable. Sex determination is a function of the ratio between a particular sex chromosome complement and the autosomes. However, several of the animal papers in this chapter will demonstrate that, from the lowest phylogenetic level considered (fish) to the highest level (primates), the relationship between the sex chromosomes and phenotypic development is not predictable under all circumstances. Thus, Chan presents data showing that natural sex reversal can occur spontaneously — with male fish sequentially becoming phenotypic females, which can actually propagate. Gresick and Hamilton, and Knight and Taber show that, under certain experimental conditions, phenotypic sex reversal or intersexuality can be brought about in fish or birds irrespective of the sex chromosome complement. Thus, even at the somatic level, a particular chromosomal complement will result in an expected phenotype only under certain conditions and within certain limitations.

Like morphological development, behavioral development must also be viewed as a bioenvironmental construct. Again, complex experimental manipulations with animals allow one to study the limits on the expected variability in behavioral development imposed by a given set of conditions.

Goy, Wolf and Eisele, in experiments on the rhesus monkey, have demonstrated that androgenization during a critical phase of fetal development resulted in complex behavioral patterns discordant for the chromosomal sex throughout the preadolescent life of the animal. Neumann and Elger (1966) administered antiandrogenic compounds to pregnant rats during a critical period of gestation; the genetic male progeny tended to behave along female lines in their sexual activity. Thus, it is evident that with certain environmental manipulations during a short critical period in fetal life, animals can be made to behave in a manner discordant to their chromosomal constitution throughout their lives.

Such studies, however, do not complicate the scene but actually simplify it, for they demonstrate that basic biological factors do indeed exist. Thus, androgens do something to developing brains, leading to permanent changes which affect the sex specific behavior throughout the lives of the animals. Therefore, by experimental manipulation, we can isolate a prenatal variable that is a contributant to future behavioral development.

In studies of human behavioral development, manipulation experiments cannot be employed; therefore, bioenvironmental interactionalism is much more difficult to view. Furthermore, since man is primarily a social animal, biological roots become easily covered over by social factors. Yet, there are several naturally occurring variants, for example, the XXY, XYY, and 45,X genotypes, that can be systematically studied developmentally. Thus, one may examine the way given biological variables interact with social variables to shape the psychological development of an individual. The chapter by Lev-Ran enumerates the many syndromes that constitute variant forms of sexual differentiation on both a chromosomal basis and a prenatal hormonal basis. Ehrhardt gives details about the psychological development of girls with the adrenogenital syndrome in another section of this book. The psychological development of boys insufficiently androgenized in utero is detailed in a chapter by Money.

Preliminary observations in the field of human behavior genetics, though often colored by serious ascertainment bias, have suggested that systematic studies of individuals with sex chromosome anomalies (aneuploidies) could offer opportunities to understand further the nature of the relationship which exists between sex chromosomic abnormalities and behavioral development. If careful, systematic, longitudinal studies could be done on behaviorally unselected populations of newborn infants with specific identifiable chromosome aberrations, it might be possible to identify some commonality in their reactive styles (that is, temperamental organization) through the matrix of the individual uniqueness expected, considering the variability of the environmental influences affecting the individual children in the study (Walzer, unpublished). This would suggest that a consideration of environmental determinants alone is insufficient to understand the complexity of human behavioral development and that nonevironmental biological factors are also relevant.

Studies of naturally occurring variants have, in the wrong hands, led to erroneous conclusions about the relationship between biological variables and behavioral development. For example, in the area of sex chromosome abnormalities and their possible relationship to behavioral development, statements have appeared emphasizing that certain chromosomal constellations (for example, XYY) caused specific behavioral abnormalities (for example, antisocial behavior). These false conclusions are, in fact, completely contrary to what one understands the relationship between these variables to be.

Many critics of human behavioral genetic studies are correct when they cannot accept the existence of a direct relationship between the genotype and the development of specific human behavior. However, they incorrectly go on to deny that there is any relationship between biological determinants and behavioral variables.

There are also 'blind believers' who have never given up the faith that ultimately every human behavior or behavioral variation will be found to have a specific measurable biological relationship between specific behavioral development and the genotype, or that there can be no relationship at all.

Behavior genetics, both animal and human, is the study of limits and variability (Money, 1970). It is concerned with the limits, both genotypic and environmental, within which a genotype can unfold into a normal phenotype. However, it accepts enthusiastically that, within these limits, a wide range of variability in phenotypic outcome is possible. A particular phenotypic constellation is the result of a dynamic interaction between the unfolding genotype and the complex bio-, psycho-, social surroundings, both pre- and postnatally.

Certain genotypic variations might narrow somewhat the variability possible in certain areas of behavioral development. The more serious the genotypic abnormality, the more limited is the variability possible in specific developmental characteristics. Within these limits, however, a broad range of variability exists which is responsive to the extensive intermixture of both biological and complex psychosocial factors. Particular phenotypic constellations appear within the limits imposed by the genotype, in response to these bio- and psycho-social factors.

The research presented in these chapters emphasizes that biological factors cannot be ignored in theoretical frameworks developed to explain the origin and organization of behavior. Further research is required to understand the way biological predispositions interact with social experiences to shape the psychological development of an individual.

BIBLIOGRAPHY

Money, J. (1970) Behavior genetics: Principles, methods and examples from XO, XXY and XYY syndromes. *Sem. Psychiat.* 2: 11—29.

Neumann, F. and Elger, W. (1966) Permanent changes in gonadal function and sexual behavior as a result of early feminization of male rats by treatment with an anti-androgenic steroid. *Endokrinologie* 50: 209—225.

CHAPTER 8

Spontaneous sex reversal in fishes

S.T.H. CHAN

In vertebrates, bisexuality is observed in most species in the chromosomes, the gonads, the sex accessories and the psychosocial patterns, but in general practice the female and male sexes may normally be distinguished according to the gonadal sex, as the testes and ovaries are the prime organs producing gametes (which form the basic units of sexual reproduction) and sex hormones (which control the body sex, the brain sex and the behavioral sex). On the criterion of gonadal sex, vertebrate sexuality can be defined either as gonochorism, in which each individual has either testes or ovaries and functions only as one sex, or hermaphroditism, where every individual in the species possesses both ovaries and testes and functions as both sexes in the life cycle. Hermaphroditism can be either 'functional in space' when both the ovarian and the testicular components mature simultaneously (simultaneous hermaphrodite) and self-fertilization is possible, or 'functional in time' when the intersexual gonad develops first as an ovary and, after functioning as female, then transforms into a testis, or vice versa. Spontaneous sex reversal in vertebrates refers to this unique biological phenomenon of hermaphroditism, functional in time, by which an organism functions naturally as both sexes in the life cycle; this is essentially a process of sequential maturation of the female and male germinal tissues in succession in relation to gonadal ontogeny (see Chan, 1970). Spontaneous sex reversal in fish is therefore, distinct from pathological or experimental sex reversals, which are generally ascribed to some unnatural conditions in which the gonadal sex of an organism is disharmonious with the genetic sex, or the body sex is disharmonious with the gonadal sex; in such instances, the organism rarely functions as both sexes in its life history.

Fish (Pisces) comprise the cartilaginous fish (Chondrichthyes) and the bony fish (Osteichthyes), the latter being subdivided into Crossopterygii and Actinopterygii. Spontaneous sex reversal is rare among the living cartilaginous fish (the Elasmobranchs) and the primitive bony fish including the ganoids and the lungfish (Dipnoi: Crossopterygii). Among the modern

Handbook of Sexology, edited by J. Money and H. Musaph
© *Elsevier/North-Holland Biomedical Press, 1977*

Actinopterygians, hermaphroditism is very common, and especially in teleost, there exists the most diversified expression of sexuality known in the
animal kingdom; nonfunctional and abnormal hermaphroditism has been
reported occasionally in most teleostean groups, while normal and functional hermaphroditism, with or without sex reversal, is known to exist commonly in Atheriniformes, Cyprinodontiformes, Aulopiformes, Stomiatiformes,
Scorpaeniformes, Perciformes and Synbranchiformes (see Atz, 1964). In the
present short chapter on spontaneous sex reversal in fish, it is intended to
avoid tedious and lengthy coverage on various taxonomical groups which will
be confusing to students unfamiliar with this field of knowledge. A selective
approach is adopted to provide some forms of concise and recent accounts
on the sparids and serranids (Perciformes), *Monopterus albus* (Synbranchiformes) and *Rivulus marmoratus* (Cyprinodontiformes), since these species
are not only the most extensively studied, but they are also the representatives of some distinctive patterns of natural sex reversal and hermaphroditism in fish.

1. THE SPARIDS AND SERRANIDS

These are the sea-breams, porgies, sea-basses and groupers in which all forms
of hermaphroditism occur, including rudimentary, simultaneous, protandrous and protogynous hermaphrodites in addition to the gonochoristic species. Atz (1964) and Reinboth (1970) provide excellent reviews on the hermaphroditic and sex-reversing species in these groups of Perciform fish.
    In the studies on spontaneous sex reversal, special attention is given to the
location and occurrence of the male and female germinal tissues in the gonad, as this is related to the structural basis for sexual changes. The gonad of
sparids is essentially an ovotestis comprising both ovarian and testicular parts
in the elongated, normally paired, structure, and there is invariably some
form of connective tissue separating male and female lobes. The ovarian
cavities of the paired gonads join and form a common oviduct posteriorly,
and along the gonadal wall there are lacunae that eventually coalesce to form
a single sperm duct; the male and female ducts open separately to the exteri-
or and this prevents the possibility of internal self-fertilization especially in
simultaneous hermaphroditic species. Spontaneous sex reversal occurs as
normal developmental events in many sparids such as the protogynous
Pagellus erythrinus (Reinboth, 1962) and the protandrous *P. acarne*
(Reinboth, 1962), *P. mormyrus* (D'Ancona, 1949) and *Sparus auratus*
(D'Ancona, 1941). In these species, the male and female lobes of the gonad
mature in succession according to the type of hermaphroditism particular to
the species. In protandrous forms, the testicular lobe matures first; as it enlarges it envelopes the ovarian part on both sides; the latter can only be observed on the inner surface of the gonad. Sex reversal from male to female
occurs at a certain time in the life history when the testicular elements

regress and the ovarian lobe proliferates and becomes functional; the male elements in the female phase may reduce to only a tiny flap of tissue along the lateral surface of the gonad. When the ovarian and testicular elements are about equally well developed, the cross-section of the gonad would be triangular with the testicular part occupying the laterally orientated apex and the ovarian along the more medial base (Fig. 1). The timing of sex reversal varies according to species and within a species. In *Sparus auratus*, the testicular elements mature during the first year of the life history and become functional in the second; sexual transformation occurs between 2 to 3 years of age when the ovarian lobe develops, and becomes functional in the third year continuing to produce ripe eggs each year for the remaining two years or so of the life history (D'Ancona, 1941). In *Pagellus acarne*, spontaneous sex reversal is found to occur in the fourth, fifth or sixth year with the actual structural change normally taking place between spawning seasons (Reinboth, 1962).

In serranids, the anatomical features of the gonad are similar to those found in sparids, except that there is normally no connective tissue separating the female and male elements, but there remains some form of localization of the ovarian and the testicular tissues within the undivided organ. The pattern of sex transformation is similar to that in sparids resulting in protogynous and protandrous sex-reversing hermaphrodites (see Atz, 1964).

It is becoming apparent that, for most of the species of sparids and serra-

Fig. 1. Cross-section through a gonad of the protandrous sparid, *Pagellus acarne*, at middle stage of sex reversal showing the male and female lobes separated by connective tissue; the ovarian elements commence to mature while the testicular lobe regresses. (Courtesy of Professor R. Reinboth)

nids studied, there seems to be generally a co-existence of both male and female germinal tissues before the onset of spontaneous sex reversal, thus providing a structural basis whereby natural transformation of the gonadal sex is possible by sequential maturation of male and female tissues in succession.

2. THE ENDOCRINOLOGY OF NATURAL SEX REVERSAL IN *MONOPTERUS*

Monopterus albus, the ricefield eel, is perhaps one of the most extensively studied among hermaphroditic fishes, especially with respect to endocrinological and biochemical aspects of the phenomenon of spontaneous sex reversal. Sex reversal in *Monopterus* was first reported by Liu (1944) who observed that small individuals are mostly female, while the large ones are male; intersexes are found in animals of intermediate size. Chan and Phillips (1967 a, b) studied the anatomy of the gonad in detail and reported, among other observations, that the pre-existence of the male germ cells before the commencement of sex change and the extensive development of interstitial Leydig tissue during sex reversal are characteristic features of special significance in this species. In the female phase, the gonad is essentially a typical teleostean ovary (Chan et al. 1967) with maturing oocytes expanding from the germinal areas, the gonadal lamellae, into the lumen of the gonad (Fig. 2A). However, unlike the ovaries of gonochoristic species, the female gonad of *Monopterus* possesses male germ cells in quiescent condition along the inner edge of the gonadal lamellae. Spontaneous sex reversal occurs at a variable age, but normally between the second and third year when the gonad fully matures as an ovary and the animal spawns as a female. In the process of structural transformation, which usually commences in the postnuptial period, there is always a loss of ovarian tissue (as a result of ovulation) together with the rapid proliferation of the male germ cells to form testicular lobules, and a parallel extensive development of interstitial Leydig tissue. The transforming gonad is therefore intersexual with both female and male elements (Fig. 2B), however, no mature eggs and sperms are found to exist simultaneously within a single gonad and the intersexual phase is always transitional, lasting for 3 to 6 months. By the next breeding season, the gonad is filled with mainly testicular lobules with active spermatogenesis (Fig. 2C). The sequential structural transformation events in the process of spontaneous sex reversal in *Monopterus* can be, and have been, studied by time-lapse biopsy investigations on the gonadal ontogeny (Chan, 1971, Chan et al., 1972a) providing evidence that the pre-existence of the male germ cells in the gonad during the mature female phase and before the onset of sex change indeed forms the structural basis of spontaneous sex reversal in this species. Sex reversal is therefore in fact sex succession in the development and maturation of the female and male germinal tissues in an hermaphroditic gonad (see Chan, 1970).

As the success of reproduction in vertebrates depends on the normal physiological functions of the gonad as a male or a female, not only in the production of mature gametes but also in the secretion of sex hormones of the corresponding sex, one major area of interest concerning sex-reversing fishes is, therefore, their hormonal mechanism(s) whereby the biochemical and endocrinological functions could adopt, or reverse, from one sex to another; a situation rarely possible in gonochoristic vertebrates, especially the higher forms. Much investigation on this aspect has been made on *Monopterus* (see Chan et al., 1974). On the aspect of gonadal sex hormones, *Monopterus*, though being a sex-reversing hermaphrodite, possesses different steroidogenic cells in the two sexual phases of the life cycle, namely, granulosa cells in the female and the interstitial Leydig cells in the male (Chan and Phillips, 1967b); both tissues show characteristics of steroidogenic cells in their activities of 3β-hydroxysteroid dehydrogenase (Tang et al., 1974), an important enzyme in the biosynthesis of sex steroids, and in their EM (electron microscopic) ultrastructures including smooth endoplasmic reticulum and mitochondria with tubular cristae (Adal, Hui and Chan, unpublished). As far as the endocrine tissue is concerned, the gonad of *Monopterus* in the female and male phase is similar to the ovary and testis, respectively, of most gonochoristic species. Studies on the production of sex steroids in vitro with radioactive precursor show that the major sex hormones, such as androstenedione, testosterone, estradiol and estrone, are produced by *Monopterus* gonads at various sexual phases. However, in the female phase estrogen predominates, while in the male phase, androgen; during the intersexual stage, a hormonal shift from estrogen to androgen occurs concomitant with the structural transformation (Chan and Phillips, 1969). In vivo studies by GLC on levels of sex steroids in peripheral plasma reveal the same hormonal patterns and shift (Chan et al., 1974). Thus all results indicate that the anatomical sex reversal in *Monopterus* is accompanied by physiological, biochemical and hormonal sex reversal, and that in the two sexual phases of the life cycle, the gonad functions in succession as two distinct entities, equivalent to the ovary and testis of gonochoristic species. Chan and co-workers (1974) discussed in depth the functional significance of the endocrine events during spontaneous sex reversal, especially aspects concerning the roles of sex steroids in the enhancement of the maturation of germ cells of the corresponding sex and the suppression at those of the opposite sex.

Since experimental sex reversal can be induced by steroid treatments on embryonic undifferentiated gonads of some gonochoristic fishes and amphibians, there are speculations that sex steroids may be responsible for spontaneous sex reversal in fish, and experimental studies on species other than *Monopterus* have so far yielded variable results (see Atz, 1964; Reinboth, 1970). In *Monopterus*, extensive experiments involving steroid administrations together with biopsy studies on gonads at various sexual phases lead to the conclusion that the administration of androgens to the female phase fails both to bring about precocious sex changes and to enhance male germ cell

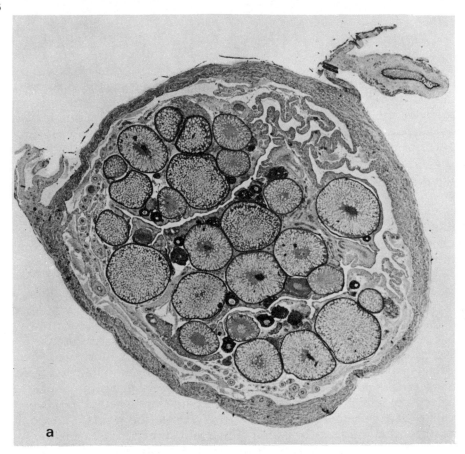

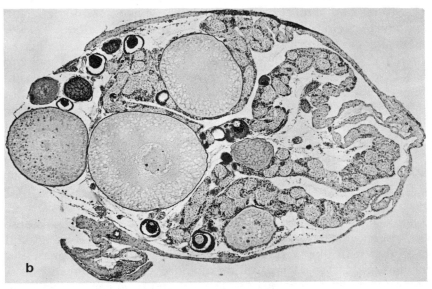

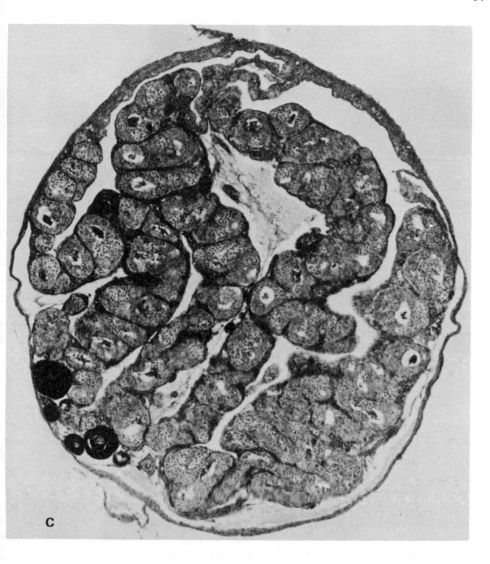

C

Fig. 2. Spontaneous sex reversal in *Monopterus albus*. (a) Female gonad with large number of maturing oocytes and follicles showing the gross appearance of a typical teleostean ovary, however, male germinal cells are present in quiescent condition along the inner edge of the gonadal lamellae (from Chan, 1970). (b) Gonad at the intersexual phase when there is a co-existence of testicular and ovarian tissues; the former show extensive development of both the interstitial Leydig cells and the testicular lobules while the latter are in degenerating state. (c) Gonad at the male stage showing the full development of testicular lobules derived from the quiescent male germ cells, the gonadal lamellae are now filled with mainly male tissues with only a few remaining degenerating oocytes; this gonad was shown by biopsy 25 weeks before to be a female entering sex reversal (from Chan et al., 1972a).

development (Chan, 1971; Chan et al., 1972b), although the same treatments to the intersexes and males show obvious spermatokinetic effects (Chan et al., 1974). As far as sex steroids and spontaneous sex reversal in *Monopterus* are concerned, it appears that, firstly, the endogenous rise in androgen during gonadal transformation is not the primary causative of sex reversal but rather is one of the series of secondary events parallel to the anatomical changes in the gonad. Secondly, the process of natural sex reversal is in some respects different from the experimental sex reversals in undifferentiated gonads of gonochorists where sex steroids could completely masculinize or femininize the gonadal development mostly via its antagonistic effects on tissue of the opposite sex in the primordial intersexual gonad. Furthermore, it appears that the response of the male germinal tissue to androgen stimulation in *Monopterus* is age-dependent, and that an appropriate endocrine environment within the gonad is essential for the normal maturation of germ cells of the corresponding sex (see Chan et al., 1974).

The hypothalamus—pituitary complex is known to control the reproductive events in vertebrate gonads, and very little is known about the relationship, if any, between the hypothalamus—pituitary functions and spontaneous sex reversal in fish. Studies on this aspect so far reported are on *Monopterus* where Chan and co-workers demonstrate by cytological and cytophysiological experiments that the anatomical structure, cell types, and function of the pituitary in this sex-reversing fish are in general similar to those reported in other gonochoristic fishes (O and Chan, 1974a, b; Chan et al., 1974, 1975). In addition, it is found that the pituitary gland of *Monopterus* contains secretions having the biological activities of mammalian FSH and LH as bioassayed by the ovarian ascorbic acid depletion (Parlow, 1961) and the ovarian hCG augmentation tests with rats; furthermore, animals at the mature female phase prior to spawning are found to have a much higher level of LH activity than any other sexual stages in the life cycle (Chan et al., 1974). These findings, together with the fact that interstitial Leydig cells are known to be under the stimulatory control of LH in most vertebrates and invariably undergo extensive development during sex change in *Monopterus*, clearly indicate the involvement of the pituitary functions in spontaneous sex reversal. Probably an increase of LH or gonadotropin secretion at a certain stage of the life cycle relates to the triggering switch mechanism, initiating the cascade of events in the process of spontaneous sex reversal in *Monopterus* (see Fig. 3). In fact, experiments with injections of mammalian LH to female *Monopterus* result in the precocious sex reversal of the treated animals (Chan et al., 1974), although such experimental sex changes are found deviating from the natural process in that they lack normal proliferation and spermatogenesis of the male germ cells, despite the extensive Leydig cell development and formation of testicular lobules. It appears either that the response of the male germinal tissue to gonadotropin is governed by some age-dependent factors or that other additional trophic factor(s) are necessary for initiating the proliferation of the male germ cells. Our most recent investigations on this aspect show that treatment with mammalian prolactin could induce to a certain degree the proliferation of the male germinal tissue in some specimens, indicating that the endogenous secretion of prolactin by the pituitary might also play a significant role in the process of spontaneous sex reversal in *Monopterus*.

Thus far, all experimental evidence derived from studies on *Monopterus* indicate that the phenomenon of spontaneous sex reversal in this protogynous species involves a cascade of endocrine events in the hypothalamo—hypophysio—gonadal axis and is closely linked with the natural physiological processes of the life cycle, growth and age.

3. ENVIRONMENTAL INFLUENCES ON SEXUALITY IN *RIVULUS MARMORATUS*

Rivulus marmoratus is an oviparous cyprinodont unique in being a simultaneous hermaphrodite normally having the eggs self-fertilized internally. All the eggs from a parent, after a period of intraparental incubation of about 2 days and an extraparental incubation of 10 days, produce isogenic descendants which are all hermaphrodites reproducing by self-fertilization. Such a specialized mode of reproduction seems to have obvious survival value in

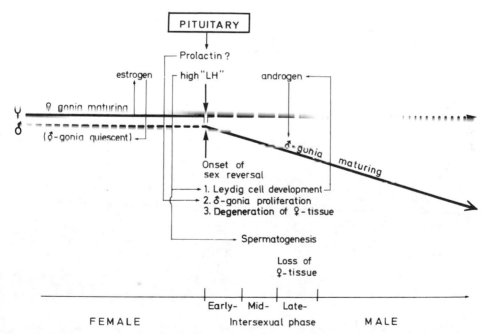

Fig. 3. A scheme summarizing the major events of spontaneous sex reversal in *Monopterus*, showing a possible switch mechanism whereby onset of the male tissue development could be initiated to displace the feminine program in the hermaphroditic gonad.

their spare and isolated occurrence in brackish habitats of alternate desiccation and tidal—pluvial flooding (Harrington, 1961). Under certain environmental influences, the hermaphroditic form would transform into a male, a process in many ways similar to spontaneous sex reversal. Aspects of the environmental control on the sexuality in *Rivulus* have been studied in depth by Harrington (1971).

Anatomically, the gonad of *Rivulus* normally develops as an ovotestis, although its gross morphology generally appears as an ovary because of the presence of large maturing follicles (Fig. 4A); testicular regions exist in the ovotestis and mature spermatozoa are usually found in the sperm duct, hence enabling the process of internal self-fertilization (Fig. 4B). During sex transformation from hermaphrodite to male, the ovarian components involute with the simultaneous and compensatory growth of the testicular elements resulting eventually in a gonad with only the male tissues; males derived from sex-reversed hermaphrodites are designated 'secondary male'. Experiments involving the control of temperature and photoperiod show that both parameters could effectively affect the expression of male sexual-

(A)   (B)

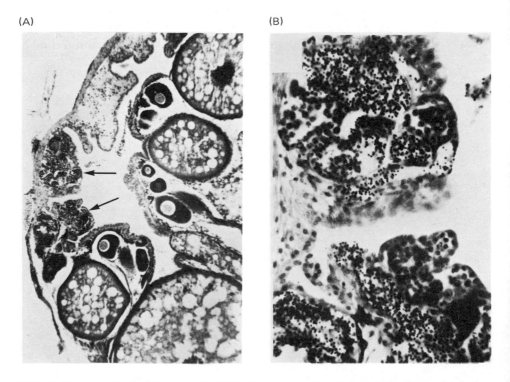

Fig. 4. Cross-sections of the gonad of *Rivulus marmoratus* showing (A) the large maturing follicles which give the gross appearance of an ovary, however, male regions exist (arrows) with the presence of spermatozoa (B) resulting in the normal process of self-fertilization in this fish (from Harrington, Biol. Bull. 132, 174 (1967)).

ity, that is the development of testicular tissues, in the gonadal ontogeny. Concerning the temperature effect, it has been demonstrated that eggs, which would have yielded ovotestis at high temperature (30°C), produce gonads with testicular tissues only when the intraparental prehatching incubation is at low temperature (20°C); such animals are called 'primary male'. A temperature threshold of $19.8 \pm 0.5°C$ and a 'thermolabile phenocritical period' in the embryonic development (Stage 31) are found essential in the sex determination of this normally hermaphroditic fish (Harrington, 1968). In addition to this temperature effect on the prehatching undifferentiated gonad of *Rivulus*, both temperature and photoperiod, when applied during the early posthatching period, are found to influence the onset of sexual transformation from hermaphrodite to secondary male. Hermaphrodites derived from high temperature prehatching incubation, but reared at high temperature (30°C) in the 'early-rearing period' change into secondary males in response to the artificial 'short day' stimuli while those of the same genotype and the same prehatching temperature but early-reared at moderate or low temperature (20°C) seldom change into males, only perhaps occasionally near the end of a life prolonged by protected conditions (Harrington, 1971). Furthermore, the onset of the responsivity to the photoperiod stimulus by hermaphrodites in their sex change varies with genotypes and hence appears to have a genotype-specific, age dependence (Harrington, 1971). These studies illustrate that there is great complexity in the problem of environmental influences on sexuality and spontaneous sex reversal, even in such an excellent experimental animal as the isogenic 'clones' of *Rivulus*.

4. PROBLEMS AND SIGNIFICANCE IN THE STUDIES OF SPONTANEOUS SEX REVERSAL IN FISH

Spontaneous sex reversal in fish exhibits wide occurrence in many unrelated groups. Students in this field must exercise caution in their consideration on each individual species, because what is known in one species might or might not necessarily apply to the others. Limited by its length, the present chapter may have oversimplified this otherwise very complex subject. Readers are therefore encouraged to consult reviews by Atz (1964), Reinboth (1970), Chan (1970), Harrington (1971) and Chan et al., (1974). The frequent occurrence, both in types and in numbers, of hermaphroditism and natural sex reversal in teleost fish has been generally considered to relate to the lack of cortex/medulla organization in the embryonic gonadal primordia and the absence of sex chromatin or sex determination system (Bullough, 1947; D'Ancona, 1949; Atz, 1964). It should be noted, however, that recent studies on *Rivulus* (Harrington, 1974) suggest that the hilar stroma in the embryonic gonad of this hermaphrodite might be the teleostean counterpart of Witschi's gonadal medulla of the amphibians, and that cytogenetic studies by Mehl and Reinboth (1974) show a possible presence of sex chromatin (Barr bodies) in liver cells of a number of hermaphroditic and. sex-reversing fish, including *Pagellus acarne*, *P. erythrinus*, *Coris julis* and *Serranus cabrilla*. The conceptual generalization on the embryonic gonadogenesis and genetic sex in fish, which are the most abundant and most diversified group in vertebrates, deserves a reappraisal as both the genetic system and the somatic tissue/germ cell interactions appear to bear close relationship to the process of sex differentiation in vertebrates and the pattern of sequential maturation of germ cells in gonads of sex-reversing fish (see Chan et al., 1974).

Information on evolution of hermaphroditism and sex reversal in fish is scanty, and the ideas that sex-reversing hermaphrodites are phylogenetically primitive (Bullough, 1947; D'Ancona, 1949) or that males could have derived from the females of a gonochoristic population by sex reversal (Atz, 1964) have never advanced beyond speculative hypotheses; the 'secondary males' of *Rivulus*, which are often misquoted as examples of the latter hypothesis, provide an example of a case of sexual transformation from hermaphrodite to male (Harrington, 1971).

The co-existence of female and male germinal tissues in gonads of most sex-reversing fish is of special significance because this undoubtedly provides the anatomical basis whereby a spontaneous reversal of the gonadal sex is possible by sequential maturation (Chan, 1970). Based on the organization of the gonad and the maturation of germ cells, Chan (1970) has emphasized the unique pattern of sexuality in spontaneous sex reversal as one of the three basic patterns in the expression of sexuality in relation to gonadal ontogeny in vertebrates; each pattern represents a series of phenotypic forms expressed during the life cycle, and is governed by a sex determination system controlling the developmental homeostasis between the male and female sexuality (Fig. 5). In simultaneous hermaphrodites, factors for development of the male and female sex are expressed in parallel, resulting in a synchronous maturation of gametes of both sexes, probably in the absence of a switch mechanism. In gonochorists, though the embryonic intersexuality, as in tetrapods, offers a bipotential capacity for the expression of both male and female sex, the system for developmental homeostatis is decisive towards one sex, resulting in the induction of development of one sex and the total suppression and destruction of the other. In sex-reversing hermaphrodites, the regulating system in relative male and female potency is probably labile, or nondecisive, resulting in the temporary suppression of one sexual part without destruction, so that in the normal ontogeny, elements of a specific sex would mature first until an intrinsic switch mechanism in the life cycle operates to initiate the development of the other sex resulting in spontaneous sex reversal. Chan (1970) maintains that these patterns of sexuality must have a genetic basis, although their expression may be affected by extragenetic or environmental influences as in many other traits.

Indeed, environmental factors such as temperature, light, sex ratio and social composition are reported to enhance or suppress spontaneous sex reversal in some fishes (see Harrington, 1971). There remains a big gap in our

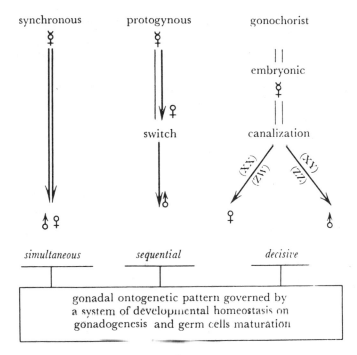

Fig. 5. Patterns of sexuality in relation with ontogeny of the gonad (from Chan, 1970).

knowledge as to how ecological factors would impose their influences to the process of sex change within the gonad. That sex reversal in *Monopterus* involves a complex series of endocrine events in the hypothalamo—hypophysio—gonadal axis (Chan et al., 1974) is the only experimental evidence so far available to account for a possible link between spontaneous sex reversal and environmental stimuli.

In conclusion, there has been in the past decade great expansion in our understanding of spontaneous sex reversal in fish which is now considered in essence as a pattern of sexuality involving a sequential maturation of the gonadal sexes in succession (Chan, 1970). Studies on the anatomical, physiological and endocrinological aspects of the phenomenon will certainly contribute knowledge of academic and scientific value, particularly in the fields of reproductive physiology, intersexuality and sex differentiation in vertebrates, for it is not unlikely that the hypothetical masculinizing mechanism in mammalian sex differentiation (Jost, 1970) and the switch mechanism for the male sexuality expression in *Monopterus* (Fig. 3) may show some distant similarities or relationship in their operative biochemistry and endocrionology. Further studies on various aspects of sex reversal, and on different species, are needed for a wider perspective on this biological phenomenon not uncommon, and in fact very successful, in fish. Gonochorism is found in most higher vertebrates and is generally regarded to have a selective advant-

104

age over hermaphroditism in ensuring cross-fertilization and fuller expression of bisexuality in both the body sex and the behavioral sex. When sex succession in the lower forms such as *Monopterus*, is a system in which the hermaphroditic gonads function separately, in different breeding seasons, as two entities as distinct as the ovary and testis of gonochoristic species, spontaneous sex reversal in fish is in effect a mechanism as good as gonochorism. Survival of the fittest!

ACKNOWLEDGEMENTS

I wish to thank Professor R. Reinboth, Dr. R.W. Harrington, Jr., The Royal Society, The Zoological Society of London, and the Biological Bulletin for their permission for some of the illustrations used in this chapter. The encouragement and contributions from many of my co-workers in the research on *Monopterus* are deeply appreciated.

This work was supported by a grant from the Nuffield Foundation, London.

BIBLIOGRAPHY

Atz. J.W. (1964) Intersexuality in fishes. In: (C.N. Armstrong and A.J. Marshal, Eds.) *Intersexuality in Vertebrates Including Man.* (Academic Press, New York) pp. 145—232.

Bullough, W.S. (1947) Hermaphroditism in the lower vertebrates. *Nature* 160: 9—11.

Chan, S.T.H. (1970) Natural sex reversal in vertebrates.*Phil. Trans. R. Soc.* B259: 59—71.

Chan, S.T.H. (1971) An ontogenetic study on natural sex reversal in *Monopterus* with some references to the effects of sex steroids on germ-cell development. *Proc. 4th Asia Oceania Congr. Endocrinol.* 128.

Chan, S.T.H. and Phillips, J.G. (1967a) The structure of the gonad during natural sex reversal in *Monopterus albus. J. Zool.* 151: 129—141.

Chan, S.T.H. and Phillips, J.G. (1967b) Seasonal changes in the distribution of gonadal lipids and spermatogenetic tissue in the male phase of *Monopterus albus. J. Zool.* 152: 31—41.

Chan, S.T.H. and Phillips, J.G. (1969) The biosynthesis of steroids by the gonads of the ricefield eel *Monopterus* at various sexual phases during natural sex reversal. *Gen. Comp. Endocrinol.* 12: 619—636.

Chan, S.T.H., O, W.S. and Hui, W.B. (1974) On the gonadal and adenohypophysial functions of natural sex reversal. In: (R. Reinboth, Ed.) *Intersexuality in the Animal Kingdom.* (Springer, Heidelberg) pp. 201—222.

Chan, S.T.H., O, W.S. and Hui, W.B. (1975) The interrenal gland and the ACTH and prolactin cells in the adenohypophysis of *Monopterus* and their roles in osmoregulation. *Gen. Comp. Endocrinol.* 27: 95—110.

Chan, S.T.H., O, W.S., Tang, F. and Lofts, B. (1972a) Biopsy studies on natural sex reversal in *Monopterus albus. J. Zool.* 167: 415—421.

Chan, S.T.H., Tang, F. and Lofts, B. (1972b) The role of sex steroids on natural sex reversal in *Monopterus. Excerpta Medica Int. Congr. Ser.* 256: 348.

Chan, S.T.H., Wright, A. and Phillips, J.G. (1967) The atretic structures in the gonad of the ricefield eel (Monopterus albus). J. Zool. 153: 527—539.

D'Ancona, U. (1941) Ulterori osservazioni e considerationi sull'ermafroditismo ed il differenziamento sessuale dell'orata (Sparus auratus). Publ. Staz. Zool. Nap. 18: 313—336.

D'Ancona, U. (1949) Ermafroditismo ed intersesualita nei Teleostei. Experientia 5: 381—389.

Harrington, R.W. Jr. (1961) Oviparous hermaphroditic fish with internal self-fertilization. Science 134: 1749—1750.

Harrington, R.W. Jr. (1968) Delimitation of the thermolabile phenocritical period of sex determination and differentiation in tho ontogeny of the normally hermaphroditic fish, Rivulus marmoratus. Physiol. Zool. 41: 447—460.

Harrington, R.W. Jr. (1971) How ecological and genetic factors interact to determine when self-fertilizing hermaphrodites of Rivulus marmoratus change into functional secondary males, with a reappraisal of the modes of intersexuality among fishes. Copeia 389—432.

Harrington, R.W. Jr. (1974) In: Int. Symp. (1974) on Intersexuality in the Animal Kingdom. Mainz. (Abstr.)

Jost, A. (1970) Hormonal factors in the sex differentiation of the mammalian foetus. Phil. Trans. R. Soc. B259: 119—130.

Liu, C.K. (1944) Rudimentary hermaphroditism in the symbranchoid eel, Monopterus javanensis. Sinensia 15: 1—18.

Mehl, J.A.P. and Reinboth, R. (1974) The possible significance of sex chromatin for determination of the genetic sex in ambisexual fish. In: Int. Symp. (1974) on Intersexuality in the Animal Kingdom, Mainz. (Abstr.)

O, W.S. and Chan, S.T.H. (1974a) A cytological study on the structure of the pituitary of Monopterus albus. Gen. Comp. Endocrinol. 24: 208—222.

O, W.S. and Chan, S.T.H. (1974b) A study on the thyroid and TSH-cells of the pituitary gland of the ricefield eel, Monopterus albus. Gen. Comp. Endocrinol. 24: 99—112.

Parlow, A.F. (1961) Bioassay of pituitary luteinizing hormone by depletion of ovarian ascorbic acid. In: (R. Rei and A. Albert, Eds.) Human Pituitary Gonadotropins (Charles C. Thomas, Springfield, Illinois) pp. 300—310.

Reinboth, R. (1962) Morphologische und funktionelle Zweigeschlechtlichkeit bei marinen Teleostiern (Serranidae, Sparidae, Centracanthidae, Labridae). Zool. Jb. (Physiol.) 69: 405—480.

Reinboth, R. (1970) Intersexuality in fishes. Mem. Soc. Endocrinol. 18: 515—544.

Tang, F., Loftts, B. and Chan, S.T.H. (1974) Δ5-3β-Hydroxysteroid dehydrogenase ac tivities in the ovary of the ricefield eel, Monopterus albus. Experientia 30: 316—317.

CHAPTER 9

Experimental sex reversal in the teleost fish, Oryzias latipes

EDWARD W. GRESIK and JAMES B. HAMILTON

1. INTRODUCTION

Prior to the establishment of the genetic basis of sex determination at the turn of the present century, it was believed that sex was established by a variety of environmental factors (Morgan, 1913). The early work on insects led to the conclusion that the sex of an individual was determined by the ratio of sets of autosomes to the number of X chromosomes, and that the Y chromosome of males was an 'empty' chromosome, inactive in sex determination (Morgan, 1913). Similar mechanisms were believed to operate in vertebrates, but relatively recently it was established that the mammalian Y chromosome is active in testicular differentiation (Ford et al., 1959).

Non-genetic factors (for example, exogenous steroid sex hormones or heat) have been shown to be capable of governing the sex phenotype in lower vertebrates. The opportunity to alter experimentally the expression of phenotypic sex provides a strong analytical tool for investigating the mecha nisms of sex determination in vertebrates.

2. CHROMOSOMAL SEX DETERMINATION IN VERTEBRATES

Sex chromosomes in the vertebrates

In mammals the male is the heterogametic sex, with an X and a Y chromosome. Among birds the female is the heterogametic sex, with a ZW constitution, while the male is homogametic with a ZZ sex complement. Among reptiles, amphibians and fishes, species occur in which sex is determined by an XX/XY or a ZZ/ZW mechanism. In many reptiles, and in most amphibians and fishes, this must be ascertained solely by following the behavior of sex-linked genes, inasmuch as the sex chromosomes are homomorphic and have yet to be identified by cytogenetic means (Ohno, 1967). This lack of

Handbook of Sexology, edited by J. Money and H. Musaph
© *Elsevier/North-Holland Biomedical Press, 1977*

morphologic differentiation of the sex chromosomes is correlated with increasingly labile sex-determining mechanisms in descent of the phylogenetic scale (Ohno, 1967).

Natural and experimental sex reversal in lower vertebrates

Natural reversal of sex is not infrequent in amphibians and fishes (Atz, 1964; Yamamoto, 1969). Synchronous hermaphrodites and consecutive hermaphrodites, both protandrous and protogynous, have been documented (Reinboth, 1970). Also among these lower forms, complete sex reversals have been produced experimentally with fully functional individuals of phenotypic sex contrary to their genotype (Yamamoto, 1969; Schreck, 1974). This seems to be impossible in mammals (Burns, 1961).

Evolution of sex chromosomes and dosage-compensation mechanisms among vertebrates

Ohno (1967) argues convincingly that the X and Y were originally an homologous pair of autosomes which bore male- and female-determining genes, respectively. As evolution proceeded, a stronger mechanism of sex determination was developed by deleting most genes except male-determining genes from the Y (or female-determining genes from the W). The X chromosome, however, bears the genes lost by the Y, and a dosage-compensation mechanism was developed (Ohno, 1967; Lyon, 1974). This is clearly seen in mammals, where one X chromosome in females is inactivated (Lyon, 1961). Thus, Ohno views the sex chromosomes as a specialized set of previous autosomes, with the X or the Z the conservative member, and the Y or the W as a highly specialized member bearing the genes determining the sex or gonadal structure of the heterogametic individual.

3. ORYZIAS LATIPES

Sex phenotype and sex genotype

Oryzias latipes, popularly known as the medaka, is a teleost fish indigenous to Japan; adults are 2—5 cm in total length. This species is gonochoristic, with testis or ovary in separate individuals (Yamamoto, 1967).

Secondary sexual characteristics are distinct and easily discernible; males, in comparison with females, possess a larger dorsal fin and a larger anal fin bearing papillary processes (Yamamoto, 1967).

The fish are either white (or unpigmented) or red (with a carotene pigment). Aida (1921) discovered that the genes for body pigment are sex-linked, and that the male is the heterogametic sex (XX/XY). In wild populations, the dominant gene, *ruby* (*R*) for red pigmentation is on the Y chromosome, while the recessive, *r* (no pigment) is on the X chromosome. The crossover rate for *Rr* alleles is 0.5%, giving a 99.5% probability that a red fish bears a Y chromosome.

Hence, by gross inspection, one can determine the sex phenotype (fins) and the sex genotype (red=*R*=Y) of these fish.

Cytogenetics

The sex chromosomes of these fish are homomorphic, and an attempt was made to distinguish an X/Y pair using banding techniques. Banding patterns

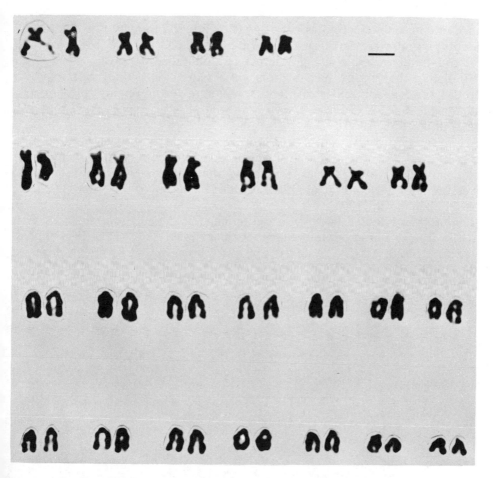

Fig. 1. Ideogram of Giemsa-banded chromosomes of adult male (XX) *O. latipes*. Spread was prepared from gill epithelial cell according to Lieppmann and Hubbs (1969). Diploid number is 48; no dimorphic sex-chromosomal pair is evident. Bar at upper right corner indicates 1 μm.

were obtained with Giemsa staining (Fig. 1) and with quinacrine, but the small size of the chromosomes (largest $< 1\ \mu$) interfered with the use of banding patterns to distinguish homologous pairs. However, it was possible to establish a diploid number of 48 in this species.

Sex reversals by feeding steroid hormones to newly hatched fry

Using *O. latipes*, Yamamoto was able to achieve complete and permanent sex reversal in either direction by raising newly hatched fry on a diet containing the appropriate steroid sex hormones. Steroid hormone treatment had to be started within the first 7—10 days of life, when the gonad was not yet fully differentiated as a testis or an ovary (Yamamoto, 1969).

Fry from a white female (X^rX^r) mated with a red male (X^rY^R) were reared on a diet containing methyltestosterone (25—50 μg/g food); some had a male phenotype and were fertile males. White males had an X^rX^r genotype, and were thus reversed females (Fig. 2, cross 1; Yamamoto, 1958).

Similarly, the fry of such a cross were reared on a diet containing an estrogen (estrone or stilbestrol), and some were fertile phenotypic females. Red females had an ovary and were sex-reversed X^rY^R males (Fig. 2, cross 2; Yamamoto, 1953, 1959).

When these two reversed offspring were crossed, the progeny, raised on a hormone-free diet; the original sex ratio of 1:1 was obtained with 50% red males and 50% white females, indicating that the sex chromosomes themselves were not affected by administration of hormone to the parents (Fig. 2, cross 3; Yamamoto, 1961).

If a cross is effected between a red female (X^rY^R) and a red male (X^rY^R), and the fry are raised without hormone, a sex ratio of 1:3 (1:2:1) is expected (Fig. 2, cross 4). The observed sex ratio, however, was usually closer to 1:2, as animals with a Y^RY^R constitution were poorly viable (Yamamoto,

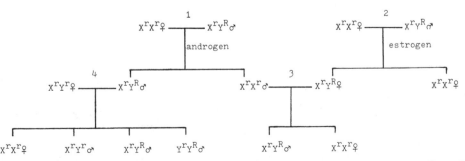

Fig. 2. Production of hormonally sex-reversed fish of XX, XY or YY genotype. Cross 1, production of male progeny; cross 2, production of female progeny; cross 3, back-cross of sex-reversed male and female; cross 4, production of YY fish. See text for details.

1955). * However, if a white sex-reversed female (X^rY^r) was used in this cross (Y^r was obtained by crossing over from X^r), Y^rY^R or Y^rY^r males were produced, which were viable (Fig. 2, cross 4; Yamamoto, 1963). By feeding estrogen to the offspring of such a cross, females of YY genotype were obtained (Yamamoto, 1963). Thus Yamamoto was able to produce either the male or female phenotype in offspring with the XX, XY or YY genotype. He claimed that the percentage of reversals was linearly related to the concentration of steroid fed (Yamamoto, 1969).

Since these pioneering experiments, several other species of teleosts have been successfully reversed by administration of steroid sex hormones to hatchlings (Schreck, 1974). In addition, other methods of reversing sex have been discovered. Loew and Larkin (1975) found that after ovariectomy of phenotypic females of the Siamese fighting fish, *Beta splendens*, the regenerated gonad was a functional testis, and the secondary sex characters and behavior became masculine.

Yamamoto (1969) interpreted his experiments to mean that the structural genes for an ovary or a testis are on the autosomes, and not on the sex chromosomes, since an ovary can be obtained in a YY individual and a testis in an XX individual. Yet, the assumption that both the X and Y chromosomes each bear the structural genes for the ovary and the testis, is also consistent with Yamamoto's findings. He believes that the sex chromosomes bear 'supergenes' which control the expression of the structural genes on the autosomes. Furthermore, he claims that the sex genes on the X and Y act by programming the production of 'sex-inducing substances', which in turn control testicular and ovarian differentiation by activating structural genes on the autosomes, and finally that the sex-inducing substances are the naturally occurring sex steroids.

4. PARADIGMATICAL SEX INDIVIDUAL

Kantor and Hamilton (1975) produced sex reversals in *O. latipes* with a modification of Hishida's method (1962), in which sex steroids are injected directly into the yolk of eggs immediately after fertilization. Hishida (1962) injected radioactive steroids and found that they were most heavily concentrated by the developing gonad where the radioactivity was still retained in high concentrations after the animals matured. Microinjection of fertilized eggs was preferable to feeding for various reasons, including delivery of known dosage and early exposure to hormones.

---

* Similarly, the Y chromosome of *Lebistes reticulatus* bears genes for body color which are lethal in homozygous combinations in YY males (Haskins et al., 1970).

Effect of varying the dosage of steroid * (Hamilton and Kantor, 1975a)

Androgen — methyltestosterone (Fig. 3)

XX fertilized eggs   Injection of XX eggs with graded doses of methyltestosterone (MT) after fertilization produced phenotypic males. A concentration of 0.2 mg/ml produced sex reversal in all living fry. Concentrations above or below 0.2 mg/ml resulted in a reduced percentage of reversals.

XY fertilized eggs   After fertilization, injection of XY eggs with MT resulted in 100% of fish with testes if the concentration of MT was 2.0 mg/ml or less. At higher concentrations some XY fish differentiated an ovary instead of a testis (that is, they are sex reversed).

YY fertilized eggs   YY eggs behave like XY with low concentrations of MT, but at high concentrations they show a smaller percentage of reversals than XY individuals. That is, they are more resistant than XY animals to differentiation of an ovary.
   This phenomenon of producing individuals with a gonad contrary to the one expected for the administered steroid is termed 'paradoxical sex reversal.' It was not seen by Yamamoto, probably because he did not administer androgens until after hatching. Paradoxical reversal with high concentrations of steroid was obtained by injecting embryos as well as eggs, but not with injections after hatching.

Estrogen — estrone acetate (Fig. 4)
Two feminizing compounds were used to effect sex reversals; the first was a natural female steroid.

XY fertilized eggs   When estrone acetate was injected into XY fertilized eggs at concentrations below 0.2 mg/ml, reversals were not obtained, and a testis developed. At higher concentrations (>1.0 mg/ml), testicular development was inhibited, and an ovary was developed (sex-reversal).

XX fertilized eggs   Similarly, when low concentrations of estrone acetate were injected into XX fertilized eggs, genotypic females developed a testis in the presence of an estrogen. At higher concentrations an ovary was formed with no paradoxical reversals.

---

* The dose of the steroid was expressed as the concentration of the hormone per ml solvent (olive oil). A droplet of oil, 0.14 0.20 mm in diameter, was injected into each egg.

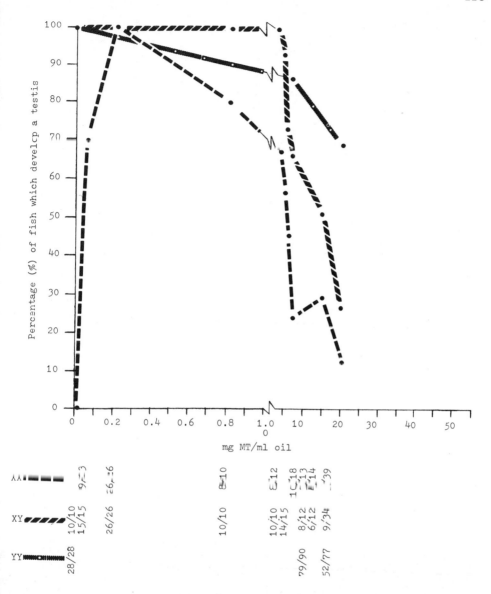

Fig. 3. Effect of varying the dose of methyltestosterone (MT) injected into fertilized eggs of *O. latipes* on the occurence of testicular differentiation in fish of three genotypes (XX, XY,YY). The number of fish which develop a testis versus the total number of fish injected is written as a fraction beneath each dose for each genotype. At low doses testicular differentiation is favored. At high doses paradoxical reversals occur in XY and YY fish, and few reversals are seen in XX fish. (Graph based on data in Hamilton and Kantor 1975a).

114

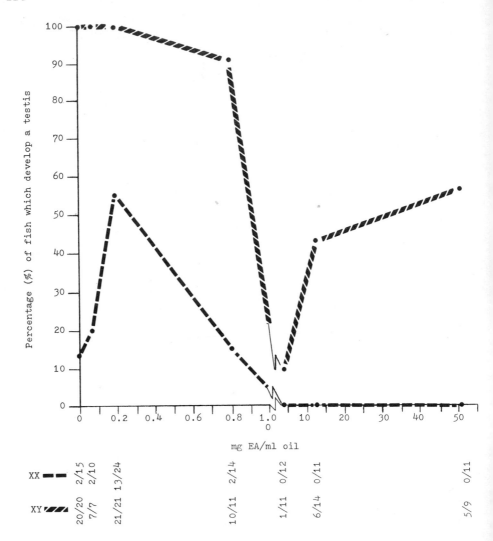

Fig. 4. Effect of varying the dose of estrone acetate (EA) injected into fertilized eggs of *O. latipes* on the occurence of testicular differentiation in fish of two genotypes (XX, XY). The number of fish which develop a testis versus the total number of fish injected is written as a fraction beneath each dose for each genotype. At low doses XY fish tend to develop a testis and resist sex reversal, while XX fish show paradoxical reversals. At higher doses testicular differentiation is reduced in XY, and completely absent in XX fish. (Graph based on data in Hamilton and Kantor, 1975a).

Progestin — ethynodiol diacetate (Fig. 5)
Ethynodiol diacetate (EDDA), a synthetic progestational steroid, was also used to effect sex reversals.

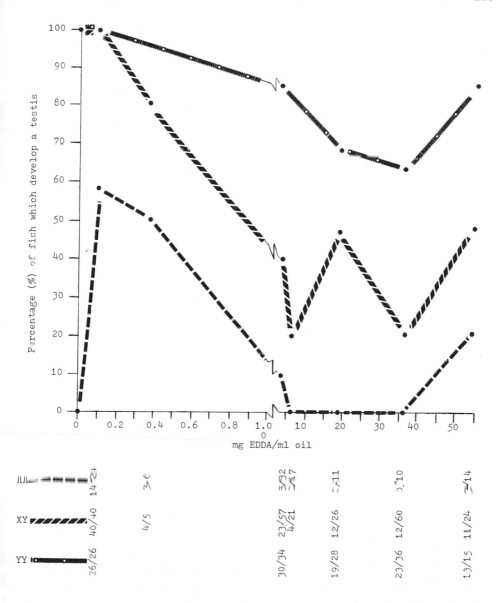

Fig. 5. Effect of varying the dose of ethynodiol diacetate (EDDA) on the occurence of testicular differentiation in fish of three genotypes (XX,XY,YY). The number of fish which develop a testis versus the total number of fish injected is expressed as a fraction beneath each dose for each genotype. At low doses testicular differentiation is favored in all three genotypes, i.e., paradoxical reversals are seen in XX fish. At higher doses all three genotypes show a reduction in testicular differentiation. (Graph based on data in Hamilton and Kantor, 1975a).

XY fertilized eggs When EDDA was administered to XY fertilized eggs at low concentrations, there was little inhibition of testicular differentiation, but at high concentrations a large percentage of animals developed an ovary. At very high concentrations paradoxical reversals occured.

XX fertilized eggs EDDA administered to XX fertilized eggs at low concentrations produced paradoxical effects. At higher concentrations all animals developed ovaries, but at the highest concentrations employed, paradoxical sex reversals were again observed.

YY fertilized eggs The response pattern to EDDA by YY fertilized eggs was similar to that exhibited by XY eggs, except that the number of reversals obtained was lower; a double Y constitution is more difficult to sex reverse than a single Y.

Thus the same response pattern is seen with androgen, estrogen and progestin: at low concentration of steroid, testis development is favored, whereas at high concentrations, ovarian differentiation can be expected.

Possible significance of paradoxical sex reversals

Yamamoto's claim that the sex-inducing substances are the naturally occuring androgens and estrogens is not supported by the findings of paradoxical reversals.

Paradoxical sex reversals have also been seen in various species of cichlid fishes (Müller, 1969; Hackmann, 1974; Hackmann and Reinboth, 1974). Androgens fed to developing cichlid fry will cause feminization of the gonad, although estrogens apparently are not capable of masculinizing this species (Hackmann, 1974). However, the effects of varying the dosage of the sex steroid have not been investigated in cichlids; such a study may reveal that paradoxical reversals in either direction may be achievable with these fish.

Finally, Yamamoto's claim about the nature of the sex-inducing substances is not supported by the findings of Tang et al. (1974) on the protogynous hermaphrodite, *Monopterus albus*. Androgens administered to females did not cause them to differentiate into males, and estrogens given to intersexual fish did not prevent them from becoming males.

All of these findings are consistent with the idea, proposed by Jost (Jost et al., 1973) that the differentiation of an ovary (female state) in organisms in which the homozygote has ovaries, represents the undifferentiated condition of the gonad, whereas production of a testis (male state) represents the induced condition. Another way of stating this is that if any means is used to block the formation of a testis, an ovary will result.

Injections of medaka eggs showed that procedures which blocked formation of a testis resulted in an ovary. Low concentrations of steroids (whether androgens, estrogens or progestins) favored induction of a testis, but high concentrations prevented testicular differentiation with the consequent appearance of the undifferentiated female state and the production of an ovary. This lack of specificity of these steroid hormones to induce either a testis or an ovary speaks strongly against these agents being the naturally occurring sex inducers.

The Y chromosome of *O. latipes* is not an empty chromosome, inasmuch as it induced formation of a testis if not interfered with. Furthermore, the influence of two doses of the Y chromosome was harder to overcome than that of one dose, meaning that inhibition of testicular differentiation was more difficult under any circumstances in YY individuals.

5. SEX REVERSALS BY THERMAL MODULATION DURING EMBRYONIC DEVELOPMENT

Fertilized eggs were ordinarily reared at room temperatures of 20 to 27°C. From fertilized eggs developing at elevated temperatures (32°C), however, 47% of XX fry differentiated a testis, and 12% of XY fry, an ovary. Development of YY eggs was not affected by elevated temperature (Hamilton and Kantor, 1975b)(Fig. 6).

From fertilized eggs that developed at 32°C and were reared after hatching at 22°C, 74% of XX fish developed a testis, whereas 8% of the XY formed an ovary instead of a testis (Hamilton et al., 1975b). Furthermore, YY fertilized eggs were not sex reversed, always developing a testis under these thermal conditions. These findings indicate that rearing of *O. latipes* at elevated temperatures favors testicular differentiation. Sex reversals by thermal means have also been reported in other fish (Harrington, 1968) as well as in amphibians (Witschi, 1929); in both cases, testicular differentiation was also favored.

The mechanism whereby these thermal factors influence sex differentiation is unknown, although some interference with enzyme systems is suggested.

The mechanism of action by heat differed from that of steroids in that (1) reversals of 100% of the animals of any given genotype were not seen, and (2) testicular differentiation was favored rather than sex reversals in either direction. These data also do not seem to support the hypothesis that the sex-inducing substances are the naturally occurring steroids.

6. EFFECT OF GENOTYPE ON SEGREGATION OF PRIMORDIAL GERM CELLS

Primordial germ cell numbers in vertebrates in general

When the number of primordial germ cells (PGCs) was counted in the indifferent gonads of various vertebrate classes, a bimodal distribution was obtained (Hardisty, 1967). For mammalian species it has been claimed that the gonads which contain larger numbers of PGCs differentiate into testes,

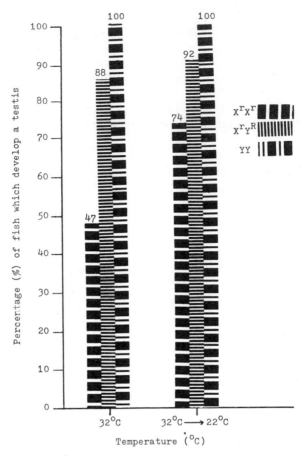

Fig. 6. Effects of temperature modulation during embryonic development on the incidence of testicular differentiation in three genotypes (XX,XY,YY) of *O. latipes*. When
fish are raised at 32°C, 47% of XX fish and 12% of XY fish are sex reversed. YY fish are
not sex reversed by thermal changes. (Based on data in Hamilton and Kantor, 1975b).

and those with fewer PGCs develop into ovaries. For amphibians and fishes,
the opposite claim was made: indifferent gonads containing many PGCs
develop as ovaries, while those with fewer PGCs develop as testes. These
studies were based solely on morphological analysis, and not on a knowledge
of the genotype of the animals. The ability to produce animals of known
genotype afforded the opportunity to investigate these claims.

PCGs in the indifferent gonads of individuals of known genotype

From XX females mated with XX males, Quirk and Hamilton (1973) obtained XX embryos which develop an ovary. From XX females mated with YY

males, they obtained XY embryos which develop a testis. PGCs were counted at 4 developmental stages, and no sex differences in their numbers were seen (Fig. 7). Both XX and XY gonads showed significantly higher numbers of PGCs at 24 hours after hatching compared to previous stages, due to gonial proliferation within the indifferent gonads on the day of hatching (Fig. 7).

Because other experiments indicated the possibility that Y eggs may be less viable than X eggs (see above), Quirk (1974) also counted the number of PGCs at the same stages in embryos with a Y contributed by the mother, that is, embryos from YY mothers mated with XX males or with YY males. The offspring so produced develop as males, and are arbitrarily designated as YX and YY to distinguish them from individuals derived from X eggs. At

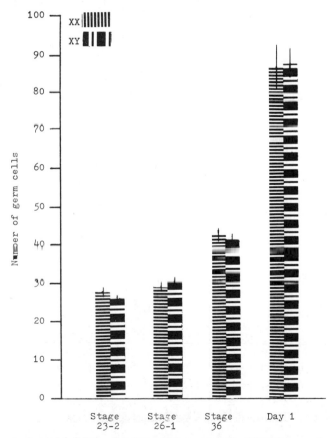

Fig. 7. Mean numbers (± S.E.) of primordial germ cells (PGCs) in embryos and fry of *O. latipes* of known XX or XY genotype. No difference in numbers of PGCs in presumptive ovaries or testes is seen at any stage examined. The increased number of cells seen on the day of hatching (day 1) in both ovaries and testes represents proliferation of gonial cells. (Based on data in Quirk and Hamilton, 1973).

each developmental stage both YX and YY offspring contained similar numbers of PGCs and fewer PGCs than offspring from X eggs (Fig. 8).

This experiment, however, did not answer the question of whether the decreased number of PGCs was due to the genetic constitution of the egg itself, or of the ovary which produced that egg (Y-effect), or to the hormonal environment in which the YY mother was raised. Thus, Quirk (1974) raised XX females under the same hormonal conditions as he had raised the YY mothers, and crossed them with YY males to produce XY embryos, or with XX males to produce XX embryos. The number of PGCs at the 4 developmental stages is similar to that seen in the original experiment on non-estrogenized females. Therefore, the reduced number of PGCs in the YX and YY gonads is due to the genetic constitution of the egg or of the ovary which produced it.

Counts of PGCs in gonads of XX or XY fry (both from X eggs), made 2 days after hatching, were bimodally distributed, with higher values in the

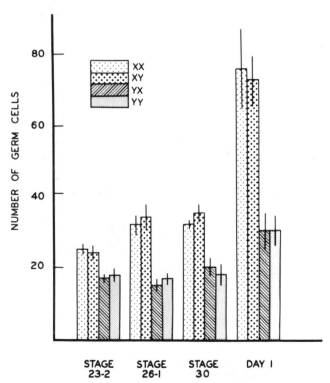

Fig. 8. Mean numbers (± S.E.) of primordial germ cells in embryos and fry of known genotypes (XX,XY,YX,YY). Fish derived from Y eggs (YX,YY) have fewer germ cells than those derived from X eggs (XX,XY). (Quirk, 1974).

future ovary (Quirk, 1974). PGCs were apparently not mitotic (or only slightly so) during migration and early colonization of the gonadal anlage, but became actively proliferative upon hatching in *O. latipes*. This finding is in agreement with Satoh and Egami (1972). Upon the onset of proliferation, a sex difference was immediately apparent, and was one of the earliest morphological expressions of gonadal differentiation in these fish.

Thus it seems that in *O. latipes* the same number of PGCs were segregated into the future ovary and testis, after which the gonial cells (either oogonia or spermatogonia) showed the first numerical differences. These findings also suggest that the X chromosome was necessary for the proper differentiation of the ovary, since eggs produced by females with only Y chromosomes showed reduced development of PGCs.

7. EFFECT OF HEAT STRESS ON EMBRYONIC DEVELOPMENT

The deleterious effects of a double Y complement on ovarian differentiation and egg development were also seen when embryos of known genotype were raised at different temperatures (Kellner, 1973). Below 17.5°C and above 35.0°C no embryos developed, whatever the genotype. Between 20°C and 32.5°C all genotypes became viable fry, but survival was better in embryos from X eggs than in those from Y eggs; at either extreme of this range of temperature, embryos from X eggs were better able to withstand heat stress.

Kellner (1973) also studied embryos of the 4 genotypes stressed by high temperatures at various times in early development. If the embryos were exposed before gastrulation, no survival to hatching was seen in those from Y eggs, since these embryos were unable to develop beyond the gastrula stage. If the embryos were stressed at various stages after gastrulation, the YY embryos also showed considerably more difficulty in survival than the YX embryos.

It is known that, before gastrulation, embryonic development depends upon information stored in the egg's RNA, and not upon the genome of the embryo itself, which is not activated until gastrulation (Davidson, 1968). When the YY embryo had to rely on its maternally derived program, survival was poor. When the embryonic genome was activated after gastrulation, the presence of an X chromosome improved the chances of survival, since the YX embryos developed just as well as XY embryos. However, YY embryos were still in difficulty after gastrulation, and this may be due to a double Y status, to the Y chromosome of the egg itself, or to the Y chromosomal constitution of the ovarian environment in which the egg was formed.

The findings from both the studies on heat stress and on development of PGCs show poorer development of eggs derived from YY mothers. Therefore, it seems that a YY constitution is not well suited to the production of hardy eggs, and that at least one X chromosome must be present for the differentiation of any ovary capable of producing fully functional eggs.

8. GONADAL STRUCTURE AND DEVELOPMENT

Structure of adult gonads

Testis

The mature testis is composed of numerous cysts containing the germ cells, an efferent duct system and interstitial cells.

In each seminiferous cyst the germ cells contained therein are all at the same stage of spermatogenesis. Each cyst is surrounded by a complete layer of cyst epithelial cells (CE), which are the teleost homologs of Sertoli cells (Gresik et al., 1974). The CE cells are squamous until spermatogenetic cells within the cyst develop into spermatids; the CE then becomes cuboidal during the conversion of spermatids to mature spermatozoa. Upon full ripening of spermatozoa, the wall of the cyst fuses with that of the efferent duct, and sperm are released into the duct lumina, where they are stored and perhaps undergo further maturation before discharge. After fusion of the cyst and ductal systems, the structure of the CE appears to be the same as the epithelium lining the efferent duct system.

In the spaces between the cysts and the ducts are steroidogenic interstitial cells, the homologs of the Leydig cells (Gresik et al., 1973). These cells are the site of biosynthesis of androgen, and possess a fine structure consistent with that role.

Ovary

The mature ovary contains a central cavity into which eggs are ovulated and stored until spawning. The cavity is continuous with the oviduct. Fertilization is external. Each oogonium is surrounded by a single layer of squamous follicular epithelial cells, which become cuboidal as the egg matures (Hirose, 1972). Interstitial cells are present, but their role in elaborating steroid hormones in this fish has not been established, although they are steroidogenic in other teleosts (Lambert and Pot, 1975).

Normal gonadal differentiation and development

Before hatching, PGCs migrate from the yolk sac endoderm to the mesodermal gonadal anlage of the posterior body wall (Onitake, 1972). At hatching the gonad is indifferent, with the same morphology in both sexes (Satoh, 1974). As in other teleosts (D'Ancona, 1956) neither cortex nor medulla is discernible in the developing gonad, which is described as a unitary indifferent gonad (Onitake, 1972).

Satoh (1974) described the fine structural features of gonadal differentiation after hatching. In the indifferent gonad the germ cells are incompletely surrounded by mesodermal stromal cells. During the first 24 hours after hatching, histologic differences are seen between the ovaries and the testes. In the ovary the PGCs are surrounded by a complete layer of follicular cells;

the latter are derived from the gonadal mesoderm and are joined together as an epithelium by desmosomes. During the first week of life, the germ cells increase in number and some of them enter meiotic prophase. Steroidogenic ovarian interstitial cells are not seen during the early establishment of ovarian structure.

In developing males the gonad maintains an indifferent structure until approximately 25 days after hatching. At this time, interstitial Leydig cells can be seen which possess the fine structural organization of the mature steroidogenic cells. Spermatogonia resemble PGCs in structure, but it is not clear whether they are surrounded by a complete layer of CE cells at this time. By 45 days after hatching, functional Leydig cells are common, and the spermatogonia, which are now enclosed in a complete CE sheath to form cysts, undergo proliferation.

Our findings on the normal course of gonadal development support those of Satoh (1974).

Gonadal development in sex-reversed fish

Preliminary observations on the fine structure of developing gonads of sex-reversed *O. latipes* indicate that the same pattern of testicular or ovarian development as described by Satoh (1974) for non-reversed fish is seen under conditions of reversal. Thus, at the end of the first week after hatching, the gonad of XX fry treated with methyltestosterone in ovo does not contain fully ensheathed gonial cells in meiotic prophase, as does a developing ovary at this age, but rather has the appearance of a developing testis. On the other hand, gonads of XY or YY individuals, sex-reversed with estrogens or progestins, show germ cells in meiotic prophase during the first week after hatching.

9. GENERAL DISCUSSION AND SUMMARY

Nature of sex-inducing substances

The occurrence of paradoxical sex reversals and of sex reversals after thermal modulation, along with the failure of sex steroids to influence the course of natural sex reversal in *M. albus* (Tang et al., 1974) speaks against the naturally occurring sex hormones as being the primary agents in determining the structural organization of developing gonads. Furthermore, in vertebrates which have been investigated, synthesis of androgens commences shortly after the morphologic differentiation of the testis (Haffen, 1970).

Role of cells present in the indifferent gonad in the establishment of gonadal sex

Primordial germ cells
PGCs of any genotype in *O. latipes* can become oogonia or spermatogonia.

124

They do not seem to play an active role in sex determination, but develop in a manner determined by the gonad into which they migrate. Their passive role in gonadal differentiation is also seen in higher forms, where the gonad apparently can develop in the absence of PGCs (Merchant, 1975).

Steroidogenic interstitial cells
Histochemically demonstrable interstitial cells and biochemically detectable steroidogenesis appear in vertebrate gonads after morphologic differentiation (Haffen, 1970). Hence, these cells also seem to be determined by the gonad, rather than vice versa.

Sertoli and follicular cells
The first morphologic signs of gonadogenesis in either sex are manifested by these two cell types. In *O. latipes* the transformation of PGCs into either oogonia or spermatogonia is heralded by their initial ensheathment by mesodermal cells of the gonadal anlage. Cells with a similar morphology are seen in the adult testis (Gresik et al., 1974) and ovary (Hirose, 1972), where they are the homologs of Sertoli and follicular cells, respectively. These cells seem to be the site of the first action of sex-determining genes. Once these cells have become committed as Sertoli or follicular cells, the PGCs are directed to differentiate into gonocytes of the appropriate sex. They may also influence the surrounding interstitial tissue to elaborate the proper sex steroids, and thus govern the differentiation of the genital tract, the external genitalia and the secondary sexual characters.

In *O. latipes* the sex steroids, in turn, might play some role in stabilizing the gonad once it has begun its differentiation. During the initial phases of their development, the Sertoli or follicular cells may still be labile and susceptible to various organizing influences, such as heat and exogenous sex steroids, which may be able at this time to override the genetic factors operating in these cells, and induce sex reversal.

BIBLIOGRAPHY

Aida, T. (1921) On the inheritance of color in a fresh water fish, *Aplocheilus latipes* Temminck et Schlegel, with special reference to sex-linked inheritance. *Genetics* 6: 554—573.
Atz, J. (1964) Intersexuality in fishes. In: (C.N. Armstrong and A.J. Marshall, Eds.) *Intersexuality in Vertebrates including Man.* (Academic Press, New York) pp. 145—232.
Burns, R.K. (1961) Role of hormones in the differentiation of sex. In: (W.C. Young, Ed.) *Sex and Internal Secretions.* 3rd edn. (Williams & Wilkins Co., Baltimore) pp. 76—158.
D'Ancona, U. (1956) Morphogénèse et différenciation sexuelle chez les poissons téléostéens. *Bull. Soc. Zool. Fr.* 81: 219—229.
Davidson, E.H. (1968) *Gene Activity in Early Development.* (Academic Press, New York.)

Ford, C.E., Jones, K.W., Polani, P.E., De Almeida, J.C. and Briggs, J.H. (1959) A sex-chromosome anomaly in a case of gonadal dysgenesis (Turner's syndrome). *Lancet* i: 711—713.

Gresik, E.W., Quirk, J.G. and Hamilton, J.B. (1973) A fine structural and histochemical study of the Leydig cell in the testis of the teleost, *Oryzias latipes* (Cyprinidontiformes). *Gen. Comp. Endocrinol.* 20: 86—98.

Gresik, E.W., Quirk, J.G. and Hamilton, J.B. (1974) Fine structure of the Sertoli cell of the testis of the teleost *Oryzias latipes*. *Gen. Comp. Endocrinol.* 21: 341—352.

Hackmann, E. (1974) Einfluss von Androgenen auf die Geschlechtsdifferenzierung verschiedener Cichliden (Teleostei). *Gen. Comp. Endocrinol.* 24: 44—52.

Hackmann, E. and Reinboth, R. (1974) Delimitation of the critical stage of hormone-influenced sex differentiation in Hemihaplochromis multicolor (Hilgendorf) (Cichlidae). *Gen. Comp. Endocrinol.* 22: 42—53.

Haffen, K. (1970) Biosynthesis of steroid hormones by the embryonic gonads of vertebrates. *Adv. Morphogen.* 8: 285—306.

Hamilton, J.B. and Kantor, R. (1975a) Lability of gonadal differentiation in the XX homogamete and increasing degrees of stability with one and two Y sex chromosomes (e.g. in XY and YY): injection of graded dosages of steroids in zygotes of *Oryzias latipes*. (In preparation).

Hamilton, J.B. and Kantor, R. (1975b) Lability of gonadal differentiation in the homogametic sex (XX) and increasing degrees of stability with one and two Y sex chromosomes (XY and YY): heat stresses at developmental stages in *Oryzias latipes*. (In preparation).

Hardisty, M.W. (1967) The numbers of vertebrate primordial germ cells. *Biol. Rev.* 42: 265—287.

Harrington, R. (1968) Delimitation of the thermolabile phenocritical period of sex determination and differentiation in the ontogeny of the normally hermaphroditic fish *Rivulus marmoratus* Poey. *Physiol. Zool.* 41: 447—460.

Haskins, C.P., Young, P., Hewitt, R.E. and Haskins, E.F. (1970) Stabilized heterozygosis of supergenes mediating certain Y-linked colour patterns in populations of *Lebistes reticulatus*. *Hereditas* 25: 575—589.

Hirose, K. (1972) The ultrastructure of the ovarian follicle of medaka, *Oryzias latipes*. *Z. Zellforsch.* 123: 316—329.

Hishida, T. (1962) Accumulation of testosterone-4-C^{14} proprionate in larval gonad of the medaka, *Oryzias latipes*, *Embryologica (Nagoya)* 7: 56—67.

Jost, A., Vigier, B., Prepin, J. and Perchellet, J.P. (1973) Studies on sex differentiation in mammals. *Rec. Prog. Horm. Res.* 29: 1 41.

Kantor, R. and Hamilton, J.B. (1975) Rapid and reliable procedures to produce in *O. latipes* fertile males and females of three sex chromosomal genotypes: YY as well as XY and XX. (In preparation).

Kellner, K.R. (1973) Development and survival of sex-chromosomal genotypes. Studies of embryonic killifish (*Oryzias latipes*) under normal conditions and under environmental stress. (Ph.D. Thesis. Downstate Medical Center, State University of N.Y., Brooklyn, N.Y.)

Lambert, J. and Pot, M. (1975) Steroidogenesis in ovarian tissue of a viviparous teleost, the guppy *Poecilia reticulata*. *Comp. Biochem. Physiol.* (B). 50: 585—590.

Lieppmann, M. and Hubbs, C. (1969) A karyological analysis of two cyprinid fishes, *Notemigonus crysoleucas* and *Notropis lutrensis*. *Texas Rep. Biol. Med.* 27: 427—435.

Lowe, T.P. and Larkin, J.R. (1975) Sex reversal in *Beta splendens* Regan with emphasis on the problem of sex differentiation. *J. Exp. Zool.* 191: 25—32.

Lyon, M. (1961) Gene action in the X-chromosome of the mouse (*Mus musculus L.*). *Nature* 190: 372—373.

Lyon, M. (1974) Evolution of X-chromosome inactivation in mammals. *Nature* 250: 651—653.

126

Merchant, H. (1975) Rat gonadal and ovarian organogenesis with and without germ cells. An ultrastructural study. *Dev. Biol.* 44: 1—21.

Morgan, T.H. (1913) *Heredity and Sex.* 2nd edn. (Columbia Univ. Press, New York.)

Müller, R. (1969) Die Einwirkung von Sexualhormonen auf die Geschlechtsdifferenzierung von *Hemihaplochromis multicolor* (Hilgendorf)-(Cichlidae). *Zool. Jahrb. Physiol.* 74: 519—562.

Ohno, S. (1967) *Sex Chromosomes and Sex-linked Genes.* (Springer Verlag, New York.)

Onitake, K. (1972) Morphological studies of normal sex-differentiation and induced sex-reversal process of gonads in the medaka, *Oryzias latipes. Annot. Zool. Japan* 45: 159—169.

Quirk, J.G. (1974) A study of the germ line in the Japanese Killifish, *Oryzias latipes*: primordial germ cell numbers in embryos of four known sex chromosomal genotypes (XX,XY,YX and YY). (Ph.D. Thesis. Downstate Medical Center, State University of N.Y., Brooklyn, N.Y.)

Quirk, J.G. and Hamilton, J.B. (1973) Number of germ cells in known male and known female genotypes of vertebrate embryos (*Oryzias latipes*). *Science* 180: 963—964.

Reinboth, R. (1970) Intersexuality in fishes. *Mem. Soc. Endocrinol.* 18: 515—543.

Satoh, N. (1974) An ultrastructural study of sex differentiation in the teleost *Oryzias latipes. J. Embryol. Exp. Morphol.* 32: 195—215.

Satoh, N. and Egami, N. (1972) Sex differentiation of germ cells in the teleost, *Oryzias latipes*, during normal embryonic development. *J. Embryol. Exp. Morphol.* 28: 385—395.

Schreck, C.B. (1974) *Control of Sex in Fishes.* (Virginia Polytechnic Institute and State University Press, Blacksburg, Va.)

Tang, F., Chan, S.T. and Lofts, B. (1974) Effect of steriod hormones on the process of natural sex reversal in the rice-field eel, *Monopterus albus* (Zview). *Gen. Comp. Endocrinol.* 24: 227—241.

Witschi, E. (1929) Studies on sex differentiation and sex determination in amphibians. II. Sex reversal in female tadpoles of *Rana sylvatica* following the application of high temperature. *J. Exp. Zool.* 52: 267—291.

Yamamoto, T. (1953) Artificially induced sex reversal in genotypic males of the medaka, (*Oryzias latipes*). *J. Exp. Zool.* 123: 571—594.

Yamamoto, T. (1955) Progeny of artificially induced sex reversals of male genotype (XY) in the medaka, (*Oryzias latipes*) with special reference to YY-male. *Genetics* 40: 406—419.

Yamamoto, T. (1958) Artificial induction of functional sex-reversal in genotypic females of the medaka (*Oryzias latipes*). *J. Exp. Zool.* 137: 227—264.

Yamamoto, T. (1959) A further study on induction of functional sex-reversal in genotypic males of the medaka (*Oryzias latipes*) and progenies of sex reversals. *Genetics* 44: 739—757.

Yamamoto, T. (1961) Progenies of sex-reversal females mated with sex-reversal males in the medaka, *Oryzias latipes. J. Exp. Zool.* 146: 163—180.

Yamamoto, T. (1963) Induction of reversal in sex differentiation of YY zygotes in the medaka, *Oryzias latipes. Genetics* 48: 293—306.

Yamamoto, T. (1967) Medaka. In: (Wilt and Wessels, Eds.) *Methods in Developmental Biology.* (T.Y. Crowell Co.) pp. 101—111.

Yamamoto, T. (1969) Sex differentiation. In: (W.S. Hoar and D.J. Randall, Eds.) *Fish Physiology*, Vol. III. (Academic Press, New York) pp. 117—175.

CHAPTER 10

Experimental sex reversal in birds

JANET S. KNIGHT and ELSIE TABER

There is an extreme sexual dimorphism to be found in the plumage, head furnishings and other secondary sexual characters of many birds, making this class of vertebrates especially valuable for intersexual studies. Also, certain characteristics of their embryological development make the experimental induction of intersexuality in birds relatively easy.

Like other vertebrates, embryos of both sexes have a pair of undifferentiated gonads, composed of varying amounts of cortical and medullary tissue; they also have two pairs of sexual ducts, Wolffian and Mullerian. Unlike other vertebrates, the right gonad of the female fails to continue its growth and differentiation and remains in a rudimentary state. Also, the right Mullerian duct in the female regresses, leaving only a rudiment at the caudal end. Otherwise, the pattern of embryonic sexual differentiation is similar to that of mammals, with the gonads developing into testes in the male and an ovary in the female, and male and female accessory organs differentiating from the Wolffian and Mullerian ducts, respectively.

Chromosomal studies in birds are confusing and the genetic mechanism of sex determination is not clear. However, it is well established that the male is the homozygotic sex (ZZ) whereas the female is heterozygous (ZW or, less frequently, ZO; Bloom, 1974). Apparently, there is no chromosomal homologue to the sex chromatin or Barr body, that is, the heteropyknotic X-chromosome, found in female mammals, although Kosin and Fujio (1970) and others have described sexual dimorphism in a heterochromatic 'sex chromatin-like body,' with a higher frequency in the female.

1. INDUCTION OF INTERSEXUALITY AFTER HATCHING

There are scattered reports of the spontaneous occurrence of intersexual birds. Some of these concern certain highly inbred strains or hybrids; some are reports of gynandromorphs or mosaics. In all of these reports, the prob-

Handbook of Sexology, edited by J. Money and H. Musaph
© *Elsevier/North-Holland Biomedical Press, 1977*

able causes of intersexuality were aberrant chromosome distribution or abnormal endocrine influences during early development.

Most reports of spontaneous intersexuality involve the masculinization of
formerly normal females, some of which had previously laid eggs. In almost
all cases, when internal examinations were made, it was found that some
pathological condition had caused atrophy or destruction of ovarian cortical
tissue and that medullary tissue remaining in the ovary and/or medullary tissue in the rudimentary right gonad had hypertrophied. (See Taber, 1964, for
references and a more detailed description of the spontaneous occurrence of
intersexuality.)

This latter type of intersexuality can easily be induced experimentally and
has been studied extensively in the domestic fowl by Domm (1927), Benoit
(1950), Kornfeld (1958), and Taber and colleagues (Taber et al., 1958,
1964; Gardner et al., 1964). Surgical removal of the single left ovary results
in hypertrophy and differentiation of the rudimentary right gonad. Histologically this is usually composed of cords or nests of medullary cells. Tubules, closely resembling those in embryonic or immature testes, but usually
containing no germ cells, are often seen. Less frequently all germinal elements, including normal appearing spermatozoa, are found. In approximately 25% of the gonads, cortical tissue also differentiates so that an ovotestis develops or occasionally, an ovary.

Immediately following sinistral ovariectomy of the brown Leghorn there
is regression of comb size and all new feathers growing in areas previously
plucked are of the male or neuter type. This is due to the lack of androgen
and estrogen, respectively, normally produced by the ovary. Subsequently,
in most cases there is pronounced growth of all head furnishings; wattles and
comb become bright red and the comb is turgid and erect as in the rooster.
The birds frequently crow and show varying degrees of male sexual behavior.
These effects are due to androgens produced by the hypertrophied right
gonad. The spurs grow and the plumage becomes entirely masculine, due to
the lack of estrogen. It may be difficult to distinguish such poulards from
normal roosters.

Frequently, at a later date (on the average of three months after ovariectomy in our experiments), new plumage reverts to the typical dull buff and
brown of the female. Such poulards are true endocrine intersexes, having the
head furnishings typical of the rooster (androgen) and the plumage of the
hen (estrogen). Also the appropriate internal target organs are stimulated
(i.e. Wolffian ducts by androgen and oviduct by estrogen). It has been suggested but not proved that estrogen is produced by cortical tissue resulting
from a secondary activation of the germinal epithelium of the hypertrophied
right gonad. However, in numerous poulards with feminized plumage, we
have failed to identify cortical tissue in serially sectioned gonads.

Groenendijk-Huijbers (1973) has reported hypertrophy of the right gonad
in chick embryos in which the left ovary was destroyed on the fourth day of
incubation. Left ovarian or testicular implants prevented this hypertrophy.

It is obvious that the presence of the normal left ovary inhibits the development of the right gonad. The mechanism of this inhibition is not clear, although it has been generally accepted that steroids produced by the ovary, via feedback on the hypothalamus and pituitary, limit gonadotropin production so that it is inadequate for the stimulation of both gonads. Although it is true that pharmacological amounts of androgen or estrogen and physiological amounts of estrogen do inhibit the development of the right gonad in sinistrally ovariectomized birds (Kornfeld, 1958; Taber et al., 1958, 1964), we have presented evidence against the above hypothesis and supporting a direct inhibitory action of a nonsteroidal substance produced by the ovary (Gardner et al., 1964).

All birds do not respond to sinistral ovariectomy as strikingly as does the domestic fowl. The Japanese quail, for example, shows limited hypertrophy of the right gonad, with no evidence of androgen production (Kannankeril and Domm, 1968), and in some birds there is no hypertrophy. In these cases one might suspect that the inhibitory substance produced by the ovary has had a permanent effect on the right gonad.

2. INDUCTION OF INTERSEXUALITY IN THE EMBRYO

The gonads

Sex reversal in the bird embryo was first conclusively demonstrated when hormone extracts and crystalline sex hormones were introduced into the chick egg prior to the time of sexual differentiation (Dantchakoff, 1935; Willier et al., 1935; Wolff and Ginglinger, 1935). In these early experiments, estrogen feminized male embryos. With lower doses the left gonad became an ovotestis but the right gonad was usually not affected. With higher doses the left gonad was indistinguishable from an ovary and the reduced right gonad contained medullary tissue typical of the right gonad of a female. Paradoxically, androsterone and dehydroandrosterone also had a feminizing effect.

Subsequent experiments on the feminization of males by exogenous hormones have been done mainly in the chicken, duck and quail (see Willier, 1939; Burns, 1961; Taber, 1964; Haffen, 1969, for literature reviews). Although experimental conditions varied (species or breed differences, dosage, injection or immersion of the egg, time of treatment and form of the hormone), the results are generally in agreement: estrogens and some androgens can induce varying degrees of ovarian differentiation in the male embryonic gonads (particularly the left).

Female gonads were not so readily transformed. Androgens had a weak masculinizing effect, causing hypertrophy and transformation of the medullary tissue into testicular cords in the right gonad of the chicken. The left ovary was usually normal but could be converted into an ovotestis with high doses. Later investigators failed to observe such transformations in duck (Lewis, 1946), turkey (Jaap et al., 1951), and chick (Erickson and Pincus, 1966).

The techniques of culture in vitro of embryonic gonads and of intracoelomic grafting have been used extensively by Wolff and his colleagues (Wolff, 1946; Wolff and Haffen, 1952; Haffen, 1970; also see Burns, 1961; Gallien, 1967, for reviews). Their results confirm those obtained by hormone administration and present additional evidence regarding the nature and action of the endogenous hormones of the embryonic gonads. When the undifferentiated left or right gonad from the female chick or duck embryo is associated with the left gonad from a male embryo in vitro, the female gonad is not altered but the male gonad is transformed into an ovary or an ovotestis. The male gonad also differentiates into an ovotestis if it is grown on culture medium containing estradiol. The chick embryonic ovary, grafted into the coelomic cavity of a male embryo, causes the persistence and differentiation of a cortex on the left testis of the host, resulting in an ovotestis. Testicular grafts do not modify a host ovary.

Grafts of the female right gonad (composed only of medullary tissue) or grafts of the left ovarian medulla (cortical tissue dissected away) also feminize the host testis (Mintz and Wolff, 1954), whereas grafts of isolated cortical fragments provoke little or no transformation (Haffen, 1963). These observations lead to the conclusion that the medulla is the site of female secretion in the embryonic ovary.

The possibility that steroid hormones, produced by the embryonic gonads, could play a role in normal gonadal differentiation (Wolff and Ginglinger, 1935; Willier, 1939; Wolff et al., 1966) has led to attempts to demonstrate whether or not undifferentiated gonads synthesize sex steroids. Scheib and Haffen (see Haffen, 1970) have observed Δ_5-3β-hydroxysteroid dehydrogenase activity in primary sex cords (medulla) just prior to histological differentiation (6½ days in the chick, 4½ days in the Japanese quail). Woods and Weeks (1969) have reported that this Δ_5-3β-HSDH reaction is positive in the genital ridge of 2-day chick embryos. Narbaitz and Adler (1966) have described agranular endoplasmic reticulum and lipids in the medullary cords at six days in the chick embryo and, according to Weniger and Zeis (1971) 6-day gonadal rudiments of the chick can transform $[1\text{-}^{14}C]$ sodium acetate into estrone and estradiol in vitro. Woods and Podczaski (1973), using an immunohistochemical method, have detected androgens in undifferentiated gonads of the 3½-day-old chick.

As stated earlier, under the influence of high doses of estrogen, embryonic left testes become morphologically indistinguishable from normal ovaries. When they are grafted into the coelomic cavity of a male embryo, they induce ovarian differentiation on the left testis of the host just as the normal ovary does (Wolff and Haffen, 1961). They show the same pattern of lipogenesis (Wolff et al., 1966), and the same distribution of Δ_5-3β-HSDH activity (Narbaitz and Teitelman, 1965) as the normal ovary. They can synthesize estrogens from [1-^{14}C]sodium acetate (Akram and Weniger, 1967). They acquire the capacity to convert dehydroepiandrosterone and testosterone to estrogens. This suggests that one effect of estrogens injected into the embryo is to stimulate an aromatization enzyme system in the gonads (Haffen, 1970). Weniger and Zeis (1973a) have shown that when dihydrotestosterone is injected, testes are feminized and can synthesize estrogens but they have not determined the sequence of biochemical and morphological events.

Experimentally induced sexual inversion is not stable. After hatching, the gonads eventually revert to those of the genetic sex even when hormone injections are continued. The mechanisms involved in the cessation of female evolution in the inverted male gonads and their return to testicular development are not well understood, but the degeneration of the cortex seems to be the primary event. Wolff and Haffen have examined the behavior of this cortex under various conditions of grafting and organ culture (see Haffen, 1969). The male 'oocytes' degenerate in the intersexual cortex (ZZ chromosome constitution) and this cortex does not survive even when it is recombined with a female medulla (ZW).

Haffen has accomplished the colonization of ovaries (ZW) by male germ cells (ZZ) in chimeric embryos of the chick and has been able to observe their development by grafting the gonadal primordia of the chimeric embryos into successive hosts. The genetically male germ cells begin development in the female direction, enter premeiosis, then undergo atresia. She has concluded that the factors responsible for the degeneration of the cortex of intersexual gonads are related to this intrinsic incapacity of male germ cells to accomplish female gametogenesis. This conclusion is supported by histochemical and ultrastructural observations of regressing intersexual gonads after hatching (Narbaitz and DeRobertis, 1970; Narbaitz, 1971). After hatching, in the hypertrophied right gonad of poulards, female germ cells can accomplish male gametogenesis (see section 1).

Accessory sex organs

Although sex reversal of the gonads is transitory, morphological alterations in the accessory organs, produced by various experimental interventions, are permanent.

Wolff and Wolff (1951) demonstrated that the neuter form of accessory sex structures in chick and duck embryos castrated by X-irradiation is, essentially, the condition found in the normal male. However, right and left Mullerian ducts persisted in both sexes. This is unlike the normal male, in which both regress, and also unlike the normal female, in which the right duct regresses.

Other studies, in vivo and in vitro, have confirmed that the male genital tubercle of the chick and duck and the syrinx of the duck are the ahormonal or neuter forms and have shown that estrogen treatment results in the development of the female forms (Lewis and Domm, 1948; Wolff, 1950; Wolff et al., 1951; Reinbold, 1951; Wolff and Wolff, 1952).

The situation with the Mullerian ducts, however, is not so simple. In the early experiments with hormone injections (Dantchakoff, 1935; Willier et al., 1935; Wolff and Ginglinger, 1935) treatment with female sex hormones resulted in partial or complete retention of both Mullerian ducts in male and female embryos. Male hormones produced various degrees of retrogression of the ducts in females. Testosterone resulted in absence of both ducts in males, but androsterone and dehydroandrosterone, which feminized the testes, caused persistence of Mullerian ducts.

Because of these confusing results, many experiments were subsequently done to determine the mode of action of the sex hormones on Mullerian duct differentiation. It was established that maintenance of both ducts of male embryos could be obtained with injection of female sex hormones, early castration, or explantation in vitro before the beginning of gonadal differentiation. In the female, regression could be obtained by injections of androgens or coelomic grafts of testes. The association of testes with undifferentiated ducts of both sexes in vitro or the addition of androgens to the medium also caused regression. When cultured in vitro after the beginning of differentiation, male ducts regressed but female ducts survived. The necrosis of male ducts was less severe when estrogen was added to the medium. Evidence was obtained that this regression of the male ducts was due to the action of proteolytic enzymes and indicated that the progress could be activated in undifferentiated or female ducts by the addition of androgen. The hypothesis was proposed that the male hormone was responsible for Mullerian duct regression and that the female hormone could play some protective or stabilizing role (Wolff, 1950, 1953; Stoll, 1950; see Burns, 1961, for review).

The rudimentation of the right Mullerian duct which occurs during normal differentiation in females, however, compounded this problem. Wolff and Wolff (1951) emphasized that the retention of both ducts in a male embryo should not be considered a sign of feminization but is the result of insufficient male hormone from the testis. A sign of feminization would be craniocaudal ('female-type') regression of the right duct. ('Male-type' regression occurs in a caudocranial direction in both ducts.) It has been suggested that regression of the right duct in the female is conditioned normally by the female hormone or some other hormone (possibly low levels of male hormone) from the female gonads (Wolff, 1953; Lutz-Ostertag, 1954; Groenendijk-Huijbers, 1962; Weniger, 1965).

Recent studies of the female right duct have indicated that its rudimentation is not analogous to the regression of the male duct (i.e. it is not an enzymatic degenerative process) but is due merely to arrested growth (Thiebold, 1973; Vergnaud et al., 1973). According to Thiebold, the right male duct is potentially subject to the same arrest but this is normally masked by the onset of the destructive process of regression in males. Therefore, two processes are involved and their causes should be investigated separately.

Recently, an increasing amount of evidence has accumulated which indicates that the Mullerian inhibitor in the male is not an androgen but some unidentified substance produced by the testis. This was foreshadowed by the early work of Stoll (1950) in which he showed that testosterone, injected into the egg, caused agenesis of Mullerian ducts but was incapable of duplicating the normal regressive action of the testis on already formed ducts. He and his co-workers have shown that the same is true for other known androgens and that the antiandrogen cyproterone does not prevent duct regression. This and other evidence led them to conclude that differentiation of the gonoducts in male birds is dependent on two secretions from the embryonic testis: one (of unknown nature) necessary for the regression of Mullerian ducts and the other (an androgen) active at a later stage in the differentiation of the epididymis and ductus deferens from the Wolffian tract (Stoll and Maraud, 1968). Recent support for this concept of a nonandrogen factor in regression has come from Weniger (1970), Weniger and Zeis (1973b), and Groenendijk-Huijbers (1974). Certain small cells of the embryonic testicular cords have been proposed as a source of this substance (Stoll et al., 1973).

3. MATING BEHAVIOR

Earlier work, mainly in the domestic fowl, has shown that testicular and ovarian hormones are usually responsible for normal male and female mating behavior; castration of the male and bilateral gonadectomy of the female (removal of the ovary followed by removal of the hypertrophied right gonad) eliminated sexual behavior. In general, male behavior could be induced in both capons (with androgen or estrogen) and bilateral poulards (with androgen; see Young, 1961, for references.)

Domm and Davis (1948) were the first to describe behavior in intersexual birds (brown Leghorn males which developed from eggs treated with estrogen). These birds, with varying degrees of feminization of gonads, ducts and plumage, were tested with normal males and females and a squatting female dummy when they were about two years old. Those with the most masculine plumage were usually at the top of the peck order and displayed male mating behavior; those with the most feminine plumage were usually at the bottom of the peck order and displayed neutral or inactive mating behavior.

The relatively recent findings that a single dose of sex steroid given at a critical time during development can produce sterility and inhibit the potential to display normal female behavior in certain mammals, have stimulated similar studies in birds.

Wilson and Glick (1970) reported that exposure of New Hampshire eggs to high levels of androgen or estrogen inhibited normal mating response in males but not in females, in contrast to the situation in mammals. The critical period for treatment was prior to the 13th day of incubation. When these male chicks were later injected with androgen, they did not develop male behavior as readily as androgen-injected controls and, when injected with estrogen, they squatted and accepted males. On the other hand, females which developed from estrogen or androgen-treated eggs laid eggs and accepted males as the normal female does.

Orcutt (1971) treated male pigeons with estrogen soon after hatching and observed altered behavior patterns, with a tendency toward the feminine, when the birds were tested 10 to 11 months later with normal males and females. He believed that estrogen had caused differentiation of neural centers mediating behavior.

Adkins and Adler (1972) have shown that exposure of adult male and female Japanese quail to short daily photoperiods results in 'functional castration' with the loss of sexual behavior. When they were subsequently treated with hormones the consequence differed significantly from the results of earlier experiments on castration followed by hormone treatment (summarized above) in that androgen had little or no effect on the females and that estrogen induced both male and female behavior in the males. Most of the estrogen-treated males were receptive to normal males, crouching and allowing mating, as would a normal female. However, when exposed to a normal receptive female, they mounted and copulated but showed little of the normal male courtship pattern. Because of this the authors concluded that males are potentially more bisexual than females.

From this brief review of selected papers, one cannot dispute the fact that the sex hormones play an important role in avian mating behavior and that their role differs from that in mammals. Although Pantic and Skaro (1974) have shown that pituitary gonadotrophs appear depressed in white Leghorns, particularly in males, following estrogen treatment of eggs, and Haynes and Glick (1974) have attempted to localize a region of the brain controlling sexual behavior in New Hampshires, the mechanisms of the control of sexual behavior in birds remains unclear.

4. SUMMARY

In the domestic fowl, removal of the single left ovary usually results in the growth and differentiation of the rudimentary right gonad into a testicular organ. Because sperm may be present, this can be considered a true sex reversal. In most cases, this gonad produces significant amounts of androgen and estrogen so that the poulard is intersexual so far as secondary sexual characteristics are concerned.

Transformation of genetically male gonads into ovaries or ovotestes can be induced by the treatment of embryos with estrogens and some androgens. The reverse (transformation of genetic ovaries into testes) is not so easily induced and has only been accomplished with high doses of androgen. These gonadal sex reversals are transitory and the gonads eventually revert to those of the genetic sex. However, intersexual conditions of the accessory sex organs which occur following various experimental treatments are permanent.

Treatment of embryos with steroid hormones at a critical time in development interferes with the subsequent sexual behavior of males but not of females, a situation essentially the reverse of that observed in mammals.

BIBLIOGRAPHY

Adkins, E.K. and Adler, N.T. (1972) Hormonal control of behavior in the Japanese quail. *J. Comp. Physiol. Psychol.* 81: 27—36.

Akram, H. and Weniger, J.P. (1967) Sécrétion d'estrone et d'oestradiol par le testicule féminizé de l'embryon de poulet. *C. R. Hebd. Seances Acad. Sci.* 264: 1806—1807.

Benoit, J. (1950) Différenciation sexuelle chez les oiseaux au cours du développement normal et de l'intersexuality expérimentale par ovariectomie.*Arch. Anat. Microsc. Morphol. Exp.* 39: 395—410.

Bloom, S.E. (1974) Current knowledge about the avian W chromosome. *BioScience* 24: 340—344.

Burns, R.K. (1961) Role of hormones in the differentiation of sex. In: (W.C. Young, Ed.), *Sex and Internal Secretions*, 3rd edn. Vol. I. (The Williams and Wilkins Co., Baltimore.) pp. 76—158.

Dantchakoff, V. (1935) Sur les effets morphogénétiques de la folliculine dans l'ébauche testiculaire du poulet. *C. R. Seances Soc. Biol. Fil.* 119: 1117—1120.

Domm, L.V. (1927) New experiments on ovariectomy and the problem of sex inversion in the fowl. *J. Exp. Zool.* 48: 31—173.

Domm, L.V. and Davis, D.E. (1948) The sexual behavior of intersexual domestic fowl. *Physiol. Zool.* 21: 14—31.

Erickson, A.E. and Pincus, G. (1966) Modification of embryonic development of reproductive and lymphoid organs in the chick. *J. Embryol. Exp. Morphol.* 16: 211—229.

Gallien, T. (1967) Developments in sexual organogenesis. *Adv. Morphogen.* 6: 259—317.

Gardner, W.A., Wood, H.A. and Taber, E. (1964) Demonstration of a myelosuppressic gonadal inhibitor produced by the ovary of the brown Leghorn. *Gen. Comp. Endocrinol.* 4: 673—683.

Groenendijk-Huijbers, M.M. (1962) The cranio-caudal regression of the right Mullerian duct in the chick embryo as studied by castration experiments and estrogen treatment. *Anat. Rec.* 142: 9—19.

Groenendijk-Huijbers, M.M. (1973) Influence of gonadal hormone administration and gonadal implantation in the compensatory growth of the embryonic chicken right ovary after early sinistral castration. *Verh. Anat. Ges.* 67: 193—196.

Groenendijk-Huijbers, M.M. (1974) Mullerian duct (Md.) regressing capability of the embryonic chicken testis. *Anat. Rec.* 178: 512.

Haffen, K. (1963) Sur l'évolution en greffes coelomiques du constituant cortical isolé des gonades femelles et intersexuées de l'embryon de poulet. *C. R. Hebd. Seances Acad. Sci.* 256: 3755—3758.

Haffen, K. (1969) Quelques aspects de l'intersexualité expérimentale chez le poulet (*Gallus gallus*) et la caille (*Coturnix coturnix japonica*). *Bull. Biol. Fr. Belg.* 103: 401—417.

Haffen, K. (1970) Biosynthesis of steroid hormones by the embryonic gonads of vertebrates. *Adv. Morphogen.* 8: 285—306.

Haynes, R.L. and Glick, B. (1974) Hypothalamic control of sexual behavior in the chicken. *Poult. Sci.* 53: 27—38.

Jaap, R.G., Ingram, R.S. and Godfrey, E.F. (1951) Embryonic sexual modification and growth in turkeys. *Ninth World Poult. Congr.* 2: 30—35.

Kannankeril, J.V. and Domm, L.V. (1968) The influence of gonadectomy on sexual characters in the Japanese quail. *J. Morphol.* 126: 395—412.

Kornfeld, W. (1958) Endocrine influences upon the growth of the rudimentary gonad of fowl. *Anat. Rec.* 130: 619—637.

Kosin, I.L. and Fujio, Y. (1970) Age and sex as factors in the occurrence of the scl-body in the liver, heart, kidney and spleen of chicken embryos. *Cytologia* 35: 577—583.

Lewis, L.B. (1946) A study of some effects of sex hormones upon the embryonic reproductive system of the white pekin duck. *Physiol. Zool.* 19: 282—329.

Lewis, L.B. and Domm, L.V. (1948) A sexual transformation of the osseus bulla in duck embryos following administration of estrogen. *Physiol. Zool.* 21: 65—69.

Lutz-Ostertag, Y. (1954) Contribution à l'etude du développement et de la régression des canaux de Müller chez l'embryon d'oiseau. *Bull. Biol. Fr. Belg.* 88: 333—412.

Mintz, B. and Wolff, E. (1954) The development of embryonic chick ovarian medulla and its feminizing action in intracoelomic grafts. *J. Exp. Zool.* 126: 511—535.

Narbaitz, R. (1971) Ultrastructural aspects of cortical differentiation in chick ovaries and intersexual gonads. *Z. Zellforsch. Mikrosk. Anat.* 118: 315—325.

Narbaitz, R. and Adler, R. (1966) Submicroscopical observations on the differentiation of chick gonads. *J. Embryol. Exp. Morphol.* 16: 41—47.

Narbaitz, R. and DeRobertis, E.M., Jr. (1970) Steroid-producing cells in chick intersexual gonads. *Gen. Comp. Endocrinol.* 14: 164—169.

Narbaitz, R. and Teitelman, G. (1965) A histochemical study of sex inversion produced by estradiol in chick embryos. *J. Embryol. Exp. Morphol.* 13: 45—50.

Orcutt, F.S., Jr. (1971) Effects of oestrogen on the differentiation of some reproductive behaviors in male pigeons (*Columba livia*). *Anim. Behav.* 19: 277—286.

Pantic, V. and Skaro, A. (1974) Pituitary cells of roosters and hens treated with a single dose of estrogen during embryogenesis or after hatching. *Cytobiologie* 9: 72—83.

Reinbold, R. (1951) Le rudiment de tubercle génital du poulet: développement embryonnaire et sensibilité aux hormones sexuelles. *Bull. Biol. Fr. Belg.* 85: 347—367.

Stoll, R. (1950) Sur la différenciation sexuelle de l'embryon de poulet. *Arch. Anat. Microsc. Morphol. Exp.* 39: 415—425.

Stoll, R., Lafitan, L. and Maraud, R. (1973) Sur l'origine de l'hormone testiculaire responsable de la régression des canaux de Müller de l'embryon de poulet. *C. R. Seances Soc. Biol. Fil.* 167: 1092—1096.

Stoll, R. and Maraud, R. (1968) Bases expérimentales d'une conception dualiste de la différenciation sexuelle des gonoductes chez le mâle des vetébrés. *Arch. Anat. Histol. Embryol.* 51: 665—671.

Taber, E. (1964) Intersexuality in birds. In: (C.N. Armstrong and A.J. Marshall, eds.) *Intersexuality in Vertebrates including Man.* (Academic Press, London) pp. 285—310.

Taber, E., Claytor, M., Knight, J., Flowers, J., Gambrell, D and Ayers, C. (1958) Some effects of sex hormones and homologous gonadotrophins on the early development of the rudimentary gonad in fowl. *Endocrinology* 63: 435—448.

Taber, E., Knight, J.S., Ayers, C. and Fishburne, J.I., Jr. (1964) Some of the factors controlling growth and differentiation of gonadal tissue in the domestic fowl. *Gen. Comp. Endocrinol.* 4: 343—352.

Thiebold, J.J. (1973) Quelques observations sur le développement du canal de Müller droit chez l'embryon de poulet. *C. R. Seances Soc. Biol. Fil.* 167: 338—339.

Vergnaud, O., Maraud, R. and Stoll, R. (1973) Sur la régression du canal de Müller droit chez l'embryon femelle de poulet. *C. R. Seances Soc. Biol. Fil.* 167: 250—252.

Weniger, J.P. (1965) Régression du canal de Müller d'embryon de poulet mâle de 8 jours cultivé in vitro au contact de gonades femelles du même âge. *Z. Zellforsch. Mikrosk. Anat.* 66: 155—160.

Weniger, J.P. (1970) Hormone testiculaire de l'embryon de poulet. *Arch. Anat. Histol. Embryol.* 53: 97—105.

Weniger, J.P. and Zeis, A. (1971) Biosynthèse d'oestrogènes par les èbauches gonadiques de poulet. *Gen. Comp. Endocrinol.* 16: 391—395.

Weniger, J.P. and Zeis, A. (1973a) Induction de la production d'oestrogènes dans le testicule embryonnaire de poulet par la dihydrotestosterone. *Biochimie* 55: 1163—1164.

Weniger, J.P. and Zeis, A. (1973b) Recherches sur la nature chimique de l'hormone testiculaire de l'embryon. *Ann. Embryol. Morphogen.* 6: 219—228.

Willler, B.II. (1939) The embryonic development of sex. In: (Allen, Danforth and Doisy, Eds.), *Sex and Internal Secretions*, 2nd edn. (Williams and Wilkins Co., Baltimore) pp. 64—164.

Willier, B.H., Gallagher, T.F. and Koch, F.C. (1935) The modification of sex development in the chick embryo by male and female sex hormones. *Proc. Natl. Acad. Sci. U.S.* 21: 625—631.

Wilson, J.A. and Glick, B. (1970) Ontogeny of mating behavior in the chicken. *Am. J. Physiol.* 218: 951—955.

Wolff, Em. (1950) La différenciation sexuelle normal et le conditionnement hormonal des caractères sexuels somatiques précoces, tubercule génital et syrinx, chez l'embryon de canard. *Bull. Biol. Fr. Belg.* 84: 119—193.

Wolff, Em. and Wolff, E. (1952) Sur la différenciation in vitro du tubercule génital de l'embryon de canard. *C. R. Seances Soc. Biol. Fil.* 146: 492—493.

Wolff, E. (1946) Recherches sur l'intersexualité expérimentale produit par la méthode des greffes de gonades à l'embryon de poulet. *Arch. Anat. Microsc. Morphol. Exp.* 00. 69—90.

Wolff, E. (1950) Le rôle des hormones embryonnaires dans la différenciation sexuelle des oiseaux. *Arch. Anat. Microsc. Morphol. Exp.* 39: 426—444.

Wolff, E. (1953) Le déterminisme de l'atrophie d'un organ rudimentaire: le canal de Müller des embryons mâles d'oiseaux. *Experientia* 9: 121—133.

Wolff, E. and Ginglinger, A. (1935) Sur la transformation des poulets mâles en intersexués par l'injection d'hormone femelle (folliculine) aux embryons. *Arch. Anat. Histol. Embryol.* 20: 219—278.

Wolff, E. and Haffen, K. (1952) Sur l'intersexualité expérimentale des gonads embryonnaires de canard cultivées in vitro. *Arch. Anat. Microsc. Morphol. Exp.* 41: 184—207.

Wolff, E. and Haffen, K. (1961) Sur la féminisation induite par les gonades mâles intersexués chez l'embryon de poulet. *Arch. Anat. Histol. Embryol.* 11 (suppl.) 275—302.

Wolff, E., Haffen, K. and Scheib, D. (1966) Sur la détection et le rôle d'hormones sexuelles dans les jeunes gonades embryonnaires des oiseaux. *Ann. Histochim.* 11: 353—368.

Wolff, E. and Wolff, Em. (1951) The effects of castration on bird embryos. *J. Exp. Zool.* 116: 59—97.

Wolff, E., Wolff, Em. and Haffen, K. (1951) Sur la différenciation in vitro de la syrinx chez l'embryon de canard. *C. R. Hebd. Seances Acad. Sci.* 233: 500—502.

Woods, J.E. and Podczaski, E.S. (1973) Androgen synthesis in the gonads of the chick embryo. *Am. Zool.* 13: 1283.

Woods, J.E. and Weeks, R.L. (1969) Ontogenesis of the pituitary gonadal axis in the chick embryo. *Gen. Comp. Endocrinol.* 13: 242—254.

Young, W.C. (1961) The hormones and mating behavior. In: (W.C. Young, Ed.), *Sex and Internal Secretions.* 3rd edn, Vol. II (Williams and Wilkins Co., Baltimore) pp: 1173—1239.

CHAPTER 11

Experimental female hermaphroditism in rhesus monkeys: anatomical and psychological characteristics

ROBERT W. GOY, JOHN E. WOLF and STEPHEN G. EISELE

1. EARLY RESEARCH

The successful experimental masculinization of the female rhesus monkey was first reported by van Wagenen and Hamilton (1943). In that study, the authors pointed out the striking similarity between virilized female rhesus monkeys and certain human infants who appear entirely like cryptorchid males at birth, but who subsequently develop in such a manner that their sex is questioned, and in whom careful examination reveals a uterus and ovaries. This description identifies the condition that has long been subsumed under the term female (pseudo-)hermaphroditism, in which the affected individual has a female gonadal sex (possessing ovaries), but external genital structures that to some degree resemble those of a male. In short, their investigations had produced a remarkable facsimile of the human disorder known as congenital adrenal virilizing syndrome, although their method of producing these masculinized females did not in any way involve direct alteration of the morphology or activity of the developing adrenal. Instead, they injected the pregnant female monkey with testosterone propionate, the esterified form of the most potent testicular hormone, and thus relied upon transfer of the injected hormone (or an altered but still active form) from the maternal circulation across the placenta to the circulation of the developing fetus.

In their initial study, only 6 pregnancies were treated with testosterone propionate, and only 4 living fetuses were obtained by caesarian section prior to term (about day 100 of the 168-day gestation period). Of the 4 fetuses obtained from treated pregnancies, 3 were genetic females and one was a genetic male. Despite the relatively small number of subjects involved, the work resulted in findings that have not since been contradicted and which provide the basis for sound generalizations. Important among these was the observation that the treatment produced no major abnormalities of development in the genetic male. Only slight hypertrophy of the prostate and male accessory glands relative to a younger control male was observed,

Handbook of Sexology, edited by J. Money and H. Musaph
© *Elsevier/North-Holland Biomedical Press, 1977*

and the testes and epididymes appeared entirely normal. Treatment of pregnancies involving genetic female fetuses, however, produced abnormalities of development that (a) involved primarily the urogenital sinus and related distal genital primordia and (b) differed according to the treatment given. When 20 mg of testosterone propionate per day were injected into the pregnant female from about the 40th through the 100th day of gestation, female offspring displayed a well-developed scrotum (devoid of gonads), a male-type urethra and phallus with slight hypospadias, prostate and bulbourethral glands of the male type, absence of an external vaginal orifice, as well as normal-appearing ovaries, fallopian tubes and uterus. Wolffian duct derivatives (ejaculatory duct, seminal vesicle, epididymis or epoöphoron, and vas deferens) were not noted. Failure to find these latter male-type structures may have been an oversight attributable to the developmental age of the animals studied, however, since later work with older subjects clearly demonstrated the presence of these structures in well-developed form (Wells and van Wagenen, 1954).

The extensive virilization obtained with this high daily dosage of 20 mg testosterone propionate was not obtained when only 5 mg per day were injected from the 69th through the 99th day of gestation. Following this treatment regimen, the female fetus did not show prostatic tissue, the urethra was not modified to the male type, the clitoris was merely hypertrophied rather than remodelled into a penis-like structure, and the external vaginal orifice and vaginal vestibule were only decreased in size rather than completely obliterated. Inasmuch as this treatment failed to produce extensive virilization, but did result in measurable deviations from the normal female, van Wagenen and Hamilton described it as a 'modified female' rather than a hermaphrodite.

The difference in effectiveness between 5 and 20 mg per day of testosterone propionate was confirmed in a later report (van Wagenen, 1949). According to that study, none of the pregnant females injected with the lower dose produced female young that appeared hermaphroditic, whereas all of the female offspring from the higher dosages were extensively virilized. The report contained two additional observations of interest. First, even with high daily doses of testosterone propionate, a complete male-type urethra failed to develop if injections stopped prior to the 63rd day of gestation. Thus, evidence was obtained to suggest that the extent of virilization was not only dose-dependent but also duration-dependent. The second finding of interest was that hermaphrodites that were allowed to live to adulthood showed menarche at the normal time and that menstrual blood traversed the penile urethra, showing that the vaginal—urethral junction was patent.

The final report of work from this laboratory (Wells and van Wagenen, 1954) provided more complete evidence for the existence of a restricted period of prenatal development during which testosterone propionate exerts its virilizing influences on the genital tract. In this report, complete anatomical descriptions were given for 9 females whose mothers had been injected with 25 mg per day of testosterone propionate beginning as early as the 23rd or as late as the 43rd day of gestation and ending at varying times from the 50th through the 124th day of gestation. In 5 cases in which the treatment persisted until the 63rd day or later in gestation, virilization was marked and the females were classified as hermaphrodites. Moreover, in all of these individuals, prostatic tissue, seminal vesicles, ejaculatory ducts, and bulbourethral glands were formed when appropriate investigations were carried out. In the remaining 4 cases, when treatment stopped prior to the 63rd day, virilization was judged to be only moderate. One additional subject was given a rather extreme treatment. Beginning on the 25th day and lasting through the 36th day of gestation, 100 mg of testosterone propionate were injected daily. Despite this very high dose, no virilization of the external genitalia or internal male duct structures was observed, presumably because the treatment ended before the beginning of the period of testosterone effectiveness.

A brief summary of these brilliant studies yields the generalization that 20—25 mg of testosterone propionate given daily from about the 40th through the 65th day of gestation produces marked virilization of female fetuses and has no measurable effect on structures of genetic male fetuses. Longer treatments may provide for augmentation of the virilized structures, but the basic masculine anatomical plan is established for the most part (the os penis may be an exception) within that 25-day period of prenatal development. Regardless of dose and duration of testosterone treatment, however, neither van Wagenen nor later investigators have succeeded in inducing complete sex reversal in the sense of completely halting gonadal differentiation in the developing female.

It is worth noting that a related line of investigation, fraught with frustrations, disappointments, and obstacles associated with the ubiquitous catastrophes of World War II, was initiated as early as 1937 by Vera Dantchakoff, whose report on prenatal virilization of rhesus females only appeared posthumously (Dantchakoff, 1950). Her technique, which was not rigorously described, differed from van Wagenen's by utilizing injections of free testosterone directly into the amniotic fluids (or occasionally into the body of the fetus). Her rationale for using this technique was based primarily on the notion that certain 'paradoxical effects' of the male hormone (for example, stimulation of the fetal uterus) were caused by transformation of testosterone as it passed through the maternal system and placenta. Her procedure generally involved an initial injection of 2.5 mg of testosterone dissolved in 0.05 ml of oil into the amniotic cavity on the 22nd day of gestation. This was followed, at unspecified intervals, with repeated injections of 5 mg of the hormone until a total of about 20 mg had been given. This work, which was never completed in accord with Dantchakoff's full hopes and intentions, is of considerable interest in the sense that it shows that dosages of the hormone that are extremely small compared to those used by van Wagenen are nevertheless effective in producing identical kinds of virilization of the genetic female fetus and in their failure to produce anomalies in the development of the genetic male.

2. EFFECTS OF DIFFERENT TREATMENTS

Because the work of van Wagenen and her colleagues so well established the beginning and end of the period when transplacental actions of testosterone propionate realize their directive influences on the anlagen of the genital tract, the work in our laboratory has followed her protocol. We have also been concerned, however, with questions regarding the effects of variation in daily dosage, duration of treatment, and the form of the administered androgen (see Table I for summary of treatments). In addition, our attention has been directed more to the psychological and behavioral consequences of the prenatal androgenization than to its morphological effects. For this reason, all of our surviving treated females have been allowed to undergo normal birth (except once when the fetus was retained to the point of peril), and to develop in social environments where their behavior could be regularly observed and records made of the frequency at which each individual performed specified kinds of responses and social acts.

The external anatomical transformations induced by the prenatal androgen treatments summarized in Table I are shown in a series of illustrations taken on the day of birth (Figs. 1—5). Our results show that 15 mg per day of testosterone propionate given from days 43—105 of gestation is adequate to achieve very complete virilization of the genital apparatus of female rhesus. Subject X-48, shown in Fig. 1, had a well-developed penis with

Table I
Summary of virilizing treatments with androgen given prenatally to female rhesus monkeys.

Female hermaprodite	Dosage (mg)	Hormone *	Day of gestation (1st—last injection)	Total no. injections	Accumulated total dosage (mg)
S-32	12.5	TP	45—153	108	1350
T-64	15	TP	44—60	17	255
V-51	15	TP	43— 59	17	255
V-85	5	TP	44—121	75	375
V-96	5	TP	41—120	80	400
X-48	15	TP	43—105	63	945
U-65	15	DHTP	43— 98	56	840
V-33	15	DHTP	45—124	79	1185
X-66	5	DHTP	42—121	79	395
Z-1	12.5	DHTP	44—103	60	750

* TP: testosterone propionate; DHTP: dihydrotestosterone propionate.

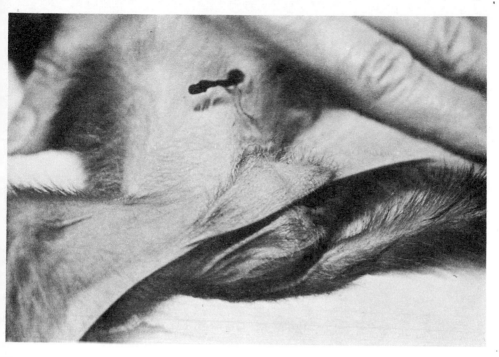

Fig. 1. Photograph taken at birth of the peripheral genitalia of a female hermaphroditic rhesus (X-48) whose mother was injected with 15 mg of testosterone propionate per day from the 43rd through the 105th day of gestation. The penis is well formed and a truly pendulus scrotum exists. There is no external vaginal orifice.

redundant foreskin, a well-defined pendulous scrotum, and no external vaginal orifice. When the same daily dosage was given for only 17 days of gestation (subject V-51, Fig. 2), the anatomical changes were less dramatic and less complete. The penis was short (and probably hypospadiac), the scrotal sac was not developed, and a ridge of tissue developed as a conspicuous median raphé brought about by the fusion of the primordial genital folds. Despite this incomplete development of masculine structures, however, the external vaginal orifice was absent from this subject as well. A lower daily dosage of testosterone propionate (5 mg as opposed to 15 mg), when given for 80 days, was more effective than the short treatment with the high dosage but less effective than 63 daily injections of 15 mg. In this subject (V-96, Fig. 3), the penis was well developed, there was no evidence of a prominent ventral median raphé, and the scrotal sac was not well defined and retained a bilobed appearance. Again, the external vaginal orifice was absent.

The androgen, dihydrotestosterone propionate, was also injected into pregnant females for comparison. Although its developmental morphological effects are of considerable interest, this androgen was chosen primarily to as-

144

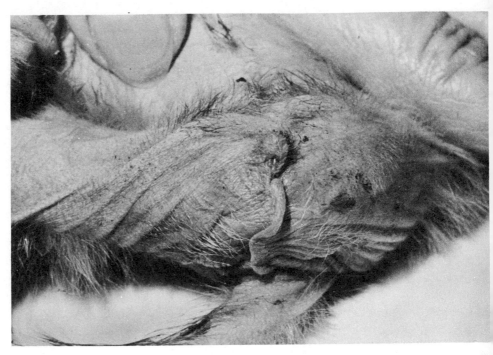

Fig. 2. Photograph taken at birth of the peripheral genitalia of a female hermaphroditic rhesus (V-51) whose mother was injected with 15 mg of testosterone propionate per day from the 43rd through the 59th day of gestation. The penis is not fully formed, hypospadias is present, and the scrotal swellings arise cephalic to the base of the phallus. A median ridge or raphé is conspicuous where a pendulous scrotum should exist. There is no external vaginal orifice.

sess its actions on behavioral development. The choice was made because in lower mammals some of the psychological masculinization resulting from injections of testosterone at early developmental stages has been attributed to the in vivo biotransformation of testosterone to estrogen, either estradiol or estrone (Ryan, 1959; Naftolin et al., 1971, 1972; Whalen and Luttge, 1971; Paup et al., 1972). Dihydrotestosterone, however, is unlikely to undergo biotransformation to an estrogen by aromatization, and its effects have been presumed to be related either to its own actions or to those of further reduced androgen. No inference should be made, however, to the effect that results obtained in rhesus monkeys with this androgen are totally independent of influences (synergistic or otherwise) of estrogen. The fetal rhesus female shows measurable concentrations of estradiol and estrone in peripheral blood which seem to be produced primarily by her own ovaries. For estrone in particular, concentrations greater than 50 pg per ml of female fetal plasma from the umbilical artery can be found as early as day 59 of gestation (Resko, 1974). Earlier developmental stages have not so far been

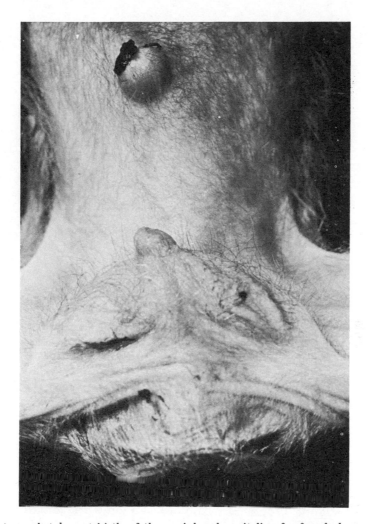

Fig. 3. Photograph taken at birth of the peripheral genitalia of a female hermaphroditic rhesus (V-96) whose mother was injected with 5 mg of testosterone propionate per day from the 41st through the 120th day of gestation. Genital structures resemble those of X-48 (Fig. 1) except that the scrotum is not as pendulous and is bilobed.

studied, but even this time is within the period of development when virilization of genitalia and masculinization of psychological traits probably occur.

Our findings to date with the androgen dihydrotestosterone, indicate that it is a less effective morphological virilizer than testosterone. Reasons for this lower efficacy are not known, but they may involve reduced transfer of the hormone from the injection site into the maternal vascular system, reduced transfer to the fetal vascular system, more rapid metabolic degradation, or a combination of these factors. Subject Z-1 (Fig. 4) was exposed to 12.5 mg of

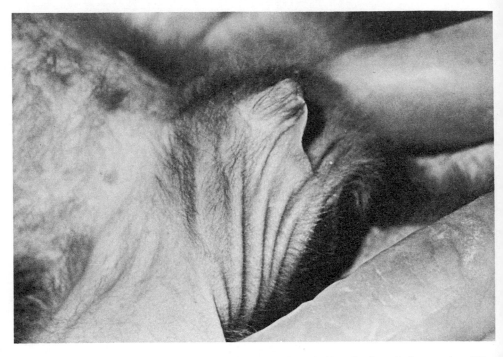

Fig. 4. Photograph taken at birth of the peripheral genitalia of a female hermaphroditic rhesus (Z-1) whose mother was injected with 12.5 mg of dihydrotestosterone propionate daily from the 44th through the 103rd day of gestation. The penis is well developed, the scrotum is not pendulous, and a median raphé is evident. The external vaginal orifice is absent.

dihydrotestosterone propionate daily for 60 days of gestational development. The penis was well developed, but the scrotum was not pendulous. A conspicuous median raphé extended from the tip of the prepuce along the ventral surface of the penis to the base of the scrotal folds. Genital characteristics shown in Fig. 4 should be compared to those shown in Fig. 1, where a very similar treatment with testosterone produced much more complete scrotal differentiation. When only 5 mg of dihydrotestosterone propionate were given daily for 79 injections (subject X-66, Fig. 5), virilization was less extensive and complete than the corresponding treatment with testosterone propionate (compare with Fig. 2). Virtually no sign of scrotal development beyond the formation of the conspicuous median raphé was in evidence. The glans penis (or clitoridis) was a barely palpable mass within the prepuce. However, both of these treatments with dihydrotestosterone propionate were as effective as the corresponding testosterone treatments in abolishing all signs of an external vaginal orifice.

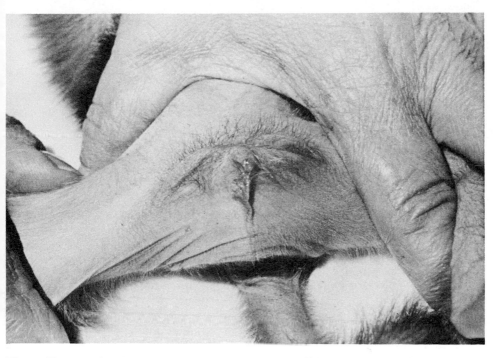

Fig. 5. Photograph taken at birth of the peripheral genitalia of a female hermaphroditic rhesus (X-66) whose mother was injected with 5 mg of dihydrotestosterone propionate per day from the 42nd through the 121st day of gestation. The phallus is underdeveloped and probably hypospadiac. Scrotal swellings are evident cephalic to the base of the phallus, and a median raphé is conspicuously present. The external vaginal orifice is absent.

0. ANDROGENS AND PREGNANCY WASTAGE

Treatments in our laboratory with these androgens are associated with increased pregnancy wastage. This result was not obtained by van Wagenen, and Dantchakoff reported that her techniques did not endanger the progressing pregnancy. The difference between our results and those of van Wagenen are difficult to explain, but they may be related to differences in diet, to differences in the degree to which females were adapted to handling, or to combinations of these and other laboratory routines. Regardless of the exact nature of the factors disposing toward wastage, only about 21% overall pregnancy wastage occurs in our laboratory in females from the general breeding colony. This percentage loss is the combined total for all types of dead or previable fetuses whether delivered at term, postterm, or aborted or resorbed prior to term. In contrast, 39%, or nearly twice as many, of treated pregnancies are wasted. The incidence of wastage is depicted in Fig. 6 for 106 normal (non-handled) females and 54 treated pregnancies. As the figure suggests, a special period of risk exists in the normal pregnancy from the

148

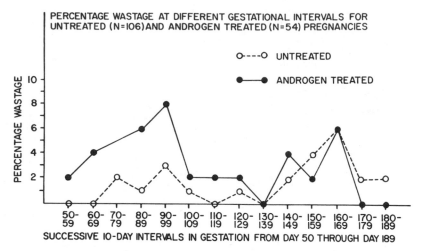

PERCENTAGE WASTAGE AT DIFFERENT GESTATIONAL INTERVALS FOR
UNTREATED (N=106)AND ANDROGEN TREATED (N=54) PREGNANCIES

Fig. 6. The distribution of pregnancy wastage at different times in the course of gestation for 106 untreated pregnancies and 54 pregnancies treated with androgen (either testosterone propionate alone or combined with dihydrotestosterone propionate).

70th through the 90th day of gestation. This remains true for treated pregnancies, but the incidence of wastage is much higher and tends to persist throughout later stages of the treated pregnancy. From the 140th through the 180th days, stillbirth losses are nearly equal in the two groups. When the data are examined by dosage of androgen, there is no convincing suggestion that higher doses cause greater wastage than lower ones. Thus, of the 40 pregnancies treated with 12.5 mg or more per day of testosterone or dihydrotestosterone propionate, 40% resulted in abortion, resorption, or stillbirth. When 10 mg or less per day were injected, 36% of the pregnancies were wasted.

4. SEXUAL DEVELOPMENT AND BEHAVIORAL DIFFERENCES

Although most of the animals discussed in this report are still immature and have not yet entered puberty, results of prior work with female hermaphroditic monkeys (Goy and Resko, 1972) indicate that a delay in menarche can be associated with prenatal virilization. Despite this delay, which on average is 7.6 months (menarche at 36.8 months in hermaphrodites compared with 29.2 months for normal females), later ovarian function can be entirely normal and ovulations occur. This latter finding agrees with Wells and van Wagenen's earlier inference based upon observation of numerous corpora albicantia in the ovaries of their hermaphrodites in terms of ovulatory ability, but our results for time of menarche disagree with their observations on the time of this event. The difference in results may be attributable in part to the fact that menarche is variable and seemingly subject to environmental factors like seasonality and stress-inducing circumstances. Alternatively, it may be related to the circumstance that the virilizing injections we have used have generally been given over a longer period of prenatal life and indeed at a later gestational age. Further observations on the hermaphrodites who are now approaching puberty and who have been produced with planned variation in duration of prenatal treatment may shed additional light on this difference. To date, from all the evidence available on rhesus monkeys, it is certain that prenatal virilization is not associated with the development of an ovulatory blockage resembling that commonly encountered in rodents exposed to testosterone propionate during the period of sexual differentiation. Moreover, even when large dosages of testosterone were injected into female rhesus on the day of birth (a procedure commonly followed and effective in short-gestational rodents like the rat), no ovulatory impairment developed (Treloar et al., 1972). There is reason to believe that some mechanism has evolved in the rhesus to protect the brain-pituitary systems regulating ovulation from the damaging effects of steroid hormones present during early stages of development. This is suggested not only by the failure of the experimental treatments to achieve ovulatory blockage in the genetic female but also by studies of the genetic male rhesus which show that the positive feedback system for the estrogen-induction of LH release is functional (Karsch et al., 1973). This hypothesized protective mechanism may have evolved in human beings as well, since it is reported that human female hermaphrodites also ovulate in adulthood (Jones and Verkauf, 1971).

There are distinct differences in the behavior of hermaphroditic female rhesus compared with normal females (Phoenix et al., 1968; Goy and Phoenix, 1971; Goy and Resko, 1972). These differences, however, have a special character. To begin with, only particular kinds of behavior seem to be altered in their form and frequency of expression. During periods of infancy and juvenile development, the specific behavior patterns affected are those in the gestural repertoire of play (play initiation, the open-mouthed play face, pursuit or chasing play, and rough-and-tumble play), agonism (threat and dominance), and sex (mounting, thrusting, and erection of the penis). For each of the behavioral elements of the play repertoire, the prenatal exposure of female fetuses to testosterone propionate and/or its metabolites results in an augmentation of the frequency of performance of these behaviors in social situations as compared with normal females. Qualitatively, the difference is exactly the same as the difference between normal males and females, and it is by virtue of the similarity in the differences between hermaphroditic and normal females on the one hand and males and females on the other that the behavior of hermaphrodites can be characterized as 'masculine'. The importance of this characterization of their behavior can be clarified by a counter illustration. If, for example, prenatal androgen induced new and bizarre types of behavior not usually found in rhesus males or females, or if it introduced distortions in behavior patterns usually displayed in the same way by all rhesus, then the effects would have to be characterized as abnormalities. In such a circumstance, the studies might be useful as curiosities or as animal psychiatric models. This is not the manner in which the prenatal androgens work, however, and although we have studied intensively over the past decade as many as 30 different kinds of behavioral responses, we have never found behavior that was modified in the hermaphrodite that did not normally differ in its expression in normal males and normal females. In short, the action of prenatal androgen is limited to those behavioral patterns that are normally sexually dimorphic.

The masculinizing effects of prenatal androgen, though evident in the play repertoire, are more conspicuous in studies of the development of the sexual repertoire. Rhesus monkeys are sexually precocious compared to many mammals in the sense that the basic motor elements of the adult sexual repertoire are displayed by infants and juveniles years before the gonadal mechanisms for reproduction have completed their full development. Two basic motor patterns are commonly displayed — mounting with foot-clasp accompanied by pelvic thrusting usually characteristic of the male, and the sexual presentation posture which is a necessary reproductive pattern in the adult female. Both are illustrated in infants at one year of age in Fig. 7. In the situation we are currently using to study the development of these behavior patterns, mounting is more characteristic of the genetic male than it is of the genetic female, but presenting is displayed equally often by both sexes. Moreover, at young ages, males are indiscriminate mounters showing no preference for a partner of a particular sex, although they may display a preference for a particular partner in their social group.

The development of mounting from about 3 to about 15 months of age has been documented for males, females, hermaphroditic females, and males treated prenatally with androgens (Fig. 8). The animals are observed daily, and the data are presented as the total frequency of mounting occurring in successive 10-day blocks of observations. During Run 1, the animals live in small social groups consisting of 4 to 6 infants and their mothers (Fig. 9). At the end of Run 1, usually at 1 year of age for the infants, mothers are separated from their infants, who are then placed in individual cages. During Run 2, the infants are removed daily from their individual cages and placed in a large observation pen in the company of their familiar peers. As shown in Fig. 8, normal males display much more mounting at all times than do normal females. Males exposed to exogenous testosterone propionate prenatally display a developmental pattern very similar to that of normal males, although the quantitative data, especially for Run 2, suggest that the prenatal treatments may have had some damaging effect. This possibility, discordant with the anatomical results, needs further evaluation. Evidence for a damaging action of excessive amounts of prenatal androgen in the developing male has been presented for short-gestational rodents (Wilson and Wilson, 1943), and comparable effects may be obtained in monkeys. Certainly, how-

Fig. 7. Mounting and presenting by infant rhesus in the postures used for reproduction by normal adults. Note the characteristic clasp of the partner's rear legs by the feet of the mounting animal. The monkeys pictured about 1 year old. (Photograph from *Primate Record*, 3 (2) Fall 1972.)

ever, there is no evidence for a precocious hypersexuality in these results. Hermaphroditic females show a complex developmental pattern. During Run 1 (Fig. 8), their performance is not greatly different from that of normal females for the first 10 blocks depicted. However, the data presented are averages for 4 female hermaphrodites produced by 3 different prenatal testosterone proprionate treatments. Two of them were treated with 5 mg per day for 75 or 80 days of gestation (V-85 and V-96, see Table I), and their total number of mounts over the 100 days of observation were 8 and 2, respectively. Another of them, S-32, received 12.5 mg per day for 108 days, and her total frequency of mounts for the 100 days of observation was 2. The other hermaphrodite, T-64, moderately well modified morphologically, received 15 mg per day for only 17 days, and she displayed no mounting during Run 1. During Run 2, after separation from the mother and housing in individual cages, all of these hermaphrodites mounted at high frequencies, including T-64, who had failed to display any mounting during the first 10 blocks of Run 1. This delay in the development of mounting for herma-

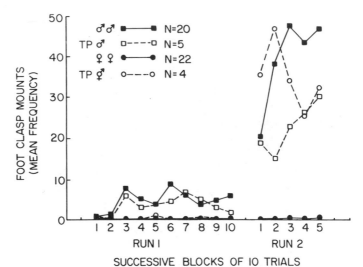

Fig. 8. The overall frequency of display of mounting behavior during the first (Run 1) and second (Run 2) years of life by normal males, normal females, hermaphroditic females, and males whose mothers were injected with testosterone propionate during gestation.

phrodites compared with normal males is difficult to interpret. If the delay were related solely to the prenatal treatment, one would expect treated males to show a similar kind of retardation. They do not, however, and the association of the delay in hermaphroditic development with the continued presence of the mothers is intriguing as evidence for a possible social mechanism (associated, perhaps, with an altered pattern of maternal care) inhibiting full expression of the masculine tendencies of hermaphrodites.

Only one female hermaphrodite given dihydrotestosterone propionate prenatally, U-65, has been studied throughout Runs 1 and 2 thus far (Fig. 10). Her mounting behavior corresponded well to that of the average male during Run 1 but was below average during Run 2. There is, unfortunately, no good explanation or hypothesis at hand to account for the lack of retardation in the development of mounting in this individual. One possibility that ought to be given further attention is the notion that dihydrotestosterone, or further reduced androgenic metabolites, act to augment the social assertiveness and social dominance of the individual so that social inhibitory influences of the mother are more easily overcome. Viewed in this light, the two different androgens studied might have different actions in the regulation of the expression of masculine behavioral predispositions as those are differentiated during prenatal life. Whereas both androgens may augment the predisposition to display mounting, only dihydrotestosterone augments the psychological trait important for overcoming the social inhibition of the expression of mounting that seems to exist during the period of mother—infant interactions.

Fig. 9. Illustration of the housing conditions for mothers and infants studied during the first year of life in the experiments described. The room is approximately 7' by 10' square, and mothers and infants are free to interact continuously.

Whether these masculinizing effects on behavior are specific to prenatal treatments with androgen, or whether they can be produced as well by post-natal treatments of genetic females, has not yet been fully decided. Only one experiment involving 3 genetic females has been carried out in regard to this question (Joslyn, 1973). In that study the females were injected with 2 mg of testosterone propionate 3 times per week beginning at 6.5 months and ending at 14.5 months of postnatal age. The injections had marked effects on growth and body weight, and injected females gained significantly more weight than control females or normal prepubertal males studied concurrent-ly, though the gains in weight were reversible after treatment ceased. In ad-dition, the injected females gained in dominance status among their peers, and during that change in status they showed increased aggressive behavior. No effects of the injections were obtained, however, on play behavior (Fig.

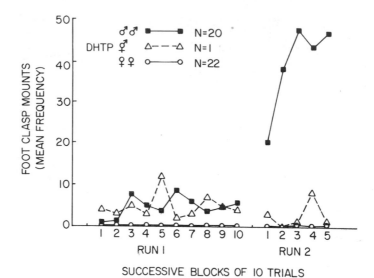

Fig. 10. The average frequency of display of mounting behavior by normal males and normal females, and the frequency of mounting by a single hermaphroditic female produced by dihydrotestosterone propionate prenatally, during the first (Run 1) and second (Run 2) years of life.

11) or on male-like mounting activity. Thus, postnatal androgen in normal genetic females may augment social assertiveness and aggressiveness without concomitantly augmenting masculine forms of play and mounting behavior. The study should be replicated, and additional androgens as well as higher dosages should be used to establish more firmly the difference in effects between androgens given prenatally and those given postnatally in this highly social species.

The rhesus monkey is extremely dependent upon social experience for development and appropriate expression of the gestures and body language involved in living with other individuals of the same species. Distortion and deficiencies in the experiential history lead inevitably to corresponding inadequacies in the social and sexual performance of the individual in later life and adulthood (Goy and Goldfoot, 1973; Goy et al., 1974). In particular, development of the mounting behavior and the subtleties involved in performing the associated gender role in a manner acceptable to normal partners are psychological traits of the greatest complexity, requiring social sophistication in multiple areas of the individual's personality structure. The task of uncovering the variables involved in adequate sociosexual adjustment is immense, and only to the extent that this has been accomplished can we hope to uncover, in turn, the factors involved in the normal development of these variables. The results we have obtained so far are promising, however, and lead to provocative hypotheses regarding the possible interactions between prenatal endocrinological conditions and the early social experiences of the individual in jointly determining the final behavioral outcomes.

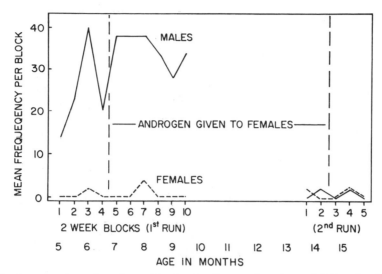

Fig. 11. Frequency of rough-and-tumble play by 3 normal males and 3 females. Beginning at 6.5 months and continuing through 14.5 months of age, the 3 females were injected 3 times weekly with testosterone propionate. (Figure reproduced from Joslyn, 1973.)

5. SUMMARY

Investigations carried out over the past 35 years in different laboratories have confirmed that androgen, administered over a critical period of gestation, exerts a strong virilizing effect on developing genetic female rhesus monkeys (*Macaca mulatta*). Recent work at the Wisconsin Regional Primate Research Center has shown that the androgen dihydrotestosterone propionate is not as potent as testosterone propionate in masculinizing the external genitalia of genetic female rhesus, for reasons not fully understood. However, dihydrotestosterone propionate and testosterone propionate are equally capable of imparting male psychological traits to genetic female rhesus monkeys treated prenatally with one of these androgens. Unlike previous studies, the Wisconsin investigations have indicated that nearly twice as many pregnancies are wasted as a result of androgen treatment in comparison to normal, untreated pregnancies.

ACKNOWLEDGEMENTS

Publication No. 15-027 of the Wisconsin Regional Primate Research Center. Support by USPHS grants RR00167 and MH21312 made this research possible, and we express our sincere gratitude. We wish to acknowledge with thanks the generosity of the Schering Corporation for supplying the testosterone propionate (Perandren) used in these studies. In addition, the talented assistance of Ms. Mary Collins and Ms. Jane Cords has made possible the collection of behavioral data on the subjects described.

BIBLIOGRAPHY

Dantchakoff, V. (1950) Sur les mécanismes différentiels dans la réalisation des sexes chez les vertébrés supérieurs (Singe, *Macacus rhesus*). *Bull. Biol. Fr. Belg.* 84: 311—340.

Goy, R.W. and Goldfoot, D.A. (1973) Experiential and hormonal factors influencing development of sexual behavior in the male rhesus monkey. In: *The Neurosciences*, Third Study Program, (MIT, Cambridge, Massachusetts) pp. 571—581.

Goy, R.W. and Phoenix, C.H. (1971) The effects of testosterone propionate administered before birth on the development of behavior in genetic female rhesus monkeys. In: (C. Sawyer and R. Gorski, Eds.) *Steroid Hormones and Brain Function*. UCLA Forum in Medical Sciences, N. 15, (University of California Press, Berkeley) pp. 193—201.

Goy, R.W. and Resko, J.A. (1972) Gonadal hormones and behavior of normal and pseudohermaphroditic nonhuman female primates. *Rec. Progr. Horm. Res.* Vol. 28 (Academic Press, New York) pp. 707—733.

Goy, R.W., Wallen, K. and Goldfoot, D.A. (1974) Social factors affecting the development of mounting behavior in male rhesus monkeys. In: (W. Montagna and W.A. Sadler, Eds.), *Reproductive Behavior*, (Plenum Press, New York) pp. 223—247.

Jones, H.W., Jr. and Verkauf, B.S. (1971) Congenital adrenal hyperplasia: Age at menarche and related events in puberty. *Am. J. Obstet. Gynecol.* 109: 292—298.

Joslyn, W.D. (1973) Androgen-induced social dominance in infant female rhesus monkeys. *J. Child Psychol. Psychiat.* 14: 137—145.

Karsch, F.J., Dierschke, D.J. and Knobil, E. (1973) Sexual differentiation of pituitary function: Apparent difference between primates and rodents. *Science* 179: 484.

Naftolin, F., Ryan, K.J. and Petro, Z. (1971) Aromatization of androstenedione by the diencephalon. *J. Clin. Endocrinol. Metab.* 33: 368—370.

Naftolin, F., Ryan, K.J. and Petro, Z. (1972) Aromatization of androstenedione by the anterior hypothalamus of adult male and female rats. *Endocrinology* 90: 295—298.

Paup, D.C., Coniglio, L.P. and Clemens, L.G. (1972) Masculinization of the female golden hamster by neonatal treatment with androgen or estrogen. *Horm. Behav.* 3: 123—132.

Phoenix, C.H., Goy, R.W. and Resko, J.A. (1968) Psychosexual differentiation as a function of androgenic stimulation. In: (M. Diamond, Ed.) *Reproduction and Sexual Behavior* (Indiana University Press, Bloomington) pp. 33—49.

Resko, J.A. (1974) Sex steroids in the circulation of the fetal and neonatal rhesus monkey: A comparison between male and female fetuses. *Colloq. Inst. Natl. Santé Rech. Med.* 32: 195—204.

Ryan, K.J. (1959) Biological aromatization of steroids. *J. Biol. Chem.* 234: 268—272.

Treloar, O.L., Wolf, R.C. and Meyer, R.K. (1972) Failure of a single neonatal dose of testosterone to alter ovarian function in the rhesus monkey. *Endocrinology* 90: 281—284.

van Wagenen, G. (1949) Induced female pseudohermaphroditism in the monkey. *Anat. Rec.* 103: 562—563.

van Wagenen, G. and Hamilton, J.B. (1943) The experimental production of pseudohermaphroditism in the monkey. In: *Essays in Biology* (in honor of Herbert M. Evans) (University of California Press, Berkeley) pp. 581—607.

Wells, L.J. and van Wagenen, G. (1954) Androgen-induced female pseudohermaphroditism in the monkey (*Macaca mulatta*): Anatomy of the reproductive organs. *Carnegie Inst. Washington Publ. 603, Contrib. Embryol.*, Vol. xxxv, pp. 93—106.

Whalen, R.E. and Luttge, W.G. (1971) Perinatal administration of dihydrotestosterone to female rats and the development of reproductive function. *Endrocrinology* 89: 1320—1322.

Wilson, J.G. and Wilson, H.C. (1943) Reproductive capacity in adult male rats treated prepuberally with androgenic hormone. *Endocrinology* 33: 353—360.

CHAPTER 12

Sex reversal as related to clinical syndromes in human beings

ARYE LEV-RAN

1. INTRODUCTION

Subjects with ambiguous genitalia are termed hermaphrodites, and their classification is determined by the histology of the gonads, irrespective of the sex chromosome constitution. Male pseudohermaphrodites are defined by the presence of testicular tissue, and female pseudohermaphrodites by the presence of ovarian tissue. In true hermaphrodites both testicular and ovarian tissues coexist. Sex reversal (ambiguous genitalia) in humans develops as a result of derangement of the embryogenesis of reproductive organs, each of which has its own quite definite period of differentiation during the embryonic and fetal periods of development.

Various forms of sex reversal can be understood from the basic processes of sex differentiation (see Federman, 1973; Grumbach and Van Wyk, 1974). The development of testis from the undifferentiated gonad requires the presence of the paracentromeric region of the short arm of the Y chromosome. It is possible that the determining factor in the development of gonads is the rate of their growth so that much earlier development of a nondifferentiated gonad results in the formation of testis. The differentiation of ovaries starts much later and requires the presence of two normal X chromosomes (exceptions are very rare). It is conceivable that the differentiation of internal reproductive organs in the female direction is stimulated by estrogens, present in large quantities in every fetus. If so, these estrogens are mainly of placental and definitely not of fetal ovarian origin. Estrogens can induce female development only if there is no strong antagonistic influence of androgens. Probably, male differentiation results from the combined action of androgens and the product of a special gene situated on the X chromosome and concerned in the response to androgens.

Testes stimulate the development of internal reproductive ducts in the male direction through their two secretions: a nonsteroid high-molecular-weight one, secreted by the fetal Sertoli cells and causing local (homolateral)

Handbook of Sexology, edited by J. Money and H. Musaph
© *Elsevier/North-Holland Biomedical Press, 1977*

atrophy of Müllerian (paramesonephric) ducts, and androgen (most probably, testosterone) inducing the development of the Wolffian (mesonephric) ducts. In addition, local presence of a testis is required for the synthesis of a high-affinity androgen-binding protein. In the presence of high levels of systemic androgens (most probably, dihydrotestosterone, locally converted from testosterone) external genitalia differentiate in the male direction. The critical period for these androgen effects is between the 12th and 17th weeks of pregnancy, when the testosterone level in male fetuses is about ten times that found in female fetuses and about equal to the level found in adult males. The level declines by 24 weeks, and at term there is no difference between the sexes in the testosterone level. The absence of sufficient androgenization leads automatically to the differentiation of external genitalia in the female direction.

The crucial factors in sex differentiation are: chromosomal constitution, testicular secretions, the level of androgens and the tissue sensitivity to androgens. Postnatal sex hormone secretions can at best modify the preexisting signs of sex reversal. Some forms of sex reversal are readily distinguishable clinically, others are not.

2. CHROMOSOMAL ANOMALIES

Chromosomal anomalies (see Grumbach and Van Wyk, 1974) appear at the time of gametogenesis, fertilization or first cleavage division. The usual results are disorders of gonadal differentiation without sex reversal. These conditions are usually included into chapters devoted to sex reversal for didactic reasons only. In rare cases, though, chromosomal anomalies are accompanied by sex reversal.

Testicular tubular dysgenesis — Klinefelter's syndrome (Becker, 1972)

The karyotype is characterized by the presence of at least one Y chromosome and at least two X chromosomes, the most usual karyotype being XXY; less frequent variants are XXYY, XXXY, and XX/XXY. The chromosomal error may occur at meiosis or early mitosis, and an advanced maternal age plays an important etiologic role. Testicular differentiation and testicular embryonic secretions are normal masculine. Drastic loss of germ cells occurs in late prenatal period and early childhood. Dysgenesis of testicular tubules with their hyalinization first appears in childhood. By early puberty spermatocytes are lost and testicular tubules become progressively hyalinized. Sometimes there is Leydig cell hyperplasia. In adults testosterone secretion is only about one fifth that of normals, and in addition androgen sensitivity of some tissues is probably diminished. Clinical features include azoospermia, diminished or absent libido, increased height, eunuchoid body build, frequently obesity with the feminine distribution of adipose tissue, bilateral gynecomastia, almost no facial hair and female-type pubic escutcheon. The size of the penis is usually normal, that of scrotum and testes small (less than 3 cm in length). Testes are usually firm. Cryptorchidism is seen very rarely, and hypospadias almost never. Some patients have structural defects of the thoracic cage or spine; many exhibit obviously abnormal personality traits (timidity, withdrawn behavior, lack of social and physical drive) and some have lowered intelligence. About one in four XXY patients is mentally retarded. The more supernumerary X chromosomes there are in the karyotype, the more pronounced are both physical changes and mental deficiency. In cases with XXXXY karyotype, hypospadias, bifid scrotum, cryptorchidism and hypoplastic phallus have been described.

A very interesting variant is found in XX males, usually of normal stature and intelligence, but with hypogonadism (not always). Three theories have been proposed to explain testicular development in the absence of Y chromosome: X—Y interchange at paternal meiosis; undetected mosaicism, and the presence of a mutant autosomal gene leading to testicular differentiation in an XX fetus.

The treatment includes resection of pubertally enlarged breasts (because of both cosmetic embarrassment and the incidence of associated cancer) and, in some cases, long-term administration of high doses of testosterone. Testosterone markedly increases external signs of masculinity (including penis) and body hair (though facial hair usually remains sparse), as well as sexual potency. The patients become more self-confident, assertive, ambitious and aggressive. Therefore this kind of treatment is not recommended for severely mentally retarded patients, nor for those with severe behavioral impairment.

Gonadal dysgeneses (Ferguson-Smith, 1965; Greenblatt, 1967; Goldberg et al., 1968)

In the majority of cases the karyotype is characterized by sex chromosome monosomy or lack of one of arms of the X chromosome in all or some of the body cells. Since one X chromosome is obligatory for life, the monosomy can by only of the 45,X (XO) type. The monosomy originates mostly from an early mitotic error or other mechanism such as meiotic nondysjunction.

Gonadal dysgenesis: Turner's syndrome
The usual karyotype is 45,X, formerly symbolized as XO, but many patients have other karyotypes: XXqi (isochromosome for the long arm), XXpi (isochromosome for the short arm), XXr (ring X chromosome), XXp- (deletion of the short arm), XXq- (deletion of the long arm) or mosaicism of the XO/ XX, XO/XXX, XO/XY and other types.

Ovarian development in the early embryonic period begins normally, but after about three months, ovaries start to regress, and by term are represented by connective tissue streaks. Germ cells degenerate since degenerating follicles cannot sustain them. One very rare variant of the syndrome with the XO/XY karyotype differs in that the streaks originate from testicular elements, but they, too, are functionally inactive. Both internal and external genitalia develop as feminine. Reports of familial clustering are very rare. The prevalence of monozygotic twinning in affected sibships is increased.

The patients suffer from both genital and somatic abnormalities. The genital ones include amenorrhea, absence of breast development at adolescence and absence or sparsity of sexual hair. In very rare cases patients with the 45,X karyotype undergo pubertal feminization, and even menstruate and become pregnant.

Somatic anomalies included stunted growth, lag of skeletal maturation in adolescence, webbed neck, widely spaced nipples, cubitus valgus, short 4th metacarpals, osteoporosis, shield-like chest, low neck hair, low set ears, epicanthus, multiple naevi, cardiac anomalies (coarctation of the aorta, aortic stenosis, etc.), renal anomalies, unexplained hypertension. Usually several of the symptoms or even the majority of them are present in the same individual. Directional sense and space and form cognition are often deranged, but verbal ability is usually normal.

Genes determining sexual development are localized on both arms of the X chromosome, and it should be remembered that both Xs are active in oögonia. It is the absence of the short arm of X (in XO, XXp- or XXqi patients) that leads to short stature and other somatic anomalies. In cases of structurally abnormal X (XXqi, XXpi, Xp-, Xq-, Xr) it is always the abnormal X that is inactivated and forms the sex chromatin body.

In XO/XX mosaicism, somatic anomalies are very few or even absent, and the greater the proportion of the XX cells, the closer is the phenotype to that of normal females. In patients with the XO/XY karyotype the streaks of the testicular remnants can secrete some androgens, resulting in clitoral hypertrophy.

The success of any treatment in accelerating growth has not been proved. Long-term substitution therapy with estrogens is effective in initiating and maintaining the menstrual cycle. In XO/XY mosaics prophylactic removal of the gonadal streak is indicated to prevent the development of gonadal tumor.

Mixed (atypical) gonadal dysgenesis (Sohval, 1964)
The usual karyotype is XO/XY. The patients have a streak gonad on one side and a severely dysgenetic testis on the other. This gonad is usually situated abdominally, but sometimes is found in the inguinal canal or even in a labium. The dysgenetic testis contains tubules with undifferentiated or Sertoli cells, Leydig cells and sometimes spermatogonia. Defective spermatogenesis causes increased gonadotropic secretion which leads to hyperplasia of Leydig cells and even tumor formation. The latter may secrete androgens, causing severe virilization, especially at puberty.

The dysgenetic testis is defective to variable extents. If the secretion of the Müllerian-suppressing substance is defective, all internal organs differentiate in the female direction, which is the usual case. Sometimes though, Müllerian-suppressing substance is secreted normally. As a result the tube is absent on the side of the dysgenetic testis, and the uterus is unicornuate. Androgen secretion is also not uniform, therefore the ductus deferens may or may not be present on the side of the dysgenetic testis (it can co-exist with the tube on the same side). Depending on the degree of secretion of androgen the external genitalia can be almost entirely feminine with only slight clitoral hypertrophy, or ambiguous, or resembling masculine genitalia with hypospadias or only with unilateral cryptorchidism. In the great majority of cases some virilization is already quite obvious at birth, therefore some of the patients (luckily, a minority only) are reared as boys. Virilization at puberty may or may not be adequate, and life as a boy may be complicated further by structural deficiency.

The patients usually have no somatic anomalies, they are amenorrheic and, unless treated, sexually infantile. Patients who virilize (especially those with Leydigoma) have a masculine body build, variable musculature, generalized hypertrichosis of the masculine type and hypertrophy of the phallic organ which despite plastic surgery, is not ideal in coital size. A patient may be clinically indistinguishable from a woman with congenital adrenal hyperplasia, but differential diagnosis is easy as the patients are chromatin-negative and excrete normal quantities of 17 ketosteroids and pregnanetriol.

The treatment in all cases includes excision of the streaks and dysgenetic testis (because of the danger of malignant changes). In patients reared as females, subsequent treatment consists of estrogenization and cosmetic measures. In those reared as males, testosterone administration and plastic surgery of external genitalia are required.

Pure gonadal dysgenesis (Simpson, 1971)

Gonadal dysgenesis can be found in some patients with the XX karyotype. Such patients have female eunuchoidism, amenorrhea and sterility. Both internal and external genitalia are feminine. An autosomal recessive inheritance has been suggested.

Some patients have an apparent XY karyotype. Clinically these patients, too, present eunuchoid proportions (the patients are usually taller than their XX counterparts), absent breasts, absent or scanty sexual hair and amenorrhea. Their external and internal genitalia are feminine, sometimes with slight clitoral enlargement. Gonadal neoplasms are frequent. The trait has been suggested as X-linked recessive or male-limited autosomal dominant. Theoretically, early embryonic castration caused by an extraneous factor, should produce the syndrome of pure gonadal dysgenesis.

The therapy consists of estrogenization. In XY patients the streaks should be removed to eliminate the danger of tumor formation.

3. TRUE HERMAPHRODITISM: AMBISEXUALITY

The majority of patients have XX karyotype, some are XX/XY mosaics, XX/XY chimeras or have XY karyotype (Pfieffer, 1974).

Clinical features are variable. According to estimate, in about one third of cases there is an ovary on one side (usually left) and a testis on the other, in 20% there are bilateral ovotestes, while in others there may be an ovotestis on one side and a testis or an ovary on the other. The obligatory feature is the presence of both ovarian and testicular tissues in the same individual. The ovaries are usually situated in their normal location; they are sometimes atrophic, but may contain follicles and even ovulate. The testes may be situated in the scrotum, in the inguinal canal or in the abdominal cavity. Usually they are atrophic with hyalinized tubuli, but in rare cases the normal structure exists and spermatogenesis may even occur. Successful pregnancy was reported in one case after the removal of an ovotestis; the other gonad was an ovary (Narita et al., 1975).

In almost all cases a uterus is present, which in the majority is rather well developed but sometimes rudimentary or bicornuate. External genitalia are extremely variable. In some patients they are almost entirely masculine with only mild hypospadias. In others the external genitalia are ambiguous with clitorine phallus, perineal hypospadias, and bifid scrotum. There are patients with almost completely feminine genitalia and only very slight clitoral hypertrophy. Inguinal hernia is present in about half the cases and can contain either a uterus or a gonad. The vagina may be well developed or be represented by a narrow cleft. At adolescence the great majority of patients exhibit both gynecomastia and some degree of masculinization; two-thirds of the patients (only chromatin-positive cases) menstruate. Because of the phallic hypertrophy, perhaps as many as two-thirds of true hermaphrodites have been reared as males.

After infancy and early childhood, treatment depends on the sex of rearing and consists of removal of contradictory or inappropriate gonadal tissue, plastic genital surgery and, when no appropriate gonad is left, in pubertal hormonal therapy. If the diagnosis is made in newborn and small children, the sex of rearing depends on the size of phallus and degree of hypospadias. Undoubtedly, in the great majority of cases, female sex of rearing is preferable.

4. MALE PSEUDOHERMAPHRODITISM

According to definition, this group includes patients with partly or completely feminine phenotype, bilateral testes and XY karyotype. This is by far the most heterogenous group, comprising patients with different mechanisms of derangement (Park et al., 1975).

Dysgenetic male pseudohermaphroditism (gonadal dysgenesis with virilization)

This form closely resembles the XY pure gonadal dysgenesis, and the development of internal genitalia is feminine. On the other hand, starting from the embryonic period of their development, the patients secrete substantial quantities of testicular androgens. This results in ambiguous external genitalia: underdeveloped epididymis, underdeveloped bifid scrotum, ambiguous phallus with chordee, perineal hypospadias. The dysgenetic testes are located in inguinal hernias or in the abdominal cavity (Chemke et al., 1970). The picture is complicated by normal male virilization at puberty. The risk of malignancy dictates that the dysgenic gonads be removed. Further surgical and hormonal measures depend on the sex of rearing.

True agonadism: testicular arrest (Parks et al., 1974)

This is a very unusual partial form of sex reversal, representing testicular arrest. The embryonic testes secrete normal or almost normal quantities of Müllerian-suppressing substance, therefore tubes, uterus and upper vagina are absent, only in very rare cases do rudimentary Müllerian derivatives survive. Androgen secretion in the first embryonic period has usually been normal, as the urethra is phallic, lower vagina absent, scrotolabial fusion complete, and in rare cases an immature epididymis is present. However, further virilization stops because of the unexplained destruction of the embryonic testes, most probably, the event occurs by the end of the third month of the embryonic life. As a result, neither Müllerian nor Wolffian derivatives develop — the first because they have already atrophied by that time, the second because of the lack of sustained androgenic stimulation. Testes are represented by insignificant vestiges which are found at laparotomy only with great difficulty. External genitalia are represented by a minuscule phallus (usually containing urethra), fused scrotolabial folds do not resemble a scrotum and a vagina is absent. No sexual maturation occurs at adolescence. The term 'agonadism' is an unfortunate misnomer since the clinical picture points to the presence of functioning testes in the embryonic period. Since all the patients should be reared as females, the treatment consists of oestrogenization and vaginoplasty.

Congenital adrenal hyperplasia in males with inborn errors of steroid synthesis in adrenals and gonads

Congenital adrenal hyperplasia is caused by one of six enzymatic defects, transmitted as autosomal recessive traits (Bongiovanni et al., 1967; New, 1968; Bongiovanni, 1972; Rosenfield, 1972). The common denominator of all the forms is impaired cortisol synthesis. As a result of negative feedback, the pituitary secretes large quantities of ACTH, which causes adrenocortical hypertrophy with excessive secretion of those steroids whose synthesis is not blocked and which accumulate before the block. In some forms of the disease the block is at a very early stage, and the result is deficient synthesis of both adrenal and gonadal steroids, since some enzymes are common to both pathways. Congenital adrenal hyperplasia accounts for about half of all patients with sex reversal, mostly females but also males. Male pseudohermaphroditism may result from insufficient masculinization of the male fetuses. If there is no block in androgen synthesis, the disease in males results in macrogenitosomia precox, which is outside the scope of this review.

20α-Hydroxylase (cholesterol desmolase) deficiency

This enzymatic defect results in a blockade of the conversion of cholesterol to pregnenolone, and, as a result, a block in the synthesis of glucocorticoids, mineralocorticoids, androgens and estrogens. The patients suffer from the so called 'lipoid adrenal hyperplasia' with severe salt-losing crises. Female genital ducts are absent, but the external genitalia are feminine. Plasma cortisol and urinary 17-ketosteroids are absent. The treatment is similar to other forms of the salt-losing adrenogenital syndrome.

Δ⁵-3β-Hydroxysteroid dehydrogenase (HSD) deficiency

This defect prevents the conversion of pregnenolone to progesterone and of dehydroepiandrosterone to androstenedione. Consequently, precursors accummulate behind the point of blockage. Deficiency of the enzyme interferes with the synthesis of glucocorticoids, mineralocorticoids, androgens and estrogens, but increased quantity of rather weak androgens (dehydroepiandrosterone and androstenediol) results in some masculinization of the external genitalia. This deficiency leads to adrenocortical insufficiency with marked salt-wasting and, in males, to pseudohermaphroditism with underdevelopment of penis, non-fusion of scrotolabial folds and preservation of vagina. In the great majority of cases the disease is fatal at an early age, in spite of hormonal treatment. Nevertheless, a number of cases have been reported in which males with pronounced hypospadias and gynecomastia reached puberty and, while on corticoids, underwent pubertal masculinization. Their testes showed spermatogenic arrest and generally diminished Leydig cells with the focal hyperplasia of the latter. In vitro studies proved partial defect of testicular enzyme without any derangement of the peripheral or hepatic Δ⁵-3β-HSD activity (Schneider et al., 1975). This example shows that the same enzymatic activity in adrenals, testes and peripheral organs may differ.

17α-Hydroxylase deficiency

The defect causes the block in the conversion of progesterone to 17-OH-progesterone and of pregnenolone to 17-OH-pregnenolone. As a result, there is a block in the synthesis of both glucocorticoids and sex steroids. On the other hand, the sysnthesis of mineralocorticoids is not affected, and life is sustained by 11-deoxycortisol (DOC) and corticosterone (mineralocorticoid with modest glucocorticoid activity). Aldosterone secretion is not very high since this hormone is secreted by adrenal glomerulosa rather than fasciculata and regulated by the renin-angiotensin system to a much greater extent than by ACTH.

Such a defect in fetal testes may result in deficient testosterone synthesis and in insufficient masculinization. The clinical picture includes mineralocorticoid excess with hypertension and hypokalemia. A male patient aged 24 was described (New, 1970) with small phallus, hypospadias, chordee, scrotal hypoplasia, left sided cryptorchidism, a small right gonad and vaginal utricle. He suffered from marked gynecomastia and had no public, axillary or facial hair. Blood pressure was only slightly elevated. Testosterone treatment was effective, facial hair appeared within several weeks.

Defects of testosterone synthesis

Steroid 17,20-desmolase deficiency (Zachmann et al., 1972)

This partial defect in adrenals and testes was described in 3 members of one family and was probably caused by a male-limited autosomal dominant or by an X-linked recessive trait. The enzymatic defect blocked synthesis of dehydroepiandrosterone and androstenedione. Urinary excretion of cortisol metabolites and of pregnanetriol was normal. There was no testosterone response to HCG, nor that of dehydroepiandrosterone to ACTH. The patients had ambiguous external genitalia and inguinal gonads at birth, severe hypospadias, but male ducts. Most probably, the enzymatic defect was incomplete, otherwise the genitalia would have been feminine.

Deficiency of testicular 17β-hydroxysteroid dehydrogenase (Goebelsmann et al., 1973; Givens et al., 1974)

This defect is unusual in that it blocks the conversion of androstenedione to testosterone in testes only. As a result, there is great increase of androstenedione in blood and of total 17-ketosteroids in urine and increased secretion of FSH and LH. The plasma level of testosterone is low. The patients are phenotypic females with separate urethral and vaginal openings, sometimes with clitoral enlargement; vagina is short and blind, there is no uterus nor tubes, but only male ducts. Breast development is variable. At adolescence clitoris progressively enlarges, and there appears severe hypertrichosis. The testes contain abundant Leydig cells but no spermatids. The treatment consists of gonadectomy and estrogenization, since almost all patients are reared as girls.

It is suggested, that Reifenstein's syndrome (hypospadias, hypogonadism, gynecomastia with postpubertal testicular atrophy) in patients reared as males is a variant of the partial 17β-hydroxysteroid dehydrogenase deficiency (Grumbach and Van Wyk, 1974).

Defect of testosterone conversion into dihydrotestosterone: pseudovaginal perineoscrotal hypospadias, or familial incomplete male hermaphroditism, type 2 (Opitz et al., 1971; Walsh et al., 1974)

The inheritance of the syndrome is probably autosomal recessive. The defect is unique in that testosterone production is normal for a male, whereas testosterone conversion into dihydrotestosterone is deficient or the hormone is not taken up by target cells. Imperato-McGinley and co-workers (1974) demonstrated a deficiency in the formation of dihydrotestosterone from testosterone secondary to 5α-reductase deficiency. Since testosterone is probably the androgen responsible for the male differentiation of the Wolffian ducts and dihydrotestosterone for the male differentiation of the urogenital sinus and urogenital tubercle, the patients present as insufficiently virilized boys with severe perineoscrotal hypospadias and dorsal prepuce; the blind vagina opens either separately or into the urogenital sinus; labioscrotal folds resemble cleft scrotum and contain grossly normal testes with epididymis; there are vasa deferentia and seminal vesicles, ejaculatory ducts empty into a short vagina. Müllerian derivatives are absent. At puberty the patients undergo sufficient virilization and gynecomastia is almost always absent. In short, internal genitalia are normally masculine and the external ones are insufficiently virilized.

It should be kept in mind that the combination of perineoscrotal hypospadias with descended testes is very unusual in patients other than intersexes, and such a combination should always arouse suspicion of male pseudohermaphroditism.

Syndromes of peripheral androgen insensitivity

Testicular feminization syndrome, or complete androgen insensitivity (Morris, 1953; Hauser, 1963; Southren, 1965)
This syndrome is transmitted as an X-linked recessive trait or a male-limited dominant one, so that half of the genetic boys are affected. The basic defect is probably reduced affinity of the cellular nuclear receptors for androgens (Amrhein et al., 1976). Therefore, not only is the reproductive tract insensitive to androgens, but anabolic effects of both testosterone and dihydrotestosterone are also lacking (Hamilton and Kliman, 1971).

In the embryonic period, the Müllerian-suppressing substance is secreted normally, therefore tubes, uterus and upper vagina are always absent. The secretion of androgens is normal, but the tissues are insensitive to them, and as a result the Wolffian derivatives are very hypoplastic and external genitalia are entirely feminine although the vagina is shallow. Testes are usually situated in the groins or in the labia majora, but are sometimes found in the abdominal cavity. The testes are immature, contain primitive spermatogonia and Sertoli cells. Usually there is no peritubular fibrosis. Leydig cells are hyperplastic and after puberty tend to form adenomas. Plasma levels of testosterone are normal for males and those of estrogens normal for females. Production rates of both estradiol and testosterone were found to be increased 2—3 fold (Wilson et al., 1974). Estrogens, whose action on peripheral tissues is unopposed by inefficient androgens, determine the clinical picture: good breast development, feminine contours, and lack of hirsuitism.

In vitro studies showed that testicular synthesis of testosterone occurred in the patients, in contrast to normal testes, via the Δ^5 pathway with the accumulation of dihydroepiandrosterone and androstenediol (Bell, 1975) that is, there is a certain defect in 3β-hydroxysteroid dehydrogenase-isomerase. This defect, though may be of secondary clinical importance only.

All the patients are reared as girls and commonly the first suspicion of abnormality arises when a seemingly normal girl fails to menstruate at puberty. Postadolescent patients have normal feminine fat distribution, well-developed breasts (sometimes with juvenile nipples), but axillary and pubic hair is usually absent or very scanty.

The testes may be prone to tumor formation, though the precise degree of risk is not known. Most specialists recommend gonadectomy after puberty with subsequent hormone replacement. Some patients require surgical deepening of the vagina.

Incomplete feminizing testes syndrome, or partial androgen insensitivity
This is a less extreme form of androgen insensitivity, with the inheritance pattern similar to the complete syndrome (Morris and Mahesh, 1963; Lenz and Pfeiffer, 1966; Crawford, 1970; Wilson et al., 1974). The most characteristic phenotype is that of a 46,XY male with severe hypospadias, small penis, chordee and/or bifid scrotum. The phallus can reach 3—6 cm; rather wrinkled labia majora can fuse to some extent, forming a kind of bifid scrotum; the vagina can be separate or joined to the urogenital sinus. Breasts are well developed, and axillary and pubic hair appear at puberty. Nevertheless, the pubertal virilization is insufficient, the body and facial hair is scarce, the voice remains high-pitched, and gynecomastia is pronounced. The testes are either of normal size or small and cryptorchid. Compared to the complete form of testicular feminization, the testes contain larger tubules with thickened membranes and abundant Leydig cells.

The syndrome presents a wide clinical spectrum. In its mildest form there can be penile urethral opening and gynecomastia or, at other times, only familial gynecomastia with sterility and without any other abnormality (Rosewater et al., 1965). Naturally, such patients are reared as boys. On the other hand, some patients may differ from cases of complete testicular feminization only by very slight clitoral hypertrophy, the presence of normal pubic and axillary hair and partial labioscrotal fusion. Such patients are reared as girls.

Testicular secretion of both estradiol and testosterone is increased and androgen insensitivity is less pronounced than in complete testicular feminization, so that testosterone can increase nitrogen retention. In vitro, a lesser degree of the 3β-hydroxysteroid dehydrogenase-isomerase deficiency was found (Bell, 1975).

Treatment depends on the sex of rearing. In the neonate, female sex assignment is preferred. Gonadectomy is often indicated because of the danger of tumorigenesis in defective testes.

Defective Müllerian regression in males (Brook et al., 1973)

This is usually the most innocuous form of sex reversal; the mode of transmission is autosomal recessive. The syndrome is diagnosed very rarely, usually by chance at laparotomy. The male patients suffer from monolateral or bilateral cryptorchidism, the testes are usually hypoplastic, and an inguinal hernia contains an underdeveloped uterus and tubes. Therefore, another name of the syndrome is 'hernia uteri inguinali'. The patients virilize at puberty and may be fertile. The treatment consists of removal of the hernial sac with uterus and tubes, and correction of cryptorchidism.

5. FEMALE PSEUDOHERMAPHRODITISM

This group includes patients with normal XX karyotype, ovaries, normal development of internal feminine genitals and with ambiguous external genitals. In a few cases no underlying reason can be found, and the only treatment necessary is plastic surgery. In other cases the reason is androgenization of the fetus. If the androgenization takes place before the end of the 3rd month of pregnancy, external genitalia are virilized with the formation of urogenital sinus, variable degree of fusion of scrotolabial and urethral folds and enlargement of clitoris. After that period excessive androgenization leads to clitoral hypertrophy only.

Prenatal androgenization of female fetuses from extraneous source (Walker and Money, 1972)

The androgenization of female fetuses was reported after the treatment of pregnant women in the first months of pregnancy by synthetic progestins (norethindrone, ethisterone, norethynodrel, medroxyprogesterone acetate) or androgens (methyltestosterone). The syndrome may be caused by the presence in the pregnant woman of an androgen-secreting tumor (arrhenoblastoma). Virilization of external genitalia is the only pathologic finding, and plastic surgery is the only treatment necessary. (There also exists a suspicion that synthetic progestins can cause hypospadias in male fetuses if the drugs are taken by women in the first 3 months of pregnancy (Aarskog, 1970).)

Congenital adrenal hyperplasia (congenital adrenogenital syndrome) in females (Bongiovanni et al., 1967; New, 1968; Bongiovanni, 1972; Rosenfield, 1972; New and Levine, 1973)

Δ^5-3β-Hydroxysteroid dehydrogenase deficiency
In genetic females partial masculinization of the external genitalia can be caused by the accumulation of weak adrenal androgens (see above).

11β-Hydroxylase deficiency

The enzyme is unique for the adrenal cortex. Its defect blocks the transformation of 11-deoxycortisol (DOC) into cortisol and of DOC into aldosterone. As a result, there is increased secretion of DOC and androgens. Excretion of 17-ketosteroids (mainly, etiocholanolone) is greatly elevated. Clinically the patients suffer from virilization, sometimes delayed to the age of puberty and rather mild, and usually also from hypertension. The treatment is similar to that for other forms.

21-Hydroxylase deficiency

This is by far the most important and common form of female pseudohermaphroditism. The enzymatic defect is at the rather distal end of the chain of reactions and blocks the synthesis of 11-deoxycortisol (and subsequently cortisol) from 17-OH-progesterone and of DOC (and subsequently aldosterone) from progesterone. Usually the enzyme deficiency is mild enough so that the cortisol production is sufficient in non-stressful situations, though at the price of enormous hyperplasia of the adrenal cortex, especially of its reticular zone. The weight of adrenals may be increased manyfold and reach 90 g. In more severe cases the block is almost complete, the cortisol deficiency is more pronounced, aldosterone secretion is low, and the patients suffer from salt-wasting with Addisonian crises (shock, hyperpigmentation, hypotension and hyperkalemia).

At birth the patients are distinguished by pronounced clitoral enlargement. Because of the labioscrotal fusion there is some narrowing of the vaginal orifice or even the preservation of the urogenital sinus. In rare cases there is complete fusion of the urethral folds resulting in penile urethra. The hypertrophied and fused folds may lead to erroneous diagnosis of male hypogonadism with bilateral cryptorchidism (and, in the vast majority of cases, hypospadias). This mistake is easy to avoid, since the combination of bilateral cryptorchidism and phallic hypertrophy is very unlikely; the problem is easily solved by the determination of the sex chromatin.

Areolae and genitalia, and sometimes hand creases are hyperpigmented due to increased secretion of adrenocorticotrophic hormone (ACTH) and melanocyte-stimulating hormone (MSH). Excretion of 17-ketosteroids (mainly, androsterone) and pregnanetriol is very high. Continued increased androgen secretion after birth leads to rapid somatic growth, and the height age is well ahead of the chronological age till the patients are 8—12 years old. However, the bone age progresses even more quickly so that the growth spurt is exhausted by about 10—14 years, if not earlier, and patients in adulthood, if untreated, have lower than normal height. Sexual hair first appears at 3—5 years and later the virilization progresses, eventually reaching the degree seen in adult males. Temporal baldness may appear. In many patients the voice becomes low-pitched. Body build is masculine with very strong musculature and underdeveloped subcutaneous fat tissue. Breasts do not develop, and the phallus continues to grow. Sexual eroticism may or may not be increased. The diagnosis is based on the finding of very high excretion of 17-ketosteroids and pregnanetriol (metabolite of 17-OH-progesterone) in a chromatin-positive subject. These biochemical findings be lacking in the first week of life, and may require repeated evaluation a short while later.

The disease is unique among syndromes of sex reversal in that virtually normal feminine development, reversing an otherwise masculinized development, can be provided by the proper treatment. Because of the danger of stunted growth, the treatment by corticoids (cortisone, prednisolone) should be started immediately after diagnosing the disease and continued indefinitely in patients reared as females. The hormonal treatment ensures almost normal puberty, and later normal menstrual cycle and even moderate prospects of pregnancy. In the previously untreated patients puberty starts when bone age reaches about 13 years, irrespective of the chronological age. Corrective surgery is necessary but not urgent. Severe clitoral hypertrophy should be corrected at an early age to save the child embarrassment, but repair of the urogenital sinus should be made in later puberty just before the expected beginning of sex life. In late-diagnosed cases cosmetic depilation is necessary. In female patients reared as males it is usually possible before the age of 2 to change the legal sex into female. In some exceptional cases the change has been effectively made even at the age of 6, but for the majority such a change is psychologically impossible after the age of 2. In such patients hormonal therapy is mandatory to prevent stunted growth, but early ovarectomy and hysterectomy are necessary to prevent early feminine puberty and menses in such boys. Many patients with salt-wasting, in addition to glucocorticoids, demand DOC or fluorohydrocortisone and salt.

6. THE PRINCIPLE OF DIFFERENTIAL DIAGNOSIS OF SEX REVERSAL

The diagnosis of most cases of chromosomal anomalies usually does not present any problem, especially if there is no sex reversal (Federman, 1967; Summitt, 1972; Grumbach and Van Wyk, 1974). One factor, however, should be kept in mind: no diagnosis can be made solely on the basis of karyotype (with the exception of classical cases of Turner XO or Klinefelter XXY). The best example is XO/XY karyotype, which can be encountered in cases of Turner's syndrome, in relatively normal males with some features of the Turner's syndrome, in patients with mixed gonadal dysgenesis or in patients with ambiguous genitalia with or without testes that may, in addition, secrete enough androgens at puberty (Pfeiffer et al., 1968).

Few cases of sex reversal demand difficult and elaborate procedures for diagnosis. In the vast majority three procedures are sufficient: determination of sex chromatin, assay for 17-ketosteroids and pregnanetriol in urine, and in some cases laparotomy. The vast majority of cases with ambiguous genitalia belong to one of the three syndromes: congenital adrenal hyperplasia caused by 21-hydroxylase deficiency, various forms of male pseudohermaphroditism (especially incomplete testicular feminization) and true hermaphroditism. The first of these is easily distinguished by high excretion of 17-ketosteroids and pregnanetriol and positive sex chromatin. Most patients with true hermaphroditism, too, are chromatin-positive, but their secretion of androgen metabolites is normal. In male pseudohermaphroditism, excretion of 17-ketosteroids and pregnanetriol is normal, and the patients are chromatin-negative. The differentiation from the chromatin-negative true hermaphroditism is possible only on the basis of the gonadal histology.

The correct recommendations as to the desirable sex of rearing in cases of sex reversal are to a large extent independent of the correct medical diagnosis and are based on the evaluation of the perspectives for adult life (Money and Ehrhardt, 1972). In simple terms, in very young children with ambiguous genitalia the sex of rearing should be determined according to the size of phallus and the prognosis of the possibility of successfully fulfilling a male sex role (the only exception being congenital adrenal hyperplasia in girls and other cases of female pseudohermaphroditism). If there is no hope for the patient to perform a male sex role in adult life, the patient should be reared as female. Since almost always it is the sex of rearing that permanently establishes the person's gender identity and role (Money and Ehrhardt, 1972; Lev-Ran, 1974), every effort should be made to predict as early as possible the most probable course of development at adolescence. In older children and adults the therapeutic measures should be governed by their actual (and not theoretically desirable) long-established gender role (Money, 1968).

7. SUMMARY

In genetic females sex reversal is usually caused by androgenization of the fetus (congenital adrenal hyperplasia or delivery of large quantities of androgens from the maternal organism). Insufficient androgenization in the genetic males can be caused by the insufficient production of testosterone, defective testosterone conversion into dihydrotestosterone, insensitivity of tissues to androgens or defective secretion of the Müllerian-suppressing substance in the embryonic period as well as by various combinations of these factors. The multiplicity of the stages and mechanisms of the sex differentiation results in the great variety of forms of sex reversal. At present the correct diagnosis of sex anomalies is possible early in life and permits one to undertake proper therapeutic measures in time and to ensure acceptable and in many cases excellent adaptation of the patient to a definite gender role.

BIBLIOGRAPHY

Aarskog, D. (1970) Clinical and cytogenetic studies in hypospadias. *Acta Paediatr. Scand.* suppl. 203: 1—62.

172

Amrhein, J.A., Meyer, W.H., III, Keenan, B.S. and Migeon, C.J. (1976) Androgen receptor studies in androgen insensitivity syndrome in man. In: (P. Lee and C. Migeon, Eds.) *Treatment of Congenital Adrenal Hyperplasias: a Quarter of a Century Later.* (University Park Press, Baltimore) in press.

Becker, K.L. (1972) Clinical and therapeutic experiences with Klinefelter's syndrome. *Fertil. Steril.* 23: 568—578.

Bell, J.B.G. (1975) Studies of in vitro steroid metabolism by testis tissue from 'complete' and 'incomplete' forms of testicular feminization. *Clin. Endocrinol.* 4: 343—356.

Bongiovanni, A.M. (1972) Disorders of adrenocortical steroid biogenesis (the adrenogenital syndrome associated with congenital adrenal hyperplasia). In: (J.B. Stanbury, J.B. Wyngaarden, and D.S. Fredrickson, Eds.). *Metabolic Basis of Inherited Disease,* 3rd edn, (McGraw-Hill Co., New York) pp. 857—885.

Bongiovanni, A.M., Eberlein, W.R., Goldman, A.S. and New, M. (1967) Disorders of adrenal steroid biosynthesis. *Rec. Prog. Horm. Res.* 23: 375—439.

Brook, C.G.D., Wagner, H., Zachmann, M., Prader, A., Armendares, S., Frenk, S., Alemán, P., Najjar, S.S., Slim, M.S., Genton, N. and Bozic, C. (1973) Familial occurrence of persistent Müllerian structures in otherwise normal males. *Br. Med. J.* 1: 771—773.

Chemke, J., Carmichael, R., Stewart, J.M., Geer, R.H. and Robinson, A. (1970) Familial XY gonadal dysgenesis. *J. Med. Genet.* 7: 105—111.

Crawford, J.D. (1970) Syndromes of testicular feminization. *Clin. Pediat.* 9: 165—178.

Federman, D.D. (1967) *Abnormal Sexual Development.* (Saunders, Philadelphia.)

Federman, D.D. (1973) Genetic control of sexual difference. *Prog. Med. Genet.* 9: 215—235.

Ferguson-Smith, M.A. (1965) Karyotype-phenotype correlations in gonadal dysgenesis and their bearing on the pathogenesis of malformations. *J. Med. Genet.* 2: 142—155.

Givens, J.R., Wiser, W.L., Summitt, R.L., Kerber, I.J., Andersen, R.H., Pittaway, D.E. and Fish, S.A. (1974) Familial male pseudohermaphroditism without gynecomastia due to deficient testicular 17-ketosteroid reductase activity. *New Engl. J. Med.* 291: 938—944.

Goldberg, M.B., Scully, A.L., Solomon, I.L. and Steinbach, H.L. (1968) Gonadal dysgenesis in phenotypic female subjects: a review of 87 cases with cytogenetic studies in 53. *Am. J. Med.* 45: 529—543.

Goebelsmann, U., Horton, R., Mestman, J.H., Arce, J.J., Nagata, Y., Nakamura, R.M., Thorneycroft, I.H. and Mishell, D.R., Jr. (1973) Male pseudohermaphroditism due to testicular 17β-hydroxysteroid dehydrogenase deficiency. *J. Clin. Endocrinol.* 36: 867—879.

Greenblatt, R. (1967) The spectrum of gonadal dysgenesis. *Am. J. Obstet. Gynecol.* 98: 151—172.

Grumbach, M.M. and Van Wyk, J.J. (1974) Disorders of sex differentiation. In: R.H. Williams, Ed.). *Textbook of Endocrinology,* 5th ed, (Saunders, Philadelphia-London) pp. 423—501.

Hamilton, C.R. and Kliman, B. (1971) Anabolic effect of dihydrotestosterone in testicular feminization syndrome. *Metabolism* 20: 870—877.

Hauser, G.A. (1963) Testicular feminization. In: (C. Overzier, Ed.) *Intersexuality.* (Academic Press, New York) pp. 255—276.

Imperato-McGinley, J., Guerrero, L., Gautier, T. and Peterson, R.E. (1974) Steroid 5α-reductase deficiency in man: An inherited form of male pseudohermaphroditism. *Science* 186: 1213—1215.

Lenz, W. and Pfeiffer, R.A. (1966) Die Genetik der Geschlechtsdifferenzierung beim Menschen. *Münch. med. Wochenschr.* 108: 1726—1731.

Lev-Ran, A. (1974) Gender role differentiation in hermaphrodites. *Arch. Sexual Behav.* 3: 391—424.

Money, J. (1968) *Sex Errors of the Body.* (Johns Hopkins University Press, Baltimore.)

Money, J. and Ehrhardt, A.A. (1972) *Man & Woman, Boy & Girl.* (Johns Hopkins University Press, Baltimore.)

Morris, J.M. (1953) The syndrome of testicular feminization in male pseudohermaphrodites. *Am. J. Obstet. Gynecol.* 65: 1192—1211.

Morris, J.M. and Mahesh, V.B. (1963) Further observations on the syndrome "testicular feminization". *Am. J. Obstet. Gynecol.* 87: 731—748.

Narita, O., Manba, S., Nakanishi, T. and Ishizuka, N. (1975) Pregnancy and childbirth in a true hermaphrodite. *Obstet. Gynecol.* 45: 593—595.

New, M.I. (1968) Congenital adrenal hyperplasia. *Pediatr. Clin. North Am.* 15: 395—407

New, M.I. (1970) Male pseudohermaphroditism due to 17α-hydroxylase deficiency. *J. Clin. Invest.* 49: 1930—1941.

New, M.I. and Levine, L.S. (1973) Congenital adrenal hyperplasia. *Adv. Hum. Genet.* 4: 251—326.

Opitz, J.M., Simpson, J.L., Sarto, G.E., Summitt, R.L., New, M. and German, J. (1971) Pseudovaginal perineoscrotal hypospadias. *Clin. Genet.* 3: 1—26.

Park, I.J., Aimakhu, V.E. and Jones, H.W. (1975) An etiologic and pathogenetic classification of male hermaphroditism. *Am. J. Obstet. Gynecol.* 123: 505—517.

Parks, G.A., Dumars, K.W., Limbeck, G.A., Quinlivan, W.L. and New, M.I. (1974) "True agonadism" a misnomer? *J. Pediatr.* 84: 375—380.

Pfeiffer, R.A. (1974) True hermaphroditism. *Helv. Paediatr. Acta.* suppl. 34: 99—110.

Pfeiffer, R.A., Lambertz, B., Friedrerszick, F.K., Distel, H., Pawlowitzki, I.H., Nicole, R., Ober, K.G. and Ruckes, J. (1968) Die nosologische Sellung des XX/XY-Mosaizismus. *Arch. Gynäkol.* 206: 369—410.

Rosenfield, R.L. (1972) Role of androgens in growth and development of the fetus, child and adolescent. *Adv. Pediatr.* 19: 171—213.

Rosewater, S., Gwinup, G. and Hamwi, G.J. (1965) Familial gynecomastia. *Ann. Intern. Med.* 63: 377—385.

Schneider, G., Genel, M., Bongiovanni, A.M., Goldman, A.S. and Rosenfield, R.L. (1975) Persistent testicular Δ^5-3β-hydroxysteroid dehydrogenase (Δ^5-3β-HSD) deficiency in the Δ^5-3β-HSD form of congenital adrenal hyperplasia. *J. Clin. Invest.* 55: 681—690.

Simpson, J.L., Christakos, A.C., Horwith, M. and Silverman, F.S. (1971) Gonadal dysgenesis in individuals with apparently normal chromosomal complements: tabulation of cases and compilation of genetic data. *Birth Defects: Original Article Series* 7: 215—228.

Solival, A.R. (1964) Hermaphroditism with "atypical" or "mixed" gonadal dysgenesis *Am. J. Med.* 36: 281—292.

Southren, A.L. (1965) Syndrome of testicular feminization. *Ad. Metab. Disord.* 2: 227—255.

Summitt, R.L. (1972) Differential diagnosis of genital ambiguity in the newborn. *Clin. Obstet. Gynecol.* 15: 112—140.

Walker, P.A. and Money, J. (1972) Prenatal androgenization of females. *Hormones* 3: 119—128.

Walsh, P.C., Madden, J.D., Harrod, M.J., Goldstein, J.L., MacDonald, P.C. and Wilson, J.D. (1974) Familial incomplete male pseudohermaphroditism, type 2. Decreased dihydrotestosterone formation in pseudovaginal perineoscrotal hypospadias. *New Engl. J. Med.* 291: 944—949.

Wilson, J.D., Harrod, M.J., Goldstein, J.L., Hemsell, D.L. and MacDonald, P.C. (1974) Familial incomplete male pseudohermaphroditism, type 1. *New Engl. J. Med.* 290: 1097—1103.

Zachmann, M., Völlmin, J.A., Hamilton, W. and Prader, A. (1972) Steroid 17,20-desmolase deficiency: new cause of male pseudohermaphroditism. *Clin. Endocrinol.* 1: 369—385.

SECTION III

Prenatal hormones and the central nervous system

Section coordinator: E. Endröczi

CHAPTER 13

Introduction

E. ENDRÖCZI

This section of the book deals primarily with the action of hormones on brain and behavior during early ontogenetic life and with the molecular bases of hormonal influences on the central nervous system (CNS) and peripheral target organs.

The endocrine control of reproduction is dominated by the CNS and the anterior pituitary peptide hormones in the mammalian species. Numerous observations indicate that, during fetal and early postnatal development, the developing brain is more vulnerable to changes in its external and internal environment than in adult age. During 'critical periods'—the exposure of the brain to certain kinds of hormonal influences, a permanent imprinting process occurs on cells involved in complex regulatory circuits so that both behavior and endocrine function may be modified in the adult animal (see reviews by Harris, 1964; Barraclough, 1967; Gorski, 1966; Flerkó, 1971; Guy and Phoenix, 1971; Levine, 1972). The critical periods differ for different species and even the name hormone may induce multiple changes in maturation of brain and behavioral correlates. The administration of hydrocortisone on postnatal day 1 is followed by a retardation of the development of certain kind of sensory function (Salas and Schapiro, 1969). However, hydrocortisone injection between the 8th and 16th postnatal days was found to facilitate the development of neuronal circuits (Vernadakis and Woodbury, 1960). Estradiol simulated the effect of hydrocortisone on brain maturation only if administered on postnatal days 4—8 (Heim, 1966; Heim and Timiras, 1963). Moreover, estradiol administration accelerated the myelination of hypothalamic centers in the early postnatal age (Curry and Heim, 1966).

The role of neonatal testicular secretion in sex differentiation of hypothalamic control of the anterior pituitary function, has been studied extensively in recent decades (Barraclough and Gorski, 1962; Harris and Levine, 1962). Testosterone administration or endogenous androgens in the critical period results in hypothalamic changes which permanently suppress the cyclic release of ovulatory hormones with loss of mating behavior.

Handbook of Sexology, edited by J. Money and H. Musaph
© *Elsevier/North-Holland Biomedical Press, 1977*

Numerous aspects of androgen sterilization are discussed in the following chapters.

Both autoradiographic and biochemical evidence indicates that sex steroids are accumulated and retained by different parts of the brain (see reviews by Stumpf, 1968; Pfaff, 1968). Comparison of the uptake and retention of labeled estradiol between brain and uterus suggests that these structures respond differently to the hormone, which might be attributed to different affinity and turnover rates of the receptors (Whalen and Maurer, 1969). Permanent changes in receptor capacity and affinity as a result of the sex steroid treatment in the critical period may explain the cellular and molecular bases of sex differentiation and androgen sterilization in rodents (see review by Flerkó, 1971). Recent studies in connection with corticosterone administration on postnatal day 3 and 6 also suggest changes of corticosterone receptors in the hippocampus of adult rats.

Relationships between effects of gonadal hormones and reproductive behavior were the subject of many electrophysiological investigations (Kawakami et al., 1967; Beyer and Sawyer, 1969; Sawyer and Gorski, 1972). In addition to the results of the influence of steroid hormones on electrophysiological correlates of reproductive behavior, electrophysiological experiments of Sawyer and Kawakami (1959) suggested that pituitary tropic hormones may exert an internal feedback action on the CNS. With unit recording techniques, Ramirez et al. (1967) and Kawakami and Saito (1967) demonstrated the direct influence of luteinizing hormone on cells in the basal—medial hypothalamic region. These observations are in accordance with the results of implantation studies which were achieved by local application of pituitary hormones into the tubero-infundibular area and which led to the concept of the 'short-loop' feedback regulation (Martini et al., 1968; Motta et al., 1968).

Regulation of the pituitary—gonadal axis at the limbic level cannot be separated from organization of reproductive behavior: both facilitory and inhibitory influences controlling sexual behavior form an inseparable unit with those involved in regulation of pituitary gonadotropic function. Both genetic factors and learned elements determine the organization of reproductive behavior which seems to be mediated primarily by the brainstem—limbic system (Lissák and Endröczi, 1965; Endröczi, 1972). Limbic structures with sensitivity to hormones play a basic role in the control of motivated behavior. However, they are also involved in the learning and memory function. Sex steroids may facilitate or inhibit the specific elements of reproductive behavior. Nonspecific motor patterns of other goal-directed behavioral reactions are also influenced by the gonadal hormones.

Humoral regulation of reproductive behavior may be categorized according to the transmitters: the long-range specific transmitters as pituitary gonadotropic hormones or sex steroids produce profound and permanent changes in the CNS during early postnatal or fetal life, and induce facilitation of reproductive motor patterns in adult age. In advance of cephalization, the facilitatory (and inhibitory) role of hormonal influences becomes more permissive, and the response of the CNS to adequate stimuli by integration of reproductive behavioral patterns in the absence of sex steroids appears to be maintained. Hormonal conditioning of motivated behavioral reactions replaces hormone-induced control of the CNS, in ascent of the phyletic scale.

Another category of transmitters, medium-range chemical mediators, produce specific biochemical changes in the anterior pituitary and modulate the secretion of tropic hormones. They are called releasing hormones or factors, and they are produced primarily in the hypophysiotropic area by parvicellular neurosecretory cells. Rapid development of the identification of different releasing hormones provides a quite new aspect of understanding regarding regulation of pituitary function by the hypothalamus. However, the existence of these releasing factors in organs other than the CNS merits some considerations (Hökfelt et al., 1975).

Classic neurotransmitters comprise the third category of mediators, as short-range transmitters, namely, acetylcholine, catecholamines and serotonin. By the use of pharmacological agents (depletors and blocking agents), the role of neurotransmitters in the control of the LH-RH and FSH-RH has been elucidated (see reviews by Kawakami et al, 1973; Knigge et al., 1973; Sawyer, 1975). Noradrenergic control of both LH and FSH seems to be accepted as a working hypothesis by many investigators. However, interference by other monoaminergic systems (dopamine and serotonin) in regulation of releasing hormones in most studies cannot be excluded.

The chapters of this section present evidence that the influence of gonadal hormones on the CNS may be manifest by change of the set-point controlling the feedback action of hormones on the hypothalamic—pituitary axis (an increased or decreased sensitivity of the limbic structures) on the one hand, and by the facilitation or inhibition of reproductive behavior on the other hand. Changes of sensitivity appear to be modulated by numerous humoral factors and neuronal events, though characteristically nonspecific in action. The specific receptors of the brain for gonadal hormones seem to control both the neuroendocrine axis of the reproductive system and its behavioral patterns.

BIBLIOGRAPHY

Barraclough, C.A. (1967) Modification in reproductive function after exposure to hormones during the prenatal and early postnatal period. In: (L. Martini and W.F. Ganong, Eds.) *Neuroendocrinology*, Vol. II. (Academic Press, New York) pp. 61—99.

Barraclough, C.A. and Gorski, R.A. (1961) *Endocrinology* 68: 68—79.

Beyer, C. and Sawyer, C.H. (1969) Hypothalamic unit activity related to control of the pituitary gland. In: (W.F. Ganong and L. Martini, Eds.) *Frontiers in Neuroendocrinology*. (Oxford University Press, London and Toronto) pp. 255—287.

Curry, J.J. and Heim, L.M. (1968) *Nature* 209: 215.

Endröczi, E. (1972) Role of short-range transmitters in hypothalamic activities. In: Neurovegetative transmission mechanisms. *J. Neural Transm.*, suppl. XI, 227—254.

Flerkó, B. (1971) Androgenization and pituitary FSH regulation. In: (C.H. Sawyer and R.A. Gorski, Eds.) *Steroid Hormones and Brain Function.* (UCLA Press, California) pp. 161—170.

Gorski, R.A. (1966) *J. Reprod. Fertil.* 1: suppl. 67—88.

Goy, W.R. and Phoenix, C.H. (1971) Perinatal hormones and the modification of adult behavior. In (C.H. Sawyer, R.A. Gorski, Eds.) *Steroid Hormones and Brain Function.* (UCLA Press, California) pp. 203—212.

Harris, G.W. (1964) *Endocrinology* 75: 627—648.

Harris, G.W. and Levine, S. (1963) *J. Physiol.* 163.

Heim, L.M. (1966) *Endocrinology* 78: 1130—1136.

Heim, L.M. and Timiras, P.S. (1963) *Endocrinology* 72: 598—604.

Hökfelt, T., Efendic, S., Hellerström, C., Hohansson, O., Luft, R. and Arimura, A. (1975) *Acta Endocrinol.* 80: 5—41 (suppl. 200).

Kawakami, M. and Saito, H. (1967) *Jap. J. Physiol.* 17: 466—486.

Kawakami, M., Seti, K., Terasawa, E. and Yoshida, K. (1967) *Prog. Brain. Res.* 27: 69—82.

Kawakami, M., Terasawa, E., Kimura, F. and Kubo, K. (1973) Correlated changes in gonadotropin release and electrical activity of the hypothalamus induced by electrical stimulation of the hippocampus in immature and mature rats. In: (K. Lissák, Ed.) *Hormones and Brain Function.* (Akadémiai Kiado, Budapest) pp. 347—374.

Knigge, K.M., Joseph, S.A., Silverman, A.J. and Vaala, S. (1973) Further observations on the structure and function of the median eminence, with reference to the organization of RF-producing elements in the endocrine hypothalamus. In: (E. Zimmerman, W.H. Gispen, B.H. Marks, D. DeWied, Eds.) *Drug Effects on Neuroendocrine Relations. Prog. Brain Res.* 39: 7—20.

Levine, S. (1972) Sexual motivation. In: (J.L. McGaugh, Ed.) *The Chemistry of Mood, Motivation and Memory.* (Plenum Press, New York) pp. 61—64.

Lissák, K. and Endröczi, E. (1965) *Neuroendocrine control of adaptation.* (Pergamon Press, Oxford.)

Martini, L., Fraschini, F., Motta, M. (1968) Neural control of anterior pituitary function. *Rec. Prog. Horm. Res.* 24: 439—496.

Motta, M., Piva, F. and Martini, L. (1970) The hypothalamus as the center of endocrine feedback mechanisms. In: (L. Martini, M. Motta, F. Fraschini, Eds.) *The Hypothalamus* (Academic Press, New York) pp. 463—489.

Pfaff, D.W. (1968) *Science* 161: 1355—1356.

Ramirez, V.D., Komisaruk, B.R., Whitmoyer, D.I. and Sawyer, C.H. (1967) *Am. J. Physiol.* 212: 1376—1380.

Salas, M. and Schapiro, S. (1969) *The Physiologist* 12: 346—354.

Sawyer, C.H. (1975) *Neuroendocrinology* 17: 97—124.

Sawyer, C.H. and Kawakami, M. (1959) *Endocrinology* 65: 622—630.

Sawyer, C.H. and Gorski, R.A. (1972) *Steroid Hormones and Brain Function.* (UCLA Press, California.)

Stumpf, W.E. (1968) *Science* 162: 1001—1004.

Vernadakis, A. and Woodbury, D.M. (1960) *Fed. Proc.* 19: 153—165.

Whalen, R.E. and Maurer, R.A. (1969) *Proc. Natl. Acad. Sci. U.S.* 63: 681—699.

CHAPTER 14

The molecular biological aspects of reproduction

E. ENDRÖCZI

1. INTRODUCTION

Administration of labeled steroid hormones is followed by accumulation of radioactivity in various organs, for example, liver, brain, kidney and thymus. It is known that the thymus does not accumulate corticosteroids when they are injected intravenously or intraperitoneally. However, these steroids have a striking involuting action on this organ (Dougherty and White, 1944; Feigelson and Feigelson, 1964). The liver concentrates adrenal cortical hormones significantly above the level in blood (Bradlow et al., 1954; Sandberg et al., 1957; Bellamy et al., 1962). The in vivo and in vitro uptake of corticosteroids cannot be compared in all cases: thus, the thymus cells concentrate corticosteroids when the hormone is given into the incubation medium (Bartlett et al., 1962; Morita and Munck, 1964; Kattwinkel and Munck, 1966; Munck, 1968). These observations clearly demonstrated that the accumulation of labeled steroid hormones does not reflect the biological activity in different target organs.

2. NONNEURONAL UPTAKE OF SEX STEROIDS

Some of the early effects of estrogen, such as histamine release, hyperemia and water imbibition of the uterus are difficult to correlate with findings concerning estrogen—receptor interaction and genome activation: these events seem to represent separate biochemical actions of estrogens (Spaziani and Szegö, 1958; Szegö, 1965). An increase of the phospholipid and glycogen content of the uterus can be detected 1—2 h following hormone treatment (Mueller, 1960; Billing et al., 1969). Total RNA and protein levels do not rise until 6 and 12 h after estradiol administration, respectively, and the rate of protein synthesis appears to be accelerated 2—4 h after estradiol administration. Thus, the lack of change in the RNA and protein concentration

Handbook of Sexology, edited by J. Money and H. Musaph
© *Elsevier/North-Holland Biomedical Press, 1977*

does not mean that estradiol-induced processes are not initiated during the early phase of hormone action. Various workers (Gorski and Nicolette, 1963; Hamilton, 1964; Gorski and Nelson, 1965) have reported an increased nuclear RNA synthesis as soon as 1 h after estradiol injection. An enhanced incorporation of precursors into RNA and phospholipid fractions could also be observed under in vitro conditions when the uterus was excised within 2 h of hormone treatment (Aizawa and Mueller, 1961; Gorski and Nicolette, 1963). Hamilton and co-workers (1965, 1968) have reported that estrogens induce a prompt increase of the incorporation of tritiated uridine into the nuclear RNA, up to a maximum of 5—6 times the control level. This rapidly synthesized RNA passes from the nucleus to the cytoplasm and may be considered as ribosomal RNA. In contrast to these observations, Billing et al. (1969) and Greenman (1970) could not find an estrogen-induced increase of RNA labeling, although they observed an increased influx of tritiated uridine into the cell which might contribute to a greater turnover rate of the intracellular uridine pool.

An increase of the RNA polymerase activity as a result of estrogen treatment could be demonstrated 2—3 h after hormone administration (Noteboom and Gorski, 1963; Gorski, 1964; Hamilton et al., 1965, 1968; Nicolette and Mueller, 1966; Gorski and Morgan, 1967; Barry and Gorski, 1971). The analysis of the sequence of the RNA produced by estrogen-induced RNA polymerase together with hybridization studies, revealed that estrogen stimulated a ribosomal-type RNA which is different from that being synthesized in the absence of estrogens (Barton and Liao, 1967; Teng and Hamilton, 1968; Trachewsky and Segal, 1968; Billing et al., 1969). This new species of RNA could be demonstrated in the rabbit uterus and liver, in the hen oviduct and even in lizards (Hahn et al., 1969; Church and McCarthy, 1970). The new RNA fraction was isolated from uterus and introduced into the luman of the uterus of ovariectomized rats, where it induced hypertrophy of the endometrium similar to that caused by estradiol administration (Segal et al., 1965; Unhjem et al., 1968; Fencl and Villee, 1971). The RNA fraction of ovariectomized rats without estrogen substitution therapy failed to produce endometrial hypertrophy.

Chromatin isolated from estrogen-treated uterus shows an increase template activity when tested in RNA polymerase system (Barker and Warren, 1966; Teng and Hamilton, 1968). Teng and Hamilton (1969) reported the synthesis of a new acidic protein following estrogen administration, which overcomes the inhibitory effect of histones on transcription at the DNA—RNA level.

The quantitative aspect of new RNA synthesis is still a subject of speculation: it seems that a longer chain is formed and the amount of RNA remains unchanged under the influence of estrogen (Barry and Gorski, 1971). It was also observed that the transport of RNA from the nucleus into the cytosol is changed during estrogen action (Church and McCarthy, 1970).

The uterotropic effect of estrogen can be blocked by pretreatment with

Actinomycin D, puromycin or cycloheximide. As inhibitors of protein synthesis can also block the estrogen-induced changes in the nucleus, the mechanism of the early metabolic events in stimulated cells is fairly obscure. Cycloheximide is a strong stimulator of uridine incorporation in the absence of estrogen and its blocking effect on estrogen-induced RNA synthesis is a puzzling problem (Hamilton et al., 1968). Both puromycin and cycloheximide block the early stimulation of phospholipid synthesis and glucose utilization in the response to estrogen administration (Mueller et al., 1961; Gorski et al., 1965; Nicolette and Gorski, 1964; Gorski and Morgan, 1967; Smith and Gorski, 1968).

Nicolette and Mueller (1966) have found that incubation of uterine tissue at 37 or 4°C maintains the estrogen-induced activation, but at 23°C the nuclear RNA polymerase activity is gradually decreased. This decline can be restored by re-incubation at 37°C. These observations led to the conclusion that a protein is necessary for activation of RNA polymerase which is stable at 4°C, though it becomes inactive at 23°C. The continuous resynthesis of the protein has been assumed when incubation is at 37°C.

Estrogen-induced activation of RNA polymerase and protein synthesis have been studied by numerous investigators. Notides and Gorski (1966) demonstrated a single radioactive peak on starch-gel when the cytosol fraction was separated from immature uterus treated with estrogen and incubated with labeled leucine under in vitro conditions. The synthesis of new protein could be blocked 30—40 min after administration of Actinomycin D. The protein could be detected 1—2 h following estradiol injection to ovariectomized or immature rabbits. Moreover, it was also found that cycloheximide did not block the synthesis of new protein (Mayol and Thayer, 1970; Barnea and Gorski, 1970; DeAngelo and Gorski, 1970). By the use of acrylamide gel electrophoresis the new protein fraction could be separated into two components (Mayol and Thayer, 1970).

The synthesis of the new protein after estrogen stimulation seems to be correlated with changes in the nuclear histone concentration. Barker (1971) reported that administration of labeled amino acids into the lumen of the uterus is followed by a rapid decline of the total histone concentration and an increase of the amino acid incorporation into the nuclear acidic protein which forms a complex with the histones (fraction F_3, arginine-rich). The synthesis of new protein in the cytosol correlated well temporally with the disappearance of histones from the nuclear compartment. The process is sensitive to Actinomycin D.

Among nonneuronal tissues, the uterus, vagina and anterior pituitary were found to accumulate and retain labeled estradiol against a marked concentration gradient with the blood (Jensen, 1960; Jensen and Jacobson, 1960; Gupta, 1960; Glascock and Hoekstra, 1959). Only unchanged estradiol could be extracted from the target organs mentioned above (Jensen and Jacobson, 1962; Stone, 1964). The estradiol is specifically bound to both endometrial and myometrial cells, although the endometrium accumulates greater amounts of radioactivity (Alberga and Baulieu, 1965; Flesher, 1965; Jensen, 1965; King and Gordon, 1966). The binding capacity of adult rat uterus is less than that of immature rat uterus (Eisenfeld and Axelrod, 1966; Hughes et al., 1969; Feherty et al., 1970). The number of available binding sites decreases with age, and the removal of ovaries is followed by a significant diminution of the binding capacity of the uterus (McGuire and Lisk, 1968; Hughes et al., 1969). The binding capacity of the uterus for estradiol varies according to the ovarian hormone production cycle, with a peak in pro-estrous state (Feherty et al., 1969; DeHertogh et al., 1971; Lee and Jacobson, 1971).

Specific estradiol binding has been observed in rat mammary gland (Sander, 1968; Sander and Attramadal, 1968), and the human (Demetricou et al., 1964; Braunsberg et al., 1967; Deshpande et al., 1967; Johansson et al., 1970).

The binding site for estradiol has a remarkable stereospecificity: it does not bind 17-epimer or estradiol-17α (Noteboom and Gorski, 1965). On the other hand, antiestrogens show a strong affinity for binding sites which will be discussed later in this chapter.

Differential centrifugation of uterine homogenate from estradiol-treated rats shows a double appearance of labeled hormone: (1) in the high-speed supernatant, and (2) in the nuclear fraction (Talwar et al., 1964; Noteboom and Gorski, 1965). It was found that almost 60—70% of labeled steroid was bound into the nuclear fraction and that the rest might be detected in the supernatant (Jensen, 1965; King and Gordon, 1966; Baulieu et al., 1967). A similar distribution of labeled estradiol was found in the anterior pituitary (King et al., 1965) and the mammary gland homogenates (Kyser, 1970). Autoradiographic studies confirmed the biochemical observations and demonstrated that most of the radioactivity is seen in the nucleus (Stumpf and Roth, 1966; Stumpf, 1968, 1969).

Ultracentrifugation in a sucrose gradient, the cytosol steroid—receptor complex appears with a coefficient to be about 8 S (Erdös, 1968; Rochefort and Baulieu, 1968). It was found that 8-S protein can be reversibly transformed into a 4-S complex in the presence of 0.2—0.4 M sodium or potassium chloride. The 4-S moiety is considered as a subunit of the 8-S moiety, although an extensive conformational change of the latter cannot be excluded (Erdös, 1968; Korenman and Rao; 1968; Jensen et al., 1969). The formation of 8-S or 4-S complex in the homogenate of the immature rat uterus is identical whether the animal was treated with estradiol or the uterine slices were incubated in a medium containing labeled estradiol (Jungblut et al., 1967; Jensen et al., 1969).

Equilibrium between the formation of 8-S and 4-S complex seems to be a temperature-dependent process. Thus, the incubation of homogenate at 37°C results in an increase of the 4—5-S complex and the 8-S complex seems to be stable when the tissue is kept at 2°C. Moreover, the transfer of the steroid—receptor complex is markedly facilitated at 37°C (Jensen et al., 1969;

Shyamala and Gorski, 1969; Rochefort and Baulieu, 1969). It seems that immature rat uterus contains about 100 fmoles of 8-S protein per mg of wet tissue, and approximately 100,000 receptor sites per uterine cell (Jensen et al., 1968). Both specific and non-specific target cells contain the 8-S receptor, although the concentration is much higher in the specific or target organs.

Taking into consideration the fact that the 8-S receptor is converted to a 4-S subunit (or shows transformational change) at body temperature, the form of the transfer of the steroid—receptor complex from the cytosol into the nucleus cannot be explained unequivocally. Jensen et al. (1967, 1968) and Musliner et al. (1970) have reported the presence of 5-S receptor in the nuclear fraction of estradiol-treated uterus. It was assumed that the 5-S receptor is responsible for transferring the estradiol from the cytosol into the nucleus. Brecher et al. (1970) and Jensen et al. (1971) suggested that the cytosol 4-S receptor is converted to a 5-S form. This conversion seems to be a temperature-dependent process which can be retarded by the addition of ethylenediaminetetraacetic acid (EDTA) and can be accelerated with an increase of the pH up to 8.5. The conversion requires the presence of estradiol and does not take place in the presence of estrone. Nevertheless, the 5-S protein cannot be regarded as an unique transfer route and binding property of the nuclear compartment. Thus, estrone is also bound specifically in chromatin tissue, although the steroid cannot be extracted in the form of a 5-S complex.

The receptor sites of the cytosol fraction show a significant decrease following estradiol administration which is associated with an increase of the labeled steroid in the nucleus (Jensen et al., 1969; Giannopoulos and Gorski, 1971). The 8-S protein has the ability to associate with basic proteins (protamine and polylysine) and is rapidly destroyed by proteases but not ribonuclease (Jensen et al., 1969, King et al., 1969, Steggles and King, 1970) Moreover, it was found that the removal of its lipid moiety by lipase is followed by its conversion to 4-S complex. The addition of mercury to the cytosol fraction resulted in the liberation of bound estradiol into the medium (Puca and Bresciani, 1970). Similarly, the administration of organic mercurials or N-ethylmaleimide to a nuclear fraction led to the release of a steroid—receptor complex with a sedimentation constant of 10—12 S. These observations revealed that sulfydryl groups are involved in the binding of estradiol to both cytosol and nuclear receptor proteins, and that the hormone—receptor complex can be liberated by cleaving the SH-bridges.

Association of estradiol with the cytosol receptor has been estimated to be in the range of 10^9—10^{10} M^{-1} for 8-S, and 10^{12} for 5-S protein (Bush, 1965; Alberga and Baulieu, 1968; DeHertogh et al., 1971; Hahnel, 1971; Puca and Bresciani, 1971). The nuclear fraction has a stronger binding affinity than the cytosol. The estradiol—receptor complex can be dissociated on incubation at 45°C and the medium contains an uncomplexed 5-S protein which is able to bind estradiol.

Purification of the 8-S protein has been difficult in that it tends to form an aggregate with cytosol components. In the presence of estradiol the 8-S protein is more stable, but aggregation is enhanced by administration of magnesium (Brecher et al., 1969; Clark and Gorski, 1969). The presence of calcium seems to stabilize the protein: it is assumed that Ca^{2+} activates an enzyme necessary to remove a part of the receptor which is responsible for aggregation (Puca, 1971). The 4-S protein was also stabilized by calcium and its conversion to the 5-S protein could also be prevented. It was found that the 4-S protein has a molecular weight of about 75,000, in contrast to the value of 20,000 given for the 8-S protein. In acrylamide-gel electrophoresis the 4-S complex appeared as a single protein band (Puca et al., 1971; DeSombre et al., 1971). The 5-S complex extracted from the nucleus undergoes aggregation to a 8—9-S form in hypotonic medium. The complex cannot be stabilized by calcium and therefore differs strikingly from the 4-S complex (DeSombre et al., 1971).

In contrast to the estradiol-binding receptor, discovery of the progesterone receptor in the uterus took much longer. Podratz and Katzman (1968) reported at first, that the mouse vagina is able to retain progesterone, but they also found that a pretreatment with estradiol markedly enhanced the accumulation of labeled progesterone. Similar observations were obtained in guinea pigs (Falk and Bardin, 1970; Milgrom et al., 1970). In chick oviducts, diethylstilbestrol treatment resulted in a 20-fold increase of progesterone binding (O'Malley et al., 1969, 1970). Moreover, Wiest and Rao (1971) demonstrated that estrogen administration led to a marked increase of progesterone binding in the rabbit uterus but not in the thigh muscle. In addition to these findings, progesterone uptake by the uterus and the vagina varied according to the estrous cycle in hamsters (Reuter et al., 1970).

In addition to the increase of the progesterone-binding capacity of the uterus after estrogen treatment, the 4.5-S progesterone—receptor complex is altered to form a new component which sediments in the 6—8-S region on sucrose gradients. These observations led to the assumption that an enhanced responsiveness to progesterone following estrogen treatment may arise through quantitative and qualitative changes in the progesterone-receptor molecule (Toft and O'Malley, 1972).

Corvol et al. (1972) have found that the guinea pig uterus contains progesterone receptor with a sedimentation constant of 7 and 3.5—4.5 S. Competition studies revealed that cortisol also bound to 3.5—4.5-S receptor but did not displace the progesterone. It was also found that incubation of the cytosol fraction at a higher temperature or an increased ionic strength results in a decrease of the 7-S and an increase of the 3.5—4.5-S complex. Species differences in the appearance of progesterone receptor complex have been demonstrated by Feil et al. (1972). Thus, mouse and rat uterus contains progesterone-binding fractions with sedimentation constants of 7 and 4 S, respectively, although the differences may be attributed to transformational changes occurring during preparation of extracts.

McGuire and Bariso (1972) could distinguish between two different progesterone binding fractions in the cytosol fraction of the rat uterus. One of them seems to be nonspecific with low affinity and high capacity. The other has a high specificity and low capacity. Attempts were made to purify the specific binder which could be detected only in the uterus and vagina but not in the spleen, stomach and liver tissues. The binding is fairly stable to both heating and dehydration. The K_d for the reaction between receptor and steroid has been calculated to be 10^{-10}, a value which is in a range to be found for estrogen receptor.

A variation of the uterine progesterone-binding capacity during the estrous cycle was demonstrated by Milgrom et al. (1971). It has a maximum of 40,000 binding sites per cell in proestrous and falls progressively during estrous to attain a 16-fold lower value in the diestrous state. The authors described a sedimentation constant of 6.7 S in proestrous, 6.7 and 4.5 S in estrous and diestrous, respectively. Obviously, implantation occurs at a moment when the receptor concentration is low.

Progesterone transfer from cytosol into the nuclear compartment results in the induction of new species of RNA which could be detected 6 h after injection (O'Malley and McGuire, 1969). By the use of DNA/RNA molecular hybridization, it was found that the progesterone administration is followed by induction of avidin synthesis in chick oviducts.

Cytoplasm from rat prostate binds tritiated progesterone and pregnenolone during incubation under in vitro conditions (10^{-8} M). It was found that SH-groups are necessary to develop the receptor—steroid complex. Sucrose gradient centrifugation revealed that the receptor has a molecular weight of $45-60 \times 10^3$, the binding is not inhibited by heating to $60°C$ or by a storage for up to one week at $4°C$. Testosterone, estradiol and 11-deoxycorticosterone are not bound to the receptor. Moreover, it was found that the liver does not contain similar binding protein (Karzmia et al., 1969).

Although the presence of progesterone binding protein seems to be well-established in the gonadal target organs, the influx of a corticosterone-binding protein which is able to bind progesterone, from the plasma into the cell cannot be excluded in species which posseses this transfer protein in the blood (Reel et al., 1970; Milgrom and Baulieu, 1970).

In the absence of cytosol receptor, the nuclei of chick oviduct do not bind progesterone but they form a complex with a steroid—4-S receptor complex (O'Malley et al., 1971). The receptor sites of the nuclei are different from those of the other tissues: the progesterone receptor is bound to an acidic nuclear protein fraction and a role for histones in the binding process seems to be unlikely (Spelsberg et al., 1971; O'Malley et al., 1971).

Androgens can be specifically accumulated in the target organs. However, some conversion of the parent molecule is also involved in the binding process. Aliapoulios et al. (1965) have reported that the infusion of canine prostate with labeled testosterone led to a number of metabolites which could be extracted from the gland in unconjugated form. The major products were as follows: dihydrotestosterone, 5α-androstane-3α,17β-diol. The conversion of testosterone to dihydrotestosterone requires an NADH-dependent testosterone 5α-reductase (Farnsworth and Brown, 1963; Shimazaki et al., 1965; Ofner, 1969).

Bruchowsky and Wilson (1968) found that only dihydrotestosterone and smaller amounts of testosterone could be extracted from the rat prostate cytosol after injection of labeled testosterone. Dihydrotestosterone showed a long half-life in the prostate, seminal vesicle and preputial gland (about 6 h), in comparison with other tissues (Anderson and Liao, 1968; Fang et al., 1968).

Prostatic cells contain chromatin-bound 5α-reductase which catalyzes the conversion of testosterone to dihydrotestosterone. Shimazaki et al. (1969) found a decrease of the enzyme activity with age. Castration also resulted in a marked decrease of the enzyme activity. The liver also contains 5α-reductase but the converted products are readily subject to conjugation with glucuronide (Schriefers, 1967).

It is well-known that dihydrotestosterone exhibits greater activity in a number of bioassays than does testosterone. Liao and Fang (1969) found 50—150% higher biological activity of dihydrotestosterone than testosterone in ventral prostate, seminal vesicle and levator ani bioassays. On the other hand, testosterone proved to be more effective in the exorbital lacrimal gland test.

Dihydrotestosterone-binding protein of ventral prostate can be destroyed by proteolytic enzymes, but it is resistant to DNAase and RNAase (Bruchowsky and Wilson, 1968; Unhjem et al., 1969). It was found that the steroid—receptor complex can be extracted by 0.4 M KCl, and the complex showed a sedimentation constant of 3 S. Incubation of labeled testosterone or dihydrotestosterone with isolated prostatic cell nuclei yielded only a small retention of the steroid. In contrast to these observations, the nuclei bound a great amount of the labeled androgens in the presence of cytosol-receptor complex. Fang et al. (1968) reported that neither testosterone nor hydrocortisone interact with the 3.5-S receptor to form a complex with dihydrotestosterone. A strong competition from estradiol and progesterone, however, could be observed in the incubation studies.

Rat epididymis cytosol fraction, labeled by incubation with testosterone or dihydrotestosterone showed two androgen-binding proteins, one of which corresponded to a high-affinity receptor for dihydrotestosterone (Ritzén et al., 1971). The mean constant of dissociation (K_d) of the high affinity component was 7×10^{-9} M. On sucrose gradient ultracentrifugation the radioactivity migrated in a single peak with sedimentation constant of 4 S. In contrast to the prostate cytosol receptor the epididymis receptor showed two peaks in acrylamide gel-electrophoresis: the prostate receptor as single peak could be identified as the slow-moving peak of the epididymis complex. Rat serum and cytosols of submandibular glands, kidney and muscle contained 3—4-S binding components, but on acrylamide gel none formed peaks of radioactivity corresponding to those of epididymis. Moreover, it was also found that the epididymis receptor has an affinity about twice as strong for dihydrotestosterone as testosterone and 17β-estradiol, and a low affinity for androstendione or 5α-androstane-3α,17β-diol.

Danzo et al. (1973) demonstrated the existence of a highly specific binding component for dihydrotestosterone in the cytosol of the caput epididymis of sexually mature rabbits. They could not detect free receptor in the corpus or the cauda of the epididymis. Another receptor which binds cortisol but not dihydrotestosterone was also discovered in these studies. Cortisol, estradiol and progesterone proved to be weak competitors for binding sites of the dihydrotestosterone receptor. It was found that the binding site is approximately 5.6×10^{-8} M per g tissue. The receptor is thermolabile and can be inactivated by incubation at 37°C. Sulfhydryl blocking agents such as N-ethylmaleimide inactivate the protein—steroid binding of the cytosol fraction.

The role of testosterone and dihydrotestosterone in regulation of cell metabolism of target organs seems to be different. Baulieu et al. (1968) have suggested that dihydrotestosterone is especially concerned with cell multiplication, whereas testosterone and its other metabolites are involved in regulation of epithelial cells and secretory processes. Gloyna and Wilson (1969) reported evidences that dihydrotestosterone plays a role in mediation of biochemical processes necessary for cell proliferation but does not simulate many of the effects of testosterone.

Unlike many other hormones, dihydrotestosterone and testosterone do not stimulate the adenyl cyclase activity of the prostate cell membrane (Rosenfeld and O'Malley, 1970). Caldarera et al. (1968) and Moulton and Leonard (1969) suggested that polyamines like spermidine and spermine may mediate some of the androgen-induced changes in the rat accessory glands. A considerable increase of the enzyme activity involved in spermidine synthesis (L-ornithine decarboxylase and putrescine-dependent S adenosyl L-methionine decarboxylase) could be observed after testosterone propionate administration in the ventral prostate of castrated rats. It seems unlikely that polyamines play a role in activation of the RNA polymerase system considering the long lag period following hormone injection (Pegg et al., 1970).

Both antiestrogens and antiandrogens compete with other sex steroids at the receptor sites. Antiestrogens such as ethamoxytriphetol (MER-25) or clomiphene, have proved to be useful tools for studying the estrogen—receptor complex (Jensen, 1962; Roy et al., 1964; Wyss et al., 1968; Callantine et al., 1967). The antiandrogen cyproterone suppressed the uptake of labeled testosterone by the prostate both in vivo and in vitro (Fang and Liao, 1969; Stern and Eisenfeld, 1969; Williams-Ashman and Reddi, 1971). Cyproterone acetate causes a marked regression of the seminal vesicle when administered to the mature male rat, and permits the vaginal development in male offspring when given to the pregnant females. Cyproterone administration resulted in a suppression of testosterone uptake by the seminal vesicle and preputial gland but did not alter the accumulation of radioactivity in the brain. Whalen and Luttge (1969) suggested that cyproterone is effective in decreasing the accumulation of labeled testosterone in those tissues which contain a significant amount of androstendione. Similar observations by Geller et al. (1969) revealed that cyproterone administration resulted in a suppression of testosterone uptake by the prostate and produced a decrease of the RNA/DNA ratio and of acid phosphatase activity.

Impairment of enzymic conversion of testosterone to dihydrotestosterone in utero is followed by the development of 'androgen-insensitivity syndrome' (Money et al., 1968; Mauvais-Jarvis et al., 1969; Northcutt et al., 1969). The patients with abdominal testes and uncomplicated XY sex genotype are insensitive to androgen therapy. The ability of accessory gland to convert testosterone to dihydrotestosterone is lacking. However, in some cases the skin is able to metabolize testosterone to a moderate extent (Wilson and Walker, 1969).

Patients with 'androgen-insensitivity syndrome' are sensitive to estrogen and show a remarkably high level of plasma androgen-binding protein (Mauvais-Jarvis et al., 1970a,b). Strickland and French (1969) found that administration of dihydrotestosterone did not induce nitrogen retention or other signs of androgen action. A lack of the specific transport protein in the cell of the target organs is assumed, and this concept is currently under investigation.

3. STEROID RECEPTORS OF PITUITARY CELLS

Anterior pituitary cells from 7-day ovariectomized rats were separated and dispersed in Hank's medium: the cells contained characteristic granules and showed RNA/DNA and protein/DNA ratios similar to those of intact pituitary tissue. When a constant number of cells was incubated with increasing concentrations of tritiated estradiol, uptake and retention of labeled steroid resulted from specific and nonspecific binding processes (Leawitt et al., 1973). The specific component had a high affinity ($K_A = 2.3 \times 10^9$ M^{-1}) and low capacity for estradiol (0.0029 pM/μg DNA). The nonspecific component had a lower affinity for estradiol and was not saturable using concentrations of estradiol up to 1.55×10^{-8} M. Scatchard's data for specific binding indicated there are approximately 1900 binding sites per cell (10.8 pg DNA). It was found that pituitary cells concentrated estradiol rapidly at 37°C, and peak uptake and retention increased rapidly, reaching a maximum at 30 min when 66% of the cellular radioactivity was localized in the nuclear fraction. Labeled progesterone, testosterone and corticosterone were not retained by cells to the extent that the estradiol was, and only a small fraction of the other steroids was bound to the nuclear compartment.

Male and female rats, both intact and castrate, showed specific binding protein for estradiol in the adenohypophysial cells. Korach and Muldon (1973) found that about 12% of added tritiated estradiol bound to an 8-S component. There was no significant difference between the uptake of the female and male pituitary tissue: 0.37 pM/mg cytosol protein for male and 0.36 pM for female. The authors reported that labeled testosterone did not form a detectable complex with 8-S protein.

In studying the uptake of labeled estradiol by the anterior pituitary cells from intact and castrated rats, it was found that ovariectomy resulted in a marked decrease of estradiol accumulation both in the uterus and the pituitary (Endröczi, 1974; Szabó and Marton, 1974). On the other hand, the administration of estradiol to ovariectomized rats resulted in a significant rise of the estradiol uptake which might be attributed to an estrogen-induced synthesis of receptor protein (Endröczi, 1974; Szabó et al., 1974). These observations indicated that continuous resynthesis of estradiol binder in the target tissue is controlled by estrogen and removal of the estrogen supply of the organism is followed by a decrease of the estradiol transport within the target cells.

Intravenous injection of labeled estradiol to 3—4-week-old ovariectomized rats is followed by accumulation of radioactivity within 5 min, both in the pituitary and hypothalamus. The cytosolic uptake in the pituitary has its peak within 5 min, the nuclear uptake is not maximal until 30 min (Mowles et al., 1971). The major part of the radioactivity is bound to macromolecules in the cytosol fraction and appears as a single peak when chromatographed on Sephadex G-75, and as a double peak on G-25. The pituitary cytosol receptor corresponds to a 4.5-S binding protein which is clearly distinct from the 8-S uterine protein. The nuclear extracts contain a 7-S receptor complex which also differs from that of the uterus, with an sedimentation constant of 4.5 S.

In contrast to the estradiol-binding capacity of the pituitary cells, testosterone uptake seems to be mediated by a receptor complex with lower affinity in rats. Sar and Stumpf (1973) reported that, after injection of tritiated testosterone, they were able to detect radioactivity of pituitary cells with dry-mount autoradiography at 5 min. After 1 h, a distinct pattern of cellular and subcellular distribution of radioactivity existed. Regional differences could be observed: the pars distalis retained and concentrated the radioactivity in the cell nuclei. The intermediate and posterior lobes did not show nuclear accumulation of labeled material. The labeled cells were identified as basophils by Gomori's trichrome stain.

McEwen et al. (1970, 1972) reported specific accumulation of labeled steroid hormones by the anterior pituitary cells. They have found that corticosterone uptake is several times higher in adrenalectomized than intact rats. Moreover, competitive-uptake studies have revealed that corticosterone, hydrocortisone and aldosterone can replace the labeled corticosterone, but dexamethasone was found to be only a weak competitor. By the use of high-speed centrifugation and separation on Sephadex G-50, corticosterone appeared as bound to a receptor with sedimentation constant of 8 S. In contrast to corticosterone, estradiol binding to the cytosol fraction was almost three times greater if the values were calculated in pM per mg cytosol protein.

Competition studies indicate that corticosterone uptake cannot be replaced by estradiol and testosterone (Endröczi, 1974). Similarly, it was found that dexamethasone administration resulting in a marked suppression of the pituitary ACTH secretion did not decrease corticosterone uptake in the pituitary (Endröczi, 1974).

4. STEROID HORMONE BINDING TO BRAIN MACROMOLECULES

Eik-Nes and Brizzee (1965) were the first who demonstrated that cortisol appears to be concentrated in the hypothalamus following administration to normal dogs. Fontana et al. (1970) reported an accumulation of cortisol in the brain nuclear fraction of eviscerated cats. Moreover, it was found that corticosterone was selectively retained by nuclei of limbic structures after systemic injection of the steroid into adrenalectomized rats (McEwen et al., 1970). In addition to these observations, a macromolecular component has been extracted from limbic nuclei which binds corticosterone (McEwen and Plapinger, 1970). Grosser et al. (1971) found that significant quantities of corticosterone were associated with macromolecules of the brain cytosol following intratectal administration of tritiated corticosterone to adrenalectomized rats. Fifteen times more steroid was found associated with proteins from adrenalectomized rats than that from control animals or adrenalectomized animals pretreated with corticosterone. Pretreatment of adrenalectomized rats with 11-dehydrocorticosterone, cortisol or cortisone decreased the amount of tritiated corticosterone found associated with protein, whereas progesterone, estradiol or testosterone did not interfere with the corticosterone binding to cytosol macromolecules.

McEwen et al. (1972) found that brain corticosterone-binding protein can be distinguished from the serum corticosterone-binding protein by several properties: (1) the brain protein is present after perfusion with a Dextran–saline solution; (2) it is precipitated by protamine sulfate; and (3) it migrates differently from the serum-binding protein in glycerol density gradients and on polyacrylamide gels containing glycerol. Moreover, it was found that brain cytosol-binding protein exchanges bound tritiated corticosterone in the medium much more slowly than does the serum binding protein.

Biochemical studies indicated that the hippocampus contains the highest concentration of corticosterone-binding sites (McEwen et al., 1969). By the use of autoradiographic technique it was demonstrated that the pyramidal neurons of the cornu ammonis (CA) and the granule neurons of the gyrus dentatus contained more radioactivity than did other regions of the brain. The nuclei of many neurons were clearly labeled but radioactivity was relatively sparse in the cytoplasm. Heavily labeled neurons were found to be concentrated in the region CA_2. The average labeling of cells in CA_1 was greater than in CA_3 and CA_4. The reduction of silver grains by radioactivity can be attributed to unmetabolized corticosterone, since it was found that at 1 h after injection of tritiated corticosterone, unchanged hormone accounted for 70—80% of radioactivity and more than 90% of radioactivity in cell nuclei of the hippocampus (McEwen et al., 1970, 1972).

Studying the uptake of tritiated corticosterone by brain slices under in vitro conditions, McEwen and Wallach (1973) found that the uptake was linear as a function of hormone concentration, while nuclear binding was saturated at 2×10^{-8} M tritiated corticosterone. Once bound to nuclei, corticosterone could not be replaced by 1×10^{-5} M unlabeled corticosterone during a 30-min incubation at 25°C. Nuclear binding was highest in hippocampus, followed by amygdala, cerebral cortex, hypothalamus, midbrain and cerebellum. In vitro studies confirmed previous in vivo findings that corticosterone binds better to hippocampal nuclei than does hydrocortisone, while progesterone does not bind to nuclei. Moreover, cytosol-binding protein has a greater affinity for corticosterone than hydrocortisone, although progesterone can displace corticosterone from binding sites in the soluble macromolecule fraction.

Comparison of blood corticosterone levels and affinities of brain binding proteins raises the question as to whether corticosterone binding sites in the brain are saturated in vivo at a resting level and thus already saturated when stress levels are attained. Whole blood levels of corticosterone in the rat can be estimated at $5—10 \times 10^{-8}$ M for the resting state and 5×10^{-7} M for a stress response. In comparison, the cytosol corticosterone-binding protein is half-maximally saturated at around 2×10^{-9} M corticosterone at 0°C. Unfortunately, determination of binding affinity at 37°C is made virtually impossible by the instability of the cytosol binding complex (McEwen and Wallach, 1973). Purification of corticosterone-binding protein from the cytosol fraction of rat brain revealed that the macromolecule is protein and has a molecular weight of approximately 200,000. The K_D was found to be 2.7×10^{-10} and 0.47 pmoles of corticosterone are bound/mg of protein (Grosser et al., 1973). The relative inability of dexamethasone to complete with corticosterone for binding sites is of great interest. The high biological activity of this synthetic steroid and its poor ability to bind to corticosterone-binding protein led to the assumption that biological potency and binding affinity to receptor macromolecules must be distinguished between in evaluation of steroid hormone actions.

The hypothalamus contains a highly specific, limited-capacity retention mechanism for estradiol (Eisenfeld and Axelrod, 1966; Kato and Villee, 1967; McGuire and Lisk, 1968). It was found that this mechanism is partially saturated by circulating levels of estrogen during proestrus, when ovarian secretion of this steroid is at its peak (McGuire and Lisk, 1968; Kato et al., 1969). Two hours after injection of tritiated estradiol, the preoptic—hypothalamic area contained 10 times more radioactivity than the blood and 1.5 times more than the cerebral cortex per mg wet weight. Moreover, it was found that the nuclear pellet prepared from the preoptic—hypothalamic region averaged a 13-fold concentration of radioactivity over that in the whole homogenate from the same tissue (Zigmund and McEwen, 1970). Pretreatment of ovariectomized rats with unlabeled estradiol 30 min before the injection of tritiated estradiol resulted in a marked decrease of the nuclear uptake of estradiol. The retention of labeled estradiol by the preoptic— hypothalamic area decreased exponentially from 30 min to 4 h. The nuclear binding reached a peak at 1—2 h and still showed high retention at 4 h.

Experiments with tritiated testosterone revealed that its uptake has a similar pattern to that of estradiol (Pfaff, 1968; McEwen et al., 1970). There are, however, basic differences between the uptake and retention mechanisms of the two steroids: (1) unlabeled estradiol injection reduced testosterone uptake in the pituitary, preoptic area, septum and olfactory bulb, in male but not in female rats; (2) unlabeled testosterone competition was only significantly more effective than unlabeled estradiol in the pituitary of the male rat; (3) estradiol enters the cell nuclei in the brain, whereas testosterone does not accumulate extensively in the nuclear compartment.

McEwen et al. (1972) reported that cyproterone administration produced a marked decrease of the testosterone uptake of limbic brain regions. In the ovariectomized female rats, cyproterone-induced suppression of testosterone uptake was found only in the pituitary and preoptic area. It is worth mentioning that other sex differences could also be found in competition studies. Thus, the administration of unlabeled testosterone reduced [^{3}H]estradiol uptake by the brain in a greater extent in female than in male rats (McEwen and Pfaff, 1970).

Nuclear-bound corticosterone and estradiol can be extracted by 0.4 M NaCl or KCl (Kato et al., 1970; McEwen and Plapinger, 1970). Calculating the amount of steroid bound to the nucleus in the different brain regions, it was found that there were 1200 molecules of estradiol per nucleus in the anterior hypothalamic region, and 23,000 molecules of corticosterone per nucleus in hippocampal cells. Many investigators accept the hypothesis that cytosol-binding protein enters into the nuclear compartment and transfers the steroid molecule into the nucleus (Jensen et al., 1969; Shyamala and Gorski, 1969). Recent observations revealed that both uterine and pituitary cells contain estradiol-binding protein in the cell nuclei after ovariectomy which can be extracted by hypertonic saline solution (Hegedüs and Endröczi, 1974; Szabó and Endröczi, 1974). These findings led to the assumption that the cytosol protein—steroid complex does not enter into the nucleus but plays a part in the transfer of the steroid into the nucleus. Disappearance of the cytosol-binding protein during the uptake process may be attributed to a transformational change of the molecule by loosening of the binding sites. On the other hand, the concentration of steroid in the nucleus is greater than can be explained by calculation from the loss of the cytosol binding sites (Szabó and Endröczi, 1974).

The role of steroid—receptor complex in genome derepression or repression has been discussed in the recent literature (Feigelson and Feigelson, 1965; Edelman and Fimognari, 1968; Hamilton, 1968; DeLuca, 1969). Intrinsic mechanisms of steroid hormone binding to the genome have not yet been elucidated. The involvement of histones and acidic proteins in the nucleus is very likely, although the mode of action seems to be dependent on the target cells. Induction of new species of RNA and proteins requires a relatively long period, and this lag period may be responsible for a delayed response of sexual steroids in brain—behavior relations. Thus, the effect of estrogen appears with a minimum latency of 16—24 h in higher mammals (Michael, 1966; Green et al., 1970). The antibiotics which interfere with RNA and protein synthesis suppressed the sex-steroid-induced changes at the hypothalamo—pituitary level (Quadagno et al., 1971; Schally et al., 1969). Moreover, in connection with the effects of corticosteroids on the RNA synthesis, Mühlen and Ockenfels (1969) found that cortisol injection produced a striking increase in the volume of the nucleoli and nuclei of the hippocampal cells in guinea pigs.

Studying the corticosterone uptake by different parts of the rat brain, we have found a close correlation between the nuclear uptake of the hippocampus and the exploratory activity of the animal (Endröczi, 1974). An inverse correlation between the hormone uptake by the nuclear compartment and the retention of a passive avoidance response was also reported in the study. Correlations between the corticosterone uptake of the hippocampus and learning activity confirmed the view that the hippocampal brainstem system is sensitive to corticosteroids and plays a basic role in controlling corticosteroid-adjusted behavior reactions (Endröczi, 1974). The involvement of corticosteroid-binding receptors in the feedback regulation of pituitary ACTH secretion, however, seems to be unlikely.

BIBLIOGRAPHY

Aizawa, Y. and Mueller, G.C. (1961) *J. Biol. Chem.* 236: 381.
Alberga, A. and Baulieu, E.E. (1965) *C. R. Acad. Sci.* Ser. D261: 5226.
Alberga, A. and Baulieu, E.E. (1968) *Mol. Pharmacol.* 4: 311.
Aliapoulios, M., Chamberlain, J., Jagarinee, N. and Ofner, P. (1965) *Biochem. J.* 98: 15P.
Anderson, K.M. and Liao, S. (1968) *Nature* 219: 277.
Barker, K.L. and Warren, J.C. (1966) *Proc. Natl. Acad. Sci. U.S.* 56: 1298.
Barker, K.L. (1971) *Biochemistry* 10: 284.
Barnea, A. and Gorski, J. (1970) *Biochemistry* 9: 1899.
Barry, J. and Gorski, J. (1971) *Biochemistry* 10: 2384.
Bartlett, D. Morita, Y. and Munck, A. (1962) *Nature* 196: 897.
Barton, R.W. and Liao, S. (1967) *Endocrinology* 81: 409.
Baulieu, E.E., Alberga, A. and Jung, I. (1967) *C. R. Acad. Sci.* Ser. D265: 454.
Baulieu, E.E., Lasnitzki, I. and Robel, P. (1968) *Biochem. Biophys. Res. Commun.* 32: 976.
Bellamy, D. (1963) *Biochem. J.* 87: 334.
Bellamy, D., Phillips, J.G., Jones, I.E. and Leonard, R.A. (1962) *Biochem. J.* 85: 537.

Billing, R.J., Barbiroli, B. and Smellie, R.M.S. (1969) *Biochim. Biophys. Acta* 190: 60.
Bradlow, H.L., Dobriner, K. and Gallagher, T.F. (1954) *Endocrinology* 54: 343.
Braunsberg, H., Irvine, W.T. and James, V.H.T. (1967) *Br. J. Cancer* 21: 714.
Brecher, P.I. and Woitz, H.H. (1969) *Endocrinology* 84: 718.
Brecher, P.I., Pasquina, A. and Woitz, H.H. (1969) *Endocrinology* 85: 612.
Brecher, P.I., Numata, M., DeSombre, E.R. and Jensen, E.V. (1970) *Fed. Proc.* 29: 249.
Bruchovsky, N. and Wilson, J.D. (1968) *J. Biol. Chem.* 243: 5953.
Bush, I.E. (1965) *Proc. 2nd Int. Congr. Endocrinol.*, London. (Excerpta Medica Found., Amsterdam) p. 1234.
Caldarera, C.M., Moruzzi, M.S., Barbiroli, B. and Moruzzi, G. (1968) *Biochem. Biophys. Res. Commun.* 33: 266.
Callantine, M.R., Clemens, C.E. and Shih, Y. (1967) *Proc. Soc. Exp. Biol. Med.* N.Y. 128: 382.
Channing, C.P. and Kammerman, S. (1973) *Endocrinology* 92: 531.
Church, R.B. and McCarthy, B.J. (1970) *Biochim. Biophys. Acta* 199: 103.
Clark, J.H. and Gorski, J. (1969) *Biochim. Biophys. Acta* 192: 508.
Corvol, P., Falk, R., Freifeld, M. and Bardin, C.W. (1972) *Endocrinology* 90: 1464.
Danzo, B.J., Orgebin-Crist, M.C. and Toft, D.O. (1973) *Endocrinology* 92: 310.
Davies, I.J. and Ryan, K.J. (1973) *Endocrinology* 92: 394.
DeAngelo, A.B. and Gorski, J. (1970) *Proc. Natl. Acad. Sci. U.S.* 66: 693.
DeHertogh, R., Ekka, E., Vanderheyden, I. and Hoet, J.J. (1971) *Endocrinology* 88: 175.
DeLuca, H.F. (1969) *Fed. Proc.* 28: 1678.
Demetricou, J.A., Crowley, L.G., Kushinsky, S., Donovan, A.J., Kotin, P. and MacDonald, I. (1964) *Cancer Res.* 24: 926.
Desphande, N., Jensen, V., Bulbrook, R.D., Berne, T. and Ellis, F. (1967) *Steroids* 10: 219.
DeSombre, E.R., Puca, G.A., Chabaud, J.P. and Jensen, E.V. (1971) *J. Steroid Biochem.* 2: 95.
Diamond, M., Rust, N. and Westphal, U. (1969) *Endocrinology* 84: 1143.
Dougherty, T.F. and White, A. (1944) *Endocrinology* 37: 1.
Edelman, I.S. and Fimognari, G.M. (1968) *Rec. Progr. Horm. Res.* 24: 1.
Eisenfeld, A.J. and Axelrod, J. (1966) *Endocrinology* 79: 38.
Endröczi, E. (1972) *Limbic system, learning and pituitary-adrenal function.* (Akad. Kiadó, Budapest) p. 165.
Endröczi, E. (1972) Pavlovian conditioning and adaptive hormones. In: (S. Levine, Ed.) *Hormones and Behavior.* (Academic Press, New York) pp. 173—207.
Endröczi, E. (1974) Behavioural and biochemical correlates of avoidance conditioning: its relation to pituitary-adrenal function. In: *Proc. Int. Congr. Psychoneuro-Endocrinol.*, Utrecht. (Elsevier Publ. Co., Amsterdam) in press.
Endröczi, E. and Szabó, G. (1974) *Acta Physiol. Acad. Sci. Hung.* in press.
Erdös, T. (1968) *Biochem. Biophys. Res. Commun.* 32: 338.
Falk, R.J. and Bardin, C.W. (1970) *Endocrinology* 86: 1659.
Fang, S. and Liao, S. (1969) *Mol. Pharmacol.* 5: 428.
Fang, S., Anderson, K.M. and Liao, S. (1968) *J. Biol. Chem.* 244: 6584.
Farnsworth, W.E. and Brown, J.R. (1963) *Natl. Cancer Inst. Monogr.* 12: 323.
Feherty, P., Robertson, D.M., Waynforth, H.B. and Kellie, A.E. (1970) *Biochem. J.* 120: 837.
Feigelson, P. and Feigelson, M. (1964) In: (G. Litwack and D. Kritchevsky, Eds.) *Actions of Hormones on Molecular Processes.* (Wiley, New York) p. 218.
Feigelson, M. and Feigelson, P. (1965) *Adv. Enzyme Regulat.* 3: 11.
Feil, P.D., Glasser, S.G., Toft, D.O. and O'Malley, B.W. (1972) *Endocrinology* 91: 738.
Fencl, M.M. and Villee, C.A. (1971) *Endocrinology* 88: 279.
Flesher, J.W. (1965) *Steroids* 5: 737.

Fontana, J.A., Walker, M.D., Casper, A.G.T., Metet, S. and Henkin, R.L. (1970) *Endocrinology* 86: 1469.

Galand, P. and Dupont-Mairresse, N. (1972) *Endocrinology* 90: 936.

Giannopoulos, G. and Gorski, J. (1971) *J. Biol. Chem.* 246: 2524.

Glascock, R.F. and Hoekstra, W.G. (1959) *Biochem. J.* 72: 673.

Gloyna, R.E. and Wilson, J.D. (1969) *J. Clin. Endocrinol.* 29: 970.

Gorski, J. and Nicolette, J.A. (1963) *Arch. Biochem. Biophys.* 103: 418.

Gorski, J. (1964) *J. Biol. Chem.* 239: 899.

Gorski, J. and Nelson, N.J. (1965) *Arch. Biochem. Biophys.* 110: 284.

Gorski, J., Noteboom, W.D. and Nicolette, J.A. (1965) *J. Cell. Comp. Physiol.* 66: suppl. 91.

Gorski, J. and Morgan, M.S. (1967) *Biochem. Biophys. Acta* 149: 282.

Green, R., Luttge, W.G. and Whalen, R.E. (1970) *Physiol. Behav.* 5: 137.

Greenman, D.L. (1970) *Endocrinology* 87: 716.

Grosser, B.I., Stevens, W., Bruenger, F.W. and Reed, D.J. (1971) *J. Neurochem.* 18:1725.

Grosser, B.I., Stevens, W. and Reed, D.J. (1973) *Brain Res.* 57: 387.

Gupta, G.N. (1960) Ph.D., Dissertation. (Dept. Biochem., Univ. of Chicago Bio-Med. Library.)

Hahn, W.E., Church, R.B. and Gorbman, A. (1969) *Endocrinology* 84: 738.

Hahnel, R. (1971) *Steroids* 17: 105.

Hamilton, T.H. (1964) *Proc. Natl. Acad. Sci. U.S.* 51: 83.

Hamilton, T.H. (1968) *Science* 161: 649.

Hamilton, T.H., Widnell, G.C. and Tata, J.R. (1965) *Biochim. Biophys. Acta* 108: 169.

Hamilton, T.H., Widnell, G.C. and Tata, J.R. (1968) *J. Biol. Chem.* 243: 408.

Hegedüs, I. and Endröczi, E. (1974) *Endokrinologie* 63: 386.

Hughes, A., Smith, S., DeSombre, E.R. and Jensen, E.V. (1969) *Fed. Proc.* 28: 703.

Jensen, E.V. and Jacobson, H.I. (1960) In: (G. Pincus and E.P. Vollmer, Eds.) *Biological activities of steroids in relation to cancer.* (Academic Press, New York) pp. 161—178.

Jensen, E.V. (1960) *Proc. 4th. Int. Congr. Biochem., Vienna*, vol. 15 (Pergamon Press, Oxford) p. 444.

Jensen, E.V. (1962) *Rec. Prog. Horm. Res.* 18: 461.

Jensen, E.V. and Jacobson, H.I. (1962) *Rec. Prog. Horm. Res.* 18: 387.

Jensen, E.V. (1965) *Proc. 2nd Int. Congr. Endocrinol., London*, (Excerpta Med. Found., Amsterdam) p. 420.

Jensen, E.V., Hurst, D.J., DeSombre, E.R. and Jungblut, P.W. (1967) *Science* 158: 385.

Jensen, E.V., Suzuki, T., Kawashima, T., Stumpf, W.E., Jungblut, P.W. and DeSombre, E.B. (1968) *Steroids* 13: 417.

Jensen, E.V., Suzuki, T., Numata, M., Smith, S. and DeSombre, E.R. (1969) *Dev. Biol.* suppl. 3: 151.

Jensen, E.V., Block, G.E., Smith, S., Kyser, K., DeSombre, E.R. (1971) In: (T.C. Hall, Ed.) Prediction of responses to cancer therapies. Biochem. Soc. Symp. 32 (U.S. Govt. Printing Office, Washington, D.C.) pp. 55—70.

Johansson, H., Terenius, L. and Thorén, L. (1970) *Cancer Res.* 30: 692.

Jungblut, P.W., DeSombre, E.R. and Jensen, E.V. (1967) *Abhandl. Dtsch. Akad. Wiss. Berlin, Klin. Med.* pp. 109—123.

Kammerman, S. and Canfield, R.E. (1972) *Endocrinology* 90: 384.

Kammerman, S., Canfield, R.E., Kolena, J. and Channing, C.P. (1972) *Endocrinology* 91: 65.

Karszina, R., Wyss, R.H., LeRoy, W.M. and Herrmann, W.L. (1969) *Endocrinology* 84: 1969.

Kato, J., Inaba, M. and Kobayashi, T. (1969) *Acta Endocrinol.* 61: 585.

Kato, J. and Vilee, C.A. (1967) *Endocrinology* 80: 567.

Kato, J., Atsumi, Y. and Muramatsu, M. (1970) *Neuroendocrinology* 3: 349.

198

Kattwinkel, J. and Munck, A. (1966) *Endocrinology* 79: 387.
King, R.J.B., Cowan, D.M. and Inman, D.R. (1965) *J. Endocrinol.* 32: 83.
King, R.J.B. and Gordon, J. (1966) *J. Endocrinol.* 34: 431.
King, R.J.B., Gordon, J. and Steggles, A.W. (1969) *Biochem. J.* 114: 649.
Koch, P.A., Neuklis, J.C., Holland, C.A., Kennedy, C.A., Weaver, R.C. and Litwack, G. (1972) *Endocrinology* 90: 1600.
Korach, K.S. and Muldon, T.G. (1973) *Endocrinology* 92: 322.
Korenman, S.G. and Rao, B.R. (1968) *Proc. Natl. Acad. Sci. U.S.* 61: 1028.
Kulin, H.E. and Reiter, E.O. (1972) *Endocrinology* 90: 1371.
Kyser, K.A. (1970) Ph.D. Dissertation. (University of Chicago, Bio-Med. Library.)
Leawitt, W.W., Kimmel, G.L. and Friend, J.P. (1973) *Endocrinology* 92: 94.
Lee, C. and Jacobson, H.I. (1971) *Endocrinology* 88: 596.
Lee, C.Y. and Ryan, R.J. (1971) *Endocrinology* 89: 1515.
Leidenberger, F. and Reichert, L.E. (1972) *Endocrinology* 91: 135.
Liao, S. and Fang, S. (1969) *Vitam. Horm.* 27: 17.
Lissák, K. and Endröczi, E. (1965) *Neuroendocrine Control of Adaptation.* (Pergamon Press, Oxford) p. 189.
Martin, J.E. (1972) *Endocrinology* 91: 594.
Mauvais-Jarvis, P., Bercovici, J.P. and Gauthier, F. (1969) *J. Clin. Endocrinol.* 29: 417.
Mauvais-Jarvis, P., Bercovici, J.P., Crepy, O. and Gauthier, F. (1970a) *J. Clin. Invest.* 49: 31.
Mauvais-Jarvis, P., Bercovici, J.P., Crepy, O., Gauthier, F. (1970b) *J. Clin. Invest.* 49: 417.
Mayol, R.F. and Thayer, S.A. (1970) *Biochemistry* 9: 2484.
McEwen, B.S. and Pfaff, D.W. (1970) *Brain. Res.* 21: 1.
McEwen, B.S., Pfaff, D. and Zigmund, R.E. (1970) *Brain Res.* 21: 17.
McEwen, B.S. and Plapinger, L. (1970) *Nature* 226: 263.
McEwen, B.S. and Wallach, G. (1973) *Brain Res.* 57: 373.
McEwen, B.S., Weiss, J.M. and Schwartz, L.S. (1969) *Brain Res.* 16: 227.
McEwen, B.S., Zigmund, R.E. and Gerlach, J.L. (1972) In: G.H. Bourne, *Structure and Function of the Nervous System.* vol. 5. (Academic Press, New York) pp. 205—291.
McGuire, J.L. and Lisk, R.D. (1968) *Proc. Natl. Acad. Sci. U.S.* 61: 497.
McGuire, J.L. and Bariso, C.D. (1972) *Endocrinology* 90: 496.
Means, R.A. (1971) *Endocrinology* 89: 981.
Means, R.A. and Vaitukaits, J. (1972) *Endocrinology* 90: 39.
Michael, R.P. (1965) *Br. Med. Bull.* 21: 87.
Milgrom, E. and Baulieu, E.E. (1970) *Endocrinology* 87: 276.
Milgrom, E., Atger, M. and Baulieu, E.E. (1970) *Steroids* 16: 741.
Milgrom, E., Atger, M., Perrot, M. and Baulieu, E.E. (1972) *Endocrinology* 90: 1071.
Money, J., Erhardt, A.A. and Masica, D.N. (1968) *Johns Hopkins Med. J.* 123: 105.
Morita, Y. and Munck, A. (1964) *Biochim. Biophys. Acta* 43: 150.
Moulton, B.C. and Leonard, S.L. (1969) *Endocrinology* 84: 1461.
Mowles, T.F., Ashkanazy, B., Mix, E. and Sheppard, H. (1971) *Endocrinology* 89: 484.
Mueller, G.C. (1960) In: (G. Pincus and E.P. Vollmer, Eds.) *Biological Activities of Steroids in Relation to Cancer.* (Academic Press, New York) pp. 129—145.
Mueller, G.C., Gorski, J. and Aizawa, Y. (1961) *Proc. Natl. Acad. Sci. U.S.* 47: 164.
Munck, A. (1968) *J. Biol. Chem.* 243: 1039.
Musliner, T.A., Chader, G.J. and Villee, C.A. (1970) *Biochemistry* 9: 4448.
Mühlen, K. and Ockenfels, H. (1969) *Z. Zellforsch. Mikrosk. Anat.* 93: 126.
Nicolette, J.A. and Gorski, J. (1964) *Arch. Biochem. Biophys.* 107: 279.
Nicolette, J.A. and Mueller, G.C. (1966) *Biochem. Biophys. Res. Commun.* 24: 851.
Northcutt, R.C., Island, D.P. and Liddle, G.W. (1969) *J. Clin. Endocrinol.* 29: 422.
Noteboom, W.D. and Gorski, J. (1963) *Proc. Natl. Acad. Sci. U.S.* 50: 250.
Noteboom, W.D. and Gorski, J. (1965) *Arch. Biochem. Biophys.* 111: 559.

Notides, A.C. and Gorski, J. (1966) *Proc. Natl. Acad. Sci. U.S.* 56: 230.
Notides, A.C. (1970) *Endocrinology* 87: 987.
Ofner, P. (1969) *Vitam. Horm.* 26: 237.
O'Malley, B.W. and McGuire, W.L. (1969) *Endocrinology* 84: 63.
O'Malley, B.W., McGuire, W.L., Kohler, P.O. and Korenman, S.G. (1969) *Rec. Prog. Horm. Res.* 25: 105.
O'Malley, B.W., Sherman, M.R. and Toft, D.O. (1970) *Proc. Natl. Acad. Sci. U.S.* 67: 501.
O'Malley, B.W., Toft, D.O. and Sherman, M.R. (1971) *J. Biol. Chem.* 246: 1117.
Pegg, A.E., Lockwood, D.H. and Williams-Ashman, H.G. (1970) *Biochem. J.* 116: 900.
Pfaff, D.W. (1968) *Endocrinology* 82: 1149.
Podratz, K.C. and Katzman, P.A. (1968) *Fed. Proc.* 27: 497.
Puca, G.A. (1971) *Fed. Proc.* 30: 1010.
Puca, G.A. and Bresciani, F. (1970) *Nature* 225: 1251.
Puca, G.A. and Bresciani, F. (1971) In: (G. Raspé, Ed.) *Advances in the Biosciences.* Vol. 7. (Pergamon Press, Oxford) pp. 97—113.
Quadagno, D.M., Shryne, J. and Gorski, R.A. (1971) *Horm. Behav.* 2: 1.
Rajaniemi, H. and Vanha-Perttule, T. (1972) *Endocrinolgoy* 90: 1.
Reel, J.R., Lee, S. and Callantine, M.R. (1969) Abstr. 51st Meeting, Endocrine Soc., St. Louis, p. 83.
Reel, J.R., Vanderwark, S.D., Shih, Y. and Callantine, M.R. (1970) Abstr. 52nd Meeting, Endocrine Soc., St. Louis, p. 83.
Reuter, L.A., Ciaccio, L.A. and Lisk, R.D. (1970) *Fed. Proc.* 29: 250.
Ritzén, E.M., Nayfeh, S.N., French, F.R. and Dobbins, M.C. (1971) *Endocrinology* 89: 143.
Rochefort, H. and Baulieu, E.E. (1968) *C. R. Acad. Sci. Ser.* D267: 662.
Rosenfeld, M.G. and O'Malley, B.W. (1970) *Science* 168: 253.
Roy, S., Mahesh, V.B. and Greenblatt, R.B. (1964) *Acta Endocrinol.* 47: 669.
Ruh, T.S., Katzeneelenbogen, B.S., Katzeneelbogen, J.A. and Gorski, J. (1973) *Endocrinology* 92: 125.
Sandberg, A.A., Slaunwhite, W.R. and Antoniades, H.N. (1957) *Rec. Prog. Horm. Res.* 13: 209.
Sander, S. (1968) *Acta Endocrinol.* 58: 49.
Sander, S. and Attramadal, A. (1968) *Acta Pathol. Microbiol. Scand.* 74: 169.
Sar, M. and Stumpf, W.E. (1973) *Endocrinology* 92: 251.
Schally, A.V., Bowers, C.Y., Carter, W.H., Arimura, A., Redding, T.W. and Saito, M (1969) *Endocrinology* 85: 290.
Schriefers, H. (1967) *Vitam. Horm.* 25: 271.
Segal, S.J., Davidson, O.W. and Wada, K. (1965) *Proc. Natl. Acad. Sci. U.S.* 54: 782.
Shain, S.A. and Barnea, A. (1971) *Endocrinology* 89: 1270.
Shimazaki, J., Kurihara, H., Ito, Y. and Shida, K. (1965) *Gumma J. Med. Sci.* 14: 100.
Shimazaki, J., Matsuhita, I., Furuya, N., Yamanaka, H. and Shida, K. (1969) *Endocrinol. Japon.* 16: 163.
Shyamala, G. and Gorski, J. (1969) *J. Biol. Chem.* 244: 1097.
Shyamala, G. and Nandi, S. (1972) *Endocrinology* 91: 861.
Smith, D.E. and Gorski, J. (1968) *J. Biol. Chem.* 243: 4169.
Spaziani, E. and Szegò, C.M. (1968) *Endocrinology* 63: 669.
Spelsberg, T.C., Steggles, A.W. and O'Malley, B.W. (1971) *J. Biol. Chem.* 246: 4188.
Steggles, A.W. and King, R.J.B. (1970) *Biochem. J.* 118: 695.
Stern, J.M. and Eisenfeld, A.J. (1969) *Science* 166: 233.
Stone, G.M. (1964) *Acta Endocrinol.* 47: 433.
Strickland, A.L. and French, F.S. (1969) *J. Clin. Endocrinol.* 29: 1284.
Stumpf, W.E. and Roth, L.J. (1966) *J. Histochem. Cytochem.* 14: 274.
Stumpf, W.E. (1968) *Endocrinology* 83: 777.

200

Stumpf, W.E. (1969) *Endocrinology* 85: 31.

Szabó, G. and Endröczi, E. (1974) *Endokrinologie* 63: 396.

Szabó, G. and Marton, I. (1974) *Proc. Int. Soc. Psychoneuroendocrinol.* Utrecht.

Szegö, C.M. (1965) *Fed. Proc.* 24: 1343.

Talwar, G.P., Segal, S.J., Evans, A. and Davidson, O.W. (1964) *Proc. Natl. Acad. Sci. U.S.* 52: 1059.

Teng, C.S. and Hamilton, T.H. (1968) *Proc. Natl. Acad. Sci. U.S.* 60: 1410.

Teng, C.S. and Hamilton, T.H. (1969) *Proc. Natl. Acad. Sci. U.S.* 63: 465.

Toft, D.O. and O'Malley, B.W. (1972) *Endocrinology* 90: 1041.

Trachewsky, D. and Segal, S.J. (1968) *Eur. J. Biochem.* 4: 279.

Tucker, H.A., Larson, B.L. and Gorski, J. (1971) *Endocrinology* 89: 152.

Unhjem, O., Attramadal, A. and Sölna, J. (1968) *Acta Endocrinol.* 62: 153.

Unhjem, O., Tveter, K.J. and Aakvaag, A. (1969) *Acta Endocrinol.* 62: 153.

Whalen, R.E. and Luttge, W.G. (1969) *Endocrinology* 84: 217.

Wiest, W.G. and Rao, B.R. (1971) In: (G. Raspé, Ed.) *Advances in the Biosciences.* Vol. 7. (Pergamon Press, Oxford) pp. 251—264.

Williams-Ashman, H.G. and Reddi, A.H. (1971) *Annu. Rev. Physiol.* 33: 31.

Wilson, J.D. and Walker, J.D. (1969) *J. Clin. Invest.* 48: 371.

Woolley, D.E., Holinka, C.F. and Timiras, P.S. (1969) *Endocrinology* 84: 157.

Wyss, R.H., Karszina, R., Heinrichs, W.L. and Hermann, W.L. (1968) *J. Clin. Endocrinol. Metab.* 28: 1824.

Zigmund, R.E. and McEwen, B.S. (1970) *J. Neurochem.* 17: 889.

CHAPTER 15

Prenatal androgenization of primates and humans

G. TÉLÉGDY

1. INTRODUCTION

It is well accepted that fetal sexual differentiation is androgen dependent. The differentiation of the Wolffian duct, urogenital sinus and genital tubercle is androgen dependent, as is the sexual differentiation of the brain.

Several reviews deal with sexual differentiation in lower mammals, and a separate chapter will summarize our present knowledge in these species. The data concerning fetal sexual differentiation and prenatal androgenization in primates, as well as in humans, is far from complete. The present chapter will summarize the data currently available on this topic.

2. SOURCE OF ANDROGENS IN PRENATAL LIFE IN PRIMATES

A number of sources can be considered for androgen formation during prenatal life; the testicles in the male fetus, adrenals, ovaries and placenta. According to the data obtained from mainly rat experiments it seems that the fetal testicles may be the most important source of androgen, which is responsible for sexual differentiation under normal physiological circumstances. However, when adrenal enzymes are deficient, producing an insufficient amount of corticosteroids, and the steroidogenetic pathway leads to an excess amount of androgen formation — as in the adrenogenital syndrome — androgen can cause a male-like, or partially male-like sexual differentiation in a female fetus. This produces an hermaphrodite or pseudohermaphrodite sexual manifestation in the offspring.

Prenatal androgen formation in Macaca mulatta

Fetal adrenal
The fetal adrenal can convert [4-^{14}C]pregnenolone and [7-^{3}H]pregnenolone

Handbook of Sexology, edited by J. Money and H. Musaph
© *Elsevier/North-Holland Biomedical Press, 1977*

sulphate to a number of progestogenic steroids as well as to such androgens as androstenedione, 11β-hydroxyandrostenedione, dehydroepiandrosterone (Gorwill et al., 1971). In perfusion studies with [4-^{14}C]progesterone injected into the umbilical vein in 20th week of gestation, androstenedione was isolated in the adrenal (Solomon and Leung, 1972).

Fetal testis

During the first trimester (45 days) of pregnancy the fetal testis can convert [4-^{14}C]pregnenolone to testosterone and Δ^4-androstenedione (Resko, 1970).

Fetal ovary

The fetal ovary at 45, 60 and 80 days of pregnancy showed no significant conversion of labeled pregnenolone to androgens (Resko, 1970). It seems that the ovary is in a quiescent stage during prenatal life.

Androgens in blood

In the umbilical artery of the rhesus fetus, androstenedione and testosterone could be found at 100, 125 and 150 days of gestation. The testosterone concentration was significantly higher in the umbilical artery of male than that of female fetuses. However, there was no difference in the androstenedione concentration between sexes. A mother bearing a male fetus had more testosterone in the peripheral and uterine plasma than a mother with a female fetus. No differences in androstenedione concentration were revealed. After birth, the plasma and testis testosterone concentration declined sharply (Resko, 1970) and remained low till about puberty, which occurs around three years of age in male rhesus (Resko, 1967).

Prenatal androgen formation in the baboon (Papio cynocephalus)

Adrenal

The adrenal is able to form 11β-hydroxyandrostenedione from androstenedione in vitro (Axelrod et al., 1973). Following injection of [7-^{3}H]pregnenolone and [4-^{14}C]dehydroepiandrosterone, 11β-hydroxyandrostenedione was isolated from both precursors (Merkatz and Solomon, 1970).

Placenta

Placenta microsomes obtained from term pregnancy were incubated with [4-^{14}C]testosterone, androstenedione, 19-hydroxy-Δ^4-androstenedione, 19-hydroxytestosterone, 19-aldosterosterone, and number of estrogens were isolated (Milewitch and Axelrod, 1971).

3. SOURCE OF ANDROGENS IN PRENATAL LIFE IN HUMANS

Fetal adrenal

The fetal adrenal can produce mainly androstenedione and 11β-hydroxyandrostenedione. Adrenal slices incubated with acetate synthesized androstenedione and 11-hydroxyandrostenedione (Bloch and Benirschke, 1959). Following perfusion of midterm fetus with acetate and cholesterol (Telegdy et al., 1970) or with acetate alone (Archer et al., 1971), androstenedione could be isolated from the adrenal. Minced adrenal tissue incubated with dehydroepiandrosterone also produced androstenedione and 11β-hydroxyandrostenedione (Villee and Driscoll, 1965). When progesterone was used as a precursor in homogenates (Solomon et al., 1958) or in minced adrenal tissue, androgen formation could be measured. After perfusion with 17α-hydroxyprogesterone of midterm human fetus, androstenedione and testosterone could be isolated from the adrenal (Solomon et al., 1970). The steroidogenetic capacity of the human fetal adrenal to form androgens from different precursors is summarized in Table I.

Fetal testis

The fetal testis obtained mainly from midterm pregnancy is able to form testosterone and also androstenedione under a number of experimental conditions. Acetate is utilized for androgen synthesis in testicular organ culture (Rice et al., 1966) and in minced fetal testicular tissue (Serra et al., 1970) as well as after perfusion of the fetus with ^{14}C-labeled sodium acetate (Mathur et al., 1972). Testicular homogenate incubated with dehydroepiandrosterone synthesized androstenedione (Bloch et al., 1962b). Minced fetal testis from pregnenolone precursor (Acevedo et al., 1961, 1963) and testis slices from

Table I
Androgen formation in human fetal adrenal.

Precursor	Source	Product	Reference
Acetate	Slice	Androstenedione, 11β-hydroxy-androstenedione	Bloch and Benirschke, 1959
	Perfusion	Androstenedione	Archer et al., 1971
Acetate and cholesterol	Perfusion	Androstenedione	Telegdy et al., 1970
Dehydroepiandrosterone	Mince	Androstenedione, 11β-hydroxy-androstenedione	Villee and Driscoll, 1965
Progesterone	Homogenate	Androstenedione	Solomon et al., 1958
	Mince	11β-hydroxy-androstenedione	Villee and Driscoll, 1965
17α-hydroxy-progesterone	Perfusion	Androstenedione, testosterone	Solomon et al., 1970

17α-hydroxypregnenolone (Ikonen and Niemi, 1966) synthesized andro-stenedione and testosterone. Progesterone could also be converted to andro-gens by testis homogenates (Bloch, 1964), minces (Acevedo et al., 1963), and slices (Bloch et al., 1962a). After perfusion with labeled 17α-hydroxy-progesterone, androstenedione and testosterone could also be isolated from testicular tissue (Solomon et al., 1970). From pooled fetal testes, testoster-one and androstenedione could be measured with gas chromatography — mass spectrometry (Huhtainen et al., 1970). The highest testosterone con-centration was seen in the testis between 11- and 17-weeks of fetal age (Reyes et al., 1973). The data concerning steroidogenesis in the human fetal testis are summarized in Table II.

Fetal ovary

The human fetal ovary has the capacity to convert minute amounts of acetate to pregnenolone and progesterone (Jungmann and Scheppe, 1968) and to metabolize progesterone (Bloch, 1964), though it is not able to form andro-gens.

Table II
Androgen formation in human fetal testis.

Precursor	Source	Product	Reference
Acetate	Organ culture	Testosterone	Rice et al., 1966
	Mince	Testosterone	Serra et al., 1970
	Perfusion	Androstenedione, testosterone	Mathur et al., 1972
Dehydroepi-androsterone	Homogenate	Androstenedione	Bloch et al., 1962b
Pregnenolone	Mince	Androstenedione, testosterone	Acevedo et al., 1961, 1963
17α-Hydroxy-pregnenolone	Slice	Androstenedione, testosterone	Ikonen and Niemi, 1966
Progesterone	Homogenate	Testosterone	Bloch, 1964
	Mince	Androstenedione	Acevedo et al., 1963
	Slice	Androstenedione, testosterone	Bloch et al., 1962a; Ikonen and Niemi, 1966
17α-Hydroxy-progesterone	Perfusion	Androstenedione, testosterone	Solomon et al., 1970
Endogenous		Androstenedione, testosterone	Huhtaniemi et al., 1970
		Testosterone	Reyes et al., 1973

Androgens in blood

In human pregnancy the maternal plasma testosterone level did not show differences between pregnancies with female and male fetuses (Mizuno et al., 1968; Rivarola et al., 1968). However, the urinary testosterone sulfate excretion in women carrying a male fetus was significantly higher than with women carrying a female fetus. At the time of delivery the testosterone or testosterone sulfate concentration in mothers with a male fetus was significantly higher than mothers with a female fetus. The testosterone concentration in the umbilical artery and vein was also significantly higher in male newborn than in female (Bertrand and Saez, 1969). In the male fetus the testosterone concentration is higher than in the female. In the male fetus the highest level was obtained at 11—17 weeks of fetal age, at the time when genital differentiation takes place (Reyes et al., 1974). When a male fetus was perfused with ^{14}C-labeled sodium acetate, testosterone could be isolated from the perfusate (Archer et al., 1971). When the human male fetus was perfused with labeled acetate and cholesterol at midterm, androstenedione could be detected in the perfusate (Telegdy et al., 1970).

4. EFFECT OF ANDROGENS ON SEXUAL DEVELOPMENT IN PRIMATES

Postnatal treatment of *Macaca mulatta* with 35 mg/kg testosterone resulted in no alteration of the time of the first appearance of menstrual bleeding, length of the menstrual cycle, gross ovarian morphology, and plasma progestin level (Treloar et al., 1972).

Prenatal toatment of the mother with testosterone propionate from postcoital day 40 till day 90 resulted in the newborn female monkey being a pseudohermaphrodite. In these offspring, phallus and scrotal rain had developed (Young et al., 1964).

The pseudohermaphroditic female monkey showed a delay in the appearance of the first menstruation. However, the subsequent established menstrual cycle was normal (Goy and Resko, 1972). Corpus luteum developed, progesterone, testosterone and androstenedione secretion from the ovary were normal; progesterone secretion from the ovary without corpus luteum was somewhat lower than in the normal monkey with the same histology of the ovary. The estrogen surge was also the same as in a comparable female.

Social behavior of the pseudohermaphrodite monkey significantly differs from the normal female control. Play initiation, rough-and-tumble play, threat, pursuit play and mounting frequencies are higher and their values tend to be closer to normal male than female (Peretz et al., 1971; Goy and Resko, 1972).

5. EFFECT OF ANDROGENS ON SEXUAL DEVELOPMENT IN HUMANS

A number of review papers have appeared on this topic (Money, 1971; Money and Ehrhardt, 1972; Ehrhardt, 1973) which will be dealt with in detail in the chapter by Ehrhardt.

Premature human infants treated with a single dose of methyltestosterone (88—22 mg/kg) failed to show any significant alteration in reproductive function when they became adults. Two subsequently became pregnant and the other had a normal menstrual cycle (Polishuk and Anteby, 1971).

Effect of prenatal androgenization on human female fetus

Progestin-induced hermaphroditism

In the 1950s progestin was used in mothers with habitual miscarriages in order to prevent abortion. An unexpected side-effect was observed in that some of the genetic females became masculinized in their external genitalia, from having an enlarged clitoris to a normal-appearing penis. The internal genitalia were normally female.

Their psychological development has been studied by Money and Ehrhardt (Money, 1971; Money and Ehrhardt, 1972; Ehrhardt, 1973). These children do not show differences in their attitudes to marriage, motherhood or infant care, however, they gave priority to having a nondomestic career rather than to full-time motherhood or housewifery. Their interest in toys was boyish in that they preferred cars, guns and trucks to dolls.

Fetal adrenogenital syndrome

Because of a genetic disturbance of 11-hydroxylase and 21-hydroxylase enzymes, the fetal adrenals produce less corticosteroids and more androgens. The androgens in genetic females induce male-like external sexual differentiation. The internal genitalia are normal, with an enlarged clitoris and empty scrotal fold. In these patients the adrenal will still produce an excessive amount of androgen after birth. The external genitalia may be corrected by surgical means, and the androgen secretion from the adrenal can be repressed by cortisone treatment.

Psychologically these children are tomboys. They also show more interest in having a career than in motherhood, more interest in boys' toys and games, and little interest in dolls and infant care.

6. SUMMARY

There is a great similarity between nonhuman primates and humans with respect to the time of sexual differentiation, source of androgens in fetal life, and also in the consequences of androgenization in genetic females. In contrast to other species, such as the rat, neonatal androgen treatment does not influence sexual differentiation either in nonhuman primates or in humans, though postnatal androgen, given in large enough doses, does have a pubertal effect.

It seems that two main sources of androgen can be considered to be responsible for normal or abnormal sexual differentiation; the testis and adrenals. The testis is the most important androgen-producing organ, secreting testosterone and androstenedione. However, testosterone seems to be responsible for normal male sexual differentiation. It takes place in the first trimester of pregnancy in humans, and perhaps somewhat later in rhesus monkeys. The role of androgen of adrenal origin can be considered an important factor influencing sexual differentiation in a pathological condition such as the adrenogenital syndrome.

Androgen treatment in the female monkey during the sexual differentiation period in pregnancy causes pseudohermaphrodite sexual differentiation, with its morphological and psychological consequences.

In the human genetic female, fetal progestin treatment or adrenogenital syndrome also causes pseudohermaphrodite newborns, with typical morphological and psychological alterations.

BIBLIOGRAPHY

Acevedo, H.F., Axelrod, L.R., Ishikawa, E. and Takaki, F. (1961) Steroidogenesis in the human fetal testis: the conversion of pregnenolone-7 ^{3}H to dehydroepiandrosterone, testosterone and 4-androstene-3,17-dione. *J. Clin. Endocrinol. Metab.* 21: 1611—1613.

Acevedo, H.F., Axelrod, L.R., Ishikawa, E. and Takaki, F. (1963) Studies in fetal metabolism. II. Metabolism of progesterone-4-C^{14} and pregnenolone-7α-H^3 in human fetal testes. *J. Clin. Endocrinol. Metab.* 23: 885—890.

Archer, D.F., Mathur, R.S., Wiqvist, N. and Diczfalusy, E. (1971) Quantitative assessment of the de novo sterol and steroid synthesis in the human foeto-placental unit. *Acta Endocrinol.* 66: 666—678.

Axelrod, L.R., Kraemer, D.C., Burdett, J. and Goldzieher, J.W. (1973) Biosynthesis of 11-hydroxyandrostenedione by human and baboon adrenals. *Acta Endocrinol.* 72: 545—550.

Bertrand, J. and Saez, J.M. (1969) Studies on the testicular function of the foetal testis in vivo. *Biochem. J.* 112: 22—239.

Bloch, E. (1964) Metabolism of 4-^{14}C-progesterone by human fetal testis and ovaries. *Endocrinology* 74: 833—845.

Bloch, E. and Benirschke, K. (1959) Synthesis in vitro of steroids by human foetal adrenal gland slices. *J. Biol. Chem.* 234: 1085—1089.

Bloch, E., Tissenbaum, B. and Benirschke, K. (1962a) The conversion of [4-^{14}C]progesterone to 17-hydroxyprogesterone, testosterone and Δ^4-androstene-3,17-dione by human fetal testosterone in vitro. *Biochim. Biophys. Acta* 60: 182—184.

Bloch, E., Tissenbaum, B., Rubin, B.L. and Dean, H.L. (1962b) Δ^5-3β-hydroxysteroid dehydrogenase activity in human fetal adrenals. *Endocrinology* 71: 629—635.

Ehrhardt, A.A. (1973) Maternalism in fetal hormonal and related syndromes. In: (J. Zubin and J. Money, Eds.) *Contemporary Sexual Behavior: Critical Issues in the 1970s.* (Johns Hopkins University Press, Baltimore) pp. 99—115.

Gorwill, R.H., Snyder, D.L., Lindholm, U.B. and Jaffe, R.B. (1971) Metabolism of pregnenolone-4-^{14}C and pregnenolone-7α-[3]-sulphate by the Macaca mulatta fetal adrenal in vitro. *Gen. Comp. Endocrinol.* 16: 21—29.

Goy, R.W. and Resko, J.A. (1972) Gonadal hormones and behavior of normal and pseudohermaphroditic non-human female primates. *Recent Prog. Horm. Res.* 28: 707—733.

Huhtaniemi, I., Ikonen, M. and Vihko, R. (1970) Presence of testosterone and other neutral steroids in human fetal testes. *Biochem. Biophys. Res. Commun.* 38: 715—720.

Ikonen, M. and Niemi, M. (1966) Metabolism of progesterone and 17α-hydroxypregnenolone by the human testis in vitro. *Nature* 212: 716—717.

Jungmann, R.A. and Schweppe, J.S. (1968) Biosynthesis of sterols and steroids from acetate-^{14}C by human fetal ovaries. *J. Clin. Endocrinol. Metab.* 28: 1599—1604.

Mathur, R.S., Wiqvist, N. and Diczfalusy, E. (1972) De novo synthesis of steroids and steroid sulphates by the testicles of the human foetus at midgestation. *Acta Endocrinol.* 71: 792—800.

Merkatz, I. and Solomon, S. (1970) The fetoplacental unit. *Clin. Obstet. Gynecol.* 13: 665—686.

Milewich, L. and Axelrod, L.R. (1971) Metabolism of 4-^{14}C testosterone by lyophilized baboon placenta microsomes. *Endocrinology* 88: 589—595.

Mizuno, M., Lobotsky, J., Lloyd, C.W., Kobayashi, T. and Murasawa, Y. (1968) Plasma androstenedione and testosterone during pregnancy and in the newborn. *J. Clin. Endocrinol. Metab.* 28: 1133—1142.

Money, J. (1971) Clinical aspects of prenatal steroidal action on sexually dimorphic behavior. In: (C.H. Sawyer and R.A. Gorski, Eds.) *Steroid Hormones and Brain Function.* (University of California Press, California) pp. 325—338.

Money, J. and Ehrhardt, A.A. (1972) Gender dimorphic behavior and fetal sex hormones. *Recent Prog. Horm. Res.* (Academic Press, New York) pp. 735—763.

Peretz, E., Goy, R.W., Phoenix, C.H. and Resko, J.A. (1971) Influence of gonadal hormones on the development of activation of the nervous system of the rhesus monkey. In: (D.H. Ford, Ed.) *Influence of Hormones on the Nervous System.* (S. Karger, Basel) pp. 401—411.

Polishuk, W.Z. and Anteby, S. (1971) Testosterone in premature babies and its effect on sexual development. *Lancet* 1: 344.

Resko, J.A. (1967) Plasma androgen levels of the rhesus monkey: Effects of age and season. *Endocrinology* 81: 1203—1212.

Resko, J.A. (1970) Androgen secretion by the fetal and neonatal rhesus monkey. *Endocrinology* 87: 680—687.

Reyes, F.I., Boroditsky, R.S., Winter, J.S.D. and Faiman, C. (1974) Studies on human sexual development. II. Fetal and maternal serum gonadotropin and sex steroid concentration. *J. Clin. Endocrinol. Metab.* 38: 612—617.

Reyes, F.I., Winterm, J.S.D. and Faiman, C. (1973) Studies in human sexual development. I. Fetal gonadal and adrenal sex steroids. *J. Clin. Endocrinol. Metab.* 37: 74—78.

Rice, B.F., Johanson, C.A. and Sternberg, W.H. (1966) Formation of steroid hormones from acetate-1-^{14}C by a human fetal testis preparation grown in organ culture. *Steroids* 7: 79—90.

Rivarola, M.A., Forest, M.G. and Migeon, C.J. (1968) Testosterone, androstenedione and dehydroepiandrosterone in plasma during pregnancy and at delivery: Concentration and protein binding. *J. Clin. Endocrinol. Metab.* 28: 34—40.

Serra, G.B., Pérez-Palacios, G. and Jaffe, R.B. (1970) De novo testosterone biosynthesis in the human fetal testis. *J. Clin. Endocrinol. Metab.* 30: 128—130.

Solomon, S., Lanman, J.T., Lind, J. and Lieberman, S. (1958) The biosynthesis of Δ^4-androstenedione and 17α-hydroxyprogesterone from progesterone by surviving human fetal adrenals. *J. Biol. Chem.* 233: 1084—1088.

Solomon, S. and Leung, K. (1972). Steroid hormones in non-human primates during pregnancy. *Acta Endocrinol.* (suppl.) 166: 178—190.

Solomon, S., Ling, W., Leung, K., Merkatz, I., Coutts, J.R.T. and MacNaughton, M.C. (1970) Metabolism of neutral steroids in pregnancy. *Excerpta Medica Int. Congr. Ser. No. 219.* 504—510.

Telegdy, G., Weeks, J.W., Archer, D.F., Wiqvist, N., Diczfalusy, E. (1970) Acetate and cholesterol metabolism in the human foeto-placental unit at midgestation. 3. Steroids synthesized and secreted by the foetus. *Acta Endocrinol.* 63: 119—133.

Treloar, O.L., Wolf, R.C. and Meyer, R.K. (1972) Failure of a single neonatal dose of testosterone to alter ovarian function in the rhesus monkey. *Endocrinology* 90: 281—284.

Villee, D.B. and Driscoll, S.G. (1965) Pregnenolone and progesterone metabolism in human adrenals from twin female fetus. *Endocrinology* 77: 602—608.

Young, W.C., Goy, R.W. and Phoenix, C.H. (1964) Hormones and sexual behavior. *Science* 143: 212—218.

CHAPTER 16

Hypothalamus and pituitary cyclicity

BÉLA HALÁSZ

1. ORGANIZATION OF THE HYPOTHALAMUS—ANTERIOR PITUITARY TARGET ENDOCRINE ORGAN SYSTEM

The function of the target endocrine organs, such as the ovaries, testes, adrenals and thyroid gland, is controlled by the central nervous system and the anterior pituitary, the former acting on the hypophysis, and the latter on the target organs.

It is a well-established fact that the mechanism of action of the nervous system is neurohumoral, that is, certain substances, called hypothalamic releasing and inhibiting factors, are produced by nerve cells located in the medial basal hypothalamus and these are released at the nerve terminals of these neurons. The substances then enter the so-called portal vascular system and are carried by the portal blood to the anterior pituitary cells (Fig. 1). The portal vascular system of the anterior pituitary is characterized by the fact that the hypophysial arteries, before reaching the pituitary, from a rich capillary network on the surface of the median eminence. Several of these capillaries penetrate into the median eminence as capillary loops. The capillary network, very close to the nerve endings containing the releasing factors, collects into portal vessels and these ramify into the sinusoids of the hypophysis (Fig. 1).

The influence of the pituitary gland on the target organs is mediated via the tropic hormones (gonadotropic, adrenocorticotropic, and others). If the hypothalamic releasing factors do not reach the hypophysis — as it is the case when the pituitary is experimentally transplanted under the renal capsule, or the connection between the hypothalamus and the pituitary is permanently interrupted by inserting a thin plate between the hypothalamus and the hypophysis — the tropic function of the gland becomes markedly reduced. In the absence of the tropic hormones, or if their blood level is very low, the gonads, adrenals and thyroid become atrophied.

It is required for all control systems that they record continuously some

Handbook of Sexology, edited by J. Money and H. Musaph
© *Elsevier/North-Holland Biomedical Press, 1977*

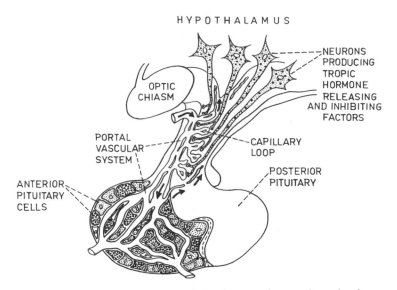

Fig. 1. Schematic illustration of the hypothalamic neurohumoral mechanism controlling the anterior pituitary. The releasing and inhibiting factors are released at the terminals of the nerve cells producing these substances and are conveyed by the portal vascular system to the pituitary.

parameters of the functional state of the target and adjust the control system to the changes. This holds true for the hypothalamo—pituitary complex. It has been known for some time that an excess of sex steroids, corticosteroids or thyroid hormones causes a decrease in gonadotropic, adrenocorticotropic, and thyrotropic hormone secretion, respectively. This feedback action is of an inhibitory nature (negative feedback). Some target gland hormones, such as estrogen or progesterone, may also exert a positive feedback action. For example, increase in blood estrogen levels can induce a release of pituitary gonadotropic hormones, as was first demonstrated by Hohlweg (1934), who found that estrogen given to infantile female rats brought about luteinization in the ovaries. In addition to the feedback of the target gland hormones (external or long feedback), there is some evidence that pituitary tropic hormones may influence their own secretion (for details see Halász, 1972).

Regarding the site of feedback action, first it was believed to be exerted at the pituitary level. Flerkó and Szentágothai (1957) furnished the first experimental evidence as to the existence of hormone-sensitive nervous structures in the hypothalamus. They showed that ovarian tissue implanted into the anterior hypothalamus inhibits pituitary gonadotropic hormone secretion. Presently, it is generally accepted that sex steroids, corticosteroids and thyroid hormones, act partly on the pituitary and partly on certain nervous structures. With regard to the site of the feedback action of the tropic hormones, it is assumed that these hormones act at the level of the nervous system.

The aforementioned facts clearly indicate that the central nervous system, adenohypophysis and peripheral endocrine organs are very closely interconnected. This is illustrated in Fig. 2.

When dealing with the organization of the endocrine control system it should be mentioned that environmental factors, such as light, smell, or temperature, as well as impulses arising within the organism, for example, from the genital tract which induce ovulation in the reflex ovulators such as the rabbit, have a great influence on this system. Environmental factors appear to be particularly important in those animals in which gonadal function shows seasonal changes. The environmental and internal stimuli act via neural routes.

Turning now to the secretory pattern of pituitary tropic hormones, there are essentially three kinds of fluctuations in the blood levels of the hormones: pulsatile rhythm, diurnal variations, and cyclic changes.

The existence of a pulsatile rhythm became evident when blood hormone levels were followed for several hours and determined at every 5 or 10 min.

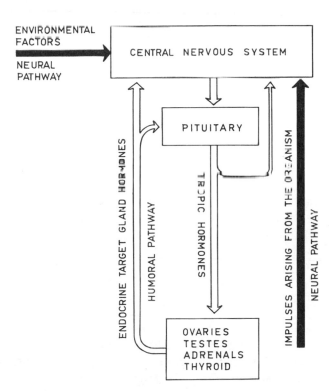

Fig. 2. A simple scheme of the organization of the central nervous system—pituitary—endocrine target gland system.

These investigations indicated that approximately at every hour there is a peak in blood hormone concentrations.

A large body of evidence indicates that in addition to pulsatile rhythm, serum hormone levels change significantly during the day. In man, for example, pituitary ACTH (adrenocorticotropic hormone) activity is high in the morning and relatively low in the afternoon. In rats it is the opposite, low in the morning and elevated in the afternoon. It is generally accepted that this pattern of hormone release is an inherited feature of the organism and that the biological clock of this rhythm resides in the central nervous system. The rhythm can be influenced but not abolished by environmental factors such as light. The diurnal ACTH rhythm is not evident in the newborn rat; it appears in the 3rd week of postnatal life (Hiroshige and Sato, 1970).

Cyclic changes are characteristic of the release pattern of gonadotropic hormones in females (except for reflex ovulators). One cycle may last for a few days, as in rats, or for four weeks or more as in human beings and other primates. In males gonadotropic hormone release is tonic.

All three kinds of hormonal changes appear to be controlled primarily by the central nervous system. For a detailed discussion of other kinds of biological rhythms see Richter (1962).

The second section of this Chapter deals with the control of tonic release of pituitary tropic hormones, and presents a brief discussion of pulsatile rhythm.

2. CONTROL OF TONIC RELEASE OF PITUITARY TROPIC HORMONES

When dealing with the tonic release of hypophysial hormones it should be recalled that if the pituitary is disconnected from the hypothalamus its hormone secretion becomes markedly reduced. This reduction is so severe that it leads to target organ atrophy, clearly indicating the fundamental role played by the nervous system in the maintenance of hypophysial function.

Tonic release of pituitary tropic hormones is presumably controlled by the medial basal hypothalamus, named the hypophysiotropic area (Halász et al., 1962, 1965; Flament-Durand, 1965). This term is based on the finding that only this hypothalamic region is capable of maintaining structure and function of the pituitary gland when transplanted into the brain. Destruction of this area results in a very significant reduction of hypophysial function. In contrast, if only the medial basal hypothalamus is left in contact with the pituitary stalk, but is separated from the rest of the brain, basal secretion of tropic hormones is well maintained (Fig. 3). Under this latter experimental condition, atrophy of the endocrine target organs does not occur; in the testes spermiogenesis and spermiohistogenesis are not altered, and the ovaries contain large follicles.

The functional capacity of the medial basal hypothalamus is not restricted

COMPLETE DEAFFERENTATION
OF THE MEDIAL BASAL HYPOTHALAMUS

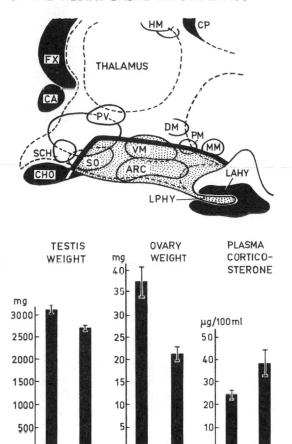

Fig. 3. (Upper) This schematic sagittal section of the rat brain illustrates the experimental model in animals with complete deafferentation of the medial basal hypothalamus. Dotted area represents the isolated region, thick line the knife cut. The isolated area is disconnected from the rest of the brain but is in intact contact with the pituitary. ARC: arcuate nucleus; CA: anterior commissure; CHO: optic chiasm; CP: posterior commissure; DM: dorsomedial nucleus; FX: fornix; HM: medial habenular nucleus; LAHY: anterior pituitary; LPHY: posterior pituitary; MM: medial mamillary nucleus; PM: premamillary nucleus; PV: paraventricular nucleus; SCH: suprachiasmatic nucleus; SO: supraoptic nucleus; VM: ventromedial nucleus. (Lower) Testis and ovary weights and afternoon plasma corticosterone levels (mean ± S.E.M.) of control animals (C) and of rats with complete deafferentation of the medial basal hypothalamus (CD). The reduced ovary weight of the rats with complete deafferentation is due to the fact that ovaries of such animals do not contain corpora lutea.

to the control of hypophysial basal activity. Some simple pituitary reactions, such as increase in pituitary ACTH or gonadotropic hormone secretion following unilateral adrenalectomy or castration, respectively, are directly mediated through this hypothalamic region. This is suggested by findings obtained in animals with a completely deafferented medial basal hypothalamus (Halász, 1969). It was found that pituitaries of rats subjected to such an operation exhibit the mentioned responses. The fact that there is a pituitary ACTH or gonadotropic hormone response to changes in blood corticosteroid or sex steroid levels favors the view that the medial basal hypothalamic region contains hormone-sensitive structures. Such an assumption is fairly well supported by the observations that neurons of this area bind estrogens and testosterone, as demonstrated by autoradiographic studies (Pfaff, 1968; Stumpf, 1968; McEwen et al., 1972).

It appears that the medial basal hypothalamus is responsible for the pulsatile rhythm. This is suggested by the finding that this rhythm is evident in animals after complete deafferentation of the medial basal hypothalamus (Blake and Sawyer, 1974).

As to the mechanism of action of the medial basal hypothalamus on the pituitary, as already mentioned, presumably this area produces the hypothalamic releasing and inhibiting factors. This assumption is supported by morphological as well as functional data. It is known from the studies of Szentágothai (1962) that the neurons of this area project to the surface zone of the median eminence, forming the tubero-infundibular tract, and terminate here, where the releasing factors are probably released. Further studies (Réthelyi and Halász, 1970) revealed that nerve cells located outside the area do not terminate in the median eminence. In accordance with these data, recent immunohistochemical investigations have demonstrated, at least for luteinizing hormone releasing factor (LH-RF) and growth hormone inhibiting factor (GIF), that LH-RF and GIF positive fibers belong to the tuberoinfundibular tract. Experiments in which releasing factor activity of various hypothalamic cell groups or regions was determined yielded further support for this theory; significant amounts of releasing factors were found only in this area of the brain (for details see Mess, 1969; Palkovits et al., 1974; Brownstein et al., 1974).

Concerning structural organization of the medial basal hypothalamus, in addition to the neurons producing the releasing factors, there is a fairly rich interconnection between the neural elements of the area. From a morphological point of view this corroborates the idea that this region may be able to control, by itself, basal secretion of pituitary tropic hormones.

3. CONTROL OF PITUITARY DIURNAL RHYTHMS AND CYCLIC GONADOTROPIC FUNCTION

The experiments carried out in animals with an isolated medial basal hypothalamus suggest on the one hand that this hypothalamic region controls tonic release of anterior pituitary hormones, while on the other hand, they indicate unequivocally that the area per se is unable to maintain diurnal variations in hypophysial activity or cyclic release of gonadotropic hormones. It has been found (Halász and Gorski, 1967; Halász et al., 1967a,b) that, following neural isolation of the medial basal hypothalamus, there are no diurnal fluctuations in ACTH secretion and rats do not ovulate (Fig. 4).

Interestingly enough, in monkeys, the medial basal hypothalamus seems to be able to control cyclic release of pituitary FSH and LH. Knobil and co workers (Knobil, 1074) found that monkeys exhibit cyclic gonadotropic hormone release following separation of the medial basal hypothalamus from the rest of the brain. (See also, below, discussion on the role of steroid feedback in the gonadal cycle.)

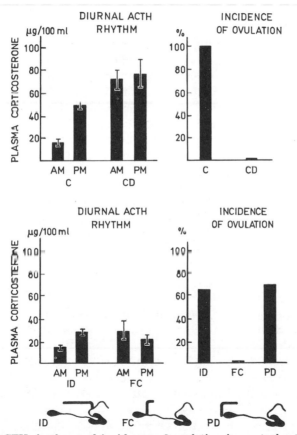

Fig. 4. Diurnal ACTH rhythm and incidence of ovulation in control rats (C) and in animals with various hypothalamic deafferentations. CD: complete deafferentation; ID: incomplete deafferentation of the medial basal hypothalamus; FC: frontal cut behind the optic chiasm; PD: deafferentation of the preoptic area. AM: in the morning; PM: in the afternoon. At the bottom the knife cut of ID, FC and PD as seen in sagittal section of the hypothalamus is illustrated (heavy line).

According to our own findings (Halász et al., 1967a,b), the critical afferents essential for both diurnal ACTH rhythm and cyclic gonadal function of the rat reach the medial basal hypothalamus from an anterior direction; interruption of the bilateral, superior and posterior connections of the region does not interfere with pituitary activity, whereas severance of the anterior connections, leaving intact all the others, blocks it (Fig. 4).

Presently it is not known which neural elements are responsible for the circadian variations. It was proposed by Moberg et al. (1971) that certain limbic structures such as the hippocampus may control diurnal ACTH rhythm. It turned out, however, that interruption of the fornix which conveys the hippocampal impulses to the preoptic region and the hypothalamus, produces only a temporary effect and the rhythm returns within a few weeks (Lengvári and Halász, 1973).

Turning to the control of cyclic gonadotropic function in the rat and guinea pig, it seems that the neural trigger for ovulation resides, at least partially, in the preoptic—anterior hypothalamic region. It has been demonstrated (Köves and Halász, 1970; Kaasjager et al., 1971) that rats ovulate after deafferentation of this region, whereas a cut behind this area blocks ovulation (Fig. 4). The sex cycle of animals with the preoptic area deafferented is, however, irregular. This suggests that other neural elements such as limbic structures — septum, amygdala, hippocampus, mesencephalon — and probably also the pineal gland, are involved in cyclic gonadal activity. Stimulation of the septal area and of the medial region of the amygdala induces ovulation (Shealy and Peele, 1957; Bunn and Everett, 1957; Everett, 1964). According to Eleftheriou and co-workers (1970), lesions of the medial amygdala complex lead to a depression of hypothalamic LH-RF activity, whereas destruction of the basolateral area of the amygdala has an opposite effect. There are some data indicating that before puberty the amygdala exerts an inhibitory influence on gonadotropic function. Lesions of this region induce precocious puberty (Elwers and Critchlow, 1960; Döcke, 1974) and stimulation of the area delayes puberty (Bar-Sela and Critchlow, 1966). With regard to the hippocampus, Kawakami and associates (1966) found LH release in response to hippocampal stimulation. Others (Velasco and Taleisnik, 1969) have postulated that the hippocampus inhibits gonadotropin release. Bilateral hippocampal lesions lead to a significant delay in puberty (Döcke, 1974). The observations of Carrer and Taleisnik (1970) favor the idea of involvement of mesencephalic structures in the control of gonadal function. They found that rats ovulate following stimulation of certain mesencephalic regions, and in contrast, LH release is blocked if other mesencephalic areas are stimulated. Very likely the epithalamo—epiphysial complex is also a member of the system. Lesions of the epithalamic region decrease fertility (de Groot, 1962). Mess and co-workers (1971) have reported that pinealectomy resulted in the appearance of irregular vaginal cycles and ovulation in persistently estrous rats made anovulatory by anterior hypothalamic lesion. This indicates that some mechanism inhibiting gonadotropin synthesis and/or release has been removed by pinealectomy. The exact role of these structures is not clarified as yet, but it is likely that some of them exert a stimulatory, and others an inhibitory influence.

As neural elements outside the medial basal hypothalamus do not terminate in the hypothalamic median eminence where the hypophysiotropic substances (releasing and inhibiting factors) presumably are released, we assume that these structures exert their influence on the pituitary via the medial basal hypothalamus, probably by modifying synthesis and/or release of the releasing and inhibiting factors produced by the hypothalamus. This view is supported by the great number of nervous connections existing between the two areas; numerous neurons of the regions outside the medial basal hypothalamus end on nerve cells of the latter area (for details, see Koikegami, 1974).

Besides the abovementioned brain regions the feedback action of sex steroids, primarily estrogen, plays a fundamental role in the control of cyclic gonadotropic function. The importance of this action is indicated by the finding, among others, that estrogen antagonists can block ovulation (Labhsetwar, 1970). Further, it is well known that the time of rupture of the ovarian follicle can be advanced by progesterone (Everett, 1948). In a 5-day cycling rat, progesterone given on the 3rd day advances ovulation by one day and this occurs at the usual period of the day. The available data suggest that, in the induction of ovulation, a positive estrogen feedback exists, which appears to be exerted partly at the pituitary level, and partly at the level of the nervous system. With regard to positive action on the pituitary it has been shown recently that estrogen increases sensitivity of the gonadotropic cells to LH-RF (Debeljuk et al., 1972; Schally et al., 1973) and thus enhances pituitary LH response to LH-RF. Sensitivity of the anterior lobe to LH-RF undergoes changes during the sexual cycle of the rat. The peak of sensitivity is at the 17th—18th h of proestrus (Aiyer et al., 1974) and this may be due to the elevated blood estrogen levels evident at this time of the cycle. A large body of evidence suggests sex steroid sensitivity of nervous elements presumably involved in the control of cyclic pituitary gonadal activity. The preoptic—anterior hypothalamic region, septum, amygdala, and hippocampus contain neurons which, like other estrogen-reactive tissue (uterus, vagina), exhibit selective uptake and binding of estrogen (for details, see Flerkó, 1973). The findings of Barraclough and co-workers (1964) and Terasawa and co-workers (1969) suggest that progesterone activates the preoptic neural trigger for ovulation. Estradiol implants in the amygdala influence pituitary gonadotropic function either by enhancing (Lawton and Sawyer, 1970) or inhibiting LH secretion (Kawakami et al., 1969). Interruption of amygdaloid and hippocampal afferents to the medial basal hypothalamus appears to alter pituitary LH response to progesterone (Velasco and Taleisnik, 1971; Brown-Grant and Raisman, 1972). One may assume that the underlying mechanism of this action is to facilitate impulse transmission between various nervous structures involved in cyclic gonadotropic hormone release; under physiological circumstances it is primarily estrogen which exerts this action.

A number of data suggest (for references see Everett, 1964) that the neurogenic stimulus which triggers ovulation in rats arises at the same time of the day. If ovulation is blocked by pentobarbital on the day of proestrus, rupture of the follicle is shifted by 24 h, and if pentobarbital is given also on the next day ovulation will take place 24 h later. Presumably a neurogenic stimulus leading to LH-RF release arises in the central nervous system, at least partly in the preoptic region of the female rat every 24 h. Whether or not this stimulus releases the ovulatory quota of LH from the pituitary may largely depend on blood estrogen and progesterone levels. As mentioned earlier, in monkeys the cyclic pattern of gonadotropic hormone release is evident after the complete isolation of the medial basal hypothalamus. Apparently in this species, and maybe also in women, the neural trigger for ovulation is, in contrast to rodents, located in this region of the hypothalamus and is probably greatly influenced by estrogen levels. On the basis of 17β-estradiol implantation studies, Karsch and his co-workers (1973b) believe that the pattern of LH secretion throughout the normal menstrual cycle of rhesus monkeys can be attributed primarily to alterations in ovarian estrogen secretion.

A permanent blockade of cyclic release of gonadotropic hormones is caused by testosterone early on in life. Pfeiffer (1936) was the first to demonstrate that ovaries implanted into adult male rats castrated at birth contain developing follicles and corpora lutea, proving that such males have cyclic gonadotropic function. On the contrary, if testes were implanted into newborn female rats, only follicles, with no cycle of ovulation, could be seen in the ovaries of the hosts when grown up. According to the latter finding, testes implanted into the newborn female rat result in a permanent blockade of ovulation. Barraclough and Leathem (1954) and Barraclough (1961) have reported that a single testosterone injection administered with the first ten days of life to female mice or rats causes sterility for the whole life, and the ovaries of such animals are polyfollicular. These observations initiated very intense work, the results of which are discussed in other chapters of this book. On the basis of the accumulated experimental evidence it is generally assumed that, independently of sex, the brain of the newborn mouse, rat or guinea pig is capable of releasing gonadotropic hormones in a cyclic manner. It is only because of the action of testosterone produced by the testes of the fetus or of the newborn that males lose this capability and show a tonic secretory pattern of gonadotropins. The site and mechanism of this action of testosterone is presently the subject of intense studies. In this context it is of great interest that [³H]estrogen uptake of the preoptic—anterior hypothalamic area of androgen-sterilized female rats (animals treated with testosterone on the first days after birth) is less than that of intact females (Flerkó et al., 1971). This suggests that in androgen-sterilized rats the estrogen-binding capacity of this region of the brain may be reduced. Flerkó and his associates assume that these changes are very important in the mechanism of action of testosterone inhibiting the cyclic release of gonadotropic hormones. It should be mentioned that according to Raisman and Field (1971), there is a sexual dimorphism in the neuropil of the preoptic area of the rat. In normal females the number of nonamygdaloid synapses on dendritic spines exceeds that of the males.

The observations by Karsch et al. (1973a) show that in primates, in contrast to rodents, exposure of the hypothalamus to androgens throughout fetal and postnatal development does not prevent differentiation of the control system that governs cyclic gonadotropic function. Whether this is related to the fact that monkeys continue to ovulate after the complete deafferentation of the medial basal hypothalamus, as mentioned earlier, is not yet clear.

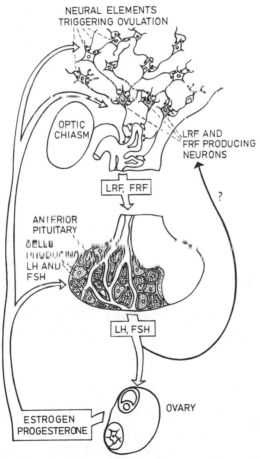

Fig. 5. A simple scheme of the system controlling ovulation and the site of action of the factors involved. FRF: follicle-stimulating hormone releasing factor; FSH: follicle-stimulating hormone; LH: luteinizing hormone; LRF: luteinizing-hormone releasing factor.

Puberty may be primarily connected with sex-steroid sensitivity of the preoptic—anterior hypothalamic region. The generally accepted view is that hormone sensitivity diminishes at puberty (Hohlweg, 1936; Byrnes and Meyer, 1951; Donovan and van der Werff ten Bosch, 1959). The observations of Ramirez and Sawyer (1965, 1966) are inconsistent with this concept. They found that the daily administration of small amounts of estrogen leads to precocious puberty. The data of Smith and Davidson (1968) suggest that the steroids may exert this action on the preoptic—anterior hypothalamic area. They have also found that estradiol implanted for 48 h into this brain region of infantile rats causes precocious puberty.

A very simple schematic illustration of the system controlling cyclic gonadotropic function is presented in Fig. 5.

BIBLIOGRAPHY

Aiyer, M.S., Fink, G. and Greig, F. (1974) Changes in the sensitivity of the pituitary gland to luteinizing hormone releasing factor during the oestrous cycle of the rat. J. Endocrinol. 60: 47—64.

Barraclough, C.A. (1961) Production of anovulatory, sterile rats by single injections of testosterone propionate. Endocrinology 68: 62—67.

Barraclough, C.A. and Leathem, J.H. (1954) Infertility induced in mice by a single injection of testosterone propionate. Proc. Soc. Exp. Biol. 85: 673—674.

Barraclough, C.A., Yrarrazaval, S. and Hatton, R. (1964) A possible hypothalamic site of action of progesterone in the facilitation of ovulation in the rat. Endocrinology 75: 838—845.

Bar-Sela, M.E. and Critchlow, V. (1966) Delayed puberty following electrical stimulation of amygdala in female rats. Am. J. Physiol. 211: 1103—1107.

Blake, C.A. and Sawyer, C.H. (1974) Effects of hypothalamic deafferentation on the pulsatile rhythm in plasma concentrations of luteinizing hormone in ovariectomized rats. Endocrinology 94: 730—736.

Brown-Grant, K. and Raisman, G. (1972) Reproductive function in the rat following selective destruction of afferent fibres to the hypothalamus from the limbic system. Brain Res. 46: 23—42.

Brownstein, M., Palkovits, M., Saavedra, J.M., Bassiri, R.M. and Utiger, R.D. (1974) Thyrotropin-releasing hormone in specific nuclei of the brain. Science 185: 267—269.

Bunn, J.B. and Everett, J.W. (1957) Ovulation in persistent estrous rats after electrical stimulation of the brain. Proc. Soc. Exp. Biol. 96: 369—371.

Byrnes, W.W. and Meyer, R.K. (1951) Effect of physiological amounts of estrogen on the secretion of follicle stimulating and luteinizing hormones. Endocrinology 49: 449—460.

Carrer, H.F. and Taleisnik, S. (1970) Effect of mesencephalic stimulation on the release of gonadotrophins. J. Endocrinol. 48: 527—539.

Debeljuk, L., Arimura, A. and Schally, A.V. (1972) Effect of estradiol and progesterone on the LH release induced by LH-releasing hormone /LH-RH/ in intact diestrous rats and anestrous ewes. Proc. Soc. Exp. Biol. 139: 774—777.

Donovan, B.T. and van der Werff ten Bosch, J.J. (1959) The hypothalamus and sexual maturation in the rat. J. Physiol. Lond. 147: 78—92.

Döcke, F. (1974) Differential effects of amygdaloid and hippocampal lesions on female puberty. Neuroendocrinology 14: 345—350.

Eleftheriou, B.E., Desjardins, C. and Zolovick, A.J. (1970) Effects of amygdaloid lesions on hypothalamic-hypophysial luteinizing hormone activity. *J. Reprod. Fertil.* 21: 249—254.

Elwers, M. and Critchlow, V. (1960) Precocious ovarian stimulation following hypothalamic and amygdaloid lesions in rats. *Am. J. Physiol.* 198: 381—385.

Everett, J.W. (1948) Progesterone and estrogen in the experimental control of ovulation time and other features of the estrous cycle in the rat. *Endocrinology* 43: 389—405.

Everett, J.W. (1964) Central neural control of reproductive functions of the adenohypophysis. *Physiol. Rev.* 44: 373—431.

Flament-Durand, J. (1965) Observations on pituitary transplants into the hypothalamus of the rat. *Endocrinology* 77: 446—454.

Flerkó, B. (1973) Hypothalamic mediation of neuroendocrine regulation of hypophysial gonadotrohic functions. In: (Greep, Ed.) M.T.P. *Int. Rev. Sci., Physiol. Sect., Ser. 1, Reproductive Physiology* (Butterworths, London) pp. 1—32.

Flerkó, B. and Szentágothai, J. (1957) Oestrogen sensitive nervous structures in the hypothalamus. Acta Endocrinol. Kbh. 26: 121—127.

Flerkó, B., Illei-Donhoffer, A. and Mess, B. (1971) Oestradiol-binding capacity in neural and non-neural target tissues of neonatally androgenized female rats. *Acta Biol. Acad. Sci. Hung.* 22: 125—130.

De Groot, J. (1962) In discussion, *Proc. Int. Union Physiol. Sci. XXII. Int. Congr. Ser.* 47: II, 623.

Halász, B. (1969) The endocrine effects of isolation of the hypothalamus from the rest of the brain. In: (W.F. Ganong and L. Martini, Eds.) *Frontiers in Neuroendocrinology*, (Oxford University Press, Oxford) pp. 307—342.

Halász, B. (1972) Hypothalamic mechanisms controlling pituitary function. *Prog. Brain Res.* 38: 97—118.

Halász, B. and Gorski, R.A. (1967) Gonadotrophic hormone secretion in female rats after partial or total interruption of neural afferents to the medial basal hypothalamus. *Endocrinology* 80: 608—622.

Halász, B., Pupp, L. and Uhlarik, S. (1962) Hypophysiotrophic area in the hypothalamus. *J. Endocrinol.* 25: 147—154.

Halász, B., Pupp, L., Uhlarik, S. and Tima, L. (1965) Further studies on the hormone secretion of the anterior pituitary transplanted into the hypophysiotrophic area of the rat hypothalamus. *Endocrinology* 77: 343—355.

Halász, B., Slusher, M. and Gorski, R.A. (1967a) Adrenocorticotrophic hormone secretion in rats after partial or total deafferentation of the medial basal hypothalamus. *Neuroendocrinology* 2: 43—55.

Halász, B., Vernikos-Danellis, J. and Gorski, R.A. (1967b) Pituitary ACTH content in rats after partial or total interruption of neural afferents to the medial basal hypothalamus. *Endocrinology* 81: 921—924.

Hiroshige, T. and Sato, T. (1970) Postnatal development of circadian rhythm of corticotropin-releasing activity in the rat hypothalamus. *Endocrinol. Japon.* 17: 1—6.

Hohlweg, W. (1934) Veränderungen des Hypophysenvorderlappens und des Ovariums nach Behandlungen mit grossen Dosen von Follikelhormon. *Klin. Wochenschr.* 13: 92—95.

Hohlweg, W. (1936) Der Mechanismus der Wirkung von gonadotropen Substanzen auf das Ovar der infantilen Ratte. *Klin. Wochenschr.* 15: 1832—1835.

Kaasjager, W.A., Woodbury, D.M. van Dieten, J.A.M.J. and van Rees, G.P. (1971) The role played by the preoptic region and the hypothalamus in spontaneous ovulation and ovulation induced by progesterone. *Neuroendocrinology* 7: 54—64.

Karsch, F.J., Dierschke, D.J. and Knobil, E. (1973a) Sexual differentiation of pituitary function: Apparent difference between primates and rodents. *Science* 179: 484—486.

Karsch, F.J., Dierschke, D.J., Weick, R.F., Yamaji, T., Hotchkiss, J. and Knobil, E.

(1973b) Positive and negative feed-back control by estrogen of luteinizing hormone secretion in the rhesus monkey. *Endocrinology* 92: 799—804.

Kawakami, M., Seto, K. and Yoshida, K. (1966) Influence of the limbic system on ovulation and on progesterone and estrogen formation in rabbit's ovary. *Jap. J. Physiol.* 16: 254—273.

Kawakami, M., Seto, K., Yoshida, K. and Miyamoto, T. (1969) Biosynthesis of ovarian steroids in the rabbit: influence of progesterone or estradiol implantation into the hypothalamus and limbic structures. *Neuroendocrinology* 5: 303—321.

Knobil, E. (1974) On the control of gonadotropin secretion in the rhesus monkey. *Recent Prog. Horm. Res.* 30: 1—46.

Koikegami, H. (1974) Anatomical considerations of modulatory effects of the limbic and paralimbic structures upon the hypothalamic hormonal or autonomic function. In: (M. Kawakami, Ed.) *Biological Rhythms in Neuroendocrine Activity.* (Igaku Shoin Ltd. Tokyo).

Köves, K. and Halász, B. (1970) Location of the neural structures triggering ovulation in the rat. *Neuroendocrinology* 6: 180—193.

Labhsetwar, A.P. (1970) Role of estrogens in ovulation: A study using the estrogen-antagonist. ICI 46, 474. *Endocrinology* 87: 542—551.

Lawton, J.E. and Sawyer, C.H. (1970) Role of amygdala in regulating LH secretion in the adult female rat. *Am. J. Physiol.* 218: 622—626.

Lengvári, I. and Halász, B. (1973) Evidence for a diurnal fluctuation in plasma corticosterone levels after fornix transection in the rat. *Neuroendocrinology* 11: 191—196.

McEwen, B.S., Zigmond, R.E. and Gerlach, J.L. (1972) *Structure and Function of Nervous Tissue,* vol. 5. (Academic Press, Inc., New York/London) pp. 205—219.

Mess, B. (1969) Site and onset of production of releasing factors. In: (Gual and Ebling, Eds.) *Progress in Endocrinology.* Int. Congr. Ser. 184 (Excerpta Medica, Amsterdam) p. 564.

Mess, B., Heizer, A., Tóth, A. and Tima, L. (1971) Luteinization induced by pinealectomy in the polyfollicular ovaries of rats bearing anterior hypothalamic lesions. In: (Wolstenholme and Knight, Eds.) *The Pineal Gland.* (Churchill, London) pp. 229—240.

Moberg, G.P., Scapagnini, U., Groot, J. de and Ganong, W.F. (1971) Effect of sectioning the fornix on diurnal fluctuation in plasma corticosterone levels in the rat. *Neuroendocrinology* 7: 11—15.

Palkovits, M., Arimura, A., Brownstein, M., Schally, A.V. and Saavedra, J.M. (1974) Luteinizing hormone-releasing hormone (LH-RH) content of the hypothalamic nuclei in rat. *Endocrinology* 96: 554—558.

Pfaff, D.W. (1968) Autoradiographic localization of testosterone-^{3}H in the female rat brain and estradiol-^{3}H in the male rat brain. *Experientia* 24: 958—959.

Pfeiffer, C.A. (1936) Sexual differences of the hypophyses and their determination by the gonads. *Am. J. Anat.* 58: 195—225.

Raisman, G. and Field, P.M. (1971) Sexual dimorphism in the preoptic area of the rat. *Science* 173: 731—733.

Ramirez, V.D. and Sawyer, C.H. (1965) Advancement of puberty in the female rat by estrogen. *Endocrinology* 76: 1158—1168.

Ramirez, V.D. and Sawyer, C.H. (1966) Changes in hypothalamic luteinizing hormone releasing factor (LHRF) in the female rat during puberty. *Endocrinology* 78: 958—964.

Réthelyi, M. and Halász, B. (1970) Origin of the nerve endings in the surface zone of the median eminence of the rat hypothalamus. *Exp. Brain Res.* 11: 145—158.

Richter, C.P. (1962) *Biological Clocks in Medicine and Psychiatry.* (Charles C. Thomas, Springfield, Ill., USA).

Schally, A.V., Redding, Z.W. and Arimura, A. (1973) Effect of sex steroids on pituitary responses to LH- and FSH-releasing hormone in vitro. *Endocrinology* 93: 893—902.

Shealy, C.N. and Peele, T.L. (1957) Studies on amygdaloid nucleus of cat. *J. Neurophysiol.* 20: 125—139.

Smith, E.R. and Davidson, J.M. (1968) Role of estrogen in the cerebral control of puberty in female rats. *Endocrinology* 92: 100—108.

Stumpf, W.E. (1968) Estradiol-concentrating neurons: topography in the hypothalamus by dry-mount autoradiography. *Science* 162: 1001—1003.

Szentágothai, J. (1962) Anatomical considerations. In: (Szentágothai, Flerkó, Mess and Halász, Eds.) *Hypothalamic Control of the Anterior Pituitary.* (Akademiai Kiadó, Budapest) pp. 19—105.

Terasawa, E., Kawakami, M. and Sawyer, C.H. (1969) Induction of ovulation by electrochemical stimulation in androgenized and spontaneously constant-estrous rats. *Proc. Soc. Exp. Biol.* 132: 497—501.

Velasco, M.E. and Taleisnik, S. (1969) Effect of hippocampal stimulation on the release of gonadotropin. *Endocrinology* 85: 1154—1159.

Velasco, M.E. and Taleisnik, S. (1971) Effects of the interruption of amygdaloid and hippocampal afferents to the medial hypothalamus on gonadotrophin release. *J. Endocrinol.* 51: 41—55.

CHAPTER 17

Sex-hormone-dependent brain differentiation and reproduction

G. DÖRNER

1. THE FEEDBACK CONTROL SYSTEM FOR REPRODUCTION

Neuroendocrine control of gonadotropin secretion

The first classical experiment in endocrinology was done by Berthold (1849). Castration of cocks resulted in atrophy of the genital organs and decrease of sexual behavior, which could be prevented by re-implantation of the testes. It was therefore suggested that a substance was produced by the testes which was responsible for the development and function of the sex organs and also for the appearance and maintenance of sexual behavior. Some 50 years later, Halban (1900) and Knauer (1900) presented similar evidence for an endocrine function of the ovary. Meanwhile the various hormones of the male and female gonads, together with many of their metabolites and precursors, have been identified and synthesized.

The gonadotropic function of the pituitary gland was first demonstrated by Aschner (1912) who observed gonadal atrophy in dogs following hypophysectomy. Subsequently, the gonadotropins were discovered by Aschheim and Zondek (1927) in our laboratories and simultaneously by Smith and Engle (1927) in America. Hohlweg and Junkmann (1932) envisaged the central nervous system as the regulator of the hypophyseal gonadotropic function, presenting for the first time a cybernetic functional unit of the central nervous system—hypophysis—gonads. Barraclough and Gorski (1961) distinguished a rostral sex center located in the preoptic suprachiasmatic region and regulating the cyclic gonadotropin secretion in females, and a caudal center located in the ventromedial arcuate region responsible for the tonic gonadotropin secretion in both sexes. Recent data suggest that structures of the limbic brain, especially of the amygdala, are also responsible for cyclic gonadotropin release in female rats (Kawakami and Teresawa, 1974; Döcke et al., 1975). These regulatory mechanisms are mediated by a gonadotropin-releasing hormone (or hormones) of the type postulated by Harris (1955),

Handbook of Sexology, edited by J. Money and H. Musaph
© *Elsevier/North-Holland Biomedical Press, 1977*

described by McCann and co-workers (1960) isolated by Schally and collaborators (1971) and synthesized by Geiger and co-workers (1971).

Present day knowledge regarding the hypothalamo—hypophyseal—gonadal system may be summarized in the following manner: In the medial basal hypothalamus a FSH/LH-releasing hormone is secreted under the influence of neurotransmitters (Kamberi, 1974). It is transported by the hypothalamo—hypophyseal portal vessels to the anterior pituitary where it stimulates gonadotropin secretion. In females, an additional cyclic sex center is responsible for the cyclically increased liberation of the gonadotropin-releaser. In consequence, a periodic over-release of hypophyseal LH occurs, promoting the induction of ovulation.

The hypophyseal gonadotropic hormones regulate the generative gonadal functions as well as the secretion of the sex hormones, which in turn regulate the physiological functions of their target organs. In this context, sex hormones produce either a predominantly inhibitory (negative) or — at least in females — stimulatory (positive) feedback effect on the hypothalamo—hypophyseal system depending on the concentration, duration of action and combination of individual hormones (estrogens, progestogens and androgens). Furthermore, sex hormones can sensitize hypothalamic mating centers to sensory stimulations which reach the diencephalon by pathways from the cerebral cortex and/or subcortex (Dörner, 1972).

Neuroendocrine control of sexual behavior

Brookhart and Dey (1941) demonstrated, by means of intrahypothalamic lesions in guinea pigs, a mating center responsible for sexual behavior patterns, distinct from the hypothalamic sex center postulated by Hohlweg and Junkmann (1932) and regulating gonadotropin secretion.

Dörner and co-workers (Dörner et al., 1968b) distinguished a male mating center located in the preoptic anterior hypothalamic area and a female center located in the hypothalamic ventromedial nucleus region. In rats of either sex, predominantly male or female sexual behavior could be selectively stimulated or abolished either by intrahypothalamic sex hormone implants or by hypothalamic electrolytic lesions in these regions. These findings were confirmed by data of other authors (Nadler, 1972; Powers, 1972; Carrer et al., 1973/74).

Moreover, the decrease of female sexual behavior following lesions of the ventromedial nucleus region was associated with a simultaneous increase of male behavior (Dörner et al., 1968a, 1969, 1975a; Roeder and Müller, 1969; Müller et al., 1974). On the other hand, lesions of the medial preoptic area resulted in decreased male and increased female behavior (Powers and Valenstein, 1972).

Therefore, the following conclusion may be drawn: different neuronal reflex circuits are responsible for male and female sexual behavior. The medial preoptic anterior hypothalamic area comprises an androgen-sensitive control center of a neuronal reflex circuit responsible for male behavior, whereas the ventromedial nucleus region includes a sex-hormone-sensitive center of a neuronal reflex circuit regulating female behavior. Antagonistic interrelationships appear to exist between both hypothalamic mating centers.

2. SEX-HORMONE-DEPENDENT BRAIN DIFFERENTIATION AND GONADOTROPIN SECRETION

Significance of the gonads for the differentiation of gonadotropin secretion

Adult female mammals are characterized by cyclic hypophyseal gonadotropin secretion, whereas male mammals show tonic gonadotropin release. Pfeiffer (1936) observed that in rats, independent of the genetic sex, the lack of testes during a critical developmental phase resulted in cyclic hypophyseal gonadotropin release, whereas the presence of testes gave rise to continuous (tonic) hypophyseal gonadotropin secretion. Thus, ovarian cycles could be induced in male rats castrated immediately after birth and implanted with ovaries after becoming adults. In contrast, ovulations could be induced neither in female rats neonatally implanted with testes nor in male rats orchidectomized after the critical neonatal masculinizing period and then implanted with ovaries. Consequently, male and female rats are born with a latent capacity for cyclic gonadotropin secretion. In the presence of testicular tissue during the first days of life, a male type of differentiation takes place, resulting in tonic gonadotropin secretion for the entire life. When testes are lacking during this critical period, a female type of differentiation occurs, independent of the presence or absence of ovaries. When becoming adult, these animals show a cyclic gonadotropin secretion.

The influence of sex hormone on the differentiation of gonadotropin secretion

Genetic females
Wilson and co-workers (1941), and Barraclough and Gorski (1961) reported that female rats androgenized during neonatal life showed acyclic ovarian function and sterility in adulthood. Takewaki (1962) then confirmed earlier findings of Wilson (1943) showing that unphysiologically high estrogen levels produced during this critical organization phase can also give rise to tonic gonadotropin secretion and acyclic ovarian function during postpubertal life. These persistent changes of gonadotropin secretion and ovarian function produced by androgens or estrogens administered during the critical differentiation period could be prevented, at least in part, by simultanous administration of high doses of progesterone (Kincl and Maqueo, 1965).

Genetic males

Barraclough and Leathem (1954) observed inhibition of testicular growth and some delay of sperm production in juvenile mice treated with high doses of androgen during neonatal life. Atrophy of testes and accessory sex glands, but apparently normal spermiogenesis, were found in neonatally androgenized adult male rats (Swanson and Van der Werff ten Bosch, 1965).

On the other hand, male rats which had been estrogenized neonatally, showed persistent atrophy of genital organs as well as permanent suppression of spermiogenesis (Kincl et al., 1963; Schiawi, 1968). The inhibitory effect of estrogens on spermiogenesis could be prevented again, at least in part, by simultaneous administration of androgen or gonadotropin during the critical neonatal period of testis development (Takasugi and Furukawa, 1972; Takasugi and Mitsuhashi, 1972).

3. SEX-HORMONE-DEPENDENT BRAIN DIFFERENTIATION AND SEXUAL BEHAVIOR

Genetic females

A remarkable observation was reported by Vera Dantchakoff (1938) which was confirmed by Phoenix and co-workers (1959). Female guinea pigs, androgenized prenatally, exhibited increased male sexual behavior after androgen treatment and decreased female behavior after estrogen treatment in adulthood. On the basis of these results, Phoenix and his co-workers distinguished a prenatal organization period and a postpubertal activation period with respect to sexual behavior in guinea pigs. During the first phase, the hypothalamus is physiologically organized, depending on the androgen level, while in the second phase the hypothalamus is activated by either androgens or estrogens. Adult females of other species, such as rats (Dörner, 1972), golden hamsters (Carter et al., 1972; Swanson et al., 1974) or rhesus monkeys (Eaton et al., 1973) showed also predominantly masculine behavioral patterns in adulthood after androgen administration during critical organization periods in perinatal or prenatal life.

Genetic males

Grady and Phoenix (1963) and Harris (1964) reported that male rats orchidectomized shortly after birth showed especially strong female sexual behavior when treated with estrogen in adulthood. Similar findings were obtained in adult male rats which had been treated with antiandrogen during perinatal life (Neumann et al., 1967). All these observations point to the significance of the androgen level during a critical differentiation phase for the development of sexual behavior.

Furthermore, it was demonstrated in different mammalian species that the prenatal or perinatal sex hormone environment can irreversibly influence not only sex-specific sexual behavior but also maternal behavior (Anderson et al., 1970), open-field behavior (Pfaff and Zigmond, 1971), aggressive behavior (Edwards, 1969; Vale et al., 1972), social behavior (Goy and Phoenix, 1971; Gorski, 1973) and sex-specific sleep patterns (Branchey et al., 1973).

4. AUTHOR'S RESEARCH WORK ON SEX-HORMONE-DEPENDENT BRAIN DIFFERENTIATION

The following findings, supplemented with the reports of others, were obtained in our laboratories:

(1) Male rats castrated on the first day of life showed predominantly heterotypical behavior, following androgen substitution in adulthood (Dörner, 1967, 1969, 1970, 1972). In other words, genetic males displaying a temporary androgen deficiency during the hypothalamic organization period, but normal or approximately normal androgen levels in adulthood were sexually excited preferentially by partners of the same sex. Similar data were obtained in golden hamsters (Johnson and Tiefer, 1972).

(2) This neuroendocrine-conditioned male homosexuality could be prevented by androgen administered during the critical hypothalamic differentiation period (Dörner and Hinz, 1971) or suppressed, at least in part, by stereotaxic lesions produced in the hypothalamic ventromedial nuclei during adulthood (Dörner et al., 1968a).

(3) The higher the androgen level during the hypothalamic differentiation phase, the stronger was the male and the weaker the female sexual behavior during the postpubertal functional phase, irrespective of the genetic sex. Even a complete inversion of sexual behavior was observed in male and female rats following androgen deficiency in males and androgen overdosage in females during the hypothalamic differentiation period. According to these findings, a neuroendocrine predisposition for primary hyposexuality, bisexuality and homosexuality may be based on different degrees of androgen deficiency in males and androgen (or even estrogen) overdoses in females during sex-specific brain differentiation (Dörner, 1969, 1970).

(4) The higher the androgen level during the critical hypothalamic differentiation period, the smaller were the nuclear volumes of neurons in the preoptic anterior hypothalamic area and in the ventromedial nuclei, and the larger the nuclear volumes of neurons in the arcuate and ventral premammillary nuclei through the entire life (Dörner and Staudt, 1968, 1969; Staudt et al., 1973). Moreover, the number of non-amygdaloid spine synapses in the preoptic area was found to be higher in normal females and neonatally castrated males than in normal males and neonatally androgenized females (Raisman and Field, 1973).

(5) In male rats castrated on the first day of life, a positive estrogen feedback effect (Hohlweg effect) could be induced similar to that in normal females, but it could not be induced in males castrated on the 14th day of

life, nor in neonatally androgenized (or estrogenized) females (Dörner and Döcke, 1964; Döcke and Dörner, 1966).

(6) A positive estrogen feedback effect could be elicited in intact homosexual men in contrast to intact heterosexual and bisexual men (Fig. 1). Thus, in homosexual men, an intraveneous injection of conjugated estrogens (20 mg Presomen®, which is comparable to Premarin®) produced a primary decrease of the LH serum level followed by a secondary increase above the initial LH values. In heterosexual and in bisexual men, on the other hand, the intraveneous estrogen administation also produced a decrease of the LH serum level which, however, was not followed by an increase above the initial LH values (Dörner et al., 1972, 1975b). This finding suggests that homosexual men may possess — at least in part — a predominantly female-differentiated brain, since in women a positive feedback action is also evocable by conjugated estrogens (Van de Wiele et al., 1970; Tanisawa et al., 1974).

(7) In female rats, unphysiologically high androgen and/or estrogen levels produced during different phases of the hypothalamic differentiation period caused anovulatory sterility and/or a neuroendocrine predisposition for female hyposexuality, bisexuality or homosexuality (Dörner et al., 1971a; Dörner and Hinz, 1972). A complete masculinization of sexual behavior in female rats was observed only following combined prenatal and postnatal androgen treatment (Ward, 1969; Sachs and Pollak, 1973).

(8) In rats of both sexes, very high androgen or estrogen doses administered during the sex-specific brain organization gave rise to permanent hypo-

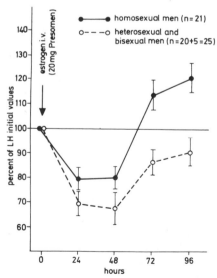

Fig. 1. Plasma LH response to an intravenous estrogen injection expressed as percent of the inital LH values in homosexual, heterosexual or bisexual men (mean ± S.E.).

gonadism (Dörner, 1972). In this context, it may be mentioned that androgens are converted to estrogens, at least in part, by neural tissues from fetal and neonatal rats (Reddy et al., 1974). In contrast to the testes of highly androgenized males, the testes of highly estrogenized males could not be stimulated by exogenous gonadotropins in adulthood (Dörner and Hinz, 1971).

In summary, the following correlational tendencies, mostly in animals, were found between changes of the androgen and/or estrogen levels during the hypothalamic differentiation phase and permanent sexual functioning during the postpubertal hypothalamic functional phase:

In a genetic male, an androgen deficiency during the hypothalamic differentiation phase may result in a more or less female differentiation of certain aspects of the brain; namely, a neuroendocrine predisposition for male hyposexuality, bisexuality, or even homosexuality, possibly associated with the evocability of a positive estrogen feedback effect.

In a genetic female, androgen or estrogen overdose during the hypothalamic differentiation phase may lead to more or less male differentiation of certain aspects of the brain, namely anovulatory sterility and/or neuroendocrine predisposition for female hyposexuality, bisexuality or homosexuality.

In both sexes, very high androgen and/or estrogen levels during the hypothalamic differentiation phase give rise to permanent hypogonadism.

In view of these findings, it may be conjectured that important disturbances of sexual functions may be based on discrepancies between the genetic sex and the sex-hormone level during the hypothalamic differentiation phase. A causal prophylaxis may become possible in the future by preventing such discrepancies during the time of sex-specific brain organization.

Three preconditions towards this aim have been achieved in our laboratories:

(a) Comparative studies of hypothalamic biomorphosis in human fetuses and rats have led to the conclusion that the critical hypothalamic differentiation period may be timed in the human between the 4th and 7th month of fetal life (Dörner and Staudt, 1972).

(b) A simple and reliable method for the prenatal diagnosis of genetic sex was developed using fluorescence microscopy of amniotic fluid cells (Dörner et al., 1973a).

(c) Significantly higher testosterone concentrations were found in amniotic fluids of male fetuses than in those of female fetuses (Dörner et al., 1973b). Moreover, during early pregnancy, significantly higher urinary values of testosterone were observed in mothers with male fetuses than in those with female fetuses (Dörner et al., 1971b; Loewit et al., 1974).

The following ontogenic organization (differentiation) rules have been deduced from our studies together with those of other groups (Fig. 2):

During the critical hypothalamic differentiation phase, an open-loop regulatory system (e.g. placenta and/or fetal hypophysis—gonad—hypothalamus) is converted into a feedback control system (hypothalamic—hypophyseal—gonadal system). The regulating variable and the regulated element of the

234

I. Prenatal open-loop regulatory system

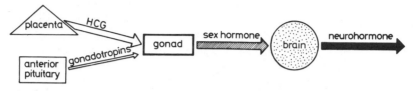

II. Postnatal feedback control system (closed-loop regulatory system)

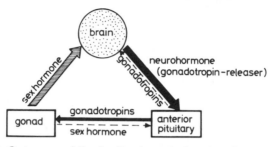

Fig. 2. Ontogeny of the feedback control system for reproduction.

primary open-loop regulatory system (for example, sex hormone and hypo-thalamus) are then transformed into the controlled condition (homeostatic variable) and the central nervous controller of the secondary feedback con-trol system (transformation rule).

The quantity of the primarily regulating and secondarily homeostatic variable (for example, sex hormone) determines during brain differentiation the quality (responsiveness) of the central nervous controller, and hence the functional and tolerance ranges of the feedback control system (determina-tion rule).

These ontogenic organization rules deduced for the hypothalamic—hypo-physeal—gonadal system regulating reproduction may also be valid for other neuroendocrine and neurovegetative systems controlling metabolism, and for neuronal behavioral systems regulating information processing (Dörner, 1974, 1976).

As shown in Fig. 3, the primarily regulating and secondarily homeostatic variables of these systems (hormones, metabolites, external signals) act on specific brain regions either as direct endogenous effectors (for example, hor-mones) or as indirect endogenous or exogenous effectors (for example, me-tabolites or external signals). The action of the indirect effectors is mediated by direct effectors, that is, by hormones produced in endocrine glands or by neurotransmitters produced in sensory receptor cells of the central nervous system (CNS).

As a preliminary conceptual model, the following theory may be ad-vanced for the effector dependent brain differentiation at the molecular level (Fig. 4):

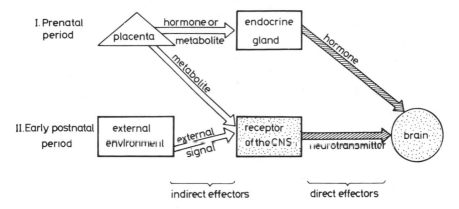

Fig. 3. Effectors as possible determinants of brain differentiation.

During the differentiation period, an effector E (for example, testosterone) activates the regulatory protein R_{D1} produced by the regulatory gene RG_{D1} and/or inactivates the regulatory protein R_{D2} produced by the regulatory gene RG_{D2}. Consequently, in the presence of the effector E during the differentiation phase, the specific regulatory gene RG_{F1} for the entire functional phase may be irreversibly activated, that is, organized or imprinted so as to result in the production of specific RNA and the regulatory protein R_{F1}, which is primarily inactive. During the functional period, this regulatory protein R_{F1} then reacts as a binding site to the same (or similar) effector E. Hence, specific structural genes (e.g. SG_{F1a} and SG_{F1b}) are now reversibly activated leading to the production of specific enzymes (1a and 1b in Fig. 4).

In the absence of the effector E during the differentiation period, the primarily active regulatory protein R_{D2} produced by the regulatory gene RG_{D2} is not inactivated and, thus, may irreversibly activate (organize or imprint) the regulatory gene RG_{F2} for the entire functional phase, resulting in the production of the primarily inactive regulatory protein RF_2. During the functional period, this regulatory protein R_{F2} then reacts as an alternative regulating site to the same (or similar) effector E. Hence, other specific structural genes (SG_{F2a} and SG_{F2b} in Fig. 4) are now reversibly activated, leading to the production of other specific enzymes (2a and 2b in Fig. 4).

Consequently, the following correlations may be assumed at the molecular level: the higher the concentration of the effector E (for example, testosterone) during the critical differentiation period, the higher is the transcribeability of RG_{F1} and, hence, of SG_{F1a} and SG_{F1b} and/or the lower is the transcribeability of RG_{F2} and, hence, of SG_{F2a} and SG_{F2b} during the functional phase and vice versa.

Although this concept should be considered hypothetical thus far, it might explain the androgen-dependent differentiation of the brain resulting in a permanently different responsiveness of the central nervous system to

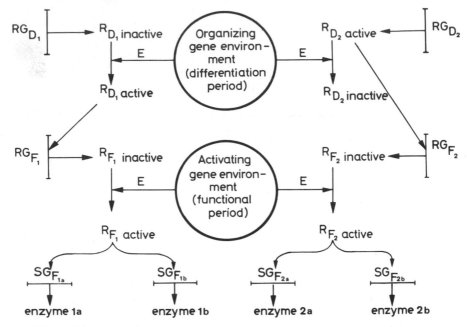

Fig. 4. Possible interactions between genetic material and gene environment.

androgen and estrogen regarding sex-specific sexual behavior as well as gonadotropin secretion.

In addition, the following findings might favor this theory:

(a) There is increasing evidence for the existence of specific receptor proteins in the cytoplasm of target cells, including the brain, that bind sex hormones (Kato, 1974). The sex hormone—protein complex is transported to the cell nucleus, binding to acidic proteins as chromatin acceptor sites (Steggles et al., 1971; Liao et al., 1972). Such receptor and/or acceptor proteins may represent, in fact, regulatory proteins of the kind discussed above (R_F).

(b) The binding capacity of the hypothalamus for estrogen and androgen during the functional phase is dependent on the androgen level during the hypothalamic differentiation phase. The higher the androgen level during the hypothalamic differentiation phase, the lower the binding capacity for estrogen and the higher for androgen during the functional phase (Flerkó et al., 1969; Tuohimaa and Johansson, 1971; Vértes and King, 1971; Dixit and Niemi, 1974; Poppe et al., 1975).

(c) The activity of specific enzymes responsible for the metabolism of sex hormones can be permanently influenced by the sex hormone level during a critical differentiation phase (Stahl et al., 1971; Tuohimaa and Niemi, 1972; Denef, 1973; Poppe et al., 1974).

(d) The androgen dependent sex-specific brain differentiation can be blocked by inhibitors of DNA, RNA and protein synthesis (Kobayashi and Gorski, 1970; Gorski and Shryne, 1972; Salaman and Birkeit, 1974).

Irrespective of the exact mechanisms at the molecular level, the following ontogenic basic rule may be deduced for fundamental processes of life: during critical organization (differentiation) periods, especially of the brain, the quantity of specific effectors (for example, sex hormone) which are to be controlled for the entire functional phase, can predetermine the quality or the responsiveness, of their own controller and, hence, the functional and tolerance ranges of their self-organizing feedback control system.

In my opinion, many functional disturbances, diseases and syndromes of reproduction, metabolism and information processing, often called 'idiopathic, genuine, primary or endogenous' thus far, may be explained etiopathogenetically by this principle and could even be prevented, at least in part, by optimizing the organizing gene environment during critical differentiation periods, especially of the brain. Therefore, 'structural teratology' should be complemented by 'functional teratology' in the future.

5. SUMMARY

Four critical ontogenic periods may be distinguished for sex-specific development in mammals:

Determination of the gonosomal sex   Fertilization of an ovum (with X-gonosome) by an androsperm (with Y-gonosome) results in a male zygote (XY), whereas impregnation of an ovum by a gynosperm (with X-gonosome) results in a female zygote (XX).

Organization of the gonads   Primordial germ cells migrate into a gonadal blastema. If the somatic cells of this blastema contain a Y-gonosome, testes will be organized, whereas in the absence of a Y-gonosome and in the presence of 2 X-gonosomes, ovaries will be differentiated.

Sex-hormone-dependent differentiation of the genital organs and the brain The organization of the gonads is followed by the differentiation of (a) male or female gonaducts (months 2—3 of fetal life in the human); (b) male or female external genitalia (months 3—4); and (c) a male or female hypothalamus (months 4—7). In the presence of testosterone-producing testes there is a male differentiation, whereas in the absence of testes a female diffentiation occurs, irrespective of the presence or absence of ovaries.

Development of the gender role   The gender role appears to be affected (a) by the sex-hormone-dependent differentiations of the external genitalia and especially of the brain, and is influenced additionally in higher mammals (b) by educational and sociocultural factors, in particular during a critical period of early postnatal life (environment-dependent determination of sexual self-identity).

Consequently, the following disorders of sex differentiation may be distinguished:

Gonosomal disorders XO (gonadal dysgenesis), XXY (sex-chromatin-positive Klinefelter's syndrome), XYY, and gonosomal mosaics.

Gonadal organization disturbances Pure gonadal dysgenesis, sex-chromatin-negative Klinefelter's syndrome, and hermaphroditism with XY or XX.

Differentiation disturbances of the genital organs and/or of the central nervous system Internal and/or external, and/or central nervous pseudo-hermaphroditism in males and females.

Disorders of the gender role Transvestitism and transexualism.

Most disorders of sex differentiation are based on gonosomal disturbances (genetic defects) or on discrepancies between the gonosomal sex and the sex-specific sex hormone status during critical differentiation periods of the internal and/or external genital organs, and/or, in particular, of the brain.

In gonosomal males, androgen deficiency during a critical differentiation period may lead to a more or less female differentiation of certain aspects of the brain, that is a neuroendocrine predisposition for male hyposexuality, bisexuality or even homosexuality, possibly associated with the evocability of a positive estrogen feedback on LH-release. In gonosomal females, on the other hand, an unphysiological increase of either the androgen and/or estrogen level during the differentiation phase may result in a more or less male differentiation of certain aspects of the brain, that is neuroendocrine predisposition for female hyposexuality, bisexuality, or homosexuality and/or (at least in some mammals) oligo- or acyclic hypophyseal gonadotropin secretion associated with a decreased or absent positive estrogen feedback effect. Finally, excessively high androgen or estrogen levels during the sex-specific brain differentiation can lead to permanent hypogonadism in both sexes.

All treatment of genetic defects is purely symptomatic. In contrast, a causal preventive therapy seems to be possible in structural and/or functional disturbances established during critical differentiation periods as lifelong effective modifications. Since important sexual disorders can be based on discrepancies between the genetic sex and the sex hormone level during the critical differentiation phases, a causal prophylaxis may become possible in future by preventing such discrepancies during these critical periods, though the possibility of undesired side effects is completely unknown, and the ethics of intervention will need to be settled.

Three preconditions towards this aim have been approximately achieved (Dörner, 1976): determination of the periods of sex-hormone-dependent differentiation; development of a reliable method for prenatal diagnosis of the genetic sex; and demonstration of different testosterone concentrations in women bearing male or female fetuses.

BIBLIOGRAPHY

Anderson, C.O., Zarrow, M.X. and Denenberg, V.H. (1970) Maternal behavior in the rabbit: effects of androgen treatment during gestation upon the nest building behavior of the mother and her offspring. *Horm. Behav.* 1: 337—345.

Aschheim, S. and Zondek, B. (1927) Hypophysenvorderlappenhormon und Schwangeren-hormon im Harn von Schwangeren. *Klin. Wochenschr.* 6: 1322.

Aschner, B. (1912) Uber die Beziehungen zwischen Hypophysis und Genitale. *Arch. Gynäkol.* 97: 200—228.

Barraclough, C.A. and Gorski, R.A. (1961) Evidence that the hypothalamus is responsible for androgen-induced sterility in the female rat. *Endocrinology* 68: 68—70.

Barraclough, C.A. and Leatham, J.H. (1954) Infertility induced in mice by a single injection of testosterone propionate. *Proc. Soc. Exp. Biol. Med. N.Y.* 85: 673—674.

Berthold, A.A. (1849) Transplantation der Hoden. *Arch. Anat. Physiol.* 42—46.

Branchey, L., Branchey, M. and Nadler, R.D. (1973) Effect of sex hormones on sleep patterns of male rats gonadectomized in adulthood and in the neonatal period. *Physiol. Behav.* 11: 609—611.

Brookhart, J.M. and Dey, F.L. (1941) Reduction of sexual behavior in male guinea pigs by hypothalamic lesions. *Am. J. Physiol.* 133:551—554.

Carrer, H., Asch, G. and Aron, C. (1973/74) New facts concerning the role played by the ventromedial nucleus in the control of estrous cycle duration and sexual receptivity in the rat. *Neuroendocrinology* 13: 129—138.

Carter, C.S., Clemens, L.G. and Hoekema, D.J. (1972) Neonatal androgen and adult sexual behavior in the golden hamster. *Physiol. Behav.* 9: 89—95.

Dantchakoff, V. (1938) Rôle des hormones dans la manifestation des instincts sexuels. *Acad. Sci. (Paris)* 206: 945—947.

Denef, C. (1973) Differentiation of steroid metabolism in the rat and mechanisms of neonatal androgen action. *Enzyme* 15: 254—271.

Dixit, V.P. and Niemi, M. (1974) Uptake of exogenous ³H-1,2 testosterone in the hypothalamus, endocrine glands and sex-accessory organs in neonatally castrated and androgenized male rats. *Endocrinol. Exp.* 8: 30—43.

Döcke, F. and Dörner, G. (1966) Tierexperimentelle Untersuchungen zur Ovulationsauslösung mit Gonadotropinen und Ostrogenen. 4. Mittl., Zur neurohormonalen Regulation der Ovulation. *Zbl. Gynäkol.* 88: 273—282.

Döcke, F., Smollich, A., Rohde, W., Okrasa, R. and Dörner, G. (1975) Studies on extra-hypophyseal sites of estrogen action in the induction of ovulation in rats. *Endokrinologie* 65: 274—287.

Dörner, G. (1967) Tierexperimentelle Untersuchungen zur Frage einer hormonalen Pathogenese der Homosexualität. *Acta Biol. Med. Germ.* 19: 569—584.

Dörner, G. (1969) Zur Frage einer neuroendokrinen Pathogenese, Prophylaxe und Therapie angeborener Sexualdeviationen. *Dtsch. Med. Wochenschr.* 94: 390—396.

Dörner, G. (1970) The influence of sex hormones during the hypothalamic differentiation and maturation phases on gonadal function and sexual behaviour during the hypothalamic functional phase. *Endokrinologie* 56: 280—291.

Dörner, G. (1972) *Sexualhormonabhängige Gehirndifferenzierung und Sexualität*. (Gustav Fischer, Jena und Springer, Wien/New York).

Dörner, G. (1974) Environment-dependent brain differentiation and fundamental processes of life. *Acta Biol. Med. Germ.* 33: 129—148.

Dörner, G. (1976) *Hormones and Brain Differentiation*. (Elsevier Amsterdam).

Dörner, G. and Döcke, F. (1964) Sex-specific reaction of the hypothalamo-hypophysial system of rats. *J. Endocrinol.* 30: 265—266.

Dörner, G., Döcke, F. and Götz, F (1975a) Male-like sexual behaviour of female rats with unilateral lesions in the hypothalamic ventromedial nuclear region. *Endokrinologie* 65: 133—137.

Dörner, G., Döcke, F. and Hinz, G. (1968a) Entwicklung und Rückbildung neuroendokrin bedingter männlicher Homosexualität. *Acta Biol. Med. Germ.* 21: 577—580.

Dörner, G., Döcke, F. and Hinz, G. (1969) Homo- and hypersexuality in rats with hypothalamic lesions. *Neuroendocrinology* 4: 20—24.

240

Dörner, G., Döcke, F. and Hinz, G. (1971a) Paradoxical effects of estrogen on brain differentiation. *Neuroendocrinology* 7: 146—155.

Dörner, G., Döcke, F. and Moustafa, S. (1968b) Differential localization of a male and a female hypothalamic mating centre. *J. Reprod. Fertil.* 17: 583—586.

Dörner, G. and Hinz, G. (1971) Männlicher Hypogonadismus mit sekundärer Hyposexualität nach hochdosierten Gaben von Ostrogenen während der hypothalamischen Differenzierungsphase. *Endokrinologie* 58: 227—233.

Dörner, G. and Hinz, G. (1972) Neuroendokrin bedingte Prädisposition für weibliche Homosexualität bei erhaltener zyklischer Ovarialfunktion. *Endokrinologie* 59: 48—52.

Dörner, G., Rohde, W., Baumgarten, G., Herter, U., Halle, H., Gruber, G., Rössner, P., Bergmann, K.H., Götz, F. and Zillmann, R. (1973a) Zur pränatalen Geschlechtsbestimmung im Fruchtwasser und peripheren mütterlichen Blut durch fluoreszenzmikroskopischen Nachweis des Y-Chromosoms. *Zbl. Gynäkol.* 95: 625—634.

Dörner, G., Rohde, W. and Krell, L. (1972) Auslösung eines positiven Ostrogenfeedback-Effekt bei homosexuellen Männern. *Endokrinologie* 60: 297—301.

Dörner, G., Rohde, W., Stahl, F., Krell, L. and Masius, W. (1975b) Neuroendocrine conditioned predisposition for homosexuality in men. *Arch. Sex. Behav.* 4: 1—8.

Dörner, G., Stahl, F., Götz, F., Rössner, P. und Halle, H. (1971b) Der Einfluss des fötalen Geschlechts auf den Androgengehalt im Frühschwangerenharn. *Endokrinologie* 58: 264—268.

Dörner, G., Stahl, F. Rohde, W., Halle, H., Rössner, P., Gruber, D. und Herter, U. (1973b) Radioimmunologische Bestimmung des Testosterongehalts im Fruchtwasser männlicher und weiblicher Feten. *Endokrinologie* 61: 317—320.

Dörner, G. and Staudt, J. (1968) Structural changes in the preoptic anterior hypothalamic area of the male rat, following neonatal castration and androgen substitution. *Neuroendocrinology* 3: 136—140.

Dörner, G. and Staudt, J. (1969) Structural changes in the hypothalamic ventromedial nucleus of the male rat, following neonatal castration and androgen treatment. *Neuroendocrinology* 4: 278—281.

Dörner, G. and Staudt, J. (1972) Vergleichende morphologische Untersuchungen der Hypothalamusdifferenzierung bei Ratte und Mensch. *Endokrinologie* 59: 151—155.

Eaton, G.G., Goy, R.W. and Phoenix, C.H. (1973) Effects of testosterone treatment in adulthood on sexual behaviour of female pseudohermaphrodite Rhesus monkeys. *Nature* 242: 119—120.

Edwards, D.A. (1969) Early androgen stimulation and aggressive behavior in male and female mice. *Physiol. Behav.* 4: 333—338.

Flerkó, B., Mess, B. and Illei-Donhoffer, A. (1969) On the mechanism of androgen sterilization. *Neuroendocrinology* 4: 164—169.

Geiger, R., König, W., Wissman, H. and Enzmann, F. (1971) Synthesis and characterisation of a decapeptide having LH-RH/FSH-RH activity. *Biochem. Biophys. Res. Commun* 45: 767—773.

Gorski, R.A. (1973) Perinatal effects of sex steroids on brain development and function. In: (E. Zimmermann, W.H. Gispen, B.H. Marks and D. de Wied, Eds.) *Progress in Brain Research*. Vol. 39 (Elsevier Scientific Publ. Co., Amsterdam) pp. 149—163.

Gorski, R.A. and Shryne, J. (1972) Intracerebral antibiotics and androgenization of the neonatal female rat. *Neuroendocrinology* 10: 109—120.

Goy, R.W. and Phoenix, C.H. (1971) The effects of testosterone propionate administered before birth on the development of behavior in genetic female Rhesus monkeys. In: (C.H. Sawyer and R.A. Gorski, Eds.) *Steroid Hormones and Brain Function* UCLA Forum Sci. No. 15 (Univ. of California Press, Los Angeles) pp. 193—202.

Grady, K.L. and Phoenix, C.H. (1963) Hormonal determinants of mating behavior; the display of feminine behavior by adult male rats castrated neonatally. *Am. Zool.* 3: 482—483.

Johnson, W.A. and Tiefer, L. (1972) Sexual preferences in neonatally castrated male golden hamsters. *Physiol. Behav.* 9: 213—217.

Halban, J. (1900) Uber den Einfluss der Ovarien auf die Entwicklung des Genitales. *Mschr. Geburtsh. Gynäkol.* 12: 496.

Harris, G.W. (1955) *Neural Control of the Pituitary Gland.* (Edward Arnold, London.)

Harris, G.W. (1964) Sex hormones, brain development and brain function. *Endocrinology* 75: 627—648.

Hohlweg, W. and Junkmann, K. (1932) Die hormonal-nervöse Regulierung der Funktion des Hypophysenvorderlappens. *Klin. Wochenschr.* 11: 321—323.

Kamberi, I. (1974) Catecholaminergic, indolaminergic and cholinergic pathway and the hypothalamic hypophysiotropic neurohormones involved in control of gonadotropin secretion. In: (G. Dörner, Ed.) *Endocrinology of Sex.* (Barth, Leipzig) pp. 80—105.

Kato, J. (1974) Sex hormone receptors in the hypothalamus and hypophysis. In: (G. Dörner, Ed.) *Endocrinology of Sex.* (Barth, Leipzig) pp. 202—217.

Kawakami, M. and Terasawa, E. (1974) Role of limbic forebrain structures on reproductive cycles. In: (M. Kawakami, Ed.) *Biological Rhythms in Neuroendocrine activity.* (Igaku Shoin Ltd., Tokyo) pp. 197—219.

Kincl, F.A., Folch Pi, A. and Herrera Lasso, L. (1963) Effect of estradiol benzoate treatment in the newborn male rat. *Endocrinology* 72: 966—968.

Kincl, F.A. and Maqueo, M. (1965) Prevention by progesterone of steroid induced sterility in neonatal male and female rats. *Endocrinology* 77: 859—862.

Knauer, E. (1900) Die Ovarientransplantation. *Arch. Gynäkol.* 60: 322—376.

Kobayashi, F. and Gorski, R.A. (1970) Effects of antibiotics on androgenization of the neonatal female rat. *Endocrinology* 86: 285—289.

Liao, S., Liang, R. and Tymoczko, J.L. (1972) Structural recognitions in the interactions of androgens and receptor proteins and in their association with nuclear acceptor components. *J. Steroid. Biochem.* 3: 401—408.

Loewit, K., Egg, D., Voigt, K. and Keusch, H. (1974) Fetale Geschlechtsbestimmung aus der mütterlichen Testosteronausscheidung in der Frühschwangerschaft. *Dtsch. Med. Wochenschr.* 99: 1656—1657.

McCann, S.M., Taleisnik, M.S. and Friedman, H.M. (1960) LH-releasing activity in hypothalamic extracts. *Proc. Soc. Exp. Biol.* 104: 432—434.

Müller, D., Orthner, H., Roeder, F., König, A., Bosse, K., Kloos, G. (1974) The effect of hypothalamic lesions on sex behavior and gonadotropic functions in the human. In: (G. Dörner, Ed.) *Endocrinology of Sex.* (Barth, Leipzig) pp. 80—100.

Nadler, R.D. (1970) Intrahypothalamic exploration of androgen-sensitive brain loci in neonatal female rats. *Trans. N.Y. Acad. Sci. Ser. II* 34: 572—581.

Napoli, A., Powers, J.B. and Valenstein, E.S. (1972) Hormonal induction of behavioral estrus modified by electrical stimulation of hypothalamus. *Physiol. Behav.* 9: 115—117.

Neumann, F., Elger, W. and von Berswordt-Wallrabe, R. (1967) Intersexualität männlicher Feten und Hemmung androgenabhängiger Funktionen bei erwachsenen Tieren durch Testosteronblocker. *Dtsch. med. Wochenschr.* 92: 360—366.

Pfaff, D.W. and Zigmond, R.E. (1971) Neonatal androgen effects on sexual and nonsexual behavior of adult rats tested under various hormone regimes. *Neuroendocrinology* 7: 129—145.

Pfeiffer, C.A. (1936) Sexual differences of the hypophyses and their determination by the gonads. *Am. J. Anat.* 58: 195—225.

Phoenix, C.H., Goy, R.W., Gerall, A.A. and Young, W.C. (1959) Organizing action of prenatally administered testosterone propionate on the tissues mediating mating behavior in the female guinea pig. *Endocrinology* 65: 369—382.

Poppe, I., Stahl, F. and Dörner, G. (1974) On sex-specific in vitro reactions of hypothalamic and hypophysial tissues for sex hormones. In: (G. Dörner, Ed.) *Endocrinology of Sex.* (Barth, Leipzig) pp. 198—200.

Poppe, I., Stahl, F., Götz, F. and Dörner, G. (1975) Different estrogen binding capacity in the medial basal hypothalamus of male and female rats. *Endokrinologie* 65: 227—228.

Powers, J.B. (1972) Facilitation of lordosis in ovariectomized rats by intracerebral progesterone implants. *Brain Res.* 48: 311—325.

Powers, J.B. and Valenstein, E.S. (1972) Sexual receptivity facilitation by medial preoptic lesions in female rats. *Science* 175: 1003—1005.

Raisman, G. and Field, P.M. (1973) Sexual dimorphism in the neuropil of the preoptic area of the rat and its dependence on neonatal androgen. *Brain. Res.* 54: 1—29.

Reddy, V.V.R., Naftolin, F. and Ryan, K.J. (1974) Conversion of androstendione to estrone by neural tissues from fetal and neonatal rats. *Endocrinology* 94: 117—121.

Roeder, F. and Müller, D. (1969) Zur stereotaktischen Heilung der pädophilen Homosexualität. *Dtsch. Med. Wochenschr.* 94: 409—415.

Sachs, B.D. and Pollak, E.E. (1973) Sexual behavior: normal male patterning in androgenized female rats. *Science* 181: 770—772.

Salaman, D.F. and Birkeit, S. (1974) Androgen induced sexual differentiation of the brain is blocked by inhibitors of DNA and RNA synthesis. *Nature* 247: 109—111.

Schally, A.V., Kastin, A.J. and Arimura, A. (1971) Hypothalamic follicle stimulating hormone (FSH) and luteinizing hormone (LH)-regulating hormone: structure, physiology and clinical studies. *Fertil. Steril.* 22: 703—721.

Schiawi, R.C. (1968) Adenohypophyseal and serum gonadotrophins in male rats treated neonatally with estradiol benzoate. *Endocrinology* 82: 983—988.

Smith, P.E. and Engle, E.T. (1927) Experimental evidence regarding the role of the anterior pituitary in the development and regulation of the genital system. *Am. J. Anat.* 40: 159—217.

Stahl, F., Poppe, I. and Dörner, G. (1971) Umwandlungsraten von Testosteron zu Dihydrotestosteron und Androsteron in Hypophyse, Hypothalamus und Kortex männlicher und weiblicher Ratten. *Acta Biol. Med. Germ.* 26: 855—858.

Staudt, J., Dörner, G., Döll, R. and Blöse, J. (1973) Geschlechtsspezifische morphologische Unterschiede im Nucleus arcuates und praemamillaris ventralis der Ratte. *Endokrinologie* 62: 234—236.

Steggles, A.W., Spelsberg, T.C., Glasser, S.R. and O'Malley, B.W. (1971) Soluble complexes between steroid hormone and target tissue receptors bind specifically to target-tissue chromatin. *Proc. Natl. Acad. Sci. U.S. (Wash.)* 68: 1479—1482.

Swanson, H., Brayshow, J.S. and Payne, A.P. (1974) Effects of neonatal androgenization on sexual and aggressive behaviour in the golden hamster. In: (G. Dörner, Ed.) *Endocrinology of Sex.* (Barth, Leipzig) pp. 61—74.

Swanson, H.E. and van der Werff ten Bosch, J.J. (1965) Modification of male rat reproductive tract development by a single injection of testosterone propionate shortly after birth. *Acta Endocrinol. (Kbh.)* 50: 310—316.

Takasugi, N. and Furukawa, M. (1972) Inhibitory effect of androgen on induction of permanent changes in the testes by neonatal injections of estrogen in mice. *Endocrinol. Jap.* 19: 417—422.

Takasugi, N. and Mitsuhashi, Y. (1972) Effects of gonadotropins on the occurence of permanent changes in the testis of mice given neonatal estrogen injections. *Endocrinol. Jap.* 19: 423—428.

Takewaki, K. (1962) Some aspects of hormonal mechanism involved in persistent estrus in the rat. *Experientia (Basel)* 18: 1—6.

Tanisawa, O., Aono, T., Minagawa, G., Miyake, A., Kawamura, K., Fukada, N., Ichii, H., Yamaji, K. and Kurachi, K. (1974) Humoral regulation of gonadotropin secretion in the female. *Psychoneuroendocrinology*, Workshop Conf. Int. Soc. Psychoneuroendocrinology (Karger, Basel) pp. 39—47.

Tuohimaa, P. and Johannsson, R. (1971) Decreased estradiol binding in the uterus and anterior hypothalamus of androgenized female rats. *Endocrinology* 88: 1159—1164.

Tuohimaa, P. and Niemi, M. (1972) In vitro uptake of tritiated sex steroids by the hypothalamus of adult male rats treated neonatally with an antiandrogen (cyproterone). *Acta Endocrinol.* 71: 45—54.

Vale, J.R., Ray, D. and Vale, C.A. (1972) The interaction of genotype and exogenous neonatal androgen: agonistic behavior in female mice. *Behav. Biol.* 7: 321—334.

Van de Wiele, K.L., Bogumil, F., Dyrenfurth, F., Ferin, M., Jewelewicz, R., Warren, M., Rizkaliah, R. and Mikhail, G. (1970) Mechanisms regulating the menstrual cycle in women. *Recent Prog. Horm. Res.* 26: 63—95.

Vértes, M. and King, R.J.B. (1971) The mechanism of estradiol binding in rat hypothalamus: effect of androgenization. *J. Endocrinol.* 51: 271—282.

Ward, I.L. (1969) Differential effect of pre- and postnatal androgen on the sexual behavior of intact and spayed female rats. *Horm. Behav.* 1: 25—36.

Wilson, J.G. (1943) Reproductive capacity of adult female rats treated prepuberally with estrogenic hormone. *Anat. Rec.* 86: 341—359.

Wilson, J.G., Hamilton, J.B. and Young, W.C. (1941) Influence of age and presence of the ovaries on reproductive function in rats injected with androgens. *Endocrinology* 29: 784—789.

CHAPTER 18

Prenatal androgenization and human psychosexual behavior

ANKE A. EHRHARDT

1. INTRODUCTION

Prenatal hormones play a crucial role in the differentiation of mammalian external genitalia. In fact, they determine whether the external sex organs will resemble those of a female or those of a male. More recently, animal experimentalists have documented that prenatal sex hormones also influence CNS differentiation and, thus, certain aspects of sex-related behavior. If androgen is present at a critical time of differentiation, the exposed animal will exhibit more male-like behavior when stimulated with androgen in adulthood. If androgen is not present, the probability increases that female-like behavior will occur after exposure to female sex hormones in adulthood. This relationship of hormones and behavior is independent of the genetic sex, that is, it can be experimentally produced contrary to the animal's genetic sex.

The study of behavior and its hormonal roots becomes more and more complex the higher one gets on the phylogenetic ladder. Physiologic and environmental factors become more intricately linked and more difficult to separate as to their etiologic contributions to any kind of behavior. Thus, it is not surprising that the presently available evidence on the effects of prenatal hormones on behavior in primates is still rather speculative and fragmentary.

2. NONHUMAN PRIMATES: PRENATAL ANDROGENIZATION IN GENETIC FEMALE RHESUS MONKEYS

The classical experiment on behavior in nonhuman primates was carried out at the Oregon Primate Research Center. There, Goy and Phoenix injected testosterone propionate into pregnant rhesus monkeys (Goy, 1968). The effect on the external genitalia of genetic female offspring was as expected:

Handbook of Sexology, edited by J. Money and H. Musaph
© *Elsevier/North-Holland Biomedical Press, 1977*

female monkeys were born with masculinized external genitalia, but with normal female internal reproductive structures. These prenatally masculinized female monkeys have been under observational study for several years as to changes in any aspect of the typically sexually dimorphic behavior of their species.

Sex differences in the behavior of young rhesus monkeys include performance of threat, play initiation, rough-and-tumble and chasing play. On each of these activities, males normally exhibit much higher frequencies than females. These sex differences of behavior in juvenile monkeys could not be solely attributed to hormonal sex differences in postnatal development since prepubertal male and female rhesus monkeys were not found to be markedly different in sex hormone levels. Thus, the question is whether one has any evidence that it is the differential exposure to prenatal androgens which affects postnatal behavioral differences between the sexes.

Prenatally androgenized females were compared in their juvenile behavior with normal male and female peers concurrently. The results of long-term behavior studies were as follows: fetally masculinized female monkeys displayed frequencies in their performance of play initiation, threat, rough-and-tumble and chasing play which were either intermediate or overlapped extensively with the normal male standard. Not only play, but also juvenile sexual behavior was modified in the prenatally androgenized females — their mounting frequencies were more similar to the mounting frequencies of male controls and exceeded those of female controls.

In adulthood, the prenatally androgenized genetic females were ovariectomized and primed with estradiol benzoate and compared with a female control group (Eaton et al., 1973). The experimental group differed in aggression. They attacked other females more vigorously and more frequently. When both groups of females were treated with testosterone propionate, the difference in aggressive behavior increased even more. The prenatally androgenized females also surpassed the control females in scores for sexual behavior such as yawning, grooming, and sexual exploration toward other females. Before and after testosterone propionate treatment, the experimental females mounted other females more frequently than did the female controls.

The experimenters concluded that the modifications in juvenile behavior of prenatally androgenized females and the differences between the two female groups in adult behavior before testosterone propionate treatment suggest that testosterone injected into the pregnant rhesus monkey can modify the central nervous system of genetic female fetuses so that they are predisposed to acquire more masculine patterns of behavior. The sexual and other types of behavior that increased in frequency after testosterone propionate treatment in adulthood indicated an increased sensitivity to the action of testosterone. One can also conclude from these experiments that some sex differences in behavior between normal male and female rhesus monkeys may well be influenced by sex differences in prenatal hormonal levels.

3. ANDROGEN EFFECTS ON HUMAN PSYCHOSEXUAL DIFFERENTIATION

When it comes to human behavior, our evidence is limited to studies on clinical populations. Such clinical groups with a known history of prenatal hormonal imbalance ranging from an excess of fetal androgens in genetic females to a cellular insensitivity to androgen in genetic males, have been in process over several years (see Money and Ehrhardt, 1972a).

Fetal androgen excess in genetic females

There are two major syndromes of prenatal androgen excess in which the human genetic female fetus is masculinized: the adrenogenital syndrome and the syndrome of progestin-induced female hermaphroditism.

The adrenogenital syndrome (AGS) is a condition in which the adrenal glands have a genetically determined defect in their function from fetal life on. The syndrome is transmitted as an autosomal recessive trait, which implies that both parents have to be carriers to produce one or several children with the illness. The genetic defect prevents the adrenal cortices from synthesizing cortisol. Instead the adrenal cortices release too much of another adrenal hormone that is androgenic in biological action, that is, a male sex hormone.

In the genetic female with AGS, excessive androgen production before birth masculinizes the external genitalia to varying degrees, in some cases only affecting the clitoris (enlargement) and in others also the formation of the labia (labial fusion). The masculinization of the genitalia is restricted to the external sex organs. The internal reproductive organs are differentiated as female. Postnatally, with proper endocrine management, the adrenal androgen output is regulated with life-long cortisone replacement therapy. With proper treatment, puberty, secondary sex characteristics, and female reproductive function are normal in female AGS patients, although menses tend to be of late onset. The masculinized external genitalia can be surgically feminized soon after birth. Thus, with proper hormonal and surgical treatment, girls with AGS grow up looking like normal girls.

Progestin-induced hermaphroditism is a condition of exogenous fetal androgenization by progestinic drugs. It occurs in genetic female offspring of mothers who have been treated with progestinic drugs during pregnancy to prevent miscarriage. The drugs sometimes have an unexpected virilizing effect on the daughters' external genitalia. The only treatment indicated is surgical correction of the genitalia. No postnatal hormonal abnormality occurs in this case.

The studies concerning the effect of prenatal hormones on behavior in human females were started at the Johns Hopkins Hospital several years ago. At the time 10 girls with progestin-induced hermaphroditism and 15 girls with early-treated AGS, between 4 and 16 years old, were evaluated and compared with matched normal control girls (Ehrhardt and Money, 1967; Ehrhardt et al., 1968; Money and Ehrhardt, 1972b).

The behavior under study has been consistently long-term childhood, adolescent, and adult sexually dimorphic behavior which could be operationally defined, assessed in detailed interviews, and analyzed on rating scales. The goal has been to look at the kind of gender-related behavior which has been shown to differentiate between normal boys and girls consistently and over a wide age range, such as play behavior, social role choices, and aspects of adult sexual behavior.

In brief, the results of these earlier studies suggested that fetally androgenized females were different from normal control girls in that they displayed a higher level of physical energy expenditure in rough outdoor play and a lesser interest in dolls and other typically female childhood rehearsal of adult female roles in fantasy and play; they were also more often identified as long-term tomboys and preferred boys over girls as playmates.

The goal of our more recent studies in Buffalo (with S.W. Baker) was to evaluate a comparable sample of fetally androgenized genetic females at another hospital to validate or disprove the findings at Johns Hopkins. In addition, we expanded the research design. In order to have both the experimental group and control group from a social environment as similar as possible, we evaluated complete families with one or more children with AGS. We also included not only genetic females but also genetic males with AGS (see below). Females with AGS were compared with female siblings, males with AGS were compared with male siblings.

The sample of our family study in Buffalo consisted of a representative 27 patients, 17 females and 10 males. Several families had more than one child with AGS. The age range was 4.3—19.9 years for the female subsample, with most of the children in middle childhood and early adolescence. The comparison sample of unaffected female siblings, namely, sisters of AGS children who do not have the disease, consisted of 11 females with a comparable age range. The families came from social classes II to V according to the Hollingshead (1957) index, with a greater number from lower than from middle and higher classes.

All patients were under long-term corrective treatment with replacement of cortisone. They had also undergone surgical correction of the external genitalia, usually in infancy or early childhood.

Every subject and her/his mother was interviewed with the same interview schedule. The items were always consistent, although the sequence was flexible so as to be unstilted in manner. All interviews were tape-recorded and subsequently transcribed. The transcribed interviews were rated according to coding scales with a range of 2—5 verbally anchored points. Agreement between answers from mothers and from children to the same aspect of the child's behavior has been found in the past to be very high (Ehrhardt, 1969), so that the answers can be pooled. Two raters tabulated the data from the transcribed interviews.

The comparisons between the patient and the various control groups were statistically tested with the Fisher Exact Test for 4-fold tables after the rating scales for each item were dichotomized.

The most pertinent results for the question of possible effects of prenatal androgens on behavior in genetic females with the adrenogenital syndrome cluster around three themes: activity and aggression; marriage and maternalism; gender role, appearance, and adolescent dating behavior (Ehrhardt and Baker, 1974).

We found in Buffalo, as in previous studies, that the girls with AGS were significantly more often described by their mothers, sisters, brothers, fathers, and themselves as having a high level of intense physical energy expenditure compared to the female siblings (Fig. 1). The behavior was long-term and specific in the sense of a high degree of rough outdoor play rather than a general elevation of activity level.

Girls with the AGS also differed in choice of playmates, significantly more often preferring boys over girls.

Our data on fighting behavior were relatively crude and centered basically only around the question: who in the family most frequently starts fights (unspecified what kind). There is a tendency for fetally androgenized girls to start fights more frequently than female siblings, but the difference was not significant.

The second cluster of pertinent results center around toy preference, response to infants, and rehearsal of adult female roles. As one can see in Fig. 2, AGS girls show a conspicuously low interest in dolls. About 80% were rated as having had little or no interest in dolls at any time during their childhood, while this was only true for a small number of female siblings. AGS girls tended to play with cars, trucks and blocks. They also expressed generally very little interest in future roles as bride and mother, but were much more concerned with future job roles. Female siblings were described as being interested in childhood rehearsal of wedding and marriage as well as of various job and career roles, and were in the latter aspect not different from the patients.

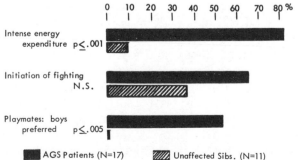

Fig. 1. Comparison of female AGS patients versus female siblings on activity and aggression. The bars represent the percentage of subjects from each group who were reported to exhibit the behavior specified by the category.

250

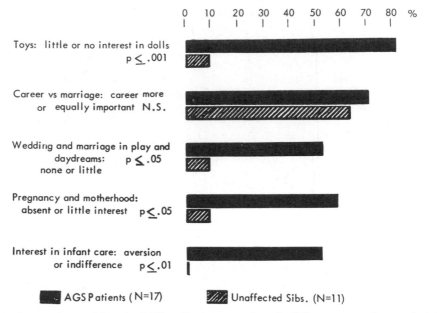

Fig. 2. Comparison of female AGS patients versus female siblings on marriage and maternalism. The bars represent the percentage of subjects from each group who were reported to exhibit the behavior specified by the category.

Girls with AGS were also more frequently described as being indifferent to small infants or expressing aversion and dislike of handling babies at home or elsewhere. In contrast to the female siblings, they often did not participate in caring for a baby at home or stayed away from babysitting or infant watching. They did not exclude the possibility of becoming a mother one day, rather their attitude was noncommittal and matter-of-fact, with no or little rehearsal in daydreams or role play about maternalism — quite in contrast to the majority of unaffected female siblings.

The next cluster of items has to do with gender role preference and with more arbitrary sex differences, such as interest in appearance (Fig. 3). If a girl tends to rough-and-tumble play and prefers boys and boys' toys, then she is traditionally identified as a tomboy. Fifty-nine percent of the patients were identified by themselves and others as a tomboy during all of their childhood, significantly different from the sample of unaffected siblings in which nobody showed this complete and long-term pattern of tomboyism, although 27% were rated as having some tomboyish traits apparent at some time during their childhood.

To the question of whether it was better to be a girl or a boy, 35% of the patient sample was undecided or thought that they might have chosen to be a boy if they could start their lives all over again. However, it is important to see these results in their proper perspective; none of the AGS girls had a

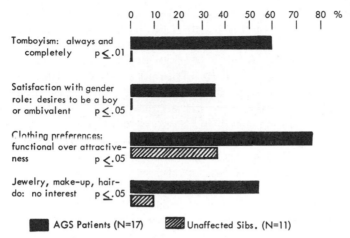

Fig. 3. Comparison of female AGS patients versus female siblings on gender role and clothing preference. The bars represent the percentage of subjects from each group who were reported to exhibit the behavior specified by the category.

conflict with their female gender identity or was unhappy about being a girl. They generally were comfortable in the female role and liked to be tomboys.

The last two items relate to interest in clothing and appearance. More girls in the patient sample preferred functional over decorative clothing and generally were not particular about the way they looked. Consistently, they were also more frequently rated as having no interest in jewelry, make-up, and hair-do than the unaffected female siblings.

Our evidence on adolescent behavior is based on too few cases to make any definitive statement. Preliminary impressions seem to indicate that AGS female patients are somewhat late in getting involved in relationships with members of the opposite sex. They seem to be slow in starting to date and having their first crush on a boy. On the other hand, there is no evidence that homosexuality is increased in the patient sample. Several of the adolescent girls expressed interest and attraction for boys, but were more reticent, not as eager, and possibly less skilled than the unaffected female siblings in getting involved in a flirtatious relationship with a boy.

Fetal androgen excess in genetic males

Exposure to high levels of prenatal androgen does not visibly affect the genetic male. At least this is true for boys with the adrenogenital syndrome. Therefore, male babies with this condition can easily go undetected at birth, unless they have some other complications, such as an increased tendency to salt loss. If not treated with cortisone, a boy with the adrenogenital syndrome will show signs of a precocious male puberty. He may have an early growth spurt and early sexual development. However, if his excessive adrenal androgens are suppressed with cortisone from an early age on, a boy with the adrenogenital syndrome will grow up looking like his normal peers.

In the Buffalo family study, we compared nine AGS boys with 11 unaffected brothers, age 4—26 years (Ehrhardt and Baker, 1974). We found the AGS boys not to be significantly different in most of the behavior aspects we assessed. They were not, for instance, more aggressive in terms of initiating fights in the family or with their peers. They were as stereotypically masculine as the sibling group in choice of playmates (boys preferred over girls), toys (cars and trucks and no dolls), and their fantasies of taking the father role in adulthood. Both male groups showed total absence of effeminacy and all of them clearly preferred the male gender role if given a choice.

The only behavior area in which the sample of adrenogenital boys differed was the area of sports and rough outdoor activities. They tended to be significantly more frequently described by themselves and their families as having a higher energy-expenditure level and were more often excellent athletes. The even higher level of physical strength and energy in sports and play activities in the AGS sample may be related to their prenatal history of a possibly even higher level of androgens compared with normal males. Six of the nine patients had been started on cortisone treatment within the first month of life; three were diagnosed and treated later, when they showed already signs of precocious puberty. With them, their higher physical energy level may have been also due to high postnatal levels of androgens before treatment. If so, it persisted even after cortisone treatment had begun to suppress their high androgen levels.

The findings on the male samples suggested that most aspects of masculine behavior development in childhood are not affected by the prenatal hormonal androgen excess in the adrenogenital syndrome. This result agrees with an earlier study on late-treated adrenogenital boys by Money and Alexander (1969).

4. ESTROGEN AND PROGESTERONE EFFECTS ON HUMAN PSYCHOSEXUAL DIFFERENTIATION

There is a lack of published, systematic behavior data on genetic females who were exposed to an estrogen and/or progesterone excess before birth. And there is only one study designed to assess the behavior development of genetic males whose mothers took estrogen and progesterone during pregnancy.

Fetal estrogen and progesterone excess in genetic males

A sample of twenty 6-year-olds and twenty 16-year-olds exposed prenatally to exogenously administered estrogen and progesterone were studied on several parameters of psychosexual development. Compared to a control group, the 16-year-olds were rated somewhat lower on assertiveness and athletic ability. The sample of 6-year-olds exposed to prenatal estrogen and progest-terone was also rated on some measures lower on aggressivity and athletic abilities (Yalom et al., 1973).

The results of this study are very difficult to interpret, since the subjects were not only exposed to prenatal estrogen and progesterone but also had mothers who were chronically ill with diabetes. Unfortunately, the investiga-tors were unable to find an adequate control group of children with diabetic mothers who had not had any steroid treatment during pregnancy. Their comparison groups consisted of sons of a few diabetic mothers (less than half of the sample in the one and less than a quarter in the other) and sons of healthy mothers, all with no known estrogen and progesterone pregnancy treatment. As the investigators of the study themselves point out, the health of the mothers is a major uncontrolled variable and may play a crucial role in the behavior differences between the experimental and control groups. Chronic illness undoubtedly has an effect on maternal behavior. It may well induce anxiety and over-protection with an influence on assertiveness and athletic abilities in sons. Therefore, one must wait to see whether the find-ings of this first study on prenatal estrogen and progesterone drug effects on postnatal masculine psychosexual development can be confirmed in a sample of children whose history is not additionally complicated by a diabetic mother.

5. PRENATAL HORMONAL EFFECTS ON INTELLIGENCE

Although it has been documented and accepted that normal males and fe-males do not differ in full IQ, the question of the effects of sex hormones on intellectual functioning was raised when studies on clinical populations with unusual hormonal histories showed that elevation of IQ values might be as-sociated with prenatal exposure to excessive progesterone and/or androgen. These findings gave rise to much speculation as to what role prenatal hor-mones may play in postnatal cognitive development. Since intelligence is only a minor interest in the discussion of psychosexual differentiation, the review of the current thinking on this issue will be brief.

Androgen effects on intelligence

Three studies at different hospitals have shown that girls and boys with the adrenogenital syndrome (and therefore exposed to high levels of prenatal androgen) tend to have an elevated general intelligence level compared to the norm (Money and Lewis, 1966; Perlman, 1973; Baker and Ehrhardt, 1974). The three IQ distributions and the mean are very similar with a significantly elevated number of above-average IQ scores in each sample, as assessed by the Wechsler Intelligence Scale (Fig. 4).

254

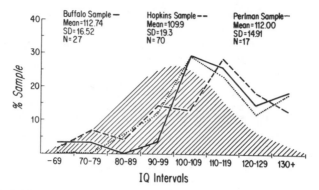

Fig. 4. Mean full IQs and frequency distributions of three independent samples of AGS patients tested at different hospitals compared with the normal distribution (from Baker and Ehrhardt, 1974).

Additional support for the hypothesis that fetal exposure to high levels of androgenic hormones may be related to elevation in intelligence came from the study on girls exposed to virilizing progestenic drugs by maternal intake during pregnancy. The mean IQ in this sample was also significantly elevated (Ehrhardt and Money, 1967).

The findings of the recent Buffalo family study have answered some of the questions raised. We compared the IQs of the sample of male and female AGS children with those of their sisters and brothers and those of their parents. All three means were significantly elevated from the norm, but not significantly different from each other (Fig. 5).

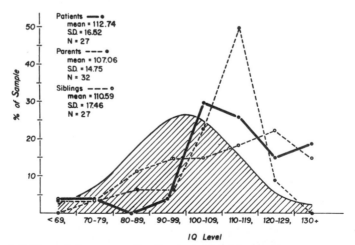

Fig. 5. Mean full IQs and frequency distributions of AGS patients, parents, and siblings in the Buffalo complete sample. The shaded area represents the expected normal distribution (from Baker and Ehrhardt, 1974).

Thus it appears that families with one or more AGS children tend to have a higher IQ. The enhancement of intellectual development cannot be attributed specifically to the prenatal and/or postnatal hormonal aspects of the adrenogenital syndrome, since patients did not differ in IQ from unaffected siblings and parents.

However, the findings cannot be attributed to social class bias since the socioeconomic background of our sample was clearly representative. If anything, it was possibly a little toward the lower end. This finding also cannot be explained by a theory that all patients who come to pediatric endocrine clinics tend to have higher IQs since studies on other endocrine samples do not support this assumption (Money et al., 1967; Ehrhardt et al., 1973; Meyer-Bahlburg et al., 1974).

Alternative hypotheses have to be considered to explain the elevated IQ in families with AGS children. There may be some linkage with the autosomal recessive transmission of the adrenogenital syndrome, since both parents and some of the siblings have to be genetic carriers. An alternative to the question of genetics is the possibility of an as yet unknown selection process of families who bring their AGS children to pediatric endocrine clinics. If such a process does exist, it seems to be unrelated to social class, since our social data did not suggest a bias toward the upper end.

Progesterone effects on intelligence

No intelligence data were reported in the already described study on estrogen and progesterone effects on masculine psychosexual differentiation (Yalom et al., 1973). However, there is a study on progesterone effects on academic performance by Katharina Dalton in England (Dalton, 1968). She reported an educational follow-up of children (both male and female) whose mothers had been given progesterone in pregnancy with no resultant masculinizing effects on the offspring. The progesterone was administered for the relief of toxemic symptoms.

Dalton matched 44 progesterone children with two control groups. One group, normal controls, consisted of next-born children listed in the labor-ward register whose mothers had a normal pregnancy and delivery. The toxemia control groups were children delivered from mothers who had toxemia during pregnancy without hormonal treatment. The educational follow-up was done on these children 9—10 years later. Ratings of school teachers on a blind basis showed that progesterone children received significantly more 'above average' grades than those of their control group. These results were significant for all academic subjects. Dalton also demonstrated a positive correlation between 'high dosage' and 'early treatment' on one hand and above-average school achievement on the other hand. Dalton did not divide her samples by sex in any of the school-performance results, so it is not possible to determine whether this was a relevant factor. She also did not report any comparable data on sibling and parent controls.

Taking all studies into account, the assumption that prenatal sex hormone exposure is related to intelligence has become less and less probable, although it cannot be completely discarded, as of yet.

6. CONCLUSION

Prenatal exposure to high levels of androgen affects psychosexual differentiation in the genetic female in terms of an increased physical energy level and a low interest in maternal caretaking. These behavior modifications are compatible with a normal female gender identity and have to be viewed as variations on an acceptable pattern of feminine behavior in our culture.

Genetic males with a history of an excess of prenatal androgen, typically have a normal male psychosexual differentiation with possibly an increased energy expenditure level.

Exposure to prenatal estrogen and progesterone may affect assertiveness and athletic abilities in genetic males, according to an unconfirmed study on diabetic mothers and their sons.

Fetal androgen excess by itself probably does not enhance intelligence, as was speculated until recent evidence has all but disproven this theory.

Prenatal progesterone exposure may be related to high academic performance, as shown in an unconfirmed study on children of toxemic mothers.

ACKNOWLEDGMENT

This paper was published previously as 'Prenatal Hormonal Exposure and Psychosexual Differentiation' in *Topics in Psychoendocrinology* (E.J. Sachar, Ed.). Grune & Stratton, New York, 1975. Reprinted by permission of Grune & Stratton, Inc.

BIBLIOGRAPHY

Baker, S.W. and Ehrhardt, A.A. (1974) Prenatal androgen, intelligence and cognitive sex differences. In: (R.C. Friedman, R.M. Richart, R.L. Vande Wiele, Eds.) *Sex Differences in Behavior.* (Wiley and Sons, Inc., New York) p. 53.

Dalton, K. (1968) Ante-natal progesterone and intelligence. *Br. J. Psychiat.* 114: 1377–1382.

Eaton, G.G., Goy, R.W. and Phoenix, C.H. (1973) Effects of testosterone treatment in adulthood on sexual behavior of female pseudohermaphrodite rhesus monkeys. *Nature New Biol.* 242: 119–120.

Ehrhardt, A.A. (1969) Zur Wirkung fötaler Hormone auf Intelligenz und geschlechtsspezifisches Verhalten. (Ph.D. thesis, University of Düsseldorf).

Ehrhardt, A.A. and Baker, S.W. (1974) Fetal androgens, human central nervous system differentiation, and behavior sex differences. In: (R.C. Friedman, R.M. Richart, R.L. Vande Wiele, Eds.) *Sex Differences in Behavior.* (Wiley and Sons, Inc., New York) p. 33.

Ehrhardt, A.A., Cotton, C. and Aceto, T. (1973) Short stature due to bone dysplasia: intelligence and personality findings. (Program and Abstracts of the Annual Meeting of the Midwestern Society for Pediatric Research, Pittsburgh).

Ehrhardt, A.A., Epstein, R. and Money, J. (1968) Fetal androgens and female gender identity in the early-treated adrenogenital syndrome. *Johns Hopkins Med. J.* 122: 160—167.

Ehrhardt, A.A. and Money, J. (1967) Progestin-induced hermaphroditism: IQ and psychosexual identity in a study of 10 girls. *J. Sex. Res.* 3: 83—100.

Goy, R.W. (1968) Organizing effects of androgen on the behaviour of rhesus monkeys. In: (R.P. Michael, Ed.) *Endocrinology and Human Behaviour.* (Oxford University Press, London) p. 12.

Hollingshead, A.B. (1957) Two-factor index of social position. (Yale University, New Haven) privately printed.

Meyer-Bahlburg, H.F.L., McCauley, E., Schenk, C., Aceto, T. and Pinch, L. (1974) Cryptorchidism, development of gender identity and sex behavior. In: (R.C. Friedman, R.M. Richart and R.L. Vande Wiele, Eds.) *Sex Differences in Behavior.* (Wiley and Sons, Inc., New York) p. 281.

Money, J. and Alexander, D. (1969) Psychosexual development and absence of homosexuality in males with precocious puberty. *J. Nerv. Ment. Dis.* 148: 111—123.

Money, J. and Ehrhardt, A.A. (1972a) *Man and Woman, Boy and Girl.* (The Johns Hopkins University Press, Baltimore).

Money, J. and Ehrhardt, A.A. (1972b) Gender dimorphic behavior and fetal sex hormones. In: (E.B. Astwood, Ed.) *Recent Prog. Horm. Res.,* vol. 28. (Academic Press, New York) p. 735.

Money, J. and Lewis, V. (1966) IQ, genetics and accelerated growth: adrenogenital syndrome. *Bull. Johns Hopkins Hosp.* 118: 365—373.

Money, J., Lewis, V., Ehrhardt, A.A. and Drash, P.W. (1967) IQ impairment and elevation in endocrine and related cytogenetic disorders. In: (J. Zubin, G.A. Jervis, Eds.) *Psychopathology of Mental Development.* (Grune and Stratton, Inc., New York) p. 22.

Perlman, S.M. (1973) Cognitive abilities of children with hormone abnormalities: screening by psychoeducational tests. *J. Learn. Disab.* 6: 26—34.

Yalom, J.D., Green, R. and Fisk, N. (1973) Prenatal exposure to female hormones. *Arch. Gen. Psychiat.* 28: 554—561.

CHAPTER 19

Prenatal deandrogenization of human beings

JOHN MONEY

1. ETIOLOGY

Experimental and iatrogenic

There are no human experimental data to compare with those from animals that are deliberately castrated, surgically or pharmacologically, in utero. Nor for ethical reasons are there ever likely to be. There are also no iatrogenic conditions of unintentionally produced deandrogenization of the genotypic male corresponding to progestin-induced masculinization of the genotypic female. The one possible exception might be in the case of sons whose mothers were given estrogen while pregnant to prevent miscarriage. However, in these cases the evidence is confounded by the fact that the pregnant mother was also usually given progestin (Reinisch et al., 1975) which is known to have a possible masculinizing effect, as judged by the effect on the genitalia of some daughters. Another confounding effect is that of the condition which threatened the pregnancy. In one study (Yalom et al., 1973), the threat to pregnancy was diabetes mellitus in the mother.

Male hermaphroditism

The spontaneously occurring syndromes in which fetal deandrogenization is inferentially known to have occurred are all recognized by reason of some form of incomplete, ambiguous, or intersexed differentiation of the reproductive system. They are all classified as male hermaphroditism. Hermaphroditism is conventionally classified on the criterion of the gonads as male (testes), female (ovaries) and true (ovotestes, or ovary and testis). The male and female types used to be distinguished from the true type by use of the prefix, pseudo-, as in male pseudohermaphroditism. All types are equally genuine.

Handbook of Sexology, edited by J. Money and H. Musaph
© *Elsevier/North-Holland Biomedical Press, 1977*

Karyotype

Fetal deandrogenization in male hermaphroditism is not, for the most part, associated with an abnormality in the number of sex chromosomes. Turner's syndrome (45,X) may, for the sake of argument, be considered an exception, for the missing 46th chromosome may theoretically be an Y or an X. In either case, the gonads fail to form. Without either testes or ovaries, the embryo differentiates as a female which, strictly speaking, is a form of deandrogenization, illustrating nature's primary adherence to the 'Eve principle,' namely, to differentiate the conceptus into an anatomical female rather than a male, regardless of chromosomal sex.

A few individuals with Turner's syndrome have a slightly enlarged clitoris and a mild degree of labial fusion. With a few androgen-secreting cells in their gonadal-streak tissue, they qualify as fetally deandrogenized hermaphrodites. A more obvious degree of genital ambiguity and of fetal deandrogenization occurs in individuals with the 45,X/46,XY mosaic. They have testes, but they are malformed, sterile, and at high risk for cancer.

Klinefelter's syndrome, 47,XXY, is only rarely associated with hypospadiac ambiguity of the genitalia and so does not qualify for the conventional diagnosis of hermaphroditism. There may be a covert and partial degree of prenatal deandrogenization, however, for in many cases there is a partial degree of deandrogenization, or incomplete virilization, at puberty. There is an increased risk of psychopathology, including sexual psychopathology and erotic inertia, associated with the syndrome. The impairment is more likely to be in target-organ response than in androgen secretion from the testes, which may also, however, be low. The possibility of covert partial, prenatal deandrogenization in Klinefelter's syndrome raises the speculative hypothesis that the same may occur in some 46,XY phenotypic males. Such an hypothesis may eventually prove to have some relevance to the etiology of gender-identity disorders, for example, male-to-female transexualism.

Deandrogenization sufficient to produce male hermaphroditism occurs primarily in fetuses with a 46,XY karotype. In some types of 46,XY male hermaphroditism, the deandrogenizing defect is known to be genetically transmitted within a family tree. In others the role of genetics has not yet been ascertained.

Prenatal hormones

Fetal deandrogenization sufficient to induce hermaphroditism, may be the end result of failure of the fetal testes to synthesize androgen in sufficient quantity, or of the required type, or at the required critical period. The failure may be a sequel to missing or defective testes, to an inborn error of metabolism affecting the synthesis of testosterone in the testes, or to a failure of the hypothalamic—pituitary stimulation of the testes.

Alternatively, fetal deandrogenization may be the end result of the failure of target-organ cells to take up and use the androgen which the testes secrete.

Fetal deandrogenization and male hermaphroditism

The classification of male hermaphroditism on the basis of deandrogenizing etiology rather than of descriptive phenomenology has a brief history of approximately ten years. Among all new cases seen, a large proportion still must be classified as miscellaneous, exact etiology unknown. Among follow-up cases, a large proportion must remain etiologically unclassifiable, chiefly because diagnostic procedures are too expensive, too time-consuming, or too involved in the unresolved legalities of informed consent.

2. SYNDROMES

Syndrome of androgen insensitivity

This syndrome was known initially as the testicular feminizing syndrome. Affected individuals are born with the unremarkable appearance of being normally female. There is no reason to be diagnostically suspicious unless the gonads descend as lumps in the groin, or unless an older sister has already alerted one to the possibility of familial recurrence. Otherwise the first diagnostic clue may be the failure of menstrual onset by mid-teenage, despite the normal development of breasts and feminine secondary sexual characteristics.

It has long been known that this syndrome is familial in occurrence, and that it is transmitted maternally, though the exact mechanism of transmission has not been established. It could be an X-linked recessive, a male-limited autosomal dominant, or a male-limited and X-linked dominant. The newest finding in endocrine research (Migeon and Meyer, personal communication) is that androgen, either endogenous or exogenous, cannot be utilized because the androgen-binding protein molecule in receptor cells is defective. In consequence, receptor cells respond only to testicular estrogen which, without androgenic competition, is sufficient to induce feminization at puberty.

Prenatally, the fetus requires only a lack of testes, not the presence of ovaries, in order to differentiate a female anatomy. Something must be added to make a male. This is the 'Adam principle.' What the fetal testes add is the masculinizing substance, androgen, and the defeminizing substance, known only as Mullerian inhibiting substance (MIS).

In the androgen insensitivity syndrome, the effect of androgen from the fetal testes is cancelled. MIS remains effective, thus inhibiting development of the Mullerian ducts into the uterus, Fallopian tubes, and innermost segment of the vagina. Herein lies the explanation for the impossibility of menstruation in women with the androgen insensitivity syndrome, despite cyclic hormone therapy; and for the eventual surgical need of vaginoplasty to ensure complete copulatory competence and pleasure.

Babies with the androgen insensitivity syndrome who are consistently reared as girls have no uncertainties about themselves as girls, women, wives, sexual partners, and mothers by adoption (Money et al., 1968; Masica et al., 1971). They grow to be womanly in their behavior, in their erotic mental imagery, and in their self-perception, even when they know the medical terminology of their diagnosis.

Syndrome of partial androgen insensitivity

This syndrome, also known as Reifenstein's syndrome, resembles complete androgen insensitivity, except that in fetal life there is partial masculinization of the external genitalia. In consequence, the baby may be assigned as a boy or a girl, dependent on local medical or midwife traditions concerning hermaphroditism in the newborn. Thus it subsequently becomes possible to match pairs of partially deandrogenized hermaphrodites concordant for prenatal history and diagnosis, but discordant for sex assignment and postnatal history contributes to the differentiation of gender identity/role (Money and Ogunro, 1974).

In the Money—Ogunro study, it was also possible to document the effects of prenatal deandrogenization when the sex of rearing is as a boy and continued deandrogenization results in pubertal feminization, requiring surgical removal of breasts. Behaviorally, it was found that deandrogenized boys are a partial, but not a complete mirror image of androgenized girls. Some of them tried in boyhood to compensate for their relative inferiority in competitive (athletic) energy expenditure. Without pubertal virilization at puberty, they had to opt out. They did not prefer girls' activities and interests, and did not have an unusual preference for rehearsing parentalism in childhood play. Because of their unvirilized, beardless appearance, and extremely small, surgically repaired genitalia, they had excessive difficulty in establishing a sex life, but none was homosexual.

It is difficult to believe that a physician would sex-reassign a daughter to a son, simply because lumps in the groin proved to be not ovarian but testicular in histological structure. In one known such instance, the child was reassigned at the age of two, even though the evidence from two similarly affected older relatives was contra-indicative. At the age of twelve, pubertally feminized and with large breasts, he was advised that he could return to being a girl in order to avert all the problems of being a beardless man without a penis. Adamantly he refused. Lacking a complete feminine gender identity, he preferred to be a eunuch and a recluse. Six years later, his decision was unchanged.

This case is remarkable testimony to the forcefulness of the experiences of late infancy and early childhood in differentiating the postnatal component of gender identity/role. Prenatally, this boy was deandrogenized. Behaviorally, he is the opposite of the tomboyish girl who was prenatally androgenized. There is no antonym for tomboyism — which is a reflection of our sexist culture. Thus, there is no noun or adjective to signify his nonconformity to the masculine macho ideal, even though he is firmly committed to living as a male.

Deandrogenization secondary to rare variants of the adrenogenital syndrome in genetic males

Lipoid adrenal hyperplasia (Prader and Siebermann, 1958) involves an enzymatic deficit (20,22-desmolase) so early in the pathway of steroid synthesis that complete failure of steroid synthesis ensues. Gonadal as well as adrenal steroids are affected, regardless of genetic sex. Genetic males differentiate female external genitalia. Owing to severe salt loss, the condition is incompatible with survival.

Deficiency of 17α-hydroxylase blocks adrenal and gonadal steroid synthesis. In the genetic male (New and Suvannakul, 1970), since the testes are unable to secrete androgen, the androgen-dependent genital anatomy differentiates as female. Puberty fails to occur unless androgen replacement therapy is given. Ideally, however, assignment and rearing should be as a girl, since the external genitalia are female.

Deficiency of 3β-hydroxydehydrogenase and isomerase (Bongiovanni, 1961) affects the sexual appearance only of genetic males. The male baby is born ambiguous-looking, with a urogenital sinus and hypospadiac phallus. The enzymatic deficit blocks the synthesis of testosterone, but permits synthesis, in both the adrenal and the testis, of a weak precursor androgen, dehydroepiandrosterone, which is physiologically deandrogenizing. Sex of assignment, should be dependent on the size of the phallus and its surgical correctability as a penis.

Deandrogenization secondary to enzyme deficit affecting androgen synthesis in the testes

Deficiency in 17-ketosteroid reductase blocks conversion of Δ^4-androstenedione to testosterone (Givens et al., 1974). The blockage in fetal life prevents complete masculinization of the external genitalia. The baby is born with hermaphroditic ambiguity of appearance. At puberty, however, secondary sexual differentiation is masculine. If rearing and surgical rehabilitation have been consistently as a male, the only remaining problem, in all probability, will be the chronic one of an excessively undersized penis.

If rearing and surgical rehabilitation have been consistently as a female, then substitution therapy with estrogen, a final-stage vaginoplasty, and adaptation to motherhood by adoption will, in all probability, be the only remaining issues.

Regardless of assigned sex, in those cases in which surgical resolution of the genital ambiguity is postponed throughout childhood, there is an increased risk of ambiguity of rearing, and of ambiguity in the differentiation of gender identity/role. Then it is necessary to make a decision regarding a sex reassignment, which should always be an elective and not an enforced procedure.

Deficiency in Δ^4-steroid 5α-reductase blocks the conversion of testicular testosterone to dihydrotestosterone (Imperato-McGinley et al., 1974) — a conversion necessary for the hormone to be utilized in some, if not all cells that require it. This blockage has, as in the case of 17-ketosteroid reductase deficiency also, a deandrogenizing effect in fetal life, but not at puberty. The hermaphroditic problems in the two syndromes are, therefore, the same.

Imperato-McGinley and associates described a family pedigree in an isolated village in the Dominican Republic. In the course of three generations, the village people have learned not to expect medical treatment for their hermaphrodites. Correctly, they have also learned to predict that their hermaphrodites will virilize at puberty, so they assign them all at birth as boys. In the earlier generations some were assigned as girls at birth, because of their female appearance, and at puberty were reassigned when they masculinized.

Imperato-McGinley and associates made the mistaken claim that at puberty 'the phallus enlarges to become a functional penis.' It is a total anatomical impossibility for a hypospadiac, hermaphroditic organ to change into a penis without surgery.

The investigators also made the mistaken claim that the hermaphrodites' sexual interest in females could be attributed to the testosterone which was not converted in their bodies to dihydrotestosterone — which is quite untenable, since even in a case of prepubertal castration with complete testosterone deficiency in teenage, a sexual interest in females, inclusive of sexual intercourse, can develop (Money and Alexander, 1967). Moreover, Imperato-McGinley and her group made no direct study of the behavioral development of the individuals whose hormones and enzymes they measured. They obtained information about gender identity and role only by hearsay, not by direct inquiry of the patients, their partners, and their parents. They had no psychologist, psychiatrist, sociologist, or other expert in behavioral science to assist them.

Deandrogenization secondary to fetal pituitary dysfunction

At least one case is known (Park et al., 1976) of a rare condition in which a baby is born looking like a female, apparently because the fetal pituitary failed to stimulate the fetal testes effectively. At the age of puberty, the testes remained dormant, until stimulated with exogenous gonadotropic hormone. Then they precipitously exerted a powerful masculinizing effect. In this well studied case, the gender identity/role was strongly feminine.

3. DIFFERENTIATION OF GENDER IDENTITY/ROLE

The syndromes of deandrogenization demonstrate the relative unimportance of the X and the Y chromosome, per se, in directly influencing gender-identity differentiation. The sex chromosomes exert their influence insofar as they program the anatomy of the gonads, which in turn programs the presence or absence of fetal testicular secretions. Most of the work of gender identity/role differentiation remains to be accomplished postnatally. The anatomical foundations of the erotic part of gender identity/role, that is of the sex role proper, is laid down prenatally. The mental content of that sex role, however, is subject to postnatal influences. Sex-coded roles (coded on the basis of genital appearance) that pertain to work, play, etiquette and legal status, are, like native language, differentiated in response to cultural conditioning in postnatal life. These sex-coded roles are grafted onto basic sexual dimorphisms in physique and reproductive role, but are not automatically preordained by them.

4. SUMMARY

In human beings, fetal deandrogenization cannot be produced experimentally and has not occurred iatrogenically. Spontaneously, it occurs in various syndromes of male hermaphroditism. In fetal life, complete deandrogenization results in complete feminization of the external genitals. Assigned sex is as a girl, differentiation of gender identity/role is feminine, and adult life is as a wife and mother by adoption. In the partial form of the syndrome, the baby appears ambiguous at birth. Fortuitously, some are assigned as males, some as females, dependent on local principles, or lack of them, regarding hermaphroditic sex assignment. In consequence, it subsequently becomes possible to match pairs of hermaphrodites, concordant for prenatal etiology and diagnosis, but discordant for sex assignment and postnatal biography. In such matched pairs, the outcome of the differentiation of gender identity/role is typically concordant with the unity or ambiguity of the sex of rearing and medical rehabilitation. A prenatal history of deandrogenization does not automatically dictate a deandrogenized gender identity/role, though it does, change the threshold for some expected, associated behavioral traits.

ACKNOWLEDGEMENT

This work was supported by USPHS Grant no. HD-00325 and funds from the Grant Foundation.

266

BIBLIOGRAPHY

Bongiovanni, A. (1961) Unusual steroid pattern in congenital adrenal hyperplasia; deficiency of 3β-hydroxydehydrogenase. *J. Clin. Endocrinol.* 21: 860—862.

Givens, J.R., Wiser, W.L., Summit, R.L., Kerber, I.J., Anderson, R.N., Pittaway, D.E. and Fish, S.A. (1974) Familial male pseudohermaphroditism without gynecomastia due to deficient testicular 17-ketosteroid reductase activity. *New Engl. J. Med.* 231: 938—944.

Imperato-McGinley, J., Guerrero, L., Gautier, T. and Peterson, R.E. (1974) Steroid 5α-reductase deficiency in man: An inherited form of male pseudohermaphroditism. *Science* 186: 1213—1215.

Masica, D.N., Money, J. and Ehrhardt, A.A. (1971) Fetal feminization and female gender identity in the testicular feminizing syndrome of androgen insensitivity. *Arch. Sex. Behav.* 1: 131—142.

Money, J. and Alexander, D. (1967) Eroticism and sexual function in developmental anorchia and hyporchia with pubertal failure. *J. Sex Res.* 3: 31—47.

Money, J., Ehrhardt, A.A. and Masica, D.N. (1968) Fetal feminization induced by androgen insensitivity in the testicular feminizing syndrome: Effect on marriage and maternalism. *Johns Hopkins Med. J.* 123: 105—114.

Money, J. and Ogunro, C. (1974) Behavioral sexology: Ten cases of genetic male intersexuality with impaired prenatal and pubertal androgenization. *Arch. Sex. Behav.* 3: 181—205.

New, M.I. and Suvannakul, L. (1970) Male pseudohermaphroditism due to 17α-hydroxylase deficiency. *J. Clin. Invest.* 49: 1930—1941.

Park, I.J., Burnett, L.S., Jones, H.W. Jr., Migeon, C.J. and Blizzard, R.M. (1976) A case of male pseudohermaphroditism associated with elevated LH, normal FSH, and low testosterone possibly due to the secretion of an abnormal LH molecule. *Acta Endocrinol.* in press.

Prader, A. and Slebenmann, R.E. (1958) Congenital adrenal insufficiency with lipid hyper hyperplasia of the adrenals and female genitalia in boys. In: (D.R. Smith and W.A. Davidson, Eds.) *Symposium on Nuclear Sex.* (Interscience, New York.)

Reinisch, J.M., Karow, W.G., Tyler, E.T. and van den Daela, L. (1975) A retrospective study of the effects of hormonal therapy during pregnancy on the intelligence of offspring: Rationale, sample description, and preliminary results. (Columbia University Teachers College, New York.)

Yalom, I.D., Green, R. and Fisk, N. (1973) Prenatal exposure to female hormones: Effect on psychosexual development in boys. *Arch. Gen. Psychiat.* 28: 554—561.

SECTION IV

Youth and sex

Section coordinator: Gunter Schmidt

CHAPTER 20

Introduction, sociohistorical perspectives

GUNTER SCHMIDT

1. TWO APPROACHES

The papers in this section deal almost exclusively with the sexuality of adolescents and young adults during this century. They provide a great deal of information concerning the present state of research by describing the sexual behavior patterns and standards of this age-group, and by analysing the relevant determinants of adolescent sexuality: the biological changes during puberty; social class; gender; and the direct influencing of sexual socialization through sex education. Initially it was planned to augment the analyses of current manifestations of adolescent sexuality with a sociohistorical paper on the problem, because it is only from a sociohistorical perspective that we gain an insight into the influence of macrosociological factors, for example, changes in the socioeconomic structure. Despite great effort, I was not able to find an author for such an essay. So, instead of writing a few integrating comments on the papers in this section, I would prefer to discuss two different sociohistorical approaches to adolescent, being totally aware of Ilenistion (1971, p. 329), who wrote: 'most efforts to marry psychology and history have ended in divorce or outright cannibalism'.

Aside from the countless historical or pseudohistorical descriptions of sexuality in the form of history of morals, and monographs dealing with specific social groups during a particular period of history (see, for example, Möller, 1969) then there are only two scientists, to my knowledge, who deal with the few historical sources on sexuality and adolescent sexuality over the last 200 or 300 years from a sociological perspective: the Belgian historian, Jos van Ussel (1968, 1970) and the American historian, Edward Shorter (1971, 1972, 1973). Both deal with the influence of industrialization of emergent capitalism on sexuality in Europe.

Handbook of Sexology, edited by J. Money and H. Musaph
© *Elsevier/North-Holland Biomedical Press, 1977*

There are significant differences in their methodological approaches to the problem. Van Ussel attempts to study and evaluate all the available sources: books on morals and sexual customs, books dealing with sexual education, works of art, medical and pedagogical literature, and belles-lettres. Shorter, by contrast, proceeds from a study of the statistics on illegitimate births between 1750 and 1950. The authors have different standpoints with respect to basic theory: van Ussel is a Marxist historian, Shorter is influenced by American positivistic sociology. Finally, both come to diametrically opposed conclusions for the period of time between roughly 1700 and 1900. For van Ussel, industrialization coincides with sexual repression and hostility toward the body; for Shorter, the same span of time is a revolution in eroticism.

2. VAN USSEL: INDUSTRIALIZATION AND SEXUAL REPRESSION

Van Ussel's central thesis is as follows: industrialization, that is, the new mode of production, demanded a new human being — a human being whose psychostructure was adapted to the demands of early capitalist industrial society and who was fundamentally different, for example, from renaissance man. Part of this new psychostructure was the new sexuality which began to be remodelled in the 16th century and reached its peak in the 19th century.

Van Ussel provides a minute description of the changes in psychostructure; however, his analysis of socioeconomic change and its interdependence with the emerging new psychostructure remains both global and unsatisfying. He points, for example, to the fact that the growth of the cities beginning in the Middle Ages and the initially slow technical development, made a constant differentiation in the division of labor possible in certain sectors of the population. This process made it necessary for more and more people, and more groups to rely on each other. Out of this arose more mutual dependency. More groups began to interact with one another in order to survive and/or to improve their standard of living. It is at this point that the development of bourgeois values begins. This was indeed demanded by the process of modernization, and it also accelerated its development. Discipline as a guarantee for complicated interaction, being able to rely on one another in terms of punctuality, exactitude and order, self-denial in order to achieve later gains, diligence and achievement, are the values which made the rise of the bourgeoisie possible and which needed to be instilled in increasing numbers of young people. During the course of this development, 'the body was transformed from an organ of pleasure to an organ of achievement. In this manner the bourgeoisie developed a morality of achievement that made it impossible to pleasurably experience sexus and eros' (van Ussel, 1970, p. 39). The individual was made available for alienated labor. The most important changes in the psychostructure of human beings between the 16th and the 19th century, according to van Ussel, are summarized as follows.

Alienation from one's own body and bodily reactions

The natural physiological reactions of the body became increasingly tabooed and repressed between the 16th and the 19th century. At the end of the Middle Ages it was thoroughly common for men and women to yawn, belch, fart, sneeze loudly, scratch themselves and such like, in public. It was not at all frowned upon. Gradually, these reactions became taboo: self-control over all of the functions of the body was the emerging value.

People attempted to distance themselves from their own natural needs. Direct connection with drive objects became interdicted: people no longer ate from a common pot with their fingers. The knife and fork increased the distance between people and their nourishment. Eating manners were invented and the satisfaction of hunger became ritualized. Defecation took place in embarrassed secrecy.

Body functions were no longer ego-syntonic. Human beings attempted to reject them as something undesirable, something that no longer belonged to one's accepted self. It was this alienation from one's own body that led to a new relationship to nudity. During the Middle Ages, even during the 16th century, van Ussel claims that everybody enjoyed illustrations of nude women and girls. He does not mention nude men and boys. It was considered normal to sleep in the nude, to go swimming in the nude, to bathe in the common village bath, and to sleep together in a bed at the inn with a stranger in the nude. During the 17th century, nudity came increasingly under attack and people became more and more preoccupied with nudity until, by the 19th century, it became tasteless to exhibit a naked table or piano leg without draping a dust-cover over it. All stimuli capable of evoking feelings of sensuousness were either to be concealed or disposed of. The paradoxical result of this development was that it led to excessive sexual excitation.

Nudity is but one example of the modes of conduct that were severly inhibited because they could stimulate the senses and jeopardize one's control over one's sensual experience. Resistance against any and all experiencing and enjoyment of visual, tactile, olfactory, and acoustic stimuli grew continuously. To deprive an environment of all stimuli, both sterile and functional in nature, was to subdue the frightening world of sensuousness.

Alienation from spontaneous feelings and emotions

The demand for self-control was not limited to the body, it also encompassed feeling and emotions. Open expression of feelings such as laughing, weeping, crying, screaming, or roaring, became more and more inhibited. Keeping one's self under control, mastering one's emotions, became a new moral virtue. Drives and emotions had to be restrained and precisely regulated. Human beings withdrew themselves increasingly from the natural events in life like birth and death, which provoke strong feelings and emotions. Living together with the physically or mentally ill became more and more taboo. In earlier times, these events more or less belonged to the sphere of public affairs in the community. Now they became something secret, something that took place behind closed doors — due more than a little to the emergence of the nuclear family.

Internalization

It was now that a fundamental restructuring of social control took place — away from outside compulsions to self-compulsions, away from the morality of shame to the morality of guilt (Taylor, 1957). In earlier times, the fear of being caught and subjected to the sanctions of the group had constituted the most important instrument of social control. 'Si non caste, tamen caute' (if not chaste, then at least cautious) was a widespread philosophical maxim throughout the sixteenth century. The old system of social control was no longer adequate for the new demands. People had to be able to rely on each other and depend on each other amidst an ever more complicated and wide-ranging network of economic and social interaction without having constantly to keep an eye on each other. This had become all the more necessary because of the increasing anonymity of social relations. The individual was no longer compelled to do something or act in a certain manner due to outside pressures; for the individual, social norms and standards became the individual's own standards; conduct and behavior were based on personal convictions. This, of course required a tremendous investment in education, yet it was a worthwhile investment, because 'a single moral theologist is more useful than ten policemen' (van Ussel, 1970, p. 40).

This restructuring of social control was primarily performed by the emerging nuclear family. It played an important role in molding the new conscience, needs and feelings, because this formative process can only take place during early childhood. This made it possible to restructure the 'pleasure-oriented child into an achieving creature' (van Ussel, 1970, p. 76). The invention of adolescence as a new phase of development — basically due to the necessity of establishing longer periods of training and education — extended the family's span of control and influence. In earlier times, there had been no such thing as adolescence in the strict sense of the term; post-pubertal boys and girls were considered to be adults. Internalization resulted in new intrapsychic modes of experience: violations and transgressions against accepted norm and standards led to conflicts even when they remained undiscovered. The former struggle between the individual and authority had now become a struggle within the individual in the form of an intrapsychic conflict.

De-socialization and individuation

People became more and more separated from each other. Social relationships took place less and less in primary groups and more and more in secondary groups. People no longer lived together in large families comprised of
three or four generations, all living under the same roof. The basic unit had
now become the small family. During the Middle Ages, the house had been
open, as it were. No, barriers existed between inside and outside. The street
led directly into the sitting-room and conversely the sitting-room was a part
of the street and the social interaction that took place in the street. Now
that the house had become sealed off, people closed themselves off from
each other. People not only created a greater distance between themselves
and their bodies, but also between themselves and others. Among the more
affluent strata, each member of the family had his or her own room. Now
individuation could take place.

Sexuality becomes a problem

Sexuality was affected by all of the four changes described. Sexuality became more and more of a problem. It no longer involved pleasure, but became increasingly associated with fear, disgust and guilt. In this manner, a
relatively simple and pleasurable aspect of human living became increasingly
menacing and sinister. A deep pessimism arose with regard to sexuality, for
example, the panic fear of its presumedly asocial explosiveness. The demand
for a unity of sexuality, marriage, love and procreation became a key value
concept. This meant that only 'pure coitus' — stripped of all its variations
and genital or non-genital tenderness, devoid of all fantasy — became the
recognized and accepted mode of conduct. Sexual modesty and prudery
were invented: nudity became taboo; sexuality became privatized, it now
took place in secrecy and even at a mutual distance to the partner. Any mention of the parts of the body, of sexual functions and activities was prohibited. Sexuality had become speechless. Because of the increasing inequality
of women — in contrast to the wife in the agrarian culture, the urbanized
wife was gradually forced out of the sphere of production — sexual repression was directed predominantly toward women. This development reached
its peak during the nineteenth century not to mention the Inquisition, three
centuries earlier. Women were looked upon as sexless creatures; sexual desire
and orgasm were considered to be an indication of loose morals, or of illness,
or of belonging to the lower social classes. However, this sexual repression
created a remarkably ambivalent situation. Its repulsiveness evoked a magic
attraction at the same time. Because of its association with fear and guilt,
sexuality took on a seductive force and an aura of enticing danger such as it
had not known before. This gave it a permanent and continuously virulent
and overpowering impetuosity. The more natural stimuli became forbidden,
the more neutral stimuli gained increasing erotic meaning. The taboo against

looking at a woman's legs or even thinking about them created a situation in which there was even something obscene about the legs of a table or a piano. The stimuli capable of arousing a sexual response became increasingly minute. Yet it was a battle against the arms of a windmill: the more people struggled against sexuality, the more the environment became sexualized. Antisexuality had become a negative sexual obsession.

Sexual prudery was but one aspect of the general psychic transformation that took place during the course of modernization. It is within this context that one must view the transformation of adolescent sexuality that took place between the sixteenth and the nineteenth century. Next to women, it was predominantly adolescents who became the victims of the antisex wave. Far into the 18th century, between 80 and 90% of the population lived in the countryside. This means that one can view the predominant premarital customs among adolescents and unmarried adults in rural regions as the most widespread pattern of behavior. This pattern involved night-courtship (bundling, Kiltgang, Nachtfreien).

Throughout most of Western Europe (as well as in the English colonies of North America), night-courtship was an accepted custom during the latter part of the Middle Ages and early modern times. In rural areas, it continued to be practiced far into the 19th and 20th centuries. It involved an institutionalized, socially controlled, generally accepted and widespread form of premarital sexuality. Certainly there were numerous variations of this custom, but common to all of them was the fact that a boy could visit a girl at night, that in the course of time a gradual escalation of intimacies took place, leading ultimately, if the parents approved of the boy, to coitus. If the girl became pregnant, then the couple married, if not, then they separated after an appropriate lapse of time. One of the important functions of this particular form of premarital sexuality was the proof of fertility, because having children was an important economic factor on the farm. The marriage itself was a quick ceremony of slight social significance. Engagement, having sexual intercouse, and becoming pregnant were the things that counted.

The bourgeoisie relinquished this form of sexual freedom, and to the degree that bourgeois model of behavior became established, night courtship disappeared. Naturally, it prevailed the longest in rural regions. Premarital intercourse became forbidden. It was a mode of conduct no longer compatible with the standard of unity of marriage, procreation, love, and sexuality outlined above. It is certain that premarital intercourse receded among bourgeois girls. That was probably not the case among the men. And yet their premarital sexuality had also changed: it was now located outside of norms; it had become an illegal act no longer capable of being an ego-syntonic experience. Due to its illegality, it became factually antisocial. There was a dissociation of love and sexuality. This was followed by the arisal of an exploitative attitude toward the premarital female partner who came from a lower social class or was a prostitute. In any event it was no longer necessary to show any sort of consideration.

The repression of adolescent sexuality reached its peak during the war against masturbation in the 19th century. In earlier times, nobody had ever really given any consideration to masturbation. In the beginning of the 18th century, it was 'discovered' that masturbation afflicted severe damage to the individual, although there are no indications that there was any increase in the incidence of masturbation. The only thing that seems to have increased was the general preoccupation with the repression of adolescent sexuality. Masturbation was looked upon as a disease, as immoral behavior that could lead to physical and mental ruin. Pedagogues and physicians developed a series of strategies and weapons to be used in the war against masturbation. These ranged from the advice to sleep on a hard bed with few covers so as to remain as cold as possible, to sadistic quasicastration devices such as, for example, spike-lined rings to be placed around the penis in such a manner as to inflict pain to it should it become erected. The war against masturbation was an attempt to "create internal order in the achievement-oriented individual" (van Ussel, 1970, p. 132). This resulted in the expulsion of the sexual activity of adolescents into the realm of guilt and fear, and in the desperate struggle of countless adolescents to behave against their own needs, but in accordance with the standards they had internalized.

The repression of adolescent sexuality is as little an isolated phenomenon as the repression of sexuality in general. According to van Ussel, it is both a symptom and a consequence of the psychostructure made necessary by the early phase of industrialization. It was the result, as van Ussel explicitly emphasizes, of socioeconomic changes and not of religious taboos. The church was a vehicle of this development, but not its decisive cause.

3. SHORTER: INDUSTRIALIZATION AND THE REVOLUTION IN EROTICISM

In much the same manner as van Ussel, Shorter also proceeds from the significant of socioeconomic factors for his analysis of sexuality. He has utilized data on the illegitimate fertility rates, and the fertility rates of young women during the past two hundred years as the basis for his study.

According to these data, there was a significant increase in the formally registered illegitimate fertility rate (births per 1000 single women) in almost every region of Europe (as well as in the New England states of the U.S.) between 1750 and 1850. The parish registers indicate that during this period the percentage of illegitimately born children rose from between 1 to 3% to between 10 and 15% of all births. In addition, the number of prebridal pregnancies (children born in wedlock, but conceived prior to marriage) also rose. Finally, the legitimate fertility rate among women, above all, among those women up to 24 years of age, rose. Shorter points out that these trends cannot be explained by a general increase in fertility, because the birth rates among women over 30 had remained constant since 1700. Indeed there was a slight decrease. It is also not a question of an extension of the span of time between conception and marriage. Shorter further excludes the explanation that the changes were due to improved procedures for reporting birth, or due to a decrease in miscarriages, and/or a rise in infanticide or abortion. For him, the most important factor is an increase in premarital sexual intercourse. 'The illegitimacy explosion probably took place, because more young people than even before were having sex before marriage' (Shorter, 1973, p. 609). This was predominantly the case among the working class and in the cities, because it was here that the changes in fertility rates were the greatest.

During the second half of the 19th century, the premarital fertility trend began to reverse itself. There was a decline both in the legitimate and the illegitimate fertility rate. This trend was also supraregional, though it began regionally at different points in time between 1810 and 1890. According to Shorter, this can not be interpreted as a decrease in the frequency of coitus and/or as a decrease in the incidence of premarital relations. In his opinion there are also no indications for a decrease in fecundity. For Shorter, the decisive factor is an improvement in, and the widespread availability of, contraceptives. This would appear to be a plausible explanation, because the invention of the vulcanization of raw rubber that took place in 1843 made it possible to produce the contraceptive condom industrially. However, Shorter does not go into the possible social factors that caused people to have fewer children, and thus to avail themselves to such a great extent of this new method of contraception. Unquestionably, subsequent to the widespread prohibition of child labor, the relative decrease of the peasant population in comparison to the municipal population, and the introduction of obligatory juvenile education, children had become a burden for an increasing number of people. They no longer provided any relief for the family.

The processes underlying the changes in the fertility of young women described above began in different classes: the reduction in the age at which coitus took place for the first time, and the increase in the incidence of premarital coitus, began in the working class and spread only slowly into the middle class. This did not become a mass transformation until the twentieth century. Conversely, the birth control movement began in the middle class and found its way into the working class only over an extended period of time.

For Shorter, the increase in the premarital behavior of working class women between 1750 and 1850 is an expression of female emancipation, of a 'growing sense of personal autonomy and independence . . . Female emancipation was, in the absence of birth control, responsible for the upward slope of the nonmarital fertility parabola, and for the increase in the marital fertility of those young women who entered marriage already pregnant' (Shorter, 1973, p. 612). According to Shorter this emancipation of working class women must be seen in the context of the social changes generated by emerging capitalism:

(a) Working class women became increasingly independent from parental and husbandly authority, because they were no longer dependent on the husband or the father economically, in so far as they were employed, which was generally the case. The fact that they were also wage laborers modified the balance of power in the family. Subordination gave way to a spirit of independence and an unwillingness to subject one's self to any kind of moral dictates on the part of the family.

(b) The ideology of capitalism was an ideology of the market place. It was an ideology of maximizing self-interest and getting ahead through personal achievement. Within the working class, including, as a result of their independence, its women too, this created a situation in which sexuality be came accepted as a form of self-realization for the sake of self-fulfillment.

(c) The middle-class could not transfer these capitalistic values into the realm of sexuality because of the greater family controls which existed. Within the working class, something which Shorter refers to as the 'proletarian subculture' made it possible to assimilate these new values rapidly. It was this transfer of capitalist values that gave the proletarian subculture its libertine moral veneer.

Shorter himself, and we must concede him this point in all fairness, characterized his explanations of the changes that took place in the sexuality of young women during the later 18th and early 19th century as highly speculative in nature. In my opinion, they are not only speculative, but also a misinterpretation of the socioeconomic condition of the working class as well as its sexuality.

4. CONCLUSION

Any discussion of the differences in van Ussel's and Shorter's viewpoints requires that one study the contradictions in their observations and in their interpretations.

With respect to their observations, one must keep in mind that van Ussel has used his sources to demonstrate an increase in the repression of adolescent sexuality, above all among adolescent girls, during the 18th and 19th centuries, concluding among other things that this resulted in a decrease in premarital relations. Shorter, on the other hand, notes an increase in premarital relations. These contradictions are probably based on the fact that the two authors were studying the behavior of different social classes: Shorter was studying the working class, van Ussel the bourgeoisie. The decrease in premarital relations in comparison to previous times and in contrast to the rural population, one can conclude, was obviously a phenomenon widespread only among bourgeois adolescents, particularly bourgeois girls.

The contradiction in interpretation lies in the fact that van Ussel attributes the destruction of sexuality, indeed of all sensuality to the early capitalist phase of industrialization, whereas, for Shorter, industrialization was responsible for the introduction of a process of sexual emancipation, particularly among women. Here, it is important to point out that Shorter by no means considers these changes to be merely quantitative in nature (greater frequency and/or incidence of premarital sexual intercourse). On the contrary, he sees qualitative changes taking place: an increase in the expressive understanding of sexuality as self-realization and a 'shift on the quality spectrum from genital to polymorphous gratification' (Shorter, 1973, p. 297). It would be all too simple to interpret these differences between van Ussel and Shorter also as class differences. Rather, Shorter's conclusions appear to me to be disputable, if not refutable.

Shorter's first 'logical chain' is as follows (1) more nonmarital pregnancies = (2) more premarital coitus relations = (3) more sexual emancipation among women. The only link in this chain of logical reasoning that appears to me to have any plausibility is the link from (1) to (2). If one attempts to connect link (1) with link (3), the questionability of Shorter's reasoning becomes most apparent: he interprets the increase in illegitimate pregnancies as a sign of female emancipation in a manner one could almost term cynical. Shorter is almost certainly correct in his estimation that working class daughters, being less economically dependent, were less subject to parental control than the daughters of bourgeois families. But why would they use this independence precisely to tie themselves down again with an illegitimate child? The high rate of illegitimacy does not indicate, as Shorter would have it, that women had become 'masters of their own fertility' (Shorter, 1973, p. 612), but rather that it was possible for them to more easily become the victims of their own fecundity under the new social conditions. However, Shorter is also oversimplifying the connection between the second and third link of the logical chain. Neither a high frequency nor a high incidence of premarital coital relations need have anything to do with sexual liberalism or emancipation. The data that have been accumulated in this century on working class sexuality (Kinsey et al., 1948, 1953; Rainwater, 1965) indicate that, in the working class, coital relations begin at a very early age, but that they are much more monotonus and prude in nature, and that for women they are both more devoid of pleasure and involve more orgasm disturbances. It would take a great deal more than the available data to justifiably pose a connection between the second and the third link. How indeed did women experience premarital sexuality? Did they really find it autonomously desirable or were they tortured by the fear of premarital pregnancy? More probably than Shorter's optimistic interpretation is the following assumption: industrialization, urbanization, exploitation and impoverishment, social insecurity, life in the ghetto, and the collapse of the family, also drove sexuality in the working class into a state of anomie in which women, as the weakest members of the class, came to bear the full brunt of this condition. The working class woman was no longer protected by the laws governing the rural custom of night-courtship, a custom that highly reduced the risks involved in premarital relations, at least to the extent that people abided by the rules. She was also not subject to the absolute parental rule of the bourgeoisie as were daughters of that class, who, despite all the other suffering it may have caused, were protected against premarital pregnancies. In this particular area of anomie, it was easy for male dominancy to assert itself. Shorter himself comes very close to this interpretation in describing increasing illegitimacy in the early 19th century as 'hit and run' illegitimacy, resulting from temporary liasions in which the partners were 'not inclined to remain together after a conception had taken place' (Shorter, 1973, p. 304). But why should a pregnant woman run off? Running off is something that would only help the man. He is the person in a position to desert from the social and economic consequences of a pregnancy. 'Hit and run' illegitimacy certainly doesn't indicate that sex is a manifestation of self-realization, but it does indicate a new manifestation of repressive behavior between men and women in a situation in which women were no longer protected by the family and a moral system. Moreover, how many of the pregnancies of lower class women were caused by men from the bourgeoisie who, owing to their double standard, did not engage in premarital sexuality with women of their own class? Many a lower class woman's pregnancy did not constitute an act of self-fulfillment, but was nothing more than an act of desperation, be it as a prostitute, or in order to obtain or keep a job.

Yet, Shorter's second line of reasoning would appear to me to be no less arbitrary. Exaggeratedly formulated, it posits that the market place ideology of capitalism led to self-fulfillment and personal autonomy and thus also to sexual autonomy among proletarian women. We would begin by pointing out that capitalism and the aggregate value system is an ideology of the bourgeoisie and that only members of this class had any chance of profiting from this ideology. It was only the sons of the bourgeoisie who had a chance of becoming someone or something through their own efforts. Why the daughters from the working class should be in such a hurry to adopt and assimilate this ideology is not clear, and even a vivid imagination does not reveal to us what could have led Shorter to this conclusion. The second mistake in this line of reasoning is that capitalism during the early phase of industrialization simply did not favor any sort of liberal sexual standards, a fact emphasized by Israel et al. (1970). During the phase of capital accumulation when all of the capitalists' income was to be re-invested for industrial progress, such things as abstaining from consumption were very important and society, that is, the bourgeoisie, propagated this very abstinence, the postponement of need satisfaction, controlling one's needs and thus controlling one's sexuality, as van Ussel has described this complex. It was the transformation from the phase of capital accumulation during early industrialization to the consumer society during the highly industrialized phase of capitalism that first made permissible the process of sexual liberalization that we have begun to observe since the turn of the century, but even more so since World War II and the beginning of the 1960s (Schmidt and Schorsch, 1975).

280

Underlying Shorter's interpretations is the middle-class prejudice with respect to working class sexuality, namely that it is natural, untarnished and uninhibited. Shorter seems to be projecting this prejudice onto simple statistical trends. However, he undoubtedly must be credited with having pointed out that the heavy increase and age change of premarital relations in the middle class, predominantly among women, in this century has its precursor in the sexual behavior of the working class, and would hardly have taken place otherwise. Smith (1973), too, has pointed out that among the general, non-middle class 'population of women, important changes in premarital sexual behavior already were under way during the late 19th century' (p. 329). According to Smith, the behavior of the educated minority converged with that of a less educated majority. The other site of the coin, the qualitative side, as Shorter refers to it, defining sexuality as self-fulfillment, the sophistication of sexuality through fantasy, imagination and the differentiation of 'polymorphous' practices is, according to everything we know today, an invention of the middle class (Kinsey et al., 1948). It is a pattern of behavior that only extended over into the working class at a later date. This would tend to indicate that the sexual liberalization observed in the course of the past decades has two historical roots emanating from different sectors of the population, leading ultimately to a convergence of the sexual behavior patterns of the middle class and (at least) the stable working class, as described in a later chapter.

BIBLIOGRAPHY

Israel, J., Gustavsson, N., Eliasson, R. and Lindberg, G. (1970) Sexuelle Verhaltensformen der schwedischen Grossstadtjugend. In: (Bergström-Walan, M.-B. et al., Eds.) *Modellfall Skandinavien? Sexualität und Sexualpolitik in Dänemark und Schweden.* (Rowohlt, Reinbek, W. Germany).

Keniston, K. (1971) Psychological development and historical change. *J. Interdiscip. Hist.* 2: 329—345.

Kinsey, A.C., Pomery, W.B. and Martin, C.E. (1948) *Sexual Behavior in the Human Male.* (Saunders, Philadelphia, London).

Kinsey, A.C., Pomeroy, W.B., Martin, C.E. and Gebhard, P.H. (1953) *Sexual Behavior. in the Human Female.* (Saunders, Philadelphia, London.)

Möller, H. (1969) *Die kleinbürgerliche Familie im 18. Jahrhundert.* (Walter de Gruyter, Berlin).

Rainwater, L. (1965) *Family Design. Marital Sexuality, Family Size, Contraception.* (Aldine Press, Chicago).

Schmidt, G. and Schorsch, E. (1975) Sexuelle Liberalisierung und Emanzipation. In: (E. Schorsch and Schmidt, G., Eds.) *Ergebnisse zur Sexualforschung.* (Kiepenheuer und Witsch, Köln).

Shorter, E. (1971) Illegitimacy, sexual revolution, and social change in modern Europe. *J. Interdiscip. Hist.* 2: 237—272. Reprinted in: (Gordon, M., Ed.), *The American Family in Social-Historical Perspective.* (St. Martin's Press, New York).

Shorter, E. (1972) Capitalism, culture, and sexuality: Some competing models. *Soc. Sci. Q.* 53: 338—356.

Shorter, E. (1973) Female emancipation, birth control, and fertility in European history. *Am. Hist. Rev.* 78: 605—640.

Smith, D.S. (1973) The data of the American sexual revolution: Evidence and interpretation. In: (M. Gordon, Ed.), *The American Family in Social-Historical Perspective.* (St. Martin's Press, New York).

Taylor, G.R. (1957) *Wandlungen der Sexualität.* (Diederichs, Köln.)

Ussel, J. van (1968) *Geschiedenis van het seksuele probleem.* (Boom en Zoon, Meppel, Netherlands.)

Ussel, J. van (1970) *Sexualunterdrückung. Geschichte der Sexualfeindschaft.* (Rowohlt, Reinbek, W. Germany) (French, Italian, Portugese and Spanish edns available.)

CHAPTER 21

Working-class and middle-class adolescents

GUNTER SCHMIDT

1. INTRODUCTION

Social class determines the socioeconomic situation of an individual, and is thus a crucial factor in determining her/his social, physiological and sexual fate. Social class defines groups which differ widely with regard to social power, property and income, education and occupation, living and working conditions, social status, and the opportunity to satisfy one's needs. Social class means social inequality. Analyzing differences in the sexuality of working class and middle class people means analyzing the influence of economic and social deprivation on sexuality.

Given the present state of research, such an analysis is a difficult task. Studies on sexual behavior are for the most part limited to the middle classes: On the one hand, members of the middle class are more accessible as subjects for sex research and are also more easily motivated to participate and cooperate in such research than is the case with members of the working class; on the other hand, the sexual behavior, norms and problems of middle class people are much more familiar to the researcher because they are the behavior, norms and problems of his own class. As the social distance between the researcher and his subjects increases, there is an increased difficulty in understanding and empathy, a reduced awareness and perception of problems, and a reduced interest and motivation for research. The sparse empirical data available for the present topic makes it necessary to augment our review of class differences among adolescents with materials dealing with studies conducted among adults.

This review is further complicated by the facts (1) that even in the few studies available highly different definitions of social class have been applied (for example: educational level, occupation, multi-level class models); (2) that very different survey methods were used (varying kinds of questionnaire and interview techniques); and (3) that very different aspects of sexuality were subjects of the studies (behavior, attitudes, or socioemotional aspects).

Handbook of Sexology, edited by J. Money and H. Musaph
© *Elsevier/North-Holland Biomedical Press, 1977*

Thus, the results arrived at are not only limited with respect to quantity; they are also quite heterogeneous. We shall, however, attempt to develop an integrated overview of the material. In this respect we shall limit ourselves to the white working and middle class (in so far as the data permit).

2. UNSTABLE VERSUS STABLE WORKING CLASS: THE CRUCIAL CUTTING POINT

The studies by Lee Rainwater (1960, 1964, 1965, 1966) are the most important contributions to the class-dependency of sexuality to date, even though his studies are based on relatively small samples and the influence of class and race were not always analyzed separately. In the early 1960s, Rainwater and his co-workers studied roughly 200 couples from the lower-lower, the upper-lower and the middle class. All of the subjects were married and less than 45 years old. Some of the results are summarized in Table I.

Rainwater (1965, 1966) was able to establish a high correlation between social class and interest and enjoyment in marital sexuality. The class-dependent drop in interest and enjoyment is still greater among women than among men. This means: (1) lower class women maintain especially often anti-sexual attitudes and resentments; they are strongly desexualized, and 54% of them, but only 14% of middle class women have a negative attitude toward sexuality, which approaches total rejection in numerous cases; (2) the inequality of sexual interest and enjoyment is much greater among lower class couples than is the case among middle class couples.

The desexualization of the woman and inequality of interest and enjoyment must diminish the mutuality of marital sexual relations. Indeed according to Rainwater (1965), significantly fewer husbands from the lower-lower class (37%) than from the middle class (70%) intended mutual fulfillment during coitus. Correspondingly, more women from the lower-lower class than from the upper-lower and middle class were of the opinion that marital sexuality was a 'duty' and not a 'pleasure'. Within the lower-lower class, sexuality is seen predominantly as a male activity. This is both an expression and a pretence for an extreme double standard. This situation leads among the women to an explicit strategy of avoidance with respect to sexual activity: excuses such as tiredness and illness are brought forth to reduce the frequency of coitus; women look forward to menstruation and childbed as an excuse to practice sexual abstinence; husbands are sent out to the bar and elsewhere to distract them from their sexual demands, all of which results in reduced coitus frequency (Rainwater, 1964, 1965).

Not only do interest and enjoyment vary from class to class; the function attributed to sexuality is class-dependent, too. Whereas men and women from the lower-lower class often expect nothing more than psychophysiological pleasure and relief, the overwhelming majority of the middle class also seek socioemotional fulfillment: A feeling of belonging to one another, of

Table I

Marital sexuality and conjugal role relationship; by social class (data from Rainwater, 1965, 1966).

	Unstable working (lower-lower) class (%)	Stable working (upper-lower) class (%)	Middle class (%)
Husband shows great interest and enjoyment in marital sex	44 (n = 59)	75 (n = 56)	78 (n = 56)
Wife shows great interest and enjoyment in marital sex	20	53	50
Wife shows mild interest and enjoyment in marital sex	26	16	36
Wife shows a slightly negative attitude toward marital sex	34	27	11
Wife rejects marital sexual relations	20 (n = 69)	4 (n = 68)	3 (n = 58)
Husband enjoys marital sex more	67	47	33
Equal enjoyment	26	51	59
Wife enjoys marital sex more	7	2	8
Segregated conjugal role relationship	72	30	0
Joint conjugal role relationship	2	16	65

giving and taking, of closeness and exchange (Rainwater 1965, 1966). Thus, one can observe a tendency toward de-socioemotionalization of sexuality in the lower-lower class. Within the middle class, sexuality is both viewed and experienced as an important social activity aimed at strengthening the relationship between man and woman whereas sexuality in the lower-lower class tends more to endanger the marriage than to strengthen it

Rainwater (1965, 1966) traces the class-dependent differences in sexuality to different conjugal role relationships. Within the middle class he found an attitude aimed toward mutuality in most couples (67%). Both partners participated in all activities within and outside of the family together, or communicated about these activities (joint relationship). Within the lower-lower class, on the other hand, an equally large majority of the couples (72%) revealed both separation and isolation in the conjugal role relationships; the couples seldom participated in common activities and there was little communication concerning such matters as family life, child-rearing, work, leisure-time activities, and such like. In other words, a segregated relationship.

Rainwater was able to prove that there is a significantly negative correlation between the degree of segregation in conjugal role relationship and both sexual interest and enjoyment, and the emphasis on the socioemotional function of sexuality. This holds true for all classes; it has led Rainwater to view segregation as a key variable in the understanding of the sexuality of the lower-lower class. Within this frame of reference, the sexual segregation of the partners is nothing more than a specific expression of the couple's general social segregation.

Simon and Gagnon (1966, 1969) trace social and sexual segregation back to the typical process of sexual socialization among male lower-lower class youth. They engage in exclusively heterosexual and coital activity at a much earlier age than middle class male youths; however, their heterosexual activity has a much greater homosocial significance. Coitus serves primarily the purpose of proving one's manliness within the male peer group. Within a class whose opportunities to prove one's status in other areas (education, job, income, property) are drastically reduced, sexuality becomes a decisive status symbol. Thus, to an even greater extent than in the middle class, sexuality within the lower-lower class is viewed within the context of performance, competition and exploitation, and is significantly less related to such factors as enjoyment, mutual satisfaction or fulfillment, and tenderness.

Other studies of the American (Komarovsky, 1967), Mexican (Lewis, 1967), Puerto Rican (Stycos, 1955) and English (Kerr, 1958) lower-lower classes which dealt with the problem of sexuality only marginally permit conclusions very similar to those arrived from Rainwater's research. Komarovsky, for example, found that the attitude that it is the duty of the woman 'to give it to her husband whether she likes it or not' (p. 83) was a much more common attitude among women of the lower-lower class than among women of the lower-middle class. Kerr found marital sexuality in the Liverpool slum area he studied to be a 'curiously mixed one. Prudery and crudeness are closely intermingled' (p. 78).

A closer look at Rainwater's data reveals that the relationship between sexuality and social class is by no means linear (see Table I). The greatest differences are to be found between the lower-lower and the upper-lower class; by contrast the differences between the upper-lower and the middle class are clearly slighter. To evaluate the significance of this fact, it is necessary to closely scrutinize Rainwater's definition of these classes:

"The lower-lower class represents . . . about 13% of the population of a city like Chicago. The people in this group . . . feel at the 'bottom of the heap' . . . They generally work at unskilled jobs, and often they work only intermittently or are chronically unemployed. Few people in this group have graduated from high school, and a great many have gone no further than grammar school. They live in slum or near-slum neighborhoods, and their housing tends to be cramped and deteriorated . . . The seasonal or intermittent nature of their jobs and their relatively impulsive spending habits often prevent them from maintaining what most Americans regard as a decent standard of living" (Rainwater, 1965, p. 24).

"The upper-lower class includes . . . 46% of Chicago's total population and is characterized by greater prosperity and stability than the lower-lower class. Upper-lower class workers generally are in semi-skilled or medium-skilled work; they are in manual occupations or in responsible but not highly regarded service jobs . . . They have generally had at least some high school education. Their families live in reasonably comfortable housing, in neighborhoods composed mainly of other manual and lower-level service workers. Although people in this group tend today to regard themselves as living the good life of average Americans, they are still aware that they do not have as much social status . . . as the middle class" (Rainwater, 1965, p. 24).

Rainwater's lower-lower class is precisely that which is described by sociologists as the unstable working class (no secure job, irregular employment, no vocational training, residence in slum areas) and the upper-lower class is that which the sociologists describe as the stable working class (relatively secure jobs or regular employment, residence outside of slum areas, at least semi-skilled). The crucial cutting point with regard to sexuality thus lies between the unstable and the stable working class.

This assumption is strengthened substantially by our studies in West-Germany (Schmidt and Sigusch, 1971a; Sigusch and Schmidt, 1971). We studied the sexual behavior of 150 male and 150 female, single, unskilled or semi-skilled workers 20—21 years of age. They belong to the 15% of the West German population with the lowest level of education, occupational training, income and social expectations. However, they belong to the stable working class, because all of them had a relatively secure job and were paid relatively good wages.

We found hardly any signs of strongly pronounced sexual segregation, or de-socioemotionalization of sexuality, or of desexualization or dissatisfaction of the women — characteristics which Rainwater found to be typical for the unstable working class. The West German workers regard sexuality as a social activity involving reciprocity. There was a strong tendency towards assimilating sexuality with personal and emotional bonds. Love and fidelity were important values; the women were not expected to be asexual or hyposexual and did not regard themselves as such. Indeed, the females experienced coitus as less satisfying and less positively than the males on the average; but this gender difference is decidedly not class-specific. It was quite remarkable that most women of the lower classes were able to have orgasms and experienced coitus with pleasure. Failure to achieve orgasm was not accepted by them with resignation, fatalism, or, out of ignorance, as natural. They tended to blame their partners for this. In contrast to Rainwater's sample, these workers were single and they were also younger. It may be that their experiences during a working class marriage will change their sexuality. However, our data point to the assumption that their marital sexuality will be similar to that which Rainwater found to be typical of the stable working class.

We find further corroboration for our cutting point hypothesis in a study conducted by Whyte (1943) three decades ago concerning the sex code of adolescents of Italian origin in a slum area of a major American city. With regard to their educational and occupational situation, these adolescents belong to the unstable working class and their sexual behavior pattern is very similar to that of the unstable working class (even though this pattern may very well be permeated with specific ethnic traditions).

The dominating characteristic of this group is an extreme double standard: the boys are expected to engage in sexual relations whenever and whereever they can; sexual intercourse with a number of girls is an important status symbol within the peer group. Whereas promiscuity has high prestige value for the boys, the girls are expected either to be virgins or to be going steady. The boys divide the girls into three groups according to their behavior: the virgins who are highly respected and protected by the boys against sexual attacks; the 'one-man-girl' who engage in sexual intercourse only with the steady boy friend, also generally respected; and the promiscuous girls who are scorned by the group and their partners. Sexual relations involve very different risks for the one-man-girls, and the promiscuous girls. If a pregnancy results, the former are nearly always married, the latter hardly ever; whereas there is hardly ever any discussion about the sexual experiences one had with one's steady girl friend, the experiences with promiscuous girls are regularly made public and serve to enhance the boy's homosocial status.

Girls who grow up in the midst of such a defaming double standard can hardly develop a positive attitude toward sexuality that is free from conflict and hostility. Within the unstable working class — to an even greater extent than in the middle class — sexuality becomes an outright battle between the sexes. The boys are out for conquests which they can brag about to their peer group in order to enhance their prestige; the girls often employ sexuality exploitatively too. In this atmosphere of reciprocal exploitation it is hardly possible to develop a sense of mutuality, or any feeling for sexuality based on emotions and tenderness and directed toward reciprocity. Here, behavior patterns are developed which are the same as those described by Rainwater with respect to the marital sexuality of the unstable working class.

Looking at the emperical evidence it would seem pertinent today to distinguish between two patterns of lower class sexuality: that of the stable and that of the unstable working class. The two are briefly described in the following sections.

Unstable working class pattern

Men and especially women of this group encounter in the emotional and psychosocial sphere of sexuality a great deal more insecurity, deprivation and frustration. Their sexual relations are often devoid of emotion and mutuality and are mechanical in nature. A powerful double standard is prevalent caused by an especially strong internationalization of gender-role stereotypes. Women regard themselves and are regarded by men as 'asexual' or at least 'hyposexual'. Correspondingly, they show little interest in sexual relations, view sexuality as a duty, experience it without desire or pleasure. For the men, heterosexuality is highly important for one's status and social exchange in the homosocial peer group.

Stable working class pattern

In this class a 'romantic' view of sexuality is widespread today. The ideal that sexuality ought to be linked to love is the prevalent norm. This results in a pronounced partner-oriented sexual behavior directed toward mutuality. Sexual desire and activity are also the domain of women. Sexual relations are satisfying for both men and women or at least ought to be. Attitudes of the double standard type occur less divisively. Contrary to the unstable working class, the stable working class does not differ in any basic sense from the middle classes with respect to sexuality. It would appear to orient itself to those liberal and romantic sexual norms which are also prevalent among the middle class today.

What are the reasons for the major differences between the unstable working class on the one hand and the stable working class and the middle class on the other hand? Rainwater's reference to the greater segregation of marital role relationships within the unstable working class serves at best to locate the phenomenon within a broader social framework, but it does not provide an explanation, because this still does not explain the genesis of this segregation.

The above described differences in the socioeconomic living conditions which separate the unstable from the stable working class point to the conclusion that a certain socioeconomic level is a prerequisite for emotionally satisfying, and mutual sexual relations enjoyable for both partners. Workers can only overcome their miserable sexual situation if they are no longer directly threatened by social misery. Social misery, insecurity with regard to one's material existence, the disintegrating and anomic effects of poverty and joblessness, the sense of helplessness in being unable to change one's situation, and the accompanying feeling of hopelessness, as well as lack of education, all tend to disintegrate social and emotional relations and thus to ruin sexuality. This means that the socioeconomic situation of an individual is one of the most powerful and basic variables correlating with the sexuality of an individual, though the exact relationship of cause and effect is unknown.

3. STABLE WORKING CLASS VERSUS MIDDLE CLASS: MINOR DIFFERENCES *

There are indeed basic similarities between the sexual patterns of the stable working class and the middle class, and they have in common that they are

---

* Kinsey et al. (1948, 1953) broke down only part of their male data according to occupation, and there was no occupational breakdown at all for their female data. Their class analyses are primarily based on educational levels. It is not possible to transpose these

both decisively different from the unstable working class. However, this does not mean that comparison of the sexual behavior of adolescents from the stable working class and the middle class reveals no differences whatsoever. On the contrary, these two classes reveal a number of differences in their behavior which we shall touch upon now briefly:

— More boys and girls from the stable working class than from the middle class have coital relations during adolescence (Table II). More recent studies on adolescents born after 1950, however, indicate very clearly that these differences have diminished considerably within the last decade (Kantner and Zelnik, 1972; Schmidt and Sigusch, 1972). During the sixties and the early seventies, the average age of middle class adolescents at first coitus dropped considerably, especially in girls (see among others, Bell and Chaskes, 1970; Christensen and Gregg, 1971; Robinson et al., 1972; Sorensen, 1973; Vener and Stewart, 1974). Among the adolescents of the stable working class on the other hand there has been little change, meaning that a gradual approximation of the average age at the first coitus is taking place. According to our data, boys from the stable working class have their first coitus on the average only six months earlier than boys from the middle class (Schmidt and Sigusch, 1972). Among the girls from the two classes there is no longer any difference (at least in West Germany). Recent studies (Schlaegel et al., 1975) confirm this trend. An especially late coital coming-out is no longer a characteristic of male or female middle class adolescents.

— There is less sexual sophistication in the stable working class with regard to sexual techniques and practices (Table III) than the middle class. Nakedness during coitus, manual stimulation of the man by the woman, and oral-genital practices are significantly less common in the stable working class than in the middle class. The data provided by Kinsey and co-workers (1948, 1953) reveal similar differences with regard to the level of education: the trend toward variation of foreplay and coital positions increases with the level of education. Members of the middle class limit their sexuality less often to coitus itself, and tend to be less monotonous sexually, and less prudish than the working class.

— The tendency within the stable working class to limit sexuality to coitus is also reflected in the data concerning masturbation. Fewer adolescents from the stable working class than from the middle class masturbate at all

---

(contd. from p. 289)
educational groups into our categories (unstable working class, stable working class, middle class). The educational group 0—8 includes subjects from the unstable working class (roughly 1/3 to 1/2) and from the stable working class; in the educational group 9—12 roughly one third of the subjects belong to the middle class. The educational groups 13 and more belong almost exclusively to the middle classes (cf. Kinsey et al., 1948, p. 328). For this reason, we shall only deal with those data provided by Kinsey in which a correlation between occupation and sexual behavior has been calculated. We shall rely also on studies which we have performed in West Germany.

Table II
Masturbation and coitus behavior; by social class.

| | USA, male (16—20 years) [a] | | | | West Germany, male and female (20—21 years) [b] | | | |
| | Stable working class | | Middle class | | Stable working class | | Middle class | |
	A [c] (n = 318)	B [c] (n = 104)	C [c] (n = 1021)	D [e] (n = 426)	Male (n = 150)	Female (n = 150)	Male (n = 395)	Female (n = 212)
Masturbation								
Active incidence [d]	87%	89%	90%	89%	57%	15%	83%	38%
Active weekly frequency	0.6	0.9	1.4	1.9	0.6	— [e]	1.5	— [e]
Coitus								
Experience (before age 21)	— [e]	— [e]	— [e]	— [e]	81%	83%	44%	33%
Active incidence [d]	77%	66%	39%	35%	71%	71%	42%	39%
Active weekly frequency	1.1	0.6	0.2	0.2	0.6	0.8	0.6	1.1

[a] According to Kinsey et al. (1948; p. 422 ff).

[b] According to Schmidt and Sigusch (1971b).

[c] A = Kinsey's occupational class 3 (semi-skilled labor); B = occupational class 4 (skilled labor); C = occupational class 6 (upper white collar); D = occupational class 7 (professional groups); social class is defined here both according to parental occupational class and to subject's own occupational class. To group A thus belong semi-skilled workers whose fathers are semi-skilled workers, too.

[d] Masturbation at least once between 16 and 20 in the US-sample; masturbation at least once within the 12 months before the study in the West German sample.

[e] No data.

Table III
Coital techniques; by social class [a]

	Stable working class (%)		Middle class (%)	
	Males (n = 104)	Females (n = 104)	Males (n = 167)	Females (n = 83)
Manual—genital, man active	93	89	97	99
Manual—genital, woman active	80	77	93	93
Cunnilingus	37	46	56	64
Fellatio	31	33	56	46
Nudity of both partners	68	80	96	99

[a] From Schmidt and Sigusch (1971b) 20—21-year-old young adults, West Germany. The table shows the percent of subjects who practiced the listed techniques at least occasionally.

and they also masturbate less often (Table II). Kinsey (1948, 1953) described similar results for subjects with low and high educational levels. The reduced masturbatory activity of working class adolescents cannot be traced back to their higher coital activity: the class differences are existent among coitus-experienced and coitus-inexperienced adolescents (Schmidt and Sigusch, 1971b). Simon and Gagnon (1969) and Gagnon and Simon (1973) have pointed to the importance of masturbation for sexual socialization during adolescence. The sexual fantasy connected with masturbation initiates a learning process by which numerous neutral stimuli and activities become sexualized or eroticized. Masturbatory fantasy, itself stimulated in part by more formal education within the middle class and the greater value placed upon fantasy in general, is certain to play an important role in the development of greater sexual sophistication within the middle class.

— Adolescents from the stable working class have more restrictive attitudes to sexuality (Schmidt and Sigusch, 1971b; Sigusch and Schmidt, 1973; Walczak et al., 1975). It was not possible to demonstrate differences in premarital sexual standards (Reiss, 1967). Nevertheless, adolescents from the stable working class, above all the girls, evaluate more unorthodox sexual activities more strictly than do middle class adolescents. This holds true, for example, for extramarital relations, masturbation and homosexuality. In addition, stable working class adolescents tend to place a greater value upon sexual fidelity than even middle class adolescents do; they (this, however, is only significant for the girls) reveal the decided intention to marry at an earlier age and tend to prefer the traditional division of labor in marriage. Although it is true that adolescents from the middle class and the stable working class both tend toward liberal sexual standards, the standards among the stable working class are still permeated with traditional values to a greater extent.

— Stable working class adolescents reveal greater gender differences than do the middle class adolescents (Sigusch and Schmidt, 1971b, 1973). This is true both for behavior and attitudes. Stable working class girls are especially sexually conservative. Thus, in the middle class sexuality tends to be less gender-specific. The greater differences prevalent in the stable working class provide for greater conflicts between males and females in sexual matters.

Thus, stable working class adolescents have heterosexual experiences at an earlier age, but remain more limited in their behavior to prude and monotonous practices and have a more restrictive attitude toward noncoital sex. The comparatively advanced average age at first coitus among middle class adolescents is probably due to their better education which keeps them economically dependent on their parents for a longer period of time, and thus more subject to their control (a control which middle class parents tend to exercise more than parents of stable working class youth). The reasons for the prudery of the stable working class can probably be found in the special nature of their social situation. Their working conditions — whose direct influence upon sexuality have not been studied to date — are manual, often physically exhausting activities that must be performed to earn a living and which do not provide much satisfaction or self-actualization, and no status or prestige. These conditions make it very difficult for people to approach and conceive of sexuality as something playful that can be enhanced with fantasy. For them sex, much the same as eating, is a serious and direct fulfillment of a physical need. It is not so important how it happens, but rather that it happens. Within the middle class, on the contrary, the process of fulfillment is artfully delayed, refined beyond the physical body-to-body aspect and maximized. Stable working class adolescents are faced with greater social problems and equipped with less education. The naturalistic conception of morality among the working class was emphasized in Kinsey (1948), where it was pointed out that the sexual behavior of the working class was judged along a dimension of natural versus unnatural; in the middle class this dimension is moral versus immoral. We might add that, in the upper-middle class, it is sophisticated versus unsophisticated. Given the lack of opportunities to achieve status, sexuality plays a more significant role in attaining male identity for adolescents from the stable working class than it does for adolescents from the middle class. Male sexuality, a sexuality aimed at proving sexual potency with women, is very important for working class boys as a proof of being a real man. This leads to a rejection of masturbation as it imperils one's manliness. For the working class girl, the family is to an even greater degree than in the middle class the only opportunity to establish and maintain one's female identity. It is for this reason, I believe, that girls from the stable working class want to marry at an early age, and why they cling strongly to the traditional model of marriage. It is also certainly true that early marriage provides an opportunity to escape from the disappointing perspectives in the world of work open to them.

As important as these differences between the stable working class and the middle class may be, the points in common between these two classes are even more significant. The adolescents of both classes today reveal a liberal, romantic love ideology. According to this philosophy, the traditional limitation of sexuality to reproduction is unanimously rejected by both boys and girls. Coital relations prior to marriage, even for adolescents, are approved by and for both sexes. However, there are strongly internationalized values that control sexual behavior: love, fidelity, the partner- or marriage-orientedness. Thus it is possible to impute a romantic love philosophy which is ultimately aimed at marriage and the family for both working class and middle class adolescents. The differences between the stable class and the middle class are only differences in emphasis within the same total concept.

The class analyses I have attempted here must be regarded as tentative. The research methods used are meager, and the aspects of sexuality dealt with are extremely limited. It is very possible that one would find much greater differences between the stable working class and the middle class if able to give more scrutiny than in the past to the emotional impact of sexuality, to the ways in which sexuality is experienced, and to the problems and conflicts involved using more qualitatively oriented research methods.

BIBLIOGRAPHY

Bell, R.R. and Chaskes, J.B. (1970) Premarital sexual experiences among coeds, 1958 and 1968. *J. Marr. Fam.* 32: 81—84.

Christensen, H.T. and Gregg, C.F. (1970) Changing sex norms in America and Scandinavia. *J. Marr. Fam.* 32: 616—627.

Gagnon, J.H. and Simon, W. (1973) *Sexual Conduct. The Social Sources of Human Sexuality*. (Chicago.)

Kantner, J.F. and Zelnik, M. (1972) Sexual experiences of young unmarried women in the United States. *Fam. Plan. Perspect.* 4: (4) 1—10.

Kerr, M. (1958) *The People of Ship Street*. (London.)

Kinsey, A.C., Pomeroy, W.B. and Martin, C.E. (1948) *Sexual Behavior in the Human Male*. (Philadelphia, London.)

Kinsey, A.C., Pomeroy, W.B., Martin, C.E. and Gebhard, P.H. (1953) *Sexual Behavior in the Human Female*. (Philadelphia, London.)

Komarovsky, M. (1967) *Blue-collar Marriage*. (New York.)

Lewis, O. (1967) *Life in a Mexican Village*. (New York.)

Rainwater, L. (1960) *And the Poor get Children. Sex, Contraception and Family Planning in the Working Class*. (Chicago.)

Rainwater, L. (1964) Marital sexuality in four cultures of poverty. *J. Marr. Fam.* 26: 457—466.

Rainwater, L. (1965) *Family Design. Marital Sexuality, Family Size, and Contraception*. (Chicago.)

Rainwater, L. (1966) Some aspects of lower class sexual behavior. *J. Soc. Iss.* 22: 2, 96—108.

Reiss, I.L. (1967) *The Social Context of Premarital Sexual Permissiveness*. (New York.)

Robinson, I.E., King, K. and Balswick, J.O. (1972) The premarital sexual revolution among college females. *Fam. Coord.* 21: 189—194.

Schlaegel, J., Schoof-Tams, K. and Walczak, L. (1975) Beziehungen zwischen Jungen und Mädchen. Sexuelle Sozialisation in Vorpubertät, Pubertät und früher Adoleszenz (I). *Sexualmedizin* 4: 206—218.

Schmidt, G. and Sigusch, V. (1971a) *Arbeiter-Sexualität. Eine empirische Untersuchung an jungen Industriearbeitern.* (Neuwied, Berlin.)

Schmidt, G. and Sigusch, V. (1971b) Patterns of sexual behavior in West German workers and students. *J. Sex Res.* 7: 89—106.

Schmidt, G. and Sigusch, V. (1972) Changes in sexual behavior among young males and females between 1960 and 1970. *Arch. Sex. Behav.* 2: 27—45.

Sigusch, V. and Schmidt, G. (1971) Lower class sexuality: Some emotional and social aspects in West German males and females. *Arch. Sex. Behav.* 1: 29—44.

Sigusch, V. and Schmidt, G. (1973) *Jugendsexualität. Dokumentation einer Untersuchung.* (Stuttgart.)

Simon, W. and Gagnon, J.H. (1966) *Heterosexuality and homosociality: A dilemma of the lower class family.* (Bloomington) mimeographed.

Simon, W. and Gagnon, J.H. (1969) On psychosexual development. In: (Goslin, D.A., Ed.), *Handbook of Socialization Theory and Research.* (Chicago.)

Sorensen, R.C. (1973) *Adolescent Sexuality in Contemporary America.* (New York.)

Stycos, J.M. (1955) *Family and Fertility in Puerto Rico. A Study of the Lower Income Group.* (New York.)

Vener, A.M. and Stewart, C.S. (1974) Adolescent sexual behavior in middle America revisited: 1970—1973. *J. Marr. Fam.* 36: 728—735.

Walczak, L., Schlaegel, J. and Schoof-Tams, K. (1975) Sexualmoral Jugendlicher. Sexuelle Sozialisation in Vorpubertät, Pubertät und früher Adoleszenz (II). *Sexualmedizin* 4: 306—325.

Whyte, W.F. (1943) A slum sex code. *Am. J. Sociol.* 49: 24—31.

CHAPTER 22

Sex education

RUDOLF MÜLLER

1. CONCEPTS OF SEXUALITY

Sex education is a planned influence on learning processes directly or indirectly related to the patterning of sexual behavior or experiences, as well as to the patterning of a value system concerning sexuality (Scarbath, 1974).

No matter how precisely one defines the goals, methods and subjects of sex education, no matter how these are divided up among the different agencies of education, and no matter how the basic question of the necessity of sex education is discussed and ultimately resolved, the prerequisite for discussing any of these problems is a more or less clear concept of sexuality and sexual development. Here, there are competing theoretical models and constructs. Current discussion is dominated by two contrasting approaches: (1) the psychoanalytical drive theory approach; and (2) the sociological or social learning approach.

Basically, the two approaches differ with respect to their fundamental assumptions concerning sexual motivation. The psychoanalytical drive theory approach posits the existence of an innate and largely autonomous developing drive. Students of the other approach consider this type of assumption to be incorrect or at least insignificant. By contrast they proceed from the assumption that strength and quality of sexual motivation develops out of a complex learning process, influenced by social norms and biological realities. Gagnon (1973) characteristically calls it a 'creation' of sexuality in early adolescence'. The pedagogical significance of these basic theoretical differences lies in the varying significance attributed to learning within the realm of sexual development.

Psychoanalytical theory describes psychosexual development as a biologically determined process which passes through differentiable phases leading ideally away from the asocial, 'polymorphous—perverse' drive-structure of the newborn child to the socialized drive-structure of the matured adult dictated by genital primacy. All of the learning processes that tend to contravene natural development are held to be basically pathogenous. Education plays only a subsidiary role in this construct. In Freud's own words, education remains "clearly within its own realm if it limits itself to completing that which is organically preformed and to giving this cleaner and deeper contours". This extremely polemic formulation of psychoanalytical, developmental theory is relativized in numerous places throughout Freud's other writings. Younger psychoanalysts are moving toward a critical re-evaluation of this approach (Miller, 1969): meanwhile, there are at present many popularizations of orthodox psychoanalytical developmental theory, above all in texts written for parents, teachers and youthworkers (Brocher, 1972; Breiner, 1972; Renshaw, 1973).

The sociological approach is primarily characterized in the negative sense by its rejection of Freud's assumptions that sexual drive develops in biologically prescribed phases and predominantly determines human development. J.H. Gagnon, one of the most prolific advocates of this approach, makes it clear that there is no compelling foundation or basis for the concept of any sexual drive as a basic biological mandate, nor for the appalling significance attributed to this drive in psychosocial development (Gagnon, 1973; Gagnon and Simon, 1973). Empirically delineable developmental phases of sexuality appear rather to be a result of standardized child-rearing patterns.

Gagnon's concept of sexual conduct is defined as, "learned behavior, not learned in the simplicity of behaviorist psychology but learned in the sense of coordination of individual and collective cultural elements, which will vary over the individual life cycle, differing within subcultures of one society and cross-culturally in both its historical and geographical dimensions" (Gagnon, 1973, p. 233). It is decisive for any understanding of both child and adolescent sexuality, in this context, that sociosexual development is conceived of as a process of individual adjustment to societal interpretations of biological facts and potentialities. Under currently existing cultural conditions in the Western world, the child does not officially begin to act and experience sexually, in the sense of adult sexuality, until early adolescence. Comparable expressions and reactions during childhood can, for the child, be completely different in their significance to the interpretations attributed to these expressions and reactions by adults.

It would be incorrect to say that psychoanalytical drive theory rejects the notion of any learning processes. On the contrary, psychoanalysis was important in contributing to the development of a concept of ego-formation as a complex learning process. However, it is the psychoanalytical assumption that, through these learning processes, the biologically preformed, developing psychosexual need-structure of the individual, which is partially dependent on external influences, is socialized towards a social reality which contradicts this very need-structure. The 'instinctual vicissitudes' of the individual are determined by the inner psychic resolution of this contradiction on the part of the individual. Orthodox psychoanalysis places the emphasis of this resolution clearly upon the redirection or rejection of these drive needs. It is only interested in the opportunities for learning available to the individual, regarding the formation of the nonpathogenetic mechanisms of drive management (for example, sublimation), and regarding the reinforcement of development toward 'genital primacy'. Thus, it is not surprising that sex educators (Kentler, 1971) make specific reference to this aspect of psychoanalytical theory.

Marxist-oriented psychoanalysts — especially the early Wilhelm Reich — detected the societally critical, even revolutionary potential of drive theory in the opportunity to demand that individual sexual drive needs be fulfilled, in opposition to the standards of bourgeois society. Reich considered the repression of the sex drive to be absolutely necessary for the maintenance of the capitalist relations of production. Marcuse's (1955) concept of 'repressive desublimization' interpreted, psychoanalytically, the contemporary sexual liberalization as a consequence of qualitatively transformed power structures in latter-day capitalism. However, both Reich and Marcuse ultimately never overcome the biologistic drive concept.

2. SEX EDUCATION AND CONCEPTS OF SEXUALITY

Both of the foregoing concepts of psychosexual development view human beings, admittedly to differing extents, as learning creatures with respect to sexuality. With regard to sexual socialization, this simply means, wanted or unwanted, planned or unplanned, nothing less than that sex education or sexual learning takes place throughout one's life — at least in the negative sense, and in the extreme case, in the form of muted sexual learning.

In order to arrive at an evaluation and conceptualization of planned sex education — in other words, of that aspect of sexual socialization that arises out of planned pedagogical measures based on more or less explicitly formulated goals, one must recognize that the above two differing approaches lead to emphasizing different aspects.

Normative orientation

The question of the normative orientation of sexual learning is basic to any concept of sex education. This question becomes all the more difficult the moment one rejects the drive-theory model and entertains the hypothesis of sexual motivational structures based only upon a learning process. This is because it is not possible to found any restrictive standardization of sexual behavior on the principally antisocial nature of sexual drives, nor on sublimation necessary for the development of culture. Nor can any of the general demands for liberalization of sexuality and freedom from repression be justified on the basis of the necessity of fulfilling biological needs. The sociological concept broadens the perspective on the many forms of societal 'scripts' of sexuality. Proceeding from the sociological concept of sexual development, it becomes overwhelmingly clear to the writer that a political analysis, evaluation and doctrine of the specific nature of the scripting of sexuality in capitalist society is an absolute necessity.

To date, Marxist-oriented social scientists have proven to be the most willing to attempt to analyze the scripting of sexuality in capitalist society. Most of this work centers around Marx's theory of commodities (see, for instance, Holzer, 1969; Reiche, 1968; Haug, 1972; Freyberg and Freyberg, 1971; Duhm, 1973).

To give an example, I would like to briefly relate one of the basic ideas to have arisen out of research, namely the concept of the occupation of the structure of needs and emotions by the illusion of the use-value of commodities.

This concept is based on the generally accepted phenomenon that commodity advertising, as well as the appearance of the commodities themselves, gives ever greater promise of fulfilling one's needs, without ever ultimately keeping that promise. The immanent contradiction between use-value and exchange-value of commodity production is becoming increasingly acute in capitalist mass production. The production of the illusion of use-value is initially oriented to the existing basic needs of people, for example sexuality.

The sexualization of countless commodities has specific modifying influences on the structure of human sexual needs. The promise of sexual fulfillment through sexualized commodities can only happen in any immediate sense to the extent that these sexual needs are already tailored to be fulfilled by commodities. For this reason it is those needs which are predominantly agitated which can be fulfilled by means of industrially manufacturable allures, as, for example, voyeuristic. On the other hand, the scripting of sexuality as an apparition of use-value in commodities is aimed at removing sexual fulfillment from the sphere of socioemotional communications between human beings, and directing them toward their relations to objects. Furthermore, the sexualized commodities becomes an important factor in the standardization of sexuality in general. This is true because there is a subtle shifting of the sexual attractions attached to commodities themselves away from them to their potential owners. In this manner, commodities attain a special use-value, that of equipping their owners with certain attributes considered to be sexually attractive.

This is, in outline form, one of the substantive aspects of the societal scripting of sexuality in our capitalist society. It would indeed be worthwhile to investigate further into these problems by studying the functions of sexual characteristics of late capitalist societies, for example, the separation of work and spare-time (work and pleasure), and the concomitant compensation functions of sexuality; or the importance of the shift from a production to a consumption morality (Gagnon and Simon, 1973).

Sex research along these lines, unfortunately, is just beginning to skim the surface (see, for instance, Rainwater, 1965; Reiche and Dannecker, 1974). However, as important as research into the state of things today may be, sex education cannot wait until the final results of this research are in. Critical sex education, constantly reflecting upon its own premises and goals, will nevertheless take a pragmatic approach to the task at hand. It will be constantly orienting itself to changing societal conditions. Naturally, as with education of any kind, it must be guided by a political ideal based upon a concept of humanity and a social order worthy of human beings.

For the author, this ideal consists of a society devoid of all material and psychic exploitation and domination of human beings by other human beings. It must be a society in which the development and fulfillment of sexual needs is not centered around and based upon serving economic ends of any sort. It must rather be based on standards established by a community of human beings living and acting as equals. Although this particular utopia defies more precise and concrete description, it is still precise enough to allow one to recognize that recent capitalist societies are not in a position to meet these criteria. It is constituent to these societies that the people living within their realm are both physically and psychically devoured and subjugated by the interests of capital, and that the sociosexual socialization of their members is largely determined by this basic structure. Capitalist society is a society engulfed in immanent contradictions. One of them is the phenomenon that by subjugating humans it also produces elements of resistance to itself. This means that we can detect dysfunctional elements of subversion both within the psychosocial structure of needs created by this society and in the opportunities it provides for fulfilling these needs.

This is not the place to expand any further on these problems. Yet our discussion does provide us with a general set of guidelines, as modest and subuniversal as they may be, with which to evaluate politically and envision planned sex education in general. The transformation of sociosexual norms, needs, attitudes, and modes of communication taking place among the younger generation during the past several years contains numerous contradictions with a high potential for conflict. The latest research on sexual liberalization points precisely to the ambivalent nature of these developments. There are three aspects.

— The extremely rapid liberalization of sexuality among youths during the past several years has certainly been induced by the total sexualization of the world of commodities. Given capital's current problems with realizing returns on its investments, it has in a sense been functional for society. However, the major discrepancies between their sexual standards and those of adults contributes to causing the adult world, that is, the society, to be called increasingly into question by the younger. And this is something that is taking place not only with respect to sexual standards.

— The sexual emancipation of women becoming massively apparent in the general increase in the unification of attitudes of boys and girls (Walczak et al., 1975) presents a contradiction, because even roughly comparable perspectives for vocational and political development for women simply do not exist. The conflict between women enjoying greater sexual self-assuredness and men who are still politically and economically dominant is certain to become more acute. The societal oppression of women is a potential for conflict that will become exceedingly difficult to control (Eliasson, 1974).

— Several more recent studies on the sexuality of youth have revealed that the liberalization of sexual behavior and sexual attitudes is limited by a moral orientation toward a value perhaps best characterized by Reiss's category of 'permissiveness with affection': sexuality is bound to love and affection and neatly integrated into a series of successive steady relationships, one of which will ultimately lead to marriage. This remarkable tendency can be interpreted ambivalently: On the one hand, love orientation often is certainly a retreat to the 'treasure island of private happiness' (Amendt, 1974). Problems in these relationships will often appear to be an indication of individual weaknesses; these weaknesses will not be critically related to the societal conditions under which interhuman relationships are doomed to take place. On the other hand, it is precisely the retreat into dual relationships and the longing for a loving partner that contains elements of unconscious protest against a society that simply does not permit such relationships. Freud (see Freud, 1974) pointed to the contradiction between a happy love relationship and society (in his eyes an immanent one): "On the one hand, love dissents against the interests of the culture, on the other hand the culture threatens love with sensitive limitations." Even if one is disinclined to accept Freud's unhistorical interpretation of this contradiction, one can still recognize that the 'romantic love ideology' of today's youth is an attempt on their part to resolve this conflict on an individual basis. What is politically and pedagogically relevant about this unpolitical attempt to arrive at a solution to the problem is its motivation — namely to create unreified partner relationships.

3. INDIVIDUALIZING OF SEXUALITY

A further difference in the conceptualization of sex education by the sociological versus the psychoanalytic approach results from a different way of looking at the relationship between individual sexual development and the societal opportunities for learning in general. Sex education based more or less explicitly on the psychoanalytical theory of sexuality tends more in the direction of quasitherapeutic steering and influencing the individual with respect to behavior, attitudes, and inner psychic conflicts. Sex education based on the sociological approach advocates giving greater consideration to the societal conditions of learning and attempting to change them.

The individualistic orientation of current sex education persists in limiting itself to the goal of equipping the child and youth in general with a specific body of knowledge, and a set of capabilities and attitudes. In this narrowly defined context, the living conditions of the individual into which this knowledge is realized are, by and large, simply ignored, that is they are not viewed as worthy of change. An individual is considered to be sexually educated, for example, if the following criteria are met (Dallas, 1972, Rogers, 1974):

Sexual knowledge:	Good
Fear or ignorance-based attitudes:	No
Humane sexual behavior:	Yes
Self-actualizing in sex:	Yes
Responsible sexual decision-making:	Yes
Sexual communication:	Good

This should not be misunderstood: these can certainly be reasonable criteria. But sex education as an institution must ask itself whether the child, the adolescent or the adult in their respective life situations are even in a position to meet these criteria. Does this society even permit attitudes toward sexuality devoid of fear, or self-actualization in sex? Is human sexual behavior nothing more than a question of the capabilities of the individual? And finally, are sexual knowledge and sexual communication to be evaluated as either meaningful or meaningless without taking a serious look at the societal situation of the individual?

It is precisely with regard to the question of sexual knowledge that one can clearly see one aspect of the individualistic orientation of current sex education: there are numerous, indeed countless, studies on the knowledge of children and adolescents (see for example Hunger, 1960; Schofield, 1965; Warren and St. Pierre, 1973) which provide us with sufficient reason for crying out more or less loudly with regard to the state of sexual knowledge. But it is relatively seldom, and then only on certain points, that these problems of knowledge are at all legitimatized with respect to the sociosexual situation of the subjects of such surveys. What, for example, does it mean for the sociosexual relationships of those students surveyed by Warren and St. Pierre if they, on the one hand, do 'not understand the basic function of the contraceptive pill' and yet are willing and have the opportunity to use the pill on the basis of expert consultation? This should serve to make it clear that providing individuals with mere knowledge can easily become an end in itself which, objectively speaking, can even detract from necessary learning goals.

Equally problematic are those concepts which expressly distance themselves from sex education aimed at the mere imparting of knowledge, claim to take a 'humanistic approach' to the problem, and attempt to create a relationship between cognitive and emotional learning with goals such as the 'capacity for love' and the 'ability for marriage' (Schuh-Gademann, 1972; Schulz and Williams, 1969). Read (1972), for example, writes the following with respect to his humanistic approach: 'In this, the first focus is upon each student and where he finds himself emotionally in his stage of sexual development and awareness'. He realizes his approach using, among other things, 'trust exercises' and 'mini-encounters'.

Concepts like these would appear to be claiming to be giving a quality to interhuman relationships through educating the individual who has increasingly less and less chance of ever realizing them. Individual training is supposed to retain that which is increasingly lost in the societally produced need structure: 'love' as an expression of unreified personal relationship between equal partners.

Any education of sexuality that prescribes for itself goals such as 'capacity for love', the 'ability for marriage', or the capacity for 'responsible sexual behavior', will end in failure if it limits itself to changing the individual and does not also — at least partially — incorporate a program aimed at changing the life situation of people in general into its concept. This also means that it will have to reduce its utopian goals which inevitably lead to frustrations and feelings of helplessness among all those concerned, particularly among teachers and youth workers and social workers. Nonetheless, criticizing the individualistic orientation of sex education we by no means want to denounce and disqualify or detract from the importance of individual educational therapeutic aid.

Sex educators involved with marginal groups or who work in ghetto schools are probably most aware of this problem, because it is here that the gap between the goals and the real possibilities for achieving these goals are the greatest. Staples (1972), for example, derived demands from his studies on black sexuality which relate sex education measures to sociopolitical changes. And the German association "Pro Familia" (a member organisation of the International Planned Parenthood Federation, IPPF) advocates a similar approach by combining sex enlightenment programs in settlements for the homeless, with practical aid measures such as providing contraceptive devices free of charge, or by also providing health care.

Back to the beginning: if one proceeds from the sociological approach to psychosexual and sociosexual development, then the individualistic abbreviation of current sexual pedagogy becomes quite clear. It claims to be able to retard and/or do away with the societally effected destruction of interhuman relationships by changing the isolated individual.

4. ISOLATION OF SEXUALITY

To point to a third shift in emphasis: while psychoanalysis advocates a concept of psychic and social development that provides the basic guidelines for all other aspects of development and socialization, the sociological approach would tend more to view sexual development as a dependent variable (Gagnon, 1973). Even current sex education — supported by the psychoanalytical theory of sexuality — reveals elements of sexual-centeredness: almost all sex education courses, programs, teaching aids, and learning materials are arranged and presented completely isolated from other areas of learning. They are all based on the assumption that sexual problems are problems sui generis that need to be tackled pedagogically of and for themselves. What used to be the one-time enlightenment lecture at school, or the facts-of-life talk between father and son, or mother and daughter, is now organised and dealt with in courses with special sexual topics and goals (Schmidt, 1974). The following catalogue of topics for a freshman seminar is a typical illustration: (1) petting and coitus; (2) masturbation; (3) venereal disease and problematic sexual behavior and; (4) abortion and sterilization. (Herold et al., 1973). This choice of topics is not merely a reaction to the problems and learning needs of students and pupils. It interprets and defines them at the same time. In a course structured in this manner it seems natural to deal only with sexuality and to ignore the nonsexual components of sexual conduct. General characteristics of social life, such as the pressures for achievement and top-rate performance, individual competition and status requirements also have a decisive effect on the molding of sexual conduct. This whole problem area remains more or less turned off in any sexual pedagogy that deals with people exclusively as sexual creatures and not simultaneously as girls, school pupils, apprentices, members of a family or simply as workers.

The atomization of the human into separate functions is, of course, typical both for the public school system and late capitalist society in general: what is never fulfilled in terms of social needs as a result of living in the modern living silos of public housing programs is supposed to be compensated for — separated neatly, of course, from the causes — through youth work and sensitivity training as public or private measures to alleviate the situation. The moral defects created by the ideology of private property ownership, and private advantage, is supposed to be corrected for through moral education at home or at school. In the same manner, sex education tries to compensate for sexual frustrations induced by societal conditions on an individual basis, without ever questioning the nonsexual foundations of these frustrations in society.

The thoughts expressed above are intended to make it clear that the psychoanalytic theory of sexual motivation and development supports an unpolitical sex education that:

— can easily do without political enlightenment and the evaluation of the societal determinants of sexual socialization, because it does not recognize how radically society scripts sexuality;

— is aimed only at qualifying the individual to deal with, and master his or her own personal sexual conflicts, because it considers the societal causes of these conflicts to be a problem of human nature;

— tendentially filters out the nonsexual determinants of sexual learning because it considers psychosexual development to be the basic and central independent variable of human development.

5. CONCLUSIONS

It would be wrong on the basis of a basic critique of sexuality oriented and individualistic sex education to come to the conclusion that all educational measures that decidedly deal with human sexuality and are aimed at individual learning process are all system-immanent and thus a priori politically compromised. All of the planning in sex education must proceed from the present level of consciousness. And in the minds of people today, sexuality is an isolated problem of its own. This means that even within the framework of politically oriented sex education it is indeed necessary to meet isolated sexual learning needs and to react to needs and problems felt to be private ones by providing individual consultation and aid — of course with the goal of making the individual aware of societal causes and consequences. Practical aid and political enlightenment is then probably the most adequate formula for the current tasks of sex education.

In defining its goal in this manner, sex education does not escape the danger of contributing to the further adjustment of people by providing practical aid, and of becoming removed from reality, and thus ineffective in terms of its political enlightenment. But at least it is not blindly subjecting itself to these dangers. It is constantly coupled to a critical reflection of society and to the political legitimacy of its own goals and measures, while oriented toward constantly adapting itself to the subjective problems of the people.

Let me point out what this means for the practical organization of sex education, particularly in schools and for extracurricular youth work.

— The determination and selection of relevant problems, topics, and subjects must proceed from the general situation of the children and adolescents as reflected in the results of surveys, observation, and other studies in the field of youth and sex research. However, this material must be interpreted politically and analysed with regard to the societal contradictions it presents. To give some examples of such contradictions:

(a) sexual liberalization versus increasing repression in job education and job situation;

(b) tendential equality for women in sexual matters coupled with continued inequality on the job and in the family (Eliasson, 1974);

(c) a flood of information dealing with sexual biology and sexual technique versus the gradual breakdown of all opportunities for emotional and social learning (particularly in the schools).

It is this type of political diagnosis which will have to be worked out ahead of time by sex educators and social workers in the field of sexology. At the same time, it is true that it can only provide a very general and by no means complete picture of the sexual situation of children and adolescents. It will have to be specified a great deal more in order to correspond to the specific situation of the learning group. This cannot take place over the heads of the individuals at which these learning processes are aimed, because the teacher or sex educator generally comes from a different background. A method must be found for making it possible for the children and adolescents to utilize their own experiences, be they immediate or didactically mediated, as the starting point of their specific learning (Scarbath, 1974; Kleinermann et al., 1971). In this manner, courses, seminars and discussions will not be structured around abstract categories of behavior (such as petting, sexual intercourse and masturbation) or according to biological topics (such as the structure and function of the sex organs), but rather according to typical conflict situations (for example. being together with a boy-friend or a girl-friend has been forbidden; a boy or a girl is too shy to seek and find a girl-friend or a boy-friend, respectively; a girl in school becomes pregnant, and such like).

— Sexuality and sex education usually take place in complex communication situations (Schmidbauer, 1974). The concept of sociosexual communication (Müller, 1973) relates the subject matter of learning and the learning situation to each other. Practical aid as a subgoal of sex education should thus be conceived of in the broad sense of the term as a contribution to the improvement of the situation of adolescents as partners in communication. This means for example:

(a) Biological sex information doesn't become legitimized simply on the basis of the fact that it is necessary to have the proper knowledge, but rather perhaps as a method for evaluating contraceptive devices or means, or for breaking down the irrational fear of masturbation or, in the field of early child training, for the establishment of sufficient security in gender identity.

(b) Learning the proper terms for things isn't important because it leads to a command of standardized, middle-class language codes, but because it serves to articulate and facilitate counseling and to aid demands made upon parents, teachers and physicians.

(c) The analysis and discussion of gender-differences and social class differences in behavior and attitudes isn't justifiable on the grounds that it is aimed at doing away with these differences, because, for one thing, that goal isn't going to be achieved in this manner. It does, however, serve to provide a better understanding of the needs and conflicts of potential partners.

(d) The discussion of problems in relationships when going steady or when married or in the family in general shouldn't be aimed at qualifying people to lead unattainably harmonious relationships, but ought to make a contribution to lowering overly elevated expectations.

— Real conflicts are indeed an important field of experience, but it is neither necessary nor advisable to provoke conflicts with the authorities, for example, for educational purposes. And yet it is one of the central tasks of planning in sex education to organize learning which, on the one hand, meets the current learning needs of pupils and, on the other hand, relates to a larger societal context. It is in this manner that pupils attain a certain potential for political enlightenment. Such learning projects are: (a) experience oriented, that is, an attempt is made to open up the total reality of certain sociosexual problems through observation (including self-observation), fact-finding missions, or exploration; (b) using a broad spectrum of methods, such as working in small groups, role-playing, information-media, short lectures, asking experts, and discussions; and (c) action-oriented, in which an attempt is made to draw immediate practical conclusions for one's self and others from the learning done in the group.

A few examples should serve to illustrate what I mean by this: pupils explore the possibilities and difficulties involved in obtaining contraceptive devices (for instance, through the purchase of condoms in a drugstore or consulting a physician), discuss their experiences and possibly re-enact the situation (physician/girl; or salesgirl/boy). Or: youths plan and execute an enlightenment campaign on contraception including confrontation with the expected resistance to such enlightenment. Or: a group of pupils publishes a 'facts of life booklet' for the other pupils in the school.

The foregoing has attempted to demonstrate that formal sex education as a subarea of sexual socialization, is influenced by the contradictions of the society in which it takes place. Even when it is explicitly politically oriented, sex education can only make a limited contribution to changing society, as long as its fundamental structure is not changed. Nevertheless, sex education, indeed education in general, can provide a counterbalance to the depoliticization of consciousness by demonstrating that apparently individual sexual problems are in reality to a great extent societal problems.

6. SUMMARY

Any concept of sex education is, at least implicitly, based on a concept of sexuality and sexual socialisation. There are contrasting approaches to this subject, (1) the psychoanalytical drive-theory approach, and (2) the sociological or social-learning approach. The pedagogical significance of these contrasting approaches lies in the varying significance attributed to learning processes within the context of sexual development.

The author's central hypothesis is that the social-learning approach can be the basis for a politically oriented sex education, while the psychoanalytic theory of sexual motivation and development supports an unpolitical sex education that:
(a) can easily do without political enlightenment and the evaluation of the societal determinants of sexual socialization, because it does not recognize how radically society scripts sexuality; (b) is aimed only at qualifying the individual to deal with and master his or her own personal sexual conflicts because it considers the societal causes of these conflicts to be a problem of human nature; and (c) tendentially filters out the nonsexual determinants of sexual learning because it considers psychosexual development to be the basic and central independent variable of human development.

Practical aid and political enlightenment is, by contrast, the author's formula for the current tasks of sex education.

BIBLIOGRAPHY

Amendt, G. (1974) *Neue Liebesromantik der Jugend. Was ist sie wert?* (Hamburg.) mimeographed.

Breiner, S.J. (1972) Psychological principles of a sex education program for grades K through 12. *J. School Health* 62: 227—232.

Brocher, T. (1972) *Psychosexuelle Grundlagen der Entwicklung.* (Opladen.)

Dallas, D.M. (1972) *Sex education in school and society.* (Windsor.)

Duhm, D. (1973) *Warenstruktur und zerstörte Zwischenmenschlichkeit.* (Köln, G.F.R.)

Eliasson, R. (1974) Doppelmoral und Lebensrollen. *Sexualmedizin* 3: 624—628

Freud, S. (1974) *Das Unbehagen in der Kultur. Sigmund Freud Studienausgabe.* (Frankfurt a.M., G.F.R.)

Freyberg, D. and Freyberg, Th. (1971) *Zur Kritik der Sexualerziehung.* (Frankfurt a.M., G.F.R.)

Gagnon, J.H. (1973) The creation of the sexual in early adolescence. In: (Graubard, S., Ed.), *From Twelve to Sixteen,* (New York.)

Gagnon, J.H. and Simon, W. (1973) *Sexual conduct. The social sources of human sexuality.* (Chicago.)

Haug, W.F. (1972) *Warenästhetik. Sexualität und Herrschaft.* (Frankfurt a.M., G.F.R.)

Herold, E.S., Eastwood, J., Epringham, C., Gall, B. and McKendry, S. (1973) Human sexuality: A student taught course. *Fam. Coord.* 22: 183—186.

Holzer, H. (1969) Sexualität und Herschaft. *Soziale Welt.* 20: 304—335.

Hunger, H. (1960) *Das Sexualwissen der Jugend.* (München and Basel.)

Kentler, H. (1971) *Sexualerziehung.* (Reinbek.)

Kleinermann, M.D., Grossman, M., Breslow, J. and Goldman, R. (1971) Sex education in a ghetto school. *J. School Health.* 61: 29—38.

Marcuse, H. (1955) *Eros and Civilisation.* (Boston.)

Miller, D.R. (1969) Psychoanalytic theory of development: A re-eveluation. In: (Goslin, Ed.), *Handbook of socialisation theory and research.* (New York.)

Müller, R. (1973) Sexualität, Kommunikation, Gesellschaft. In: (W. Fischer et al., Eds.) *Inhaltsprobleme in der Sexualpädagogik.* (Heidelberg.)

Rainwater, L. (1965) *Family design. Marital sexuality, family size, and contraception.* (Chicago.)

Rainwater, L. (1966) Some aspects of lower class sexual behavior. *J. Soc. Iss.* 22: No. 2, 96—108.

Read, D.A. (1972) Developing sexual awareness: a humanistic approach. *J. School Health.* 62: 330—333.

Reiche, R. (1968) *Sexualität und Klassenkampf.* (Frankfurt a.M., G.F.R.)

Reiche, R. and Dannecker, M. (1974) *Der gewöhnliche Homosexuelle.* (Frankfurt a.M., G.F.R.)

Renshaw, D.C. (1973) Sex education for educators. *J. School Health.* 63: 645—650.

Rogers, R.S. (ed.) (1974) *Sex education. Rationale and reaction.* (Cambridge.)

Scarbath, H. (1974) Sexualerziehung. In: (C. Wulf, Ed.) *Wörterbuch der Erziehung.* (München and Zürich.)

Schmidbauer, W. (1974) Kommunikation, Sexualität, Partnerschaft. *Sexualmedizin* 3: 637—640.

Schmidt, G. (1974) Totale Sexualmedizin? *Sexualmedizin.* 3: 497—504.

Schofield, M. (1965) The sexual behavior of young people (London.)

Schuh-Gademann, L. (1972) *Erziehung zur Liebesfähigkeit.* (Heidelberg.)

Schulz, E.D. and Williams, S.R. (1969) *Family life and sex education.* (New York.)

Staples, R. (1972) Research on black sexuality: Its implication for family life, sex education, and public policy. *Fam. Coord.* 21: 183—187.

Walczak, L., Schlaegel, J. and Schoof-Tams, K. (1975) Sexualmoral Jugendlicher. Sexuelle Sozialisation in Vorpubertät, Pubertät und früher Adolescenz (II). *Sexualmedizin* 4: 306—325.

Warren, C.L. and St. Pierre, R. (1973) Sources and accuracy of college students' sex knowledge. *J. School Health.* 63: 588—590.

CHAPTER 23

Changing sociosexual mores*

IRA L. REISS

1. THE PAST: MYTH AND REALITY

One of our most prevalent myths is that in past centuries the typical form of courtship was that of two virgins meeting, falling in love, and doing very little with each other sexually. They then married, learned about sex together in the marital bed, and remained faithful to each other until death separated them. I am certain that some couples did have exactly that type of experience and I would go even further and grant that this happens in some cases today. But the key point is that I am sure it was never the common pattern for the majority of Americans. The evidence for this exists in large part in historical records. We know, for example that in Massachusetts at a well-known church in the last part of the 18th century one in every three women who married confessed fornication to her minister. The major reason for making such a confession would be that the woman was pregnant and if she did not make that confession at her marriage, the baby could not be baptized. Many other girls who were nonvirginal but not pregnant would likely not confess fornication to their minister. This was the time of bundling in New England and many ministers blamed the high premarital pregnancy rates on that custom. It is probable that much of the pregnancy occurred after engagement. Engagements in those days were very seldom broken and thus were more akin to actual marriage. In any case it seems clear that at the time of the formal marriage, the sexual innocence of many couples was questionable.

The double standard

If we look at male nonvirginity, the picture becomes even more extreme.

---

* Revised version of 'Premarital sexuality: Past, present and future'. In: (I.L. Reiss, Ed.) Readings on the Family System. (Holt, Rinehart & Winston, New York) 1972.

Handbook of Sexology, edited by J. Money and H. Musaph
© *Elsevier/North-Holland Biomedical Press, 1977*

Certainly the history of the western frontier was not one of male virginity. In fact it was quite the contrary. The western frontier was settled largely by males and this male-dominated society had a heavy reliance on prostitution. The very term 'red light district' comes from the custom of girls in prostitution houses leaving a red lantern in the window so that the cowboys riding into town would know 'where the action was'. 'Gunsmoke' notwithstanding, dance hall girls did more than dance. In the typical case the upstairs rooms were where the girls would entice the customers to take them and then collect a suitable fee for the sexual services rendered.

One example that illustrates the sexual orientation of the 19th century is afforded by the Philadelphia World's Fair of 1876. The aspect of that fair that echoed around the country was the introduction of the first vulcanized rubber condom for males. This condom was on display at the Fair and created a great deal of interest. Previous to that time condoms were made out of animal skins and a vulcanized rubber condom was a notable advance. But in a culture that was largely practicing abstinence, this contraceptive advance would hardly have received so much notice. However, in a society where prostitution was common and where people were concerned with avoiding venereal disease and unwanted pregnancy, such an advance was important. It was about this same time that the diaphragm and the pessary cap were invented. A few decades later, by the time of World War I, knowledge of these contraceptive techniques had spread widely among the wealthier and better educated classes and did create an impact of major importance on their sexual behavior. I will speak of this impact very shortly.

Not only is it mistaken to think of earlier generations of Americans as people who mostly entered marriage virginally, but this view would be erroneous for virtually any society. I have examined the historical and cross-cultural record rather closely and have found no society, at any time in history, in which the majority of even one generation of its males remained virginal on reaching physical maturity — say age twenty or so. This is not an argument against a single standard of abstinence, it is rather a statement of the fact that no society has been able to achieve abstinence for both sexes unless they sanctioned either child marriage or very youthful matings. It is not difficult to understand why no society has been able to produce a generation of virginal males. The reason is very likely that since males are in power in almost all societies, it is unlikely that they would structure that societal system so as to deny themselves access to sexual pleasures before marriage.

General trends

According to our best information the majority of American women have been entering marriage nonvirginal for over fifty years. Kinsey's findings indicated that about half the women born in the 1900—1910 decade were nonvirginal at marriage. This proportion rose only slightly until the late 1960s but since then it seems to have risen rapidly. Sometime around the first

world war the proportion of nonvirginal women doubled from about 25—
50% and during the late 1960s the proportion probably has risen from about
50% to 70 or 75%. In the fifty years from World War I to the late 1960s the
predominant change was not in the proportion of women nonvirginal but
rather in the attitudes of women and men toward premarital sexuality.
During that half-century, guilt feelings were reduced, the public discussion
of sex increased radically, probably the number of partners increased, and
the closeness to marriage required for coitus to be acceptable decreased. For
males, other changes were occurring. Males were becoming more discriminate; they were beginning to feel that sex with someone they felt affection
for, person-centered sex, was much to be preferred to body-centered coitus.
The male partners were shifting from the prostitute and the lower-class female to the girl next door. One of the most dramatic decreases that has constantly evidenced itself during the 20th century is the rapid decline in the
proportion of males, particularly college-educated males, who have experienced frequent intercourse with a prostitute. That proportion today is probably only a small percentage.

Full equality in the sexual sphere is not possible today given the different
priorities of family and occupational roles that males and females have. This
is a point that present-day Women's Liberation adherents have often made.
Regardless of whether one agrees with all the beliefs of Women's Liberation,
this particular point seems sociologically well established. If females think
that getting married and starting a family is their first priority in life and place occupational ambitions secondary to this, then they will view sex in terms
of these goals. This means that they will consider whether copulating with a
boy will waste time in their search for a mate; whether this boy will tell
others what happened and thus hurt their chances of getting married; whether having intercourse will make a boy more seriously committed to marriage
or less; and so forth. These concerns are nowhere near as potent to a male,
for he is not so strongly oriented toward marriage as his primary life goal. In
the middle class his primary goal will be an occupational career and having
premarital intercourse is not very likely to matter one way or the other in
terms of that goal. Surely men today are oriented toward marriage but the
immediate pressures felt by such a marriage goal are considerably less than
those felt by females. A male is not so concerned with the time wasted in an
affair, nor is he so worried about the impact of the word getting around that
he is having an affair. In fact, in many circles news of such an affair might
enhance his image as an exciting date or a romantic interest for females.

The role of contraception

One of the key factors that encouraged the sexual liberalization of women,
particularly in the middle and upper classes, was the contraceptive revolution of the late 19th century. It is about one hundred years since the vulcanized rubber condom, the pessary cap, and the diaphragm made their ap-

pearance on the scene. To be sure these methods were known and at first used predominantly by the upper 20 or 30% of the population. There were contraceptive measures available from the Biblical method of 'withdrawal' to Casanova's method of placing a hollowed out lemon rind over the cervix. What was new about the late 19th century methods was that they were extremely effective in preventing pregnancy, and they occurred at a time when there was a large group of well-off people with a strong demand for such techniques. Let me briefly elaborate on this.

Ever since Priscilla told John to speak for himself, it has been clear to historians of the family that the American courtship system was to a very high degree run by the participants in it and not directly controlled by parents. By the late 19th century this meant that due to the size and complexity of the new urban centers and the fact that even in 1890 almost 4 million women were working, parents could not possibly know the people that their children were dating. This autonomy of dating coupled with the high risk taking and the pleasure emphasis that youth culture has always exhibited meant that the desire for sexual pleasures would be relatively strong. Being alone with an attractive person of the opposite sex for several hours on a date exposed one to high temptation. Yet the upper- and middle-class groups in this country were considerably concerned with having legitimate children. Thus sexual desires were present but so was the inhibitory influence of a strong desire to avoid illegitimate offspring. The development of very effective contraceptive methods that would avoid pregnancy in the late 19th century afforded a way out of the dilemma. By the time of the first world war, condoms were available in a variety of places and their usefulness was widely known. The better-off male could use them and have intercourse with relative safety from venereal disease and also with the comfort that he was unlikely to impregnate his partner. This meant that he would be more likely to feel free to copulate with the girl next door. Females, too, became aware that males could avoid impregnating them and this must have had an important impact on their sexual orientations. It was mainly married women who used diaphragms, but the attitude that males could prevent pregnancy with condoms and that females too had available methods lessened the view of pregnancy as an uncontrollable consequence.

The new middle-class and upper-class permissiveness was not based on the difficulty of economically sound marriages, nor on the fatalism or social disorganization that was so common in the lower classes. The new middle- and upper-class permissiveness was based on an ethic of person-centered sexuality that stressed intimacy with those with whom one was in love. It also stressed a rational control of undesired consequences such as venereal disease and premarital pregnancy. The ethic of freedom of choice, equalitarianism, and pursuit of happiness is stronger in this new middle- and upper-class sexual emancipation. Thus the early thrust of the new sexuality that appeared around World War I was related to contraceptive advances that made possible both sexual pleasure and the avoidance of unwanted pregnancies.

2. THE CURRENT SCENE

The impact of the pill

The topic of contraception affords a bridge into the current situation regarding premarital sexuality. Many people believe that the availability of the pill contraceptive, starting about 1960, has had a major impact on sexual beliefs and behaviors. I think this case has been oversold. As noted above, I do believe that in the past the condom and diaphragm did have such an impact on the middle and upper classes. This was so because these classes wanted to participate in sexual behavior, but also wanted desperately to avoid pregnancy. In addition, they had no other highly effective techniques readily available. Under such conditions the introduction of effective techniques can have a dramatic impact. The doubling of the female nonvirginity rates around World War I was partially a result of this force. Of course, diversity in norms, changes in religious controls, and urban-industrial development also were important causal variables contributing to the growth of the new permissiveness.

More important than its effectiveness is the fact that the pill places the control of contraception in the hands of the female. Furthermore it does this in a way that still allows the act to occur spontaneously since the pill does not have to be taken in conjunction with the act of coitus. The consequences of this are multiple. For some females the thought of being constantly ready for coitus is not acceptable. They want to be carried away by romantic feelings of the moment and they want the male to be the aggressor, and for the male to plan to be ready for coitus. This attitude leads to a high risk of pregnancy and is often heard in unwed mother's homes.

A second result of the contraceptive control being in female hands is that the female comes to value sexuality much more highly than before. Her risks of conception are reduced and her abilities to enjoy the erotic aspects of sex and view herself as a sexual creature are increased. This is a slow process in it is not reinforced by many other aspects of our type of courtship. It is part of the increased similarity of men and women in their view of sexuality. Women today are more likely than before to value sex for its own sake and men are more likely today to value sex with affection. As I have noted above, the sexes still differ in that women are more oriented to affectionate sexuality, and men more oriented to body-centered sexuality, but each sex has increasingly learned to appreciate the major orientation of the other. In sum then the importance of the pill, in my mind, is not that it is so effective contraceptively but that it places the burden of contraception on the female and, therefore, forces her to think about her own sexuality.

The legitimacy of choice

Probably the major characteristic of the current premarital sex scene is the felt legitimacy of the sexual choice. More than any other characteristic this one epitomizes what has changed in the last half-century. It is no longer a secretive choice of sexual codes that is made privately and with great guilt, if the choice is not abstinence. There is still an element of privacy and still an element of psychological qualms often present, but the degree of change is vast. Boys have always talked openly with other males, about certain aspects of their sexual lives, and this continues. However, there is change here, too, in that more males seem willing to admit they have difficulties sexually, in their thinking as well as in their behavior. The mask of the naturalness of sex for males is increasingly being put aside. Furthermore, the affectionate affair is being protected by privacy except from close friends. Here then is a change for males in the area of sexual communication. Conversely, females do talk more about their affairs, although most fully with their very close friends.

The choice of how to think and behave sexually is now accepted as an important choice for young people to make, and they are seriously exploring the full range of possibilities in their conversations with same and opposite sex friends. It is true that there are many parents today who do not accept the legitimacy of such sexual choices, and who believe that only abstinence is the proper path. But the majority of young people believe the choice is legitimately theirs in sex as it is in politics, religion, and other personal areas of their existence.

Generation versus role changes

My comment above on parent—child differences concerning the legitimacy of the sexual choice might mislead the reader into thinking that the basic change in premarital sex is a generational one. During the early 1960s I selected several samples of high school students, college students, and one national sample that was chosen to represent the nation. The results of this study, one of the few to utilize a representative national sample for intensive analysis of sexual relationships before marriage, were published in my 1967 book, The Social Context of Premarital Sexual Permissiveness. One of our most interesting findings was that the difference between 55-year-olds and 25-year-olds was not very dramatic. However, the differences between people of the same age who were single, married without children, or married and parents of dating-age children were indeed dramatic. For example, 45-year-old bachelors were highly acceptant of premarital intercourse, whereas 45-year-old married people without children or with little children were much less acceptant, and 45-year-old married people with teenage or older children were the least acceptant of premarital intercourse. People of the same age are of the same generation and yet their differences are much greater than people who are of different ages and generations. Thus it is the specific role we play that is most important in how we feel about premarital sexuality.

The same parents who themselves participated in premarital coitus may well change and become less permissive as they move into the parental role. The reasons for this are not hard to find. The parent does not experience the pleasures of sex that his child is undergoing, nor is he exposed to the temptations of being with an attractive person of the opposite sex on a date. In addition, the parent is held responsible by the community if his daughter becomes pregnant or his child contracts venereal disease. We found that even older siblings were low on sexual permissiveness compared to their younger siblings because as older siblings they were put into parentlike supervisory roles. Thus the roles an individual plays in society are a major factor in determining his level of acceptable premarital activity. It follows then that there are 45-year-old bachelors who are more sexually liberated than some 20-year-olds. Thus young people are not all involved in the new changes in sexuality nor are older people excluded from such changes.

The forces that promote premarital permissiveness on the part of young people in their courtship roles are also not hard to understand. If we were to invite a sociologist from another country to visit our country and examine our courtship system and tell us what he thinks it accomplishes sexually and how it operates, what would he say? He would note that the average young person dates for approximately ten years and that at least during the last five years of that period, the typical pattern of dating involves (1) the use of some sort of drug such as alcohol or pot, (2) the occurrence of dancing with movements that are clearly genital and sexual in meaning, and (3) a period of time at the end of each date when the couple are supposed to be allowed privacy. That privacy is very often supplied by the young person's parents. The living room of the girl is a very common place for the last hour of a date to take place. It is also the most common place for a girl to start having intercourse. Her parents are upstairs usually 'trusting her to behave properly.' It is not typical for parents to spy on their youngsters and try to catch them copulating. These parents also teach that love is a key justification for behavior and being self-reliant is important. Such values unintentionally help to develop an acceptance of sexuality on the part of their children.

Our foreign sociologist would surely look upon this system and note that it is well organized to promote sexual intimacies between young people. I feel sure that if we presented him with the figures showing the majority of females and almost all males entering marriage nonvirginally, his amazement would not be that the figures are so high but, to the contrary, that they are so low. The question that needs answering is not why do so many people have premarital intercourse? That can easily be understood by examining our type of courtship — the key question is why do so few people have premarital intercourse? How does anyone go through years of such an intimacy-promoting type of courtship institution and avoid having intercourse? The answer to this question resides in good measure in the basic emphasis by females, and increasingly also by males, on person-centered coitus. Such coitus stresses the value of close ties to another person, and thus puts limits on casual coitus and imposes difficulties in locating proper sex partners. Our marriage-for-love type of system implies that person-centered sexual behavior should be involved in some way in our courtship institution, and thus such a development is not surprising. It is these monogamous norms that have much to do with the control of coitus when it occurs. This is especially true for females. Males are still more body centered and therein lies part of the "battle of the sexes."

In a very basic, fundamental sense, all Americans regardless of age are involved in the changes that are occurring in our sexual orientations. How could it be otherwise? Parents of the young people who are involved in premarital sex cannot ignore the greater openness of discussion of sex because much of it occurs right in the home. Also, parents themselves are encouraged by sex education courses in the public schools, by courses in adult education, by articles in the popular press, by the mass media, and in many other ways to think more carefully and fully about the meaning of sex. This is not simply a youth rebellion, it is a cultural change rooted in our rapid movement toward a post-industrial society.

The stress of our civilization today is increasingly on self-realization, personal fulfillment, and happiness, and thus situational ethics is a very compatible philosophy, for it allows for a self-designed ethical system. Large segments of Americans at all age levels are involved in this search for self-discovery and for a more personally designed life style. I am sure that America will still have shared-patterns of life styles and will not atomize into over 200 million different life styles. But I am equally sure that the variety of tolerated life styles has increased at all age levels. The point I am making is the extensiveness of this search for selfhood.

One other important area of change is a convergence of sexual standards and behavior patterns of the lower and middle classes. These changes have been dealt with in Chapter 21 by Schmidt.

3. THE NEXT DECADES: THE LIKELY OUTCOME

Given the above situation regarding the past and present, what can we say about the future of sex during the balance of this century?

Physiological differences

It should be clear that there is no physiological barrier to sexual equality. The data we have from the Kinsey studies and also from the Masters and Johnson studies show clearly that there are more women who can achieve multiple orgasms then there are men, and that some female rates of orgasm are far beyond what any male can hope to achieve. The lack of representative samples is not so serious a matter in this conclusion, for we are certain that no group of males exists who can achieve orgasm every few minutes over and over again as many females do. The high-performing young male is capable at most of six or seven orgasms an hour, and the few who exceed this do not even approach the extreme end of the older female's orgasm curve. If one were to venture a conclusion, the most probable one would be that women's orgasmic ability is greater on both ends of the curve; that is, more women fall in both the nonorgasmic category and the multiple orgasmic category. Males are more clustered toward the center. Although it is entirely possible that females who are nonorgasmic could be psychologically trained to be orgasmic, it is not very likely that males could ever be trained to be as capable of multiple orgasms as are females. Thus overall, the advantage, orgasmically, would seem to go to the female.

Now, of course, there is more to sex than orgasms. It could still be true that males have some advantages in the ease with which they develop erotic imagery. Kinsey believed the male cortex afforded such an advantage. As a sociologist, I would tend to posit learning as the key factor in determining the sexes' different ability to "turn on", but one cannot be sure at this point. The most important conclusion to draw here is that, whatever innate differences exist between the sexes, one can bring up males and females to be relatively equal in their sexual orientation. The evidence for this comes from cross-cultural studies that report societies in which the sexes are relatively equal in their desire for coitus. Also, even within our own society vast differences exist between female groups, and these differences would seem to be based on training and experience.

Trends in nonvirginity

What about some of the newer trends? For example, what is likely to be the percent of premaritally nonvirginal females and males in the remaining decades of this century? First, we should note that the percent of nonvirginal males has been about 85—90% for generations. Thus there is little room for change here. Nevertheless, as pointed out earlier, there is change going on in the attitudinal area and in the type of partners with whom males have coitus. In the case of females there was an increase in the World War I period from about 25% to about 50% nonvirginal by the time of marriage. There has been no indication of any change in this proportion, except during the period from the late 1960s to date. During this recent period reports of studies showing 40% of the 20-year-old college girls to be nonvirginal have appeared. The Kinsey data from the 1940s showed only 20% of the 20-year-old college girls nonvirginal. These data are not decisive, conclusive evidence of a sharp increase in female nonvirginity, however. For example, if such an increase were occurring, one would expect to see some evidence of increased female sexuality in an increase in the number of partners of women, and in the percentage of women who masturbate, and the frequency of masturbation. Few such changes have been reported. Thus it is possible that college girls today are copulating sooner and thereby reaching the peak percentage of 50% sooner, without adding to the total percent nonvirginal. Unless one were to follow a college sample through to marriage, it would be hard to draw definite conclusions. College girls do have a greater likelihood of marrying today than they had in the 1940s, and much of a female's coital performance is related to being ostensibly or actually in love and engaged. Therefore, it may be that there is more reported coitus because of an earlier marriage age for college girls, and partially because more of them are in the serious courtship process that leads to marriage during their college years. However, the studies by Bell and Christensen and others are consistent regarding increases in nonvirginity. Also, if 40% of the 20-year-olds are nonvirginal, it is difficult to conclude that by marriage the rate will be only 50%. Bell does find that his more recent sample of coeds had more partners and required less affection than in his older 1958 sample. Finally, Kantner and Zelnik (1972) in a study of 4600 15—19-year-old girls found 46% of the 19-year-old girls were nonvirginal. So the evidence pushes toward a conclusion of significant increases in female nonvirginity. *

In 1960 I published a book entitled, Premarital Sexual Standards in America in which I attempted to sum up what research evidence told about sexual orientations in America. I predicted then that sometime by the end of the 1960s we would witness a noticeable rise in the percentage of nonvirginal females. It seemed to me that behavior and attitude were coming into balance around 1960 and, according to my interpretation of the evidence, that usually meant that behavior would then move forward again. Until 1970 I held to the belief that the expected increase in nonvirginity had not yet occurred. I still feel that the evidence is not fully in, but the data coming in are so consistent in their findings of higher nonvirginity rates at specified ages, that I am willing to assert that the change predicted has occurred, and that the actual premarital nonvirginity rate is now probably close to 75% for females.

The 1970s, I believe, will be to the last few decades of this century what the 1920s were to the decades of the first half of this century. More specifically, this decade will set the pace for the next few decades and afford clear outlines of the emerging life style. In the decade preceding the 1920s the older sexual orientations were attacked from a variety of perspectives. A new urban-industrial life style was then emerging and the developing liberal attitudes toward divorce, sex, and women had taken hold and were to evolve gradually during the next forty years. Then in the 1960s the same process of rapid change that occurred before 1920 was again present. Between 1915

---

* At least in some northwest European countries female nonvirginity has been (and is) traditionally more widespread than in the USA. The reported percentages of married women having had premarital intercourse are: Germany, total population, birth years 1900—1930: 70% (L. v. Friedeburg, 1954); West-Germany, university students, birth years 1935—1945: 90% (H. Giese and G. Schmidt, 1968); Sweden, total population, birth years 1910—1940: 94% (H.L. Zetterberg, 1969); Sweden, total population, birth years 1940—1950: 96% (H.L. Zetterberg, 1969).

and 1920 the divorce rates doubled and we were in the midst of a major war. Likewise between 1963 and 1973 the divorce rates doubled and we were again in the midst of a major war. Many alternative approaches to sex and the family were put forth in the realms of suggestions regarding abortion, life-long unions, living together, swinging, and female sexual orientations. What we are witnessing now is the culmination of the exploration of new life styles in the area of sex. The sixties spelled out many of the new possibilities and the seventies will lead to collective choices and priorities that will define these alternatives and their estimated worth in a way that will likely last a few decades.

Living together

Situational ethics has made us aware of the variety of choices that may be viewed as legitimate, and has moved us away from the view that only one choice is legitimate. The key characteristic of the seventies will be the awareness and toleration of a larger variety of alternative life styles. For example, living together has recently become a much more noticeable and popular custom on college campuses. Some people have reacted to this custom by viewing it as the death knell of marriage. That view is mistaken on two grounds. First, marriage need not be a legal contract. Indeed, most societies in the world lack a legal system and thus could not have legal marriage. Marriage can be celebrated by a meal together as in the Trobriand Islands, by requesting a common room as in some Israeli Kibbutz, or by an elaborate church wedding as in some segment of American society. If a new custom of marriage came into America in the form of couples living together, that could still be considered marriage. The test of whether a custom symbolizes marriage is whether the custom sanctions parenthood. If living together were accepted as a way for two people to become parents, then it would indeed be a new marriage custom. From the data I have seen from Eleanor Macklin, Michael Johnson and others it appears that, as a general rule, living together on American campuses is not a substitute for marriage because most of the couples involved do not want children, and are quite careful to avoid them. Most of these couples, however, seem to plan on a legal marriage someday — a marriage that is to take place when they do want children.

Experimentation in sex

Actually, a proper perspective for viewing living together is to see it as one of many developments that epitomize the emphasis on the value of experimentation. We can see evidence of this in the use of drugs 'just to see what it is like.' We see it in the area of sex in the reduced occurrence of quick self-labeling. For example, people are less likely to label themselves as homosexual because of one homosexual experience or as loose women because of one affair. Today young people seem to have more of a 'shoppers' attitude toward their sexual lives. They know they will experiment with different kinds of sexual relationships, but they also know that they need not continue any kind of sexuality that they find not to their liking. They reduce thereby the stigma of any one type of sexual encounter and increase the importance of experimenting in order to find which sexual life style suits them best. Living together is one outcome of such a philosophy.

We have opened up premarital sexuality for public debate, experimentation, and moral examination to a much greater extent than any previous generation in America. But in terms of the possible areas that such a debate could consider, it is still a rather narrow dialogue.

Control of the consequences of sex

One issue that has been central in the new openness regarding human sexuality is that of abortion. Like the pill, the liberalization of abortion laws puts the control of sexuality more in the hands of females and thereby helps in the development of their own sense of sexuality. They are no longer so likely to conceive of sex as something that happens to them and over which they have little control. Females now have control over their own sexuality and its consequences to a degree unmatched in Western history. This situation will continue in the remaining decades of the 20th century.

A qualification is in order here. The discussion above of the greater control over consequences, greater rationality in choices, and greater experimentation may lead to the view of the current scene as a neat, organized group of clear-thinking young people carefully reasoning out their sexual identities. That is not necessarily so. For example, one does not expect knowledge of how to avoid such unwanted consequences as pregnancy, to guarantee that such knowledge will be properly utilized. In the study of Kantner and Zelnik it was found that the vast majority of nonvirginal females (15—19 years old) only sometimes used contraceptive methods. When all is said and done, nature has not relinquished birth as part of her scheme of things!

One other point is the potentiality of sex interfering with the full development of a love relationship. Love relationships have high levels of self-revelation. Clearly sex is one level of revelation that is present in courtship relations; but we are still learning how to keep the sexual revelation from blocking other areas of revelation. People in love have often at times found out how to do this, but many others have failed. Males, for example, due to a lack of sexual opportunities may focus on 'scoring' and not bother to try to get to know the other rewards a particular relationship may possess. Females may stress their sexual attractions to the point where they fail to develop or present other aspects of themselves. Carelessness regarding pregnancy can make an otherwise developing relationship undergo a crisis that may lead to its termination. In many ways sex can act as a block to the growth of a relationship, and it should be clear that this can be the case whether the couple is kissing or copulating. This is not an argument against copulation — it is a statement of the fit of any type of sex in a relationship. The focus on sexual attractions is not present just in couples who copulate, it is present in some degree in nearly all couples. Many couples seem able to place sex in perspective and develop other aspects of their relationship; some couples can do this by having intercourse and thereby relieving that tension, whereas others are able to do it by sexual behavior short of coitus. The point I am making is that this generation seems to value honesty, totalistic types of relationships, and 'telling it like it is.' Such an open relationship can best be achieved if one knows how to keep sex from interfering with its growth and, equally important, how to utilize sex to help in developing a totalistic type of relationship.

4. CONCLUSIONS

Our sexual customs are changing, in accord with the emphasis in post-industrial society, concerning the quality of human relationships rather than material things. We can emphasize the human relationship in sex because we are learning very fast how to take care of the disease and pregnancy consequences of premarital intercourse, and by doing this we have increased the moral quality of the sexual choice. We can most often avoid, if we are careful, the unwanted consequences of sex, namely pregnancy and venereal disease, and thus we cannot use them as final reasons for our sexual decisions. We must delve deeper into the sexual relationship and decide whether we feel that our personality growth and that of our partner will be helped or hindered by having a sexual relationship of one sort or another. We can examine the potential impact of the relation upon ourselves and the others who are involved. It is just such an examination that has led to the popularity of situational ethics, for it is abundantly clear that for some people having premarital coitus would contribute to the development of responsibility, the ability to relate to people, a sense of integrity, and self realization. For other people having premarital coitus might lead to exactly the opposite set of consequences. As Alex Comfort put it a few years ago, this is the first generation that Western society has called upon to make a truly moral, intelligent choice of sexual life styles. Other generations were spared the choice by virtue of the social straitjackets they were wearing.

The question arises regarding the mental health impact in the next few decades of our orientation today toward premarital sexuality. What will be the rewards and the costs? These are, of course, difficult to generalize about. However, it seems that we can already discern a different type of cost. Psychiatrists do report that whereas generations ago people would seek help because they could not get started sexually, today they may seek help because they cannot stop sexually. It seems that our type of evolving system is more conducive to getting people started sexually, particularly females. The culture's definition that the individual has the responsibility for determining the specific controls of his sexual life style means that outside societal support is not (particularly for females) as ever present, or so narrow, as it was for past generations; and it is this that leads to control being one of the key personal problems of the current sexual scene.

I believe that in a very few years there will be a noticeable increase in the closure we reach on sexual questions. The 1960s opened up the doors on a wide range of possibilities. The 1970s are going to reach closure on many of the issues raised by this wider range of possible sex behavior. We will have learned to live with a greater range of choice, and we will learn more about the consequences of the newer choices confronting us.

The new sexuality offers a variety of forms of sexual expression and individualizes choice to a greater extent, and this should be a mental health advantage. The older sexual morality was a procrustean bed. If an individual did not fit, the society did not offer alternatives but rather tried to cut that individual down to size. The key advantage of the new sexuality is also its key disadvantage, namely, the increased possibility of choice. The advantages of choice are obvious — a person can choose a sexual life style more suited to himself. The disadvantage of greater freedom of choice is that we run the risk of choosing 'fool's gold.' In short, we may choose some course of action that yields temporary satisfaction but in the long run destroys more valuable parts of our life style. For example, we may choose to have a weekend with a sexually attractive person we just met and thereby alienate a person we love. Freedom of choice imposes the responsibility for restraint on the individual. The social restraints must be minimized for the freedom to be more than a facade, and this means that the possibility for individual error must be accepted. The choice of life style and the value judgements involved are individual choices. Social science can help in gaining understanding and perspective, but the final judgement is one we must each make, alone.

BIBLIOGRAPHY

Bell, R.R. and Chaskes, J.B. (1970) Premarital sexual experience among coeds: 1958—1968. *J. Marr. Fam.*, 32 (February) 81—84.

Christensen, H.T. and Gregg, C. (1970) Changing sex norms in America and Scandinavia. *J. Marr. Fam.*, 32 (November) 616—627.

Comfort, A. (1967) *The Anxiety Makers.* (Nelson, London.)

Cuber, J.F. and Harroff, P. (1965) *The Significant Americans.* (Appleton-Century-Crofts, New York.)

Hunt, M. (1974) *Sexual Behavior in the 1970's.* (Playboy Press, Chicago.)

Johnson, M.P. (1969) Courtship and commitment: A study of cohabitation on a University Campus. (Master's Thesis; unpublished, University of Iowa.)

Kantner, J.F. and Zelnik, M. (1972) Sexual experiences of young unmarried women in the United States, *Fam. Plan. Perspect.* 4 (October) 9—18.

Kinsey, A.C., Pomeroy, W.B. and Martin, C.E. (1948) *Sexual Behavior in the Human Male.* (Saunders, Philadelphia.)

Kinsey, A.C.. Pomeroy, W.B., Martin, C.E. and Gebhard, P.H. (1953) *Sexual Behavior in the Human Female.* (Saunders, Philadelphia.)

Klassen, A.D. and Levitt, E.E. (1975) Public attitudes toward sexual behaviors: The latest investigation of the Institute for Sex Research. *Arch. Sex. Behav.*, in press.

Macklin, E.D. (1972) Heterosexual cohabitation among unmarried college students. *Fam. Coord.* 21 (October) 463—473.

Masters, W.H. and Johnson, V.E. (1966) *Human Sexual Response.* (Little, Brown, Boston).

Reiss, I.L. (1960) *Premarital Sexual Standards in America.* (Macmillan-Free Press, New York.)

Reiss, I.L. (1967) *The Social Context of Premarital Sexual Permissiveness.* (Holt, Rinehart and Winston, New York.)

Reiss, I.L. (1973) *Heterosexual relationships: Inside and outside of marriage,* (General Learning Press, Morristown, New Jursey) pp. 1—29.

Reiss, I.L. (1976) *Family Systems in America.* 2nd edn. (Holt, Rinehart and Winston, New York.)

Simon, W., Berger, A.S. and Gagnon, J.H. (1972) Beyond anxiety and fantasy: The coital experience of college youth. *J. Youth Adolescence,* 1, 203—222.

Sorensen, R. (1973) *Adolescent Sexuality in Contemporary America.* (World Publ. New York.)

CHAPTER 24

The imagery of sex

DONN BYRNE

1. INTRODUCTION

One of mankind's more intriguing attributes is the ability to generate internal imaginative experiences which can recreate past events, anticipate future occurrences, or create novel scenes which bear no relationship to reality. This capacity for imagery serves numerous functions ranging from simple amusement to contingency planning. One of the more curious aspects of imaginative activity, however, is the effect it has on the motivational—emotional responses of the individual who generates the fantasy and of anyone to whom the fantasy is communicated.

The self-arousal properties of imagination can be easily demonstrated for oneself by recalling or anticipating specific interpersonal situations appropriate to anger, depression, fear, or joy. If they are sufficiently vivid, such imaginative activities can evoke the appropriate physiological and psychological accompaniment. Similarly, external cues such as words, drawings, photographs, or motion pictures are able to elicit the same kinds of responses, and it is logical to assume that imaginative processes serve as mediators. For example, a magazine photograph of a rich, moist chocolate cake plus a succulent description of its taste and texture can elicit images of cakes which, in turn, evoke the salivary response and the desire to eat. Because of these arousal effects of internal and external imaginative cues, human beings are not dependent on the occurrence of actual interpersonal interactions to evoke such emotions as anger, nor on internal physiological deficits to evoke such motives as to eat. In the realm of sexual activity, it should not be surprising to find that precisely the same mechanisms are operative. We can be

* Work on this manuscript was supported in part by Grant SOC 74-15254 from the National Science Foundation.

Handbook of Sexology, edited by J. Money and H. Musaph
© *Elsevier/North-Holland Biomedical Press, 1977*

sexually aroused by our fantasies whether these are self-generated or triggered by the externalized fantasies of others.

In the present chapter, sexual imagery will be examined with respect to psychological and physiological reactions to erotic stimuli, the meaning of erotic fantasies for human sexuality, group differences in sexual imagery, and the importance of sexual fantasies for human sexual behavior.

2. PSYCHOLOGICAL AND PHYSIOLOGICAL REACTIONS TO EROTIC IMAGERY

When individuals generate sexual fantasies or when they are exposed to external stimuli which elicit such fantasies, they react both sexually and affectively.

Sexual arousal

The most obvious and best documented effect of erotic stimulation is that of sexual excitement. It appears that the thought processes which are generated in response to erotic material most often lead the individual to respond as if he or she were a participant in the situation. Specifically, sexual desire increases, and the body responds as though in preparation for the sexual act.

Verbal reports of sexual excitement

When experimental investigations of response to erotica were first undertaken, societal restraints were sufficiently strong that the typical study involved only male subjects who were exposed to relatively mild stimuli such as photographs of unclad females (Clark, 1952). In a few experiments, sexual activity was described verbally (Byrne and Sheffield, 1965). In the past decade, dramatic societal changes in sexual permissiveness have been paralleled by equally pervasive changes in psychological research on human sexuality. The most obvious changes have been the use of photographs and motion pictures of individuals engaged in every possible type of sexual activity, and the increased use of female subjects (Schmidt and Sigusch, 1970; Byrne et al., 1973).

The most common response measure in all such experiments has been some version of a simple rating scale in which subjects indicate their degree of sexual arousal or excitement. With numerous investigations involving married and unmarried individuals, residents of a variety of Western nations, and both sexes, it has become possible to make a few generalizations about the arousal value of various types of stimuli presented in various media.

When experimenters make a direct comparison between types of stimulus presentation, few differences appear. It seems that the imaginative processes set in motion by words, photographs, or movies lead to approximately equal levels of self-reported arousal. For example, photographic slides of various sex acts result in the same arousal level as verbal descriptions of those same activities (Byrne and Lamberth, 1971). There are data indicating that photographs are slightly more arousing than comparable line drawings (Levitt and Hinesley, 1967) and that movies are more arousing than still pictures (McConaghy, 1974). The greatest difference reported in such studies, however, is of special interest in the present context. When Byrne and Lamberth (1971) asked subjects to imagine a specific series of sexual activities, they were considerably more aroused than other subjects who actually read stories or viewed slides which depicted those activities.

With respect to specific themes, the studies suggest a surprising uniformity in that most subjects report the greatest arousal in response to depictions of sexual intercourse in varied positions, genital caresses, fondling of the female breasts, fellatio, and cunnilingus. The least arousing material consists of acts of sadism, male nudes, and male homosexual acts such as fellatio and anal intercourse.

Physiological indications of arousal
Zuckerman (1971) reviewed the kinds of physiological response measures which have been used as indicators of sexual arousal. Many of these involve relatively nonspecific indications of activation or anxiety such as the galvanic skin response, heart rate, pupil dilation, and electrocortical measures. Research has also shown that exposure to erotic stimuli leads to an increase in urinary acid phosphatase in males (Barclay, 1970). In addition, males viewing a sexually explicit movie show an increase in plasma testosterone while males viewing a neutral film show no increase (Pirke et al., 1974). With respect to all of these physiological measures, there is evidence that they are influenced also by variables other than erotic stimulation.

In contrast to other arousal states such as anger, fear, or thirst, sexual excitement is accompanied by unique and quite specific observable physiological reactions. That is, there are specific genital responses including glandular secretions and changes in volume and temperature. The most extensive observations and detailed measurement of physiological changes during the sexual act have been provided by Masters and Johnson (1966). Thus, there is laboratory documentation of the effect of sexual excitement on circulatory changes in erectile tissue and on preparatory genital lubrication in both sexes. If the response to fantasy material is like that of response to an actual sexual partner, the same bodily reactions would be expected to occur.

The male response is, of course, easier to observe and measure, and several investigators have utilized a device to measure penis volume and hence the degree to which an erection occurs (Freund et al., 1965). Related devices utilize a strain gauge which indicates changes in penile circumference (Bancroft et al., 1966). Research using these instruments has demonstrated that erections occur in response to such erotic stimuli as movies (Howard et al., 1971) and in the absence of external stimuli when subjects simply think about sexual activities (Laws and Rubin, 1969). Measures of female responsiveness are used much less frequently, but Jovanovic (1971) has developed a balloon-like instrument which indicates vaginal contractions and a device to record temperature changes in the clitoris. A device to measure vaginal pressure pulse and blood volume was shown to indicate differential responses to erotic and nonerotic films (Geer et al., 1974). In general, then, the use of physiological measuring devices has shown that erotic stimuli and erotic imaginings bring about bodily changes identical to those observed in actual interactions with a sexual partner.

In much of the laboratory research on sexual behavior, of course, it is impractical or impossible to request subjects to permit direct recording of their sexual reactions. A surprisingly easy way to obtain relevant physiological information without the expense or embarrassment of penile or vaginal attachments has been developed by the Hamburg group (Schmidt and Sigusch, 1970). Subjects are asked to respond to a questionnaire in which they indicate the presence or absence of various bodily reactions while viewing erotic slides or movies. Over two-thirds of the individuals of each sex report some physiological reaction to the erotica. Most males indicate having an erection and 25% of them indicate the occurrence of some pre-ejaculatory emission. Analogously, most females report genital sensations and 28% indicate vaginal lubrication.

Behavioral correlates of sexual arousal
A few investigators have examined other aspects of subjects' behavior during their exposure to erotica. Amoroso and co-workers (1971) found that subjects spent more time looking at erotic slides as the slides increased in arousingness. In a study of interpersonal behavior, Griffitt and his colleagues (1974) found that sexually aroused subjects spent more time looking at opposite-sex strangers than did nonaroused subjects.

Affective and judgemental responses

In addition to the arousal aspects of internal and external erotic images, research interest has also been focused on the emotional and evaluative reactions to erotica. That is, sexual stimuli do not simply lead to arousal but are also embedded in a matrix of other reactions including anxiety, fear, anger, pleasure, curiosity, and so on. Presumably, such concomitant emotional states have become linked with sexuality by means of simple associative conditioning. Further, evaluative judgments as to the goodness and badness of sexual imagery seem to be determined by these learned affective responses.

Affective responses
Whenever investigators assess the emotional reactions of those exposed to erotica, it is universally found that the post exposure feeling state is different from the pre-exposure state. For example, in an investigation involving response to sexual stories, Schmidt and co-workers (1973) found increases in

general emotional activation and agitation, greater feelings of emotional instability and tension, and an increase in negative emotional reactions.

Such studies also report individual differences in emotional responses, and there have been several attempts to identify the antecedents and correlates of positive versus negative emotional reactions to sexuality. In an effort to delineate such an affective dimension more precisely, Byrne and co-workers (1974) presented marital partners with a series of erotic slides or stories and subjected the post-experimental emotional reactions to a factor analysis. Instead of the expected unidimensional response, it was found that there are two orthogonal dimensions. Subjects respond from low to high along a generally positive dimension and, independently, along a generally negative dimension. As a result, it is possible to classify emotional reactions to erotica roughly into four distinct categories as shown in Table I. It is hypothesized that numerous aspects of actual sexual behavior vary among these four categories of individuals.

Evaluative judgments

In the reinforcement-affect theory of evaluative responses, it has been proposed that our attitudinal judgments about any stimulus object are a simple reflection of the affect associated with that object (Clore and Byrne, 1974). That is, when we say that we like something, we only mean that it elicits positive feelings in us. When we dislike something, we mean that it elicits negative feelings. Complexities arise, however, because few people seem to

Table I
A four-fold classification of emotional reactions to erotic stimuli.

Positive affective response	Negative affective response	
	Low	High
High	*Prosex* Sexual imagery associated with pleasant, exciting, intriguing feelings without negative overtones	*Ambivalent* Sexual imagery associated with strong positive and negative feelings, suggesting an approach—avoidance conflict about sexuality
Low	*Emotionless* Sexual imagery is not associated with strong positive or negative feelings, suggesting either indifference to sexuality, satiation with erotica, or repression of affective responses	*Antisex* Sexual imagery is associated with unpleasant, angry, depressing feelings without positive overtones

be able to limit their evaluations to a simple expression of their own affective responses. Instead, people tend to attribute their feelings to qualities intrinsic to the object itself. Erotica, for example, is not just experienced as pleasant or unpleasant and hence liked or disliked; rather, people tend to assert that erotica itself is good or bad. A second step is then taken — that of justifying or vindicating one's evaluations. Thus, if erotic images elicit pleasant emotions, they not only must be intrinsically good, but it is asserted that exposure to erotica has positive effects such as improved mental health, greater human happiness, and a less totalitarian society. More dramatically, if erotic images elicit negative emotions, they not only must be intrinsically bad, but it is asserted that exposure to erotica has negative effects such as moral depravity, sex crimes, and anarchy.

Consistent with this formulation, individuals whose own emotional responses are high on the negative dimension and low on the positive one, label many more erotic themes as pornographic than do those with the opposite pattern of emotional responses (Byrne et al., 1974). Similarly, the antisex individuals are much more in favor of legal restrictions on erotica such as censorship than are the prosex individuals. Presumably, the progression is from 'erotica makes me feel uncomfortable' to 'erotica is pornographic' to 'erotica is dangerous and must be controlled.'

Despite these individual variations, there is some agreement within any given subject population that certain themes are disgusting. For example, conventional heterosexual couples are most likely to label as pornographic depictions of male or female homosexual acts, sadomasochistic themes, and group sex (Byrne and Lamberth, 1971). It seems likely that subjects who are homosexual, sadomasochist, or devotees of swinging would not share these evaluative judgments.

3. EROTIC FANTASIES AND HUMAN SEXUALITY

Erotica as a uniquely human enterprise

The importance of hormones in controlling sexual arousal decreases as one moves up the evolutionary scale (Beach, 1969). In less-developed mammalian species such as the rat, a primary determinant of sexual behavior is the hormonal output of the ovaries and testes (Lisk, 1970). Beach suggests that the difference between rats and primates is attributable to the relative size of the neocortex; thus, the sexuality of the higher mammals is controlled in large part by the central nervous system. It follows, then, that the human sex drive has more of a psychological than a physiological base.

Not only can human beings become aroused in response to internal and external sexual images, they apparently have sought to do so throughout recorded history. The prehistoric origins of erotic fantasies are obviously not available to us, but it can be noted that some of the earliest drawings and carvings include depictions of genitalia and of sexual acts. In fact, it seems accurate to assert that progressive developments in art, technology, and communication skills are almost immediately put to use in depicting and communicating sexual images. There are countless examples of our species' long-standing interest in representing and communicating erotic images, and of our ingenuity in utilizing all available artistic and technological skills in this enterprise. Prior to the 20th century, erotic creations included Latin American clay figures, African phallic statues, bas-relief sculptures in Indian temples, Pompeian frescoes, sexual paintings by artists such as Rembrandt, underground erotic stories and novels of Victorian England, and photographic postcards from 19th century France. In the current century, advancing technology has given us the stag movie and multitudes of sexually explicit 8-mm loops suitable for home viewing, the rampant sexuality of familiar comic strip characters in 'Tijuana bibles,' humor-oriented erotic 'party records,' audio tapes of sexual encounters complete with sound effects, the big-budget full-color sex movies of the 1970s, and the videotaped erotica currently available in certain motels.

Why are erotic images created and communicated?

We have seen that our species has the ability to create sexual images, the tendency to be aroused by them, and the apparent desire to spend time and effort in this pursuit. Though it may seem a naive question, not much effort has been devoted to explaining why such behavior occurs. Among the few answers that have been offered is the suggestion that all such erotic activities are evidence of perversity and moral depravity or that they represent conspiratorial efforts to subvert and debauch others. For example, a letter to *Playboy* magazine suggests that pornography is inherently evil. A letter to the Norman (Oklahoma) *Transcript* expresses the belief that erotica is a menace to humanity. A letter to the St. Louis, Missouri, *Globe-Democrat* sees pornography as a poison to body and soul. If erotica is seen as evil and threatening, it is not surprising that its presence is attributed to a sinister plot on the part of Communists to brutalize Americans (according to a former Indiana congressman) or on the part of capitalists to distract Czechoslovakians from political concerns (according to the Soviet Young Communist League). A more all-purpose explanation was provided in medieval Europe when Satan was seen as the perpetrator of sexual fantasies. Sexual dreams and nocturnal orgasms, for example, were believed to be caused by the stealthy ministrations of succubi and incubi.

It is possible to suggest four primary reasons that may help to explain the human propensity for exposing ourselves to internal and external erotic images.

Erotica as a source of knowledge
When individuals are asked to specify the primary source of their knowledge

about sex, very few name their parents, schools, or churches. Instead, the most important sex educators seem to be friends of the same age with pornography as supplementary source material.

Though very little research has been directed at this question, retrospective accounts by adults suggest that the details of sexual anatomy and the complexities of copulation are often communicated most clearly and most specifically by erotic stories and pictures. In the movie, *Summer of '42*, there was an excellent portrayal of the eager curiosity of adolescent boys examining an illustrated medical text. Though our laws and mores prohibit it, it seems likely that the exposure of youngsters to erotica could be an effective and economical teaching device. Unselected erotica unfortunately can also be a source of misinformation about sex, and hence its potential value is usually diluted by society's refusal to acknowledge its pedagogical role.

Once the basic anatomical aspects of genitalia are understood and their interactive properties mastered, there are still two major ways in which erotic images continue to be educational and informative. First, there are all the variations in intercourse positions, paragenital sexual acts, and multiparticipant sexuality. In effect, educational erotica can progress from introductory to intermediate and advanced sexual behavior. Second, there is a different type of knowledge imparted by sexual fantasies, one which touches on very important psychological concerns. According to Festinger (1954), human beings have a need for social comparison. We constantly seek information as to where we stand in reference to others with respect to ability, skills, opinions, and so forth. Such comparison processes provide us with a sense of who we are and inform us of areas in which change would be desirable. The one aspect of human behavior which historically has been the least open to direct social comparison is that of sexuality. Through erotica, sexual behavior is, however, put on public display and thus it becomes possible for the viewer to assess his or her abilities and proclivities, at least in comparison with the depicted individuals. Of course, any distortions of reality in erotica unfortunately lead to erroneous bases for social comparison.

Erotic images as aphrodisiacs
Because sexual activity in our species is largely under cognitive control, it follows that we can, to a surprising degree, regulate our sexual behavior by creating erotic fantasies or sharing the fantasies of others. In effect, we can become excited whenever we wish to do so. Though much time, effort, money, and wishful thinking have been directed toward the search for an effective aphrodisiac, many individuals have learned that they are carrying one of the most powerful instruments for stimulation in their own imagination. The arousal properties sought in ginseng roots, rhinocerous horn, stag antlers, or cantharides can be obtained easily and reliably by exposure to stories, pictures, and thoughts involving sexual activity.

Not only are sexual images utilized to obtain self-arousal, but their motivating properties have long been utilized in attempts to manipulate the arousal of others — most often by males attempting to arouse females. There are numerous historical and literary references to such uses of erotica. The anonymous author of 'My Secret Life' in the early 1800s in England recounts several examples of seduction aided by erotic books, pictures, and conversations. On the basis of his laboratory findings, Griffitt (1973, p. 337) notes, 'If, in fact, males attempt to arouse female partners sexually by exposing them to erotica, the present data suggest that their efforts would be generally successful . . .'

Erotic images, arousal and pleasure

Many drive-arousal theories suggest that motivation is based primarily on unpleasant physiological states of either deprivation or painful stimulation. When such states become sufficiently noxious, the organism behaves in such a way as to reduce the drive. Drive reduction is reinforcing, and, with human beings at least, the accompanying emotional state is described as one of pleasure. It also follows that the stronger the drive, the greater the drive reduction when the appropriate goal is achieved. Common experience tells us that the greater the drive reduction, the more intense the accompanying pleasure. It is a truism that food tastes best when one's mealtime is delayed, that great thirst enhances the pleasurable qualities of even a glass of water, that sleep deprivation makes it all the more delightful to lie down in a comfortable bed, and so forth.

When the relationships outlined above are extrapolated to the area of sexuality, it seems plausible to suggest that erotic images act to increase drive level and that any subsequent orgasm would involve increased drive reduction and hence intensified pleasure. If this analysis is correct, it means that imaginative fantasies can serve to enhance sexual gratification. There is some research evidence indicating that fantasy is widely used for this purpose. For example, Hariton and Singer (1974) found that the majority of their sample of married women regularly have sexual fantasies during intercourse. These fantasies are not associated with sexual or marital difficulty but simply serve to increase desire and to heighten pleasure.

Imagination versus reality

Reality is restrictive for a variety of reasons. One advantage of imaginative activities is that they can go beyond the confines of reality in allowing one to engage vicariously in activities which are legally and/or morally condemned, which are physically impossible, or which might be intriguing at the level of fantasy but acutely unpleasant in actual fact.

Both in commercially distributed erotica and in self-reports of fantasies, sexual behavior frequently involves tabooed or illegal activities. Though the taboos and the laws change over time, and though they vary across localities, it is clear that rape, adultery, prostitution, homosexuality, anal sex, and sadism, for example, have played a much larger role in our public and private fantasies than has, say, the heterosexual intercourse of spouses in the dorsal—ventral position, female supine. It also seems safe to assume that more individuals have thought about and become aroused by the idea of quasi-illicit activities such as group sex, for example, than have actually had the opportunity or the willingness to engage in the activity.

In addition, realistic obstacles can be overcome by imaginative activities. Anyone can dream the impossible dream and engage in whatever sexual acts with whatever person or persons one chooses. The most unattractive female can be the lust object of matinée idols, equally unattractive males can make easy conquests of famous sex godesses. In imagination, no one need worry about the size or shape of any anatomical feature. There is no frigidity or impotence, and unrequited desire is unknown. Even at a more mundane level, sexual fantasies are much simpler than the real world in which individuals must deal with the details of steering wheels, motel clerks, brassiere hooks, shoes and socks. This idea is described well by Erica Jong (1973) in 'Fear of Flying', when she presents her fantasy of the 'zipless fuck' which was '. . . more than a fuck. It was a platonic ideal. Zipless because when you came together zippers fell away like rose petals, underwear blew off in one breath like dandelion fluff. Tongues intertwined and turned liquid.'

Finally, many excitingly imagined activities would be much less exciting and much less pleasant if they actually occurred. Perhaps a prime example is rape. Females may report rape fantasies as arousing and pleasurable, but actual rape, in contrast, involves fear, pain and humiliation. Similarly, many individuals who are turned on by sadomasochistic themes in fantasy would be repelled by the stark reality of administering or receiving pain. Sexual imagery can sometimes be preferable to its real-life counterparts.

4. GROUP DIFFERENCES IN RESPONSE TO SEXUAL IMAGERY

Because individuals differ greatly in the extent to which they are aroused by erotica, and in their emotional and evaluative reactions, there has been considerable interest in determining whether these differences are associated with other identifiable characteristics.

Religious behavior and response to erotica

It is frequently reported that Catholics in the U.S. respond more negatively to erotic stimuli than do individuals with other religious beliefs. Both Catholics and Protestants are more favorable toward legal restrictions on erotica than are agnostics and atheists. An isolated finding of possible interest is that Protestants and Catholics are more sexually aroused by themes of erotic sadism than are atheists and agnostics (Byrne and Lamberth, 1971).

Frequency of church attendance is generally found to be unrelated to sex arousal (Schmidt et al., 1969). With respect to evaluations of erotica, it is consistently found that the more frequently an individual attends church, the more likely he or she is to indicate negative and restrictive attitudes about sexual stimuli (Reed and Reed, 1972).

Personality variables

Authoritarianism
The California F-Scale (Adorno et al., 1950) is a measure of the attitudes and beliefs underlying acceptance of fascistic, antidemocratic ideology. Individuals scoring high on this dimension possess such characteristics as rigid adherence to conventional values, the tendency to submit to authority and to aggress against those in the outgroup who deviate, the tendency to use projective defense mechanisms, and an exaggerated concern with the sexual behavior of others.

Though this personality dimension is usually found to be unrelated to degree of sexual arousal in response to erotica, it is consistently found that authoritarianism is positively associated with unfavorable attitudes toward many aspects of sexuality. For example, authoritarians are more likely than equalitarians to classify nude paintings, such as Chabas' *September Morn*, as pornographic (Eliasberg and Stuart, 1961). Explicit sexual material is also rated as more pornographic by authoritarians than by equalitarians. In addition, those high in authoritarianism respond to erotica with negative emotional responses, and they are in favor of imposing legal restrictions on the production and sale of erotic material (Byrne and Lamberth, 1971).

Conservatism—Liberalism
Perhaps in part because many different measures of the liberal—conservative dimension and many different stimulus conditions have been employed in research, the relationship between this variable and degree of arousal has not been established with consistency (Schmidt et al., 1969; Wallace and Wehmer, 1972). The importance of specific themes may explain much of the inconsistency. For example, conservatives are found to be more aroused than liberals by photographs of nudes but less aroused by photographs depicting such themes as petting, coitus from the rear, and fellatio (Schmidt et al., 1969).

Findings relevant to evaluative judgments are much more consistent. Political conservatives tend to make more negative judgments about erotica than do liberals. Such political differences have been attributed to conservative fears that unbridled sexuality is somehow a threat to the orderly functioning of society and an attack on the status quo. For this reason, they tend to favor censorship in order to avoid unduly arousing the lusts of the populace and to support repressive legal actions against those who behave in an unorthodox manner sexually.

Sex guilt
Mosher (1966) defines sex guilt as a generalized expectancy for self-punish-

ment whenever standards of proper sexual conduct are violated or even contemplated. Though sex guilt is unrelated to degree of arousal following exposure to erotic films, subjects high in guilt rate the films as more pornographic, disgusting, and offensive than do those low in guilt; guilt is also related to increased negative feelings in the 24 hours following the film experience (Mosher, 1971).

Sex differences

It has long been believed that females are much less interested in sex than males. It is males, not females, who have been the sexual aggressors, the creators and consumers of pornography, and the ones who are most obviously motivated to seek sexual information and titillation. Generations of women have been taught to satisfy the sexual demands of a husband as an obligatory marital duty; Eleanor Roosevelt told her daughter, "Sex, my dear, is a thing a woman must learn to endure". Others have been advised to feign sexual interest in order to avoid losing the spouse to one who is a better bedroom actress. Even Alex Comfort (1972, p. 73) regards the sexes as quite different in arousability in that, 'Male sex response is triggered easily . . . like putting a quarter in a vending machine.' Current research in this area suggests that much of our conventional wisdom about sex differences must be revised.

Male and female arousal

One aspect of sex differences for which there is some documentation is the disinterest of females in erotic stimuli and their low ability to respond sexually to such material. On the basis of their extensive interviews, Kinsey and co-workers (1953) concluded that females are indifferent to pornography because it has no effect on them erotically. Despite many changes in sexual attitudes and behavior since the 1950s, survey research in the 1970s reveals much the same self-reported sex differences (Abelson et al., 1971).

When experimental investigations of response to erotica began to include women subjects, the findings yielded a surprise. Among unmarried college students in Hamburg, Germany (Sigusch et al., 1970) and in Manhattan, Kansas (Griffitt, 1973), and among married couples in West Lafayette, Indiana (Byrne and Lamberth, 1971), males and females were found to report equal levels of arousal in response to erotic stories, photographs, and movies! Approximately the same percentages of each sex group also report some physiological responsiveness to erotic stimuli (Schmidt and Sigusch, 1970), and both sexes are equally aroused by sexual stories with and without expressed affection (Schmidt et al., 1973). While such findings seem to surprise some males and invite their sarcastic incredulity (Kempton, 1970), females are more apt to agree to their validity. For example, one female graduate student upon learning of this research told the author how relieved she felt. For years, she had believed herself to be somehow abnormal because she found erotica highly arousing.

The discrepancy between folk wisdom and survey research on the one hand and experimental findings on the other is not difficult to explain. If society teaches women that it is not appropriate for them to be interested in erotica, and indicates the unacceptability for them of any expression of interest, most women will, reasonably or unreasonably, accept those proscriptions. When asked in surveys whether they are aroused by erotic stimuli and pornography, they will reply in the negative either because they have had little or no contact with erotica, or because it would be embarrassing or socially undesirable to admit such an aberration. In a laboratory, by contrast, contact with erotica is determined by the experimenter and the admission of arousal is facilitated by the research procedures. The Victorian author of 'My Secret Life' and some of his companions, knew of the artificiality of female disinterest in erotica over a century ago: "And a baudy book, they won't look at till you've fucked them? — Oh! Won't they! — They would at church if you left them alone with it" (Anonymous, 1966, p. 583).

Sexual experience does seem to play a role in female responsiveness to sexual imagery. Griffitt (1975) found that female arousal when viewing erotica is a positive function of amount of heterosexual experience. It follows that as the sexual permissiveness of society increases, female responsiveness to sexual stimuli should also increase.

Sex differences in fantasy content

Despite the recent revelations concerning previous misconceptions about female sexuality, it should be pointed out that there are some male—female differences in the kind of fantasy material which is arousing. In a study of undergraduates at Michigan State University, Barclay (1973) asked males and females to create their own sexual fantasies. He reported marked sex differences in that males wrote stories which sounded like typical hard-core pornography with unemotional, highly sexed characters and the use of a great deal of visual imagery. Females, in contrast, created more diverse fantasies usually featuring strong emotional elements of either love or being taken by force.

Sex differences are also found in responding to erotic images created by others. Not surprisingly, members of each sex report greater arousal in response to a solitary nude of the opposite sex then to one of the same sex (Griffitt, 1973). Also, both sexes are more aroused by a movie of an opposite sex individual masturbating than of a same sex individual masturbating (Schmidt, 1974). While males and females who are married do not differ in the extent to which they are aroused by themes of cunnilingus and fellatio (Byrne and Lamberth, 1971), unmarried males tend to be more aroused by depictions of oral sex than are unmarried females (Griffitt, 1973). Differential experience would seem to explain these findings of premarital sex differences which do not occur among married couples. Griffitt (1975) has found that twice as many unmarried college males have experienced fellatio and cunnilingus as have unmarried college females and that such experience is related to the extent of the reported oral sex. It is thus suggested that among married individuals, experiential differences between the sexes disappear, and hence sex differences in arousability to oral sex themes also disappear.

Masturbation fantasies are especially interesting, because it can be assumed that individuals who are masturbating are inhibited by no external constraints, and thus tend to focus on the type of sexual interaction which is most arousing to them. The masturbation fantasies reported by Hunt (1974) are shown in Table II. It may be seen that the most common fantasy for both sexes is that of intercourse with the one they love. Beyond that, males and females tend to differ in the content of their masturbation fantasies. Men are more likely than women to imagine intercourse with strangers, group sex with multiple partners, and forcing someone to have sex; women are more likely than men to imagine various sexual activities they would never actually engage in, being forced to have sex, and having homosexual relations.

Affective and evaluative responses

Because males and females have traditionally been taught according to a double standard of social acceptability regarding sexuality, it is reasonable to expect that females would be more likely than males to associate erotic images with anxiety, disgust, and other negative emotional states. A great many females have been taught to avoid sexual excitement in order to protect themselves against the advances of rutting males. Even the most sexually liberated female learns to be wary of possible exploitation on the part of

Table II
Comparative masturbation fantasies of males and females. (Data from Hunt, 1974.)

	Percentage of sample reporting each type of fantasy	
	Males	Females
Reported equally by males and females:		
Intercourse with a loved person	75	80
Reported more frequently by males than by females:		
Intercourse with strangers	47	21
Group sex with multiple partners of the opposite sex	33	18
Forcing someone to have sex	13	3
Reported more frequently by females than by males:		
Doing sexual things you would never do in reality	19	28
Being forced to have sex	10	19
Homosexual activities	7	11

males. Thus, many females might well equate the arousing properties of sexual imagery with danger. It has been found, for example, that for females negative affect is the primary determinant of evaluative judgments about erotica, while male judgments are based on an interactive combination of positive and negative affect (Byrne et al., 1974).

Among undergraduate college students, Griffitt (1973) found that females who had viewed erotic slides were more disgusted, angry and nauseated, than were males; the females also were more likely to favor restrictive legislation to control pornography. After reading an erotic story, females reported more negative emotional responses (feeling disgusted, shocked, quarrelsome and irritated) than did males, while the reverse was true with respect to feeling gregarious, driven and impulsive (Schmidt et al., 1973). Thus, women expressed avoidance reactions after exposure to sexual images while men indicated activation. Such differences are even more strongly evidenced in response to aggressive sexual themes, such as in a movie depicting rape (Schmidt, 1974).

One area in which males express more negative emotional reactions than do females is in response to a movie showing an individual of their own sex masturbating (Schmidt, 1974). Presumably, the homosexual implications of being interested in such a scene are more threatening to males than to females.

5. THE IMPORTANCE OF SEXUAL FANTASIES FOR HUMAN SEXUAL BEHAVIOR

So far in this chapter, it has been assumed that sexual fantasies are created primarily to enhance personal satisfaction. It is always possible, however, that additional consequences may be brought about by indulgence in sexual fantasies. A frequently asked question is whether or not such fantasy activity may bring about changes in overt behavior.

Does exposure to sexual imagery instigate unacceptable sexual behavior?

One of the most controversial questions in the study of social influence processes is whether or not overt behavioral acts are instigated by exposure to imaginative representations of violence, sexuality, or whatever. Surely one of the major fears of those who favor censorship of erotica is that the consequence of displaying sexual books, plays, photographs, or movies to the public is the subsequent acting-out of the depicted scenes by the spectators. What are the relevant data?

Short-term behavioral effects of imaginative arousal
Though direct evidence concerning the effects of erotica on overt behavior was completely lacking until the last few years (Cairns et al., 1971), the ex-

periments conducted under the auspices of the Commission on Obscenity and Pornography (1970) plus equally recent work conducted at various research centers such as the one at Hamburg have provided a body of relevant data.

The findings have been something of a disappointment both to those who advocate emotional liberation through sexual freedom, and to those who fear that rampant sexuality will be displayed in the streets after each showing of a pornographic film. The most general conclusion is that sexual books, movies, and photographs have very little effect on subsequent behavior. Some investigators report no measurable changes in behavior (Howard et al., 1971), and any reported changes tend to involve mild increases in the subjects' existing sexual habits such as masturbation (Amoroso et al., 1971) or coitus with the usual sexual partner (Cattell et al., 1972). Even these moderate increases in sexual activity seem to be limited to the brief period immediately following exposure to erotica. For example, Mann and co-workers (1971) presented either sexual or nonsexual films to married couples once a week for four weeks, obtained their daily sexual records for these weeks plus the following four weeks, and found increased sexual activity in the experimental group only on the nights the erotic films were shown.

Erotica and sex crimes
It would be premature to conclude on the basis of such experiments as those mentioned above, that erotica could have no ill effects on behavior. For one thing, it is not possible to probe the null hypothesis. More importantly, experimental studies to date have been quite circumscribed with respect to subject samples. That is, the subjects have primarily been drawn from university populations in which relatively bright, well-educated, emotionally adjusted, middle-class individuals volunteered to participate. If the same studies were repeated with dull, uneducated, maladjusted denizens drawn from the lowest socioeconomic strata of society, perhaps the results would be quite different. Some findings are available, however, in which the subject population was not restricted.

In 1969, the laws of Denmark were changed to permit all forms of explicit sexual material to be sold. Thus, across that country it became possible for adults to purchase books and magazines and attend movies and live sex shows without restraint. Even if only a minuscule portion of the population is adversely affected by exposure to erotica, the result should have been a frightening rise in Danish sexual crimes. As is widely known by now, sex crimes actually showed a 30% decrease in 1969, and the decline has continued. Though it is impossible to assert that the availability of erotica was responsible for the decrease in rapes, child molestation, Peeping Tomism, and homosexual offenses, the data are certainly consistent with that hypothesis (Commission on Obscenity and Pornography, 1970).

The other type of evidence is that dealing with retrospective studies of convicted sex criminals to determine whether they report an unusually large amount of contact with pornography either during their youth or in the period immediately preceding the criminal act. Such studies tend to show that sex offenders actually report less contact with erotica than is true for comparable nonoffenders (Goldstein et al., 1971). Once again, the specific data are open to question. It could be that sex offenders actually spend a lifetime saturated with erotica but are motivated to conceal this fact from prison researchers in order to present what they consider to be a socially acceptable facade.

Erotic imagery an a safety value
Despite the limitations of the data, the sum total of the results of the laboratory experiments, the Danish experience, and the study of sex criminals, is a consistent one. On the basis of present knowledge, one could best conclude, however tentatively, that erotica has not been shown to have negative effects on sexual behavior and, if anything, seems to act as a deterrent to sexual crimes. How could this be?

The most obvious possibility, and the most difficult to verify, is that when individuals are able to indulge their sexual fantasies, they are less inclined to feel it necessary to act out these fantasies in anti-social acts (Crepault, 1972). If that is true, erotica which is sufficiently arousing to evoke masturbation should be the most effective deterrent of all. For example, when the potential voyeur can vicariously and harmlessly peep into as many bedrooms as he likes on the movie screen, he can masturbate while witnessing such imagery, and/or he can relive the manufactured scenes in his own masturbatory fantasies. It is easy to ridicule or condemn the men who furtively masturbate under their raincoats at a pornographic movie. If, however, the choice is between this and the commission of a sex offense against an unwilling victim, it is clear which alternative is preferable.

It might also be added that this proposed safety-valve function of erotica can probably be credited with various beneficial effects that are unrelated to sexual crimes. The individual who is unable to attract a sexual partner can at least live a partially satisfying existence with the help of erotic images and masturbation. When an individual is separated from his or her sexual partner, self-produced or commercial sexual fantasies help relieve the frustration. It is even possible that many less-than-perfect marriages are maintained by the sexual fantasies of one or both partners during masturbation and/or intercourse. Spouses who would otherwise be unhappy can attain satisfaction by imagining more desirable partners or forbidden acts.

Does exposure to sexual imagery have any long-range effects on sexual attitudes and behavior?

Despite existing evidence that erotic stimuli have only moderate short-term effects on overt sexual behavior, the very real possibility remains that research to date has not been adequately designed to test more subtle, more gradual, and ultimately more important effects. The difference can be illustrated with an analogy. Racial intolerance was an integral part of the presentations of the American entertainment industry throughout most of our history, and blacks were routinely presented in stereotypic terms and demeaning roles. This policy changed rather abruptly following World War II. With motion pictures based on themes of racial tolerance, the creation of black superstars, and the use of integrated scenes in television commercials, the public today is exposed to very different images than was true in the prewar era. Have such changes in the entertainment world had any effects on changing the attitudes and the behavior of the audience with respect to race? It seems apparent that the answer is 'yes,' but the antecedent—consequent relationship is essentially impossible to establish because the changes in the media are inextricably confounded with other changes in our society. Further, any such effects are not likely to have been instantaneous. The cummulative effects of exposure to such images over a long period of time, and across generations, is another matter. Many behavioral scientists are convinced that these experiences are very influential in altering our interracial views and actions.

With respect to sexual attitudes and behavior, precisely the same effects seem eminently plausible. In research on nonsexual behavior, it has been established that the specific activities of the depicted characters may be imitated (Bandura et al., 1963). It seems very probable that exposure to erotica would also result in specifically imitative sexual behavior. Because overt sexual acts do not occur in the typical laboratory investigation, a way has not yet been found to document these effects.

Altering sexual behavior via alterations in sexual fantasies
There is a good deal of psychological research which indicates that manipulations of the content of imaginative fantasies are followed by parallel alterations in relevant behavior (McClelland, 1965). In addition, therapists in a variety of disciplines report the utilization of various aspects of imaginative activity as a step in altering behavior.

Some forms of therapy involve instructing the patient to engage in specific imaginative activity in a context which facilitates the association of that fantasy with a positive affective state. One such procedure is desensitization. The therapist attempts to reduce anxiety by asking the patients to say words or imagine scenes beginning with the least threatening and working up toward the most threatening. This is a counterconditioning procedure in which the imagined object or activity gradually comes to evoke feelings of safety and relaxation rather than fear and anxiety. It is not much of an extension to suggest that anything which induces people to think about anxiety-evoking sexual acts under nonthreatening conditions could be expected to have effects analogous to those of desensitization therapy.

The positive affect associated with a calm, relaxed state can be intensified by the administration of positive reinforcement as the imaginative activity occurs. In the sexual realm, guided masturbation is a technique whereby specific fantasies can become associated with the pleasures of masturbation and orgasm. Denholtz (1974) reported a case in which a nonorgasmic female was instructed to imagine being raped as she masturbated. The rape fantasy made sexual excitement acceptable in that she was not responsible for what was done to her; a series of such fantasy—masturbation pairings led to the resolution of her orgasmic difficulties. This same therapist also reports using a variant of that technique to change a patient's goal object. A male homosexual patient is asked to masturbate along with whatever fantasy he wishes, but to think of a female at the point of climax. On subsequent trials, the role of the female sex object is shifted progressively further into the fantasy sequence until the masturbation fantasy is totally oriented toward a member of the opposite sex. Fantasy conditioning can also occur as part of everyday activities. For example, Denholtz (1973) instructs a male homosexual patient to think of pleasant things (music, flowers) whenever he sees a reasonably attractive female and to think of unpleasant things (penis with a bad-smelling ulcer) whenever he sees a male to whom he is attracted. The goal is to alter the positive and negative qualities of sexual cues and hence to alter overt sexual behavior by altering covert fantasy behavior.

These same general procedures are also used in conjunction with external stimuli, usually in the form of photographic slides. Again, an individual can be taught to modify his behavior through the association of a given image with pleasurable affective responses such as relaxation or masturbatory activity. Presumably, it is in this way that we ordinarily learn, developmentally, to associate particular images with sexual excitement and fulfillment. Conceptually, there is little difference between what one incidentally learns via a masturbation fantasy and what one learns in a therapist's office in which a photographic slide is presented while the patient masturbates.

Possible effects of erotic imagery on sexuality

Let us take as an example a female who has never engaged in fellatio, is made somewhat anxious by even thinking of it, and has no desire to alter her attitudes or behavior. Leaving aside the question of the prudence of her views, we can simply say that in a sexually restrictive society, there would be little or no reason to expect this behavior to change. She could easily avoid thinking about the topic, and external representations of fellatio would seldom if ever be thrust upon her. In many parts of the world in recent years, such an individual would find it very difficult to avoid verbal and pictorial fantasies involving oral stimulation of the penis. In movies, books, and popular magazines, she would be repeatedly exposed to the idea that fellation is an acceptable, expected, pleasurable aspect of heterosexual relationships. It is proposed that such exposure results in a progressive series of changes in the sequence described below.

Step I. Attitude change via familiarization and desensitization We have already noted the therapeutic use of densensitization which indicates that repeated exposure to an anxiety-evoking stimulus leads to decreased anxiety. More generally, Zajonc (1968) has proposed that repeated exposure to any stimulus results in more favorable evaluations of that stimulus. Over a period of months or years, our hypothetical female is exposed directly or indirectly to material contained in such books as 'Portnoy's Complain', such movies as *Deep Throat*, and such plays as *Let My People Come*. Each time that the topic of fellatio arises, there should be less and less anxiety. The expected result is a more favorable evaluation of fellatio. It is hypothesized that exposure to sexual images tends to bring about changes in evaluative responses such that attitudes toward the depicted sexual activity are gradually changed from negative to neutral to mildly positive.

Step II. Tolerance and imaginative rehearsal Once there has been an attitudinal shift, the individual is able to think about the activity in question without being blocked by anxiety and the necessity to vindicate the negative feelings by means of negative attributions. For example, it would now be possible for our female more easily to tolerate the idea that others are engaging in fellatio without condemming them for it. Hunt (1974) describes many instances in which there is increased tolerance in the United States for various sexual practices such as anal intercourse, even among those who have never engaged in such acts. The ability to think about a given sexual activity without anxiety also means that such thoughts can occur during masturbation or coitus. There is evidence that erotic stimuli, especially pictorial stimuli, directly influence the masturbatory and coital fantasies of both males and females (Schmidt and Sigusch, 1973). In effect, the individual becomes involved in an active conditioning procedure much like the guided masturbation technique used in therapy. The end result is that a previously forbidden act such as fellatio may become a stimulus for arousal, sexual pleasure, and orgasm.

Step III. Behavioral change It is proposed that the new associations which the individual learns are apt to be followed by changes in overt behavior. For example, if the idea of fellatio has become an exciting and pleasurable one, the inclination is to try it out in real life. In this way, the erotic images prevalent in the culture become transferred to private erotic images which are later translated into overt behavior.

It should be added that this three-step process is not inevitable because of numerous possible disruptions and that each progressive step has a lower probability of occurrence than the previous one. Thus, more people change their attitudes as a result of repeated exposure than become actively engaged in imaginative rehearsal, and fewer still try out the imagined scene in overt behavior. For the population as a whole, however, the net long-range result of sexual explicitness should be (1) more favorable attitudes toward the depicted activities, (2) an increase in tolerance for the activities and in private fantasies about the activities, and (3) an increase in the frequency of the activities themselves. Because of the very nature of the process being described, no single experiment can pinpoint the effects very convincingly, but changes in the explicitness of erotic images in our society have obviously occurred concomitantly with changes in sexual attitudes, tolerance, and overt practices.

The kinds of effect attributed to sexually explicit material may be interpreted by many as beneficial, in that increasing numbers of people may be learning to be less anxious about many aspects of their sexual lives and to obtain more joy from engaging in a variety of sexual practices. A word of caution is in order, however. In the example, changes were described with respect to fellatio, a rather typical primate activity. The example could have been rape, flagellation, or pederasty. Though we as citizens may disagree about which sexual acts are acceptable and which are detrimental to society, we can all agree that at least some erotic activities, especially violent ones, should not be encouraged. If our present knowledge and theorizing of the generalizability of the effect of erotic images on human behavior proves to be generally correct, even the most permissive and tolerant will reconsider the wisdom of selective censorship.

6. SUMMARY

It is well established that exposure to erotic images results in sexual arousal as measured by verbal reports, physiological indicators of excitement, and behavioral changes. In addition, erotica elicits positive and negative affective responses which, in turn, mediate various evaluative judgments.

Throughout history, human beings have created external representations of sexual activities in the form of drawings, stories, poems and recently, photographs, recordings and movies. It was suggested that these erotic images function as a source knowledge about sex, as cognitive aphrodisiacs, as a way to enhance sexual pleasure, and as a way to go beyond the confines of reality.

Differential response to erotica has been found to be related to religious affiliation and frequency of church attendance and to personality variables such as authoritarianism, conservatism—liberalism, and sex guilt. Though it has long been believed that females are less aroused by sexual imagery than are males, recent experimental evidence indicates a lack of sex differences. There are some male—female differences in the specific themes that are most arousing, in the content of self-created sexual fantasies, and in affective responses.

The effects of sexual fantasies on human sexual behavior have not been investigated intensely until recent years. Experiments show that the short-term behavioral effects of imaginative arousal are limited to brief periods of time and to behaviors already in the individual's sexual repertoire. There is no evidence linking sex crimes to exposure to erotica, except some indications of a negative effect. A possible explanation is that erotic imagery provides a safety valve for unacceptable sexual desires. The long-range effects of exposure to erotica are more difficult to establish. Psychotherapists have shown that alterations in sexual fantasies can lead to alterations in sexual behavior. Hypothetically, repeated exposure to erotica may lead to more favorable evaluations of the depicted acts, and favorable evaluations may lead to increased tolerance and to imaginative rehearsal of these acts, following which, actual engagement in the behavior may follow. Nonetheless, this sequence needs to be tested empirically, not only for one, but for all known forms and variants of human erotic activity.

ACKNOWLEDGEMENT

The author wishes to thank the Information Service of the Institute for Sex Research, Indiana University, for assisting in the bibliographic search.

BIBLIOGRAPHY

Abelson, H., Cohen, R., Heaton, E. and Suder, C. (1971) National survey of public attitudes toward and experience with erotic materials. In: *Technical Report of the Commission on Obscenity and Pornography*, Vol 6, pp: 1—137. (U.S. Government Printing Office, Washington, D.C.)

Adorno, T.W., Frenkel-Brunswik, E., Levinson, D.J. and Sanford, R.N. (1950) *The Authoritarian Personality*. (Harper, New York.)

Amoroso, D.M., Brown, M., Pruesse, M., Ware, E.E. and Pilkey, D.W. (1971) An investigation of behavioral, psychological, and physiological reactions to pornographic stimuli. In: *Technical Report of the Commission on Obscenity and Pornography*, Vol 8, pp: 1—40. (U.S. Government Printing Office, Washington, D.C.)

Anon. (1966) *My Secret Life*. (Grove, New York.)

Bancroft, J.J., Jones, H.G. and Pullan, B.R. (1966) A simple transducer for measuring penile erection, with comments on its use in the treatment of sexual disorders. *Behav. Res. Ther.* 4: 239—241.

Bandura, A., Ross, D. and Ross, S.A. (1963) Imitation of film-mediated aggressive models. *J. Abn. Soc. Psychol.* 66: 3—11.

Barclay, A.M. (1970) Urinary acid phosphatase secretion in sexually aroused males. *J. Exp. Res. Pers.* 4: 233—238.

Barclay, A.M. (1973) Sexual fantasies in men and women. *Med. Aspects Hum. Sex.* 7: 205—216.

Beach, F.A. (1969) It's all in your mind. *Psychol. Today* 3 (2) 33—35, 60.

Byrne, D., Cherry, F., Lamberth, J. and Mitchell, H.E. (1973) Husband-wife similarity in response to erotic stimuli. *J. Pers.* 41: 385—394.

Byrne, D., Fisher, J.D., Lamberth, J. and Mitchell, H.E. (1974) Evaluations of erotica: Facts or feelings? *J. Pers. Soc. Psychol.* 29: 111—116.

Byrne, D. and Lamberth, J. (1971) The effect of erotic stimuli on sex arousal, evaluative responses, and subsequent behavior. In: *Technical Report of the Commission on Obscenity and Pornography*, Vol 8, pp: 41—67. (U.S. Government Printing Office, Washington, D.C.)

Byrne, D. and Sheffield, J. (1965) Response to sexually arousing stimuli as a function of repressing and sensitizing defenses. *J. Abn. Psychol.* 70: 114—118.

Cairns, R.B., Paul, J.C.N. and Wishner, J. (1971) Psychological assumptions in sex censorship: An evaluative review of recent research (1961—1968). In: *Technical Report of the Commission on Obscenity and Pornography*, Vol 1, pp. 5—21. (U.S. Government Printing Office, Washington, D.C.)

Cattell, R.B., Kawash, G.F. and DeYoung, G.E. (1972) Validation of objective measures of ergic tension: Response of the sex erg to visual stimulation. *J. Exp. Res. Pers.* 6: 76—83.

Clark, R.A. (1952) The projective measurement of experimentally induced levels of sexual motivation. *J. Exp. Psychol.* 44: 391—399.

Clore, G.L. and Byrne, D. (1974) A reinforcement-affect model of attraction. In: (T.L. Huston, Ed.) *Foundations of Interpersonal Attraction*. (Academic Press, New York.) pp: 143—170.

Comfort, A. (1972) *The Joy of Sex*. (Crown, New York.)

Commission on Obscenity and Pornography (1970) *The Report of the Commission on Obscenity and Pornography*. (U.S. Government Printing Office, Washington, D.C.)

Crépault, C. (1972) Sexual fantasies and visualization of "pornographic scenes." *J. Sex Res.* 8: 154—155.

Denholtz, M.S. (1973) An extension of covert procedures in the treatment of male homosexuals. *J. Behav. Ther. Exp. Psychiat.* 4: 305.

Denholtz, M. (1974) *Behavior therapy in sexual disorders*. Paper presented at the Institute for Sex Research, Bloomington, Indiana.

Eliasberg, W.G. and Stuart, I.R. (1961) Authoritarian personality and the obscenity threshold. *J. Soc. Psychol.* 55: 143—151.

Festinger, L. (1954) A theory of social comparison processes. *Hum. Relat.* 7: 117—140.

Freund, K., Sedlacek, F. and Knob, K. (1965) A simple transducer for mechanical plethysmography of the male genital. *J. Exp. Anal. Behav.* 8: 169—170.

Geer, J.H., Morokoff, P. and Greenwood, P. (1974) Sexual arousal in women: The development of a measurement device for vaginal blood volume. *Arch. Sex. Behav.* 3: 559—564.

Goldstein, M., Kant, H., Judd, L., Rice, C. and Green, R. (1971) Experience with pornography: Rapists, pedophiles, homosexuals, transsexuals, and controls. *Arch. Sex. Behav.* 1: 1—15.

Griffitt, W. (1973) Response to erotica and the projection of response to erotica in the opposite sex. *J. Exp. Res. Pers.* 6: 330—338.

Griffitt, W. (1975) Sexual experience and sexual responsiveness: Sex differences. *Arch. Sex. Behav.* 4: 529—540.

Griffitt, W., May, J. and Veitch, R. (1974) Sexual stimulation and interpersonal behavior: Heterosexual evaluative responses, visual behavior, and physical proximity. *J. Pers. Soc. Psychol.* 30: 367—377.

Hariton, E.B. and Singer, J.L. (1974) Women's fantasies during sexual intercourse: Normative and theoretical implications. *J. Consult. Clin. Psychol.* 42: 313—322.

Howard, J.L., Reifler, C.B. and Liptzin, M.B. (1971) Effects of exposure to pornography. In: *Technical Report of the Commission on Obscenity and Pornography*, Vol 8, pp: 97—132. (U.S. Government Printing Office, Washington, D.C.)

Hunt, M. (1974) *Sexual Behavior in the 1970's*. (Playboy, Chicago.)

Jong, E. (1973) *Fear of Flying*. (Holt, Rinehart and Winston, New York.)

Jovanovic, U.J. (1971) The recording of physiological evidence of genital arousal in human males and females. *Arch. Sex. Behav.* 1: 309—320.

Kempton, M. (1970) A feelthy commission. *The New York Review of Books* 15 (9): 24—25.

Kinsey, A.C., Pomeroy, W.B., Martin, C.E. and Gebhard, P.H. (1953) *Sexual Behavior in the Human Female*. (Saunders, Philadelphia.)

Laws, D.R. and Rubin, H.B. (1969) Instructional control of an autonomic sexual response. *J. Appl. Behav. Anal.* 2: 93—99.

Levitt, E.E. and Hinesley, R.K. (1967) Some factors in the valences of erotic visual stimuli. *J. Sex Res.* 3: 63—68.

Lisk, R.D. (1970) Mechanisms regulating sexual activity in mammals. *J. Sex Res.* 6: 220—228.

Mann, J., Sidman, J. and Starr, S. (1971) Effects of erotic films on sexual behavior of married couples. In: *Technical Report of the Commission on Obscenity and Pornography*, Vol 8, pp: 170—254. (U.S. Government Printing Office, Washington, D.C.)

Masters, W.H. and Johnson, V. (1966) *Human Sexual Response.* (Little Brown, Boston.)

McClelland, D.C. (1965) Toward a theory of motive acquisition. *Am. Psychol.* 20: 321—333.

McConaghy, N. (1974) Penile volume responses to moving and still pictures of male and female nudes. *Arch. Sex. Behav.* 3: 565—570.

Mosher, D.L. (1966) The development and multitrait-multimethod matrix analysis of three measures of three aspects of guilt. *J. Consult. Psychol.* 30: 25—29.

Mosher, D.L. (1971) Psychological reactions to pornographic films. In: *Technical Report of the Commission on Obscenity and Pornography*, Vol 8, pp: 255—312. (U.S. Government Printing Office, Washington, D.C.)

Pirke, K.M., Kockott, G. and Dittmar, F. (1974) Psychosexual stimulation and plasma testosterone in man. *Arch. Sex. Behav.* 3: 577—584.

Reed, J.P. and Reed, R.S. (1972) P.R.U.D.E.S. (Pornography research using direct erotic stimuli). *J. Sex Res.* 8: 237—246.

Schmidt, G. (1974) *Sex Behavior: Current Research Report.* Paper presented at the Institute for Sex Research, Bloomington, Indiana.

Schmidt, G. and Sigusch, V. (1970) Sex differences in responses to psychosexual stimulation by films and slides. *J. Sex Res.* 6: 268—283.

Schmidt, G. and Sigusch, V. (1973) Women's sexual arousal. In: (J. Zubin and J. Money, Eds.), *Contemporary Sexual Behavior: Critical Issues in the 1970's*, pp: 117—143. (Johns Hopkins University Press, Baltimore.)

Schmidt, G., Sigusch, V. and Meyberg, V. (1969) Psychosexual stimulation in men: Emotional reactions, changes of sex behavior, and measures of conservative attitudes. *J. Sex Res.* 5: 199—217.

Schmidt, G., Sigusch, V. and Schäfer, S. (1973) Responses to reading erotic stories: Male-female differences. *Arch. Sex. Behav.* 2: 181—199.

Sigusch, V., Schmidt, G., Reinfeld, A. and Wiedemann-Sutor, I. (1970). Psychosexual stimulation: Sex differences. *J. Sex Res.* 6: 10—24.

Wallace, D.H. and Wehmer, G. (1972) Evaluation of visual erotica by sexual liberals and conservatives. *J. Sex Res.* 8: 147—153.

Zajonc, R.B. (1968) Attitudinal effects of mere exposure. *J. Pers. Soc. Psychol. Monogr.* suppl. 9: 1—27.

Zuckerman, M. (1971) Physiological measures of sexual arousal in the human. *Psychol. Bull.* 75: 347—356.

CHAPTER 25

Puberty: physical maturation and sexual behavior

HEINO F.L. MEYER-BAHLBURG

1. INTRODUCTION

Puberty denotes the developmental period of attaining the capacity for reproduction. It is a time of rapid conspicuous changes in body size and appearance which are associated with the maturation of internal reproductive structures and based on major alterations of endocrine function. Beyond the somatic transition from childhood to adulthood, puberty — in western indus trialized societies — marks the onset of adolescence, the period of 'growing up' towards adult status in social, psychological and legal terms. Adolescence sets the stage for the development of sexual behavior as a function of both the somatic and psychosocial processes.

2. PHYSICAL MATURATION

The pubertal growth spurt

One of the major events of puberty is the growth spurt, that is, a transient increase of growth velocity or growth rate of the body, which results in the attainment of adult size. Fig. 1 illustrates this phenomenon in both sexes. The upper part of the figure shows the overall growth curves; the lower part demonstrates how the annual rate of growth falls steadily throughout childhood, picks up again rather suddenly at the time of puberty (this is the 'growth spurt') and declines to zero in later adolescence, when skeletal maturation is completed and the growth potential exhausted. Actually, there are wide interindividual variations in the slope of the growth curve, the age at onset of the pubertal spurt, the shape of this spurt, and its peak growth velocity.

Some of the variability is due to socioeconomic differences: generally, children and adolescents from higher socioeconomic levels with, thereby,

Handbook of Sexology, edited by J. Money and H. Musaph
© *Elsevier/North-Holland Biomedical Press, 1977*

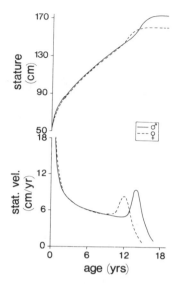

Fig. 1. Above: growth in stature in the average boy (solid line) and girl (interrupted line). Below: growth velocities at different ages of the average boy (solid line) and girl (interrupted line). (Reprinted, with permission, from Marshall, 1975.)

better nutritional conditions, tend to grow more rapidly (Tanner, 1962; Takahashi, 1966). There are also marked sex differences. Whereas both boys and girls are of comparable stature until the end of childhood, their growth curves diverge in puberty. Boys start their growth spurt about two years later than girls do. Thereby, at the onset of their own growth spurt, boys are already taller (on the average, by 10 cm) than girls usually are when they start growing faster. In addition, boys have, on the average, a higher peak growth velocity than girls. Consequently, girls who are in the midst of their pubertal growth spurt tend to be taller than boys of the same age, but when the boys catch up in pubertal development, the girls fall behind and end up with a shorter adult stature than the boys.

The growth spurt is not restricted to body size. Practically all muscular and skeletal components of the body are included (Tanner, 1975). Bone and muscle diameters increase, and boys show a considerably higher increase in number and size of muscle cells than girls do. Consequently, physical strength increases rapidly in both sexes with boys surpassing the girls (Fig. 2). Subcutaneous fat decreases in most boys and in some girls. All these changes combined result in the characteristic adult sex differences in body build: most conspicuously, the relatively greater height and broader shoulders in men, the relatively wider hips in women. There are many internal sex differences, for instance in blood chemistry, that develop in puberty but which will not be discussed here (Tanner, 1975).

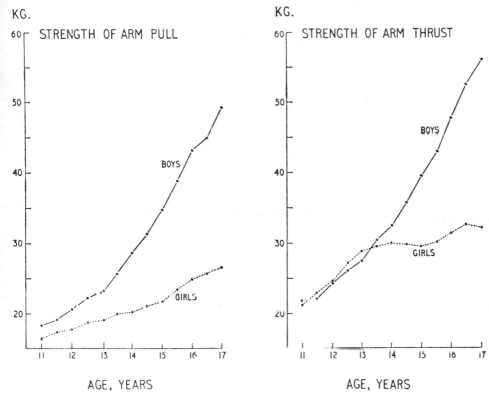

Fig. 2. Strength of arm pull and arm thrust from age 11 to 17 yrs. Mixed longitudinal data; 65—93 boys and 66—93 girls in each age group. (Reprinted, with permission, from Tanner, 1962.)

Development of secondary sexual characteristics

Another major accentuation of male and female external appearance is brought about by the development of secondary sexual characteristics. The typical sequence of events is shown in Fig. 3.

In girls (Marshall and Tanner, 1969), the first sign of puberty is usually the appearance of 'breast buds', that is, an elevation of the breast and nipple as a small mound, with the areolar diameter enlarging over the infantile status. In some girls, the appearance of pubic hair precedes breast budding, but in the majority it follows. Axillary hair typically appears about two years after the start of pubic hair growth. More or less concurrently with the external changes, internal sexual structures including the uterus grow and mature also. Uterine development must probably have reached a definitive stage for menarche, the first menstrual period, to occur which usually happens after the peak of the height spurt has been passed. However, menarche by itself does not signify the attainment of full reproductive capacity. Early menstru-

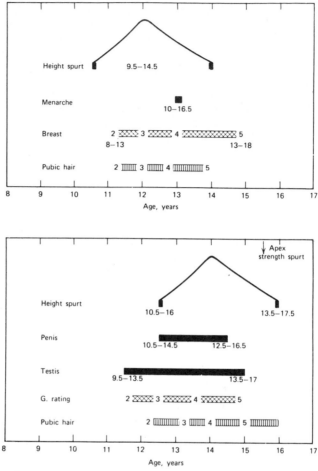

Fig. 3. Diagram of sequence of pubertal events in the average girl and boy. The numbers placed directly below the bars indicate the range of ages within which each event charted may begin and end. The numbers placed between the bars marked Breast, Pubic hair, and G. (for Genital) rating denote entry into the respective Tanner stages. The bars marked Penis and Testis represent the period of accelerated growth of these organs. (Reprinted, with permission, from Marshall and Tanner, 1970.)

al cycles are often anovulatory, that is, do not produce fertile eggs, and postmenarchal 'adolescent sterility' may last from one year to 18 months.

On the average, pubertal changes in boys begin only about 6 months later than in girls. The general impression of an overall considerably earlier maturation of girls is largely due to the fact that the growth spurt (with its concomitant somatic changes) is placed earlier in the sequence of pubertal changes in girls than in boys; the average boy has his growth peak two years later than the average girl.

The earliest sign of pubertal changes in boys (Marshall and Tanner, 1970) is a growth acceleration of testes and scrotum, often accompanied by thinning and reddening of the scrotal skin. Simultaneously or shortly after, pigmented pubic hairs start to appear. About a year later, spurts in penile growth and height begin. Coinciding with the penile growth spurt, the male internal sexual structures, for instance the seminal vesicles and the prostate, enlarge and develop. Their maturation is the prerequisite for the first ejaculation of seminal fluid which tends to occur about a year after the beginning of accelerated penile growth (Tanner, 1975). Approximately one third of all boys show a distinct enlargement of the breasts around the middle of puberty which usually regresses after about a year. About 2 years after the onset of pubic hair growth, axillary hair appears; there is also an increase in axillary sweating due to an enlargement of axillary sweat glands. At about the same time, facial hair starts to grow. It usually begins at the corners of the upper lip, then spreads out to form the mustache, later extends to the upper part of the cheeks, and finally forms the beard. More toward the end of the growth spurt, the voice breaks and deepens, often in a very gradual process. Starting in adolescence, the hair line above the forehead recedes; this process becomes more marked in adulthood.

For clinical and research purposes, several scales for the normative characterization of pubertal status have been developed. Most widely used are Tanner's photographic and descriptive standards of breast and pubic hair development in girls, and genital and pubic hair development in boys (see Tanner, 1975; colored standards are available in van Wieringen et al., 1971). The standards are comprised of 5 stages. (There is a 6th stage of pubic hair development in 80% of the males and 10% of the females.) Stage 1 is always prepubertal, stage 5 (and 6) adult (compare Fig. 3). In addition, Tanner (1975) has published centile standards for age ranges of pubertal developmental stages.

In Fig. 3, the timing given represents average values for European and North American girls and boys. Even within this relatively homogeneous group, there are wide variations in the timing of pubertal events: in girls, for instance, the onset of breast budding varies from age 8 to 13 years, and menarche ranges from age 10 to 16.5 years. In boys, the acceleration of testicular growth may start anywhere from age 9.5 to 13.5. The penile growth spurt starts between age 10.5 and 14.5 and the penis reaches adult size between age 12.5 and 16.5. The development of pubic hair may continue into adulthood. In contrast to the age at which the pubertal events occur, the sequence of events is much less variable. However, the sequence is not identical for all boys or all girls; also the rate of passing through the whole sequence varies considerably between individuals, and some sexual characteristics may mature relatively faster than others. Thus, both adolescent girls (especially between the ages of 11 and 14 years) and boys (particularly the age group 13 to 16 years) show a tremendous variation in somatic developmental status, which is one of the important factors explaining the typical problems of adolescent self-image and behavior.

The age at onset of puberty varies with many factors, genetic as well as environmental (Tanner, 1975). Consequently, there are differences even between Western European countries. For example, the current mean age of menarche is 12.5 years in Germany, 13.0 years in England, and 13.4 years in Switzerland (Bierich, 1975). Socioeconomic status has a strong influence (Tanner, 1966): menarche, for instance, occurs several months earlier in girls of higher social class than of lower social class. This has been demonstrated in as different geographic regions and racial groups as Danes or African Bantu (Burrell et al., 1961), Indians (Israel, 1959) or Rumanians (Stukovsky et al., 1967). Higher social class usually implies better living conditions, including nutrition, sleep and exercise, and these may be the major factors accounting for class differences in rates of growth in childhood as well as in timing of the growth spurt and of menarche.

Increased growth in childhood and early onset of menarche may in fact be tied together by the critical weight hypothesis according to which menarche occurs in females who have reached a 'critical weight' associated with a decline in metabolic rate and with achievement of a characteristic body composition (Frisch and Revelle, 1970). More recent studies have shown that menarche may correlate more closely with body composition than with the critical weight (Frisch et al., 1973; Osler and Crawford, 1973) and the direction of the causal relation is under investigation (Crawford and Osler, 1975)

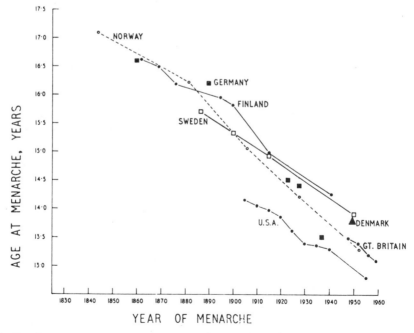

Fig. 4. Secular trend in age at menarche. (Reprinted, with permission from Tanner, 1962.)

though the validity of the findings has been questioned on statistical grounds (Johnston et al., 1975).

A particularly interesting phenomenon is the acceleration of puberty. In western countries, the onset of puberty seems to have dropped in age consistently over the last 150 years (Tanner, 1962, 1975). For example, the age of menarche has fallen from 17 to 13 years during this period (Fig. 4). Acceleration of puberty has also been demonstrated in non-Caucasian populations, for instance, in China (Tanner, 1968) or in Japan (Asayama, 1976). Most likely, this secular trend is due to the complex changes in nutrition, social conditions and public health which have been brought about by the technological development of the modern industrialized society.

Endocrine changes of puberty

Underlying the conspicuous changes of puberty in growth and sexual maturation are changes in the hypothalamic—pituitary—gonadal and —adrenal systems which lead to an increased secretion of male and female sex hormones. Since reliable methods for the measurement of pituitary, gonadal and adrenal hormones have only recently been developed, our knowledge of the complex endocrinology of puberty is still limited (for overviews see Grumbach et al., 1974; Tanner, 1975). Some of the representative findings follow.

For girls, Winter and Faiman (1973) found in a cross-sectional study that systematic changes in hormone levels coincided with the first signs of puberty. The first appearance of labial hair or of a subareolar breast bud (thelarche) was accompanied by rises in the mean plasma concentrations of FSH, estradiol and testosterone, whereas levels of serum LH did not become significantly elevated over prepubertal values before pubertal stage 3. The typical findings for girls are illustrated in Fig. 5 which shows typical serial serum concentrations of estradiol and progesterone in seven girls who are at different stages of development. It is not until several months after menarche that adult levels of estradiol appear as well as its cyclical variation which, in association with LH peaks of ovulatory magnitude and a normal luteal rise in serum progesterone levels, is the prerequisite of the final attainment of reproductive capacity.

It is noteworthy that hormonal changes predate the onset of conspicuous pubertal changes. Mixed cross-sectional/longitudinal data of the same authors (Faiman and Winter, 1974) showed small increments of gonadotropins in prepubertal girls between age 6 and 10 years, and a steep rise thereafter, whereas serum estradiol did not change noticeably before age 10.

Analogous data are available for boys. Cross-sectional studies show that serum gonadotropins in males rise gradually between age 6 and 10 — again, in the prepubertal period — whereas significant rises in plasma testosterone tend to occur after this period. Fig. 6 shows the steep increase of plasma testosterone levels in relation to the pubertal stages. These findings have been basically confirmed in a recent mixed cross-sectional/longitudinal study

358

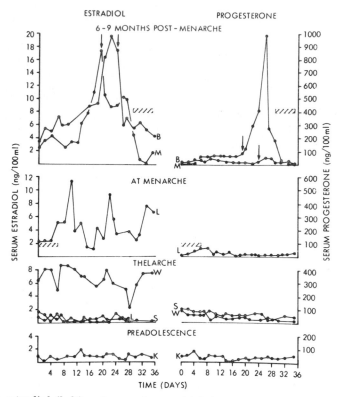

Fig. 5. Serum estradiol (left) and progesterone (right) in perimenarchal girls. The hatched bar denotes menses. The arrows indicate the time of the LH/FSH peak in the postmenarchal girls. (Reprinted, with permission, from Winter and Faiman, 1973.)

by Lee and co-workers (1974). LH levels rose throughout puberty, the initial rise of LH occurring before testosterone concentrations were significantly increased. Testosterone levels rose progressively from before the appearance of sexual hair until an adult distribution was achieved. Noticeable genital growth started before testosterone concentrations increased and continued after elevations of testosterone were no longer detectable. The question of which hormone or hormone combination causes what pubertal event cannot yet be answered in satisfactory detail except for the well-established fact that testosterone has a major role in the development of male sexual characteristics and estrogens a major role in female puberty. There are numerous gonadal hormones in both sexes and some of the pubertal changes cannot be explained without taking into account adrenal androgens whose secretion also increases around the time of puberty (Lee and Migeon, 1975).

The mechanism by which the timing of puberty is regulated is not yet understood. All available evidence points to the assumption that it is not primarily the peripheral glands, nor the pituitary gland, but the brain itself,

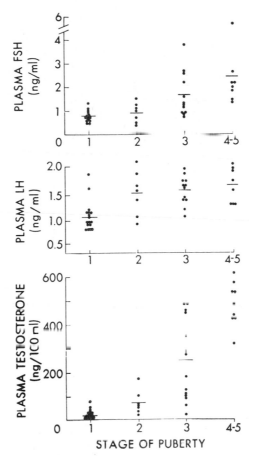

Fig. 0. Correlation between plasma FSH, LH, testosterone, and the stage of puberty. The horizontal bars indicate the mean concentration for each stage of puberty (Reprinted, with permission, from August et al., 1972.)

especially the hypothalamus, which is responsible. The currently most wide-ly shared theory is the one proposed originally by Hohlweg and Dohrn (1932) on the basis of rat experiments, according to which puberty is in-duced by a change in sensitivity to circulating sex steroids of a sexual center in the central nervous system which regulates gonadotropin secretion. In its present form, the theory states that the hypothalamic gonadotropin-regul-ating mechanism of the prepubertal individual is much more sensitive to the negative feedback effects of circulating androgens and estrogens than in the adult. Thus, the low levels of sex hormones in the prepubertal individual are sufficient to suppress the release of gonadotropin-releasing factor from the hypothalamus and thereby the secretion of FSH and LH. With the approach of puberty, the hypothalamic negative feedback receptors show a progressive decrease in sensitivity to the sex steroids. Consequently, the secretion of pi-

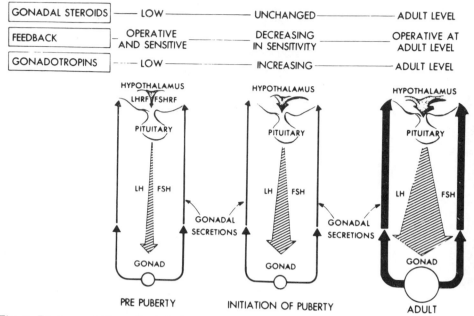

Fig. 7. Diagram of the pubertal changes in the hypothalamic–pituitary–gonadal system. LHRF and FSHRF stands for hypothalamic releasing factors of LH and FSH. (Reprinted, with permission, from Reiter and Kulin, 1972.)

tuitary gonadotropins increases, stimulating an increased production of sex hormones which, in turn, leads to the development of the secondary sex characteristics (Grumbach et al., 1974). Fig. 7 depicts this theory in graphic form. According to Grumbach and co-workers, during mid- to late puberty, a second and positive feedback mechanism matures which provides the capacity to exhibit an estrogen-induced LH surge to effect ovulation in the female.

Another pubertal event is the establishment of episodic or pulsatile secretion of gonadotropins which, during puberty only, is associated with an augmentation of secretion synchronous with sleep (Boyar et al., 1972). Since this phenomenon appears to be independent of gonadal activity, it underlines the active role of the central nervous system in the initiation of puberty.

3. SEXUAL BEHAVIOR

Sexual behavior in childhood

The potential for sexual arousal and even orgasm is probably already present in early infancy. Although it is doubtful that erections shown by male neonates are an indication of specific sexual arousal, unambiguous incidences of self-induced orgasms have been described in very young children of both sexes. Kinsey and co-workers (1948) estimated that more than half of all boys are capable of achieving orgasm at age 3 to 4 years and almost all boys could do so 3 to 5 years before reaching puberty (there are no comparable estimates for girls). In general, prepubertal boys seem to have erections more rapidly and react with arousal to a wider range of (often nonsexual) stimuli than adolescents and adults (Ramsey, 1943; Kinsey, et al., 1948); they also appear to be more capable of multiple orgasms.

Although self-exploration and self-manipulation of the genitalia are quite common in prepubertal children, masturbation in the strict sense of deliberate self-stimulation is relatively uncommon. For instance, not more than 13—16% of the boys and girls in the Kinsey samples had done so before the age of 10 (Kinsey et al., 1948, 1953). By contrast, the majority of prepubertal children have some sociosexual experience, that is, engage in sexual play activities with another partner (Table I). In the Kinsey sample, 57% of the adolescent and adult males and 48% of the females reported at least one sociosexual incident at prepubertal age. This is probably an underestimate of the real frequency because when boys were asked before puberty, 70% admitted such experiences. 10% of the males reported sociosexual experiences for age 5 years, and the percentage increased gradually to a maximum of 39% for age 12 with a slight decline afterwards. Females reported lower incidence figures. 10% admitted sociosexual experiences for age 5; the peak percentage was 14 at age 9, again followed by some decline. All these figures clearly contradict the (psychoanalytic) notion of middle childhood as the 'latency' period when sexuality is dormant.

Usually, sociosexual play in childhood is only sporadic and lacks the regularity of adolescent or adult life. The majority of these childhood sexual activities do not involve full sexual relations but are confined to exploratory sexual play (Tables II and III). On the other hand, in 55% of all males and in 17% of all females who reported any heterosexual play in childhood, coital

Table I
Incidence of sociosexual play in prepubertal children (data from Kinsey et al., 1948, 1953).

	Girls	Boys
Incidence of any sociosexual play (%)		
Report by prepubertal children	No data	70
Recall by adolescents and adults	48	57
Incidence of any heterosexual play (%)	30	40
Incidence of any homosexual play (%)		
Report by prepubertal children	No data	60
Recall by adolescents and adults	33	48

362

Table II
Heterosexual play in prepubertal children: Techniques and continuation into adolescence.
Educ. level indicates years of schooling. (Data from Kinsey et al., 1948, 1953.)

	Girls	Boys
Techniques of heterosexual play		
(% heterosexually active pop.)		
Exhibition	99	100
Manual	52	81
Oral	2	9
Vaginal insertions (finger, objects)	3	49
Coital	17	55
With adolescent/adult partners		
(at least 5 years older)	24	No data
Continuation into adolescence		
(% heterosexually active pop.)		
Petting	13	65
Coitus	8	55

	Petting	Coitus
Boys: Educ. level 0—8	77	74
Educ. level 9—12	67	54
Educ. level 13+	30	19

play, that is, an attempt to effect genital union, had been part of it and may have occurred with some frequency, particularly in boys with lower socio-economic background. In both boys and girls, there seems to be a somewhat higher frequency of homosexual than heterosexual play which is probably a

Table III
Homosexual play in prepubertal children: Techniques and continuation into adolescence.
Educ. level indicates years of schooling. (Data from Kinsey et al., 1948, 1953.)

	Girls	Boys
Techniques of homosexual play		
(% of homosexually active pop.)		
Exhibition	99	100
Manual	62	67
Anal (mainly femoral)	—	17
Vaginal insertions (finger, objects)	18	—
Oral	3	16
Continuation into adolescence	5	42
(% homosexually active pop.)		
Educ. level 0—8	No data	51
Educ. level 9—12	No data	43
Educ. level 13+	No data	23

reflection of the sex segregation typical for childhood play activities in general.

It should be emphasized that all descriptive terms used like 'homosexual play' or 'coital play' are strictly defined in terms of overt behavior and do not imply that the child who engages in some such behavior necessarily acts with the same or a similar set of motives as the adult would.

Sexual behavior in normal puberty

According to Kinsey and co-workers (1948, 1953), there are striking differences between the sexes in psychosexual development during puberty. Boys show a sudden upsurge in sexual activity which may begin a year or more before the onset of puberty is noticeable; they usually reach their life peak in terms of orgasmic frequency within a year or two after the onset of puberty. Most of this early activity is self-masturbation. For two-thirds (68%) of the boys in the Kinsey sample, self-masturbation provided the first ejaculation; for the remaining ones, nocturnal emissions and heterosexual coitus provided the first ejaculation. By age 15, 82% of the boys were experienced in masturbation to orgasm.

In girls, by contrast, the gradual and steady increase in the accumulative incidence of erotic arousal and orgasmic response which was observed before puberty continues into puberty and beyond; women do not reach their maximum rate of orgasm until their middle 20s to 30s. Of the relatively small percentage of girls in the Kinsey sample who experienced orgasm during puberty (20% by age 15), the majority (84%) used masturbation as the most important outlet. For the average male, adolescence is the age of highest orgasmic frequency with 3.4 outlets per week in the Kinsey sample whereas the corresponding figure for sexually active females (including masturbation) was around 0.5 orgasms per week.

With respect to sociosexual activities, it appears from Kinsey's data that there is a slight decrease in their incidence just before puberty. However, there is still a significant proportion of children who continue their prepubertal heterosexual or homosexual activities into puberty (Tables II and III), particularly in the lower educational levels. The majority of adolescents have their first coital experience considerably later than their first ejaculation or menarche, and the average female has this experience later than the average male. This is the case, not only in Western societies, but also elsewhere as shown in Japanese data from 1959—60 (Figs 8, 9). Although the various studies in Western countries are not strictly comparable because of sampling problems and other methodological differences, they show similar trends. In the U.S. samples of Kinsey and co-workers (1948, 1953), 24% of the males and 3% of the females had coital experience by 15 years of age. In Schofield's (1965) survey of English teenagers, 30% of the males aged 17 to 19 years and 16% of the females of this age reported coital experience. Sorensen's (1973) study in the U.S. registered premarital intercourse in 59%

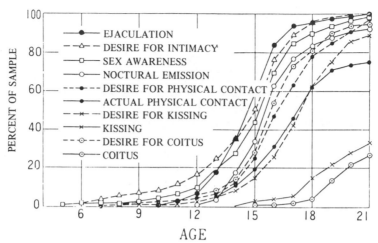

Fig. 8. Male Japanese students' sexual development and experience: accumulative incidence. (Reprinted, with permission, from Asayama, 1975.)

of the boys and 45% of the girls aged 15 to 19 years. In general, the more recent studies appear to show a decrease in age at first coital experience, particularly for females so that the sex difference is shrinking (see data and references in Schmidt and Sigusch, 1972).

Kinsey and co-workers (1948, 1953) had demonstrated a strong influence of social class (educational level) on psychosexual development. Fig. 10 gives a more recent illustration of such factors in an American national random sample of both black and white female subjects. Apparently, intercourse ac-

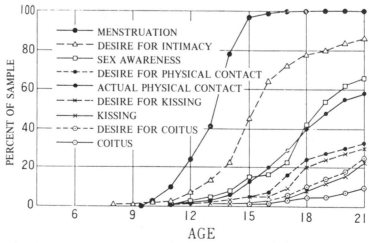

Fig. 9. Female Japanese students' sexual development and experience: accumulative incidence. (Reprinted, with permission, form Asayama, 1975.)

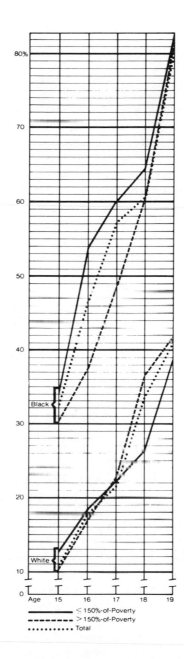

Fig. 10. Never-married young women 15—19 years of age who have had intercourse, for single years of age, by race and poverty status (100%-of-poverty is the poverty level as defined by the US government). (Reprinted, with permission, from Kantner and Zelnik, 1972.)

tivity starts earlier in low socioeconomic strata of society than in higher ones and earlier in blacks than in whites even when socioeconomic level is controlled (Kantner and Zelnik, 1972).

Unfortunately, there are no studies available that correlate directly assessed somatic and endocrine changes in puberty with sexual behavior. From the studies reported to date, it is very apparent that puberty by itself does not determine the start of mature sexual behavior. Socioeconomic status, sex role definitions, technological and ideological changes of society — all these factors have a strong influence on psychosexual development. Most likely, psychosexual competence is not an innate capacity that is activated during puberty, but the end result of a complex social learning process involving childhood as well as adolescence (Gagnon and Simon, 1973).

Still, puberty has an important influence of its own. To a large extent, this influence is due to the somatic and endocrine changes. Adolescents have to form a new body image; they focus much attention on differences in physique because of the great variability of the rate of pubertal development. The degree of masculinity or femininity of appearance in combination with stature strongly affects the adolescent's attractiveness to and acceptance by the other sex. Moreover, the adults' responses to and expectations from adolescents change with the latters' degree of physical maturation. Size and musculature determine, especially in boys, how much they can engage in athletic and other physical activities. Thus, pubescent girls and boys enter multiple new social roles that form the context of their psychosexual development.

There is also evidence that the sex hormones do not only prepare the physical apparatus for mature sexual behavior but that they do have direct effects on the nervous system, and thereby on sexual behavior, as well. It is unlikely that mature sexual behavior patterns would develop as easily without these (hormonal) effects. Thus, the role of puberty for psychosexual development may well be largely permissive, that is, puberty may be necessary for mature sexual behavior to occur but is not sufficient in itself to bring about mature psychosexual development. Both the social and hormonal influences on sexuality will be discussed in subsequent chapters.

Sexual behavior in pubertal disorders

Most adolescents and adults have some expectations of what girls or boys in their early teens should look like or behave like. Deviations from the usual timetable of pubertal development occasion the differentiation of several variables that are usually highly correlated: chronological age, physique age, psychosocial age — the latter of which can be broken down conveniently into academic age, recreational age and psychosexual age (Money and Clopper, 1974). In errors of pubertal timing, physique age is advanced or retarded in relation to chronological age. It depends largely on the particular environment — social pressures from peers and adults, whether or not and to what extent the psychosocial age will coincide with or deviate from the physique age on the one hand and the chronological age on the other. Usually, the adolescent will be aware of these discrepancies. The degree of his or her emotional response, and the quality of coping will depend largely on support from the outside.

Precocious puberty

It is somewhat arbitrary where the line is drawn between 'early normal' and pathologically early or precocious puberty. Many endocrinologists will agree with Bierich's (1975) definition by which the term sexual precocity is used for girls, if they show signs of sexual maturity before their 6th birthday (and menarche before their 8th birthday) and for boys, if signs of sexual maturity appear before their 8th birthday. Precocious puberty can be secondary to a variety of more general medical abnormalities, including a lesion in the brain or the peripheral endocrine glands. It can also be idiopathic or spontaneous without any other physical disorder. A girl with precocious puberty typically has to cope with an early growth spurt putting her on the growth level of other children who are 2 or 3 years older than her chronological age, so that a 6 year-old girl may be as tall as somebody who is 8 or 9 years old. At the same time, she will begin to develop pubic and axillary hair, breast enlargement and menstruation.

One of the major concerns of parents and teachers of precociously developing children is often the fear of an early sexual interest and behavior. In a follow-up study of 15 girls with idiopathic precocious puberty (age 10—25 years) by Money and Walker (1971), the only study that deals with this particular issue, masturbation and sex play did not appear to be increased, although normal sexual curiosity occurred more or less consistent with age and independent from the precocious puberty. Premarital intercourse did not occur earlier than normally expected (age 17 years and up), with the exception of one girl who became pregnant at age 11 and was the only mother in the sample. Thus, precocious sexual behavior is not a frequent concomitant of precocious puberty. This result is in close agreement with studies on 'early normal' maturing girls who showed only a slight tendency to start their sexual activity earlier than their peers (Kinsey et al., 1953).

Precocious puberty occurs less frequently in boys than in girls. The overall psychosocial effects in boys with precocious puberty are similar to the ones in girls. Parental fear is even higher than with girls that their sexual behavior will become a problem at an early age; however, this fear seems to be largely unwarranted. Studies of the psychological development of precocious puberty in boys have shown that sociosexual behavior is typically only moderately ahead of chronological age, although erotic fantasies and masturbation may occur somewhat earlier than usual. Psychosexual development was found to be normal for boys, with no signs of homosexuality (Money and Alexander, 1969; Money and Ehrhardt, 1972).

Studies on 'early normal' maturing boys, in contrast to studies on similar girls, have shown that their sexual behavior starts noticeably earlier and remains on a higher frequency level than that of their peers (Kinsey et al., 1948).

Delayed puberty

The diagnosis of idiopathic delayed puberty is as much a matter of convention as the definition of idiopathic precocious puberty (Prader, 1975). Most boys aged 15 or 16 who are not yet in puberty will be unhappy and many of them seek professional help. Just by statistical definition, there must be the same percentage of girls with delayed puberty but relatively much fewer of them come to medical attention because they do not seem to suffer as much as boys.

Most clinicians seem to agree that the onset of puberty two or three years after the median age justifies concern and the label 'delayed puberty'. There are many physical conditions that may cause delayed onset of puberty, and the most common type is idiopathic or constitutional delay of puberty. The delayed adolescent faces multiple disadvantages. In comparison with his peers, he falls behind in size and strength, and faces teasing and sometimes physical harassment by peers. If he is not able to keep up with his peers in some way, he may withdraw which usually implies missing out on all the typical experiences of one's age group and having less of an opportunity of acquiring the teenage skills of same-sex socializing and heterosexual contact and bonding. These transient developmental deficiencies may have long-term effects. Several longitudinal studies in which late maturers were compared to early (not precocious) or normal maturers, like the classical California Adolescent Growth Study, found not only the described disadvantages of late pubertal development during adolescence (Jones and Bayley, 1950), but also relative delays in their career status and 'organizational leadership' (Ames, 1957) as well as in marriage and number of children (Peskin, 1967) in adulthood. Clinical studies of severe forms of delayed puberty also show psychological and psychosexual delay to be present (Lewis et al., 1973; Money and Wolff, 1974) though it is difficult to disentangle the influence of pubertal delay per se from other contributing factors, especially short stature.

Induced puberty

In the case of idiopathic precocious and delayed puberty, only timing is in error. The hypothalamic—pituitary—gonadal feedback system is functioning normally although its action is starting too early or too late. In other cases the defect is more permanent so that puberty will never occur spontaneously. For those patients, it becomes of utmost importance for their psychological growth and development that puberty is induced by a sex-appropriate hormone regimen.

Our clinical experience has been that there are no dramatic uncontrollable directly CNS-mediated behavioral effects of sex hormone treatment, except for erections in boys. Usually, for both boys and girls, sex hormone treatment constitutes a boost to morale especially when the body begins changing visibly.

Often an upswing in mood and assertiveness occurs, and later also in sexual feelings, sexual fantasies, and interests. Hypopituitary or hypogonadal male patients usually do not assume full heterosexual relations without hormone treatment. Particularly important is the timing of the induction of puberty. If the appropriate sex hormone treatment can be started at a time when the patient's peers go into puberty, psychosocial as well as psychosexual development seem to be largely normal. The more treatment is delayed, the greater is the chance of maldevelopment. The evidence for this issue comes from studies of Turner's syndrome (Money and Mittenthal, 1970; Perheentupa et al., 1974), hypogonadism in males (Money and Alexander, 1967; Bobrow et al., 1971), and hypopituitarism (Huffer, 1964; Meyer-Bahlburg, 1975; Money and Clopper, 1975). Induction of puberty after age 20 often does not lead to normal psychosexual development. A number of older (hypopituitary) patients have even refused to start sex hormone treatment or ceased taking it later. It is unclear if this negative reaction towards treatment is due to a generally poorer physiological response to exogenous sex hormones (Zachman and Prader, 1970) or to a psychological rigidity and contentment with the patient's particular status at that age.

Principles of psychological management of disorders in puberty have been described in detail elsewhere (Ehrhardt and Meyer-Bahlburg, 1975; Money, 1968; Pinch et al., 1974).

In general, the clinical evidence from pubertal disorders strongly supports an interactive view in the theory of psychosexual development: physical and hormonal changes are necessary for normal psychosocial and psychosexual development in adolescence, but even if they are present, normal psychosexual development is dependent on the social integration of the individual in his society and especially in his peer group.

4. SUMMARY

Puberty is the developmental period of attaining the capacity for reproduction. It involves the adolescent growth spurt and the development of the secondary sex characteristics including the maturation of internal reproductive structures. These changes are caused by hormonal factors. The complex endocrine mechanism of puberty is not yet fully understood.

Sexual behavior is already present in childhood but its quantity and quality changes in adolescence. Puberty is only one factor among several others that contribute to psychosexual development. Studies of the psychological consequences of pubertal disorders lend support to the assumption that the physical and hormonal changes of puberty as well as social learning are necessary for the development of mature sexual behavior.

BIBLIOGRAPHY

Ames, R. (1957) Physical maturing among boys as related to adult social behavior. *Calif. J. Educat. Res.* 8: 69—75.

Asayama, S. (1976) Sexual behavior in Japanese students: comparisons between 1974, 1960 and 1952. *Arch. Sex. Behav.* 5, in press.

Asayama, S. (1975) Adolescent sex development and adult sex behavior in Japan. *J. Sex Res.* 11: 91—112.

August, G.P., Grumbach, M.M. and Kaplan, S.L. (1972) Hormonal changes in puberty: III. Correlation of plasma testosterone, LH, FSH, testicular size, and bone age with male pubertal development. *J. Clin. Endocrinol. Metab.* 34: 319—326.

Bierich, J.R. (1975) Sexual precocity. In: (J.R. Bierich, Ed.) *Disorders of Puberty, Clinics in Endocrinology and Metabolism*, Vol. 4, No. 1, (W.B. Saunders, London, Philadelphia, Toronto) pp. 107—142.

Bobrow, N.A., Money, J. and Lewis, V.G. (1971) Delayed puberty, eroticism and sense of smell: a psychological study of hypogonadotropinism, osmatic and anosmatic (Kallmann's syndrome). *Arch. Sex. Behav.* 1: 329—344.

Boyar, R., Finkelstein, J., Roffwarg, H., Kapen, S., Weitzman, E. and Hellman, L. (1972) Synchronization of LH secretion with sleep during puberty. *New Engl. J. Med.* 287: 582—586.

Burrell, R.J.W., Healy, M.J.R. and Tanner, J.M. (1961) Age at menarche in South African Bantu schoolgirls living in the Transkei Reserve. *Hum. Biol.* 33: 250—261.

Crawford, J.D. and Osler, D.C. (1975) Body composition at menarch: the Frisch-Revelle hypothesis revisited. *Pediatrics* 56: 449—458.

Ehrhardt, A.A. and Meyer-Bahlburg, H.F.L. (1975) Psychological correlates of abnormal pubertal development. In: (J.R. Bierich, Ed.) *Disorders of Puberty, Clinics in Endocrinology and Metabolism*, Vol. 4, No. 1, (W.B. Saunders, London, Philadelphia, Toronto) pp. 207—222.

Faiman, C. and Winter, J.S.D. (1974) Gonadotropins and sex hormone patterns in puberty: clinical data. In: (M.M. Grumbach, G.D. Grave and F.E. Mayer, Eds.) *The Control of the Onset of Puberty*, (John Wiley & Sons, New York, London, Sydney, Toronto) pp. 32—61.

Frisch, R.E. and Revelle, R. (1970) Height and weight at menarche and a hypothesis of critical body weight and adolescent events. *Science* 169: 397—398.

Frisch, R.E., Revelle, R. and Cook, S. (1973) Components of weight at menarche and the initiation of the adolescent growth spurt in girls: Estimated total water, lean body weight and fat. *Hum. Biol.* 45: 469—483.

Gagnon, J.H. and Simon, W. (1973) *Sexual conduct. The social sources of human sexuality.* (Aldine, Chicago.)

Grumbach, M.M., Grave, G.D. and Mayer, F.E. (Eds.) (1974) *The control of the onset of puberty.* (John Wiley & Sons, New York, London, Sydney, Toronto.)

Hohlweg, W. and Dohrn, M. (1932) Über die Beziehungen zwischen Hypophysenvorderlappen und Keimdrüsen. *Klin. Wochenschr.* 11: 233—235.

Huffer, V., Scott, W.H., Conner, T.B. and Lovice, H. (1964) Psychological studies of adult male patients with sexual infantilism before and after androgen therapy. *Ann. Intern. Med.* 61: 255—268.

Israel, S. (1959) The onset of menstruation in Indian women. *J. Obstet. Gynecol. Br. Emp.* 66: 311—316.

Johnston, F.E., Roche, A.F., Schell, L.M. and Wettenhall, H.N.B. (1975) Critical weight at menarche. *Am. J. Dis. Child.* 129: 19—23.

Jones, M.C. and Bayley, N. (1950) Physical maturing among boys as related to behavior. *J. Educat. Psychol.* 41: 129—148.

Kantner, J.F. and Zelnik, M. (1972) Sexual experience of young unmarried women in the United States. *Fam. Plan. Perspect.* 4: 9—18.

Kinsey, A.C., Pomeroy, W.B. and Martin, C.E. (1948) *Sexual Behavior in the Human Male*. (W.B. Saunders, Philadelphia, London.)

Kinsey, A.C., Pomeroy, W.B., Martin, C.E. and Gebhard, P.H. (1953) *Sexual Behavior in the Human Female*. (W.B. Saunders, Philadelphia, London.)

Lee, P.A., Jaffe, R.B. and Midgley, A.R. Jr. (1974) Serum gonadotropin, testosterone and prolactin concentrations throughout puberty in boys: a longitudinal study. *J. Clin. Endocrinol. Metab.* 39: 664—672.

Lee, P.A. and Migeon, C.J. (1975) Puberty in boys: correlation of plasma levels of gonadotropins (LH, FSH), androgens (testosterone, androstenedione, dehydroepiandrosterone and its sulfate), estrogens (estrone and estradiol) and progestins (progesterone and 17-hydroxyprogesterone). *J. Clin. Endocrinol. Metab.* 41: 556—562.

Lewis, V.G., Money, J. and Bobrow, N.A. (1973) Psychologic study of boys with short stature retarded osseous growth, and normal age of pubertal onset. *Adolescence* 8: 445—454.

Marshall, W.A. (1975) Growth and sexual maturation in normal puberty. In: (J.R. Bierich, Ed.), *Disorders of Puberty, Clinics in Endocrinology and Metabolism*, Vol. 4, No. 1, (W.B. Saunders, London, Philadelphia, Toronto) pp. 3—25.

Marshall, W.A. and Tanner, J.M. (1970) Variations in the patterns of pubertal changes in boys. *Arch. Dis. Child.* 45: 13—23.

Marshall, W.A. and Tanner, J.M. (1969) Variations in pattern of pubertal changes in girls. *Arch. Dis. Child.* 44: 291—303.

Masica, D.N., Money, J. and Ehrhardt, A.A. (1971) Fetal feminization and female gender identity in the testicular feminizing syndrome of androgen insensitivity. *Arch. Sex. Behav.* 1: 131—142.

Meyer-Bahlburg, H.F.L. (1975) Sexuality in idiopathic hypopituitarism. Paper presented at 1st Annu. Meet. Int. Acad. Sex Res., Stony Brook, N.Y., Sept. 12—14, 1975.

Money, J. (1968) *Sex Errors of the Body*. (Johns Hopkins Press, Baltimore.)

Money, J. and Alexander, D. (1967) Eroticism and sexual function in developmental anorchia and hyporchia with pubertal failure. *J. Sex Res.* 3: 31—47.

Money, J. and Alexander, D. (1969) Psychosexual development and absence of homosexuality in males with precocious puberty. *J. Nerv. Ment. Dis.* 148: 111—123.

Money, J. and Clopper, R.R. (1974) Psychosocial and psychosexual aspects of errors of pubertal onset and development. *Hum. Biol.* 46: 173—181.

Money, J. and Clopper, R.R. (1975) Postpubertal psychosexual function in post-surgical male hypopituitarism. *J. Sex Res.* 11: 25—38.

Money, J. and Ehrhardt, A.A. (1972) *Man & Woman, Boy & Girl*. (Johns Hopkins University Press, Baltimore, London.)

Money, J. and Mittenthal, S. (1970) Lack of personality pathology in Turner's Syndrome: Relation to cytogenetics, hormones and physique. *Behav. Genet.* 1: 43—56.

Money, J. and Walker, P.A. (1971) Psychosexual development, maternalism, nonpromiscuity, and body image in 15 females with precocious puberty. *Arch. Sex. Behav.* 1: 45—60.

Money, J. and Wolff, G. (1974) Late puberty, retarded growth and reversible hyposomatotropinism (psychosocial dwarfism). *Adolescence* 9: 121—134.

Osler, D.C. and Crawford, J.D. (1973) Examination of the hypothesis of a critical weight at menarche in ambulatory and bedridden mentally retarded girls. *Pediatrics* 51: 675—679.

Perheentupa, J., Lenko, H.L., Nevalainen, J., Niittymäki, M., Söderholm, A. and Taipale, V. (1974) Hormonal therapy in Turner's Syndrome: growth and psychological aspects. *Pediatria XIV*. (XIV (1974) Int. Congr. Pediat.) Vol. 5, Growth and Development. Endocrinology. (Buenos Aires, Editorial Medica Panamericana, S.A.) pp. 121—127.

Peskin, H. (1967) Pubertal onset and ego functioning. *J. Abnorm. Psychol.* 72: 1—15.

Pinch, L., Aceto, T., Jr. and Meyer-Bahlburg, H.F.L. (1974) Cryptorchidism. In: (L.C. King, Ed.) *Pediatric Urology, The Urologic Clinics of North America*, Vol. 1, No. 1

(W.B. Saunders, Philadelphia, London, Toronto) pp. 573—592.

Prader, A. (1975) Delayed adolescence. In: (J.R. Bierich, Ed.) *Disorders of Puberty, Clinics in Endocrinology and Metabolism*, Vol. 4, No. 1 (W.B. Saunders, London, Philadelphia, Toronto) pp. 143—155.

Ramsey, G.V. (1943) The sexual development of boys. *Am. J. Psychol.* 56: 217—233.

Reiter, E.O. and Kulin, H.E. (1972) Sexual maturation in the female: Normal development and precocious puberty. *Pediat. Clin. North Am.* 19 (3) 581—603.

Schmidt, G. and Sigusch, V. (1972) Changes in sexual behavior among young males and females between 1960—1970. *Arch. Sex. Behav.* 2: 27—45.

Schofield, M. (1965) *The Sexual Behavior of Young People*. (Longmans, Green & Co. Ltd., London.)

Sorensen, R. (1973) *Adolescent sexuality in contemporary America*. (World Publishing, New York.)

Stukovsky, R., Valsik, J.A. and Bulai-Stirbu, M. (1967) Family size and menarcheal age in Constanza, Roumania. *Hum. Biol.* 39: 277—283.

Takahashi, E. (1966) Growth and environmental factors in Japan. *Hum. Biol.* 38: 112—130.

Tanner, J.M. (1975) Growth and endocrinology of the adolescent. In: (L.I. Gardner, Ed.), *Endocrine and Genetic Diseases of Childhood and Adolescence*, 2nd edn. (W.B. Saunders, Philadelphia, London, Toronto) pp. 14—64.

Tanner, J.M. (1968) Earlier maturation in man. *Sci. Am.* 218: 21—26.

Tanner, J.M. (1966) Growth and physique in different populations of mankind. In: (P.T. Baker and J.J. Weiner, Eds.) *The Biology of Human Adaptability*, (Clarendon Press, Oxford) pp. 45—66.

Tanner, J.M. (1962) *Growth at Adolescence*, 2nd edn, (Blackwell Scientific Publications, Oxford).

van Wieringen, J.C., Wafelbakker, F., Verbrugge, H.P. and de Haas, J.H. (1971) *Growth Diagrams 1965, Netherlands*. (Wolters-Noordhoff, Groningen, Netherlands.)

Winter, J.S.D. and Faiman, C. (1973) The development of cyclic pituitary-gonadal function in adolescent females. *J. Clin. Endocrinol. Metab.* 37: 714—718.

Zachmann, M. and Prader, A. (1970) Anabolic and androgenic effect of testosterone in sexually immature boys and its dependency on growth hormone. *J. Clin. Endocrinol. Metab.* 30: 85—95.

SECTION V

Hormones and sexual behavior in adulthood

Section coordinator: J. Herbert

CHAPTER 26

Introduction

J. HERBERT

Clinical, scientific and social needs now demand that our knowledge of sexual behavior shall be based firmly on experimental evidence. The realization that hormones play a major part in controlling both the levels and direction of sexual activity was an epoch-making event in the science of sexual behavior. The chapters in this section survey the rapidly growing body of knowledge defining the way these chemical substances regulate behavior, or are themselves regulated and modified by behavioral events in the animal's immediate or past experience. One chapter deals also with the role of odoriferous substances or pheromones which influence sexual behavior.

Although workers familiar with the behavior of rodents, carnivores and ungulates have for many years acknowledged the operation of endocrine factors in determining sexual behavior, more recent studies on nonhuman primates have shown that they, too, are influenced by hormones to a degree thought unlikely only a few years ago. Extension of this knowledge to man has already begun, and is likely to form a major area of investigation in the years to come. Both similarities and differences in the relationship between hormones and sexual behavior in primates and nonprimates are revealed by the chapters in this section; awareness of these findings is critically important for anyone seeking to understand, or treat, aberrations in human sexuality.

Handbook of Sexology, edited by J. Money and H. Musaph
© *Elsevier/North-Holland Biomedical Press, 1977*

CHAPTER 27

Regulation of sexual behavior by hormones in male nonprimates

INGEBORG L. WARD

1. INTRODUCTION

The male's function in the reproductive cycle of a species often has been underrated by those reproductive physiologists who consider the male contribution merely as one of supplier of the sperm needed to fertilize the female ova. Only recently has there developed a fuller appreciation of the multiple purposes fulfilled by the often elaborate behavioral mechanism through which the male finally deposits sperm into the vagina of the female. In many species, various components of the male's courtship and copulatory pattern have been shown to constitute critical stimuli triggering discrete neuro-endocrine changes within the female essential toward making her a reproducing organism. Two examples will suffice to illustrate this point.

The typical rat copulatory sequence, emitted over a 10—20 minute period, involves repeated posterior mounting of the female and a series of 4—10 intromission responses (vaginal penetrations) before culminating in ejaculation. While this may appear to be a inefficient behavioral pattern, since only the final response attains the objective of sperm emission, closer inspection reveals that without the stimulation provided by repeated penile thrusts to vaginal—cervical receptors the probability of achieving pregnancy is reduced (Adler, 1969; Adler et al., 1970). Twenty percent of female rats in whom ejaculation is preceded by 0—2 intromissions become pregnant as compared to 84% receiving 6—19 intromissions. Penile thrusting is believed to trigger cervical opening, thus facilitating sperm transport, as well as activating release of progesterone, the ovarian hormone needed for implantation of the fertilized ovum unto the uterine wall.

Preparation of this article was supported in part by Grant HD-04688 from the National Institute of Child Health and Human Development.

Handbook of Sexology, edited by J. Money and H. Musaph
© *Elsevier/North-Holland Biomedical Press, 1977*

Similarly, in many animal species, including carnivores, marsupials and insectivores, ovulation does not occur spontaneously. Rather such 'reflex ovulators' require mechanical stimulation of vaginal—cervical receptors to induce release of sufficient gonadotropic hormone to catapult the mature ova out of the ovary (Everett, 1961; Diakow, 1971).

Male reproductive behavior patterns are largely under the control of testicular hormones. However, the mechanisms by which androgen influences sexual behavior vary considerably at different stages of ontogenetic development. During prenatal and in some species neonatal development, androgenic steroids are secreted by the fetal testes and exert an organizing action. The presence of these hormones differentiates the tissues destined to mediate adult sexual behavior in a masculine direction. Associated with the induction of a male potential is a concomitant suppression of female behavior. In the absence of gonadal steroids, which is the natural condition in the case of genetic females, the reverse occurs, namely, organization of the female potential and suppression of the male. In adult organisms the primary function of these same steroids is to activate the behavioral potentials established during the perinatal differentiation stages (see reviews by Young, 1961; Phoenix et al., 1968; Valenstein, 1968; Ward, 1974). It is the goal of this chapter to discuss the activational rather than organizational role of testicular hormones in the mediation of sexual behavior in adult males.

2. TESTOSTERONE AND MALE COPULATORY BEHAVIOR

Although weak sexual responses occasionally are exhibited by prepuberal males of many species, the appearance of the full functional pattern coincides with puberty and the second onset of testicular hormone secretion. The activation and dependence of the male's sexual drive on testicular hormones ranks among the first and most thoroughly investigated problems in the history of sex research. As a result, a number of general principles can be enumerated which apply to a wide range of mammalian species.

Castration of adult males

A decline in copulatory behavior is discernible soon after gonadectomy (Stone, 1927; 1932; Beach and Pauker, 1949; Grunt and Young, 1952; Lincoln et al., 1972). This behavioral deficit can be alleviated if exogenous testosterone is administered (Moore and Price, 1938; Stone, 1939; Sollenberger and Hamilton, 1939; Seward, 1940; Beach and Pauker, 1949). The decrease in sexual potency as well as the restorative effects of androgen therapy are relatively gradual processes. Suppression of behavior following hormone withdrawal may require weeks, months, or even years to be fully accomplished. Furthermore, while there is an overall decrease in sexual behavior following gonadectomy, all components of the male copulatory pattern are not equally vulnerable (Stone, 1939; Beach and Holz-Tucker, 1949; Beach and Pauker, 1949; Grunt and Young, 1953; Whalen et al., 1961; Davidson, 1966a). Generally, ejaculation * is the first response to drop from the male's behavioral repertoire, followed more gradually by the intromission pattern and, finally, by the lower-order mounting responses. Low degrees of mounting may persist indefinitely in a large percentage of castrates. Following androgen replacement, reinstatement of the various components of the total pattern occurs in the reverse order of their disappearance with larger quantities of androgen being required to restore ejaculation than intromission or mounting (Beach and Holz-Tucker, 1949; Grunt and Young, 1953).

Exogenous testosterone treatment of adult males

There is a limited amount of evidence to indicate that the rate and quality of male sexual behavior is directly proportional to circulating androgen titers. If endogenous testosterone levels of intact rats or rabbits are augmented by injections of testosterone propionate, the time required for ejaculation to occur is decreased and the total number of ejaculations emitted per unit of time is increased (Beach, 1942a; Cheng and Casida, 1949; Cheng et al., 1950). Indeed, in the rat, male sexual excitability may be so intensified that copulation is attempted with such low-incentive animals as juvenile males, nonreceptive females, or anesthetized estrous females (Beach, 1942a). In addition, as a few castration and replacement studies suggest, with sufficiently high androgen therapy, copulatory behavior not only is restored but exceeds precastration levels. Beach and Holz-Tucker (1949) injected various dosages of testosterone propionate into gonadectomized male rats. A minimum dosage of 50—70 μg/day was required to maintain behavior at precastration levels. Dosages below that resulted in deterioration of behavior, while higher dosages potentiated performance well above precastration base line levels. Similar effect have been obtained with hamster (Beach and Pauker, 1949). However, the potentiating effect of a high androgen dosage cannot be demonstrated using castrated guinea pigs (Grunt and Young, 1952), nor is it a universal finding in studies utilizing rats (Beach and Fowler, 1959; Larsson, 1966a).

Persistence of copulation following castration

Although the quantity and quality of copulatory behavior decreases markedly following castration, there is considerable variability among males with regard to the length of time required before the behavior is persistently ab-

---

* The term, ejaculation, used within the context of this chapter refers solely to the final behavioral component of the male copulatory pattern and need not necessarily be accompanied by seminal emission.

sent. Some individuals within a species cease to copulate altogether within a few days while others continue to exhibit even the ejaculatory pattern for a year or more after castration (Stone, 1927; Beach and Holz, 1946; Beach and Pauker, 1949; Grunt and Young, 1953; Rosenblatt and Aronson, 1958a, b; Davidson, 1966a; Beach, 1970). This variability exists despite a relatively uniform drop in plasma testosterone titers to undetectable levels within six hours of gonadectomy (Resko, 1970; Resko and Phoenix, 1972). One explanation for such an apparent paradox is that, in the absence of gonadal testosterone, the adrenal cortex might increase its output of other androgens sufficiently to support continued copulation. However, this does not appear to be the case since simultaneous castration and adrenalectomy of male hamsters (Warren and Aronson, 1956; 1957), cats (Cooper and Aronson, 1958), dogs (Schwartz and Beach, 1954; Beach, 1970), or rats (Bloch and Davidson, 1968) neither alters the rate of loss of sexual potency nor eliminates the variability among individuals with regard to its persistence.

A second factor tested for its possible contribution toward the maintenance of copulatory behavior in gonadectomized animals is the amount of precastration mating experience. While Rosenblatt and Aronson (1958a,b; Rosenblatt, 1965) found that sexually experienced cats retained copulatory behavior considerably longer after gonadectomy than did cats with little or no previous mating experience, no such correlation can be demonstrated in either rats (Stone, 1927; Bloch and Davidson, 1968) or dogs (Hart, 1968b).

Interaction of androgens with organismic and environmental factors

The lack of adrenal involvement and limited contribution of copulatory experience to the persistence of sexual behavior following castration led to a renewed search for other variables which interact with testicular hormones to control adult copulatory behavior. It seems clear that while androgen facilitates male sexual behavior, the target tissues on which the hormone acts are not uniform among animals, since considerable variability is seen in the dependence upon and reactivity to gonadal steroids. Several variables have been identified which critically influence the extent to which, in the adult, androgen is able to activate the full copulatory pattern.

Genetic factors
Young and his collaborators have been particularly successful in demonstrating the existence of genetic differences correlated with varying degrees of sexual vigor. This parameter was discovered in the following manner. Several strains of guinea pigs differing in male sexual drive were identified. To assess whether these differences simply reflected variations in endogenous androgen levels, all were castrated and treated with testosterone propionate (Riss and Young, 1953; Valenstein and Young, 1953; Riss et al., 1955). The precastration differences persisted despite identical postcastration plasma androgen titers. Similarly, male guinea pigs from a homogenous strain were

designated to be high, medium or low-performance copulators on the basis of tests with receptive females. Following gonadectomy and androgen replacement, the three groups reverted to the same level of response as was displayed during precastration tests (Grunt and Young, 1952, 1953). The rate at which copulatory behavior disappeared following castration varied among the three groups, low-drive animals ceasing to ejaculate within one week of gonadectomy, medium-drive animals after three weeks, and high-drive animals after nine weeks. Furthermore, unlike the earlier findings of Beach and Holz-Tucker (1949) with rats, administration of large quantities of testosterone did not increase sexual performance above precastration levels in any of the groups tested. Even 4–20 times the amount of androgen required to restore behavior in normal males, failed to increase the total number of copulatory responses emitted by the low-drive animals above that shown prior to castration (Riss and Young, 1954).

Prepuberal social factors

Early social experience also exerts a critical influence on whether males acquire copulatory skills. Removal of male guinea pigs (Riss et al., 1955; Valenstein et al., 1955; Valenstein and Young, 1955; Valenstein and Goy, 1957; Gerall, 1963a) or rats (Zimbardo, 1958; Folman and Drori, 1965; Gerall et al., 1967b; Gruendel and Arnold, 1969; Spevak et al., 1973) from their siblings shortly after birth severely impairs adult sexual behavior. Most juvenile males raised in total isolation from members of their own species are unable to copulate when given access to receptive females in adulthood. More limited behavioral deficits occur in males raised in partial isolation, that is, separated from socially housed males or females by a wire mesh screen which prevents manipulative interactions but does not block passage of conspecific auditory, visual or olfactory cues (Gerall, 1963a; Gerall et al., 1967b; Spevak et al., 1973). In these males, the development of sexual inadequacies cannot be prevented by administering androgen prepuberally (Riss et al., 1955; Valenstein et al., 1955), nor are they reversed by exogenous androgen treatment in adulthood (Valenstein and Young, 1955). The only therapy found to be effective in a limited number of cases seems to be prolonged housing with females in adulthood (Valenstein and Goy, 1957; Gerall et al., 1967b).

It appears that the expression of masculine sexual patterns is more dependent upon the sensitivity or responsiveness of the central tissues upon which androgen acts than on minor fluctuations in adult steroid titers, provided that sufficient hormone is present to exceed the minimum threshold for behavioral activation. The sensitivity of the target tissue in turn is determined by genetic predisposition, the presence of androgen during fetal sexual differentiation stages, and adequate prepuberal socialization. Adult gonadal steroids activate existing behavioral potentials but cannot alter, exceed, or substitute for various organismic and environmental variables which interact to set the upper and lower limits of the basic potential.

Prepuberal androgen and precocity

While the full male copulatory pattern normally appears at puberty, there are indications that sexual behavior could be exhibited at an earlier age, if sufficient androgen were available. Whereas male rats normally begin to copulate at about 55 days of age, daily injection of testosterone propionate to prepuberal males will advance the age at which ejaculation and intromission patterns appear by as much as 20 days (Stone, 1940; Beach, 1942b; Larsson, 1967). However, very high dosages of androgen are needed to induce precocious ejaculatory behavior (Baum, 1972, 1973; Goldfoot and Baum, 1972). Five or even 500 μg/100 g body weight of testosterone propionate failed to accelerate the appearance of copulation (Baum, 1972, 1973), while 1000 μg per animal were effective (Beach, 1942b; Baum, 1972). It is unlikely that the variability in age at which ejaculation first appears among normal male rats is due to slight differences in endogenous androgen titers, since the dosage demonstrated to accelerate maturation exceeds the capacity of the normal testes to synthesize and release hormone. However, at least in the rat, the complete male copulatory pattern appears to be fully organized in prepuberal males, although the androgen threshold for behavioral activation is very high compared to that of mature males. While daily injections of 75 μg testosterone propionate are sufficient to restore full copulatory capacity to adult castrated male rats (Beach and Holz-Tucker, 1949), a dosage in excess of 500 μg is required to activate this same pattern in prepuberal animals.

The generality of this finding is limited by the outcome of studies done with other species. Neither prenatal (Gerall, 1963b) nor postnatal treatment with testosterone propionate (Riss et al., 1955; Gerall, 1958, 1963b) advanced the age at which intromission or ejaculation patterns first appeared in the guinea pig. A slight increase in the number of lower level mounting responses, accompanied by an increased attentiveness to estrous females, was noted, but the authors point out that this might better be viewed as increased sexual arousal than accelerated maturation since untreated prepuberal guinea pigs also display such patterns but at lower rates. However, none of the guinea pig studies employed androgen doses as high as those found to be effective in the rat. Thus, the discrepancy between the rat and the guinea pig does not necessarily reflect true species differences.

Prepuberal castration

Since prepuberal androgen, under certain circumstances, accelerates sexual maturation, the question arises as to whether prepuberal castration alters the potential for normal adult copulatory behavior. Early reports on both the rat (Moore and Price, 1938) and guinea pig (Sollenberger and Hamilton, 1939; Seward, 1940) indicated that this is not the case, provided that androgen replacement is instituted in adulthood. In a systematic investigation of the rat, Beach and Holz (1946) castrated males at 21, 48, 100, 150 or 350 days of age and tested them three months later, following extensive androgen treatment. All copulated normally, indicating that the tissues involved in the expression of adult sexual behavior do not require exposure to prepuberal testicular secretions for normal functioning.

There are two exceptions to the above. First, if males are castrated before the perinatal process of sexual differentiation is completed, a potential for intromission and ejaculation fails to develop. Thus, male rats castrated within the first 5 days after birth are entirely unable to execute the full copulatory pattern in adulthood, even following extensive androgen replacement therapy (Beach and Holz, 1946; Grady et al., 1965; Gerall et al., 1967a; Larsson, 1966b). If castration is delayed until day 7 or 10, the process of sexual differentiation is complete and only androgen in adulthood is required to activate the full pattern. Secondly, while all components of the male copulatory pattern appear in the rat at about 55 days of age, there are discrete differences between the mating sequence executed by pubertal and older males. Larsson and co-workers (Larsson, 1956, 1958; Larsson and Essberg, 1962) have shown that older male rats achieve ejaculation after fewer intromission responses than do pubertal males. This maturation of the pattern is due to prolonged exposure to endogenous androgen rather than increased age or sexual experience. Intact, sexually naive males given their first copulatory test at 200 days of age show the full mature pattern while prepuberally castrated males given androgen replacement therapy beginning at 200 days of age display the pubertal pattern (Larsson, 1967). Thus, withholding prepuberal androgen will delay maturation of the copulatory sequence, but does not block its ultimate appearance.

3. THE LOCUS OF ACTION OF ANDROGENS

Considerable controversy still exists as to the most critical site on which androgen exerts its behavior-potentiating effects. The peripheral morphology (specifically the penis), the spinal cord, and the diencephalon have been extensively investigated.

Penile factors

The penis functions in a dual capacity, both receiving sensory information and executing motor responses vital to the display of well integrated copulatory patterns. Furthermore, its morphological integrity is clearly androgen dependent. Castration causes atrophy (Beach and Holz, 1946; Grady et al., 1965; Gerall et al., 1967a; Beach, 1970) and ultimately loss of the capacity for erection (Rosenblatt and Aronson, 1958). Loss of erectile capacity can be induced also by removal of a portion of the penile bone, and has been shown to block totally the execution of intromission and ejaculation responses in sexually experienced male rats (Beach and Holz, 1946). In addition, in many species, for example, the rat and cat, there are cornified papillae or penile spines embedded in the epithelial folds of the glans penis which when mechanically stimulated by contact with the vaginal wall will innervate numerous touch corpuscles located directly under the base of each spine (Beach and Levinson, 1950; Aronson and Cooper, 1967). These structures are believed to constitute a major source of sensory input from the penis to the central nervous system and to contribute to general sexual arousal. Following castration, these spines regress and finally disappear (Beach and Levinson, 1950; Aronson and Cooper, 1967), reappearing in direct proportion to the quantity of androgen replacement. Since the loss and reinstatement of copulatory behavior associated with steroid withdrawal or administration roughly parallels the distribution of penile spines, it has been suggested that, as the size and number of penile receptors fluctuates, so does the intensity of stimulation associated with the act of intromission, with direct consequences on the continued execution of such responses. However, all authors hasten to point out that these spines are not likely to mediate the only action which androgen exerts either on the penis or on other tissue implicated in the control of sexual behavior (Beach and Levinson, 1950; Aronson and Cooper, 1967).

Penile spines are important but not critical for normal sexual arousal. The correlation between loss of copulatory behavior and penile receptors following castration is far from perfect. Aronson and Cooper (1967) have shown that the regression of penile spines follows an orderly and predictable course in the cat. Very little change occurs in the first week. By two months the spines are reduced to half size, while by six months they have totally disappeared. However, sexual behavior may be entirely lost within two weeks after castration, before the spines have undergone much degeneration, or persist for over a year, long after the spines have totally involuted (Rosenblatt and Aronson, 1958a,b). Furthermore, deteriorative changes in penile spines and general testicular morphology can be prevented totally if castrated males are chronically treated with peripherally acting androgens such as fluoxymesterone (Beach and Westbrook, 1968) or dihydrotestosterone (McDonald et al., 1970; Feder, 1971; Whalen and Luttge, 1971; Beyer et al., 1973). Despite accessory structures indistinguishable from those of testosterone-treated males, such animals show the deficient copulatory pattern associated with castration. This would strongly suggest that maintenance of the penis and accessory structures alone is insufficient to sustain copulatory behavior.

Tactile sensitivity also can be reduced by direct application of a local anesthetic to the penile shaft. This procedure temporarily blocks activation of all skin receptors, including penile spines, without necessarily interfering with erection (Adler and Bermant, 1966). Mature sexually experienced rats or cats exposed to such treatment will cease to intromit, ejaculate or exhibit spinal penile reflexes for as long as the anesthetic is active (Carlsson and Larsson, 1964; Adler and Bermant, 1966; Aronson and Cooper, 1968; Hart,

1972; Larsson and Södersten, 1973). Similarly, bilateral surgical sectioning of the dorsal nerve of the penis will chronically impair transmission from mechanoreceptors located on the penile shaft. Despite the ensuing loss of penile sensitivity, erection continues in the cat (Aronson and Cooper, 1968) but not in the rat (Larsson and Södersten, 1973). However, in both species, the surgical deafferentation blocks intromission and ejaculation responses. The impairment appears to be in the male's ability to orient himself properly with regard to the female's vagina, so that vaginal detection and penetration (intromission) becomes difficult. In all of the studies in which penile sensitivity was impaired, sexual arousal appeared normal, since high levels of mounting persisted in almost all animals. Alterations occurred in the quality rather than quantity of copulatory behavior.

The importance of sensory input from the penis must also be evaluated in light of the recent finding of Cooper and Aronson (1974) that castration does not alter neural discharge from penile mechanoreceptors. Evoked potentials obtained by applying standardized pressure stimuli to various portions of the penile shaft revealed that neither the threshold for neural discharge nor the total amount of activity generated varied between intact and castrated male cats.

Spinal factors

The spinal cord has also been identified as a site of androgenic action. In a series of elegant studies, Hart demonstrated that spinal reflexes mediating erection and ejaculation are androgen dependent (Hart, 1967, 1968a,b). When continuous pressure is applied to the base of the penis, male rats in whom the spinal cord has been transected at the mid-thoracic level will show erection and other reflexes consisting of 'long and short penile flips'. These genital responses decline markedly following castration but are reinstituted by androgen. Two lines of evidence indicate that the action of the systemically administered androgen was exerted directly on spinal elements rather than peripheral targets. Castrated spinal rats in which genital responses had dropped to a low baseline level showed marked and rapid recovery of spinal reflexes when testosterone was implanted directly into the cord via cannula (Hart and Haugen, 1968). Since there were no differences in seminal vesicle weight between males receiving spinal androgen versus cholesterol, it was concluded that insufficient hormone had leaked into the systemic circulation to induce peripheral effects. Thus, the recovery of function was the consequence of direct action on spinal neurons and not of reinstatement of peripheral penile sensitivity. Conversely, maintenance of normal penile morphology through systemic injections of the peripherally acting androgen, dihydrotestosterone, did not support penile reflexes in castrated spinal males (Hart, 1973).

Diencephalic control

Application of androgen directly to a number of brain sites will restore copulatory behavior in castrated males. The most effective of these sites appear to be the medial preoptic—anterior hypothalamic area (Davidson, 1966b; Lisk, 1967; Barfield, 1969; Johnston and Davidson, 1972; Kierniesky and Gerall, 1973; Christensen and Clemens, 1974). The posterior hypothalamus has been variously found either to be unresponsive to intracranial androgen (Lisk, 1967; Christensen and Clemens, 1974), moderately responsive (Davidson, 1966; Johnston and Davidson, 1972) or fully responsive (Kierniesky and Gerall, 1973). More variability is reported with regard to other extrahypothalamic sites. However, it seems safe to conclude that localized treatment with androgen of discrete diencephalic sites known to concentrate testosterone (Pfaff, 1968; Sar and Stumpf, 1973; Resko et al., 1967) restores ejaculatory capacity in castrated rats. Since negative sites are often in close proximity to positive placements, it seems likely that the steroid action was relatively specific to the central sites in which it was placed and did not spread extensively into adjacent brain areas. Similarly, although slight stimulation of peripheral morphology is almost always found in intracranial testosterone implant studies, this is not considered to contribute toward the restoration of copulatory behavior. The recovery of penile morphology typically is slight and thus unlikely to result in significant enhancement of penile sensitivity. Furthermore, sexual morphology is also stimulated in animals where the brain implant of androgen fails to restore copulatory behavior.

4. SUMMARY

Normal levels of copulatory behavior in adult males require the presence of testicular hormones. Sexual behavior declines if androgen is withdrawn and is potentiated if exogenous testosterone is administered. Androgen exerts its activational influence on sexual behavior by acting on substrates which vary as a function of genetically mediated predispositions, the presence of androgen during critical fetal stages of development, and adequate prepuberal socialization acquired through habitation with members of the same species. While the presence of prepuberal androgen may accelerate sexual behavioral maturation in some animals, it is not critical toward its ultimate development. Various tissues have been identified which both take up androgen and play a role in the mediation of copulatory behavior. Specifically, the penis, spinal cord and diencephalon appear to be the three most critical targets through which androgen exerts its potentiating effects on male sexual behavior. Of these, the diencephalon is probably the most important, since the complete male sexual pattern is displayed by castrated males if androgen is implanted directly into discrete hypothalamic sites. Selective androgenization of only the peripheral morphology or spinal cord fails to potentiate behavior or restores only selected components of the pattern.

ACKNOWLEDGEMENT

The assistance of O. Byron Ward, Jr. in the writing and editing of this manuscript is gratefully acknowledged.

BIBLIOGRAPHY

Adler, N.T. (1969) Effects of the male's copulatory behavior on successful pregnancy of the female rat. *J. Comp. Physiol. Psychol.* 69: 613—622.

Adler, N. and Bermant, G. (1966) Sexual behavior of male rats: Effects of reduced sensory feedback. *J. Comp. Physiol. Psychol.* 61: 240—243.

Adler, N.T., Resko, J.A. and Goy, R.W. (1970) The effect of copulatory behavior on hormonal change in the female rat prior to implantation. *Physiol. Behav.* 5: 1003—1007.

Aronson, L.R. and Cooper, M.L. (1967) Penile spines of the domestic cat: Their endocrine-behavior relations. *Anat. Rec.* 157: 71—78.

Aronson, L.R. and Cooper, M.L. (1968) Desensitization of the glans penis and sexual behavior in cats. In: (M. Diamond, Ed.), *Perspectives in Reproduction and Sexual Behavior,* (Indiana University Press, Bloomington) pp: 51—82.

Barfield, R.J. (1969) Activation of copulatory behavior by androgen implanted into the preoptic area of the male fowl. *Horm. Behav.* 1: 37—52.

Baum, M.J. (1972) Precocious mating in male rats following treatment with androgen or estrogen. *J. Comp. Physiol. Psychol.* 78. 356 007.

Baum, M.J. (1973) Hormonal stimulation of precocious mating in male rats without antecedent effects on sexual clasping or ambulation. *Physiol. Behav.* 10: 137—140.

Beach, F.A. (1942a) Effects of testosterone propionate upon the copulatory behavior of sexually inexperienced male rats. *J. Comp. Psychol.* 33: 227—247a.

Beach, F.A. (1942b) Sexual behavior of prepuberal male and female rats treated with gonadal hormones. *J. Comp. Psychol.* 34: 285—292b.

Beach, F.A. (1970) Coital behavior in dogs: VI. Long-term effects of castration upon mating in the male. *J. Comp. Physiol. Psychol.* 70: (No. 3, Part 2), 1—32.

Beach, F.A. and Fowler, H (1959) Individual differences in the response of male rats to androgen. *J. Comp. Physiol. Psychol.* 52: 50—52.

Beach, F.A. and Holz, A.M. (1946) Mating behavior in male rats castrated at various ages and injected with androgen. *J. Exp. Zool.* 101: 91—142.

Beach, F.A. and Holz-Tucker, A.M. (1949) Effects of different concentrations of androgen upon sexual behavior in castrated male rats. *J. Comp. Physiol. Psychol.* 42: 433—453.

Beach, F.A. and Levinson, G. (1950) Effects of androgen on the glans penis and mating behavior of castrated male rats. *J. Exp. Zool.* 114: 159—168.

Beach, F.A. and Pauker, R.S. (1949) Effects of castration and subsequent androgen administration upon mating behavior in the male hamster (Cricetus auratus). *Endocrinology* 45: 211—221.

Beach, F.A. and Westbrook, W.H. (1968) Dissociation of androgenic effects on sexual morphology and behavior in male rats. *Endocrinology* 83: 395—398.

Beyer, C., Larsson, K., Pérez-Palacios, G. and Morali, G. (1973) Androgen structure and male sexual behavior in the castrated rat. *Horm. Behav.* 4: 99—108.

Bloch, G.J. and Davidson, J.M. (1968) Effects of adrenalectomy and experience on post-castration sex behavior in the male rat. *Physiol. Behav.* 3: 461—465.

Carlsson, S.G. and Larsson, K. (1964) Mating in male rats after local anesthetization of the glans penis. *Z. Tierpsychol.* 21: 854—856.

Cheng, P. and Casida, L.E. (1949) Effects of testosterone propionate upon sexual libido and the production of semen and sperm in the rabbit. *Endocrinology* 44: 38—48.

Cheng, P., Ulberg, L.C., Christian, R.E. and Casida, L.E. (1950) Different intensities of sexual activity in relation to the effect of testosterone propionate in the male rabbit. *Endocrinology* 46: 447—452.

Christensen, L.W. and Clemens, L.G. (1974) Intrahypothalamic implants of testosterone or estradiol and resumption of masculine sexual behavior in long-term castrated male rats. *Endocrinology* 95: 984—990.

Cooper, M. and Aronson, L. (1958) The effect of adrenalectomy on the sexual behavior of castrated male cats. *Anat. Rec.* 131: 544 (abstract).

Cooper, K.K. and Aronson, L.R. (1974) Effects of castration on neural afferent responses from the penis of the domestic cat. *Physiol. Behav.* 12: 93—107.

Davidson, J.M. (1966a) Characteristics of sex behavior in male rats following castration. *Anim. Behav.* 14: 266—272a.

Davidson, J.M. (1966b) Activation of the male rat's sexual behavior by intracerebral implantation of androgen. *Endocrinology* 79: 788—794b.

Diakow, C. (1971) Effects of genital desensitization on mating behavior and ovulation in the female cat. *Physiol. Behav.* 7: 47—54.

Everett, J.W. (1961) The mammalian female reproductive cycle and its controlling mechanism. In: (W.C. Young, Ed.) *Sex and Internal Secretions*, 3rd Ed., Vol. 1, (Williams and Wilkins Co., Baltimore) pp. 497—555.

Feder, H.H. (1971) The comparative actions of testosterone propionate and 5α-androstan-17β-ol-3-one propionate on the reproductive behaviour, physiology and morphology of male rats. *J. Endocrinol.* 51: 241—252.

Folman, Y. and Drori, D. (1965) Normal and aberrant copulatory behaviour in male rats (R. Norvegicus) reared in isolation. *Anim. Behav.* 13: 427—429.

Gerall, A.A. (1958) An attempt to induce precocious sexual behavior in male guinea pigs by injections of testosterone propionate. *Endocrinology* 63: 280—284.

Gerall, A.A. (1963a) An exploratory study of the effect of social isolation variables on the sexual behaviour of male guinea pigs. *Anim. Behav.* 11: 274—282a.

Gerall, A.A. (1963b) The effect of prenatal and postnatal injections of testosterone propionate on prepuberal male guinea pig sexual behavior. *J. Comp. Physiol. Psychol.* 56: 92—95b.

Gerall, A.A., Hendricks, S.E., Johnson, L. L. and Bounds, T.W. (1967a) Effects of early castration in male rats on adult sexual behavior. *J. Comp. Physiol. Psychol.* 64: 206—212.

Gerall, H.D., Ward, I.L. and Gerall, A.A. (1967b) Disruption of the male rat's sexual behaviour induced by social isolation. *Anim. Behav.* 15: 54—58.

Goldfoot, D.A. and Baum, M.J. (1972) Initiation of mating behavior in developing male rats following peripheral electric shock. *Physiol. Behav.* 8: 857—863.

Grady, K. L., Phoenix, C.H. and Young, W.C. (1965) Role of the developing rat testis in differentiation of the neural tissues mediating mating behavior. *J. Comp. Physiol. Psychol.* 59: 176—182.

Gruendel, A, D. and Arnold, W.J. (1969) Effects of early social deprivation on reproducive behavior of male rats. *J. Comp. Physiol. Psychol.* 67: 123—128.

Grunt, J.A. and Young, W.C. (1952) Differential reactivity of individuals and the response of the male guinea pig to testosterone propionate. *Endocrinology* 51: 237—248.

Grunt, J.A. and Young, W.C. (1953) Consistency of sexual behavior patterns in individual male guinea pigs following castration and androgen therapy. *J. Comp. Physiol. Psychol.* 46: 138—144.

Hart, B.L. (1967) Testosterone regulation of sexual reflexes in spinal male rats. *Science* 155: 1283—1284.

Hart, B.L. (1968a) Sexual reflexes and mating behavior in the male rat. *J. Comp. Physiol. Psychol.* 65: 453—460.

Hart, B.L. (1968b) Role of prior experience in the effects of castration on sexual behavior of male dogs. *J. Comp. Physiol. Psychol.* 66: 719—725b.

Hart, B.L. (1972) Sexual reflexes in the male rat after anesthetization of the glans penis. *Behav. Biol.* 7: 127—130.

Hart, B.L. (1973) Effects of testosterone propionate and dihydrotestosterone on penile morphology and sexual reflexes of spinal male rats. *Horm. Behav.* 4: 239—246.

Hart, B.L. and Haugen, C.M. (1968) Activation of sexual reflexes in male rats by spinal implantation of testosterone. *Physiol. Behav.* 3: 735—738.

Johnston, P. and Davidson, J.M. (1972) Intracerebral androgens and sexual behavior in the male rat. *Horm. Behav.* 3: 345—357.

Kierniooky, N.C. and Gerall, A.A. (1973) Effects of testosterone propionate implants in the brain on the sexual behavior and peripheral tissue of the male rat. *Physiol. Behav.* 11: 633—640.

Larsson, K. (1956) *Conditioning and Sexual Behavior in the Male Albino Rat.* (Almkvist and Wiksell, Stockholm.)

Larsson, K. (1958) Age differences in the diurnal periodicity of the sexual behavior. *Gerontologia* 2: 64—72.

Larsson, K. (1966a) Individual differences in reactivity to androgen in male rats. *Physiol. Behav.* 1: 255—258.

Larsson, K. (1966b) Effects of neonatal castration upon the development of the mating behavior of the male rat. *Z. Tierpsychol.* 23: 867—873.

Larsson, K. (1967) Testicular hormone and developmental changes in mating behavior of the male rat. *J. Comp. Physiol. Psychol.* 63: 223—230.

Larsson, K. and Essberg, S. (1962) Effect of age on the sexual behavior of the male rat. *Gerontologia* 6: 133—143.

Larsson, K. and Södersten, P. (1973) Mating in male rats after section of the dorsal penile nerve. *Physiol. Behav.* 10: 567—571.

Lincoln, G.A., Guinness, F. and Short, R.V. (1972) The way in which testosterone controls the social and sexual behavior of the red deer stag (Cervus elaphus). *Horm. Behav.* 3: 375—396.

Lisk, R.D. (1967) Neural localization for androgen activation of copulatory behavior in the male rat. *Endocrinology* 80: 754—761.

McDonald, P., Beyer, C., Newton, F., Brien, B., Baker, R., Tan, H.S., Sampsom, C., Kitching, P., Greenhill, R. and Pritchard, D. (1970) Failure of 5α-dihydrotestosterone to initiate sexual behaviour in the castrated male rat. *Nature* 227: 964—965.

Moore, U.L. and Price, D. (1938) Some effects of testosterone-propionate in the rat. *Anat. Rec.* 71: 59—78.

Pfaff, D.W. (1968) Autoradiographic localization of radioactivity in rat brain after injection of tritiated sex hormones. *Science* 161: 1355—1356.

Phoenix, C.H., Goy, R.W. and Resko, J.A. (1968) Psychosexual differentiation as a function of androgenic stimulation. In: (M. Diamond, Ed.) *Perspectives in Reproduction and Sexual Behavior*, (Indiana University Press, Bloomington) pp. 33—49.

Resko, J.A. (1970) Androgens in systemic plasma of male guinea pigs during development and after castration in adulthood. *Endocrinology* 86: 1444—1447.

Resko, J.A., Goy, R.W. and Phoenix, C.H. (1967) Uptake and distribution of exogenous testosterone-1,2-^{3}H in neural and genital tissues of the castrated guinea pig. *Endocrinology* 80: 490—498.

Resko, J.A. and Phoenix, C.H. (1972) Sexual behavior and testosterone concentration in the plasma of the rhesus monkey before and after castration. *Endocrinology* 91: 499—503.

Riss, W., Valenstein, E.S., Sinks, J. and Young, W.C. (1955) Development of sexual behavior in male guinea pigs from genetically different stocks under controlled conditions of androgen treatment and caging. *Endocrinology* 57: 139—146.

Riss, W. and Young, W.C. (1953) Somatic, psychological, and androgenic determinants in the development of sexual behavior in the male guinea pig. *Am. Psychol.* 8: 421. (abstract).

Riss, W. and Young, W.C. (1954) The failure of large quantities of testosterone propionate to activate low drive male guinea pigs. *Endocrinology* 54: 232—235.

Rosenblatt, J.S. (1965) Effects of experience on sexual behavior in male cats. In: (F.A. Beach, Ed.) *Sex and Behavior.* (John Wiley and Sons, Inc., New York) pp. 416—439.

Rosenblatt, J.S. and Aronson, L.R. (1958a) The influence of experience on the behavioural effects of androgen in prepuberally castrated male cats. *Anim. Behav.* 6: 171—182.

Rosenblatt, J.S. and Aronson, L.R. (1958b) The decline of sexual behavior in male cats after castration with special reference to the role of prior sexual experience. *Behaviour* 12: 285—338.

Sar, M. and Stumpf, W.E. (1973) Autoradiographic localization of radioactivity in the rat brain after the injection of 1,2-^{3}H-testosterone. *Endocrinology* 92: 251—256.

Schwartz, M. and Beach, F.A. (1954) Effects of adrenalectomy upon mating behavior in castrated male dogs. *Am. Psychol.* 9: 467—468 (abstract).

Seward, J.P. (1940) Studies on the reproductive activities of the guinea pig. III. The effect of androgenic hormone on sex drive in males and females. *J. Comp. Psychol.* 30: 435—449.

Sollenberger, R.T. and Hamilton, J.B. (1939) The effect of testosterone propionate upon the sexual behavior of castrated male guinea pigs. *J. Comp. Psychol.* 28: 81—92.

Spevak, A.M., Quadagno, D.M., Knoeppel, D. and Poggio, J.P. (1973) The effects of isolation on sexual and social behavior in the rat. *Behav. Biol.* 8: 63—73.

Stone, C.P. (1927) The retention of copulatory ability in male rats following castration. *J. Comp. Psychol.* 7: 369—387.

Stone, C.P. (1932) The retention of copulatory activity in male rabbits following castration. *J. Genet. Psychol.* 40: 296—305.

Stone, C.P. (1939) Copulatory activity in adult male rats following castration and injections of testosterone propionate. *Endocrinology* 24: 165—174.

Stone, C.P. (1940) Precocious copulatory activity induced in male rats by subcutaneous injections of testosterone propionate. *Endocrinology* 26: 511—515.

Valenstein, E.S. (1968) Steroid hormones and the neuropsychology of development. In: (R.L. Isaacson, Ed.), *The Neuropsychology of Development.* (John Wiley and Sons, Inc., New York) pp: 1—39.

Valenstein, E.S. and Goy, R.W. (1957) Further studies of the organization and display of sexual behavior in male guinea pigs. *J. Comp. Physiol. Psychol.* 50: 115—119.

Valenstein, E.S., Riss, W. and Young, W.C. (1955) Experiential and genetic factors in the organization of sexual behavior in male guinea pigs. *J. Comp. Physiol. Psychol.* 48: 397—403.

Valenstein, E.S. and Young, W.C. (1953) Resistance of strain differences in male sex drive and growth to maternal influence prior to weaning in the guinea pig. *Anat. Rec.* 117: 604 (abstr.).

Valenstein, E.S. and Young, W.C. (1955) An experiential factor influencing the effectiveness of testosterone propionate in eliciting sexual behavior in male guinea pigs. *Endocrinology* 56: 173—177.

Ward, I.L. (1974) Sexual behavior differentiation: Prenatal hormonal and environmental control. In: (R.C. Friedman, R.M. Richart and R.L. Vande Wiele, Eds.) *Sex Differences in Behavior.* (John Wiley and Sons, Inc., New York) pp: 3—17.

Warren, R.P. and Aronson, L.R. (1956) Sexual behavior in castrated-adrenalectomized hamsters maintained on DCA. *Endocrinology* 58: 293—304.

Warren, R.P. and Aronson, L.R. (1957) Sexual behavior in adult male hamsters castrated-adrenalectomized prior to puberty. *J. Comp. Physiol. Psychol.* 50: 475—480.

Whalen, R.E., Beach, F.A. and Kuehn, R.R. (1961) Effects of exogenous androgen on sexually responsive and unresponsive male rats. *Endocrinology* 69: 373—380.

Whalen, R.E. and Luttge, W.G. (1971) Testosterone, androstenedione and dihydrotestosterone: Effects on mating behavior of male rats. *Horm. Behav.* 2: 117—125.

Young, W.C. (1961) The hormones and mating behavior. In: (W.C. Young, Ed.) *Sex and Internal Secretions,* 3rd edn, Vol. 2 (Williams and Wilkins Co., Baltimore) pp: 1173—1239.

Zimbardo, P.G. (1958) The effects of early avoidance training and rearing conditions upon the sexual behavior of the male rat. *J. Comp. Physiol. Psychol.* 51: 764—769.

CHAPTER 28

Regulation of sexual behavior by hormones in female nonprimates

H.H. FEDER

1. INTRODUCTION

During sexually active periods, male mammals secrete, in more or less tonic fashion, testicular hormone in amounts adequate to maintain spermatogenesis, secretory activity of the genital tract, morphological and histological integrity of internal and external genital tissues, adenohypophyseal release of gonadotropic hormones, and the capacity of central neural tissues to mediate the display of sexual behavior. It is characteristic of male mammals that all of these functions of testicular secretions are manifested simultaneously. Spontaneously ovulating female mammals, by contrast, typically show a sequential, rather than simultaneous, activation of the various tissues (genital, hypophyseal, neural) involved in reproduction. The steroid hormones most significant for maintaining cycles of sequential activity of reproductive tissues in females are estrogen and progestins. The nature of the role played by estrogen in this process is similar among a wide range of species, but the nature of the role played by progestins changes markedly among species. The first sections of this chapter will deal with various ways in which progestins facilitate the action of estrogen in activating the expression of female sexual behavior and in linking the timing of this behavior to the timing of ovulation.

In several nonprimate species there is evidence that steroids not only promote or facilitate the display of sexual behavior, but they may also have the effect of suppressing or inhibiting female sexual responses. Progestins, in particular, have been demonstrated to possess such inhibitory properties. This seemingly paradoxical situation will form the basis for the final section of the chapter.

Handbook of Sexology, edited by J. Money and H. Musaph
© *Elsevier/North-Holland Biomedical Press, 1977*

2. FACILITATION OF SEXUAL BEHAVIOR BY PROGESTERONE AND ESTROGEN IN RODENTS

Endogenous hormonal events in some female rodents

Rats

Under controlled conditions of laboratory lighting, nonpregnant female white rats show cyclic periods of sexual behavior known as estrous behavior, sexual receptivity, or heat, lasting about 8 to 13 hours, once every 4 or 5 days. Ovulation occurs 'spontaneously' once every 4 or 5 days, usually towards the end of each period of estrous behavior (Bermant and Davidson, 1974). One of the most important behavioral elements of the period of sexual receptivity is the assumption of the lordosis posture. Lordosis is characterised by immobilisation, elevation of the head and a deep concave arching of the back which elevates the rump and permits intromission by a male (Komisaruk, 1974). Changes in estrogen and progesterone levels normally precede display of lordosis, and ensure that lordotic behavior will have a close temporal relationship with ovulation.

On the first day after sexual receptivity and ovulation have occurred, in the absence of the induction of pregnancy or pseudopregnancy, the plasma concentrations of estrogen, progesterone and luteinizing hormone (LH) are low (Brown-Grant, 1971). Follicle-stimulating hormone (FSH) concentrations are elevated, and this probably acts to stimulate growth of a fresh set of ovarian follicles (Daane and Parlow, 1971). On the second day after ovulation, the levels of plasma FSH, LH, and estrogen are low. There is a detectable increase in plasma progesterone level reflecting some degree of steroid secretory activity in the recently formed corpora lutea or in the interstitial tissue (Eto et al., 1962; Hashimoto et al., 1968; Feder et al., 1968a; Uchida et al., 1969). On the third day of a 4-day cycle, the progesterone level declines and plasma FSH and LH remain low. However, estradiol-17β begins to be produced in larger quantities by growing ovarian follicles (Naftolin et al., 1972; Schwartz, 1974; Shaikh and Shaikh, 1975). Increases in ovarian estrone secretion also occur at about this time, but their significance is unclear (Shaikh and Shaikh, 1975). The elevated estradiol level has multiple effects, one of which is to prime neural tissues destined to mediate lordosis behavior (Young, 1961) as well as ovulation (Brown-Grant, 1971). Another effect is the induction of an increase in adrenocortical secretion (Kitay, 1963; Bartosik et al., 1971). One of the steroids released by the adrenal cortex is progesterone (Feder et al., 1968a; Resko, 1969; Holzbauer et al., 1969) and the light-dependent circadian pattern of release of adrenal progesterone on the morning of the fourth day of a 4-day estrous cycle has been found to be an important element in entraining the timing of LH release to the light–dark cycle (Feder et al., 1971; Nequin and Schwartz, 1971; Lawton, 1972; Mann and Barraclough, 1973). In the morning of the fourth day, plasma estradiol levels have reached a peak, and the rise of estradiol to a critical point induces release of a surge of the gonadotropins FSH and LH, during the afternoon of the fourth day of a 4-day cycle (Brown-Grant, 1969; Ferin et al., 1969; Kalra, 1975). This gonadotropin surge has two important and related consequences. First, it acts on the mature ovarian follicle(s) to ensure that they will undergo their final spurt of preovulatory growth, and then rupture within about 8 to 12 hours after release of the gonadotropins. Second, the gonadotropic surge stimulates the preovulatory ovary to secrete large quantities of progesterone (Feder, et al., 1968a; Barraclough et al., 1971). This preovulatory progesterone acts in synergy with the previously secreted estradiol to promote the display of sexual receptivity at precisely the time at which the ovulatory mechanism has been set irrevocably into motion. In rats, secretion of preovulatory progesterone therefore plays a significant role in linking the timing of display of female sexual behavior to the timing of their ovulation. A recent experiment by Powers (1970) further serves to illustrate the importance of preovulatory progesterone for lordosis behavior. He ovariectomized rats shortly before the expected preovulatory progesterone peak or shortly after the peak had been reached. Only in the second case was lordosis displayed consistently. This finding suggests that during a normal 4-day estrous cycle not enough estrogen is produced endogenously to promote sexual receptivity, and that secretion of preovulatory progesterone provides the last bit of hormonal stimulation necessary for full expression of estrous behavior.

Hamsters

The hamster has a very regular 4-day estrous cycle under controlled laboratory lighting conditions (Brown-Grant, 1971). By contrast with rats, estrogen (estradiol + estrone) levels in peripheral plasma are relatively high throughout the hamster estrous cycle, and patterns of estrone and estradiol plasma levels show little correspondence with each other (Baranczuk and Greenwald, 1973). As in rats, estradiol concentrations in hamsters reach their peak on the morning and early afternoon of the day of the surge of gonadotropin release from the pituitary. Just after the gonadotropin surge, there is a massive release of progesterone from the preovulatory ovary (Lukaszewska and Greenwald, 1970). This preovulatory progesterone facilitates the action of estrogen on lordosis behavior (which lasts about 16 hours in hamsters) and links the timing of sex behavior to the timing of ovulation, as in rats (Ciaccio and Lisk, 1971a). Like the rat, the hamster exhibits only a brief period of slight luteal-phase activity two days after ovulation, and this period of progesterone secretion does not appear to have behavioral significance (Lukaszewska and Greenwald, 1970). No role of adrenal progesterone in entrainment of ovulation to the light—dark cycle has been demonstrated for hamsters, as it has for the rat.

Guinea pigs

In contrast to rats and hamsters, guinea pigs have estrous cycles of 16—18 days duration. Lordosis behavior is displayed for about 8 consecutive hours, and ovulation invariably occurs towards the end of the period of sexual receptivity (Young, 1969). Estrogen levels are low throughout the cycle and it has been difficult to demonstrate changes in the concentration of estrogen in the systemic circulation (Challis et al.,1971; Sasaki and Hanson, 1974). However, measurements of estradiol in ovarian-vein plasma show a significant rise during days 15 to 18 of the cycle. Estrone is secreted at a fairly steady rate throughout the cycle (Joshi et al., 1973).

Progesterone values in the systemic circulation are low when compared with values for rats (Feder et al., 1968b). However, changes in the concentration of progesterone are readily detectable in systemic plasma. One period of elevated progesterone level occurs from the third through the eleventh day after ovulation (that is, during the luteal phase) but this appears to have no direct bearing on the promotion of lordosis behavior. Another period of high progesterone concentrations in plasma occurs on about the 16th day of the cycle, just at the start of lordosis behavior and about 8 hours prior to ovulation (Feder et al., 1968b). This preovulatory peak of progesterone lasts for only a few hours, and serves in guinea pigs, as it does in rats and hamsters, to facilitate the action of estrogen on lordosis and to link the display of lordosis to the occurrence of ovulation (Joslyn et al., 1971). The guinea pig adrenal gland, although capable of secreting progesterone (Feder and Ruf, 1969), probably does not have a significant role in entraining sexual behavior and ovulation to the light—dark cycle.

Exogenous hormones and activation of female behavior in rodents

Rats
A combination of endogenously secreted estrogen and progesterone facilitates lordosis behavior in the course of a normal estrous cycle (see above). Experiments with exogenous hormones have extended understanding of the relationships of these hormones to the expression of behavior.

Early workers established that ovariectomized rats did not exhibit sexual receptivity to males (Young, 1961). However, lordosis can be induced in ovariectomised rats when an experimenter probes the cervix with a plastic rod (Komisaruk, 1974). Injection of estrogen to ovariectomised rats facilitates display of lordosis in response to males or to cervical probing (Boling and Blandau, 1939; Komisaruk, 1974), but sequential administration of estrogen followed 24—48 hours later is even more effective than estrogen alone (Boling and Blandau, 1939: Beach, 1942a).

Current views on hormonal influences on rat sexual behavior can be most conveniently summarized by first considering the role of estrogen and deferring discussion of progestin. First, how hormone-specific is the interaction between estrogen and lordosis? Several estrogens (estradiol-17β, estrone, estrone-3-sulphate, estriol) and some androgens which can be converted to estrogens (for example, testosterone) facilitate lordosis in ovariectomized rats (Beach, 1942b; Pfaff, 1970; Beyer et al., 1971). Estradiol-17β is the most potent of these substances (Beyer et al., 1971), but since estriol is capable of promoting lordosis yet incapable of being biotransformed to estradiol-17β, the argument cannot be made that there is an absolutely specific relationship between estradiol-17β and display of lordosis.

A second line of inquiry into the role of estrogens in lordosis is concerned with their central neural sites of action. Intracerebral implantation of estradiol-containing cannulae into ovariectomized rats stimulates lordosis when cannulae are located in the preoptic area, anterior hypothalamus, basolateral amygdala, habenula and septum (Dörner et al., 1968; Lisk, 1962; Rodgers and Law, 1968). Lesioning of the anterior hypothalamus or preoptic area leads to inability of ovariectomized animals of several species to exhibit lordosis in response to exogenous estrogen (Sawyer, 1960), but the data for rats are ambiguous (Law and Meagher, 1958; Kennedy, 1964; Lisk, 1967; Singer, 1968). Such lesion data suggest that estrogens act by stimulating particular diencephalic loci. However, other recent research has shown that lesions of the preoptic area (Powers and Valenstein, 1972), posterior hypothalamus (Law and Meagher, 1958) and septal region (Komisaruk et al., 1972; Nance et al., 1974) as well as olfactory bulb removal (Moss, 1971; Edwards and Warner, 1972) or chemical depression of cerebral cortical activity (Clemens, 1971; Ross et al., 1973a) may enhance display of lordosis in estrogen-primed rats. This set of findings suggests that these brain areas may exert tonic inhibitory effects on lordosis (Beach, 1967) and that inhibition (or destruction) of these 'inhibitory' areas enhances the actions of estrogen on behavior.

Administration of radioactively labeled estradiol to adult ovariectomised rats permits experimenters to localize sites at which estradiol is concentrated within the nervous system. By use of scintillation counting and autoradiographic methods the following picture has emerged: radioactive estradiol concentrates primarily in the hypothalamus and preoptic area (McEwen and Pfaff, 1973). Some estradiol-concentrating properties are also shown by septum and amygdala, and even by portions of the spinal cord (Keefer et al., 1973). In the neural target tissues for estradiol, the estradiol tends to concentrate within the nuclear portions of individual neurones (Stumpf, 1968; Zigmond and McEwen, 1970). This has given rise to the hypothesis that estrogen influences sex behavior by acting on hypothalamic cell nuclei to induce protein synthesis. Preliminary evidence for this notion comes from the findings that some antiestrogenic substances which presumably compete with estrogen for cytoplasmic or nuclear receptors in neural target cells also suppress female behavior (Arai and Gorski, 1968; Komisaruk and Beyer, 1972; Ross et al., 1973b; Whalen and Gorzalka, 1973) and that protein synthesis inhibitors such as actinomycin-D also prevent expression of lordosis after estrogen treatment (Whalen et al., 1974). However, specific proteins which are produced by hypothalamic cells as a result of estrogen action and which are required for display of sexual behavior have not yet been demonstrated.

We turn now to the role of progestin in promoting lordosis. In ovariectomized, adrenalectomized rats, estradiol administration leads to display of lordosis even when no progestin is given (Davidson et al., 1968). Thus, progestin is not an absolute requirement for lordosis behavior in rats, but is rather a facilitator of estrogen action. Of all the naturally occurring progestins which have been tested for facilitatory actions on lordosis, progesterone is the most effective (Whalen and Gorzalka, 1972). Lordosis is exhibited very soon (less than 1 hour) after intravenous administration of progesterone (Lisk, 1960; Meyerson, 1972). By way of contrast, the estrogen-conditioning process for lordosis requires about 16—24 hours (Green et al., 1970). The well-known anesthetic properties of progesterone are probably not responsible for its effects on lordosis, because no positive correlation exists between anesthetic potency and lordosis-promoting potency in a series of progestins (Meyerson, 1967). Brain lesioning techniques have not been used to study loci of progesterone action either in terms of enhancing or suppressing lordosis. Implantation of cannulae containing progesterone into specified neural sites indicates positive sites for lordosis facilitation in midbrain reticular formation (Ross et al., 1971) and in basal hypothalamus (Powers, 1972). Radioactive progesterone administered to ovariectomized rats is concentrated in the following rank order in brain homogenates: midbrain tegmentum > hypothalamus > cerebral cortex and hippocampus. In contrast to estradiol, progesterone is extensively and rapidly metabolized to other progestins, and the contrast in estrogen-concentrating ability between hypothalamus and cerebral cortex is more marked than the contrast in steroid-concentrating ability between midbrain and cerebral cortex homogenates for progesterone (Whalen and Luttge, 1971; Wade et al., 1973). The absence of specific antiprogesterone agents which exert effects at the neural level is one of the factors hindering research into biochemical mechanisms of progesterone action on behavior. One idea proposed for a mechanism of progesterone action is an inhibition of the serotonin system (Meyerson, 1964; Kow et al., 1974).

Recently, it has been found that luteinizing hormone releasing factor (LH-RH, a peptide) given to estrogen-primed, ovariectomized rats facilitates lordosis (Moss and McCann, 1973; Pfaff, 1973). It is not known whether or not this facilitatory effect of LH-RH on behavior is mediated by the same factors that are responsible for the lordosis-activating properties of progesterone.

Hamsters

As for rats and guinea pigs (Young, 1969) ovariectomy leads to cessation of lordosis behavior in hamsters and replacement therapy with estradiol preparations is not as effective in restoring lordosis as replacement therapy with estradiol followed 24—28 hours later by an injection of progesterone (Lisk, 1970; Ciaccio and Lisk, 1971b).

Selective uptake of radioactively labeled estradiol into the hypothalamus has been demonstrated in hamsters, by scintillation counting and autoradiographic techniques (Feder et al., 1974; D.W. Pfaff, personal communication), but both sets of techniques also show that the hypothalamus/cerebral cortex ratio of radioactivity is much lower for hamsters than for rats. This may be a factor contributing to the relative insensitivity of estrogen-activated neural tissues mediating lordosis behavior in hamsters (Frank and Fraps, 1945). Intracerebral implants of estrogen preparations into ovariectomized hamsters induce lordosis only if the implanted cannulae are large gauge and are placed in the anterior dorsal hypothalamus (Ciaccio and Lisk, 1973).

Progesterone, radioactively labeled, is taken up in higher quantities in hamster midbrain than in other brain areas (Wade et al., 1973). However, no evidence exists for selectivity or saturability of this midbrain progesterone uptake mechanism or for a relationship of this uptake mechanism to the expression of lordosis. Intracerebral implant studies have not yet indicated a specific neural focus for facilitation of lordosis by progesterone in hamsters (Lisk et al., 1972).

No facilitatory effects of LH-RH on lordosis have been seen in ovariectomized, estrogen primed hamsters (H. Siegel, personal communication).

Guinea pigs

Work with ovariectomized guinea pigs using the techniques of lesioning brain tissue (Brookhart et al., 1941) or implanting estradiol benzoate intracranially (Morin and Feder, 1974a) indicates that the preoptic area, anterior hypothalamus and basal hypothalamus are primary estrogen-sensitive areas mediating lordosis. Systemic injection of radioactive estradiol confirms that the guinea pig hypothalamus contains a specific, saturable uptake mechanism for estradiol (Feder et al., 1974) which involves the cell nuclei (Feder and Wade, 1974). However, attempts to antagonize the early effects of estrogen on guinea pig lordosis behavior by means of the antiestrogen MER-25 have been unsuccessful (Feder and Morin, 1974) and the antiestrogen CIS-clomiphene actually appears to facilitate lordosis under certain conditions (W.A. Walker and H.H. Feder, unpublished).

Progesterone, in very small quantities, facilitates lordosis in ovariectomized, estrogen-primed guinea pigs (Morin and Feder, 1974b). The exquisite sensitivity of guinea pigs to this action of progesterone may be related to high uptake, long retention and low rate of metabolism of progesterone in neural tissues (Wade et al., 1973). Rats, which are far less sensitive to the behavioral effects of progesterone, metabolize progesterone much more rapidly than do guinea pigs (Wade et al., 1973). Intracerebral implants of progesterone facilitate lordosis when they are placed in the medial basal hypothalamus (Morin and Feder, 1974c), and some evidence exists for specific, saturable nuclear progesterone receptors in the hypothalamus (Sar and Stumpf, 1973). Receptor uptake does not guarantee a behavioral correlate, however. Thus in the guinea pig, homogenates of midbrain take up even more radioactive progesterone than homogenates of hypothalamus (Wade and Feder, 1972) though no facilitatory effects on lordosis are seen after implantation of progesterone in guinea pig midbrain (Morin and Feder, 1974d).

We have been unable, thus far, to demonstrate a facilitatory effect of LH-RH on lordosis in guinea pigs (W.A. Walker and H.H. Feder, unpublished).

2. FACILITATION OF SEXUAL BEHAVIOR BY PROGESTERONE AND ESTROGEN IN SHEEP

Endogenous hormonal events in sheep

Sheep, like guinea pigs, are spontaneous ovulators with estrous cycles of 16—18 days duration. As in guinea pigs, there is a prolonged period of luteal functioning (Brown-Grant, 1971; Short, 1972). Heat occurs 18—24 hours before ovulation. This temporal linkage between heat and ovulation appears less precise than for guinea pigs, suggesting that a different method of linkage is utilized by sheep.

Plasma estrogen levels during the estrous cycle are low for the first 15 days after ovulation, but a striking increase in estradiol-17β levels occurs between days 15 and 17 (in a 17-day cycle), with peak levels obtaining just prior to the surge of gonadotropin release on day 17 (Moore et al., 1969). Plasma progesterone concentrations rise markedly from the third day after ovulation through the twelfth and reach a plateau from days 12—15 (luteal phase). After day 15 there is a sharp decline in plasma progesterone titers and, in contrast to rodents, no increase in plasma progesterone occurs in response to the LH surge in the preovulatory period (Stabenfeldt et al., 1969; Thorburn et al., 1969). Since sheep display estrous behavior at about the time of the LH surge, does this mean that progesterone plays no role in facilitating lordosis in sheep? Or does it mean that the role played by progesterone in sexual behavior of sheep differs from the role it plays in rodents? Experimental evidence for the second alternative has been produced by the use of exogenously administered steroids.

Exogenous hormones and activation of female behavior in sheep

Ovariectomized sheep given estrogen injections do not show as intense sexual responses as sheep given a regimen of progesterone injections followed by cessation of progesterone treatment for 24—28 hours, and then initiation of estrogen treatment (Robinson, 1955; Moore and Robinson, 1957). It can be easily recognized that this exogenous hormone regime exactly parallels the endogenous hormonal events which occur in intact sheep undergoing a normal estrous cycle. That is, a prolonged period of elevated progesterone levels (of luteal origin) precedes a decline in progesterone concentrations (as the corpus luteum undergoes involution). This decline is followed about 2 days later by a rapid increase in estrogen secretion and the onset of heat. Thus, in sheep the progesterone which facilitates heat by readying the animal for estrogen action is of luteal origin. In guinea pigs (which have an extended luteal phase) and in other rodents, luteal progesterone or progesterone preconditioning has not been shown to facilitate sex behavior (H.H. Feder and E. Peretz, unpublished). Instead, estrogen readies the rodent for the facilitatory effects of preovulatory progesterone. Such species differences in the sequencing of estrogen and progesterone are intriguing, and could shed light on the cellular actions of these hormones.

4. FACILITATION OF SEXUAL BEHAVIOR BY ESTROGEN ALONE IN OTHER SPECIES

Some spontaneously ovulating species such as cows, sows, mares and dogs show no pre-ovulatory surge of progesterone secretion (Hansel and Echternkamp, 1972; Smith and McDonald, 1974; Smith et al., 1970) and estrogen alone is sufficient for inducing heat in ovariectomized subjects (Robertson, 1969; Leathem, 1938). However, estrogen-primed cows (Melampy et al., 1957) and dogs (Beach and Merani, 1968) given progesterone show a facilitation of sexual behavior.

Reflex ovulators such as the rabbit secrete enough estrogen to support display of sexual receptivity in the absence of progestin (Eaton and Hilliard, 1971). The same is probably true of cats, which can be induced to display heat by implantation of estrogenic compounds intrahypothalamically (Harris et al., 1958). Even in these cases one might be able to detect, under appropriate experimental conditions, facilitatory actions of progesterone on neural tissues mediating sexual behavior (rabbits; Sawyer and Everett, 1959).

It is possible that in species such as cows, dogs and rabbits there is a residual ability of estrogen-primed neural tissues to respond to facilitatory behavioral effects of exogenous progesterone, although these neural tissues are not normally called upon to respond to pre-ovulatory progesterone during the course of the copulatory phase of a normal reproductive cycle. There is insufficient evidence regarding the question of whether in species such as cows, sows or dogs there is a facilitatory action of progesterone of luteal origin on neural tissues which will subsequently be exposed to estrogen and which mediate female behavior (Robertson, 1969).

5. SUPPRESSION OF FEMALE SEXUAL BEHAVIOR BY PROGESTERONE

In a variety of nonprimate female mammals, progesterone inhibits the display of sexual behavior (sheep and goat: Phillips et al., 1946; cows: Melampy et al., 1957; ferrets: Marshall and Hammond, 1945; rabbits: Makepeace et al., 1937; guinea pigs: Goy et al., 1966; hamsters: Lisk, 1969; rats: Whalen and Nakayama, 1965). Related progestins may also have suppressive effects on female sexual responses (for example, in guinea pigs, 5α-dihydroprogesterone: Czaja et al., 1974).

The guinea pig is particularly interesting to study because progesterone possesses both strong facilitatory and strong inhibitory activities on lordosis in this species. Experimentally, this is an appropriate species in which to assess the extent of overlap or separability of facilitatory and inhibitory brain mechanisms responsive to progesterone. This experimental problem takes on an additional dimension of complexity in so far as progesterone may exert more than one type of inhibitory influence on lordosis in guinea pigs. In order to illustrate these different types of suppressive effects of progesterone on lordosis, three different experimental paradigms are necessary.

Inhibitory effect A

The first group of experiments with ovariectomized guinea pigs involves giving systemic injections of hormones according to the following schedule:

GROUP	HOUR 0	HOUR 36	PRESENCE OF SEXUAL RESPONSES AT HOUR 40
I	Estradiol benzoate	Progesterone	High percentage of animals show lordosis
II	Estradiol benzoate + progesterone	No steroid injection	Reduced percentage of animals show lordosis
III	Estradiol benzoate + progesterone	Progesterone	Reduced percentage of animals show lordosis

This schedule was used experimentally by Goy and Phoenix (1965) and Zucker and Goy (1967) and clearly demonstrated that when progesterone was administered simultaneously (or within 6 hours of estrogen treatment) lordosis behavior not only was not facilitated (Group II), but was actively suppressed (Group III). Thus, when progesterone is administered before estrogen has had an adequate period of time to act on neural tissues mediating behavior, the effect of the progesterone is suppressive. Neither the site nor the mechanism of this action of progesterone is known. Current research in this laboratory by Babetta Marrone is aimed at testing the hypothesis that this particular suppressive action of progesterone is exerted in the same areas of the diencephalon (preoptic area, anterior hypothalamus, and medial basal hypothalamus) as those in which estradiol is maximally concentrated and maximally effective in inducing lordosis. A related idea which is also being tested, is that progesterone inhibits uptake of radioactive estradiol into cell nuclei in these diencephalic sites. Both of these predictions rest on the notion that the suppressive action of progesterone in Group III is due to a direct interference by progesterone with estrogen uptake and retention in the basal diencephalon.

Inhibitory effect B

The second experimental design used to illustrate a suppressive action of progesterone on lordosis in ovariectomized guinea pigs may be summarized as follows:

GROUP	HOUR 0	HOUR 36	HOUR 60	PRESENCE OF SEXUAL RESPONSES AT HOUR 64
IV	Estradiol benzoate	Progesterone	Progesterone	Reduced
V	Estradiol benzoate	No steroid injection	Progesterone	Not reduced

By use of this type of design (Zucker, 1966; Morin and Feder, 1974b) it can be recognized that one injection of progesterone (at hour 36 in Group IV) suppresses the facilitatory behavioral effects of a subsequent injection of progesterone (at hour 60 in Group IV). The site and mechanism of this second type of inhibitory effect of progesterone are also unknown. However, there is evidence that estrogen-primed guinea pigs given an intracerebral implant of progesterone in the mesencephalic tegmentum (at hour 36) do not show lordosis, or show impaired lordosis after receiving a systemic injection of progesterone at hour 40 (Morin and Feder, 1974b). Because estradiol implants in the mesencephalon of guinea pigs do not induce lordosis (Morin and Feder, 1974a) and because the guinea pig mesencephalon does not take up estradiol very avidly or selectively (Feder et al., 1974), one may reason that this second type of inhibitory action of progesterone is not attributable to a direct antagonism between estrogen and progesterone at the same neural sites. Furthermore, this second type of inhibitory effect of progesterone occurs when estrogen conditioning is complete. If the mechanism underlying this type of inhibitory action of progesterone does not involve direct antagonism of estradiol, what alternative explanations can be sought? One possibility is that mesencephalic progesterone stimulates activity of the serotonin or dopamine systems, and the increased activity of either or both of these systems affects the arousability of forebrain tissues to which they project. This idea is currently being tested in this laboratory by William Crowley. Preliminary results suggest that dopamine and serotonin agonists suppress lordosis induced by estrogen and progesterone in ovariectomized guinea pigs. Cell bodies of neurons that use dopamine as a neurotransmitter are located in the substantia nigra of the midbrain (Ungerstedt, 1974), and mesencephalic implants of progesterone in the substantia nigra suppress lordosis in guinea pigs (Morin and Feder, 1974d).

Inhibitory effect C

The final type of suppressive effect of progesterone on lordosis in guinea pigs is discernible in the following groups of ovariectomized subjects:

GROUP	HOUR 0	HOUR 36	CHARACTERISTICS OF LORDOSIS
I	Estradiol benzoate	Progesterone	Heat duration about 8 h; lordoses strong
VI	Estradiol benzoate	No steroid	Heat duration variable can last much longer than 8h; lordoses usually weak

A proportion of females displays lordosis in response to estradiol benzoate alone (Group VI). These females tend to display weaker responses which are, however, spread over a longer period of time than the stronger responses shown by animals given sequential treatment with estrogen and progesterone (Boling et al., 1938). Thus, progesterone apparently has a role in defining the length of estrous receptivity in guinea pigs. The mechanisms and sites of this activity of progesterone are unknown but the process does not appear to be a passive one. That is, lordosis responses do not cease merely because progesterone levels decline. This was demonstrated by giving ovariectomized, estrogen-primed guinea pigs multiple injections of progesterone at short intervals (Morin and Feder, 1973). Even though this procedure results in the maintenance of elevated progesterone levels in the circulation, estrous receptivity lasts only about 2.7 hours longer than usual. The estrus-terminating properties of progesterone might be attributable to: (a) impedance of estrogen-sensitive brain areas; (b) development of refractoriness of brain sites normally responsive to behavior-facilitating effects of progesterone, as a result of prolonged exposure to progesterone; or (c) a shift in balance between the activity of progesterone-sensitive brain sites (possibly in the hypothalamus) mediating facilitation of lordosis and progesterone-sensitive brain sites (possibly in the mesencephalon) mediating suppression of lordosis. According to the last idea, the facilitatory effects of progesterone would be exerted first at the hypothalamic level, but the balance would eventually shift as the inhibitory influences of the mesencephalon continue to build up. This would account for the slight prolongation (2.7 hours) of estrous receptivity seen in animals given multiple progesterone injections, if one supposed that the additional progesterone threw the balance in favor of the facilitatory system, but only for a short time.

6. SUMMARY

Estrogens (particularly estradiol-17β) activate female sexual behavior in a wide variety of nonprimate species. The role of progesterone in the activation of female behavior varies markedly among species. In rodents such as rats, hamsters and guinea pigs, a period of estrogen conditioning prepares the neural tissues for a behavior-facilitating action of pre-ovulatory progesterone. In ewes, a period of luteal progesterone secretion conditions the neural substrates of behavior for activation by estrogen. In cows, dogs and rabbits progesterone probably has little or no role in activation of sexual behavior under normal circumstances, but experimental manipulations suggest that neural tissues are capable of responding to behavior-facilitating actions of exogenous progesterone.

Progesterone also suppresses female sexual behavior in a variety of nonprimates, but the mechanisms of this effect of progesterone are unknown.

ACKNOWLEDGEMENTS

I am grateful to William Crowley, Margaret Johns, Babetta Marrone and William Walker for discussions regarding this chapter and for reading the manuscript. I also express my gratitude to Regina Harris for typing the manuscript. Because this review is necessarily brief I was regretfully not able to refer to many excellent and relevant publications on the subject of hormones and female sex behavior.

This work was supported by USPHS Grant NIH-HD 04467 and NIMH Career Development Award K2-MH-29006. Contribution Number 244 of the Institute of Animal Behavior.

BIBLIOGRAPHY

Arai, Y. and Gorski, R.A. (1968) Effects of anti-estrogen on steroid induced sexual receptivity in ovariectomized rats. *Physiol. Behav.* 3: 351—353.

Baker, L.N., Ulberg, L.C., Grummer, R.H. and Casida, L.E. (1954) Inhibition of heat by progesterone and its effect on subsequent fertility in gilts. *J. Anim. Sci.* 13: 648—657.

Baranczuk, R. and Greenwald, G.S. (1973) Peripheral levels of estrogen in the cyclic hamster, *Endocrinology* 92: 805—812.

Barraclough, C.A., Collu, R., Massa, R. and Martini, L. (1971) Temporal interrelationships between plasma LH, ovarian secretion rates and peripheral plasma progestin concentrations in the rat: effects of nembutal and exogenous gonadotropins. *Endocrinology* 88: 1437—1447.

Bartosik, D., Szarowski, D.H. and Watson, D.J. (1971) Influence of functioning ovarian tissue on the secretion of progesterone by the adrenal glands of female rats. *Endocrinology* 88: 1425—1428.

Beach, F.A. (1942a) Importance of progesterone to induction of sexual receptivity in spayed female rats. *Proc. Soc. Exp. Biol. Med.* 51: 369—371.

Beach, F.A. (1942b) Male and female mating behavior of prepuberal male and female rats treated with gonadal hormones. *J. Comp. Psychol.* 34: 285—292.

Beach, F.A. (1967) Cerebral and hormonal control of reflexive mechanisms involved in copulatory behavior. *Physiol. Rev.* 47: 289—316.

Beach, F.A. and Merani, A. (1968) Coital behavior in dogs, IV. Effects of progesterone in the bitch. *Proc. Natl. Acad. Sci. U.S.* 61: 442—446.

Bermant, G. and Davidson, J.M. (1974) *Biological Bases of Sexual Behavior.* (Harper and Row, New York.)

Beyer, C., Morali, G. and Vargas, R. (1971) Effect of diverse estrogens on estrous behavior and genital tract development in ovariectomized rats. *Horm. Behav.* 2: 273—277.

Boling, J.L. and Blandau, R.J. (1939) The estrogen-progesterone induction of mating responses in the spayed female rat. *Endocrinology* 25: 359—364.

Boling, J.L., Young, W.C. and Dempsey, E.W. (1938) Miscellaneous experiments on the estrogen-progesterone induction of heat in the spayed guinea pig. *Endocrinology* 23: 182—187.

Brookhart, J.M., Dey, F.L. and Ranson, S.W. (1941) The abolition of mating behavior by hypothalamic lesions in guinea pigs. *Endocrinology* 28: 561—565.

Brown-Grant, K. (1969) The effects of progesterone and of pentobarbitone administered at the dioestrous stage on the ovarian cycle of the rat. *J. Endocrinol.* 43: 539—552.

Brown-Grant, K. (1971) The role of steroid hormones in the control of gonadotropin secretion in adult female mammals. In: (C.H. Sawyer and R.A. Gorski, Eds.) *Steroid Hormones and Brain Function.* (University of California Press, Los Angeles) pp. 269—288.

Challis, J.R.G., Heap, R.B. and Illingworth, D.V. (1971) Concentrations of oestrogen and progesterone in the plasma of non-pregnant, pregnant and lactating guinea-pigs. *J. Endocrinol.* 51: 333—345.

Ciaccio, L.A. and Lisk, R.D. (1971a) Hormonal control of cyclic estrus in the female hamster. *Am. J. Physiol.* 221: 936—942.

Ciaccio, L.A. and Lisk, R.D. (1971b) The role of progesterone in regulating the period of sexual receptivity in the female hamster. *J. Endocrinol.* 50: 201—207.

Ciaccio, L.A. and Lisk, R.D. (1973) Central control of estrous behavior in the female golden hamster. *Neuroendocrinology* 13: 21—28.

Clemens, L.G. (1971) Perinatal hormones and the modification of adult behavior. In: (C.H. Sawyer and R.A. Gorski, Eds.) *Steroid Hormones and Brain Function.* (University of California Press, Los Angeles) pp: 203—214.

Czaja, J.A., Goldfoot, D.A. and Karavolas, H.J. (1974) Comperative facilitation and inhibition of lordosis in the guinea pig with progesterone, 5α-pregnane-3,20-dione, or 3α-hydroxy-5α-pregnan-20-one. *Horm. Behav.* 5: 261—274.

Daane, T.A. and Parlow, A.F. (1971) Periovulatory patterns of rat serum follicle stimulating hormone and luteinizing hormone during the normal estrous cycle: effects of pentobarbital. *Endocrinology* 88: 653—663.

Davidson, J.M., Rodgers, C.H., Smith, E.R. and Bloch, G.J. (1968) Stimulation of female sex behavior in adrenalectomized rats with estrogen alone. *Endocrinology* 82: 193—195.

Dörner, G., Döcke, F. and Moustafa, S. (1968) Differential localization of a male and a female hypothalamic mating centre. *J. Reprod. Fertil.* 17: 583—586.

Eaton, L.M., Jr. and Hilliard, J. (1971) Estradiol-17β, progesterone and 20-α-hydroxy-pregn-4-en-3-one in rabbit ovarian venous plasma. I. Steroid secretion from paired ovaries with and without corpora lutea: effect of LH. *Endocrinology* 89: 105—111.

Edwards, D.A. and Warner, P. (1972) Olfactory bulb removal facilitates the hormonal induction of sexual receptivity in the female rat. *Horm. Behav.* 3: 321—332.

Eto, T., Masuda, H., Suzuki, Y. and Hosi, T. (1962) Progesterone and pregn-4-en-20α-ol-3-one in rat ovarian venous blood at different stages in reproductive cycle. *Jap. J. Anim. Reprod.* 8: 34—40.

Feder, H.H., Brown-Grant, K. and Corker, C.S. (1971) Pre-ovulatory progesterone, the adrenal cortex and the "critical period" for luteinizing hormone release in rats. *J. Endocrinol.* 50: 29—39.

Feder, H.H. and Morin, L.P. (1974) Suppression of lordosis in guinea pigs by ethamoxytriphetol (MER-25) given at long intervals (34—46 hr.) after estradiol benzoate treatment. *Horm. Behav.* 5: 63—72.

Feder, H.H., Resko, J.A. and Goy, R.W. (1968a) Progesterone levels in the arterial plasma of pre-ovulatory and ovariectomized rats. *J. Endocrinol.* 41: 563—569.

Feder, H.H., Resko, J.A. and Goy, R.W. (1968b) Progesterone concentrations in the arterial plasma of guinea-pigs during the oestrous cycle. *J. Endocrinol.* 40: 505—513.

Feder, H.H. and Ruf, K.B. (1969) Stimulation of progesterone release and oestrous behavior by ACTH in ovariectomized rodents. *Endocrinology* 69: 171—174.

Feder, H.H., Siegel, H. and Wade, G.N. (1974) Uptake of 6,7-³H estradiol-17β in ovariectomized rats, guinea pigs, and hamsters: correlation with species differences in behavioral responsiveness to estradiol. *Brain Res.* 71: 93—103.

Feder, H.H. and Wade, G.N. (1974) Integrative actions of perinatal hormones on neural tissues mediating adult sexual behavior. In: (F.O. Schmitt and F.G. Worden, Eds.) *The Neurosciences, Third Study Program,* (M.I.T. Press, Cambridge, Mass.) pp. 583—586.

Ferin, M., Tempone, A., Zimmering, P.E. and Van de Wiele, R.L. (1969) Effect of antibodies to 17β-estradiol and progesterone on the estrous cycle of the rat. *Endocrinology* 85: 1070—1078.

Frank, A.H. and Fraps, R.M. (1945) Induction of estrus in the ovariectomized golden hamster. *Endocrinology* 37: 357—361.

Goy, R.W. and Phoenix, C.H. (1965) Inhibitory actions of progesterone. *Am. Zool.* 5: 725 (abstr.).

Goy, R.W., Phoenix, C.H. and Young, W.C. (1966) Inhibitory action of the corpus luteum on the hormonal induction of estrous behavior in the guinea pig. *Gen. Comp. Endocrinol.* 6: 267—275.

Green, R., Luttge, W.G. and Whalen, R.E. (1970) Induction of receptivity in ovariectomized female rats by a single intravenous injection of estradiol-17β. *Physiol. Behav.* 5: 137—141.

Hansel, W. and Echternkamp, S.E. (1972) Control of ovarian function in domestic animals. *Am. Zool.* 12: 225—243.

Harris, G.W., Michael, R.P. and Scott, P.P. (1958) Neurological site of action of stilboestrol in eliciting sexual behaviour. In: (G.E.W. Wolstenholme and C.M. O'Connor, Eds.). *Ciba Foundation Symposium on the Neurological Basis of Behaviour, 1957,* (Little, Brown and Co., Boston, Mass.) pp. 236—254.

Hashimoto, I., Henricks, D.N., Anderson, L.L. and Melampy, R.M. (1968) Progesterone and pregn-4-en-20α-ol-3-one in ovarian venous blood during various reproductive status in the rat. *Endocrinology* 82: 333—342.

Holzbauer, M., Newport, H.H. Birmingham, M.K. and Traikov, H. (1969) Secretion of pregn-4-ene-3,20-dione (progesterone) in vivo by the adrenal gland of the rat. *Nature* 221: 572—573.

Joshi, H.S., Watson, D.J. and Labhsetwar, A.P. (1973) Ovarian secretion oestradiol, oestrone, 20-dihydroprogesterone and progesterone during the oestrous cycle of the guinea-pig. *J. Reprod. Fertil.* 33: 177—181.

Joslyn, W.D., Feder, H.H. and Goy, R.W. (1971) Estrogen conditioning and progesterone facilitation of lordosis in guinea pigs. *Physiol. Behav.* 7: 477—482.

Kalra, S.P. (1975) Observations on facilitation of the preovulatory rise of LH by estrogen. *Endocrinology* 96: 23—28.

Keefer, D.A., Stumpf, W.E. and Sar, M. (1973) Estrogen-topographical localization of estrogen-concentrating cells in the rat spinal cord following 3H-estradiol administration. *Proc. Soc. Exp. Biol. Med.* 143: 414—417.

Kennedy, G.C. (1964) Hypothalamic control of the endocrine and behavioural changes associated with oestrus in the rat. *J. Physiol.* 172: 383—392.

Kitay, J.I. (1963) Pituitary-adrenal function in the rat after gonadectomy and gonadal hormone replacement. *Endocrinology* 73: 253—260.

Komisaruk, B.R. (1974) Neural and hormonal interactions in the reproductive behavior of female rats. In: (W. Montagna and W.A. Sadler, Eds.) *Reproductive Behavior.* (Plenum Press, New York) pp. 97—130.

Komisaruk, B.R. and Beyer, C. (1972) Differential antagonism, by MER-25, of behavioral and morphological effects of estradiol benzoate in rats. *Horm. Behav.* 3: 63—70.

Komisaruk, B.R., Larsson, K. and Cooper, R. (1972) Intense lordosis in the absence of ovarian hormones after septal ablations in rats. (Abstr. 2nd Annul. Meet. Soc. Neurosci., Houston, Texas) p. 230.

Kow, L.M., Malsbury, C.W. and Pfaff, D.W. (1974) Effects of progesterone on female reproductive behavior in rats: possible modes of action and role in behavioral sex differences. In: (W. Montagna and W.A. Sadler, Eds.) *Reproductive Behavior.* (Plenum Press, New York) pp. 179—210.

Law, D.T. and Meagher, W. (1958) Hypothalamic lesions and sexual behavior in the female rat. *Science* 128: 1626—1627.

Lawton, I.E. (1972) Facilitatory feedback effects of adrenal and ovarian hormones on LH secretion. *Endocrinology* 90: 575—579.

Leathem, J.H. (1938) Experimental induction of estrus in the dog. *Endocrinology* 22: 559—567.

Lisk, R.D. (1960) A comparison of the effectiveness of intravenous, as opposed to subcutaneous, injection of progesterone for the induction of estrous behavior in the rat. *Can. J. Biochem. Physiol.* 38: 1381—1383.

Lisk, R.D. (1962) Diencephalic placement of estradiol and sexual receptivity in the female rat. *Am. J. Physiol.* 203: 493—496.

Lisk, R.D. (1967) Sexual behavior: Hormonal control. In: (L. Martini and W.F. Ganong, Eds.) *Neuroendocrinology,* Vol. 2 (Academic Press, New York) pp. 197—239.

Lisk, R.D. (1969) Progesterone: role in limitation of ovulation and sex behavior in mammals. *Trans. NY Acad. Sci.,* Ser. II, 31: 593—601.

Lisk, R.D. (1970) Mechanisms regulating sexual activity in mammals. *J. Sex Res.* 6: 220—228.

Lisk, R.D., Ciaccio, L.A. and Reuter, L.A. (1972) Neural receptor mechanisms for estrogens and progesterone and the regulation of ovulation and sex-related behavior in mammals. *Gen. Comp. Endocrinol.* suppl. 3: 553—564.

Lukaszewska, J.H. and Greenwald, G.S. (1970) Progesterone levels in the cyclic and pregnant hamster. *Endocrinology* 86: 1—9.

Makepeace, A.W., Weinstein, G.L. and Friedman, M.W. (1937) The effect of progestin and progesterone on ovulation in the rabbit. *Am. J. Physiol.* 119: 512—516.

Mann, D.R. and Barraclough, C.A. (1973) Role of estrogen and progesterone in facilitating LH release in 4-day cyclic rats. *Endocrinology* 93: 694—699.

Marshall, F.H.A. and Hammond, J., Jr. (1945) Experimental control by hormone action of the oestrous cycle in the ferret. *J. Endocrinol.* 4: 159—168.

Melampy, R.M., Emmerson, M.A., Rakes, J.M., Hanka, L.J. and Eness, P.G. (1957) The effect of progesterone on the estrous response of estrogen-conditioned ovariectomized cows. *J. Anim. Sci.* 16: 967—975.

Meyerson, B.J. (1964) The effect of neuropharmacological agents on hormone-activated estrous behaviour in ovariectomized rats. *Arch. Int. Pharmacodyn. Ther.* 150: 4—33.

Meyerson, B.J. (1967) Relationship between the anesthetic and gestagenic action and estrous behavior-inducing activity of different progestins. *Endocrinology* 81: 369—374.

Meyerson, B.J. (1972) Latency between intravenous injection of progestins and the appearance of estrous behavior in estrogen-treated ovariectomized rats. *Horm. Behav.* 3: 1—9.

Moore, N.W., Barrett, S., Brown, J.B., Schindler, I., Smith, M.A. and Smyth, B. (1969) Oestrogen and progesterone content of ovarian vein blood of the ewe during the oestrous cycle. *J. Endocrinol.* 44: 55—62.

Moore, N.W. and Robinson, T.J. (1957) The behavioral and vaginal response of the spayed ewe to estrogen injected at various times relative to the injection of progesterone. *J. Endocrinol.* 15: 360—365.

Morin, L.P. and Feder, H.H. (1973) Multiple progesterone injections and the duration of estrus in ovariectomized guinea pigs. *Physiol. Behav.* 11: 861—865.

Morin, L.P. and Feder, H.H. (1974a) Intracranial estradiol implants and lordosis behavior of ovariectomized guinea pigs. *Brain Res.* 70: 95—102.

Morin, L.P. and Feder, H.H. (1974b) Independence of progesterone induced facilitation and inhibition of lordosis behavior in ovariectomized guinea pigs. *Horm. Behav.* 5: 7—12.

Morin, L.P. and Feder, H.H. (1974c) Hypothalamic progesterone implants and facilitation of lordosis behavior in estrogen-primed ovariectomized guinea pigs. *Brain Res.* 70: 81—93.

Morin, L.P. and Feder, H.H. (1974d) Inhibition of lordosis behavior in ovariectomized guinea pigs by mesencephalic implants of progesterone. *Brain Res.* 70: 71—80.

Moss, R.L. (1971) Modification of copulatory behavior in the female rat following olfactory bulb removal. *J. Comp. Physiol.* 74: 374—382.

Moss, R.L. and McCann, S.M. (1973) Induction of mating behavior in rats by luteinizing hormone-releasing factor. *Science* 181: 177—179.

McEwen, B.S. and Pfaff, D.W. (1973) Chemical and physiological approaches to neuroendocrine mechanisms: attempts at integration. In: (W.F. Ganong and L. Martini, Eds.) *Frontiers in Neuroendocrinology.* (Oxford University Press, New York) pp. 267—335.

Naftolin, F., Brown-Grant, K. and Corker, C.S. (1972) Plasma and pituitary luteinizing hormone and peripheral plasma oestradiol concentrations in the normal oestrous cycle of the rat and after experimental manipulation of the cycle. *J. Endocrinol.* 53: 17—30.

Nance, D.M., Shryne, J. and Gorski, R.A. (1974) Septal lesions: effects on lordosis behavior and pattern of gonadotropin release. *Horm. Behav.* 5: 73—81.

Nequin, L.G. and Schwartz, N.B. (1971) Adrenal participation in the timing of mating and LH release in the cyclic rat. *Endocrinology* 88: 325—331.

Pfaff, D.W. (1970) Nature of sex hormone effects on rat sex behavior: specificity of effects and individual patterns of response. *J. Comp. Physiol. Psychol.* 73: 349—350.

Pfaff, D.W. (1973) Luteinizing hormone-releasing factor potentiates lordosis behavior in hypophysectomized ovariectomized female rats. *Science* 182: 1148—1149.

Phillips, R.W., Fraps, R.M. and Frank, A.H. (1946) Ovulation and estrus in sheep and goats. In: (E.T. Engle, Ed.) *The Problem of Fertility.* (Princeton University Press, Princeton) pp. 11—48.

Powers, J.B. (1970) Hormonal control of sexual receptivity during the estrus cycle of the rat. *Physiol. Behav.* 5: 831—835.

Powers, J.B. (1972) Facilitation of lordosis in ovariectomized rats by intracerebral implants. *Brain Res.* 48: 311—325.

Powers, B. and Valenstein, E.W. (1972) Sexual receptivity: facilitation by medial preoptic lesions in female rats. *Science* 175: 1003—1005.

Resko, J.A. (1969) Endocrine control of adrenal progesterone secretion in the ovariectomized rat. *Science* 164: 70—71.

Robertson, H.A. (1969) The endogenous control of estrus and ovulation in sheep, cattle, and swine. *Vitam. Horm.* 27: 91—130.

Robinson, T.J. (1955) Quantitative studies on the hormonal induction of oestrus in spayed ewes. *J. Endocrinol.* 12: 163—173.

Rodgers, C.H. and Law, O.T. (1968) Effects of chemical stimulation of the "limbic system" on lordosis in female rats. *Physiol. Behav.* 3: 241—246.

410

Ross, J., Claybaugh, C., Clemens, L.G. and Gorski, R.A. (1971) Short latency induction of estrous behavior with intracerebral gonadal hormones in ovariectomized rats. *Endocrinology* 89: 32—38.

Ross, J.W., Gorski, R.A. and Sawyer, C.H. (1973a) Effects of cortical stimulation on estrous behavior in estrogen-primed ovariectomized rats. *Endocrinology* 93: 20—25.

Ross, J.W., Paup, D.C., Brant-Zawadzki, M., Marshall, J.R. and Gorski, R.A. (1973b) Effects of cis- and trans-clomiphene in the induction of sexual behavior. *Endocrinology* 93: 681—685.

Sar, M. and Stumpf, W.E. (1973) Neurons of the hypothalamus concentrate (^{3}H) progesterone or its metabolites. *Science* 182: 1266—1268.

Sasaki, Y. and Hanson, G.C. (1974) Correlation between the activities of enzymes involved in glucose oxidation in corpus luteum and the concentration of sex steroids in systemic plasma during the reproductive cycle of the guinea pig. *Endocrinology* 95: 1213—1218.

Sawyer, C.H. (1960) Reproductive behavior. In: (J. Field, Ed.) *Handbook of Physiology Section 1: Neurophysiology.* Vol. 2 (Am. Physiol. Soc., Washington, D.C.) pp. 1225—1240.

Sawyer, C.H. and Everett, J.W. (1959) Stimulatory and inhibitory effects of progesterone on the release of pituitary ovulating hormone in the rabbit. *Endocrinology* 65: 644—651.

Schwartz, N.B. (1974) The role of FSH and LH and of their antibodies on follicle growth and on ovulation. *Biol. Reprod.* 10: 236—272.

Shaikh, A.A. and Shaikh, S.A. (1975) Adrenal and ovarian steroid secretion in the rat estrous cycle temporally related to gonadotropins and steroid levels found in peripheral plasma. *Endocrinology* 96: 37—44.

Short, R.V. (1972) Role of hormones in sex cycles. In: (C.R. Austin and R.V. Short, Eds.) *Reproduction in Mammals Book 3: Hormones in Reproduction.* (University Press, Cambridge) pp. 42—72.

Singer, J.J. (1968) Hypothalamic control of male and female sexual behavior in female rats. *J. Comp. Physiol. Psychol.* 66: 738—742.

Smith, I.D., Bassett, J.M. and Williams, T. (1970) Progesterone concentrations in the peripheral plasma of the mare during the estrous cycle. *J. Endocrinol.* 47: 523—524.

Smith, M.S. and McDonald, L.E. (1974) Serum levels of luteinizing hormone and progesterone during the estrous cycle, pseudopregnancy and pregnancy in the dog. *Endocrinology* 94: 404—412.

Stabenfeldt. G.H., Holt, J.A. and Ewing, L.L. (1969) Peripheral plasma progesterone levels during the bovine estrous cycle. *Endocrinology* 85: 11—15.

Stumpf, W.E. (1968) Estradiol-concentrating neurons: topography in the hypothalamus by dry-mount autoradiography. *Science* 162: 1001—1003.

Thorburn, G.D., Bassett, J.M. and Smith, I.D. (1969) Progesterone concentration in the peripheral plasma of sheep during the oestrous cycle. *J. Endocrinol.* 45: 459—469.

Uchida, K., Kadowaki, M. and Miyake, T. (1969) Ovarian secretion of progesterone and 20α-hydroxy-pregn-4-en-3-one during rat estrous cycle in chronological relation to pituitary release of luteinizing hormone. *Endocrinol. Jap.* 16: 227—237.

Ungerstedt, U. (1974) Brain dopamine neurons and behavior. In: (F.O. Schmitt and F.G. Worden, Eds.) *The Neurosciences, Third Study Program,* (MIT Press, Cambridge, Mass.) pp. 695—704.

Wade, G.N. and Feder, H.H. (1972) (1,2-^{3}H) Progesterone uptake by guinea pig brain and uterus: differential localization, time-course of uptake and metabolism, and effects of age, sex, estrogen-priming and competing steroids. *Brain Res.* 45: 525—543.

Wade, G.N., Harding, C.F. and Feder, H.H. (1973) Neural uptake of (1,2-^{3}H) progesterone in ovariectomized rats, guinea pigs and hamsters: correlation with species differences in behavioral responsiveness. *Brain Res.* 61: 357—367.

Whalen, R.E. and Gorzalka, B.B. (1972) The effects of progesterone and its metabolites on the induction of sexual receptivity in rats. *Horm. Behav.* 3: 221—226.

Whalen, R.E. and Gorzalka, B.B. (1973) Effects of an estrogen antagonist on behavior and on estrogen retention in neural and peripheral target tissues. *Physiol. Behav.* 10: 35—40.

Whalen, R.E., Gorzalka, B.B., DeBold, J.F., Quadagno, D.M., Ho, G.K. and Hough, J.C., Jr. (1974) Studies on the effects of intracerebral actinomycin D. implants on estrogen-induced receptivity in rats. *Horm. Behav.* 5: 337—343.

Whalen, R.E. and Luttge, W.G. (1971) Differential localization of progesterone uptake in brain, role of sex, estrogen pretreatment and adrenalectomy. *Brain Res.* 33: 147—155.

Whalen, R.E. and Nakayama, K. (1965) Induction of oestrous behaviour. facilitation by repeated hormone treatments. *J. Endocrinol.* 33: 525—526.

Young, W.C. (1961) The hormones and mating behavior. In: (W.C. Young, Ed.) *Sex and Internal Secretions* 3rd edn, Vol. 2 (Williams and Wilkins, Baltimore) pp. 1173—1239.

Young, W.C. (1969) Psychobiology of sexual behavior in the guinea pig. In: (D.S. Lehrman, R.A. Hinde and E. Shaw, Eds.) *Advances in the Study of Behavior.* Vol. 2 (Academic Press, New York) pp. 1—110.

Zigmond, R.E. and McEwen, B.S. (1970) Selective retention of estradiol by cell nuclei in specific brain regions of the ovariectomized rat. *J. Neurochem.* 17: 889—899.

Zucker, I. (1966) Facilitatory and inhibitory effects of progesterone on sexual responses of spayed guinea pigs. *J. Comp. Physiol. Psychol.* 62: 376—381.

Zucker, I. and Goy, R.W. (1967) Sexual receptivity in the guinea pig: inhibitory and facilitatory actions of progesterone and related compounds. *J. Comp. Physiol. Psychol.* 64: 378—383.

CHAPTER 29

Pheromones and sexual behavior

E.B. KEVERNE

1. INTRODUCTION

Mammals use all their senses in assessing their environment and the functions of the different systems overlap extensively. Olfactory signalling has, in this last decade, received particular attention and has been shown to be of great importance in mammalian sexual behavior. The significance of olfactory communication lies in its persistence over time, which allows information to be transmitted even in the absence of the signalling animal. Olfactory signals are implicated not merely in sexual behavior and attraction, but also in territorial marking and defense, individual recognition, and the evocation of maternal and aggressive behavior.

A system of terminology for studying olfactory communication was suggested by Karlson and Butenandt (1959), who introduced the term 'pheromone', a word derived from the Greek, *pherein* (to transfer) and *hormon* (to excite). Pheromones are substances secreted by an animal externally with specific effects on the behavior or physiology of another individual of the same species. Although originally defined in the context of insect communication, the meaning of the word pheromone has since been extended to include chemical communication in a broader sense, and in all species, while the ability to detect and exploit odors appears to reach its highest degree of development among mammals. Care must be taken when describing complex mammalian responses not to imply the degree of stereotypy which exists in insect behavior.

Three kinds of response to pheromones are now recognised among mammals (Bruce, 1970). Primer pheromones alter the physiology and consequent behavioral repertoire of the receptor animal. This type of response is slow to develop and demands a prolonged stimulation which is mediated through the nervous and endocrine systems.

If the pheromone produces a more or less immediate change in the behavior of the recipient, it is said to have a releaser effect (Wilson, 1963). Sex at-

Handbook of Sexology, edited by J. Money and H. Musaph
© *Elsevier/North-Holland Biomedical Press, 1977*

tractants constitute a large and important category of the releaser pheromones. Olfactory imprinting at a critical stage in the development of the neonate has also been shown to be of importance in some mammalian species, and may result in a permanent modification of sexual preference as in the behavior of the adult mouse (Marr and Gardner, 1965). Hence, there are the three levels at which pheromones might influence sexual behavior, but to deal with all of them in detail is not the purpose of this chapter. Several review articles have been written which deal in some detail with primer pheromones (Bronson, 1968, 1971; Bruce, 1970; Dominic, 1969; Vandenbergh, 1975; Whitten and Bronson 1970). The function of this chapter is to consider sex-attractants in mammalian sexual behavior.

2. RODENTS

Rats

Olfactory cues are probably of some importance in the reproductive behavior of the rat, for under seminatural conditions the estrous female has been observed to range further than normal from her burrow, leaving her scent on the ground and objects she passes. These scent markings are examined by males and probably provide the cues for tracking the female to her burrow. Certainly, in a laboratory choice situation, the male rat prefers the odor of an estrous female to that of a diestrous female or another male (Le Magnen, 1952)). However, the ability to demonstrate this preference for estrous female odors is dependent on prior sexual experience, which suggests it is a learned response. Although castrated males are capable of distinguishing between the odors of receptive and nonreceptive females when given a substantial (nonsexual) reward, under normal circumstances castrated males fail to respond differentially to either odor (Stern, 1970). These odors are probably present in the female's urine, since sexually experienced adult male rats investigate urine-soiled bedding from estrous females for longer than soiled bedding from nonreceptive females (Lydell and Doty, 1972). The female rat has also been shown to display a preference for intact male odors over odors from the castrate, especially when the female was sexually experienced or in the receptive phase of her cycle. The importance of these sex-odor preferences could be one of mutual attraction between sexual partners at estrus. Certainly, depriving the rat of its sense of smell by olfactory bulb ablation alters the sexual behavior in both males and females. This in the male takes the form of longer latencies and fewer ejaculations in a given period, while in the female the olfactory bulbs appear to inhibit other neural structures, such that bulb removal enhances the expression of lordotic behavior.

Mice

Urination in the mouse has been observed to change in response to the social environment: males produce far more urine than females in male—female encounters, and females urinate less during female—female encounters. Urination may thus play an adaptive part in social encounters, being relatively ample in the presence of a partner of the opposite sex where proximity and attraction is of biological advantage (Reynolds, 1971). Moreover, urine from adult male mice has been shown to elicit a significantly greater amount of sniffing by the female than urine from castrated males (Scott and Pfaff, 1970). The attractive components appear to have their origin in the preputial gland, and the preference response of females to preputial gland extracts is strong and consistent, but is lost during pregnancy or under the influence of progesterone, which may be of selective value since male urine is also known to contain a pregnancy-blocking primer pheromone (Bronson and Caroum, 1971). The attractant properties of male urine for female mice is paralleled by female urine especially that from estrous females serving to attract male mice (Davies and Bellamy, 1974). Thus, in the mouse, as in the rat, there appears to be mutual attraction of sexes by substances present in urine of both males and females. Female mouse urine also contains a pheromone possessing aggression-inhibiting properties when applied to males, but until chemical identification proceeds it is as yet unclear whether or not these two properties are due to the same compound which can produce a different behavioral effect dependent on the social context. This may likewise be true for the preputial component of male urine which attracts females but increases aggression between males. Olfactory bulb ablation completely abolishes the display of sexual behavior in male mice, and in female mice attenuates the estrogen—progesterone induced display of sexual receptivity. Since, however, such lesions can produce significant behavioral effects not necessarily related to a sensory deficit, the interpretation of these results is limited.

Hamsters

When the receptive female golden hamster is sexually stimulated, an abundant, highly odorous substance, which has a stimulating or releasing effect on the sexual behavior of the male hamster, exudes from her genital region. The male hamster sniffs and licks this vaginal discharge before and intermittently throughout mating. If this secretion is applied to the fur of a male, other males respond to him as though to a female and attempt to mate with him (Murphy, 1973; Lisk et al., 1972). Moreover, the mating behavior of the male hamster is totally eliminated following removal of both olfactory bulbs (Murphy and Schneider, 1970). Even less drastic methods of inducing anosmia peripherally interfere with the male's mounting behavior. Some workers, however, have found normal mating behavior following this technique (Powers and Winans, 1973), unless damage to the vomero-nasal organ also occurred (Powers and Winans, 1975). In contrast, female hamsters show normal lordosis behavior in response to the male following either peripheral or central anosmia, suggesting a sex-difference in the importance of olfaction for sexual behavior.

3. CARNIVORES

Canidae

Scent marking in the Canidae probably serves a number of functions, but as far as sexual attraction is concerned, there is evidence for the influence of olfactory stimuli from the female upon the male, and several sources of attractants have been suggested. Urine is perhaps the most significant source of attractants and many females mark only during the period preceding estrus and estrus itself (Kleiman, 1966). The bitch urinates more frequently when in heat, and only part of the bladder contents are expelled at each micturition, hence making a series of odor trails which converge upon her territory. Males have been attracted over long distances to estrous bitches. Female urine used as a lure has attracted male foxes and coyotes. Moreover, the urine from females in heat is preferentially discriminated from nonestrous urine by sexually active males (Beach and Gilmore, 1949).

In an attempt to trace the source of male attractants, experiments involving removal of the reproductive tract have been conducted, in which removal of the ovaries, anal glands and uterus were without effect on the attractiveness of the estrogenized female. Removal of the whole reproductive tract including the vulva and vestibule resulted in a loss of attractiveness and, although these females showed courtship behavior, the male would sniff and turn away and even attack the female if she persisted (Gier, 1960). These results indicated that the attractant odor was produced in the vestibule or the vulva of the female. Male dogs would investigate cotton swabs impregnated with vaginal secretions for longer periods than they would those from anestrous females (Beach and Merari, 1970). Progesterone greatly enhances the stimulus value of these vaginal secretions, and males show increased sniffing and licking of the vulva when females received both estrogen and progesterone.

Yet another source of sex attractants appears to be the anal gland secretions of the estrous bitch. When wiped over the rump of anestrous females, these secretions sexually excited males into mounting and copulation (Donovan, 1969). When the same procedure was performed with secretions from anestrous females, the male showed little interest. The anal gland secretions of one canine, the red fox, have been chemically investigated. Albone and Fox (1971) identified a series of saturated carboxylic acids (C_2 to C_6), but no concurrent behavioral studies were conducted with purified acids to confirm that these were involved in sexual attraction.

Thus it seems that three sources of sex-attractants exist in the Canids, including urinary, vaginal and anal gland secretions. Since all three sources are in close proximity, one has to be certain that no cross contamination occurs during experimental investigations. However, it is possible that urinary odors serve to direct males to estrous females from a distance, while vaginal secretions from the same females are involved in sexual arousal during courtship behavior. Secretions taken from within the female's anal gland may, under normal circumstances, not be readily available to males. Moreover, the remarkable similarity in some chemical components (short chain aliphatic acids) found in both anal gland secretions and vaginal secretions, could also be a source of confusion to the dog, and might in part account for the attractant properties of the anal gland secretions. However, in experienced male dogs, mating behavior does not depend exclusively on olfactory stimulation since peripheral anosmia is without apparent effect on sexual behavior, presumably because males compensate with other sensory information. This does not necessarily imply that odor cues serve no function in attracting males to estrous bitches, but in contrast to some rodents, sexual performance in dogs is not dependent on an olfactory input.

Felidae

During the courtship behavior of cats, the male has been observed to establish an area as 'familiar' by spraying it with urine and anal gland secretions. The estrous female, when introduced into such an area formerly occupied by the male, displays crouching and treading, but not if the cage is first washed thoroughly with disinfectant. Lissak (1962) reported that the odor of valeric-acid induced estrous-like behavior in the female cat, namely, head shaking and rolling, while catnip has been described as evoking similar responses (Todd, 1963). These compounds may have mimicked an attractant pheromone which was present in the urine or anal gland secretions of male cats, since an ether-extracted fraction of urine from males, but not females, elicited the head shaking and rubbing response seen in the estrous female cat.

4. UNGULATES

There is an increasing amount of evidence to suggest that olfaction is of fundamental importance to the stimulation of sexual behavior in many ungulate species, and similar responses are observed following genital inspection. This olfactory response, originally termed 'flehman' by Schneider (1930), is almost invariably in response to close genital sniffing.

Cattle

Hart and co-workers (1946) demonstrated that olfactory cues are of importance in arousing the sexual drive of bulls. The bull showed no interest in the nonestrous cow, but smearing such a cow's genital area with a mixture of vaginal mucous and urine from an estrous donor cow resulted in the bull's mounting and serving an affixed artificial vagina twice in five minutes. Similarly, when plastic gloves used rectally to palpate a cow in estrus became smeared with fecal matter and anal gland secretions and then were rubbed around the tail of an anestrous cow, the bull selected this cow from a row of animals and sniffed and stopped behind her (Donovan, 1967).

Horses

Olfactory stimulation of the stallion is derived from different parts of the mare's body including the external genitalia, muzzle and particularly the groin and neighboring parts (Berliner, 1959). Unlike the adult, young stallions showed a poor sexual response to a dummy, but sexual behavior was readily elicited from them when the dummy was sprinkled with urine from an estrous mare; 37% of the stallions then mounted it (Wierzbowski and Hafez, 1961).

Sheep

The method by which rams detect estrous ewes has long been considered to involve olfactory cues. Kelley (1937) concluded that rams were able to detect estrous ewes by the characteristic odor of vaginal secretions and claimed to have confused rams by wiping the swabs from the perineal region of estrous ewes onto the vulva of nonestrous ewes. Others have failed to find any significant change in the courtship behavior of rams rendered temporarily anosmic by topical anesthesia, but Lindsay (1965), using rams with olfactory lobes ablated, found anosmic rams to approach both estrous and nonestrous ewes at random. Normal rams were able to select among the two categories and preferentially approached estrous ewes. However, the ability of anosmic rams to mate successfully was not impaired and, although their precopulatory behavior was modified, they displayed practically no foreplay preceding the actual mating attempt.

Pigs

Signoret and Mesnil de Buisson (1961) have experimentally partitioned the stimuli which elicited the mating stance in the sow. The rutting sow shows an immobilizing reflex in the presence of the boar and in 50% of cases the same reflex can be triggerd by exerting pressure on the back of the estrous female in the male's absence. Acoustic signals produced by the boar had some effect in promoting the mating stance, but olfactory signals were of primary importance. Sows in pens impregnated by the odor of the boar were readily induced to give a mating stance in 81% of cases, but the pheromones responsible were not identified.

Chemical analysis of compounds isolated from the fat of mature pigs showed the presence in the boar of an odorous 5α-androst-16-en-3-one, which was absent from the fat of the castrate and the female. The corresponding steroid alcohol, 3α-hydroxy-5α-androst-16-ene, occurs in considerable concentration in the submaxillary salivary gland of the boar (Patterson,

1968), and both steroids are present in the saliva, imparting a musty odor to the breath of the animal. During the mating behavior of the boar, the male approaches the sow giving a series of grunts, noses the vulva and champs his jaws, producing copious saliva, and it was suggested that olfactory cues might have originated from the male in this way. Trials using aerosol sprays containing the two Δ16 androgen steroids have shown that, in the absence of the boar, the characteristic response of the estrous female to back pressure can be elicited when the spray is used in some 50% of sows previously negative (Melrose et al., 1971).

Other workers (Eibl and Wettke, 1964) have shown that a few millilitres of seminal fluid from a boar, deposited on the snout of a sow showing incomplete signs of heat, will make the animal responsive to back pressure in the majority of cases. It has also been suggested that the preputial gland is the site of sex-odor production, and that this depends upon the presence of male sex-hormones (Dutt et al., 1959). Melrose and co-workers (1971) found that a mixture of preputial fluid and urine was effective in promoting a response to back pressure in up to 62% of estrous sows that had not previously responded in the absence of the boar. Marked differences have been found between the biochemical composition of salivary gland pheromones and boar preputial fluid, in which, under conditions of acid pH, low molecular weight fatty acids predominate, whereas under conditions of alkaline pH, the principle odorous components are phenols, ammonia and amines. The proportions of the various components also vary dependent on the degree of bacterial activity in the mixture.

Deer

The flehman display is shown by the male antelope in response to sniffing the female's urine during precopulatory behavior. The black-tailed deer has been observed to pick up the scent and follow the trail of a female in, or approaching heat (Golly, 1957). This species also display the flehman face in response to urine and is able to detect those females approaching heat several days before the event, as assessed by increases in sniffing the genitalia and attempts to mount. In the red deer, the vaginal mucus at estrus was described as possessing a strong penetrating smell, and throughout the mating season there was a second odor which was sweet and musty, and which may have been the stag's rutting odor following mounting. In the early stages of estrus, clear fluid mucus dripped from the vagina and from the end of the hind's tail (Guinness et al., 1971). Stags were observed to sniff areas where estrous females had been lying, and after the estrous hind had urinated, the stag would rush up, sniff out the exact spot, and then show flehman. As estrus progressed, the hind gradually became more reluctant to run away, and would allow the stag to place his chin on her rump during the chase, or nuzzle and lick her vulva. The pheromones responsible for attracting males are not yet known but a series of acid lactones have been isolated from the tarsal scent gland, and are thought to be important in mutual recognition (Müller-Schwarze, 1971).

Elephant

In the Asiatic elephant, secretions from the urine or vagina may be involved in chemical communication. After touching the female in the region of the urogenital sinus, the male frequently places his trunk into his mouth, a chain of events comparable to the flehman reaction shown in other ungulates and termed urine testing (Eisenberg et al., 1971). Observations of sexual behavior during encounters between males and females indicated that the male played an active role in detecting estrus, and the frequency of urine testing altered significantly during various phases of the cycle. During diestrus after the initial urine test, the male paid no further attention to his partner for the rest of the observation period. As the female came into and passed out of estrus, there was a marked increase in the frequency of the male's scenting the urogenital sinus of the female.

There is perhaps also an olfactory influence from males on the behavior of female elephants. Females seen standing downwind of males, but not in visual communication, would turn and approach the male following the unsheathing of his penis. Females show an olfactory interest in the male, and touch and sniff most frequently in the vicinity of the penis sheath, but also smell the male in the area of his temporal gland and at the mouth mucosa.

5. PRIMATES

Prosimians

In the prosimian primates olfactory signals play an important role in communication between the sexes. Complex behavioral patterns involving 'stink-fights', urine marking, and scent-gland marking have evolved (Petter, 1965; Jolly, 1966). *Lemur catta* females have been observed to perform genital marking with the labia widely reflected and the inner surface pressed firmly against the marked surface, but whether these odor cues serve as attractants or primers in the activation of estrus remains to be determined. Other species of *Lemuroidea* perform olfactory marking with urine, a feature shared in common with the male loris and lesser bush baby.

Monkeys

In the squirrel monkey, urine marking is elicited during sexual excitement. Among males, genital inspection of females or the areas occupied by females is more frequent on receptive days (Latta et al., 1967). It was the view of Marler (1965) that olfactory communication played little part in the distance communication of monkeys and apes, although he pointed out that urine of estrous females seemed to convey information about their condition to males in the group. Certainly, field studies of several primate species have revealed that scenting of the females' anogenital region by males is a common, almost routine occurrence in the cercopithicus monkey, the howler monkey, the dusky titi, the night monkey and the patas monkey. In the talapoin monkey, males have been observed to look at or smell the females' sexual skin area more frequently and for longer periods around midcycle than during the early follicular or late luteal phases of the menstrual cycle (Scruton and Herbert, 1970). Scent marking regularly preceeds and follows copulation in marmosets, and scent marking as well as intensive licking and sniffing of the partner's marks and genitals is a regular component of courtship behavior (Epple, 1970).

Carpenter (1942) first noticed the vaginal exudate from the rhesus monkey (*M. mulatta*) to possess a characteristic odor which he thought might provide additional stimuli attracting males to females. This may be related to the persistent close following of females by males that has been observed in field studies, from which it has been suggested males receive some sort of cue about the state of the female's receptivity. Jay (1965) perceived a strong smelling vaginal discharge in toque macaques (*M. oinica*) and observed males to examine the genitalia of most females in the group each day. Bonnet macaques (*M. radiata*) have rarely been seen to present for copulation unless solicited by the male, which involved flipping the tail aside, olfactory examination of the genitalia, and on occasions, insertion of a finger followed by sniffing and tasting of the secretions. In the pigtail macaque (*M. nemestrina*) the male displays a posture similar to flehman following olfactory inspection of the female's genitalia, while the stump-tailed macaque (*M. arctoides*) sniffs, fingers and licks the female's perineal region prior to copulation. Although olfactory cues from the urine of receptive females are not ruled out, it would appear from these observations that in the macaques the secretions of the vagina serve some communicative function in reproductive behavior. This is certainly in agreement with findings for the rhesus monkey, where olfactory information concerning the sexual status of the female occurs by way of a pheromone of vaginal origin (Michael and Keverne, 1970).

To test this proposition experimentally, use was made of operant conditioning techniques, in which male rhesus monkeys were required to press a lever in order to raise a partition which physically separated them from a female partner, but through which they could both see and smell the partner. Males had to work with some dedication, pressing the lever 250 times to gain access to the female. They regularly responded for ovariectomized partners treated with estrogen, but rarely performed when faced with untreated ovariectomized females. Temporarily depriving these males of their sense of smell did not markedly affect either their pressing for, or behavior with the estrogen-treated females; these females were presumably remembered as being attractive because of previously rewarding sexual experiences with them. However, the temporarily anosmic male failed to respond for unfamiliar ovariectomized females after these females were administered estrogen, and shown to be sexually stimulating to normal males.

When the olfactorily deprived males had their sense of smell restored they readily began pressing for access to these females. That is to say, anosmia did not markedly impair the males' sexual arousal and sexual activity with familiar estrogenized females, but anosmic male rhesus monkeys were not able to detect the onset of attractiveness which estrogen promoted in their unfamiliar partners. These results were consistent with the hypothesis that estrogenized female rhesus monkeys produced substances which stimulated the sexual interest of their male partners via the olfactory sense.

The preoccupation of males with the female's genital region suggested this might be an obvious place at which to start looking for male sex attractants. Therefore, we studied the effects on male behavior of transferring vaginal secretions from estrogenized donor monkeys to ovariectomized, unattractive recipient partners. Application of vaginal secretions to the sexual skin area of recipients, which were themselves quite unreceptive to males, nevertheless resulted in a marked stimulation of the male partner's sexual activity. To determine the chemical nature of the substances in vaginal secretions responsible for these powerful behavioral effects, extraction and fractionation procedures were used in conjunction with behavioral assay methods. These resulted in the identification of a series of short-chain aliphatic acids, (C_2–C_6) which, when applied to the sexual skin area of unattractive females in concentrations equivalent to those in estrous vaginal secretions, markedly provoked male sexual behavior with some females.

The effectiveness of these pheromones in stimulating male sexual activity in the rhesus monkey varies, however, according to social conditions: with some partners, and in certain tests, no sexual stimulation occurs. As more males were tested, it became evident that the response to pheromone varied between individuals, and also depended in part upon the female partner with whom they were paired. Whereas some females treated with the natural pheromone readily evoked a sexual response from the male, other females when treated in the same manner failed to do so. Perhaps of even more interest is the different types of behavior which these odor cues can stimulate. Such olfactory stimulants can produce mounting and ejaculation, but in the presence of certain females the male may, instead, masturbate to ejaculation. The same male when paired with another ovariectomized female treated with pheromonal, estrous vaginal secretions in precisely the same manner, may display no overt sexual behavior, but will groom the female for longer. In other instances there will be marked reduction in the male's aggressive behavior. It could be argued that we are dealing with more than one odor cue, and that the vaginal secretion contains a grooming stimulant and an aggression-reducing pheromone, in addition to the sex attractant. My own opinion is that the coding for the behavioral response is not restricted to the olfactory cue, but is integrated in higher areas of the neocortex. Hence, the response to pheromones in these highly evolved social primates is not stereotyped, and differs from that in insects which is stereotyped. Thus, when considering this aliphatic acid mixture in the rhesus monkey, our present understanding of the term pheromone may not be appropriate, for what applies to some males may not be true for others, or indeed, for the same male with a different female partner. Clearly, olfactory cues are but one ingredient of female attractiveness.

As more pairs have been tested, data have accumulated providing a direct comparison of the synthetic acid mixture and the original vaginal secretions; the latter were effective in more tests. Additional constituents are known to be present in the rhesus monkey vaginal secretion, and two such components (phenylpropanoic acid and p-hydroxyphenylpropanoic acid) have characteristic strong odors of their own, but fail in themselves to stimulate male sexual activity when applied to the female's sexual skin. Their addition to the aliphatic acid mixture did, however, improve the latter's effectiveness, which now became almost equivalent to the natural vaginal secretion. There is an indication here that these other components may have an enhancing effect on the sexual stimulating properties of the synthetic pheromone. Perhaps, therefore, the odorous components of the vaginal secretion in toto represent the pheromone complex for some males, while others are readily stimulated by the fatty acid mixture which, in any case, probably mimics the most odorous components of the vaginal secretion.

Although these fatty acids are readily recovered from the rhesus monkey by vaginal lavage, we do not know whether their source is primarily glandular or as an exudate through the vaginal wall. There is evidence that microbial action plays a part in producing the vaginal secretion, since acid concentrations increase during incubation of the vaginal lavage, while autoclaving the lavage, or treating the vagina with penicillin prevents production of these substances. It seems probable, therefore, that the production of acidic pheromones depends upon the bacteria of the vagina, and that the ovarian hormones exert their influence on acid production in the intact animal by determining the availability of nutrients (in the form of cornified cells and mucus) for the bacteria.

The ovarian hormones may also affect the availability of the pheromone by changes in the tonus of the muscle folds in the vaginal wall, influencing flow rates to the exterior. Here, estrogen-dependent changes in the coloration of the sexual skin might facilitate dissemination of the odor. Reddening of the sexual skin is caused by increased vascularity and is associated with a localized increase in skin temperature. Hence, at times of intense reddening, under the influence of estrogen, there would be an improved surface for the volatilization of sex-attractant pheromones.

The dependence of pheromone production on bacterial activity indicates the existence of a rather novel symbiotic relationship. This relationship is probability not unique to the rhesus monkey, since similar aliphatic acids are also present, but in differing concentrations, in the vaginal secretions of several species of old-world primates, and also in humans. Although the importance of these acid odors in other species has yet to be determined, their widespread distribution in the anal glands of the cat and fox, the preputial gland of the boar, and chin gland secretions of the rabbit may be of some behavioral significance.

Humans

One can only speculate on the significance of these aliphatic acids in the human, where they characterize both vaginal and underarm body odors. Their presence does not, per se, signify a causal relationship between odor cues and the sexual behavior of the human male. True, the human male can distinguish variation in the pheromonal odors relative to the phases of the menstrual cycle in the rhesus monkey. In some islands of the Pacific, body odors are regarded as erotic, particularly those arising from the woman's genitalia. In tribes of Southern New Guinea armpit odors are said to be of social significance. To demonstrate friendship for a departing visitor, the host wipes sweat from the visitor's armpits with his finger, smells it, and then rubs his finger on his own chest. A parallel is found in a higher primate, the lowland gorilla; males attempt to touch the female's genitals or armpits, particularly around the estrous period, and then sniff their fingers before wiping them over their chest.

Western man now takes great pains to disguise or repress body odors. It could be argued that odoriferous stimulation or provocation might be disruptive to our social order. Clearly, cultural determinants are of great significance in human behavior, and if we consider the complexity and plasticity in the response of the male rhesus, then the further social evolution of man may make the search for an olfactory aphrodisiac with sexual releasing properties a profitless task. This is not to say that these odors play no part in human sexual behavior, but that to give them significance as sex-attractants underestimates the complexity of human behavior.

What then might be the effect of these odor cues on human behavior? It appears from our behavioral results with the rhesus monkey that at least two separate neural pathways are involved in the integration of olfactory cues. It is possible that sexual attraction involving releaser pheromones is brought about via olfactory connections to the pyriform cortex and neocortical regions before passing on to the hypothalamus. This neural circuitry I envisage as serving an integrative function, with the neocortex analogous to a computer incorporating certain go and no-go programs. As I have already stated, the rhesus monkey's behavior incorporates a number of no-go programs; for example, the modifying effects of partner preference, past experience with certain females, and the presence of other males. If we consider the human with infinitely more complex behavior patterns involving traditions, rituals, religions and past experiences, there are many variables which might constitute no-go programs, making it meaningless to look for any overt behavioral response. If, on the other hand one considers odor cues in the context of sexual performance as an autonomic response, then the findings for the rhesus monkey may be more transferable, in a similar context, to the human.

In the rhesus monkey, withdrawal of the sex-attractant from the female partner usually results in a loss of male interest, but occasionally males maintain their sexual arousal and, paradoxically, show increased mounting and thrusting prior to a loss of sexual interest. Moreover, if the estrogenized female donor is given progesterone, her vaginal secretions lose their sexual stimulating properties when applied to the recipient. However, prior to the male's loss of sexual interest there is a marked increase in his mounting and thrusting. Since the only change in all these experiments is the odor of the female partner, I interpret this increased mounting behavior as an increase in male sexual performance to compensate for the odor deficit of the female partner; that is, an increase in tactile input compensating for decreases in another sensory cue, namely, the olfactory cue. Similarly, following reversal of anosmia there may be an increase in male ejaculations with no marked increase in mounting or thrusting. Here the introduction of the olfactory sense with an attractive female improves the sexual performance of the male, and briefly increases the frequency of his ejaculations. In this context of sexual performance, it is possible that a second, more direct, olfactory input to the hypothalamus exists, probably involving only a few synapses or even being monosynaptic. This I envisage as being analogous to tactile input, as in genital stimulation, with the hypothalamus serving as an area of integration, while the threshold for response is modulated by hormonal status. Since there are no limits to the definition of attractiveness in the human, a distinction may be made between attraction and sexual performance or erotic arousal, and it is in this context of performance that one might consider a role for these odors in man.

6. CONCLUDING REMARKS

In order to demonstrate a behavioral response to pheromones, animals are best studied in the laboratory where environmental variables can be minimised or at least accurately quantified. Only in the laboratory can progress be made towards chemical identification of attractant pheromones when performed in conjunction with a repeatable behavioral assay system. Efforts should be made to use, as an assay, a behavioral response which is part of the animal's natural repertoire, and not simply a preference of one odor over another. Sexual attraction is not readily defined in either man or animals, and since olfactory cues are but one of a number of sensory ingredients, care must be taken to isolate the odor cues from other sensory information. Often this involves elaborate experimental manipulations, whereupon the relevence of such findings to the natural behavior of the animal may not be appropriate. This is particularly true where surgical techniques involving ablation of the olfactory bulbs are carried out, and nonsensory side effects impose severe limitations on the conclusions that can be drawn about behavioral changes related to olfaction in itself.

If we consider the way olfactory information is transmitted to induce a behavioral event, then at least two separate neural pathways can be envisaged. Any olfactory pathway which results in an animal being attracted to another animal is clearly of a complex nature, since attraction in this sense can be modified by any number of variables including past experiences and partner preferences. Such neural circuitry requires complex integration, and is probably represented neuroanatomically by olfactory pathways which enter the pyriform cortex, are relayed to the thalamus and on to the prefrontal area of the neocortex before returning to the anterior hypothalamus. In taking this circuitous route, access to the neocortical neuron pool is achieved and information may be integrated and modified before being relayed to the brain's sex-coordination region or center. Sexual performance on the other hand can be modified by odor cues or their absence (as in bulbectomized animals), and since this behavioral modification requires no access to the programming of the neocortex, such information might influence the brain's sex center more directly. The neural pathway of this center is probably represented by the amygdala and from here via the stria terminales to the anterior hypothalamus. Hence, direct olfactory information to the brain's sex-center could influence sexual performance at a level below the threshold of conscious awareness.

There are a number of points which emerge from studies so far conducted which might serve as guide lines to future investigations. The absence of a stereotyped response seems to be characteristic of those mammalian pheromones so far studied, unlike the phenomenon observable in insect behavior for which the term, pheromone, was originally introduced. Rarely is a response evoked in 100% of applications, and in the primate, and perhaps also the mouse, the behavior pattern initiated depends upon the social context. Moreover, those pheromones chemically identified appear to be odor complexes consisting of a number of compounds rather than a single constituent. This again contrasts with the findings for insect pheromones, such as bombykol and gyplure, which serve as attractants in the silkworm and gypsy moths. In conclusion then, the sexual response of mammals to odor cues, unlike that of insects, is complex and, although odors are clearly of great importance to attraction, mammalian sexual behavior depends upon multiple sensory cues.

BIBLIOGRAPHY

Albone, E.S. and Fox, M.W. (1971) Anal gland secretion of the red fox. *Nature* 233: 569—570.

Beach, F.A. and Gilmore, R. (1949) Responses of male dogs to urine from females in heat. *J. Mammals* 30: 391—392.

Beach, F.A. and Merari, A. (1970) Coital behaviour in the dog. V. Effects of oestrogen and progesterone on mating and other forms of social behaviour in the bitch. *J. Comp. Physiol. Psychol.* suppl. I, 1—22.

Berliner, V.R. (1959) The oestrous cycle of the mare. In: (H.H. Cole and P.T. Cupps, Eds.) *Reproduction in domestic animals.* (Academic Press, New York) pp. 67—289.

Bronson, F.H. (1968) Pheromonal influences on mammalian reproduction. In: (M. Diamond, Ed.) *Reproduction and Sexual Behaviour.* (Indiana Univ. Press) pp. 341—361.

Bronson, F.H. (1971) Rodent pheromones. *Biol. Reprod.* 4: 344—357.

Bronson, F.H. and Caroum, D. (1971) Preputial gland of the male mouse: attractant function. *J. Reprod. Fertil.* 25. 279 282.

Bruce, H.M. (1970) Pheromones. *Br. Med. Bull.* 26: 10—13.

Carpenter, C.R. (1942) Sexual behaviour of free ranging rhesus monkeys (*Macaca mulatta*). II. Periodicity of oestrous, homosexual autoerotic and non-conformist behaviour. *J. Comp. Psychol.* 33: 143—162.

Davies, V.J. and Bellamy, D. (1974) Effects of female urine on social investigation in male mice. *Anim. Behav.* 22: 239—241.

Dominic, C.J. (1969) Pheromonal mechanisms regulating Mammalian Reproduction. *Gen. Comp. Endocrinol.* 2: 200—267.

Donovan, C.A. (1967) Some clinical observations on sexual attraction and deterence in dogs and cattle. *Vet. Med. Anim. Clin.* 62: 1047—1051.

Donovan, C.A. (1969) Canine anal glands and chemical signals (Pheromones). *J. Am. Vet. Med. Assoc.* 155: 1995—1996.

Dutt, R H , Simpson, E.C., Christian, J.C. and Barnhart, C.E. (1959) Identification of preputial glands as the site of reproduction of sexual odours in the boar. *J. Anim. Sci.* 18: 1557.

Eibl, K. and Wettke, H. (1964) Artificial insemination of pigs using CO_2-inactivated boar semen. *Vet. Rec.* 76: 856—858.

Eisenberg, J.F., McKay, G.M. and Jainndeen, M.R. (1971) Reproductive behaviour of the Asiatic Elephant (*Elphas maximus maximus* L.) *Behaviour XXXVIII* 3(4) 193—225.

Epple, G. (1970) Quantitative studies on scent marking in the Marmoset (*Callithrix jacchus*). *Folia Primatol.* 13: 48—62.

Gier, H.T. (1960) Estrous cycle in the bitch; vaginal fluids. *Vet. Scope* 5: 2—9.

Golly, F.B. (1957) Gestation period, breeding and fawning behaviour of Columbian Black-tailed deer. *J. Mammal.* 38. 116 120.

Guinness, F., Lincoln, G.A. and Short, R.V. (1971) The reproductive cycle of the female red deer (*Cervus elaphus*). *J. Reprod. Fertil.* 27. 427 438.

Hart, G.H., Mead, S.W. and Regan, W.M. (1946) Stimulating the sex drive of bovine males in artificial insemination. *Endocrinology* 39: 221—223.

Jay, P. (1965) Field studies. In: (A.M. Schrier, H.F. Harlow and F. Stollnitz, Eds.) *Behaviour of Non-Human Primates.* (Academic Press, New York) pp. 525—529.

Jolly, A. (1966) *Lemur Behavior, A Mudagascar Field Study.* (Univ. of Chicago Press, Chicago.)

Karlson, P. and Butenandt, A. (1959) Pheromones (ectohormones) in insects. *Annu. Rev. Entomol* 4: 39—58.

Kelley, R.B. (1937) Studies in fertility of sheep. *Bull. Counc. Ind. Res. Aust.* no. 112.

Kleiman, D. (1966) Scent marking in the Canidae. *Symp. Zool. Soc. Lond.* 18: 167—177.

Latta, J., Hopf, S. and Ploog, D. (1967) Observations on mating behaviour and sexual play in the squirrel monkey (*Saimiri sciureus*). *Primates* 8: 229—246.

Le Magnen, J. (1952) Les phenomenes olfacto-sexuels chez le rat blanc. *Arch. Sci. Physiol.* 6: 295—332.

Lindsay, D.R. (1965) The importance of olfactory stimuli in the mating behaviour of the ram. *Anim. Behav.* 13: 75—78.

Lisk, R.D., Ziess, J. and Ciacco, L.A. (1972) The influence of olfaction on sexual behaviour in the male golden hamster (*Mesocricetus auratus*). *J. Exp. Zool.* 181: 69—78.

428

Lissak, K. (1962) Olfactory-induced sexual behaviour in female cats. *Proc. I.U.P.S.* 22: 653—656.

Lydell, K. and Doty, R.L. (1972) Male rat odour preferences for female urine as a function of sexual experience, urine age and urine source. *Horm. Behav.* 3: 205—212.

Marler, P. (1965) Communication in monkeys and apes. In: (I. De Vore, Ed.) *Primate Behaviour.* (Holt, Rinehart and Winston, New York) pp. 544—584.

Marr, J.N. and Gardner, L.E. (1965) Early olfactory experience and later social behaviour in the rat: preference, sexual responsiveness and care of young. *J. Genet. Psychol.* 107: 167—174.

Melrose, D.R., Reed, H.C.B. and Patterson, R.L.S. (1971) Androgen steroids associated with boar odour as an aid to the detection of oestrus in pig A.I. *Br. Vet. J.* 127: 495—502.

Michael, R.P. and Keverne, E.B. (1970) Primate sex pheromones of vaginal origin. *Nature* 225: 84—85.

Murphy, M.R. (1973) Effects of female hamster vaginal discharge on the behaviour of male hamsters. *Behav. Biol.* 9: 367—375.

Murphy, M.R. and Schneider, G.E. (1970) Olfactory bulb removal eliminates mating behaviour in the male golden hamster. *Science* 167: 302—304.

Müller-Schwarze, D. (1971) Pheromones in Blacktailed deer. *Anim. Behav.* 19: 141—152.

Patterson, R.L.S. (1968) Identification of 3α-hydroxy-5-androst-16-ene as the musk odour component of boar sub-maxillary salivary gland and its relationship to the sex odour taint in pork meat. *J. Sci. Fd. Agric.* 19: 434—438.

Petter, J.J. (1965) The lemurs of Madagascar. In: (I. De Vore, Ed.) *Primate Behaviour* (Holt, Rinehart and Winston, New York) pp. 292—319.

Powers, J.B. and Winans, S.S. (1973) Sexual behaviour in peripherally anosmic male hamsters. *Physiol. Behav.* 10: 361—368.

Powers, J.B. and Winans, S.S. (1975) Vomeronasal organ: critical role in mediating sexual behaviour in male hamsters. *Science* 187: 961—963.

Reynolds, E. (1971) Urination as a social response in mice. *Nature,* 234: 481—483.

Schneider, K.M. (1930) Das Flehmen. *Zool. Gart.* 43(4) 183—198.

Scott, J.W. and Pfaff, D.W. (1970) Behavioral and electrophysiological responses of female mice to male urine odours. *Physiol. Behav.* 5: 407—411.

Scruton, D.H. and Herbert, J. (1970) The menstrual cycle and its effect on behaviour in the talapoin monkey (*Miopithecus talapoin*). *J. Zool. Lond.* 162: 419—436.

Signoret, J.P. and Mesnil de Buisson, F. (1961) Etude du comportement de la truie en oestrous. *Proc. IV Int. Congr. Anim. Reprod. Artif. Insem.* (The Hague) pp. 171—175.

Stern, J.J. (1970) Responses of male rats to sex odours. *Physiol. Behav.* 5: 510—524.

Todd, M.B. (1963) The catnip response. *Ph.D. thesis.* (Harvard Univ. Cambridge, Mass.)

Vandenbergh, J.G. (1975) Hormonal correlates of behavior. In: (B. Eleftheriou and J.P. Sprott, Eds.) *Hormones, Pheromones and Behavior.* (Plenum Press, New York) pp. 551—584.

Whitten, W.K. and Bronson, F.H. (1970) Role of pheromones in mammalian reproduction. In: (J.W. Johnson, D.C. Moulton and A. Turk, Eds.) *Advances in Chemoreception.* (Appleton, Century Crofts, N.Y.)

Wierzbowski, S. and Hafez, E.S. (1961) Analysis of copulatory reflexes in the stallion. *Proc. IV Int. Congr. Anim. Reprod.* (The Hague) pp. 176—179.

Wilson, E.O. (1963) Pheromones. *Sci. Am.* 208: 100—114.

CHAPTER 30

Cerebral monoamines and sexual behavior

B.J. EVERITT

1. INTRODUCTION

Results from a great number of experiments have consistently implicated the hypothalamus as one area in the brain which is sensitive to sex hormones and which may, therefore, be a site at which they act to control sexual behavior (see Davidson 1972). Thus, implants of testosterone into the medial preoptic area consistently restore the sexual activity of male castrates, while those of estradiol placed slightly more caudally (into the medial anterior hypothalamus) restore the sexual activity of female castrates. In the case of the female monkey, whose receptivity depends on adrenal and ovarian androgen (not estrogen), implants of testosterone in the anterior hypothalamus restore to normal the unreceptivity which follows bilateral adrenalectomy (Everitt and Herbert, 1975).

The important, and as yet unanswered, question which arises from the above information is concerned with the nature of the link between hormones and the central nervous system (CNS). How do hormones modulate neural activity and hence alter behavior? The problem is as applicable to sexual as to other hormone-dependent behavior. One approach has been to study the way that hormones alter monoamine neurotransmitter activity in various areas of the CNS (for example, the hypothalamus and midbrain) and it is with this approach that this chapter is concerned.

The basic premise is that hormones may alter neural activity by directly or indirectly modulating monoamine neurotransmitter activity. The hypothalamus (which is known to be involved in sexual activity) and other structures of the 'limbic' brain contain particularly large amounts of the neurotransmitters serotonin, noradrenaline, dopamine and adrenaline (Fuxe et al., 1975). These limbic structures also specifically accumulate sex hormones (Kow et al., 1974). Changes in the neurotransmitters could therefore provide the link between sexual behavior and its controlling hormones.

Handbook of Sexology, edited by J. Money and H. Musaph
© *Elsevier/North-Holland Biomedical Press, 1977*

Methodology

In order to investigate this complex problem, several approaches have been employed. Pharmacological studies in which a wide variety of drugs modifying amines (Table I) have been used to study sexual behavior have given most of the information available at present. A knowledge of the distribution of monoamine neurons in the CNS, together with the development of neurotoxic drugs has led to the development of anatomical studies in which the effects on sexual behavior of destroying specific amine-containing pathways has provided a complementary approach to the pharmacological studies. Neurochemical studies provide the alternative strategy, namely, of varying an animal's hormonal status and investigating the effects on various aspects of monoamine neurotransmitter activity. These three approaches taken together have given some insight into the complex interaction between hormones and cerebral monoamines in the control of sexual behavior.

Pharmacological studies

The basic strategy of pharmacological experiments is to give drugs which affect transmission in an aminergic system. They may be given to castrate animals whose sexual activity is low, owing to treatment with subeffective doses of hormones, in order to see if the aminergic drugs increase sexual activity; or they may be given to intact animals or to castrates treated with effective

Table I

Drugs mentioned in the text and their principal actions

Drug	Effect
Amphetamine	dopamine and noradrenaline releaser
Fenfluramine	5-HT (and dopamine) releaser
Chlorimipramine	5-HT uptake inhibitor (mainly)
Protryptline	noradrenaline uptake inhibitor (mainly)
Pimozide, Spiroperidol and Haloperidol	dopamine receptor blocker
Chlorpromazine	dopamine and noradrenaline receptor blocker
Phenoxybenzamine	noradrenaline receptor blocker
Piperoxane and Yohimbine	α-adrenergic receptor blocker—high dose ?adrenaline receptor blockers—low dose (see text)
Propranolol	β-adrenergic receptor blocker
Cinanserin, Methysergide, Mesorgydine	5-HT receptor blockers
d-LSD	?inhibition of 5-HT neurons—low dose 5-HT receptor stimulator—high dose
ET495 and apomorphine	dopamine receptor stimulators
Reserpine and Tetrabenazine	Amine depletors
p-Chloromethamphetamine	Long lasting depletion of 5-HT ? inhibits synthesis

doses of hormones, in order to see if the drug treatment decreases sexual activity.

2. SUBPRIMATE MAMMALS: FEMALE

Indoleamines

Meyerson has been largely responsible for the ever-increasing interest in monoamines as related to sexual behavior and the experimental strategies for studying the problems which are set out above. His observation (1964) that reserpine (which depletes all cerebral amines) could be substituted for progesterone to induce lordosis behavior (the most commonly used indicator of sexual receptivity in the female rat) led him to suggest that 'monoaminergic central nervous pathways exist which mediate heat inhibition'. Further experiments (1964a,b,c) involving the use of monoamine-oxidase inhibitors (MAOI) and the monoamine precursor 5-hydroxytryptophan (5-HTP) suggested that the monoamine, 5-hydroxytryptamine (5-HT) (Fig. 1) was largely responsible for the observed effects on sexual behavior. Thus, depletion of 5-HT led to an increase in receptivity, while elevation of 5 HT levels inhibited estrogen—progesterone-induced receptivity. Meyerson's hypothesis is that 5-HT-containing neurons act to inhibit estrous behavior, and that hormones induce estrous behavior by removing or attenuating activity in these inhibitory neurons. This hypothesis has received support, notably from experiments in which *p*-chlorophenylalanine (PCPA), a depletor of brain serotonin, was given to female rats (Everitt et al., 1975), mice (Hansult et al., 1972) and

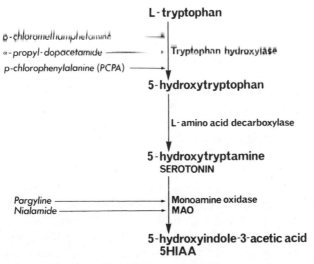

Fig. 1. Pathway for the synthesis and breakdown of 5-hydroxytryptamine. Drugs interfering with enzymes are shown to the left in italic script.

cats (Hoyland et al., 1970). In these experiments PCPA produced an increase in sexual activity.

The fact that 5-HTP prevents the behavioral effects of PCPA argues strongly for the conclusion that depletion of 5-HT is the basis of the behavioral change. Implantation of a 5-HT receptor blocker (antagonist) in the hypothalamus of estrogen-treated female rats will cause an increase in lordotic responding (Ward et al., 1975), as does systemic d-lysergic acid diethylamide (LSD) which, in low dosage, inhibits 5-IIT neurons (Everitt et al., 1975).

Conversely, elevated 5-HT levels produced by combined MAOI/5-HTP treatment, inhibit hormonally-induced receptivity in female rats (Meyerson, 1964a). Blocking uptake of 5-HT (with tricyclic compounds such as chlorimipramine) or releasing 5-HT (as with fenfluramine) will prolong the postsynaptic actions of the amine, and, as a result, inhibit hormone-induced receptivity (Everitt et al., 1975).

Occasional reports which seem to run contrary to the data outlined above may largely be explained by differences in experimental approaches (see Whalen et al., 1975).

Catecholamines

Until recently, pharmacological investigation has centered around 5-HT despite the fact that most, if not all, the treatments described above result in alterations in catecholamine levels as large as, or even greater than alterations in 5-HT levels. Ahlenius and his co-workers (1972) purported to show, however, that PCPA altered sexual behavior in female rats only if catecholamine levels were depressed. These data are themselves controversial (Zemlan et al., 1973; Everitt et al., 1975), but the finding that α-methyl-p-tyrosine, a specific depletor of catecholamine, increased receptivity in female rats (Ahlenius et al., 1972; Everitt et al., 1974) provides clear evidence for catecholamine involvement — but which catecholamine? By using drugs which more specifically alter dopamine and noradrenaline transmission, it has recently become possible to assign separable roles to those amines in the control of sexual behavior in females.

The neuroleptic drugs, pimozide and spiroperidol, which specifically block dopamine receptors, cause a marked increase in lordosis frequency in estrogen-treated rats (Everitt et al., 1974). This suggests that dopamine has an inhibitory action on female sexual behavior. Support for such an idea comes from the finding that drugs which stimulate dopamine receptors also inhibit hormone-induced receptivity (Everitt et al., 1974).

The addition of amphetamine to pimozide and spiroperidol produces a relative increase in noradrenaline activity (due to release of both noradrenaline and dopamine caused by amphetamine in the presence of blocked dopamine receptors) while at the same time increasing lordotic responding above the level induced by the neuroleptics alone (Everitt et al., 1975). This suggested to us that noradrenaline may have an excitatory role, particularly since blockade of both dopamine and noradrenaline receptors, with or with-

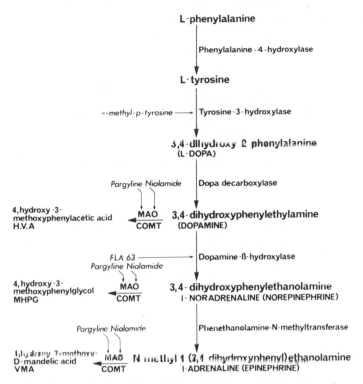

Fig. 2. Pathway for the synthesis and breakdown of the catecholamines, dopamine, noradrenaline and adrenaline. Drugs interfering with enzymes are shown to the left in italic script. COMT = catecholamine-o-methyltransferase.

out amphetamine, has no effect (that is, no increase) on receptivity. This interpretation was supported by the finding that phenoxybenzamine (which blocks noradrenaline receptors) and FLA63 (which inhibits dopamine-β-hydroxylase and hence lowers cerebral noradrenaline levels) both inhibit, to some extent, estrogen—progesterone-induced receptivity (Everitt et al., 1975). But the picture is confused, since Ahlenius and co-workers (1975) report that FLA63 may increase receptivity if given in low doses, whilst protryptylene (an inhibitor of noradrenaline uptake) may inhibit hormone-induced receptivity which, if noradrenaline is excitatory, it should not do (Everitt and Fuxe, unpublished). Part of this confusion is due to the fact that drugs which interfere with noradrenaline transmitter mechanisms will almost inevitably have some effect on adrenaline which appears to be the transmitter in a large system of neurons projecting from the brain stem — thus, the latter may have opposite effects to the former.

Ward and co-workers (1975) reported the rather surprising finding that ostensible β-adrenergic blocking agents enhanced the receptivity of female rats when placed in the hypothalamus. It has often been suggested that adrenaline may preferentially occupy β-receptors in the CNS (see Furchgott,

1967, for review). This is particularly important since Hökfelt and colleagues (1974) recently described a system of adrenaline neurons (neurons showing immunofluorescent labelling to the adrenaline-forming enzyme, phenethanolamine-N-methyltransferase), distribution of which closely parallels that of noradrenaline neurons and which, therefore, may have nerve terminals in the hypothalamus. A number of drugs with β-receptor blocking properties have now been seen to induce receptivity in estrogen-treated female rats (Everitt and Fuxe, unpublished) while two drugs which, in low dosage, seem specifically to inhibit adrenaline neurons (yohimbine and piperoxane; see Fuxe et al., 1974) have the same effect (Everitt et al., 1975). If β-adrenergic receptors are occupied preferentially by adrenaline (and not noradrenaline), and if Fuxe and co-workers' hypothesis of the actions of yohimbine and piperoxane are correct, then the functional importance of hypothalamic adrenaline may become clearer. Since the late 1940s, adrenaline itself has been implicated in another neuroendocrine system — the control of ovulation — so perhaps this puzzle is a little nearer solution.

These pharmacological data suggest that indoleamines and catecholamines are involved in the control of female sexual behavior. 5-HT, dopamine and adrenaline appear to have similar, inhibitory roles while noradrenaline may be excitatory. The way these systems are altered by way of hormones and their interaction provides a fascinating problem for future research.

Understanding the mechanisms by which drugs modify behavior is, of course, fundamentally important in explaining their behavioral effects. Thus, several workers have suggested that drugs such as reserpine, PCPA and α-methyl-p-tyrosine (αMPT) affect the sexual behavior of estrogen-treated castrate females indirectly by causing the release of adrenal progesterone (which thus induces receptivity), since adrenalectomy (which itself disturbs cerebral amines) is said to inhibit the effects of these drugs (see Paris et al., 1971; Eriksson and Södersten, 1973). There are, however, reports to the contrary (Zemlan et al., 1973; Everitt et al., 1974), which raise not only problems of interpretation, but also of methodology. It is an unfortunate fact of pharmacological experiments of the kind reported above that many variables — dose of drugs, time after injection of observation, behavioral techniques (such as pairing a female with one or two males, or manual stimulation to elicit lordosis, etc.) — are rarely the same in different experiments. Manual stimulation of a female rat's back and vagina whilst probing the cervix with a glass rod is not the same as a mount by a male. Large and small doses of a drug such as PCPA have different effects on amines, and there are enormous strain (as well as species) differences in response to a drug. These are some of the factors which contribute to the differing results of apparently similar experiments (see also below). Thus, 2—6 h after PCPA injection, the increase in lordosis seen in ovariectomized females may be prevented by adrenalectomy, and may well be due to removal of progesterone from this source, but this is unlikely to be the case 24, 48, 54 or 72 h after injection since, even in the rat, some degree of refractoriness to progesterone develops.

It is equally unlikely that the increases in receptivity seen 5—10 min. after central administration of 5-HT receptor blockers or systemic LSD are due to adrenal progesterone release, since the time course appears to be too short. In addition, elevated 5-HT levels will prevent the actions of endogenous or exogenous progesterone. Any hypothesis which seems to explain the effects of drugs on sexual behavior solely in terms of adrenal progesterone release is, therefore, inadequate; and it must be acknowledged that different mechanisms may explain the effects of a drug at different times after injection or after different dosages.

3. SUBPRIMATE MAMMALS: MALE

Research on the effects of drugs on male sexual behavior began a little later than that on females, but has since followed an explosive course. Methodological problems similar to those described above make interpretation of some of the data very difficult, since male—male interactions are often employed, sometimes in groups as large as 10 animals or in pairs with one partner (the untreated one) anesthetized. Furthermore, mounting behavior is often taken as the only measure of sexual behavior, and this may not be the best indicator of increases or decreases in sexual activity, while the use of poorly defined terms such as 'hypersexual', 'aphrodisiac' and 'sexual excitement' has led to considerable misunderstanding in interpreting the quoted effects of a drug (or hormone) on sexual behavior.

Indoleamines

Shillito (1969) first observed increased mounting behavior in adult male rats (in all-male groups) treated with large doses of PCPA. Many other studies of homosexual mounting behavior have lent support to the hypothesis that 5-HT is involved in this type of male behavior. Thus, Tagliamonte and co-workers (1969) observed increased sexual activity in groups of rats treated with PCPA, an effect enhanced by injection of pargyline (a monoamine oxidase inhibitor) and prevented by injection of the 5-HT precursor 5-HTP. The changes in sexual behavior were paralleled by those in brain 5-HT concentrations. Similar findings have been reported for cats (Ferguson et al., 1970) and rabbits (Tagliamonte et al., 1969), though it should be borne in mind that the experimental conditions in these studies vary considerably, and that the so-called 'hypersexuality' consists of an increase among treated animals in their mounting of others in large all-male groups, or of anesthetized animals (Ferguson et al., 1970), or of individuals of another species (Fratta et al., 1975).

Depletion of 5-HT as a cause of these alterations in sexual behavior is further suggested by work with other drugs which preferentially inhibit 5-HT neurons (for example, methysergide and mesorgydine; Benkert and Eversmann, 1972). These 5-HT inhibitors induce an increase in sexual activity. The neurotoxic drug 5,6-dihydroxytryptamine (which destroys 5-HT and noradrenaline-containing neurons when injected intraventricularly) induced homosexual mounting behavior in intact rats (Da Prada et al., 1972a). It is strange that the more potent 5,7-DHT injected intracerebrally produced no change in heterosexual copulatory activity (Larsson, Everitt and Fuxe, unpublished).

The association of low 5-HT levels with increased mounting behavior also seems to apply to the heterosexual activity of male mammals. Several groups (Sheard, 1969; Sjoerdsma et al., 1970; Ahlenius et al., 1971; Salis and Dewsbury, 1971) report increases in a number of components of sexual behavior (not simply mounting) after treatment with PCPA. These effects are particularly prominent if so-called 'sexually sluggish' animals are used (Sjoerdsma et al., 1970), but completely absent in 'vigorous copulators' (Whalen and Luttge, 1970), which again emphasizes the importance of defining experimental conditions and the behavioral state of the animals being tested.

Almost all the studies mentioned have been carried out on intact males which have, therefore, endogenously secreted testosterone which itself may be altered by drug treatments. The studies of Malmnäs (1973), which clearly confirmed the role of 5-HT in male sexual behavior, among other findings, were carried out on castrate males treated with a dose of testosterone that maintained a submaximal level of sexual activity on which the increase/decrease effects of a variety of drugs were observed. A feature which has emerged from other drug studies is the role of testosterone. Gessa and co-workers (1970) reported that PCPA induces homosexual mounting only in the presence of testosterone, a finding confirmed by Mitler and co-workers (1972), who suggested also that PCPA-induced heterosexual copulation is not testosterone-dependent. However, del Fiacco and his colleagues (1974) quite clearly demonstrated that PCPA does not increase male—female copulatory behavior in the absence of testosterone. The importance of testosterone is not confined to the effects of drugs modifying 5-HT transmission (see below).

Catecholamines

Early reports of 'hypersexuality' in Parkinsonian patients on L-DOPA therapy (see Goodwin 1971) led to many investigations of the role of dopamine in male sexual behavior. Results obtained with the amine depletors reserpine and tetrabenazine were inconsistent. Both increases in sexual behavior (Soulairac and Soulairac, 1961; Dewsbury, 1971; Dewsbury and Davis, 1970), and decreases (Malmnäs 1973) were reported. However, the finding that MAOI in combination with PCPA increased sexual activity more than did PCPA alone (see above) led to a re-appraisal of the effects of drugs which affect dopamine, since this combined treatment produces a high dopamine : 5-HT ratio in the CNS (Tagliamonte et al., 1969). Subsequently, L-DOPA alone or in combination with a peripheral decarboxylase inhibitor was reported to induce a marked increase in homosexual mounting behavior in all-male groups of rats (Benkert, 1972; Da Prada et al., 1972b). Similar results are seen in castrate male rats treated with submaximal doses of testosterone (Malmnäs, 1973), and in 'sexually sluggish' male rats paired with females. However, both Hyyppä and co-workers (1971) and Gray and co-workers (1974), who used intact sexually vigorous males, reported that these treatments had no effect, which suggests that sexual behavior may be stimulated only in animals showing submaximal performance.

Apomorphine (a dopamine-receptor stimulating agent) has similar effects to L-DOPA, and haloperidol (a dopamine-receptor blocker) inhibits the effects of L-DOPA and apomorphine (Gessa and Tagliamonte, 1974). Both results argue strongly for the suggestion that dopamine has an opposite (that is, stimulatory) role to that of 5-HT in the control of sexual behavior in the male. Malmnäs (1973) reported that alterations in noradrenaline levels have either inconsistent or no effects on male sexual behavior. An explanation for this has been outlined above.

It is clear from this account that drugs which modulate cerebral monoamine transmitter activity have profound effects on the sexual activity of subprimate mammals. Dopamine apparently has opposite effects on the sexual behavior of males and females; drugs which depress dopamine activity increase sexual receptivity in females but decrease sexual behavior in males, and vice versa. The presence of testosterone in males (see Malmnäs, 1973, Baraldi and Bertolini, 1974; Gessa and Tagliamonte, 1974) or of estrogen in females (see Everitt et al., 1975) is critical for the effect of drugs on sexual behavior. Manipulating monoamines does not compensate for a total lack of hormones and presents the problem of the extent to which hormones induce behavioral changes by modulating amines (see below).

4. PRIMATES INCLUDING MAN

Studies of the effects of drugs on, and the role of amines in, human sexual behavior are more numerous than those on monkeys. So far as monkeys are concerned, Perachio and Marr (quoted by Zitrin et al., 1973) reported that a single, large dose of PCPA induced changes in the male rhesus monkey's sexual behavior which they interpreted as an increase. Dement showed that PCPA did not change the frequency of masturbation of two males housed alone, nor the sexual behavior of one male housed with two female adolescents. Scruton and Herbert (personal communication) observed no alterations in the sexual activity of male rhesus monkeys treated with PCPA or L-DOPA though they acknowledge that this result is due more to methodology than to a real absence of effects of the drugs, since their males were already performing at a high, if not maximal, rate. A much more effective strategy is to try to restore behavior that has been impaired. Thus, PCPA in low dosage reverses the unreceptivity induced by adrenalectomy in estrogen-treated female rhesus monkeys (Gradwell et al., 1975). The only other compounds effective in this way are testosterone and androstenedione (see introduction). In other words, 5-HT depletion may be substituted for a hormone in inducing sexual receptivity. Here is persuasive evidence that the two may be related and, since 5-HTP both prevents the effect of PCPA and induces unreceptivity in intact females (Gradwell et al., 1975) that there is specific involvement of 5-HT.

Interest in amines and human sexual behavior owes more to casual observations of increased sexual activity allegedly in response to L-DOPA therapy of Parkinsonian patients than to the many animal studies of L-DOPA. Several such reports had appeared (Jenkins and Groh, 1970; Calne and Sandler, 1970) before the effects of L-DOPA on sexual function were looked at more closely, first by Hyyppä and co-workers (1970) and later by Benkert (1973). Increases are reported in both studies, but the careful study of Benkert shows the effects to be slight and not improved by the addition of androgen. Investigating sexual function in drug-dependants, Gossop and co-workers (1974) reported that it is not impaired in male oral amphetamine users, but that severe sexual dysfunction occurs in female amphetamine addicts. There is a parallel here with the suggested inhibitory role of dopamine in female sexual behavior (Everitt et al., 1974) and no inconsistency with the excitatory role dopamine is reported to have in men and other male animals.

So far as 5-HT is concerned, Cremata and Koe (1968) reported no increase in libido after PCPA administration in male prisoner volunteers. Sjoerdsma and colleagues (1970) similarly found no increase in sexual activity after PCPA treatment. Sicuteri (1974), on the other hand, demonstrated that, in patients complaining of migrane and sexual dysfunction, PCPA in combination with testosterone significantly increases sexual activity (measured as erections induced by erotic imagery).

The studies of Benkert (1973) give us most information concerning the role of 5-HT in man. p-Chloromethamphetamine (PCMA, which depresses brain 5-HT levels for long periods), methysergide, or PCPA all in combination with mesterolone (an androgen) increase erectile capacity, ejaculations and libido.

The state of knowledge concerning the role of amines in the sexual behavior of rats hardly justifies the use of drugs which modify neurotransmitters in the treatment of human sexual disorders. The hormones which control the sexuality of female monkeys are different from those in rats. The aminergic mechanisms may be similar, but to take this as a basis for clinical treatment would seem ill-advised at present. No conclusive experiments have been performed on the effects of drugs on the sexual behavior of male monkeys, and it is a large jump from rats and rabbits to man.

5. ANATOMICAL STUDIES

If sex hormones induce sexual behavior by acting on monoamine-containing neurons in the CNS, it is of fundamental importance to determine their site of action. The anatomical distribution of 5-HT, dopamine- and noradrenaline-containing neurons, and the courses taken by their ascending axons have been studied with the use of fluorescence histochemistry (see Fuxe and Jonsson, 1974; Ungerstedt, 1971). 5-HT cell bodies lie principally in the dorsal and medial raphe nuclei of the caudal mesencephalon, and noradrenaline cell bodies are present in the reticular formation of the medulla and pons. Noradrenaline and 5-HT terminals are found throughout hypothalamus, septum, amygdala and limbic cortex. Cortical noradrenaline terminals originate from the locus coeruleus. The dopamine innervation of structures including the nucleus accumbens, amygdala and limbic cortex (prepyriform, entorhinal, cingulate) originates in the ventral midbrain tegmentum (cell group A10; Dahlström and Fuxe, 1964) and zona compacta of the substantia nigra (medial A9; Dahlström and Fuxe, 1964). Details of the projections may be found elsewhere (Ungerstedt, 1971; Fuxe and Jonsson, 1974; Fuxe et al., 1975). In general terms, the dopamine, noradrenaline and 5-HT axons run in the medial forebrain bundle (mfb), diverging as mfb courses through the rostral mesencephalon and lateral hypothalamic area (see Fig. 3).

Electrolytic lesions of the mfb within the hypothalamus disrupt the sexual behavior of intact male rats (Caggiula et al., 1973; Hitt et al., 1973), and the masculine behavior manifested by spayed female rats treated with testosterone (Modianos et al., 1973). Estrogen—progesterone-induced receptivity in female rats is, however, unaffected by similar mfb lesions (Modianos et al., 1973). The problem in interpreting these data is that the mfb is not a unitary structure, containing as it does dopamine, noradrenaline and 5-HT axons, as well as descending projections from forebrain to brainstem. Caggiula and co-workers (1973) looked more carefully at the site and extent of the lesions and correlated these with both the behavioral deficit and the degree of depletion of telencephalic noradrenaline and 5-HT. A significant correlation appeared between decreased noradrenaline levels and sexual impairment of male rats, but none in the case of 5-HT. It would, perhaps, have been more informative to measure hypothalamic/septal noradrenaline and 5-HT (see below). But these data suggest that noradrenaline facilitates male sexual activity, although this does not emerge from the pharmacological experiments described above. However, electrolytic lesions (see above) themselves destroy substantial amounts of the hypothalamus and thus, perhaps, some of the cells controlling the behavior itself.

Kow and co-workers (1974), in reviewing the literature and their own work, suggest that the 5-HT projection from the raphe nuclei to the septum (via the mfb) is the site of action of progesterone in females. They work on the hypothesis proposed by Meyerson (1964a) that when this system is active, lordosis (that is, receptivity) is inhibited, and that one of the ways in which progesterone acts is to inhibit this system, thus disinhibiting the postsynaptic sites to which it projects and which supposedly underlie the appearance of lordosis. Thus, they note that septal lesions may induce lordosis, even in the absence of estrogen and progesterone (Komisaruk et al., 1972),

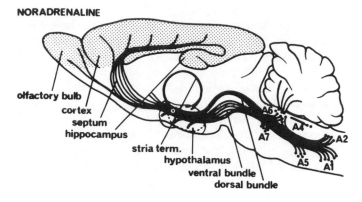

NORADRENALINE

olfactory bulb
cortex
septum
hippocampus
stria term.
hypothalamus
ventral bundle
dorsal bundle

A6 A4 A2 A7 A5 A1

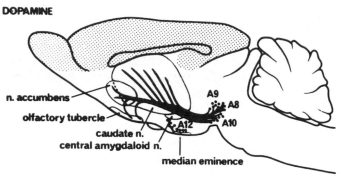

DOPAMINE

n. accumbens
olfactory tubercle
caudate n.
central amygdaloid n.
median eminence

A9 A8 A12 A10

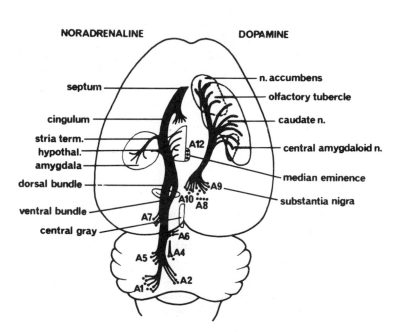

NORADRENALINE   **DOPAMINE**

septum
cingulum
stria term.
hypothal.
amygdala
dorsal bundle
ventral bundle
central gray

n. accumbens
olfactory tubercle
caudate n.
central amygdaloid n.
median eminence
substantia nigra

A12 A9 A10 A8 A7 A6 A5 A4 A1 A2

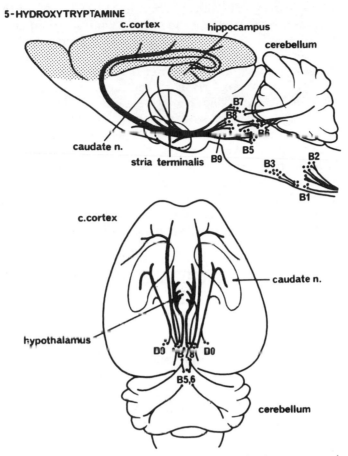

Fig. 4. Distribution of dopamine and noradrenaline and 5-hydroxytryptamine neurons in the rat brain (from Ungerstedt, 1971; Fuxe and Jonsson, 1974).

while septal stimulation may inhibit receptivity induced by these hormones (Malsbury and Pfaff, 1973). Depletion of 5-HT (see above), also induces receptivity in estrogen-treated females.

According to the hypothesis of Kow and co-workers, destruction of the raphe nuclei or mfb (which carries 5-HT projections) should induce receptivity, since these procedures decrease forebrain 5-HT levels (Heller and Moore, 1965; Sheard, 1973). Whether or not such lesions facilitate lordosis is not known, but extensive lesions of the raphe do not induce alterations in the sexual behavior of male rats despite a lowering of 5-HT levels (Sheard 1973). However, a more refined approach is possible. It makes use of both the recently discovered location of a medial ascending 5-HT pathway (which originates in the raphe and innervates the diencephalon; Fuxe and Johnsson, 1974) and the new neurotoxic dihydroxytryptamines (for example, 5,7-DHT) which can be used selectively to destroy 5-HT axons (Everitt et al., 1975). Such lesions are selective and small. They destroy very little, if any, of the surrounding brain, and may be made outside the hypothalamus and raphe. Destruction of this 5-HT pathway in this way results in a 75% decrease of hypothalamic 5-HT (Baumgarten et al., 1973) and causes a significant increase in the sexual receptivity of estrogen-treated castrate females when compared with controls (Everitt et al., 1975). A proportion of the females also became aggressive. This is the first anatomical evidence which links 5-HT-containing neurons with sexual behavior and may well represent the site of action of progesterone. Indeed this hormone will induce receptivity if implanted in the midbrain (Ross et al., 1971). Where estrogen acts is still a puzzle. Its presence is critical for progesterone (Kow et al., 1974), drugs and lesions (Everitt et al., 1975a,b) to induce receptivity. There is poor overlap between estrogen uptake sites and 5-HT-containing cell bodies and terminals (Pfaff and Keiner, 1973; Kow et al., 1974). Perhaps dopamine and noradrenaline neuronal systems hold the key and should be investigated along the lines set out above.

6. NEUROCHEMICAL STUDIES

If, as seems likely, 5-HT, dopamine and noradrenaline participate normally in the central regulation of sexual behavior (and, indeed, of anterior pituitary function also), it is reasonable to predict that changes in the concentration of circulating hormones would influence levels, turnover, release, synthesis (via the controlling enzymes) or metabolism of monoamines in the brain. Considerable effort has been put into investigating the problem, and it is impossible to review all the literature here. However, certain approaches which have yielded much data will be summarized.

During the estrous cycle, after castration (Bernard and Paolino, 1974) and following treatment with sex hormones, alterations in the levels of 5-HT, dopamine and noradrenaline are observed in various areas of the brain (see Wurtman, 1971; Janowsky et al., 1971 for reviews). The problem with such data is that alterations in levels do not disclose the mechanisms which underly them. Thus high levels could reflect increased synthesis, low utilization or decreased breakdown — each implies very different changes in neuronal activity.

Clearly, measuring turnover of amines ought to provide more information but, unfortunately, there is lack of agreement about how to measure turnover, as well as what the measurement itself means (see Wurtman, 1971, for discussion). In rats, an increase in noradrenaline turnover follows castration (Anton-Tay and Wurtman, 1968). Estrogen and progesterone may decrease noradrenaline turnover in diencephalon/brainstem while 5-HT turnover in whole brain is increased by estrogen, an effect prevented by progesterone (Everitt et al., 1975a,b). In monkeys, 5-HT turnover is decreased by testosterone (which induces receptivity) and increased by progesterone (which induces unreceptivity; Gradwell et al., 1975). Such results can be listed indefinitely, but they give only correlates of hormonal treatment with little insight into the mechanisms by which the changes occur.

Direct effects of the hormones on enzymes concerned with synthesis and breakdown of monoamines could be one such mechanism. Thus, oral contraceptives decrease brain monoamine oxidase activity (Marchi and Cugurra, 1974). Progestational steroids inhibit tyrosine hydroxylase activity in vitro (Beattie and Soyka, 1973). Catechol-o-methyl transferase activity is depressed during estrus and inhibited in vitro by estrogen and progesterone (see Janowsky et al., 1971).

Recently, work has been done on the effects of hormones on the uptake by synaptosomes or brain slices of radioactively labeled 5-HT, noradrenaline and dopamine. The implication here is that hormones are directly interfering with the uptake mechanisms of the neuron (and, perhaps, with amine release; Janowsky et al., 1971). Such effects could be responsible for the changes in turnover mentioned above (Schubert et al., 1970). Estrogen and progesterone have been seen to inhibit noradrenaline and dopamine uptake in various areas of the brain (Janowsky et al., 1971; Nixon et al., 1974; Hackman et al., 1973; Endersby and Wilson, 1974; Everitt et al., 1975b) while 5-HT uptake may apparently be increased, decreased or unaffected by sex hormones (Hackman et al., 1973; Everitt et al., 1975a; Wirz-Justice et al., 1974).

None of the above studies on uptake, enzyme activity, turnover and levels are comparable with each other since, methodologically, they differ in so many ways. Large, clearly pharmacologic doses of hormones are used. Progesterone is often given on its own (a situation which never occurs physiologically), and the hormones are often introduced in high concentration to an in vitro medium. We have made some attempt to look at turnover and amine uptake using in vivo treatments with hormones in small doses commonly used to induce receptivity in females (Everitt et al., 1975b). Until some such standardization is introduced into this work the data will remain confused and inconclusive.

What emerges from these studies? The realization that hormones have marked effects on monoamine metabolism and neuronal processes. This alone justifies further and more careful studies, and also suggests that the effects of drugs which induce sexual behavior arise, in part at least, by mimicking the actions of hormones on amine-containing neurons.

7. CONCLUSIONS AND COMMENT

The pharmacologic and anatomic data presented here demonstrate that alterations in monoaminergic neurotransmission can induce changes in the sexual behavior of male and female mammals, including man, and provide an anatomical basis for these observations. A key problem is to demonstrate that drug-induced alterations in monoamines in some way reflect the actions of hormones on monoamines in inducing sexual behavior. In other words, one needs to ascertain if the mechanisms differ even though the end result is the same. For example, estrogen, testosterone, or drugs which deplete 5-HT all induce 'nonspecific' changes in behavior which may be interpreted as an increased responsiveness to behavior-eliciting stimuli in any modality (Weissman and Harbert, 1972; Vernikos-Danellis, 1972; Everitt et al., 1975). Thus it could be predicted that animals so treated would show increased sexual behavior in a situation where the cues impinging on the animal are primarily sexual, as compared with increased aggressive behavior when the cues are aggressive and so on. Indeed this may occur (Sheard, 1969; Weissman and Harbert, 1972). However, it is equally important to recognize that specific and nonspecific interpretations are not mutually exclusive. The effects of estrogen on sexual behavior (specific) and eating and wheel-running (nonspecific) are a case in point (see Everitt et al., 1975).

Since hormones do have marked effects on amine metabolism and behavior, the two may be linked. Anatomical investigations show some overlap between sites in the brain where implants of hormones induce sexual activity, where steroid uptake can be demonstrated, and where monoamine cell bodies and terminals are in abundance.

To clarify the problems, more refined approaches are necessary, and these are already possible. An extremely sensitive radioenzymatic assay technique allows the analysis of amine metabolism in individual nuclei of the brain (see Saavedra et al., 1974). This technique, combined with investigations of the effects of drugs implanted locally within the brain (see Ward et al., 1975), particularly in combination with neurochemically specific lesions of pathways (see Everitt et al., 1975b) and an increasingly refined behavioral analysis should allow the questions to be formulated properly and the answers to follow in due course.

8. SUMMARY

Depressing 5-hydroxytryptamine activity in the CNS induces sexual behavior in male and female mammals. Elevating dopamine levels in males or depressing it in females has similar effects. Altering noradrenaline or adrenaline levels has less clear behavioral consequences. Whether or not changes in amines underlie the way in which hormones modulate neural activity to induce sexual behavior is an important and as yet unanswered question. Various anatomical and neurochemical investigations support a positive answer, and justify more detailed experiments. The degree to which animal psychopharmacological data can be applied to the treatment of human sexual behavioral disorders remains equivocal.

BIBLIOGRAPHY

Ahlenius, S., Eriksson, H., Larsson, K., Modigh, K. and Södersten, P. (1971) Mating behaviour in the male rat treated with p-chlorophenylalanine methyl ester alone and in combination with pargyline. *Psychopharmacologia* 20: 383—388.

Ahlenius, S., Engel, J., Eriksson, H., Modigh, K. and Södersten, P. (1972) Importance of central catecholamines in the mediation of lordosis behavior in ovariectomized rats treated with estrogen and inhibitors of monoamine synthesis. *J. Neural Transm.* 33: 247—255.

Ahlenius, S., Engel, J., Eriksson, H., Modigh, K. and Södersten, P. (1975) On the involvement of monoamines in the mediation of lordosis behaviour. *Adv. Biochem. Psychopharmacol.* (in press).

Anton-Tay, F. and Wurtman, R.J. (1968) Norepinephrine turnover in rat brains after gonadectomy. *Science* 161: 1245.

Baraldi, M. and Bertolini, A. (1974) Penile erections induced by amantadine in male rats. *Life Sci.* 14: 1231—1235.

Baumgarten, H.G., Björklund, A., Lachenmayer, L. and Nobin, A. (1973) Evaluation of the effects of 5,7-dihydroxytryptamine on serotonin and catecholamine neurons in the rat CNS. *Acta Physiol. Scand.*, suppl. 391: 1—19.

Beattie, C.W. and Soyka, L.F. (1973) Influence of progestational steroids on hypothalamic tyrosine hydroxylase activity in vitro. *Endocrinology* 93: 1453—1455.

Benkert, O. (1972) L-dopa treatment of impotence: A clinical and experimental study. In: (S. Malitz, Ed.) *L dopa and Behavior.* (Raven Press, New York) pp. 73—79.

Benkert, O. (1973) Pharmacological experiments to stimulate human sexual behaviour. In: (T.A. Ban et al., Eds.) *Psychopharmacology, Sexual Disorders and Drug Abuse.* (North Holland, Amsterdam) pp. 489—495.

Benkert, O. and Eversmann, T. (1972) Importance of the anti-serotonin effect for mounting behavior in rats. *Experimentia* 28: 532—533.

Bernard, B.K. and Paolino, R.M. (1974) Time-dependent changes in brain biogenic amine dynamics following castration in male rats. *J. Neurochem.* 22: 951—956.

Caggiula, A.R., Antelman, S.M. and Zigmond, M.J. (1973) Disruption of copulation in male rats after hypothalamic lesions: A behavioral, anatomical and neurochemical analysis. *Brain Res.* 59: 273—287.

Calne, D.B. and Sandler, M. (1970) L-dopa and Parkinsonism. *Nature* 226: 21.

Cremata, V.Y. and Koe, B.K. (1968) Clinical and biochemical effects of fenclonine. a serotonin depletor. *Dis. Nerv. Syst.* 29: 117—160.

Da Prada, M., Carruba, M., O'Brien, R.A., Saner, A. and Pletscher, A. (1972a) The effect of 5,6-dihydroxytryptamine on sexual behaviour of male rats. *Eur. J. Pharmacol.* 19: 288—290.

Da Prada, M., Carruba, M., O'Brien, R.A., Saner, A. and Pletscher, A. (1972b) L-dopa and sexual activity of male rats. *Psychopharmacologia* 26: 135.

Dahlström, A. and Fuxe, K. (1964) Evidence for the existence of monoamine neurons in the central nervous system. IV. Distribution of monoamine nerve terminals in the central nervous system. *Acta Physiol. Scand.* 64: suppl. 247: 39—85.

Davidson, J.M. (1972) Hormones and reproductive behaviour. In: (H. Balin and S. Glasser, Eds.) *Reproductive Biology* (Excerpta Medica, Amsterdam.)

Del Fiacco, M., Fratta, W., Gessa, G.L. and Tagliamonte, A. (1974) Lack of copulatory behavior in male castrated rats after p-chlorophenylalanine. *Br. J. Pharmacol.* 51: 249—251.

Dewsbury, D.A. (1971) Effects of tetrabenazine on the copulatory behavior of male rats. *Eur. J. Pharmacol.* 17: 221—226.

Dewsbury, D.A. and Davis, H.N. (1970) Effects of reserpine on the copulatory behavior of male rats. *Physiol. Behav.* 5: 1331—1333.

Endersby, C.A. and Wilson, C.A. (1974) The effect of ovarian steroids on the accumulation of ^{3}H-labelled monoamines by hypothalamic tissue in vitro. *Brain Res.* 73: 321—331.

Eriksson, H. and Södersten, P. (1973) A failure to facilitate lordosis behaviour in adrenalectomized and gonadectomized estrogen-primed rats with monoamine synthesis inhibitors. *Horm. Behav.* 4: 89—97.

Everitt, B.J., Fuxe, K. and Hökfelt, T. (1974) Inhibitory role of dopamine and 5-hydroxytryptamine in the sexual behaviour of female rats. *Eur. J. Pharmacol.* 29: 187—191.

Everitt, B.J., Fuxe, K., Hökfelt, T. and Jonsson, G. (1975a) 5,7-Dihydroxytryptamine (5,7-DHT) and the behavior of female rats. *J. Pharmacol.* 6: 25—32.

Everitt, B.J., Fuxe, K., Hökfelt, T. and Jonsson, G. (1975b) Pharmacological and biochemical studies on the role of monoamines in the control by hormones of sexual receptivity in the female rat. *J. Comp. Physiol. Psychol.* 89: 556—572.

Everitt, B.J., Gradwell, B.P. and Herbert, J. (1976) Neural mechanisms regulating sexual receptivity in female rhesus monkeys. In: (M. Sandler and G.L. Gessa, Eds) *Sexual Behavior. Pharmacology and Biochemistry.* (Raven Press, New York) pp. 181—191.

Everitt, B.J. and Herbert, J. (1975) The effects of implanting testosterone propionate into the central nervous system on the sexual behaviour of adrenalectomised female rhesus monkeys. *Brain Res.* 86: 109—120.

Ferguson, J., Henrickson, S., Cohen, H., Mitchell, G., Barchas, J. and Dement, W. (1970) Hypersexuality and behavioural changes in cats caused by administration of *p*-chlorophenylalanine. *Science* 168: 499—501.

Fratta, W., Biggio, G., De Montis, G., Olianas, M.C. and Mereu, G.P. (1975) Effect of tryptophan-free diets on sexual behaviour and EEG patterns in male animals. *Adv. Biochem. Psychopharmacol.* (in press).

Furchgott, R.F. (1967) The pharmacological differentiation of adrenergic receptors. *Ann. NY Acad. Sci.* 134: 553—567.

Fuxe, K. and Johnsson, G. (1974) Further mapping of central 5-hydroxytryptamine neurons: Studies with the neurotoxic dihydroxytryptamines. *Adv. Biochem. Psychopharmacol.* 10: 1—12.

Fuxe, K., Lidbrink, P., Hökfelt, T., Bolme, P. and Goldstein, M. (1974) Effects of piperoxane on sleep and waking in the rat: Evidence for increased waking by blocking inhibitory adrenaline receptors on the locus coeruleus. *Acta Physiol. Scand.* 91: 566—567.

Fuxe, K., Hökfelt, T., Everitt, B.J., Johansson, O., Jonsson, G., Lidbrink, P., Ljungdahl, Å. and Ogren, S.-O. (1975) Anatomical and functional studies of monoamines in the limbic system. *Proc. VIIth Int. Congr. Neuropathol., Hungary* (in press).

Gessa, G.L., Tagliamonte, A., Tagliamonte, P. and Brodie, B.B. (1970) Essential role of testosterone in the sexual stimulation induced by *p*-chlorophenylalanine in male animals. *Nature* 227: 616—617.

Gessa, G.L. and Tagliamonte, A. (1974) Role of brain monoamines in male sexual behavior. *Life Sci.* 14: 425—436.

Goodwin, F.K. (1971) Behavioural effects of l-dopa in man. *Seminars Psychiat.* 3: 477—492.

Gossop, M.R., Stern, R. and Connell, P.H. (1974) Drug dependence and sexual function: A comparison of intravenous users of narcotics and oral users of amphetamines. *Br. J. Psychiat.* 124: 431—434.

Gradwell, P.B., Everitt, B.J. and Herbert, J. (1975) 5-Hydroxytryptamine in the central nervous system and sexual receptivity of female rhesus monkeys. *Brain Res.* 88: 281—293.

Gray, G.D., Davis, H.N. and Dewsbury, D.A. (1974) Effects of l-dopa on the heterosexual copulatory behavior of male rats. *Eur. J. Pharmacol.* 27: 367—370.

Hackmann, E., Wirz-Justice, A. and Lichtsteiner, M. (1973) The uptake of dopamine and serotonin in rat brain during progesterone decline. *Psychopharmacologia* 32: 183—191.

Hansult, C.D., Uphouse, L.L., Schlesinger, K. and Wilson, J.R. (1972) Induction of estrus in mice: Hypophyseal-adrenal effects. *Horm. Behav.* 3: 113—121.

Heller, A. and Moore, R.Y. (1965) Effect of central nervous system lesions on brain monoamines in the rat. *J. Pharmacol. Exp. Ther.* 150: 1—9.

Hitt, J.C., Byron, D.M. and Modianos, D.T. (1973) Effects of rostral medial forebrain bundle and olfactory tubercle lesions upon sexual behavior of male rats. *J. Comp. Physiol. Psychol.* 82: 30—36.

Hökfelt, T., Fuxe, K., Goldstein, M. and Johansson, O. (1974) Immunohistochemical evidence for the existence of adrenaline neurons in the rat brain. *Brain Res.* 66: 235—251.

Hoyland, V.J., Shillito, E.E. and Vogt, M. (1970) The effect of parachlorophenylalanine (PCPA) on the behavior of cats. *Br. J. Pharmacol.* 40: 659—667.

Hyyppä, M., Rinne, U.K. and Sonninen, V. (1970) The activating effect of L-dopa treatment on sexual function and its experimental background. *Acta Neurol. Scand.* 46: suppl. 43: 223.

Hyyppä, M., Lehtinen, P. and Rinne, U.K. (1971) Effect of l-dopa on the hypothalamic, pineal and striatal monoamines and on the sexual behavior of the rat. *Brain Res.* 30: 265—272.

Janowsky, D.S., Fann, W.E. and Davis, J.M. (1971) Monoamines and ovarian hormone-linked sexual and emotional changes: A review. *Arch. Sex. Behav.* 1: 205—218.

Jenkins, R.B. and Groh, R.H. (1970) Mental symptoms in Parkinsonian patients treated with L-dopa. *Lancet* II: 177.

Komisaruk, B.R., Larsson, K. and Cooper, R. (1972) Intense lordosis in the absence of ovarian hormones after septal ablation in rats. *Program and Abstracts, Soc. Neurosci.* (2nd Annu. Meet.). 200 (abstr. No. 51.10)

Kow, L.-M., Malsbury, C.W. and Pfaff, D.W. (1974) Effects of progesterone on female reproductive behavior in rats: Possible modes of action and role in behavioral sex differences. In: (W. Montagna and W.A. Sadler, Eds.) *Reproductive Behavior* (Plenum, New York) pp. 179—210.

Malmnäs, C.-O. (1973) Monoaminergic influence on testosterone-activated copulatory behavior in the castrated male rat. *Acta Physiol. Scand.*, suppl. 395: 1—128.

Malsbury, C. and Pfaff, D.W. (1973) Suppression of sexual receptivity in the hormone-primed female hamster by electrical stimulation of the medial preoptic area. *Program and Abstracts, Soc. Neurosci.* (3rd Annu. Meet.). 100 (abstr. No. 56)

Marchi, M. and Cugurra, F. (1974) The effect of long term oral treatment of rats with contraceptive steroids on tissue MAO. *Eur. J. Pharmacol.* 25: 407—410.

Meyerson, B.J. (1964a) Central nervous monoamines and hormone induced estrus behaviour in the spayed rat. *Acta Physiol. Scand.* 63: (suppl. 241) 1—32.

Meyerson, B.J. (1964b) The effect of neuropharmacological agents on hormone-activated estrus behaviour in ovariectomised rats. *Arch. Int. Pharmacodyn. Ther.* 150: 4—33.

Meyerson, B.J. (1964c) Estrus behaviour in spayed rats after estrogen or progesterone treatment in combination with reserpine or tetrabenazine. *Psychopharmacologia* 6: 210—218.

Mitler, M.M., Morden, B., Levine, S. and Dement, W. (1972) The effects of parachlorophenylalanine on the mating behaviour of male rats. *Physiol. Behav.* 8: 1147—1150.

Modianos, D.T., Flexman, J.E. and Hitt, J.C. (1973) Rostral medial forebrain bundle lesions produce decrements in masculine, but not feminine, sexual behavior in spayed female rats. *Behav. Biol.* 8: 629—636.

Nixon, R.L., Janowsky, D.S. and Davis, J.M. (1974) Effects of progesterone, β-estradiol, and testosterone on the uptake and metabolism of ^{3}H-norepinephrine, ^{3}H-dopamine and ^{3}H-serotonin in rat brain synaptosomes. *Res. Commun. Chem. Pathol. Pharmacol.* 7: 233—236.

Paris, C.A., Resko, J.A. and Goy, R.W. (1971) A possible mechanism for the induction of lordosis by reserpine in spayed rats. *Biol. Reprod.* 4: 23—40.

Pfaff, D. and Keiner, M. (1973) Atlas of estradiol-concentrating cells in the central nervous system of the female rat. *J. Comp. Neurol.* 151: 121—158.

Ross, J.W., Claybough, C., Clemens, L.G. and Gorski, R.A. (1971) Short latency induction of oestrous behaviour with intracerebral gonadal hormones in ovariectomized rats. *Endocrinology* 89: 32—38.

Saavedra, J.M., Palkowitz, M., Brownstein, M.J. and Axelrod, J. (1974) Serotonin distribution in the nuclei of the rat hypothalamus and preoptic region. *Brain Res.* 77: 157—165.

Salis, P.J. and Dewsbury, D.A. (1971) *p*-Chlorophenylalanine facilitates copulatory behaviour in male rats. *Nature* 232: 400—401.

Schubert, J., Nybäck, H. and Sedvall, G. (1970) Effect of antidepressant drugs on accumulation and disappearance of monoamines formed in vivo from labelled precursors in mouse brain. *J. Pharm. Pharmacol.* 22: 136—139.

Sheard, M.H. (1969) The effect of *p*-chlorophenylalanine on the behaviour in rats: relation to 5-hydroxytryptamine (5-HT) and 5-hydroxyindoleacetic acid. *Brain Res.* 15: 524—528.

Sheard, M. (1973) Brain serotonin depletion by *p*-chlorophenylalanine or lesions of raphe neurons in rats. *Physiol. Behav.* 10: 809—811.

Shillito, E. (1969) The effect of p-chlorophenylalanine on social interactions of male rats. *Br. J. Pharmacol.* 36: 193P—94P.

Sicuteri, F. (1974) Serotonin and sex in man. *Pharmacol. Res. Commun.* 6: 403—411.

Sjoerdsma, A., Lovenberg, W., Engelman, K., Carpenter, W.T., Wyatt, R.J. and Gessa, G.L. (1970) Serotonin now: clinical implications of inhibiting its synthesis with *p*-chlorophenylalanine. *Ann. Intern. Med.* 73: 607—629.

Soulairac, A. and Soulairac, M.-L. (1961) Action de la reserpine sur le comportment sexuel du rat male. *C. R. Seances Soc. Biol.* 155: 1010—1012.

Tagliamonte, A., Tagliamonte, P., Gessa, G.L. and Brodie, B.B. (1969) Compulsive sexual activity induced by p-chlorophenylalanine in normal and pinealectomized male rats. *Science* 166: 1433—1435.

Ungerstedt, U. (1971) Stereotaxic mapping of the monoamine pathways in the rat brain. *Acta Physiol. Scand.*, suppl. 367: 1—48.

Vernikos-Danellis, J. (1972) Effects of hormones on the central nervous system. In: (S. Levine, Ed.) *Hormones and Behavior*. (Academic Press, New York).

Ward, I.L., Crowley, W.R., Zemlan, F.P. and Margules, D.L. (1975) Monoaminergic mediation of female sexual behavior. *J. Comp. Physiol. Psychol.* 88: 53—61.

Weissman, A. and Harbert, C.A. (1972) Recent developments relating serotonin and behavior. *Annu. Rep. Med. Chem.* 7: 47—58.

Whalen, R.E. and Luttge, W.G. (1970) *p*-Chlorophenylalanine methyl ester: an aphrodisiac? *Science* 169: 1000—1001.

Whalen, R.E., Gorzalka, B.B. and De Bold, J.F. (1975) Methodological considerations in the study of animal sexual behavior. In: (M. Sandler and G.L. Gessa, Eds) *Sexual Behavior. Pharmacology and Biochemistry*. (Raven Press, New York).

Wirz-Justice, A., Hackmann, E. and Lichtsteiner, M. (1974) The effect of estradiol diproprionate and progesterone on monoamine uptake in rat brain. *J. Neurochem.* 22: 187—189.

Wurtman, R.J. (1971) Brain monoamines and endocrine function. *Neurosci. Res. Prog. Bull.* 9: 172—297.

Zemlan, F.P., Ward, I.L., Crowley, W.R. and Margules, D.L. (1973) Activation of lordotic responding in female rats by supression of serotonergic activity. *Science* 179: 1010—1011.

Zitrin, A., Dement, W.C. and Barchas, J.D. (1973) Brain serotonin and male sexual behavior. In: (J. Zubin and J. Money, Eds) *Contemporary Sexual Behaviour: Critical Issues in the 1970s*. (Johns Hopkins University Press, Baltimore) pp. 321—338.

CHAPTER 31

The neuroendocrine basis of sexual behavior in primates

J. HERBERT

1. INTRODUCTION

Primates are distinguished by possessing large brains. The effect this has on behavior is an all-pervasive characteristic of the order, particularly intriguing in the case of sexual behavior. Sexual activity is, of course, of the greatest phylogenetic antiquity, and those parts of the brain involved, as shown by studies, principally on the rat (see chapters by Ward and Feder), are the hypothalamus and the limbic system, themselves ancient structures which have changed very little during evolution as compared with the neocortex. Neurohumoral mechanisms in primates have been studied comparatively with those species such as the rat, which are equipped with less developed brains. Various methods are used to assess the role of such factors in the sexual behavior of primates; in general, these can be divided into those which seek to understand which hormones are particularly concerned with regulating behavior, and those which focus on the area of the brain responsive to the humoral agent.

2. ENDOCRINE STUDIES

The female

The reproductive cycle
The easiest way to detect the possibility of an endocrine influence on behavior is to determine whether sexual interaction, which can be studied under a variety of conditions, varies predictably with the phases of the reproductive cycle. In prosimians, the most primitive primates, sexual activity appears to be strictly circumscribed by the female's cycle (Evans and Goy, 1968). Prosimian and nonprimate females such as rodents resemble one another in this respect. Prosimians have a well marked breeding season, which also

Handbook of Sexology, edited by J. Money and H. Musaph
© *Elsevier/North-Holland Biomedical Press, 1977*

points to strict endocrine control of mating, though individual contributions of changes in the male and the female have still to be analyzed adequately (Eaton, 1973).

Both old and new world monkeys, though widely separated both geographically and phylogenetically, show changes in behavior during the female cycle. Though more information is available from old world than new world species, the number of species studied is still limited. Copulation seems most likely to occur near midcycle (that is, at the time of ovulation) and least likely during the period immediately following, (that is, during the luteal phase; Rowell, 1972). Though many factors, both individual and social (see chapter by Hanby) can modify the way in which the menstrual cycle changes behavior, the basic pattern remains relatively constant, though somewhat less predictable than in the estrous cycle of nonprimate females so far extensively studied. The limited information available on apes suggests that they, too, display rhythmic changes in sexual behavior, more marked in gorillas and chimpanzees than orang-utans (Young and Orbison, 1944; Goodall, 1969; Nadler, 1975). Rhythmic changes have also been reported in women. Earlier investigations tended to report highest levels of sexual activity near menstruation (particularly shortly after menstruation) rather than at midcycle as in other primates (Stopes, 1937). In some more recent studies (Udry and Morris, 1968), rates of sexual intercourse have been reported as maximal near midcycle, though there are still many reports of levels being highest during the early part of the cycle rather than at midcycle. The latter seems reproductively more advantageous unless Darwinian selection has operated in humans so as to reduce fertility.

Such findings in primates do no more than suggest strongly that endocrine fluctuations occurring during the menstrual cycle alter behavior. Biological and social functions of cyclic changes need to be studied directly. Furthermore they indicate that though endocrine control of behavior still occurs in female primates, as compared with nonprimates, the effects of hormones may be more variable. The role of the individual hormones remains to be elucidated.

Hormones and sexual behavior
The contemporary approach is to devise a quantitative method of measuring sexual behavior, and then to produce, by experimental means, an endocrine 'steady state' which corresponds, so far as possible, with a chosen point in the menstrual cycle. Thus the daily or even hourly changes in behavior which occur naturally, are avoided, and observations are made while animals are under more controlled conditions. Combined with equally precise hormone assays, a powerful method of analyzing behavior then becomes available, which allows the role of a given hormone upon a given behavioral component or group of components to be assessed; this one may call the behavioral point of action of the hormone. Subsequently, the tissue on which the hormone acts to produce its effects (which can be called the somatic point of action) can be determined (Herbert, 1974). Studying laboratory-prepared

animals differs in one important respect from studying intact animals because the effects produced by rising or falling hormone levels are disregarded, though it is possible that these fluctuations are important.

The first procedure is to determine the changes in behavior resulting from ovariectomy. In rats this results in its almost complete abolition (see chapter by Feder). Though prosimians might be highly hormone sensitive, adequate experimental evidence on ovariectomized animals is still needed. However, several different species of monkey have been studied after ovariectomy. The operation reduces sexual interaction with males, though to varying degrees in different individuals and under different conditions. Giving an estrogen such as estradiol-17β (the principal estrogen secreted by the ovary) stimulates sexual interaction and thus mimics the situation observed at midcycle, when estrogen levels are naturally highest (Herbert, 1970). If an estrogen-treated female is then given progesterone, replicating the humoral conditions of the luteal phase, sexual activity declines once again, as can be observed during the normal menstrual cycle (Herbert, 1974).

Behavioral analysis clearly shows that estradiol promotes the female's sexual attractiveness: the male becomes more eager to mate, initiates more sexual interaction, and more readily responds to the female's sexual invitations. Progesterone has a converse effect, the female becoming less attractive. These effects are transmitted to the male rhesus monkey, at least partly, by vaginal pheromones, which are discussed fully in the chapter by Keverne. Thus, estrogen has its principal somatic point of peripheral action on the female's vagina. Increasing evidence suggests that androgen also plays an important part in the female's sexual activity. Ovariectomized female monkeys given androgen display increased attempts to solicit mounting from the males; that is, they are more actively receptive (Trimble and Herbert, 1968). Removing the adrenals from ovariectomized females, and hence the remaining source of all androgen, makes them unreceptive even though they are given estrogen and thus remain sexually attractive to the male. The critical nature of androgens becomes apparent if such animals are given a small dose of testosterone or androstenedione, when their behavior becomes fully receptive once again (Everitt et al., 1971).

These experiments allow a humoral explanation of the rhythmic changes in sexual interaction which occur during the primate menstrual cycle. During the earlier follicular phase, the female is moderately receptive and attractive since both estrogen and androgen levels are at mid-point. Near midcycle both hormone levels become elevated (Knobil, 1974; Persky, 1974), which results in increasing attractiveness and receptivity, and in maximal levels of sexual interaction with the male. After ovulation, the newly formed corpus luteum secretes increasing amounts of progesterone, which counteracts the effects of estrogen and makes the female less attractive. Progesterone may also interfere with the effect of androgen and so induce unreceptivity, though the evidence for this is now under scrutiny. However, androgen levels fall during the second half of the cycle partly at least as the result of an elevated progesterone level (Hess and Resko, 1973). Thus both decreased attractiveness and, possibly, reduced receptivity, contribute to the conspicuous low point in sexual behavior discernible during the luteal phase (Bullock et al., 1972; Saayman, 1973). Just before menstruation the corpus luteum wanes and this results in the heightened level of activity which can be observed in some animals at this time.

There is little experimental evidence on the role of hormones in the sexual behavior of female apes, though that of female chimpanzees is apparently reduced by castration (Young and Orbison, 1944). The problems of defining and measuring human sexuality have been referred to and need not be elaborated further. Nevertheless, clinical evidence suggests that similar hormonal mechanisms may exist in human females as in monkeys. Ovariectomy, or cessation of ovarian function at the menopause, is said not to result in diminution of the human female's 'libido' (Kinsey et al., 1953; Waxenburg et al., 1960). However, it has long been known that giving androgen to women might intensify their sexual desire (Salmon and Geist, 1943), and removal of the adrenals has been reported to reduce libido, in marked contrast to the inconspicuous effects of ovariectomy (Waxenburg et al., 1959). Whether treating adrenalectomized women with androgen can restore their sexual interest has not, it appears, been reported. Though much more work needs to be done, particularly on the factors modifying basic endocrine effects on human behavior, such evidence as there is points to conspicuous similarities between what is known of the hormonal control of behavior in monkeys and in women.

The male

Breeding season
Since in males there is no feature corresponding to the female's menstrual cycle, natural observation pointing to endocrine control of mating behavior relies on the way in which this activity varies between the breeding and non-breeding seasons, and the correlation between changes in behavior and alterations in testicular size or blood levels of androgen. For example, most male prosimians show marked seasonal alterations in behavior, which can be linked, to some degree, with changes in spermatogenesis (Petter-Rousseaux, 1964). Some male rhesus monkeys also show diminishing sexual activity at certain times of the year (usually the summer) which can be correlated with changes in other androgen-dependent tissues such as the color of the sexual skin (Vandenberg, 1965), though the unavailability of sexually attractive females at the same time is a complicating factor of such studies, and it is known that the male's hormonal levels may fluctuate in consonance with those of the female (Rose et al., 1974).

Hormones and sexual behavior
Castrated male prosimians have not apparently been studied. A number of

reports, both early and more recent, suggest that castration diminishes sexual activity in male monkeys (Thorek, 1924; Phoenix, 1973), though the effects may take a long time to become fully apparent (as in some nonprimate males, for example, dogs). Individual variations are as prominent in male as in female primates; persistence of sexual activity is not correlated with residual plasma testosterone levels (Wilson and Vessey, 1968; Wilson et al., 1972). Castrating infantile male rhesus monkeys has no long-lasting effect on juvenile play-mounting or erectile capacity (Phoenix, 1973).

Testosterone, as expected, can restore behavior to at least a proportion of castrated male monkeys, though after a prolonged period of hormone deficit target tissues may become less sensitive to the hormone. Dihydrotestosterone (DHT), a principal metabolite of testosterone, can also stimulate sexual behavior in castrated male rhesus (Resko and Phoenix, 1972), in contrast to experimental results on the rat (see chapter by Ward).

There is much anecdotal literature on the effects of castration and testosterone administration to man. Many reports indicate that castration during adult life may result in various degrees of impotency and reduction of desire (the two, may, of course, vary independently) though many cases apparently exist in which sexual activity was retained for many years after castration. In general, the effects seem rather similar to that seen in male monkeys, though the information from the latter is also limited. In men, it is sometimes said that the belief that castration will impair sexual performance is an important factor in determining the behavior results of this operation (McCullagh et al., 1973). Castration has more profound effects if carried out prepubertally than later. The need for contemporary studies on the effect of castration is evident.

Giving testosterone to castrated men has led to improved capacity for erection and ejaculation as well as to increase of sexual drive (see Money, 1961). The possible mechanisms for the way this might be achieved have not yet been studied, but are considered further in the next section. There is a recent report which suggests the possibility that administering luteinizing hormone releasing factor (LH-RF) may potentiate sexual behavior in men who do not show a worthwhile response to testosterone (Mortimer et al., 1974), a finding which will recall that of Moss and McCann (1973) who reported that LH-RF can substitute for the action of progesterone in inducing lordosis (that is, receptive behavior) in female rats.

3. NEURAL MECHANISMS

The female

Understanding of the function of the nerve supply to the genitalia of the female primate is still very limited. The nerve supply to the clitoris relative to the well known role of this organ in erotic sensation and orgasm has not been adequately studied experimentally. There is no information on the results of clitoridectomy in the sexual behavior of nonhuman female primates. Clitoral erection has been produced by electrically stimulating the brain in squirrel monkeys; the effective sites are those bordering the third ventricle in the thalamus, hypothalamus and upper midbrain, which correspond to those which mediate penile erection in the male (Maurus et al., 1965). Though much attention is currently being given to the role of vaginal pheromones in sexual behavior (see chapter by Keverne), it is not yet known whether neural pathways can mediate the production of pheromones. Likewise, the role of neural pathways in the pattern of vaginal contraction which were described by Masters and Johnson (1966) in human females during orgasm is not yet know. Electrical changes after genital stimulation have been detected in the preoptic area in the hypothalamus of the female rhesus monkey (Chhinna et al., 1968) which indicates that sensory information from the genitalia reach this part of the brain.

Recent investigations have centered on the hormonal sites of action in the female monkey's brain with respect to regulation of sexual behavior. Testosterone implanted into the anterior hypothalamus of adrenalectomized (unreceptive) female rhesus monkeys results in a return to normal behavior (Everitt and Herbert, 1975). This suggests that androgen in female monkeys may have a site of action in the brain similar to that of estrogen in the female rat (see chapter by Ward). Other areas of the female brain have still to be explored to determine whether or not hormone sensitive foci exist which are important in regulating sexual behavior. There is as yet no convincing experimental evidence of the direct effect of estrogen on the brain of the female monkey with respect to sexual behavior, though further work is required.

Recent studies on rats have suggested that monoamines may be concerned in the regulation of sexual behavior (see chapter by Everitt). The same may apply to female primates, since administration of substances (for example, p-chlorophenylalanine) which deplete 5-HT can replicate the action of testosterone on the adrenalectomized monkeys and restore normal levels of sexual receptivity (Gradwell et al., 1975). The present state of knowledge, which is still fragmentary, thus seems to indicate that a hormone-sensitive area exists in the anterior hypothalamus of the female monkey which responds to testosterone (or other androgens) and which modulates the level of sexual receptivity. Thus though the area of the brain corresponds with that fulfilling a similar function in the rat, the effective hormonal stimulus differs between the two species. Since the anterior hypothalamus contains large amounts of 5-HT, it is possible that androgens have their effect on monkeys by influencing the action of this neurotransmitter in the anterior hypothalamus. Definitive evidence on this point has still to be obtained. Since a similar neurochemical mechanism may also apply to the rat (see chapter by Everitt) it seems to be the hormonal stimulus which differentiates the two species, rather than the effects that the hormone has on the brain.

The male

Rather more is known about the role of the external genitalia in the sexual behavior of the male primate than of the female. The glans penis of the male monkey is covered by a large number of epidermal spines which overlay dermal papillae containing neural receptors. Castration results in these spines' disappearing, in the same way as in the rat and the cat (Herbert, 1974). Penile spines have not been described in man. The precise role these penile spines play in sensory input is still obscure, though they are generally believed to increase the activity of the underlying receptors and hence the sensory input reaching the male's central nervous system during mating. However, it is equally probable that their principal function is to increase sensory input to the female. Sectioning the penile dorsal nerve of male monkeys causes characteristic effects on their behavior. Ejaculation is practically abolished if both nerves are sectioned completely; thrusting becomes irregular and incoordinated. Intromission and mounting are, however, less severely affected (Herbert, 1973). The afferent input responsible for ejaculation thus travels over the dorsal nerves of the penis. It has clinically been demonstrated in men with complete spinal transection that the neural reflex responsible for ejaculation exists in the lumbar cord. Though there is no direct experimental evidence available on primates, the neural outflow which induces ejaculation probably travels over the lumbar sympathetic nervous system. Clinically it is found that lumbar sympathectomy in man delays or prevents ejaculation (Johnson, 1968). However, as in the case of other spinal reflexes, there are descending pathways from the brain which can regulate or modulate these spinal mechanisms. Thus, central nervous stimulation as well as local excitation of the penis or spinal cord can induce ejaculation (see below).

Work on carnivores suggests that the parasympathetic outflow is chiefly responsible for the changes in blood flow to the penis involved in erection (Semans and Langworthy, 1938). There is no corresponding experimental work on this pathway in primates as yet. In nonprimates there is evidence of a close functional relationship between the blood level of steroid hormones and noradrenaline in the autonomic nervous system supplying the genitalia of both males and females, which may have a role to play in the behavioral consequences of castration (Owman et al., 1974).

Studies which seek to implicate particular parts of the male primate's brain in sexual behavior have been made in three ways. Investigation of hormone-sensitive neural areas can be done by localized implanting of androgens (such as testosterone) into the castrated animal's brain to determine which sites result in the restoration of sexual activity. Such studies have yet to be reported. A less specific way of exciting the brain is by passing an electric current through an implanted electrode. This technique has two problems: it uniformly stimulates an area of the brain in a manner which may bear little or no relationship to physiological stimulation, and the results may be difficult to interpret. For example, brain stimulation causing erection may signify either that a motivational state has been produced by the stimulus or, more simply, that the efferent motor pathway altering blood flow in the penis has been directly set in operation. Furthermore, in many monkeys, sexual signals may serve functions which have a wide nonerotic significance. For example, male rhesus monkeys may mount as part of their aggressive or dominance behavior, and squirrel monkeys show a genital display which includes penile erection, in rather similar context (Ploog et al., 1963), demonstrating that penile erection after electrical stimulation of the brain (or any other procedure) may represent changes in activity of neural mechanisms determining behavior which differs from primary sexual activity.

Neocortical stimulation is fairly ineffective in inducing penile erection, though there are sensitive areas in the medial orbital cortex and adjacent anterior cingulate regions. The midline (periventricular) part of the thalamus and hypothalamus bordering the third ventricle are also sensitive loci (as in the female). Whether stimulation affects an afferent pathway, or links up with an efferent system is not clear. On the basis of studies on squirrel monkeys principally by Maclean and Ploog (see Maclean et al., 1963; Ploog, 1967), the neural system travels over the medial forebrain bundle in the hypothalamus, passing laterally and caudally through the pons and medulla in a pathway lying lateral to the cerebral peduncle, but distinct from the somatic motor pathway. Stimulating the substantia nigra relatively easily induces penile erection. This has been correlated with impotence in Parkinsonian patients (Maclean et al., 1963), and may also be related to a functional role for dopamine in sexual behavior in rats as demonstrated in more recent work (see chapter by Everitt). Another implication is that the effects of stimulating the medial forebrain bundle may relate to its ascending (aminergic) fibers rather than, or as well as, descending components.

Ejaculation has been effected by electrically stimulating the preoptic area of the hypothalamus in a rhesus monkey (Robinson and Mishkin, 1966). In this case ejaculation was preceded by penile erection (though the more peripheral mechanisms underlying the two functions may be rather different; see above). Following ejaculation, the current threshold necessary to evoke further penile erection became markedly raised, suggesting the existence of a neurophysiologically refractory period corresponding to the well-known behavioral state. Copulation by males with rhesus females has also been invoked by electrically stimulating the hypothalamus. The response could be modified by the presence of a second male (particularly a more dominant one) or the hormonal or individual characteristics of the female (Perachio et al., 1973).

Only limited knowledge about sexual behavior in male primates can be gained from experiments in which parts of the brain are destroyed. The well known Klüver—Bucy syndrome which results from bilateral damage to the amygdalae induces unselective sexual and ingestive behavior towards objects not usually associated with such activity in normal animals. These results, however, are probably examples of more widespread effects on behavior and illustrate a problem inherent in such studies: the effects of lesions (or stimulation) may be critically dependent on the conditions under which they are studied. In situations where sexual stimuli predominate, effects on sexual behavior will be observed, but this does not necessarily indicate that a specifically 'sexual' part of the brain is being explored.

Neural inputs which regulate the male primate sexual activity have been studied. Two have already been considered: tactile input to the penile dorsal nerve, and olfactory input (see Koverne's chapter). The former seems likely to reach the hypothalamus directly or so the neurophysiological evidence suggests. The latter may do likewise, though cortical structures could intervene. A third category of input is represented by visual signals which, in the monkey, are gestures such as the female's sexual presentation or invitation, as well as, presumably, less well defined visual characteristics of individual females which modify their sexual attractiveness. This input is highly likely to need neocortical processing, since only the neocortex seems to possess the mechanism necessary to analyse such complex information. Presumably there exists some pathway communicating the results of visual analysis with those parts of the brain such as the hypothalamus, which are more specifically concerned with sexual activity. This pathway, if it exists, has not been traced, though connections between the neocortex and hypothalamus have recently been described (Kievit and Kuypers, 1975).

The fragmentary state of knowledge about the neuroendocrine basis of the male primate sexual behavior needs no reiteration. The same applies, with minor qualification, to the female. Enough can be discerned for it to be concluded, however, that information obtained from nonprimates such as the rat may not necessarily be applied to the study of man and other primates without qualification.

BIBLIOGRAPHY

Bullock, D.W., Pavis, C.A. and Goy, R.W. (1972) Sexual behaviour, swelling of the sex skin and plasma progesterone in the pigtail macaque. *J. Reprod. Fertil.* 31: 225—236.

Chhina, G.S., Chakrabarty, A.S., Kaur, K. and Anand, B.K. (1968) Electroencephalographic responses produced by genital stimulation and hormone administration in sexually immature rhesus monkeys. *Physiol. Behav.* 3: 579—584.

Eaton, G.G. (1973) Neural-endocrine determination of sexual behaviour in simian and prosimian females. In: (C. Phoenix, Ed.) *Primate Reproductive Behaviour.* (Karger, Basel) pp. 20—35.

Evans, C.S. and Goy, R.W. (1968) Social behaviour and reproductive cycles in captive stumptailed lemurs (*Lemur catta*). *J. Zool.* 156: 181—197.

Everitt, B.J., Herbert, J. and Hamer, J.D. (1971) Sexual receptivity of bilateral adrenalectomised female rhesus monkeys. *Physiol. Behav.* 8: 409—415.

Everitt, B.J. and Herbert, J. (1975) The effects of implanting testosterone propionate in the central nervous system on the sexual behaviour of the female rhesus monkey. *Brain Res.* 86: 109—120.

Goodall, J. (1969) The behaviour of free living chimpanzees in the Gombe Stream Reserve. *Anim. Behav. Monogr.* 1: 165—311.

Gradwell, P.B., Everitt, B.J. and Herbert, J. (1975) 5-Hydroxytryptamine in the central nervous system and the sexual receptivity of female rhesus monkeys. *Brain Res.* 88: 281—293.

Herbert, J. (1970) Hormones and reproductive behaviour of rhesus and talapoin monkeys. *J. Reprod. Fertil.* suppl. 4: 119—140.

Herbert, J. (1973) The role of the dorsal nerves of the penis in the sexual behavior of the male rhesus monkey. *Physiol. Behav.* 10: 293—300.

Herbert, J. (1974) Some functions of hormones and the hypothalamus in the sexual activity of primates. *Prog. Brain Res.* 41: 331—348.

Hess, D.L. and Resko, J.A. (1973) The effects of progesterone on the patterns of testosterone and oestradiol concentrations in the systemic plasma of the female rhesus monkey during the inter-menstrual period. *Endocrinology* 92: 446—453.

Johnson, J. (1968) *Disorders of Sexual Potency in the Male.* (Pergamon Press, Oxford.)

Kievit, J. and Kuypers, H.G.J.M. (1973) Basal forebrain and hypothalamic connections to frontal and parietal cortex in the rhesus monkey. *Science* 187: 660—662.

Kinsey, A.L., Pomeroy, W.A., Martin, C.E. and Gebhard, P.H. (1953) *Sexual behaviour of the human female.* (Saunders, Philadelphia.)

Knobil, E. (1974) On the control of gonadotrophic secretions in the rhesus monkey. *Rec. Prog. Horm. Res.* 30: 1—46.

MacLean, P.D., Dennison, R.H. and Dua, S. (1963) Further studies on cerebral representation of penile erection: caudal thalamus, midbrain, pons. *J. Neurophysiol.* 16: 273—293.

Masters, W.H. and Johnson, V.E. (1966) *Human Sexual Response.* (Churchill, London.)

Maurus, M., Mitra, J. and Ploog, D. (1965) Cerebral representation of the clitoris in ovariectomised squirrel monkeys. *Exp. Neurol.* 13: 283—288.

McCullogh, E.P., McCullogh, D.R. and Hickan, M.A. (1933) Diagnosis and treatment of hypogonadism in the male. *Endocrinology* 17: 49—63.

Money, J. (1961) Sex hormones and other variables in human eroticism. In: (W.C. Young, Ed.) *Sex and Internal Secretions.* Vol. II (Williams and Wilkins, Baltimore) pp. 1383—1400.

Mortimer, C.H., McNeilly, A.S., Fisher, R.A., Murray, M.A.F. and Besser, G.M. (1974) Gonadotrophic-releasing hormone therapy in hypogonadal males with hypothalamic and pituitary disfunction. *Br. Med. J.* 4: 617—621.

Moss, R.L. and McCann, S.M. (1973) Induction of mating behavior in rats by luteinizing hormone releasing factor. *Science* 181: 177—179.

Nadler, R.D. (1975) Sexual cyclicity in captive lowland gorillas. *Science* 189: 813—814.

Owman, C., Sjöberg, N.O. and Sjöstrand, N.O. (1974) Short adrenergic neurons, a peripheral neuroendocrine mechanism. In: (M. Fujinara and C. Tanaka, Eds.) *Amine Fluorescence Histochemistry* (Igaku-Shoin, Tokyo) pp. 47—66.

Perachio, A.A., Alexander, M. and Marr, L.O. (1973) Hormonal and social factors affecting evoked sexual behaviour in rhesus monkeys. *Am. J. Phys. Anthropol.* 38: 217—232.

Persky, H. (1974) Reproductive hormones and moods during the menstrual cycle. In: (R.C. Friedman, R.M. Richart and R.C. Vande Weile, Eds.) *Sex differences in Behavior.* (Wiley, New York) pp. 455—466.

Petter-Rousseaux, A. (1964) Reproductive physiology and behaviour in the Lemur uroidea. In: (J. Buettner-Janusch, Ed.) *Evolutionary and Genetic Biology of Primates.* Vol. I. (Academic Press, New York) pp. 91—131.

Phoenix, C.H. (1973) The role of testosterone in the sexual behaviour of laboratory male rhesus. In: (Phoenix, C., Ed.) *Reproductive Behaviour.* (Karger, Basle) pp. 99—122.

Ploog, D.W., Blitz, J. and Ploog, F. (1963) Studies on social and sexual behaviour of the squirrel monkey. (*Siamiri sciureus*) *Fol. Primatol.* 1: 29—66.

Ploog, D.W. (1967) The behaviour of squirrel monkeys (*Siamiri sciureus*) as revealed by sociometry, bioacoustics and brain stimulation. In: (S.A. Altmann, Ed.) *Social Communication Among Primates*. (Univ. Chicago Press, Chicago) pp. 149—184.

Resko, J.A. and Phoenix, C.H. (1972) Sexual behaviour and testosterone concentrations in plasma of the rhesus monkey before and after castration. *Endocrinology* 91: 499—503.

Robinson, B.W. and Mishkin, M. (1966) Ejaculation evoked by stimulation of the preoptic area in monkey. *Physiol. Behav.* 1: 269—272.

Rose, R.M., Bernstein, I.S., Gordan, T.P. and Catlin, S.F. (1974) Androgens and aggression; a review and recent findings in primates. In (R.L. Holloway, Ed.) *Primate Aggression, Territoriality and Xenophobia*. (Academic Press, New York) pp. 275 304.

Rowell, T.E. (1972) Female reproductive cycle and social behaviour in primates. In: *Advances in the Study of Behaviour* 4: (Academic Press, New York) pp. 69—105.

Saayman, G.S. (1973) Effects of ovarian hormones on the sexual skin and behaviour of ovariectomised baboons (*Papio ursinus*) under free-ranging conditions. In: (C. Phoenix, Ed.) *Primate Reproductive Behaviour*. (Karger, Basle) pp. 64—98.

Salmon, V.J. and Geist, S.H. (1943) The effect of androgens upon libido in women. *J. Clin. Endocrinol. Metab.* 3: 275—238.

Semans, J.H. and Langworthy, D.R. (1938) Observations on the neurophysiology of sexual function in the male cat. *J. Urol.* 40: 836—844.

Stopes, M. (1937) *Married Love*. (Harper, New York.)

Thorek, M. (1924) Experimental investigations of the role of the Leydig, seminiferous and sertoli cells and effects of testicular transplantation. *Endocrinology* 8: 61—90.

Trimble, M.R. and Herbert, J. (1968) The effect of testosterone or oestradiol upon the sexual and associated behaviour of the adult female rhesus monkey. *J. Endocrinol.* 42. 171—185.

Udry, J.R. and Morris, N.M. (1968) Distribution of coitus in the menstrual cycle. *Nature* 220: 593—596.

Vandenberg, J.G. (1965) Hormonal basis of sex skin in male rhesus monkeys. *Gen. Comp. Endocrinol.* 5: 31—34.

Waxenburg, S.E., Drellich, M.G. and Sutherland, A.N. (1959) The role of hormones in human behaviour: I. Changes in female sexuality after adrenalectomy. *J. Clin. Endocrinol. Metab.* 19: 193—202.

Waxenburg, S.E., Finkbeiner, J.A., Drellich, M.G. and Sutherland, A.N. (1960) The role of hormones in human behaviour: II. Changes in sexual behaviour in relation to vaginal smears of breast cancer patients after oophorectomy and adrenalectomy. *Psychosom Med.* 22: 435—442.

Wilson, A.P. and Vesse, S.H. (1968) Behaviour of free ranging castrated rhesus monkeys. *Fol. Primatol.* 9: 1—14.

Wilson, M., Plant, T.M. and Michael, R.P. (1972) Androgens and the sexual behaviour of male rhesus monkeys. *J. Endocrinol.* 52: ii.

Young, W.L. and Orbison, W.D. (1944) Changes in selective features of behaviour in pairs of oppositely-sexed chimpanzees during the sexual cycle and after ovariectomy. *J. Comp. Psychol.* 37: 107—143.

CHAPTER 32

Social factors affecting primate reproduction

J.P. HANBY

1. INTRODUCTION

Most monkeys, apes and humans live in social groups. The aim of this chapter is to show how the sexual behavior of group-living primates is affected by heritage, rearing conditions, and more immediate social contexts.

That sexual practices of the individual are affected by the particular group into which the individual is born may seem obvious. Nevertheless, it is still unclear just what practices are affected, how much, and by what specific social factors. For instance, homosexual behavior in humans and other social primates has been variously thought to be the product of social conditions (as in prisons), family background (both genetic and social), societal custom (as among the Romans), hormonal imbalance, and of mental imbalance — or even to be perfectly normal.

The basic assumption of this section is that homosexual and all other sexual behavior exhibited by humans can be better understood by placing human behavior in the broader context of primate behavior. The study of captive and free-ranging nonhuman primates has revealed that some behavior is common to all group-living primates, and some the product of special, definable circumstances. Variability in primate sexual behavior can be related to many different factors, as a glance at the section headings of this Handbook illustrates. Here primarily the general factors resulting from social organization are considered in order to clarify what is basic and what is modifiable in our primate sexual repertoire.

2. PHYLOGENETIC PREDISPOSITIONS

Most of the 250-odd species of primates live in social groups. The smallest group consists of one adult male and female and their young, for example, gibbons. The largest consists of many of both sexes and all ages, for example,

Handbook of Sexology, edited by J. Money and H. Musaph
© *Elsevier/North-Holland Biomedical Press, 1977*

macaques. Since the concern here is with the social factors that influence primate sexual behavior, the focus will be on the old world monkeys and apes (the catarrhines) because in addition to being more like humans in terms of biochemistry, behavior and environment, these species have more known about them, both in the wild and in captivity.

Certain physical, social and behavioral characteristics of monkeys and apes are particularly relevant to understanding their sexual interactions: (1) the reddening or swelling of the sexual skin in some species; (2) the lack of strict breeding seasons and the occurrence of copulation at practically all stages of the female menstrual cycle in most species; (3) the variability of copulatory patterns; (4) the rules of social organization, as in a ranking system; and (5) the appearance of sexual gestures in a wide variety of social situations.

Physical attributes

Sex skin coloration and swelling, the breeding season, and female cyclicity are three factors that affect the timing, frequency, and appearance of much sexual behavior. These factors are directly related to hormonal state and are dealt with elsewhere in this volume. Most of the primates that are considered in this section show slight to very conspicuous physical signs of sexual state, and mating is often not confined to a particular time of year or to the middle of a female's menstrual cycle. This is especially true of the medium-to-large mixed social units. The solitary and small-family species have fewer conspicuous physical and behavioral signs of sexual state.

Copulatory patterns

Variability in posturing and other components of courtship and copulation seem most obvious in the mixed social groups. Except for humans, the usual copulatory posture involves a rear approach by the male (some examples are shown in Fig. 1) but ventro-ventral and many other variations have been observed in some species (for example, stumptail and Japanese monkeys; Bertrand, 1969; Chevalier-Skolnikoff, 1974; Hanby and Brown, 1974). Variability or flexibility in courtship and copulatory sequences increases with different kinds of rearing conditions, especially in captivity.

Males of different species require varying numbers of mounts or intromitted thrusts before they can ejaculate. In most species, the male mounts once, but some macaques and baboons require multiple mounts. The number of thrusts per mount varies not only with the species (Michael et al., 1973) but with the male's age and idiosyncracies. For instance, young and old males may require more intromissions or more thrusts than males in their prime, and the duration of a man's intromission before ejaculation is said to be culturally linked (Ford and Beach, 1951).

Ejaculation is fairly easy to recognize in adult males for it involves a cessation of thrusting, bodily rigor, and usually some sign of ejaculate. The

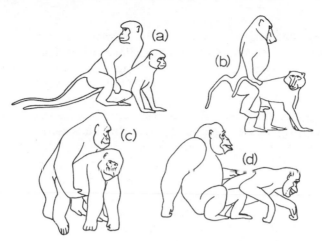

Fig. 1. Some copulatory postures. (a) Adult male and female langurs (from photo by Jay), (b) Adult male and female anubis baboons (from photo by McGinnis), (c) Adult male and female gorillas (from photo by D. Sorby), (d) Adult male and female chimpanzees (from photo by D. Bygott)

comparable pattern in nonhuman females is seldom seen but has been described for a few captive stumptail macaques, *Macaca speciosa* or *arctoides* (Chevalier Skolnikoff, 1974). Some researchers have inferred female orgasm from 'reaching back' in the captive rhesus monkey (Zumpe and Michael, 1968) or from jumping away movements or vocalizations in wild chacma and anubis baboons (Saayman, 1970; Rowell, Packer, H. and F. Plooj, personal communication), and in wild chimpanzees (McGinnis, personal communication). Whether such behavior or the uterine contractions of a female rhesus recorded during a male's ejaculatory mount (Michael, 1971) are comparable to a human female's orgasm remains to be shown (see Burton, 1971). It cannot be assumed that only human females have orgasms. If other primate females have orgasms as inconsistently or subtly as do some women, that may explain why observers find it difficult to document them without more direct physiological measurements.

Social organization

The sizes, sex and age ratios of primate groups vary considerably. These composition factors alone regulate the number of sexual partners available for any one individual. Most groups of macaques, baboons, chimpanzees and gorillas are large and contain both sexes and all ages; therefore individuals have more opportunities for mating with a variety of partners. Potential mates are more limited when there is a social system characterized by small reproductive units as in the hamadryas baboons and Bedouin harem groups or in monogamous pairs. Monogamous systems are rare in primates, and most individuals seem to mate with whomever they can, given the restrictions imposed by group composition and social structure, and, to a much lesser degree, individual preference.

Internal organization of groups affects partner availability both directly and indirectly. Individuals of certain age classes often leave their natal group and are thus not available within that group, but only within other groups they might join. Social hierarchies based on kinship groups (Missakian, 1972) and aggressiveness (Bernstein, 1970) affect mate selection directly. Certain species have patterns of fatherly care or allow differential access to infants and thus indirectly affect familiarity of individuals with one another. Subgroup patterns within the group further affect relationships between individuals and thus sexual relations (Hanby, 1975). While general social status and existing relationships strongly affect the availability and selection of sexual partners, the sexual relationship in turn affects other social relations. Sexual relationships between individuals affect social organization by promoting familiarity, alliances and friendships and establishing kinship. Conversely, the social organization of all primate societies imposes regulation of sexual relationships in various ways.

Sociosexual behavior

The term sociosexual (Zuckerman, 1932) refers to behavior that is commonly seen in the context of heterosexual copulation but also in other social situations. Sociosexual patterns include: presentation, investigation and manipulation of the genitals; mounting; penile erection; pelvic thrusting; intromission; ejaculation, orgasm; embracing; hip touching; clinging; kissing, caressing, nuzzling, lipsmacking and various vocalizations. Sociosexual behavior forms a large part of the social repertoire and mainly occurs in contexts involving a mild or high degree of tension or excitement, as in greeting, play and disturbance. From their developmental origins, most of the elements seem more related to comfort giving and seeking then to any other motivational system (Hanby, 1976). In the past, sociosexual behavior has been variously labeled as strictly sexual, pseudosexual, aggressive or dominant (Hamilton, 1914; Kempf, 1917; Zuckerman, 1932; Maslow, 1936; Wickler, 1967). Some examples of the diverse contexts and appearance of some sociosexual patterns are shown in Fig. 2.

Human observers have interpreted sociosexual patterns differently, usually as sexual or aggressive, according to biases not often clear to the observers themselves. Some biases are gender related. It is genuinely difficult to interpret any particular interaction unless details are known about the situation, and especially about the participants. Monkeys and apes seem to be far better at interpreting actions than are their human observers, but even so one can observe cases in which a particular individual appears confused. For example, a young male Japanese monkey was observed to mate with a sexually receptive female. He mounted her in series but on occasion between mounts he would run back to his mother and mount her (no intromission with the mother was observed). This son—mother mounting could be interpreted as sexual and incestuous, but other interpretations could be made given other

Fig. 2. Some sociosexual patterns (all drawn from photographs in cited work). (a) An adult female anubis baboon presents to another adult female and her recent infant (Hall and DeVore, 1965). (b) 'Social buffering' in Barbary macaques. Two males hold an infant which one has brought over to the other; the recipient raises the infant's bottom and inspects it (Deag, 1974). (c) Mutual genital holding during excitement between two immature stumptail macaques (Bertrand, 1969). (d) An infant anubis baboon presents to an adult male putting foot and tail into contact (Ransom and Rowell, 1973). (e) Mounting between two guinea baboons after an agonistic interaction (A. Mertl). (f) A mount between two bonnet macaque males (the recipient is reaching back to touch the testicles of the mounter) in a greeting situation (Simonds, 1965). (g) An adult female chimpanzee approaches and presents her bottom to an adult male who gently extends a hand to touch it (Bygott). (h) Two adult male chimpanzees show excitement and genital holding during a period of calling by distant chimpanzees (Bygott).

items of information: the male was young, in his first reproductive year; the other female was his age mate but of a much higher rank than himself and was skittish (he [was] mounting off); his mother had always been tolerant of [her] sons (and she had many) approaching and contacting her; and in this species the infants and juveniles commonly mount and ride on mothers in situations of excitement and stress. Thus the son—mother mounting could also be interpreted as comfort or reassurance seeking, or as confusion between these and sexual expression.

The motivational bases for sociosexual interactions are by no means always clear but it is doubtful that many of the patterns are strictly dependent on sexual hormones. Mounting and presenting, for instance, both seem to be independent of gonadal hormones (Phoenix et al., 1967). Sociosexual behavior is widespread and relatively frequent in the terrestrial mixed groups of primates. Phylogenetically, sociosexual patterns appear to have developed as a (Missakian, 1969, 1972; Erwin et al., 1974) because much more is known causes and the functions of sociosexual behavior need more investigation, a broader perspective concerning the hormones, situations and individuals involved.

3. DEVELOPMENTAL DEPENDENCIES

Early social experience is crucial to the development of mature sociosexual patterns. No matter what the adult levels of sexual hormones, if a monkey has lacked experience and interaction with other monkeys, sociosexual behavior is grossly abnormal. Research, mainly on rhesus macaques and chimpanzees, has made it abundantly clear that early rearing restrictions negatively affect adult social and sexual behavior (see reviews on rhesus by Harlow and Harlow, 1969; and Sackett, 1968; and on chimpanzee and gorilla by Riesen, 1971; and Nadler, 1974). Much of the early work on this problem needs re-evaluation and care in interpretation in the light of other research (Missakian, 1969, 1972; Erwin et al., 1974) because much more is known now about the behavior of free-ranging primates living in more complex social groups (see Hanby, 1976, for review). Thus normal or natural development can be traced and compared to that in the laboratory under specific rearing regimes.

Development of sociosexual behavior

Infant macaques, baboons and chimpanzees show early sociosexual behavior, including thrusting, mounting, attempted and even achieved intromissions, genital play, presenting and embracing. In wild and captive groups which include all ages and both sexes, males seem to develop their basic copulatory repertoire, except for ejaculation, by the end of their first year. In anubis baboons, infant males appear to show even an orgasmic pattern (Owens, 1973). It is apparent that the presence of adult females, including the mother, greatly facilitates the linking of the erection—thrust—mount—intromit sequence. Adult females allow or even encourage infant and juvenile males to mount and intromit. In free-ranging groups mothers and others often carry youngsters on their backs. This dorsal riding pattern helps them to learn to respond appropriately to mount and dismount gestures as well as to learn to mount properly.

Female infant and juvenile macaques and baboons seldom mount but, when they do, their posturing is correctly oriented and may even involve the adult heterosexual pattern of footclasping. More often, however, infant and juvenile females are embrace—thrust and mount—thrust partners for infant males and thereby seem to acquire both maternal and sexual experience with their young companions.

Female macaques begin irregularly cycling as young as age $2\frac{1}{2}$ years, and they and the females of some other species may show juvenile swellings (VanWagenen, 1972). Pubertal onset and regular cycling greatly increase a female's participation in sexual activity and she may conceive by age $3\frac{1}{2}$. Males do not usually show ejaculation until age $4\frac{1}{2}$ in wild and captive mixed groups, even though they show increased levels of testosterone by age 3 or so in the laboratory (Resko, 1967), and can inseminate females at that age under special laboratory circumstances (Maple et al., 1973). In captivity, chimpanzee males and females reach puberty at about 7—8 and 6—10 years of age, respectively, (McGinnis, 1973), and maybe 2—3 years later in the wild (Teleki, Hunt and Pfifferling, in preparation). Adolescence in these and most other primates is a rather prolonged period between the onset of puberty and achieving full growth and integration into the troop.

Long before the changes, both social and physiological, that come with puberty, young primates who have grown up in mixed groups show a differentiation of copulatory patterns from those related patterns for giving or requesting contact or comfort. Adolescence seems to be a time for smoothing and integrating these patterns, and most important, linking of behavior to physiological changes. Thus, sexual readiness becomes linked to gratification achieved in heterosexual contacts, and reassurance remains clearly linked to other partners and other situations. Both the copulatory and the contacting/comforting systems become linked to physiological states, partners and contexts, but the former system seems to become increasingly stereotyped while the latter remains relatively more variable in form and context.

By full adulthood, usually several years after puberty, individuals show species-specific as well as individual patterns, and their behavior serves also to initiate the young. Since primate behavior is so modifiable and the rearing period so long, individuals and groups can develop variants on the basic patterns. This whole process seems to depend on a relatively critical time in development, during infancy and the juvenile period. If there are restrictions regarding partners and situations, or models and leaders, sociosexual patterns change.

Social restrictions during development

The most extreme restriction is complete isolation from others. Even when from birth onward, surrogate, terry-cloth covered, warmed pseudomothers are offered in the place of live mothers adult sociosexual behavior is totally inadequate. Attempts at rehabilitation in the juvenile or adult period by allowing experience with other animals has only meager effects (Meier, 1965; Harlow et al., 1966; Harlow and Harlow, 1969; Missakian, 1969). There are signs that specific kinds of experience, for example, with younger, nonthreatening partners, or very patient experienced partners may improve sexual performance (Mason, 1960; Davenport and Rogers, 1970). Unfortunately, though copulatory performance might be improved, there is little indication that patterns appropriate for getting along with other group members in nonsexual situations, or for child-rearing are affected positively.

Foster-rearing, notably by humans, produces monkeys or apes that show peculiar sexual behavior, if any, though occasionally an individual may appear relatively normal (Rowell, personal communication; Lemmon, 1970 and Lemmon and Temerlin, 1974, on chimpanzees). Rearing with only the animal's mother seems to improve the probability that the offspring will eventually be able to reproduce and to participate in group activity in adulthood (Hinde and Spencer-Booth, unpublished and Spencer-Booth, 1969; Chamove, 1973; and, on chimpanzees, Lemmon, 1970). Rearing monkeys with peers only produces animals with adequate behavior as adults in the sense that they do breed (Chamove, 1973; Harlow and Harlow, 1969; Sackett, 1968).

A system of early rearing that might be expected to produce individuals that were relatively normal in their sociosexual behavior is rearing first with the mother with subsequent exposure to peers. However, compared with those reared in mixed groups from birth, the mother-then-peer-raised monkeys show deficiencies and delays in their sociosexual patterns. For example, Goy and Goldfoot (1974) compared rhesus mother-and-peers vs. mother-then-peers and found that the latter produced (a) males that developed the correct mounting posture later, (b) males that were unable to mount females properly after puberty, and (c) males that never mounted at all. That hormonal factors are less important than social ones was shown by the fact that castrate males and pseudohermaphrodite females exhibited the same deficiencies in sexual behavior as did their like-raised controls.

Another example of the kinds of behavior seen after a rearing regimen of mother-then-peers is that reported by Erwin and co-workers (1973). Rhesus monkeys were reared for 7 months with mothers, then housed with but one member of the same sex, then, at puberty, they were exposed to a member of the opposite sex. The pairs heterosexually matched at puberty showed a wide variety of unintegrated elements of sociosexual behavior: correct and disoriented mounting and presenting, fellatio, premature ejaculation (mounting and ejaculating before intromission was achieved), refusal of sexual advances, much aggression, and high frequencies of sexual activity interspersed with various other behavior. Each pair exhibited a unique style or interaction pattern. After such pubertal heterosexual experience, it was determined that one pair of males reared together actually preferred one another as sexual partners (with anal intromission) to females (Erwin and Maple, unpublished; see also Maple, Ch. 94).

Retardation of the development of integrated sociosexual patterns and the appearance of highly idiosyncratic patterns is reminiscent of some human behavior (see Masters and Johnson, 1970). The monkeys described above had not integrated elements of behavior into smooth copulatory sequences or friendly, nonsexual contact sequences as wild monkeys at the same age do. The restriction of opportunities to link certain behavioral sequences to certain partners and situations produces monkeys with delayed and distorted sociosexual behavior. Likewise, humans are often subjected to a variety of restricted rearing practices, and may show behavior similar to that of deprived monkeys.

As adults, primates with limited early experience apparently have to work out a pattern that allows members of a pair to associate peacefully if they are to copulate. Peaceful associations with others in noncopulatory situations requires even more elaborate patterns. Restricted rearing produces idiosyncratic or impaired patterns of behavior involving much aggression and withdrawal and an obvious confusion of sexual and nonsexual gestures. In adults with less restricted early rearing, sexual partners are distinct from those one might call friends or companions in nonsexual situations. Some human cultures show a similar distinction with men and women associating for primarily reproductive reasons, whereas they may associate with members of their own sex for companionship (Marshall and Suggs, 1971). In Western cultures, with restricted rearing and traditional monogamy, heterosexual pairs are expected to provide the members with sexual, contacting and companionship gratifications. This overlap may promote monogamy as well as problematic behavior.

The study of nonhuman primates in a greater variety of rearing conditions, simulating human rearing practices, and attending more to the general sociosexual repertoire (as well as to purely sexual acts) should reveal much about the ways in which our own sociosexual patterns develop. Of course, direct observation of human behavior would help, too. In all studies, more attention needs to be given to the interaction between the type of maternal or paternal care and the development of relations with others. For example, one might ask whether permissive mothers have babies who interact sociosexually at an earlier age or at higher frequencies than do those of restrictive mothers.

4. CONTEXTUAL CONSTRAINTS

Given the influence of early rearing, it is not surprising that adult primates show wide individual differences in the quality and quantity of sociosexual interactions. Early rearing shapes the behavior to which each individual is genetically predisposed, but there remain more immediate social factors that contribute both regularity and variability to sociosexual acts. These social factors primarily affect partner availability and thus partner selection. It is the latter which affects genetic transmission and ongoing social organization. Partner selection in free-ranging primates is difficult to study for obvious reasons: both partners must be considered and selection may be as much a matter of acceptance as of active choice; also, observation conditions are seldom ideal. Laboratory studies suffer from numerous restrictions in partner availability, time, housing, and so forth. For these reasons, partner availability, which can be studied in most situations, will receive more attention in the following discussion than will partner selection.

Partner availability is regulated in all primate groups. Death from predation, illness, or old age removes individuals, and destruction of the habitat diminishes groups, but even under undisturbed conditions individuals, especially males, leave and join other groups. The degree of integration into a group profoundly affects the appearance and frequency of sociosexual acts and status. Status is a broad term that refers to the position that an individual has in the web of relationships with others in a group; in this paper only dominance and kinship relationships will be focused upon, as they are the most studied. Partner familiarity, group traditions, and some other social factors will be considered briefly.

Group attachment

Long-term studies on free-living groups of monkeys and apes have provided evidence that group transfer is a predictable primate pattern. Movement between groups affects the sociosexual availability of partners and the frequency of sociosexual behavior. Group transfer is most common in adolescent males, but this varies from species to species and group to group.

Long-term observations on rhesus monkeys have established that it is the young males who transfer mainly during breeding season (Boelkins and Wilson, 1972). Drickamer and Vessey (1973) summarized 6 years of study on this species and found that the average age of leaving was 4 years, although special social circumstances (such as the sex ratio, or the departure of peers) may force or entice a younger animal away. All males were found to have left their natal group by prime adulthood (7 years). Sexual opportunities apparently increase for the transferring males. Lindberg (1969) found that transfers were most common during the breeding season and the males copulated with the females in the newly joined group. Males who shifted relatively permanently copulated at a significantly higher frequency per observation hour.

Japanese monkey males of all ages transfer and it is usually the young who are most mobile. Norikoshi and Koyama (1974) reported on 8 years of study of wild Japanese monkeys and found that almost none of the males over $4\frac{1}{2}$ years old stayed in the troop with which their mothers and close female relatives lived. Males transferred mainly during the breeding season. It has been suggested that the subordinate males in any age class and those with more attachment to peers than to the remainder of the maternal group were the most likely to leave.

Observations on wild anubis baboons have also revealed that all males leave their natal group before reaching 8 years of age (Packer, 1976). Males who do not leave at puberty have definitely fewer opportunities for mating. Upon shifting to a new group these young males form consort relations with estrus females, and become integrated into the group.

A young male hamadryas baboon may attach himself to a harem (one-male) group of an older male but his opportunities for mating are limited (Kummer, 1968). He may also form his own unit by 'kidnapping' a female, usually young, from some other group. The females of this species have a special place in the social structure, in that they form estrous swellings and mate at a very early age ($2\frac{1}{4}$) even though they do not conceive until a year or more later. The relationship between the young male and his juvenile consort includes many maternal (for example, cuddling), as well as sexual components and this overlap in sociosexual system may well promote attachment between the individuals.

Langur males shift groups and may do so especially when population densities are high (Sugiyama, 1965; Sugiyama et al., 1965; Rudran, 1973). New langur males may even kill the infants in their adopted groups. New males thereby significantly increase their potential genetic contribution as they promptly inseminate the females. Such aggression also firmly establishes their social status (Parthasarathy and Rahaman, 1974). Initial sexual activity is very high (Sugiyama, 1965), and other drastic social changes occur such as fighting between males which may affect fertility (see subsequent sections).

Siamang males and females leave their families at adolescence and then appear to spend a considerable period establishing a relationship with a member of the opposite sex. Sexual behavior seems to increase the probability that a pair will stay together (Aldrich-Blake and Chivers, 1973). Gorilla males and females also change groups (D. Fossey, personal communication), though it is not clear how sociosexual behavior is affected. Chimpanzees are unusual and more like humans in that it is the female who commonly transfers (Nishida and Kawanaka, 1972; Tutin, unpublished; Pusey, unpublished). Adolescent females often move quite long distances into the range of another chimpanzee community and mate with the resident males. They seem to go through a period of adolescent sterility. When they do conceive or give birth they may stay in their new community or return to their original one.

Sexual behavior and general sociosexual gestures (such as male—male mounting) seem to be especially common in situations of entry or re-entry of an individual into a group. Increased sexual activity (usually not distinguished from interactions that may not have sexual components) has been noted in most cases of group transfer, reunion, introductions, the formation of new groups and in situations of excitement or stress (rhesus, Hamilton, 1914; Kempf, 1917; Bernstein and Mason, 1963; Conaway and Koford, 1965; Joslyn, 1967; pigtail monkeys: Bernstein, 1969; Tokuda et al., 1968; Japanese monkeys: Kawai, 1960; Miyadi, 1967; Hanby, 1974; stumptail monkeys: Bertrand, 1969; chimpanzees: Goodall, 1968a,b; Bygott, 1974; and see Fig. 2).

The appearance of such behavior seems to be relatively independent of the sex hormonal state of the males and females. Saayman (1973) found that there was no close response relationship between amounts of estradiol administered to chacma baboon females and their sexual behavior upon being released near a new group. However, in this species it is the male who usually transfers, which may mean it would be more profitable to investigate the effects of hormones on the males, or on the resident females. The menstrual cycle state in hamadryas baboon females also did not affect their immediate acceptance by males (Kummer, 1968, 1973). Increased sociosexual activity in cases of group change or partner change may be more a result of adrenal than gonadal hormones though the hormonal bases remain largely uninvestigated. There is also a large component of contact or comfort seeking and giving in such situations. More recording of details of the interactions would be illuminating.

Dominance status

Most large groups of primates have some sort of dominance system; agonistic interactions are often one-way (A hits B, B aquiesces to A) such that the individuals can be ranked in a linear or near-linear manner. The rank an individual has in the dominance hierarchy may affect his or her sociosexual behavior.

Male dominance

There is no widespread positive correlation between a male's rank in a dominance hierarchy and his opportunities to mate, the production of offspring or the frequency and direction of other sociosexual behavior. However, what evidence there is, is confined to mixed groups; family units as in gibbons and siamangs or in one-male groups such as hamadryas baboons, must be excluded from consideration from lack of information on overall dominance relations between the adult males.

A positive relationship between a male's dominance and his sexual activity has been found for some groups of macaques (Carpenter, 1942; Altman, 1962; Conaway and Koford, 1965; Kaufman, 1965; Loy, 1969; Hanby et al., 1971) and baboons (DeVore, 1965; Packer, 1976). However, as Loy (1969) put it, 'there is no striking correlation between dominance rank and frequency of mating'. In other words, the positive correlations are not very high, are variable over time (Eaton, 1974), and the variables to be correlated are often ambiguous. Dominance rank is confounded with age, and mating can mean consorting without intercourse, or ejaculation or a number of other, often undefined components of behavior. On the whole, dominance is an unsatisfactory concept by itself (see Bernstein, 1970).

A more fruitful line of inquiry seems to be to examine a number of attributes of specific males and social situations. In this way it can be shown that rank is largely a function of a male's age (Bygott, 1974, on chimpanzees) and it is the prime adult males who usually copulate the most and have the most (different) female partners (Hanby et al., 1971, on Japanese monkeys). Nevertheless, within the age category of prime adult, males differ as to their sexual activity and it is often the most dominant or 'alpha' males that have the highest frequencies (Hanby et al., 1971; Eaton, 1973, on the same troop of Japanese monkeys). Kaufman (1965) found that when two young rhesus males became high ranking rather quickly, their copulatory frequency also dramatically increased.

Low-ranking males, or those continually defeated in fights, may have low levels of testosterone that may correlate with both copulatory and aggressive behavior. The direction of cause and effect is unknown. Some low-ranking males do seem to have retracted testicles and pale sex-skin color in Japanese monkeys, and there is some evidence that the mere presence of dominant males in a group will inhibit younger or less-dominant males from engaging in sexual activity (personal observations on celebes, Japanese and rhesus macaques; also Koford, 1963; Hinde and Spencer-Booth, 1967; Kaufman, 1965).

More direct evidence for the effects of social factors on hormonal state come from research by an interdisciplinary team at the Yerkes primate center in Atlanta (Rose et al., 1971, 1972; Gordon and Bernstein, 1973). In an all-male group there was a relationship between testosterone, dominance rank, and frequency of aggressive behavior. In order to clarify whether the higher level of testosterone in a dominant or an aggressive male preceded or was consequent upon its social position, a second study was undertaken. Adult males were allowed access to sexually receptive females, with a resultant increase in testosterone level. Upon exposure to a large group of males and defeat in fights, the testosterone level fell. Social and experiential varibles clearly affect the male's androgen level.

Presumably, low-ranking males may have low levels of testosterone. Nevertheless, they do copulate with females and under less stressful conditions than in the above-cited studies, their testosterone levels may well be as high as those of higher ranking males (Eaton and Resko, 1974). Participation in mating activity by low-ranking males has repercussions on their relationships with other group members even if they do not sire offspring. In any case, a male's status changes throughout his life, and opportunities for high rank always exist.

Female reproductive state can affect male mating opportunities, regardless of rank. For instance, Japanese macaque males at and before puberty, and low-ranking males of all ages, copulated when there were many sexually active females in their group (Hanby et al., 1971) The following year, most of the females had infants and were lactating, a state that inhibits mating activity (Tanaka et al., 1970; Hanby et al., 1971). That year, the number of low-ranking and prepubertal males that participated in breeding greatly diminished (Hanby and Brown, 1974). Thus, rank appeared to be more important in the second year and may usually be more related to mating frequency under conditions of limited access to partners (see, for example, DeVore, 1965).

Dominance rank seems to be of relatively less importance to sexual activity than to overall status in the group and the availability of partners. Nevertheless, when all other factors are controlled, high dominance does appear to promote participation in breeding activity. High dominance itself seems to result from a combination of factors such as maturity, integration into the group, familiarity with group members, and to a very small degree from aggressiveness; testosterone may be more an effect than a cause.

Male dominance and other sociosexual behavior

There is a common notion that dominance rank is related to nonsexual mounting and presenting. Wickler (1967) reviewed a good deal of the literature that purports to show a relation between dominance, aggression and sociosexual gestures. His conclusion was that the mounter was sexually motivated but the recipient probably was not. Thus presenting was primarily a primate tactic to divert aggression into sexual activity. There is not much support for this view.

It is now known that species that have a strict breeding season with coinciding changes in sexual hormone levels also mount in the nonbreeding season. For instance, in a study by Gordon and Bernstein (1973), two all-male groups of rhesus were caged next to a mixed group with males and seasonally receptive females. One of the all-male groups could see the mixed group, while the other all-male group, which was housed equally close, could only smell and hear them. During the breeding season of the mixed group, the all-male group that could see the sexual behavior of the males and females, showed mounting among themselves. Some of the mounting was of the series pattern typical of heterosexual copulation, and the males also had the seasonal change in testosterone level. The other all-male group showed only the usual type of male—male mounting and no homosexual behavior, nor seasonal change in testosterone level. It is unlikely that the male—male mounting so often seen in macaques, baboons and chimpanzees is related to sexual hormones. There is also little evidence to support the notion that sociosexual gestures such as mounts, presenting and genital touching are related to dominance, for they do not appear in agonistic situations nearly so often as in exciting or tense situations. I have previously reviewed the data that has been offered to relate dominance to sociosexual behavior between males (Hanby, 1974). There is little evidence of dominant males mounting subordinates, though there is more evidence that presentation is a gesture of deference by subordinates to more dominant, and usually older animals. Most commonly, sociosexual gestures appear to function as tension reducing, comforting or appeasing mechanisms rather than as sexual or dominance expressions. Indeed, equating the mounter's role with maleness or dominance and the recipient's with femaleness and submission, is an outmoded and outworn concept.

Female status and sociosexual behavior

There are as yet few studies that mention the relation between a female's rank in a social hierarchy and the direction or frequency of her sociosexual encounters. The picture that exists is clouded by the lack of precise knowledge of reproductive state, and general confusion about what determines rank, but there are some studies that clearly indicate an interaction between female rank and her sociosexual behavior.

Laboratory studies have generally used the pair or triad test, an experimental paradigm for the evaluation of an animal's sexual behavior. A female is put into a male's cage, or vice versa, or both into a special cage, for periods of 10—60 min or more. In these situations most adult male and female monkeys will copulate. If not, they may well be excluded from further experiments. Also, in such situations a female's menstrual cycle relates more closely to her sexual behavior than it does under freer conditions (see reviews by Herbert, 1970; Rowell, 1972). When another female is introduced to the pair, sexual behavior may be modified from that predictable from hormonal level (Herbert, 1968). Female dominance is one factor that modifies such behavior.

Given two estrogen-treated females, a male copulated most frequently with the more dominant of the two (Perachio et al., 1973). If estrogen was withdrawn from the dominant female, the male would still not mount the subordinate unless she was only slightly less dominant than the other. Thus, female relationships can affect a male's sexual behavior was well as their own.

Another study showed further intricacies of female dominance and sexual behavior. Goldfoot (1971) studied fifteen adult, intact female pigtail macaques relative to sexual swelling, progesterone level, and phase of the menstrual cycle. He then formed two types of temporary group composed of three females: multiphase, or each female in a different state of the cycle (one early follicular or just swelling, one preovulatory or peak swelling, and one midluteal or deflating) and monophase, or all three females in the same cycle state. The fifteen females were placed in triads and observed as a triad, and then with three vasectomized males presented one by one to the female group for 15 min apiece. Dominance ranks were based on the way the monkeys maintained central or peripheral areas of the room, showed eye aversion, displacement of one female by another, or any overt agonistic interactions.

In the multiphase groups the preovulatory or fully swollen female showed significantly more sexual and social behavior directed towards the male, and received the most sexual behavior from the male. However, the probability that any preovulatory female would show such increases depended on her dominance status. The first and second ranking females both showed increased sexual behavior when swollen but the third ranking female did not. In monophase groups, the most dominant animal always showed the highest frequencies of sexual behavior. Social dominance among the females was unrelated to ovarian condition, and did not change when a male was added to the triad of females. These results demonstrate the interaction between dominance and the display of sexual behavior. Goldfoot concluded: "Endocrine factors increase the probability that insemination occurred at an optimum time for conception, while social factors operated to decrease the probability of conception in females who were in positions of very low dominance" (1971, p. 339).

Whether dominant females suppress the sexual behavior of the lower ranking females, or whether males are not attracted to subordinate females is an open question. Both probably affect behavior. That rhesus males show decided preferences for individual females has been shown by Herbert (1967, 1969) who equated females for endocrine condition. Everitt and Herbert (1969) also found that withdrawal of estrogen from the preferred female depressed but did not completely reverse preferential treatment by the male. Female preferences for males and vice versa are probably formed with familiarity and experience.

Dominance may be more important under confined or crowded conditions than in other situations. For instance, in captive groups of rhesus monkeys that had access to indoor enclosures, the single adult male and a subordinate female might be found mating in one part of the pen while the group was in another part (personal observations). When the entire group was locked out for the morning observation period, the males usually were seen to mate with only the dominant female. Likewise, in a captive troop of Japanese monkeys enclosed in a two-acre space, the subordinate males and females (regardless of the rank of the particular partner) often hid or fled from very dominant individuals. They also roamed about the enclosure more than the dominant monkeys when mating (Hanby, 1972). Wild monkeys and apes also show this general tendency for shy or lower-ranking individuals to avoid others of their groups and to avoid human observers when they are mating. For example, in gorillas, it was only after several years that Fossey was able to observe mating with any frequency; Schaller (1963) also mentions the difficulty of observing mating. Whether this avoidance is due to the male or female is not clear but there is some reason to believe it is the female, since in most species she is the one who initiates, accepts or solicits sexual behavior, and is also the one who is often attacked by other group members, when she is estrous (rhesus and Japanese monkeys: Carpenter, 1942; Sugiyama, 1967; Stephenson, 1973).

Probably of much greater importance to a female's status in the group is how many offspring or kin she may have. In fact, her dominance or aggressiveness may well be a product of her family ties. High-ranking females often seem to have the most extensive family connections and usually many offspring. Genealogical relations are important to all phases of the individual's life but can be studied only over long periods of time. The relationship between genealogy and mating is only beginning to be understood in any primate species (Missakian, 1972; Norikoshi and Koyama, 1975; Enomoto, 1975). One factor of special importance is the birth of a baby. Females without offspring tend to be of lower rank, and the prime or dominant males often do not mate with a female until she has had an infant. Somehow the presence of an infant changes a female's overall status in the group (personal observations on rhesus, celebes and Japanese macaques).

Kinship and familiarity

Closely related individuals or those that have had a relatively long period of contact early in life appear to have few sexual interactions in adulthood. There seems to be some degree of familiarity that is necessary for individuals to have sexual relations, but too much familiarity inhibits such relations. Copulation between mother and son, for example, is very infrequent in primates (rhesus: Sade, 1968; Loy, 1969; Japanese macaques: Enomoto, 1974; Hanby, unpublished). Sade (1968) suggested on the basis of one observed case that the mother's superior dominance rank inhibits a son from mating with her. It seems far more likely that an early close attachment or high degree of familiarity between the two inhibits sexual arousal. Other sociosexual patterns such as grooming are more habitual, and may preclude sexual interactions.

The early attachment may be the critical factor rather than any genetic relationship. Thus, in a troop of Japanese macaques, a high-ranking male protected and defended and spent much time with two orphan females (who were probably totally unrelated to him). He did not mate with either female when they became sexually active. In contrast, a young female who had spent some periods of time as a juvenile with the lowest ranking male in the troop, tried repeatedly to get him to mount her when she reached puberty. He avoided her much of the time but did copulate with her on occasion (Hanby, unpublished).

Kaufman (1965) mentioned that two rhesus males just reaching puberty mounted their mothers and one copulated, but the circumstances are not clear. In a captive, newly formed group of rhesus monkeys with no fully adult males, a female repeatedly solicited her pubertal son, who avoided her but did finally mount her (Meier, 1965). Also, in a captive setting, a young rhesus male mounted his mother repeatedly after a separation from her (Harlow et al., 1966). In all these cases there is some indication of social disturbance and much of the mounting or even copulation (ill-defined in the above studies) may have more to do with the social setting than sexual behavior. There are as yet no documented cases of long term sexual relations between mother and son in any undisturbed species of nonhuman primates.

Brother—sister pairs may mate in primate groups (rhesus: Loy, 1960; Japanese macaques: Hanby et al., 1971) but it is not a common phenomenon. This is probably because males tend to transfer to some other group at adolescence, while females usually remain in their natal group. Since females begin breeding earlier than males in all the catarrhines, they would also probably have already formed some preferences for certain male partners, and the younger brothers, when they do become sexually active would not have easy access to a sister. In addition to availability, early attachment or contact between siblings may inhibit sexual relations in adulthood. It has been reported that kibbutz children who have been reared together in close contact do not marry one another, nor do they have sexual relations after childhood, though they remain very close in affection (Shepher, 1971). Adolescent mobility combined with the inhibition that appears to result from early close tactile contact seem to account for the lack of incest (in its narrow sense), without the need to postulate verbal or other overt social restrictions.

Kinship and familiarity affect other aspects of sociosexual activity as has been mentioned in the foregoing discussion of male and female status. Males, even if they remain in their natal groups, appear not to mate with females in their genealogies nor with those with whom they spend much time (Enomoto, 1974, on Japanese monkeys). Nevertheless, some degree of familiarity between partners seems necessary for the two to enter into a sexual relationship (or add sex to their previously established relationship). Thus, baboons, macaques and chimpanzees all have patterns of courtship or precopulatory activity that are more extensive the less familiar the partners. After some years or many mating episodes, partners appear to have abbreviated precopulatory and idiosyncratic copulatory patterns. Partner preferences become clearer with increasing familiarity both in the laboratory and field in chimpanzees (Tutin and McGrew, 1973a,b; Tutin, 1976 and unpublished). There may be too much familiarity, as judged by the evidence that monkeys caged together for years show lower rates of sexual relations and may cease to copulate at all (rhesus: Harlow, personal communication; Hanby, personal observations).

The relationship between degree and type of familiarity and overall relations between individuals and their mating activity or sexual attractiveness is an interesting line of inquiry. Many social factors regulate the amount of time individuals can spend together and also the types of behavior that are allowed. For instance, in a troop of Japanese monkeys, a male and female began a mounting series some weeks after the breeding season (dated as of the last observed ejaculation). The pair were promptly attacked by both males and females in the group. The degree of familiarity and the interactions that are permissible may well determine much of what is interpreted as sexual preference and the frequency of sexual acts.

Group traditions and other social factors

As more groups of the same species are studied in different habitats, it is becoming clear that courtship, copulation and more general sociosexual patterns vary from group to group. For instance, females mount males or males carry females around on their backs as part of their consortship behavior in only some groups of wild and captive Japanese monkeys (Stephenson, 1973; Hanby and Brown, 1974). Male—male mounting in this species also varies from common to absent in different groups.

The participation of adult males in infant handling varies from species to species and group to group, and may change over time. For instance, Burton (1972) described a very active role of young and adult males in the socialization of Barbary macaque infants, but this seems not to have been the case in the past. Other groups of this species show a highly developed treatment of infants in male—male interactions which Deag has termed agonistic buffering (Deag and Crook, 1971; Deag, 1974). It involves much inspection of infant genitalia (see Fig. 2b).

Most of the young of the species that have been discussed show a wide variety of attention to copulating or consorting adults: they will often stare at, follow, harrass or physically interfere with mating pairs (Japanese macaques, rhesus and celebes: Hanby and Brown, 1974; irus macaques: deBenedictis, 1973; anubis baboons: Owens, 1973; vervet monkeys: Struhsaker, 1967; chimpanzees: Goodall, 1968a,b; McGinnis, 1973; gorillas: Fossey, personal communication). Such behavior may sometimes lead to what might be termed imitation. For example, Rowell (1966) describes young wild olive baboon males that 'often danced round a copulating pair making repeated coughs and touching them'. The young males may then go off and mount a partner, usually female (see also Owens, 1973). Such behavior seems to be a matter of general arousal or excitement on the part of the youngsters, related perhaps to novelty, conflict, curiosity, fear, or sexual interest. Observation of mating pairs may lead to mounting or other activity with subsequent gratification or punishment by others in group-living primates. In the laboratory or confinement, such observation may lead to self-biting, masturbation, or other signs of arousal and frustration (Hanby, personal observations; Bertrand, 1969). Under normal, group-living conditions, arousal may often lead to sociosexual interaction, the specific type determined by age, status, time of year, early rearing, adult experience, and hormonal condition.

5. SUMMARY

Human and nonhuman groups that include both sexes and all ages, all the year and for year after year, have evolved complex ways of maintaining group integrity. Many components of behavior that can be interpreted as friendly, contact-promoting and aggression-reducing may also appear in the context of heterosexual copulation. Such sociosexual behavior, and copulatory behavior as well, have a long and vulnerable period of development, and depend largely on the availability of interacting conspecifics.

Group integrity is combined with some system for the transfer of new individuals from group to group. This genetic and social interchange usually depends on a wide repertoire of gestures that indicate unaggressive or friendly intentions. Sexual and the more general sociosexual gestures are very important in establishing nonaggressive contact that promotes familiarity and integration.

The degree of integration into a group affects the number and kinds of alliances and friendships, which in turn affects the overall status of the individual and ultimately his or her reproductive success. Social position constantly changes in primate groups, and these changes may correlate with hormonal level. Sexual behavior in all group-living primates must be considered with reference to these general phylogenetic predispositions, developmental dependencies, and the immediate contextual constraints.

480

BIBLIOGRAPHY

Aldrich-Blake, P. and Chivers, D. (1973) On the genesis of a group of siamans. *Am. J. Phys. Anthropol.* 38: 631—636.

Anthoney, T.R. (1968) The ontogeny of greeting, grooming and sexual motor patterns in captive baboons. *Behaviour* 31: 358—372.

Beach, F.A. (Ed.) (1965) *Sex and Behavior.* (Wiley, New York.)

Bernstein, I.S. (1970) Primate status hierchies. In: *Primate Behaviour* Vol. I. (Academic Press, New York.)

Bernstein, I.S. (1969) Introductory techniques in the formation of pigtail monkey troops. *Fol. Primatol.* 10: 1—19.

Bernstein, I.S. and Mason, W.A. (1963) Group formation in rhesus monkeys. *Anim. Behav.* 11: 28—31.

Bertrand, M. (1969) The behaviour repertoire of the stumptail macaque. *B. bl. Primatol.*, II. (Karger, Basle.)

Boelkins, R.C. and Wilson, A.P. (1972) Intergroup social dynamics of the Cayo Santiago rhesus (*Macaca mulatta*) with special reference to changes in group membership by males. *Primates* 13: 125—140.

Burton, F.D. (1971) Sexual climax in *Macaca mulatta. Proc. 3rd. Int. Congr. Primatol. Zurich.* Vol. 3 (Karger, Basle) pp. 181—191.

Burton, F.D. (1972) The integration of biology and behaviour in the socialization of *Macaca sylvana* of Gilbralter. In: (F.E. Poirier, Ed.) *Primate Socialization.* (Random House, New York) pp. 29—62.

Bygott, D. (1974) Agonistic behaviour and dominance in wild chimpanzees. (Ph.D. thesis, Cambridge University.)

Carpenter, C.R. (1942) Sexual behaviour of free ranging rhesus monkeys (*Macaca mulatta*). I: Specimens, procedures and behavioural characteristics of estrus. II: Periodicity of estrus, homosexual, autoerotic and non-conformist behaviour. *J. Comp. Psychol.* 33: 113—142, 142—162.

Chalmers, N.R. (1972) Comparative aspects of early infant development in some captive Cercopithecines. In: (F.E. Poirier, Ed.) *Primate Socialization.* (Random House, New York) pp. 63—82.

Chamove, A.S. (1973) Varying infant rhesus social housing. *J. Inst. Anim. Tech.* 24(1) 5—15.

Chevalier-Skolnikoff, S. (1974) Male—female, female—female, and male—male sexual behaviour in the stumptail monkey, with special attention to the female orgasm. *Arch. Sex. Behav.* 3(2) 95—115.

Conaway, C.H. and Koford, C.B. (1965) Estrous cycles and mating behaviour in a free-ranging band of rhesus monkeys. *J. Mammal.* 45: 577—588.

Davenport, R.K. and C.M. Rogers (1970) Differential rearing of the chimpanzee: A project survey. *The Chimpanzee* 3: 337—360.

Deag, J. (1974) A study of the social behaviour and ecology of the wild Barbary macaque, *Macaca sylvanus.* (Ph.D. thesis, Bristol Univ.)

Deag, J. and Crook, J. (1971) Social behaviour and agonistic buffering in the Wild Barbary Macaque *Macaca sylvanus* L. *Fol. Primatol.* 15: 183—200.

de Benedictis, T. (1973) The behaviour of young primates during adult copulation: Observations of a *Macaca irus* colony. *Am. Anthropol.* 75: 1469—1484.

DeVore, I. (1965) Baboon sexual behavior. In: (F.A. Beach, Ed.) *Sex and Behavior.* (Wiley, New York).

Drickamer, L.C. and Vessey, S.H. (1973) Group changing in free-ranging male rhesus monkeys. *Primates* 14(4) 359—368.

Eaton, G. (1974) Male dominance and aggression in Japanese macaque reproduction. In: (W. Montagna, Ed.) *Reproductive Behaviour.* (Plenum Publishing Corp. New York) pp. 287—297.

Eaton, G. and Resko, J. (1974) Plasma testosterone and male dominance in a Japanese macaque (*Macaca fuscata*) troop compared with repeated measures of testosterone in laboratory males. *Horm. Behav.* 5: 251—259.

Enomoto, T. (1975) The sexual behavior of wild Japanese monkeys. In: (S. Kondo, M. Kawai and A. Ehara, Eds) *Contemporary Primatology*. (Karger, Basel) pp. 275—279.

Erwin, J., Maple, T., Mitchell, G. and Willott. (1974) A follow-up study of isolation and mother-reared rhesus monkeys paired with preadolescent conspecifics in late infancy: cross-sex pairings. *Dev. Psychol.* 10: 808—814.

Erwin, J., Mitchell, G. and Brandt, E. (1973) Initial heterosexual experiences of three-year-old rhesus macaques. Paper presented to Annu. Meet. Int. Soc. Dev. Psychobiol. (San Diego, California.)

Everitt, B. and Herbert, J. (1969) Ovarian hormones and sexual preferences in rhesus monkeys. *J. Endocrinol.* 43: xxxi (abstr.)

Ford, C.S. and Beach, F.A. (1951) *Patterns of Sexual Behaviour*. (Harper and Brothers, New York) 307 pp.

Goldfoot, D. (1971) Hormonal and social determinants of sexual behaviour in the pig-tail monkey (*Macaca nemistrina*) In: (G. Stoelinger and J. v.d. Werff Ten-Bosch, Eds.) *Normal and Abnormal Development of Brain and Behaviour*. (Leiden Univ. Press, Leiden, Netherlands) pp. 325—342.

Goodall, J. van Lawick (1968a) The behaviour of free-living chimpanzees in the Gombe Stream Reserve. *Anim. Behav. Monogr.* 1, 165—311.

Goodall, J. van Lawick (1968b) A preliminary report on expressive movements and communications in the Gombe Stream Chimpanzees. In: (P.C. Jay, Ed.) *Primates - Studies in Adaptation and Variability*. (Holt, Rinehart and Winston, New York, London) pp. 313—374.

Gordon, T.P. and Bernstein, I.S. (1973) Seasonal variation in sexual behaviour of all-male rhesus troops. *Am. J. Phys. Anthropol.* 38: 221—226.

Goy, R.W. and Goldfoot, D.A. (1974) Experiential and hormonal factors influencing development of sexual behaviour in the male rhesus monkey. In: *The Neurosciences, Third Study Program*. (M.I.T. Press, Cambridge, Mass.)

Hamilton, G.V. (1914) A study of sexual tendencies in monkeys and baboons. *J. Anim. Behav.* 4: 295—318.

Hanby, J.P. (1975) The social nexus: problems and solutions in the portrayal of primate social structures. Symp. 5th Int. Primatol. Soc. Nagoya, Japan. pp. 25—42

Hanby, J.P. (1976) Sociosexual development in primates. In: (P.P.G. Bateson and P.H. Klopfer, Eds.) *Perspectives in Ethology Vol. 2* (Plenum, New York) in press.

Hanby, J.P. and Brown, C.E. (1974) The development of sociosexual behaviours in Japanese macaques *Macaca fuscata*. *Behaviour* 49: 152—196.

Hanby, J. (1974) Male-male mounting in Japanese macaques. *Anim. Behav.* 22: 839—849.

Hanby, J., Robertson, L. and Phoenix, C. (1971) Sexual behaviour in a confined troop of Japanese macaques. *Fol. Primatol.* 16: 123—143.

Harlow, H.F. and Harlow, M.K. (1962) Social deprivation in monkeys. *Sci. Am.* 207(5) 136—146.

Harlow, H.F. and Harlow, M.K. (1969) Effects of various mother-infant relationships on rhesus monkey behaviours. In: (B.M. Foss, Eds.) *Determinants of Infant Behaviour* Vol. 4 (Methuen, London.)

Harlow, H.F., Harlow, M.K., Dodsworth, R.D. and Arling, G.L. (1966a) Maternal behaviour of rhesus monkeys deprived of mothering and peer associations in infancy. *Proc. Am. Phil. Soc.* 100(1) 58—66.

Harlow, H.F., Joslyn, D., Senko, M. and Dopp, A. (1966b) Behavioural aspects of reproduction in primates. *J. Anim. Sci.* 25: 49—67.

Herbert, J. (1967) The social modification of sexual and other behaviours in the rhesus monkey. In: (D. Starck, R. Schneider and H. Kohn, Eds.) *Progress in Primatology*. (Gustav Fischer Verlag, Stuttgart.)

482

Herbert, J. (1969) Neural and hormonal factors concerned in sexual attraction between rhesus monkeys. *Proc. 2nd Int. Congr. Primatol.* Vol. 2 (Karger, Basle) pp. 41—49.

Herbert, J. (1970) Hormones and reproductive behaviour in rhesus and talapoin monkeys. *J. Reprod. Fertil.* suppl. 11: 119—140.

Hinde, R.A. (1970) *Animal Behaviour.* (McGraw Hill Co., New York.)

Hinde, R.A. (1971) Development of Social Behaviour. In: (A.M. Schrier and F. Stollnitz, Eds.) *Behaviour of Nonhuman Primates.* Vol. III. (Academic Press, New York, London) pp. 1—68.

Hinde, R.A. and Spencer-Booth, Y. (1967) The effect of social companions on mother-infant relations in rhesus monkeys. In: (D. Morris, Ed.) *Primate Ethology.* (Weidenfield and Nicholson, London.)

Joslyn, D. (1967) Behaviour of socially experienced juvenile rhesus monkeys after eight months of late social isolation and maternal-offspring relations and maternal separation in juvenile rhesus monkeys. (Unpublished Ph.D. thesis, U. Wisconsin.)

Kaufman, J.H. (1965) A three-year study of mating behaviour in a free ranging band of rhesus monkeys. *Ecology* 46(4) 500—512.

Kawai, M. (1960) A field experiment on the process of group formation in the Japanese monkey (*Macaca foscata*) and the releasing of the group at Ohirayama. *Primates* 2: 181—252.

Kempf, E.J. (1917) The social and sexual behaviour of intra-human primates with some comparable factors in human behaviour. *Psychoanal. Rev.* 4: 147.

Koford, C.B. (1963) Rank of mothers and sons in bands of rhesus monkeys. *Science* 141: 356—357.

Kellar, C.J., Beckwith, W.C. and Edgerton, R.B. (1968) Sexual behaviour in the ARL Colony chimpanzees. *J. Nerv. Ment. Dis.* 147: 444—459.

Kummer, H. (1968) Social organization of hamadryas baboons. *Bibliotheca Primatol.* 6 (S. Karger, New York.)

Kummer, H. (1973) Dominance versus possession: An experiment on hamadryas baboons. *Symp. IVth Int. Congr. Primatol.* Vol. 1 (Karger, Basle) pp. 226—231.

Kummer, H., Götz, W. and Angot, W. (1974) Triadic differentiation: and inhibitory process protecting pair bonding in baboons. *Behaviour* 49(1—2) 62—87.

Lemmon, W.B. (1970) Experiential factors and sexual behaviour in male chimpanzees. *Medical Primatology.* Proc. 2nd Conf. Exp. Med. Surg. Primates, New York 1969 (Karger, Basle) pp. 432—440.

Lemmon, W.B. and Temerlin, J.W. (1974) The development of human oriented courtship behaviour in a human reared chimpanzee female. (Paper presented at 5th Int. Primatol. Congr., Nagoya, Japan.)

Lindberg, D.G. (1969) Rhesus monkeys: mating season mobility of adult males. *Science* 16: 1176—1178.

Loy, J. (1969) Estrous behaviour in free-ranging rhesus monkeys (*Macaca mulatta*) a study of continuity and variability. (Ph.D. thesis, Northwestern Univ., Chicago, Illinois.)

Maple, T., Erwin, J. and Mitchell, G. (1973) Age of sexual maturity in laboratory-born pairs of rhesus monkeys. *Primates* 14(4) 427—428.

Marshall, D.S. and Suggs, R.C. (Eds.) (1971) *Human Sexual Behaviour.* (Basic Books Inc., New York.)

Maslow, A.H. (1936) The role of dominance in the social and sexual behavior of infra-human primates: III. A theory of sexual behavior of infra-human primates. *J. Genet. Psychol* 48: 310—338.

Mason, W.A. (1960) The effects of social restriction on the behaviour of rhesus monkeys: I. Free social behaviour. *J. Comp. Physiol. Psychol.* 53: 582—589.

Masters, W.H. and Johnson, V.E. (1970) *Human Sexual Inadequacy.* (Little, Brown and Co., Boston.)

McGinnis, P. (1973) Sexual behaviour of chimpanzees. (Ph.D. Thesis, Cambridge.)

Meier, G.M. (1965) Other data on the effects of social isolation during rearing upon adult reproductive behaviour in the rhesus monkey (Macaca mulatta). Anim. Behav. 13: 228—231.

Mertl, A. (1963) Baboon social behaviour. (M.A. thesis, Univ. of Chicago.)

Michael, R.P. (1971) Neuroendocrine factors regulating primate behaviour. In: (L. Martini and F. Ganong, Eds.) Neuroendocrinology. (Oxford Univ. Press, New York) pp. 359—398.

Michael, R.P., Wilson, M. and Plant, T.M. (1973) Sexual behaviour of male primates and the role of testosterone. In: (R.P. Michael and J.H. Crook, Eds.) Comparative Ecology and Behaviour of Primates. (Academic Press, London) pp. 236—313.

Missakian, E.A. (1969) Reproductive behaviour of socially deprived male rhesus monkeys (Macaca mulatta). J. Comp. Physiol. Psychol. 69: 403—407.

Missakian, E. (1972) Genealogical and cross-genealogical dominance relations in a group of free-ranging rhesus monkeys (Macaca mulatta) on Cayo Santiago. Primates 13(2) 169—180.

Mitchell, G. and Brandt, E.M. (1972) Paternal behaviour in primates. In: (F. Poirier, Ed.) Primate Socialization. (Random House, New York) pp. 173—206.

Miyadi, D. (1967) Differences in social behaviour among Japanese macaque troops. In: (Stark, Schneider and Kuhn, Eds.) Progress in Primatology (Gustav Fisher Verlag, Stuttgart)

Nadler, R. (1974) Determinants of variability in reproductive behavior of captive gorillas. In: (S. Kondo et al., Eds) Proc. Symp. 5th Congr. Int. Primatol. Soc. (Japan Science Press, Tokyo) pp. 207—216.

Nishida, I. and Kawanaka, K. (1972) Inter-Unit-Group relationships among wild chimpanzees of the Mahali Mountains. In: (T. Umesao, Ed.) Kyoto Univ. African Studies. Vol. 7, pp. 1—169.

Norikoshi, K. and Koyama, N. (1975) Group shifting and social organization among Japanese monkeys. Symp. 5th Cong. Int. Primatol. Soc. Japan.

Owens, N. (1973) The development of behaviour in free-living baboons. Papio anubis. (Ph.D. thesis, Univ. of Cambridge.)

Packer, C. (1976) Group transfer by male anubis baboons. (Ph.D. thesis, Cambridge Univ.)

Parthasarathy, M.D. and Rahaman, H. (1974) Infant killing and dominance assertion among the Hanuman langur. In: (S. Kondo et al. Eds) Proc. Symp. 5th Congr. Int. Primatol. Soc. (Japan Science Press, Tokyo).

Perachio, A.A., Alexander, M. and Marr, L.D. (1973) Hormonal and social factors affecting evoked sexual behaviour in rhesus monkeys. Am. J. Phys. Anthropol. 38: 227—232.

Phoenix, C., Goy, R. and Young, C. (1967) Sexual Behaviour: General aspects. In: (L. Martini and F. Ganong, Eds.) Neuroendocrinolgoy II. (Academic Press, New York) pp. 163—196.

Ransom, T.W. and Rowell, T.E. (1972) Early social development of feral baboons, In: (F.E. Poirier, Ed.) Primate Socialization. (Random House, New York) pp. 105—144.

Resko, J. (1967) Plasma androgen levels of the rhesus monkey: Effects of age and season. Endocrinology 81: 1203—1225.

Riesen. (1971) Nissens observations on the development of sexual behaviour in captive-born, nursery-reared chimpanzees. The Chimpanzee 4: 1—18.

Rose, R.M., Gordon, T. and Bernstein, I.S. (1972) Plasma testosterone levels in the male rhesus: Influences of sexual and social stimuli. Science (N.Y.) 178: 693—695.

Rose, R.M., Holaday, J.W. and Bernstein, I.S. (1971) Plasma testosterone, dominance rank and aggressive behaviour in male rhesus monkeys. Nature 231: 366—368.

Rosenblum, L.A. and Kaufman, I.C. (1966) Laboratory observation of early mother-infant relations in pigtail and bonnet macaques. In: (S.A. Altmann, Ed.) Social Interaction Among Primates. (Univ. Chicago Press, Chicago.)

484

Rowell, T.E. (1972) Female reproductive cycles and social behaviour in primates. *Adv. Study Behav.* 4: 69—105.

Rudran, R. (1973) The reproductive cycles of two subspecies of purple-faced langurs (*Presbytis senex*) with relation to environmental factors. *Fol. Primatol.* 19: 41—60.

Saayman, G.S. (1970) The menstrual cycle and sexual behaviour in a troop of free-ranging chacma baboons, *Papio ursinus. Fol. Primatol.* 12: 81—111.

Saayman, G.S. (1973) Effects of ovarian hormones upon the sexual skin and mounting behaviour in the free-ranging chacma baboon (*Papio ursinus*). *Fol. Primatol.* 17: 297—303.

Sackett, G.P. (1968) Exploratory behaviour of rhesus monkeys as a function of rearing experience and sex. *Dev. Psychol.* 6: 260—270.

Sade, D.S. (1968) Inhibition of son-mother mating among free-ranging rhesus monkeys. *Sci. Psychoanal.* 12: 18—38.

Shepher, J. (1971) Self-imposed incest avoidance in second generation kibbutz adults. (Ph.D. thesis, Rutgers Univ., State Univ. New Jersey.)

Simonds, S.E. (1965) The bonnet macaque in South India. In: (I. DeVore, Ed.) *Primate Behaviour: Field studies of monkeys and apes.* (Holt, Rinehart and Winston, New York) pp. 175—196.

Spencer-Booth, Y. (1969) The effects of rearing rhesus infants in isolation with their mothers on their subsequent behaviour in a group situation. *Mammalia* 33: 80—86.

Stephenson, G.R. (1973) Testing for group specific communication patterns in Japanese macaques. *Symp. IVth Int. Congr. Primatol.,* Vol. I (Karger, Basle) pp. 51—75.

Struhsaker, T. (1967) Behaviour of vervet monkeys (*Cercopithecus aethiops*) *Univ. Calif. Publ. Zool.* 82: 1—74.

Sugiyama, Y. (1965) On the social change of hanuman langurs (*Presbytis entellus*) in their natural condition. *Primates* 6: 381—418.

Sugiyama, Y., Yoshiba, K. and Parthasarathy, M.D. (1965) Home range, mating season, male group and inter-group relations in hanuman langurs (*Presbytis entellus*). *Primates* 6(1) 73—106.

Tanaka, T., Tokuda, K. and Kotera, S. (1970) Effects of infant loss on the interbirth interval of Japanese monkeys. *Primates* 11: 113—117.

Tokuda, K., Simons, R. and Jensen, G. (1968) Sexual behaviour in a captive group of pigtailed monkeys (*Macaca nemestrina*). *Primates* 9: 283—294.

Tutin, C. (1976) Exceptions to promiscuity in a feral chimpanzee community. (Ph.D. thesis, Univ. of Edinburgh.) in press.

Tutin, C.E.G. and McGrew, W.C. (1973a) Sexual behaviour of group-living adolescent chimpanzees. Proc. IVth Int. Congr. Primatol. *Am. J. Phys. Anthropol.* 38: 195—200.

Tutin, C.E.G. and McGrew, W.C. (1973b) Chimpanzee copulatory behaviour. *Fol. Primatol.* 19: 237—256.

Van Wagenen, G. (1972) Vital statistics from a breeding colony: Reproduction and pregnancy outcome in *Macaca mulatta. J. Med. Primatol.* 1: 3—25.

Whalen, R. (1971) The ontogeny of sexuality. In: (H. Moltz, Ed.) *The Ontogeny of Vertebrate Behaviour.* (Academic Press, London) pp. 229—261.

Wickler, W. (1967) Socio-sexual signals and their intra-specific imitation among primates. In: (D. Morris, Ed.) *Primate Ethology.* (Weidenfeld and Nicolson, London.)

Zuckerman, S. (1932) *The Social Life of Monkeys and Apes.* (Kegan Paul, London.)

Zumpe, D. and Michael, R.P. (1968) The clutching reaction and orgasm in the female rhesus monkey (*Macaca mulatta*). *J. Endocrinol.* 40: 117—123.

CHAPTER 33

Endocrine abnormalities and sexual behavior in man

JOHN MONEY and TOM MAZUR

1. HORMONAL HYPOSECRETION OR DEFICIT

Sex hormone deficit

The hypothalamic–pituitary–gonadal axis mediates the effects of sex hormones on target cells. Once clinical signs point to a possible sex hormone deficit, a differential diagnosis is made by determining, through various endocrine tests, at what level in the axis the deficiency occurs, or whether the deficit is one of hormonal uptake by target tissues.

Hypogonadism
Primary hypogonadism occurs if the gonads, by being either defective or absent, are primarily responsible for a hyposecretion of either testosterone or oestrogen. If, however, the hyposecretion of testosterone or oestrogen from the gonads is the result of a defect at the hypothalamic–pituitary level the diagnosis is hypogonadism secondary to hypogonadotropinism. *

Examples of primary hypogonadism are prepubertal and postpubertal castration in both males and females, spontaneous bilateral anorchia or hyporchia in males, and Turner's syndrome (see below).

Regardless of etiology, the effects of hypogonadism upon sexual behavior are similar, as are the effects of hormonal treatment. Both effects are outlined by Money and Daléry (Ch. 103) and so are not repeated here in detail. Briefly stated, hypogonadism correlates with behavioral hyposexuality. If puberty has not taken place, there is an additional complication of juvenile and/or eunuchoid physique and appearance. The discrepancy between physique age and chronological age retards social maturation and social age. Without puberty, childhood sexuality continues. In males, this includes erec-

---

* For complete endocrine details, consult Wilkins (1965), Williams (1974) or Gardner (1975).

Handbook of Sexology, edited by J. Money and H. Musaph
© Elsevier/North-Holland Biomedical Press, 1977

tions and does not rule out intercourse. There is no ejaculate, though some semblance of climactic feeling may occur. In females, lack of lubrication inhibits intercourse. Compared with ordinary adolescents, those with failed puberty are relatively sexually inert and romantically indifferent.

In postpubertal hypogonadism, the behavioral sexual sequelae are individually variable. In males, the ejaculate always disappears, but erection and orgasmic feeling may persist, even for years. In females, vaginal lubrication ceases, as it does postmenopausally, without loss of orgasmic feeling. In both sexes there may be either a gradual or rapid increase in sexual apathy and inertia. Some males report an increased fatiguability.

Hypogonadotropinism
The sexual behavioral effects of hypogonadism secondary to hypogonadotropinism follow the same final common pathway.

Hypogonadotropinism may be a primary defect of pituitary function, or the pituitary dysfunction may be secondary to a hypothalamic defect in releasing factors that act directly on the pituitary to secrete gonadotropins.

Hypogonadotropinism in Kallmann's syndrome is associated with impairment of the sense of smell (anosmia or hyposmia). In addition to the behavioral effects of sex-hormone deficit, there is, in Kallmann's syndrome, an increased risk of psychopathology.

Growth hormone deficiency (hyposomatotropinism) may coexist with hypogonadotropinism in both sexes. The affected boy or girl grows up to be both dwarfed in stature and impaired in prepubertal maturation, even when the best therapeutic results are obtained. They are at a disadvantage with respect to achieving social maturity because they look too short as well as too juvenile for their age.

Hypogonadotropinism or hyposomatotropinism, separate or together, are associated with an unusual frequency of difficulty in pair bonding or falling in love, though not with establishing companionship or friendship. A possible hypothesis to explain this deficit is that the hypothalamic regulation of the pituitary, and a possible pair-bonding mechanism, are both impaired (Bobrow et al., 1971).

Short-statured girls with delayed or impaired puberty have cosmetics, fashion wigs, and padded bras commercially available to help overcome immaturity of teenaged appearance prior to hormonal induction of puberty. There are no corresponding aids for boys.

Turner's syndrome
Girls with Turner's syndrome lack ovaries. They share with hypopituitary girls the problems of short stature and of being reliant on hormonal therapy to induce puberty. Associated with the chromosomal defect basic to the syndrome — typically, 45,X — are various possible physical deformities, including anomalies of appearance. A girl with Turner's syndrome may therefore have added difficulty in attracting a male partner to respond romantical-

y and/or sexually (Money and Mittenthal, 1970). This problem is enhanced when induction of puberty is therapeutically postponed in favor of allowing more time for increased growth in stature. Nonetheless, girls with Turner's syndrome fare relatively well throughout life, and are remarkably free of psychopathology (Money and Mittenthal, 1970). A low threshold for emotional arousal, a characteristic of the syndrome, may help explain their equanimity.

Idiopathic delayed puberty

Idiopathic delayed puberty is also known as constitutional delay of growth and adolescence. The diagnosis signifies normal pubertal maturation, but at a late age of onset. It affects both boys and girls, but is more common in boys. In girls menstrual delay or irregularity is more common than delay of other pubertal feminization.

Idiopathic delayed puberty like hypogonadotropinism creates an age discrepancy in which physique age lags behind chronological age, with social age somewhere in between (Money and Clopper, 1974). For this reason, brief hormonal therapy to induce puberty is indicated, especially after age fifteen, height and bone age permitting. Appropriate hormone therapy for a brief period of time induces onset of puberty in both males and females. Catch-up growth in social age is then possible. The treatment does not necessarily relieve concomitant psychopathology, if present, for which psychotherapy is indicated.

Hermaphroditism and microphallus

Idiopathic delayed puberty sometimes occurs in association with microphallus in male hermaphroditism, but not in female hermaphroditism. It may also be associated with nonhermaphroditic microphallus, though not invariably so. In both conditions, it is possible to anticipate puberty of the penis done by applying testosterone cream to the penis for a few months in infancy and/or childhood. In this way the boy's morale is increased during the developmental years. In the hermaphrodite, surgical repair is facilitated. The treatment does not, however, overcome the handicap of an excessively small, thin penis, shorter than two standard deviations from the mean, that is, shorter than 8.7 cm (3.5 in) when erect in adulthood. In some adolescent and adult cases, the morale is sturdy enough to permit the use of a prosthetic, strap-on penis as an erotic augmenter in coitus — with further morale-building effect.

Klinefelter's syndrome

Klinefelter's syndrome is identified by a chromosomal anomaly (47,XXY) in phenotypic males with such symptoms as small testes and sterility. After puberty, males with Klinefelter's syndrome tend to be tall and long-limbed. Sometimes they develop breasts like those of an adolescent girl. They require corrective surgery.

As a group, males with Klinefelter's syndrome tend to manifest sexual and general inertia, with or without lower than average testosterone levels. Hormonally, it is more likely that there is an abnormality of androgen uptake in the target tissues than of androgen production in the testes. Rehabilitation of both sexual and general inertia may be facilitated by a course of high dosage androgen treatment. Behavioral counseling (Money et al., 1974) or psychotherapy, including the family if necessary, may also be indicated, as the incidence of psychopathology is increased by the supernumerary chromosome.

Reversible hyposomatotropic dwarfism

Reversible hyposomatotropic dwarfism (psychosocial dwarfism) is so named because the deficiency in growth hormone (somatotropin) is reversible upon change of domicile. So also are various behavioral pathologies of the syndrome (Money et al., 1976). The syndrome occurs in both males and females. If untreated, it may be associated with delayed puberty. If so, rapid progress into puberty follows change of domicile (Money and Wolff, 1974).

Other hormonal deficits

There are other hormonal deficits that indirectly affect the hypothalamic-pituitary—gonadal axis and/or sexual behavior. Sexual hypofunctioning in both male and female may occur secondary to systemic debility in hypothyroidism, Addison's disease, hypoparathyroidism, and hypoaldosteronism. Rarely, in hypothyroidism of childhood, there may be a precocious activation of pituitary gonadotropin which induces premature partial puberty and lactation.

In diabetes mellitus, it has been shown that sexual impotence in the diabetic male is due to a neurological lesion of nerve fibers that control erection (Faerman et al., 1974). Formerly, it was considered by some that a defect in gonadotropin might be implicated.

Hyposomatotropinism may occur without hypogonadotropinism, namely in one form of hypopituitary dwarfism. The sexual behavior of individuals with this diagnosis closely parallels that of people with hypogonadotropinism (Clopper et al., 1976), despite the fact that they undergo their own puberty and require no sex-hormone therapy. In both types of dwarfism there may be a deficit, as yet conjectural, in the neural mechanism of pair-bonding. In addition, short stature itself may inhibit the establishment of love relationships.

2. HORMONAL HYPERSECRETION OR EXCESS

Sex hormone excess

An excess of sex hormone may be defined, in one sense, as excessive relative to timing of appearance and chronological age. The prime example is in precocious onset of puberty (Money and Daléry, Ch. 103). Precocious puberty may be complete or partial. Partial precocity occurs as thelarche (breast enlargement only), adrenarche or pubarche (pubic hair only, with or without axillary hair). Complete precocity may be concordant with anatomical sex, or discordant, as in the virilizing female adrenogenital syndrome (see Chapter 18 by Ehrhardt).

Precocious pubertal maturation of the body is accompanied by erotic mental changes similar to those of normally timed puberty, except that the content of erotic imagery and type of erotic practice more closely parallels chronological and/or social age than physique age.

Discordant precocious puberty creates the same problems as discordant hormonal function later in life, for sex hormones do not determine the masculinity or femininity of erotic disposition, behavior, or desire.

An excess of sex hormone may be defined in a second sense as excessive in absolute amount, not simply in relation to age. The sex hormones are unlike other hormones, for example, cortisol, thyroid or parathyroid hormone, in that they do not hypersecrete so as to produce syndromes of toxic effect. Any excess of sex concordant hormone is apparently excreted in the urine. Thus there are no primary problems, symptoms or syndromes of sexual behavior which can be attributed to an excess of any one of the sex concordant hormones in either sex. An excess of sex discordant hormone produces, in the female, somatic virilization, and in the male, somatic feminization, before being secreted as surplus, in the urine.

Other hormonal hypersecretions

In hypersecretion of hormones other than the sex hormones, the first effect is toxic. Then, without treatment, a general systemic debilitation follows. Sexual functioning, if affected, is secondary to the systemic debility.

In acromegaly (characterized by progressive enlargement of the bones of the hands, feet and face), growth hormone secretion from the pituitary is excessive while sex hormones are within normal limits. Thus, the sexual inertia reported by patients cannot be attributed to a lessening of sex hormone.

The pituitary hormone, prolactin, regulates among other things, milk secretion. In excess, as in cases of pituitary tumor, it may induce galactorrhea (milk flow) and/or hypogonadism in either males or females, though not inevitably so. There have been no systemic studies of the relationship between excessive prolactin secretion and sexual behavior. Clinically, however, a few males with high prolactin levels have reported being impotent.

There have been no systematic studies of the relationship between hyperparathyroidism and sexual functioning. Anecdotal clinical impressions indicate no specific correlation, except that in the advanced, untreated stage hyperparathyroidism is a sexually as well as a generally debilitating systemic disease.

An occasional patient with hyperthyroidism (thyrotoxicosis) may report a transient increase in sexual activity, along with general hyperkinesis in the early stages of the disorder. More often, overactivity expresses itself as agitation, and is systemically and sexually debilitating. In the rare, paradoxical form of the disease, apathetic hyperthyroidism, sexual apathy is included.

Hyperaldosteronism is a very rare syndrome — so rare that there are apparently no records of its effects upon sexual functioning.

In Cushing's disease, the pathognomic symptoms are secondary to adrenocortical hypersecretion of glucocorticoid (cortisol). The pituitary is usually involved also, either primarily or secondarily, by releasing an excess of adrenocorticotropic hormone. Excessive amounts of exogenously administered cortisol, as is well known, can precipitate psychosis. The nonspecific psychopathology for which Cushing patients are at risk may, therefore, be secondary to their excessive cortisol production. Persistence of psychopathology after hormonal or surgical correction of the adrenal cortices, suggests also a possible neural involvement, presumably from hypothalamic pathways. Sexual functioning is not known to be systematically impaired in Cushing's syndrome, except as secondary to the systemic debility of the disease and/or the effect of concurrent psychopathology on human relationships.

3. INCONGRUOUS HORMONAL SECRETION

Incongruous hormonal secretion refers to either the incongruous ratio of estrogen and androgen or the incongruous usage at the cellular level, as for example, in the androgen-insensitivity syndrome. Hormonal incongruity is not responsible for transexualism, transvestism or homosexuality. Therefore, androgen is not applicable as treatment for any one of these three conditions (see Chapter 102 by Money and Walker).

Adolescent gynecomastia, gynecomastia in Klinefelter's syndrome (47, XXY), and the partial or total prenatal feminization of the external genitalia and, at puberty, of the breasts in the androgen-insensitivity syndrome are the effects of hormonal incongruity on the genetic male.

When the gender identity has differentiated as male, breast development in a teenaged boy is a mortification. Embarrassment may be so acute as to forbid seeking medical attention. Surgery (mastectomy) is almost always needed. Rarely, in XXY cases, there will be an associated history of transexualism, and the patient insists on keeping the breasts and being surgically sex reassigned.

Hermaphrodites with the androgen-insensitivity syndrome are commonly reared as girls from birth. They differentiate a female gender identity, and they value their breasts.

The counterpart of gynecomastia in the male is hirsutism, with the voice deepening; and clitoral hypertrophy in the female. The process for such virilization may start prenatally, namely in the adrenogenital syndrome (see

Chapter 18 by Ehrhardt). The pathognomic virilism of the adrenogenital syndrome may also be of late onset, usually around the age of puberty.

Postpubertal masculinization in the form of hirsutism and a male body and pubic hair pattern may also appear in the Stein—Leventhal syndrome. This syndrome is characterized by polycystic ovaries, amenorrhea, sterility, and hormonal abnormality. Similarly, postpubertal hormonal virilization may be secondary to an androgen-producing adrenal tumor. Androgen, in the genotypic female who has lived her life as a female and differentiated a female gender identity does not change the gender identity. The change in voice pitch and body appearance is mortifying. Secondarily, it may handicap sexual life, even though increasing orgasmic response. The voice change cannot be reversed. Only electrolysis will completely get rid of facial and body hair.

In those rare cases of virilizing hermaphroditism where assigned sex and gender-identity differentiation are male, the masculine signs of somatic puberty are welcomed.

4. DISORDERS OF CYCLICITY

The hypothalamic—pituitary axis is not cyclic in genetic, prenatally androgenized males. Problems of cyclicity in the genetic female may or may not be related to a presumed, covert prenatal androgenic effect on the hypothalamus. In adulthood, inhibition of cyclicity may be secondary to panic, as in wartime bombing. Usually, there is no clear-cut etiology. In any case, suppression of the menstrual cycle in women, regardless of etiology, affects fertility rather than eroticism and copulatory function. The exception is when eroticism and copulation themselves constitute a threat and source of covert panic.

It is not known whether the cyclic premenstrual tension syndrome is or is not associated with endocrine abnormality.

5. SUMMARY

Hypogonadism, primary or secondary to hypogonadotropinism, induces some degree of behavioral hyposexuality. The additional complication of juvenility of appearance, with or without dwarfism, introduces a discrepancy between chronological age and physique age which retards social maturation and social age, including the age of romantic interest. Various other additional complications are syndrome specific, such as the gynecomastia of Klinefelter's (47,XXY) syndrome.

Deficiency of hormones other than gonadal hormones indirectly induces behavioral hyposexuality, secondary to general debilitation. The same applies to other endocrine syndromes of hormonal excess. Excessive amounts of the sex hormones themselves are not toxic, and are not associated with behavioral changes unless they are sex-incongruous. Increased estrogen or progesterone in the male has a functional, reversible castrating effect on behavior. Increased androgen in the female commonly increases the frequency of sexual activity, or desire for it, and intensifies orgasmic feeling. Incongruous or cross-sex hormonal excess does not change masculinity or femininity of sexual orientation. Thus sex hormones are not applicable to the treatment of homosexuality. Disorders of cyclicity in the female are not known to be induced by gonadal hormones; they affect fertility but not sexual behavior.

ACKNOWLEDGEMENT

This work was supported by USPHS Grant no. HD-00325 and funds from the Grant Foundation, New York.

BIBLIOGRAPHY

Bobrow, N.A., Money, J. and Lewis, V.G. (1971) Delayed puberty, eroticism, and sense of smell: a psychological study of hypogonadotropinism, osmatic and anosmatic (Kallmann's syndrome). *Arch. Sex. Behav.* 1: 329—343.

Clopper, R., Adelson, J. and Money, J. (1976) Postpubertal psychosexual function in male hypopituitarism without hypogonadotropinism after growth hormone therapy. *J. Sex Res.* 12: 14—32.

Faerman, I., Glocer, L., Fox, D., Jadzinsky, M. and Rapaport, M. (1974) Impotence and diabetes. Histological studies of the autonomic nervous fibers of the corpora cavernosa with impotent males. *Diabetes* 23: 971—976.

Gardner, L.I. (1975) *Endocrine and Genetic Diseases of Childhood and Adolescence.* 2nd edn. (W.B. Saunders, Philadelphia).

Money, J., Annecillo, C., Van Orman, B.. and Borgaonkar, D.S. (1974) Cytogenetics, hormones and behavior disability: comparison of XYY and XXY syndromes. *Clin. Genet.* 6: 370—382.

Money, J., Annecillo, C. and Werlwas, J. (1975) Hormonal and behavioral reversals in hyposomatotropic dwarsfism. In: (E.J. Sachar, Ed.) *Hormones, Behavior, and Psychopathology.* (Raven Press, New York.)

Money, J. and Clopper, R. (1974) Psychosocial and psychosexual aspects of errors of pubertal onset and development. *Hum. Biol.* 46: 173—181.

Money, J. and Mittenthal, S. (1970) Lack of personality pathology in Turner's syndrome: Relation to cytogenetics, hormones and physique. *Behav. Genet.* 1: 43—56.

Money, J. and Wolff, G. (1974) Late puberty, retarded growth and reversible hyposomatotropinism (Psychosocial Dwarfism) *Adolescence* 9: 121—134.

Wilkins, L. (1965) *The Diagnosis and Treatment of Endocrine Disorders in Childhood and Adolescence,* 3rd edn. (Charles C. Thomas, Springfield, Illinois).

Williams, R.H. (1974) *Textbook of Endocrinology,* 5th edn. (W.B. Saunders, Philadelphia).

SECTION VI

Customs of family formation and marriage

Section coordinator: Preben Hertoft

CHAPTER 34

Introduction

PREBEN HERTOFT

The papers in this section describe how different sexual norms, attitudes and habits are, from one society to another, regarding past and contemporary cultures. The connection between social conditions and sexual morals is stressed. It is impossible to reflect on the sexual traditions in a country without knowing something about the background factors, social laws and beliefs, influencing the daily life in that country and subculture. Human sexuality is part of a totality and cannot be treated in isolation or disintegrated from the social background as such, whether the discussion is about premarital sexual relationships, marriage customs, divorce frequency, children born out of wedlock, or other subject. Therefore, it will always be futile trying to transfer sexual norms from one country to another without considering the contexts to which they belong. If one wishes to change the sexual norms in a culture, it implies a change of the social conditions; and vice-versa, if the social conditions are changed in a society, the result will often be a change of the sexual mores. And this is what is seen nowadays. Some people want to believe that certain human institutions, for example marriage, is a fundamental, established, unchanged institution through the times. But it is not so. The fact is that, in Catholic as well as in Protestantic countries, the laws regulating marriage have been altered quite often. For long periods during history it has been difficult to make a sharp distinction between marital and nonmarital relationships. Further, there is a tradition in many cultures for sexual relationships among youngsters outside marriage. Personally, I have often been surprised by the preoccupation of some American investigators regarding premarital versus marital sex, and in my ears — and I suppose in Polynesian ears too — a question like, "Is there a relationship between premarital petting and marital success" sounds funny, though it might have some sense in the American culture. Also I have wondered why some people believe that a permissive attitude to premarital sex is the same as an acceptance of cohabitation with anybody.

The papers in this section show us that sex morals are not statically and

Handbook of Sexology, edited by J. Money and H. Musaph
© *Elsevier/North-Holland Biomedical Press, 1977*

eternally valid but on the contrary something very variable from one culture to another. What is blameless and quite natural in one society is dubious in another culture or subculture. What one generation or one ethnic group takes for granted has no relevance for another generation, another ethnic group, and so on. In previous more static, isolated societies it was possible to develop and maintain relatively permanent rules for sexual life so that all the inhabitants knew what was 'wrong' and 'right'. Some societies developed very restrictive rules, others more permissive ones, but usually each society found that their special way of living represented the only acceptable, 'natural' manner. Today it is different. Societies are not static and not isolated and the fast changes in social conditions and influences from other cultures are followed by fast changes in sexual mores. Today, inside the same society, we find a wide variety of sexual norms. It makes life more difficult and confusing for those depending on strict rules. But to persons who are able to establish their own choices and norms, the present societies give more possibilities than the former to realize a sexual life in accordance with their own personality.

It is unwise to try and put back the clock. What we can do is to face the new conditions and to help those who are confused to make their own choices, and to realize that there are many ways of living and that different ways of living inside the same society only make life richer and more stimulating.

CHAPTER 35

The American heritage of three traditions of pair-bonding: Mediterranean, Nordic and Slave

JOHN MONEY

1. MORAL TRADITIONS

The evidence both of history and comparative ethnology show that there are many highly divergent conventions, all equally viable, of integrating human pair-bonding, mating, and breeding into the totality of a society's customs. It requires a fair degree of sophistication, however, for the members of any given society to recognize the arbitrariness and moral relativity of its own, or any other society's customs and conventions. People everywhere are culture bound, which means that they tend to perceive their own customs, sexual and otherwise, not as traditions of history but as ethical absolutes, moral imperatives, or theological dogmas.

In American society today, it is difficult for the average citizen, steeped in Christian tradition regardless of religious affiliation, to accept as moral the sexual orthodoxy of the Polynesian culture of American Samoa, of the Eskimo culture of Alaska, or of the American Indian culture in various of its local and tribal traditions. It is equally difficult for these same citizens to accept as legitimate and moral the sexual customs of a different community, race, age, or creed, should they happen to be divergent from their own. Here lies the basis of the socioeconomic gap, the racial gap, the religious gap, and the generation gap, with respect to sexual morals.

2. MEDITERRANEAN TRADITION

For the majority in America today, orthodox sexual morality, supported by political, religious and other public institutions, is in the tradition of the virgin bride and the double standard. This tradition is often dubbed, in a derogatory way, the Judeo-Christian tradition. In actual fact it antedates the Judeo-Christian tradition, perhaps for millenia. There is no way to retrieve its actual history and development, unless it be by means of a kind of science

Handbook of Sexology, edited by J. Money and H. Musaph
© *Elsevier/North-Holland Biomedical Press, 1977*

fictional reconstruction of history. It is more a scientific than a fictional speculation that the virgin bride and double standard tradition had its origins east of the Mediterranean, rooted in the origins of cities and of slavery.

The building of cities gave a great impetus to slavery, and vice versa, for it is not possible to build great edifices without a hierarchical organization of power to control production, distribution and consumption. Slaves work for the aggrandizement of their owners, and they are owned. The status of being owned is readily generalizable from being owned as a worker to being owned as a sexual partner. Wealthy men in power, could, therefore, each possess a harem of his own women. In a patriarchal society, wealthy and powerful males thus would sequester an excess of female breeding partners. In consequence, there would be too few remaining females for the abundance of unattached, nonwealthy and nonpowerful males. For them, in the Mediterranean tradition of the virgin bride (or concubine) and the double standard, the public harem or whorehouse became, in the absence of any other sexual institution, a matter of social necessity.

In our own time, Western culture became heir to this ancient eastern Mediterranean system, as recorded in the Bible, and enshrined in current Christian doctrine. The system is particularly well preserved in pure form in Mediterranean and Latin American Catholic cultures. In these cultures, the virginity of the nubile young woman is ensured by a vigorous system of chaperonage behind locked iron gates. The young men, early in adolescence, are tacitly informed that they should prove their masculinity in the company of whores.

Elsewhere in Western culture, the Mediterranean system of the virgin bride and the double standard has been less well preserved, possibly because it always suffered by comparison with the completely different Nordic system, details of which are reported in Chapter 36 by Hertoft.

3. NORDIC TRADITION

Though named Nordic by reason of the whereabouts of its present-day survival, the origin of the betrothal system of the north is lost in prehistory and cannot be traced. It institutionalized betrothal as ceremonially more important than marriage. Betrothal signified a couple's intention to become pregnant and demonstrate their ability to establish a family unit. Marriage simply confirmed the achievement. Without the baby, the marriage was unlikely to take place.

The culture of the betrothal system was not a city-building culture, but one of farming and fishing hamlets in which the family was the cooperative and productive unit. The family was the foundation of society, not in the shibbolethic sense in which this expression is used today, but in actual fact. Families lived on more or less equal terms with respect to food, shelter and clothing, and so did males and females. The betrothal system was one of equality between the sexes, totally disparate from the discriminatory sexism of the system of the virgin bride and the double standard. Thus one may epitomize the system of the North as the system of betrothal and sexual equality.

Within historical times, the system of the North was transplanted from Scandinavia and Scotland westward across the Atlantic to Greenland and Iceland, where it still exists, and to the New England colonies, where it fell into disuse in the 19th century. In New England it was known as bundling. In the same century, remnants of the system could be traced southward through eastern Europe to the Alps. One may infer that the Nordic system once encompassed all of tribal Europe and that it was displaced by the encroachment of the Mediterranean system, until eventually it survived chiefly on the distant and rural northern perimeter of Mediterranean culture.

In the Scandinavian countries, the encroachment was never complete. Even as Scandinavia became urbanized after the Middle Ages, the betrothal system became urbanized also. In other words, even after the legalization of the Mediterranean marriage tradition in Scandinavia, the right of young couples to establish a sex life prior to the formality of the wedding has always been tolerated in a way totally alien to the culture of Catholic countries of the Mediterranean south.

4. ROMANTIC PAIR-BONDING

The Northern tradition of betrothal and equality of the sexes has always recognized the phenomenon, which exists among human beings as well as some other species, of pair-bonding on the basis of the intense romantic and possessive attraction between two partners. That is to say, young people matched themselves together as lovers, and then received family endorsement. By contrast, in a marriage arranged by a professional matchmaker, or the parents, of which the child marriages of the Hindu tradition are an extreme example, the family decides on the partnership, and the partners endorse it as lovers, if they can.

Among us human beings, the phenomenon of pair-bonding as lovers is distinct from bonding as copulators or breeding pairs. Subjectively, it is known as falling in love or being in love, and objectively as the love affair. There is no simple noun by which to name the experience, nor a verb to identify it unequivocally. Love is too broad in its nonerotic implications, and lust is too specific in its copulative implications, as well as being morally stigmatized.

This semantic difficulty in the English language may well be a hitherto unrecognized derivative of the Mediterranean tradition of the virgin bride and the double standard. The Mediterranean tradition, in its original form, did not prescribe pair-bonding on the basis of falling in love. Rather, it prescribed that a man's family select his partner, or at least consent to his own selection. The man presented his proposed virgin bride to his own family.

Having obtained their consent, he then claimed her from her father. In former times, the claim involved overt negotiation regarding the economic factor, the dowry, which, in more recent times, is more covertly taken into consideration.

The tradition whereby the man claims his bride from her father, no longer in its pristine form, has persisted into contemporary times, in the symbolic ritual in today's marriage ceremony in which the bride's father gives her away. The change from a negotiated marriage to one based on romantic pair-bonding can be traced to the ideology of the Troubadors in the 12th century.

5. ROMANTIC AND CONJUGAL LOVE

History has not left for us a record of all the facts, but it is likely that the Troubadors can be construed as having mediated a compromise between the traditions of the North and of the Mediterranean. In their poems and songs they enshrined a philosophy of romantic love, but it was always a love, if not unrequited, then unconsummated in sexual intercourse. The Mediterranean tradition had been incorporated into church doctrine at this time, but copulation itself had the status of the depravity of original sin. The triumph of the Troubadors was to leave original sin to the church, and to liberate love for youth. Western culture has been saddled with the dichotomy ever since. Young people still today struggle to reconcile love and sex — to be in love before they copulate, even though being in love proves only to be an empty, verbal formula, in some instances.

Given the ecclesiastical climate of the 12th century, there was probably no other way of relaxing the intense antisexualism of the era than that achieved in the compromise whereby romantic love was distinguished from conjugal love. Socially and psychologically this compromise corresponds with the Church's doctrinal change toward the worship of the Virgin, for which the Cathars and the Waldenses had formerly been persecuted as heretics. Contemporary science also flourished: this was the age of Peter Abelard, Roger Bacon, and the so-called Little Renaissance.

6. SEX, SCIENCE AND HERESY

On the pendulum of Western history, antisex, antiscience, and antiheresy have always parallelled one another, as have sex, science, and heresy. The relaxation of the 12th century was followed by the horrors of the Inquisition which prescribed death by burning for heresy, for teaching scientific knowledge, and for falsely confessing under torture to having dreamed of copulating with the devil.

One could be burned alive as late as the 18th century for confessing a dream, which one had not had, of carnal knowledge with the devil. It is, then, not surprising that carnal knowledge in an actual act of copulation has always been something of a trauma for many millions of people since the 12th century. Anyone who works in a sex therapy clinic knows that coitus is still a trauma for many people today, married or single, male or female. The trauma manifests itself in many devious and insidious symptoms and malfunctions.

As the worst excesses of the Inquisition waned, people were no longer tortured and burned because of what had taken place in their sexual imaginations. What they imagined became replaced by what they did. Adultery and homosexuality both became targets of suspicion. Both are activities that a majority of people think they can expect themselves to avoid. The majority today feel more safe in scapegoating homosexuality than adultery. The persecution of homosexuality still persists. Ascertainment and interrogation methods derived from the Inquisition are still used by the secret police of United States military in connection with homosexuality. Quite literally, it is permissible to establish guilt by reason of accusation, and to discharge the accused dishonorably.

In the aftermath of the Inquisition, the universal suspect in sexual traffic with the devil was not the adulter nor the homosexual but the masturbator. Masturbation is at least as universal as cohabiting with the devil formerly was believed to be. Thus a simple displacement from witchcraft to masturbation may explain the appearance, in the 18th century, of a new doctrine of masturbation as a cause of all those ills that formerly had been attributed to witchcraft and devil possession. Though medically and scientifically the doctrine is totally without support, it held immense prestige in the Victorian era and traumatized and impaired the psychosexual development of untold numbers of young people.

The Victorian era is commonly epitomized and despised as the era of sexual negation and repression. It was also the era of sexual hypocrisy. Therein lies the key to Victorianism. It was, par excellence, the era of compromise, of tolerating contradiction and the incompatible — of having one's cake and eating it too. It was the age of Darwin that preached the Book of Genesis, and the age of Freud that legislated sexual prudery. It invented birth control and sent family planners to jail. It sanctified the family, while making prostitution big business, and condoned keeping a mistress on the side. It extolled sexual normalcy, but forbade sex education in schools. It abhorred homosexuality, but segregated its young people into homosexual environments.

The Victorian era set of the stage for our own. We have not changed much, except for a fluctuatingly increased degree of freedom from repression in sexuality, science, and the expression of heretical ideas.

7. THE BIRTH-CONTROL AGE

In sex, the special challenge of the 20th century stems from the discovery of birth control. It affects each one of us in our daily lives, as much as did the discovery of fire millenia ago.

The rubber condom was the first effective method of birth control. It was exhibited to the public for the first time in 1876 at the Philadelphia Exhibition, celebrating the 100th anniversary of the U.S. The birth-control age did not begin in earnest, however, until the late 1920s, with the discovery of the latex rubber process. The latex condom was thin, effective, cheap, mass produced, and mass distributed. Since then, as is well known, other methods of birth control have been perfected, most recently the pill and the IUD, and more are to come.

Birth control, like the automobile, challenged the established culture, at first beyond its capacity to absorb the new invention into its way of life. Birth control challenged not only the material culture, but also the moral order. The reaction of each generation of adults since the birth-control age began has chiefly been one of struggling with their own personal morality vis-a-vis birth control. With their own children, they become either electively mute, or they communicate as though time halted when they themselves were teenagers. Even when they condone sex education in schools, it is very likely with an express proviso excluding mention of coitus and birth control. In consequence, the newly developing group of teenagers is left too much on its own to formulate its own morality for coming to terms with birth control. To complicate matters, the age for arriving at this formulation has been decreasing, as the age of the onset of puberty becomes lower. When Bach conducted his choir at the St. Thomas Church in Leipzig in the 18th century, boys sang soprano until age 17. Today their voices break at 13 or 14.

8. RECREATIONAL AND PROCREATIONAL SEX

Young people reared today in the Western tradition of the nuclear family are aware that the 20th century version of the tradition of the virgin bride and the double standard is not holding up very well. Many of them have had the experience of traumatic family relationships, separation and divorce. Even when divorce resolves interpersonal trauma, the result is not so satisfactory for a developing child as is a family in which the parent—child bonds are strong and positive. A child does not divorce either his father or his mother.

In the majority of divorce cases, the children are not yet fully grown. The figures are high: over one third of American marriages end in divorce. It is doubtful that any society can afford the ill effects of so many divorces on so many of its children, without eventually having to overhaul its breeding practices.

The youth generation of the birth-control age may already be effecting this overhaul in its restoration of betrothal. The new institution of betrothal differs from the old Nordic one because of birth control. A young couple now decide to establish a premarital sex life together not in order to prove that they can procreate, but because they can plan not to procreate. They belong to the second generation in all the history of mankind for whom recreational sex in adolescence and young adulthood can be predictably separated from procreational sex. They are able to test the viability of their erotic pair-bonding before they embark on parenthood and the marital contract for the legal protection of offspring.

9. AMERICAN SLAVE TRADITION

In American culture, the Mediterranean and Nordic traditions of pair-bonding and procreation are augmented by another great tradition, that of American slavery. The extent to which African tribal customs of procreation may have survived in the New World is not known. It is known, however, that American slaves could not marry, for marriage is a legal right, and they were denied all legal rights. In consequence, a couple had no legal obligation to stay together as parents. Whether they formed a family unit, or were separated, was at the discretion of their owner. The humanism of slave owners was variable, just as is the humanism of industrial employers today. Some slaves did establish long-lasting sexual and parental bonds. Others were bred together, as in animal husbandry. In some instances children were sold off; and in others, families were dispersed as a safeguard against mutiny.

By and large the system worked to separate young parents from their children during the working day. The strong and healthy of either sex, mothers as well as fathers, were daily put to forced labor. The elderly and infirm slaves were charged with the care of the young. In other words, the care of children was the responsibility of the grandparental, not the parental generation. The older couples were the ones who settled down into house-keeping arrangements, as though married. They had no economic responsibility for the children they reared: food, clothing and shelter were provided by the plantation manager, and were typically less than first rate.

In accordance with the well known anthropological principle of cultural lag, the tradition of slavery — the tradition of required early pairing and grandparental child care — has persisted since emancipation. It is found among Blacks chiefly, though not exclusively those of lower income, who have stayed rural or moved to urban ghettos. Unchanged is the tradition that young people have young love affairs and early parenthood. The young father knows, and is proud of his child. But he usually stays living with his own family, and the girl with hers. When the love bond dissolves, the young parents go their separate ways. The girl's mother and her husband accept responsibility for the care of the grandchild; and the young mother herself goes out to work every day.

One major change is that, when finances fail, the department of welfare replaces the plantation boss. The allotments are as inadequate for proper child rearing as they were before the emancipation.

The tradition of early pairing and grandparental child care is as viable and morally valid as any other tradition, provided it is fully integrated into all the cultural institutions of the society in which it exists. In America today it is not integrated into the economics of the majority culture, except insofar as it is exploited, by the very majority who morally condemn it, as a means of ensuring a pool of poverty and the cheap labor derived therefrom.

If the American culture could find a positive way of integrating the culture of the aftermath of slavery into the economics of the majority culture giving it equal status, then it would have much to contribute to the majority culture. The culture of slavery does not deny the sexuality of the young. In this respect, it may already have been borrowed into the renaissance of betrothal. Reciprocally, the tradition of slavery may already be borrowing from the betrothal system the formula of recreational sex with contraception, prior to embarking on procreational sex.

10. SUMMARY

Moral traditions of pair-bonding and procreation are culturally and sociologically relative. Each tradition is viable insofar as it interlocks with the other traditions and institutions of which a culture is comprised. The American heritage comprises the Mediterranean tradition of the virgin bride and the double standard; the Nordic tradition of betrothal and sexual equality; and the slave tradition of required breeding and grandparental child rearing.

In Western history, the Troubadors of the 12th century broke the aceticism of their forebears by glorifying the concept of romantic love, but at the expense of conjugal (procreative) love. The split has haunted Western sexuality every since. The Inquisition was the darkest age of antisexuality in Western culture. The Victorian era, tolerant of contradition, set the stage for the birth control age, and the contemporary search for a new ethic of recreational as well as procreational sex. A renaissance of the betrothal custom may unify the Mediterranean, the Nordic and the slave traditions.

ACKNOWLEDGEMENTS

This work was supported by USPHS Grant no. HD-00325 and funds from the Grant Foundation, New York.

CHAPTER 36

Nordic traditions of marriage: the betrothal system

PREBEN HERTOFT

1. TRADITION, OLD AND NEW

The traditions of a nation may exist in their own obscure way, without many people being aware of them, or even admitting that they adhere to them. It may even happen that certain contemporary standards of behavior are looked upon as breaks in tradition, whereas, when they are studied more closely, they prove to be rooted far back in ancient times. Paradoxically, it may become currently a vogue to follow ancient customs and, at the same time, to consider these ancient ways of living to be an expression of breaking with more recent tradition — a deplorable decadence of the times!

The fact that a tradition is old does not mean that it has any value, and a break with tradition does not necessarily imply a deterioration. An example of an unheeded, traditional way of living with its roots far back in the past in the Scandinavian countries is that here it has almost always been the custom for sexual intercourse to be initiated before marriage.

It can hardly be denied that in the present century this custom has been and continues to be quite common in all classes of the community. Evidence is not lacking. Yet it is not exactly common knowledge that there exists a centuries-old tradition for premarital intercourse in our countries.

Georg Hansen (1963) recorded that people formerly were well aware of this tradition. With regard to conditions at the end of the 18th century he wrote: "Other clergymen who wanted to teach the peasants that it was disgraceful for their daughters to enter into relationships with chance farm boys were regarded with distrust. They could not be in earnest. It had always been so. As long as the girl did not conceive, it was quite all right, but should she become pregnant, the young couple could marry. The parents had been similarly indiscrete. What had been good enough for them, could also be good enough for their children. It was a peculiar idea for the clergy to hold a different opinion, and older people would not like it, if clerical opinion found favour among the young people". This is an example, among many others, of

Handbook of Sexology, edited by J. Money and H. Musaph
© *Elsevier/North-Holland Biomedical Press, 1977*

an older generation's distrust of new ways and habits, although it is quite different from the usual attitude. Furthermore, the quotation bears witness to a conflict between two culture groups, who could not understand each other. All investigations show that the peasants and the common people in the towns almost universally accepted premarital intercourse, whereas the middle classes and the nobility came to disapprove such standards of behavior as they became more 'cultured'

In order to understand the tradition underlying premarital intercourse in Scandinavia, it is necessary to have some knowledge of the historical development of marriage in Denmark, Norway, Sweden and Finland, and of the form of courtship which is known in Denmark under the name of 'nattefrieri' (night courtship, bundling, kiltgang) and which, in the opinion of some research workers, still exerts an influence on the present sexual morality not only of the Scandinavian countries, but of all of Europe and the English-speaking world.

2. NIGHT-COURTSHIP ('NATTEFRIERI')

Several treatises have dealt with this extremely ancient custom of courtship which is known to have been common among many peasant communities in the Scandinavian countries, in neighboring countries of Eastern Europe as far south as the Alps, in Scotland and Northern England, and to have spread as far as to the New England colonies in America. (Peters, 1781; Hübertz, 1834; Sundt, 1855; Wikman, 1937; Doten, 1938.)

Night-courting traditionally was a warm-weather institution, for the rigors of a northern winter dictated that all members of the household keep warm at night around the great log fireplace of the communal kitchen and living room. When winter ended, and people segregated into their separate sleeping quarters, the single girls of the household took to their special sleeping quarters in the girls' house (Fig. 1). Typically they occupied the loft, accessible by anterior ladder, of a small storage barn. Once inside the building, the girls could fasten the door. Their guests would join them by climbing a rope ladder thrown down from the upper window.

As guests to join them, they might invite up a roving band of youths who, of a summer evening, went about the countryside to serenade the girls whom they wanted to meet. The girls would recognize the boys by their voices, and so would decide whether or not to welcome them — or rather, whether one particular girl wanted to meet one particular boy. After a period of general sociability, if it became obvious that a couple wanted to be left alone then, on subsequent occasions it would be arranged for the boy to stay alone with the girl overnight.

Staying overnight did not imply that sexual intercourse would automatically take place. He who was allowed to stay had to comply with a traditional set of rules. At first he must sleep with all his clothes on, and above the

Fig. 1. Girls' house, 20th century restoration, Finland. By courtesy, Professor M. Niemi.

covers; then clothed, but under the covers, until finally he and his girlfriend agreed to copulation.

It was at this point that the couple announced to their families and the community their intention of betrothal, and the appropriate festivities were celebrated. If no pregnancy ensued, then marriage was not obligatory. In fact, without a pregnancy, marriage might be discouraged.

This betrothal system among peasant communities of the past left no problems regarding paternity. Under the conditions of urban industrialization, greater anonymity opened more opportunity for irresponsibility regarding paternity, until the age of birth control. Effective contraception has given new viability to the betrothal custom, since the beginning of copulation no longer predicates parenthood.

In Denmark the night-courting custom does not seem to have followed quite the same pattern as in the other Scandinavian countries, but close interrelationship between young people can be seen as far back as the middle ages.

In the middle of the last century, the custom was still very widespread in Norway, Sweden, Finland and Iceland. Up to the present time it has been followed occasionally in remote rural districts. As late in 1941 it is said to have been observed on the Orkney Islands (Jonsson, 1951; Reynolds, 1951).

3. MARRIAGE

The present conception of marriage in the Scandinavian countries rests partly on the viewpoints of old Northern law, and partly on the views of Christianity, as it appears from Canon Law, and later on from the Lutheran views on marriage. Not until the 18th century were definite legal rules for church marriage created in Sweden.

Characteristic features of old Northern law were that the celebration of marriage was determined by two separate acts: the agreement of the parties prior to marriage, or betrothal, and the wedding ceremony, the marriage. The betrothal was a contract which was entered into before witnesses. At the wedding ceremony itself the bride was given to the bridegroom by her father or her guardian. Both acts were purely secular. If the betrothal was followed by actual union, the parties were considered to be validly married.

Gradually the influence of the Church on the establishment of marriage became more and more widespread in the north. Formerly, the secular wedding ceremony was followed by a second ceremony in church. The nature of this church ceremony changed at a later date from being voluntary to compulsory. Following the Lutheran reformation, some confusion arose as to the actual time at which marriage was legally entered into. Gradually the rules became obscure and to a certain extent contradictory, and in this field also a reform became necessary. In 1582 the authorities tried to clarify the position by making definite rules for the celebration of marriage in Denmark.

It was laid down that all who wished to enter into matrimony should first be betrothed, this betrothal taking place before a priest and five witnesses and, furthermore, that the banns should be read from the pulpit on three consecutive Sundays prior to the solemnization of the marriage. Evidently the intention was to suppress the more informal marriage agreements, so that betrothal followed by actual union no longer, in effect, made the marriage valid. Although it was not expressly said that a church ceremony was an absolute condition for a valid marriage, it was, however, laid down that betrothed couples should not live together before marriage. Not until a century later, in 1683, was a church ceremony made a condition for the validity of a marriage, but the betrothal ceremony was retained and, far into the 18th century, this resulted in a great proportion of couples living together immediately after betrothal without the church ceremony. In most cases the authorities accepted this practice tacitly, and children resulting from unions of this nature were almost always considered legitimate, particularly amongst the lower classes. Not until 1799 was the condition abolished whereby a marriage should be preceded by betrothal and rules necessary for a valid marriage established, which rules were very similar to those prevailing today.

Sexual union without the blessing of the authorities has always been known, witness the numerous premarital conceptions. One knows from Church Registers that, in the 18th century, when the betrothal ceremony was still valid, 30—35% of first-born children were born so soon after betrothal that conception must have taken place before betrothal. It is not surprising, therefore, that almost 50% of brides in rural areas were pregnant at the time of their church marriage, and that the percentage was even higher among the common people in the towns (Hansen, 1957). A statistical study from the end of the 19th century shows that at two thirds of the weddings the bride was pregnant or had borne a child before she was married (Rubin and Westergaard, 1890). Similar figures are available from the present century. Auken (1953) found that 49% of married women were pregnant when they entered into marriage and that 99% of sexually experienced women had had sexual intercourse before marriage.

Hence, the tradition of initiating sexual intercourse before marriage is old in the Scandinavian countries. The official rules prevailing throughout the years did not have very much influence on the customs of the people. When, today, it is accepted in our countries that young engaged couples have sexual intercourse, this attitude represents a long unbroken tradition. The Scandinavian countries are not communities without rules, but communities which have developed their own rules and standards on the basis of their own premises, other than those observed, for example, in the American or the Mediterranian traditions. However, development in the Northern countries is no isolated phenomenon, but one which presents many features similar to those in other countries. Presumably, it will be more correct to refer to differences of degree than to absolute differences. Perhaps we have only succeeded in our northern countries, assisted by a certain tradition, to establish a somewhat better agreement between the actual and the expected sexual customs, including customs of premarital intercourse, than in many other countries. In this respect, it has been a little easier for us to accept what people really do.

BIBLIOGRAPHY

Auken, K. (1953) *Undersøgelser over unge kvinders sexuelle adfærd*. With English summary — Investigation into the Sexual Behaviour of Young Women. (Rosenkilde & Bagger, Copenhagen.)

Doten, D. (1938) *The Art of Bundling*. (Farrar & Rinehart, New York.)

Hansen, G. (1957) *Sædelighedsforhold blandt Landbefolkningen i Danmark i det 18. Århundrede.*Morality situation among the rural population in Denmark in the 18th century. (Det. Danske Forlag, Copenhagen.)

Hansen, G. (1963) Kvinde og mand (Woman and man). In: (A. Steensberg, Ed.) *Dagligt Liv i Danmark*. (Nyt Nordisk Forlag, Copenhagen.)

Hertoft, P. (1968) *Undersøgelser over unge mænds seksuelle adfærd, viden og holdning*. With English summary — Investigation into the Sexual Behavior of Young Men. (Akademisk Forlag, Copenhagen.)

Hübertz, J.R. (1834) *Beskrivelse over Ærø*. Description of Ærø (Gyldendal, Copenhagen.)

Jonsson, G. (1951) Sexualvanor hos svensk ungdom. (Sexual habits among Swedish youth). *Official Report no. 41, 1951*. (Swedish Government, Stockholm.)

Peters, S. (1781) *General History of Connecticut*. (London.)

510

Reynolds, R. (1951) *Beds*. (Doubleday, New York.)

Rubin, M. and Westergaard, H. (1890) *Ægteskabsstatistik*. Statistics of marriage. (Copenhagen.)

Sundt, E. (1855) *Om Giftermaal i Norge*. On marriage in Norway. (Christiania, Oslo.)

Wikman, K. (1937) Die Einleitung der Ehe. *Acta Acad. Ab.*, Humaniora IX, 1, Aabo.

CHAPTER 37

The Polynesian extended family

BENGT DANIELSSON

1. KINSHIP

A Polynesian living on an island where the traditional culture is still intact has an enviably secure position within a social system whose main components are the lineage and the extended family. Each individual takes pride in reciting his genealogy, often as many as twenty or thirty generations back to a more or less mythical ancestor, and shares a common territory with a group of men and women tracing descent from the same ancestor. Descent is reckoned through both the father and the mother, with a preference for the former mode, resulting in a nonunilineal, nonexogamous lineage, for which Firth (1957) has coined the special term 'ramage'. It can therefore be said that the Polynesian kinship system is more flexible than usually is the case among pre-literate peoples.

The kinship terminology is strongly classificatory, the same term being used for all individuals belonging to the same generation, both of lineal and collateral descent. As a rule, classificatory brothers and sisters and their spouses, children and parents live together in an extended family household that easily comprises fifteen or twenty persons. With the same, typically Polynesian permissiveness, children, when marrying, can chose whether they want to live with the bride's or the bridegroom's parents, and occasionally it even happens that they set up their own neolocal household.

In spite of their extensive genealogical knowledge, the Polynesians have special terms only for two generations above one's own, the word for grandparent being used for all preceeding ancestors. For generations below one's own they have often, but not in all the islands, separate terms for as many as four generations. Seniority is carefully indicated among individuals of the same generation and sex. For instance, the Eastern Polynesian words *tuakana* (the elder one) and *teina* (the younger one) are used either about two brothers or about two sisters, but never to indicate the relative age of a brother and sister. First cousins are regarded as siblings, and the same terms as those

Handbook of Sexology, edited by J. Money and H. Musaph
© *Elsevier/North-Holland Biomedical Press, 1977*

denoting brothers and sisters are used. In this case, however, seniority is not determined by the cousins' own age but by their parents' relative age.

The basic differences between the Polynesian and the Western or European way of reckoning descent are shown in Fig. 1.

The European way of reckoning kinship is given in small letters, the Polynesian in capitals. EGO is the starting point. While a European has special words for parents and their brothers and sisters, a Polynesian uses the same term, *metua*, *matua*, *makua*, or other variant, depending on the local dialect. Grandparents are all called *tupuna*, *tipuna*, *kupuna*. All nephews, nieces and cousins' children are called children, *tama*, *kama*, and all their offspring in the generation below are grandchildren, *mokopuna*, *mo'otua*.

It must be stressed here that the kinship terminology is matched by a corresponding affective behavior. Thus every child on the son—daughter level has as protectors and educators not only their biological parents but also their uncles and aunts, and the mutual feelings and attitudes between all these 'children' and 'parents' are socially and not biologically determined. In the same manner, the fact that a man uses the same word, *vahine*, for his wife's sisters, and a woman the same word, *tane*, for her husband and his brothers indicates well that brothers-in-law and sisters-in-law are allowed to have intercourse together. Captain Bligh (1937) noted for instance in Tahiti in 1789: "An elder brother has connection with another brother's wife, and the younger brothers with the different brother's wives, whenever opportunities offer, without giving offense. It is considered no infidelity, for I have known a man to have done the act in the presence of his own wife, and it is a common thing for the wife to assist the husband in these amours" (II, p. 78). This leads quite naturally to levirate marriages, or the custom often referred

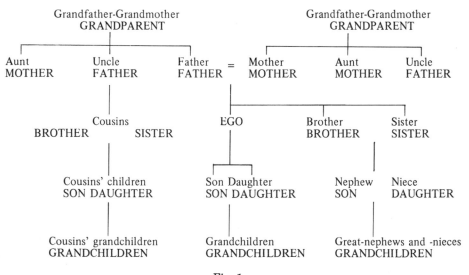

Fig. 1.

to in the Bible, requiring a widowed man to marry by preference a sister of his deceased wife.

Enumeration of household members in a Polynesian extended family will show, more likely than not, one or more adopted children. How common adoption still is today is shown by the following census of the twenty-seven households that existed in 1950 on the small atoll of Raroia, in the Tuamotu islands (Danielson, 1957, p. 218).

Household number	Children		Household number	Children	
	Given away	Adopted		Given away	Adopted
1	—	—	14	2	1
2	—	—	15	—	1
3	—	—	16	—	2
4	—	—	17	—	1
5	—	—	18	—	3
6	—	—	19	—	1
7	—	1	20	1	—
8	—	1	21	2	1
9	3	2	22	—	2
10	2	1	23	1	1
11	—	4	24	—	—
12	2	—	25	1	1
13	3	2	26	—	2
			27	2	—

Robert Levy (1970, p. 83—4) has made these important points concerning this widespread custom: "In form, Polynesian and Micronesian adoption is relatively frequent, public, casual, and involves only partial transfer of the adopted child to the new family. Western adoption is relatively infrequent, private, formal, and involves an almost complete transfer, limited in principle only by incest considerations. The message in the Polynesian and Micronesian adoption is that relationships between all parents and children are fragile and conditional. The form of Western adoption mutes from community awareness the impact of the breaking of the biological relationship and thus protects the essential Western orientation that relationships between all parents and children are categorical."

2. MARRIAGE PATTERNS

Before the Polynesians were converted to one or another of the various forms of Christian faith, introduced by a succession of competing missionaries, marriages which European observers defined as polygamous were socially approved, although, for economic and practical reasons, common only among the upper classes of the highly aristocratic Polynesian society. As almost everywhere else in the world, it was also a male privilege, with the exception of the Marquesas islands. But the difference is more apparent than real, for a Marquesan woman living in a polyandrous union had very little power and authority, additional husbands being chosen and directed not by her but by her first husband. Socially, the principal husband was moreover always regarded as the father of all children to whom his wife gave birth. It can therefore very well be said that what one observed in the Marquesas islands was not so much a polyandrous family as a union between a man married to a woman and several other men.

Everything seems to indicate that the polygamous families in Polynesia functioned smoothly. The explanation may be found in these wise rules, adhered to in all islands:
— The wives were placed in order of rank
— Work was divided between them
— They had separate houses or sleeping places
— The husband visited them in turn

To quote a person with a first-hand experience, this is how William Mariner (1818, II, p. 31) reported a Tongan woman whom he met in 1810:

"She thought the custom of having only one wife a very good one, provided her husband loved her. If not, it was a very bad one, because he would tyrannize over her more; whereas, if his attention was divided between five or six, and he did not behave kindly towards them, it would be very easy to deceive him."

Another instance where the marriage pattern was even more strongly determined by the class structure was the existence, although rare, of incestuous unions in certain families of exalted lineage. On the whole, the Polynesians rule out many more unions as incestuous than usually is done in Western type societies, and these quite logically corresponded to all persons who were classificatory siblings and cousins down to the fifth degree. But quite exceptionally, in Hawaii, a high chief sometimes married his biological sister, due to the overruling desire to preserve the purity of their aristocratic blood.

Whereas adolescent sexuality, at least before conversion to Christianity took place, was heartily approved and even encouraged, the accepted ideal after marriage was strict fidelity. But here again, there were important exceptions along class lines to both rules. For instance, the daughters of high chiefs were to remain virgins, so as to avoid misalliances with commoners which might result in the birth of children of less noble status. To achieve this, the girls were given attendants who watched them closely day and night, and their marriage partner was carefully chosen by their parents, with no say for themselves. In Samoa, where this custom has been best preserved, such a noble virgin, or *taupo*, still fulfills an important social function as an official village hostess and enjoys an immense prestige. She is given the best food, and although she engages in a number of feminine occupations, like bark-cloth making and mat plaiting, she is freed from all hard work. Surprisingly enough, the same abstinence is not required of the unmarried sons of high chiefs. Or it may not be so strange after all, considering that the males in all Polynesian islands enjoy so many more privileges than the females. Another excellent example of this double standard is provided by the many co-marital affairs which the chiefs and other noblemen indulged in, without suffering any negative sanctions. On the contrary, they were invariably praised in songs and stories for their prowess.

3. SEX AND RELIGION

There is no doubt that the main rationale behind all these discriminatory practices was of a religious nature, and since religion was the most important strand in the social fabric in Polynesia, it is necessary to outline briefly the principal tenets. As in Christian religion, the creation myth of the Polynesians assigned already from the very beginning of things an inferior position to woman, for she was modelled from a heap of sand and infused with life by the male god Tiki. Handy (1927, p. 227) neatly sums up the implications of this: "Man was the embodiment of the divine procreative *mana* that was always associated with nature superior; while woman, sprung from earth or sand into which life was breathed or impregnated, forever belonged, by reason of her origin and the dualism of nature, with the earth or nature inferior."

Not only were women considered inferior but also spiritually unclean. As a first consequence, women could neither hold priestly offices nor take part in divine service. However, this interdiction was to a large extent compensated for by their similarly motivated unworthiness to be killed and offered to the gods, in the quite numerous islands where human sacrifices occurred.

In the political sphere, where nothing was ever done without consulting the gods, women were, of course, equally handicapped. Although the first-born child had highest rank, it seldom happened in chiefly families that a daughter succeeded her father. In the event of her being the first child, she usually had to content herself with a high-sounding title, whilst one of her brothers ruled. Only in rare cases, when there was no male heir, did a woman become chief — provided that she also possessed exceptional powers of leadership. Such women took over all duties of a ruler, except the religious ones, and were often daring and skillful commanders in war.

Last but not least, these religious beliefs had practical consequences for all women, both of noble birth and commoners, in their family life. Owing to their spiritual uncleanliness, they must not touch the food eaten by men, or even eat in their presence. This taboo required that men and women had separate huts or places for cooking and eating their food. This necessitated the construction of quite a huge compound for each household, of which Fig. 2 is a typical plan.

The grouping of the huts naturally varied, as well as their form, which in

516

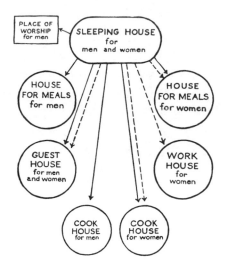

Fig. 2. Building plan for Polynesian household.

some islands was rectangular instead of oval or round. In a chief's household there were often one or several more huts for additional wives. The solid lines connect houses which the men could visit, the broken lines houses which the women could visit.

The account of the early navigators and missionaries provide abundant evidence of the seriousness with which the Polynesians took these ordinances. The following quotation from Crook's Marquesan journal (p. 27) will suffice to make the point: "Anything which a woman passes over cannot be used again, and if it is something that has passed over the head of a man, the consequences are highly calamitous, and the death of the offender the only expiation. This indeed has been inflicted on women for eating out of their husband's gourds or calabashes. Disease, death, wounds and defeat in war are supposed to originate in the breach or neglect of taboo rules." Even today, after the religious motivation has long since been forgotten, men and women often eat apart in many Polynesian households which otherwise follow Western ideals and comprise European type furniture, refrigerators, gas stoves, radios and TV sets!

4. UNWANTED FREEDOM

Although these discriminations and interdictions along sex lines were religiously motivated, this did not mean that the sexual act itself was ever condemned as something evil and sinful. On the contrary, the gods had shown by their frequent and joyful matings that sex was a positive value, in all circumstances. This explains the complete sexual freedom that all youths engaged in with all willing partners. Married people were restricted to a limited number of persons of the opposite sex. Sometimes, at least so far as males were concerned, they might have partners of the same sex.

No contraceptive devices, either mechanical or chemical, were known. Many pregnancies occurred therefore among the young girls. This never met with social disapproval, but if the child were unwanted on practical or social grounds, an abortion was attempted, with the help of herbal decoctions or violent massage. Sometimes the pregnant girl preferred to wait until the child was born, before she and her family decided whether she wanted to keep it or not. If not, it was immediately suffocated with a piece of damp bark-cloth. Whilst, at the time of the European exploration of Polynesia, abortion was widespread, infanticide was recorded as a common practice only in Hawaii, Tahiti, Rarotonga and New Zealand.

5. CULTURE SHOCK

The arrival and subsequent establishment of Europeans in the Polynesian islands resulted in what Alan Moorehead has aptly called "the fatal impact" — the almost total destruction of the old culture and the physical annihilation, through diseases, liquor and fire-arms, of up to 80 or 90% of the islanders within less than fifty years. After having remained stationary up to the 1920s, the native population is again increasing at an ever faster rate, and no efficient birth control programs have been introduced. This threatening demographic trend could theoretically result in larger extended families and a strengthening of kinship ties. Unfortunately, the opposite is happening, because the whole economic system has in the meantime changed from a simple subsistence economy to a more and more complex money economy. This forces the members of the same family to seek work individually, in separate trades and in different localities. What one actually witnesses is that the extended family, which until recently represented one of the very few surviving social institutions from pre-European times, and which offered the best protection against the culture shock for the Polynesian islanders, is now rapidly breaking up.

BIBLIOGRAPHY

Biggs, B. (1960) *Maori Marriage*. (Wellington, N.Z.)
Bligh, W. (1937) *The Log of the Bounty*. (London.)
Collocott, E.E.V. (1923) Marriage in Tonga. *J. Polynesian Soc.* 4 (New Plymouth, N.Z.)
Crook, W.P. (unpublished) *Journal*. (Manuscript in Mitchell Library, Sydney, Australia.)
Danielsson, B. (1953) Tuamotuan kinship terms. *Ethnos* 3—4 (Stockholm.)
Danielsson, B. (1956) *Love in the South Seas*. (London.)
Danielsson, B. (1957) *Work and Life on Raroia*. (London.)
Deihl, J. (1932) The position of woman in Samoan culture, *Primitive Man* 2—3 (Sydney.)

518

Firth, R. (1957) A note on descent groups in Polynesia, *Man* LVII (London.)

Goldman, I. (1970) *Ancient Polynesian Society.* (Chicago.)

Handy, C. (1927) *Polynesian Religion.* (Honolulu.)

Handy, C. (1958) *The Polynesian Family System in Ka'u.* (Wellington.)

Holmes, L.D. (1958) *Ta'u, Stability and Change in a Samoan Village.* (Wellington.)

Knoche, W. (1912) Geschlechtsleben auf der Osterinsel, *Z. Ethnol.* (Berlin.)

Levy, R. (1970) Tahitian adoption as a psychological message. In: (Carroll, Ed.) *Adoption in Eastern Oceania.* (Honolulu.)

Mariner, W. (1818) *An Account of the Natives in the Tonga Islands.* (London.)

Opler, M. (1943) Woman's social status and the forms of marriage. *Am. J. Sociol.* 2.

CHAPTER 38

Sex training and traditions in Arnhem Land *

JOHN MONEY, J.E. CAWTE, G.N. BIANCHI and B. NURCOMBE

What happens in a culture where children in infancy are permitted and expected to play games of sexual intercourse? This was the question that took
me to join my Australian colleagues on Elcho Island, in Arnhem Land, on
the shore of the Arafura Sea, of the Northern Territory of Australia. We
knew in advance that the Aboriginal Australians of Arnhem Land traditionally had a culture which did not taboo sexual play in infancy. I wanted to find
out whether this feature of the traditional culture might still persist among
these isolated people and, if so, what effect their childhood sexual experience might have on sexual behavior in later life. It did not take me long to
get the first question answered. Within a few days of my arrival, I heard a
story from an elementary school teacher which told me what I wanted to
know.

The group at the back of the room laughed with that peculiar squeal
characteristic of Yolngu Aboriginal children when something is funny and
playfully dangerous or risky. Their mission teacher had missed the joke. Her
Yolngu teaching assistant had trouble translating it for her. The vernacular of
the children's speech had 'bad' words for which she had not been taught an
English equivalent — words like nigi nigi. ** According to one preteenager,

---

* Contribution to symposium on Medical Ethnopsychology in Aboriginal Australia:
Acculturation Stresses. First published in Br. J. Med. Psychol. (1970) 43 pp. 383—399.
** Nigi nigi (pronounced 'niggi niggi' as below) is also a nonsense word in an Australian
student song in which the verses progressively name parts of the body, thus:

With my hand on myself
What have I here
This is my joymaker
My mother dear
Joymaker, joymaker
Niggi niggi naggi nool
That's what they taught me
When I went to school.

In the 1920s, a commercially popular song had the title 'Diga Diga Doo'.

Handbook of Sexology, edited by J. Money and H. Musaph
© *Elsevier/North-Holland Biomedical Press, 1977*

nigi nigi is 'junior language' from Darwin, meaning sexual intercourse. The stir in the classroom was in response to the report of an eight-year-old that two six-year-old relatives at the camp-fire the previous night had given a demonstration of nigi nigi, to the accompaniment of everyone's hilarity. The Yolngu prefer to sleep outdoors in family groups around a camp-fire, whether they own a modern house or a makeshift shelter cabin, except perhaps in the rainy season. Traditionally they always slept outdoors, for they erected no dwellings — only temporary canopies against the sun or the rain.

1. INFANTILE COITAL PLAY

Among the Yolngu children of Arnhem Land it is not peculiar that school-aged boys or girls should consider it funny, but not wrong, to tell of other children playing at sexual intercourse. They are simply expressing the attitude of their elders and their culture. To the casual white observer, biased by a prudish morality, it may seem that the Yolngu are careless, indifferent or promiscuous in matters of sex, but that is not so. Their standards differ from our own, but they are standards, nonetheless, to be adhered to. One such standard, very surprising to middle-class Australians and Americans, is that children may play at making the movements of sexual intercourse. They know that they are playing at what older people do to reproduce the species. It is much the same as a kitten playing at hunting, but using only a dry leaf or seed pod, in preparation for the real thing later. Probably all children are meant by nature to play sexually. Monkeys, in fact all the primates in their native habitat, rehearse in the playfulness of infancy various movements and postures that will later be used in earnest in reproducing the species.

Yolngu children are not instructed by their parents or elders about sexual intercourse, nor do they learn from observing adults, unless perhaps by accident. Parents do not give sex instruction to the young, and normally they seek privacy or darkness when they themselves copulate with their respective partners. Little children do, however, learn by what they see. What they see may be the paly of other children scarcely older than themselves, or the play and sexual activity of older children and teenagers on whom they are spying, 'in the bush'.

The publicly acceptable sexual play of small children loses its sanction somewhere around the age of eight or nine. No definite age can be given because the Yolngu do not traditionally keep track of numbers and ages. In pidgin English, their counting, it is said, used to be: one, two, three, little mob, big mob! Even a boy of 14 whose birth date can be verified in his school record, is liable to say he is '10, 9, 11'. Nonetheless, he knows, on the basis of stature and maturation, that tradition defines a boy ready at the age of eight or nine to go through the initiation ceremony of circumcision, or dhapi.

2. CIRCUMCISION CEREMONY

The timing and arrangement of the dhapi ceremony are made by the mother's brother, a man who is as important in a boy's life as his father. If several boys are of suitable age, a joint ceremony may be arranged, so that a large part of the community becomes intimately involved. In any case, the occasion is one for public rejoicing. The history of the people is celebrated in mimetic dance and chanting to the accompaniment of the rhythmic drone pipe, or didgeridoo, and clapsticks. The evening ceremony continues until the morning star rises. After daylight it continues until the climactic moment when the ceremonial initiates among the elders carry the boy off, safe from the view of girls and women, encircling him in close formation. One of them lies on his back on the ground, the boy lying face upward upon him and pinioned in a locked embrace. Another man holds down the boy's legs. A third does the actual cutting. In ancient times a stone knife was used. Today the instrument is a razor blade. The cutting is more likely to be a series of dissection movements than swift incision. The boy may cry out with the pain. Immediately the foreskin is removed, the men in charge carry the boy into the bush nearby where he is passed through the smoke of a fire for spiritual cleansing. The bleeding of his penis is stopped by cauterizing with a piece of hot charcoal and the application of hot wet leaves. He returns to his home camp-fire and there rests and recuperates for about a week.

The meaning of the ceremony is, like the origin of circumcision itself, lost in the unrecorded annals of prehistory. My own theoretical guess is that it represents a substitute for, and attenuation of, a still earlier practice of human sacrifice. One may see a similarity with the way in which the symbol of the Crucifixion became a substitute for, and attenuation of, the animal sacrifice of Old Testament times. Among the Australian Aborigines of a past era, the ritual of circumcision may also have had a magical function of symbolic wounding as a protection against being speared. All to readily one might have been speared as the result of a sorcerer's accusation, according to the mortuary vengeance system whereby any one totemic group of the Yolngu lived in fear of murder and decimation by the others.

Today the young boy about to undergo his dhapi is given no specific instruction in advance. He may have learned something by witnessing another ceremony and he may have had information passed on by older boys. He does not know exactly what will be done to him, nor when, nor what will be the pain. The experience becomes, therefore, part of a training in stoicism, resignation to suffering and indifference to wounding or killing others, if tradition demands it. The tradition of blood revenge is now all but extinct, but stoicism when in pain still is an Aboriginal trait. In an earlier era a male's stoicism would be put to the test by more than circumcision, for eventually the septum of his nose would be pierced so as to hold a bone ornament, and the skin of his chest, shoulders and arms would be incised so as to raise decorative scars.

However much the Aboriginal boy fears his initiation rite of dhapi, he invariably says that he wants it or is glad that he had it. Different boys have different rationalizations as to why it is necessary. One said that the penis would get to be like a hook, another that he would get a sickness, and another that without the dhapi 'we don't get married'. Socially, the ceremony gives status to a boy as a member of the masculine sect, so to speak. It officially sanctions his right to the ceremonial knowledge and ritual which is the exclusive prerogative of men. It gives him access to his father's inherited right to reproduce ancestral totemic rituals, dances, chants, designs and sacred objects. The ceremony also places on him the obligation to obey the complicated totemic rules of social permissions and avoidances, especially as they apply to one's promised partners in marriage. One obligation imposed by these totemic rules is linguistic. The partner whom one may marry should belong to a linguistic and tribal-totemic or clan group different from one's own.

3. LINGUISTIC GROUPS

All Yolngu children eventually learn at least two forms of speech, the father's and the mother's. In infancy they speak the mother's language, changing to the father's language later. By the time a boy has had his dhapi ceremony, he should officially be using his father's tongue exclusively.

There are approximately 19 different variations of language or dialect spoken by the thousand people living on or near the Elcho mission station where we worked. This diversity of tongues is an anachronism now that the once nomadic and highly dispersed Yolngu have coalesced together in village life — chiefly since World War II. The situation is less chaotic than it might seem to be. People do understand each other, partly because of the similarity of some of the dialects, and also because the children who become proficient in several variants through their contacts with other children are forging a new multiply-shared language. Thus when a girl gets sent to her 'promise man' in marriage, the likelihood is that the two will have a common language of exchange even if it is not the official tongue of the clan to which either belongs. The new generation of school-educated children also have English.

4. AVOIDANCY RELATIONSHIP

Another social obligation that a boy must certainly respect after his dhapi ceremony is that of respectful avoidance of his future mother-in-law. The two must not address each other directly, but only through an intermediary, in much the same way as a very formal doctor in our society does not ask questions directly of a patient lying in the bed before him, but addresses his inquiries instead to the resident or intern, standing there beside him.

Women who, by reason of their totemic classification, may never become mothers-in-law to a boy need not be avoided and never spoken to; but they are of special significance to him because he must respectfully avoid their daughters. His own sisters are in this category, and also those first cousins who are the daughters of his mother's sister (who, by reason of sisterhood polygamy, may be not only his cousins but his own half-sisters as well), or the daughters of his father's brother. A school teacher who does not understand this obligation of respectful avoidancy can create an untenable and socially destructive situation in the classroom by assigning a boy and a girl, incompatible because of their totemic avoidance relationship, to sit next to each other in the same two-person desk. In play groups the complexities of who may play with whom become unmanageably difficult, which is perhaps why when children congregate, they tend, regardless of age, to segregate themselves by sexes. This same tendency persists through teenage and adulthood. At all public assemblies, like Friday night outdoor movies in the school yard, the overwhelming majority of the people segregate themselves by age and sex. In the intimacy of the home and its outdoor campfire, by contrast, where all the people present know their totemic avoidance classification vis-à-vis one another, one may observe young people of both sexes close to one another in groups.

5. MARRIAGE CLASSIFICATION

Which women are eligible to be a male's mother-in-law is a matter that is decided before his birth — or, for that matter, before his conception. Mathematically, one may classify the society in the same way a biologist schematizes an experimental breeding design in a dual 2×2 table (Fig. 1). Instead of having strains of mice, one has 'strains' of Yolngu: four of them classified as Dhuwu type and four of them as Yirritja type. The mating is fixed, so that each Dhuwa strain is matched with its own special Yirritja strain. However, one alternative matching is permitted as a second choice. Thus if all a man's available partners have been used up, then one, and only one, second choice 'strain' is permitted. If all his available partners in that alternative strain have been used up, then the hapless man should resign himself to spending his life single, unless in the future an eligible widow might become available. There is no corresponding problem for a woman, since she can go to a man who already has one wife or more.

Actually, this dual 2×2 system is said to be a fairly modern borrowing from the Arunda people of the central desert of Australia. The older system which it purports to replace, though not completely, is even more restrictive, for it simply dictates that a male shall have his mother's brother's wife for a mother-in-law. All of her daughters (his first cousins), no matter how many, will be his wives. If his mother had only one brother, whereas he himself has three or four brothers younger than himself, then that is his good luck and

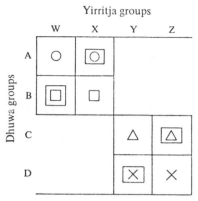

Fig. 1. Groups permitted to intermarry can be schematized in a dual 2 × 2 table. Symbols enclosed in squares indicate second choice; others, first choice.

his brothers' misfortune. He gets all the cousins as wives and his brothers get none.

6. THE PROMISE SYSTEM

The marriage system as it actually functions today, despite the increased latitude of the dual 2 × 2 system, does in fact leave some young men without a single female whom they are eligible to marry. Any girl to whom such a youth may wish to pay attention is a girl who knows that the system has already committed her to another male, and one who may be twice or even three times her age. This older man may already have up to five or more wives, but the system identifies him as the young girl's 'promise man'. Seldom is he willing to permit her not to come to him. Any other man who tried to claim her must pay. In the old days, the payment usually meant being speared, that is murdered. Today the payment is literal and means the money of a bride price. The price may well be excessive, and there are some examples of extortion on an indefinite basis, without ever agreement to a settlement. One man has handed over his savings for seven years. He is an active supporter of the mission and therefore risked opprobrium when he and his girl friend tried the extreme expedient of having a child. Still, her 'promise man', already the husband of three wives, refuses to release her from her obligation to come to him. The father will not, therefore, sanction her going to marry, or even to live with, her child's father. The two lovers must see one another surreptitiously, using whatever ruses and opportunities they can to meet one another.

The tyranny of the promise system is seen in reverse when the time comes for a second promise girl to go to a man who is mission educated and well advanced in acculturation. The man is then confronted with a cruel dilemma: whether to obey the Aboriginal law, take his second wife and betray the mission, or to obey the white law and betray his elders. For some men his dilemma has proved the turning point in their careers. They have turned their back on all they have achieved in the new order. To obey the Aboriginal law of taking a second wife is for them an all-or-nothing decision, irreconcilable with what the mission would prefer. So they quit their mission careers, to the bewilderment of the missioners who saw a bright future ahead, and returned to a quasi-nomadic, imperfectly acculturated way of life.

7. SAFEGUARDS OF THE PROMISE SYSTEM

A system or tradition of behavior is good or effective only in proportion to the allegiance that it elicits and sustains among the people. One safeguard built into the promise system in former times allowed for the transfer of a promise girl from one man to another. Thus an old man in the 'granny' generation might be due to receive his fourth or fifth promise wife, a teenaged girl. He might decide to give her to a young man, one of his half-brothers or clan brothers, who had neither wife nor promise girl, and whose only hope, otherwise, was that a promise girl would eventually be born for him, or be freed by widowhood. The young couple would then settle down to routine family life.

Another safeguard, also of long history, permitted an older brother with more than one wife to lend one of them to a younger brother, or at least absolved the older brother from the responsibility of revenge, should he find this younger brother cohabiting, from time to time, with one of his wives. The woman's status as wife of the older brother remained unchanged. Responsibility for paternity would not become an issue since, although the necessity of copulation for conception is taken for granted, the actual occurrence of conception is correlated not with copulation alone, but with the decision of benevolent spirits. The concept here corresponds to the idea, in our own society, of praying for a pregnancy. In the secular sense, it recognizes the fact that conception does not invariably follow copulation.

Imprecision concerning the correlation between copulation and paternity fitted well into another safeguard of the promise system in older times, namely the kunapipi rite. The songs and dances of kunapipi, combining myth and ancestral history, celebrate fertility. The ceremonies extend over a week or so, during which time men and women not promised to one another, but correctly matched by totemic clan, may have sexual intercourse together. Needless to say, Christian missionaries have not been able, by reason of their own moral philosophy, to condone kunapipi. The Yolngu in the outstations may today still celebrate the rite, however, making a compromise with the mission leadership by having only a 'little' kunapipi.

8. PROMISE SYSTEM VERSUS FALLING IN LOVE

The promise system does not prevent boys and girls in teenage from falling in love with partners to whom they are not promised. The promise system and the love-affair system exist side by side in irreconcilable juxtaposition. Officially, a girl must go obediently to her promise man when her mother tells her so. Equally officially she must illicitly flirt, making bold and open sexual suggestions to a youth to whom she is attracted. The young man, too, must follow the same formula of bold but illicit sexual invitation, culminating in a secret rendezvous and sexual intercourse in the bush, probably after dark.

An illicit love-affair generates for both the boy and the girl the tension and excitement of gambling, lest their identities be revealed. For the boy, it is a case of walking knowingly into a trap, and for the girl of knowing that she deliberately led him there. In former times the pair might take off by foot or canoe to a far distant camp, in the hope of escaping the offended promise man until he had cooled off and was willing to take a material compensation. But by far the greater likelihood was that the offended promise man would respond with a feeling of having no choice: only the death of the intruding lover would be sufficient revenge. Once marked for murder, a young man had no foolproof means of escape from the treachery that would almost certainly get him, in the long run. His death would then need to be avenged by the death of the one who killed him.

Only violation of sacred places compared with 'woman trouble' as a provocation for vengeance feuding. Falling in love thus was a highly dangerous business. It occupied a central position, quite literally, in the old order of things, in the balance of life and death, regeneration and extinction. Love led to violence. Violence got rid of male lovers. Lust and aggression both having been taken care of by death, the shortage of men could then be offset by polygamy — and a self-perpetuating system was in existence. Such a system is self-limiting with regard to population growth: one man can multiply impregnate plural wives, but he cannot guarantee the survival of all their progeny — and the progeny of Aboriginal Australia has always been remarkably low, like that of neighboring New Guinea, as compared with the millions of nearby Indonesia, India and the Asian continent.

9. BREAKDOWN OF THE PROMISE SYSTEM

One of the cracks observable in the breakdown of the promise system today may quite possibly be a tradition in itself. This is the concession made to certain young adult men whose fathers have widely acknowledged social prestige and power. Such a young man gets by with what are, within the promise system, adulterous unions. No sanctions are brought to bear on him for breeding with a woman who is not one of his promises and who, in the Western system, would be his mistress or concubine.

Of far greater importance, however, is another crack, well and truly observable in the wall of the promise system today. It is created by young people themselves. To them it is unimportant that polygamy under the promise system and the feuding system may have served the society well in the nomadic days of their ancestors. Today prescribed feuding has almost finished and the people see themselves as no longer doomed to self-extinction. Moreover, under the new conditions of village living, nutrition, disease and mortality are successfully regulated. The birth rate is exceptionally high, at 5 per hundred per annum. The sex ratio is no longer unequal. Young men are not content to have celibacy imposed on them in order to permit older men to have more than one wife, and they lack any capacity to turn to homosexuality as an interim outlet.

One sign of the pressure from the young people is that, after first capitulating, they finally won out over the conservatism of their elders, and gained permission to hold a Saturday night social gathering, outdoors, in the monsoonal dry season. The elders had been afraid that, if permitted to dance together, teenagers and young adults would establish relationships together outside the promise system. The elders therefore forbade mixed dancing, with the resultant spectacle of young men and young women in separate groups doing the twist, and surreptitiously making eyes at one another, whenever they could.

Among the elders of the village council it was an open secret that the Saturday night social gave young adults not promised together a too easy opportunity to go down in the darkness to the beach and copulate together. Some, if not all, members of the council, reconciled themselves to this latter practice, using the hypothesis that the Yolngu need to build up their own Aboriginal population, immediately, in order to compete with an influx of more and more whites. No contraceptive techniques have yet been made available to the Yolngu, primarily as a consequence of *laissez-faire* rather than of an explicit policy on family size and planning. The council's worry was not the possible breeding of feelings, but of the possible mismatching of Yirritja with Yirritja or Dhuwa with Dhuwa. This mismatching would be a catastrophe, for the child would have no proper relatives, under the terms of kinship tradition.

The anachronism of polygamy and the promise system is one of the points of acculturation at which the stress between the old and the new, the traditional and the changing, is maximal. Perhaps there should be instituted a system of worthwhile stipendiary rewards for all men who, having one wife, relinquish their extra promise girls to young men who have none.

10. CLOTHING AND NUDITY

The onset of sex education of the Yolngu may be traced to the ancient tradition of soothing fretful infants by stroking their sex organs. This tradition implies a lack of prurience or guilt regarding the genitals which is evident also in the relaxed attitude towards infantile nudity. An ancient custom of the Yolngu, surviving into the present century, was to wear no clothes at all, even at night when they might feel too cold after the camp-fire had burned to ashes. There was one aged man who refused in 1968 to relinquish his lifelong custom of defeating the mid-day heat by resting naked under a makeshift canopy. The children in the preschool, adjacent, would point him out to their teacher as an oddity. At the same time of day, many mothers rest with their infants, in the shade of their living quarters, wearing only a skirt. If whites approach, they usually contrive to put a top on. Children below school age unselfconsciously wear nothing at all. They enter preschool at the age of four. Some of them insist on wearing clothes to school — cotton shorts for the boys, pants and skirts or dresses for the girls — in order to conform to the model of their older brothers and sisters in primary school. Some might come to preschool naked. Before the indoor activities begin, and before they are given something to eat, all the children, boys and girls together, are soaped under a shower and dressed in clothing issued and laundered by the school. Now that they have adopted clothing, Yolngu children, and many adults too, wear it as they used to wear their naked skin, and are reluctant to remove it. They have always lived in close symbiosis with the earth, unoffended by what Westerners recoil from as mud, dirt and grime, and do not feel compelled to remove clothing to prevent its becoming soiled. Nor is it removed if they go in the sea to swim, which they do relatively little. We found that the boys would make no compromise with nudity in order to go swimming, at least in front of white men, and were embarrassed and amazed that we would dry off in their presence. Men once did their ceremonial dances with their bodies covered only with body paint. Now they wear baggy cotton-print diapers of early 19th-century missionary design, and respect them as traditional!

Despite the shame of nakedness they will eventually acquire, Yolngu children, it is obvious, grow up completely well informed of the external anatomical differences between the sexes. They take elimination for granted and in infancy do it wherever the need dictates. Because it is permitted in their play, they take for granted the bodily contact of the sexes in copulation. Whether their playing at sexual intercourse with pelvic thrusts is a spontaneous emergence — as apparently it is in lower primates — or whether it is a sequel to copying other children, is an issue still to be decided. Though this form of playfulness in infants and young children is publicly acceptable to Yolngu adults, it is tacitly understood throughout the culture that, by middle childhood, it will be kept respectfully out of sight.

11. SEXUAL PLAY OF CHILDHOOD

By the letter of the law, heterosexual play after middle childhood, even though covert, should be only between a boy and a potential promise girl of like age — or at least a girl from the correct totemic or clan group. By this time, a boy has had his dhapi ceremony and is supposed to conform to the ways of men. Therefore he ought not to practicipate in sexual play with a girl who is promised to someone else. It would be a far worse transgression, however, should he engage in sexual play with a girl whose mother had the totemic avoidancy classification that would exclude her ever becoming his mother-in-law. This girl would definitely not be promised to him. Moreover, she would not under any circumstances he permitted to become his wife. When parents discover that their children or adolescents have been away after sundown, they may suspect the likelihood of sexual intercourse. Their primary anxiety is not the occurrence of intercourse, but whether the couple would be properly matched according to totemic avoidancy criteria. In our own Western society, one can vicariously feel the power of this Yolngu anxiety by equating totemic avoidancy groups with religious groups — Catholic, Protestant, Jewish, Black Muslim — and by considering the intensity of feeling generated in some families if the children cross religious lines in their dating and premarital intercourse, to say nothing of marriage.

A Yolngu couple who ought not to be pairing off together do not easily have privacy or secrecy available to them for sexual play. Ahead of time it is common, therefore, for them to use sign language to declare their intentions and lay their plans for where and when to meet. Signals in eye talk and finger talk can be made to appear as inadvertent movements to onlookers. Yolngu sign language is so highly developed that people were able to communicate back and forth with two deaf-mutes in the village with apparently uninterrupted fluency.

Though we had no way of taking a census or other tally, we have the impression that boy—girl agreements to meet were not very common in the prepubertal years as compared with later.

12. SEXUAL SWEARING

In these earlier years sexual play is not excluded and tabooed, but it takes second place to the rigid formalities of the totemic avoidancy taboos. Boys and girls can be playful by resorting to the traditional system of teasing one another with curse words of sexual connotation. The curse terms sound very pale in literal translation, since they simply lay a curse on various organs of the body, including the genitals, or else describe them as ridiculously big or deformed, and so forth. There does not seem, to a European ear, to be much emotive value in saying: a curse on your eyes. However, one young teenager who had learned Australian sailors' cursing in English gave the equivalent translation as: fuck you bloody bastard in the eyes — which has plenty of emotive value to Australians, perhaps even more than to Americans.

13. GIRLS' SEXUAL PLAY

Children have another more direct way of circumventing the restrictions on childhood sexual play secondary to totemic avoidancy taboos. Two or more girls together, for example, might decide to play house. One would take the role of the father. When the time comes for sexual intercourse, the 'father' might simulate the coital motions of the male, possibly using a finger or stick to insert into the partner's vagina. So far as could be ascertained, the counterpart in boys' games, wherein a younger boy would impersonate a female's sexual position for an older partner, is uncommon and seems to have been associated with delinquency in puberty, i.e. from around age 13 to the middle teens. In the case of girls, there has been no known association of their coital play with delinquency, nor with subsequent lesbian interests which are apparently unheard of in adulthood. Coital play also does not appear to be associated with undue emphasis on masturbation in girls. Female masturbation has the status of a childhood activity — a diluted form of coital play when no partner is present. In the context of the moral teaching of the mission, some Yolngu girls and women officially frown upon stimulation of the vagina, alone or in unmarried pairs. It qualifies as adultery, according to their usage of Biblical terminology. The Yolngu use of the vagina in girls' coital play may also, however, be interpreted as a childhood rehearsal phenomenon of the same order as playing mother to a doll improvised from a stone or branch of leaves.

For Yolngu girls, even more than boys, it is probably essential to the maintenance of the polygamous promise system that their childhood experience with sex allows coitus to be emotionally uncomplicated, like killing birds or lizards to eat, or watching a baby breast-feeding. By the time she goes to her promise man, a girl must have been prepared to perform sexually with him, even though she may not be in love with him, or may even feel repelled by his appearance and age.

14. WIVES AND CO-WIVES

A girl must be ready to be taken away from her family by her promise man, perhaps as soon as she has her first menstruation at 12 or 13. Whereas this early age is the youngest that a girl may go to her promise man, the majority are settled with a husband by age 16. Some men agree, however, to allow the promise girl to continue her education into late teenage by attending the high school in Darwin, approximately 300 miles away. Before she goes to live with her promise man, a girl may, in some instances, not have seen him before, if he comes from one of the neighboring Yolngu settlements of which the nearest is 50 or 60 miles distant. He may be 40 or 50 years old, or older. She may even be the fifth or sixth wife in the entourage, others of whom may be her sisters. She will get only as much attention from her man as he decides to give her, and her sex life will be at his bidding.

A wife may or may not have to live with her co-wives and their children under the same shelter and around the same camp-fire. In the least acculturated type of housing, situated in the 'bottom camp', a dwelling is no more than an improvised shanty made of discarded corrugated sheet metal and scrap wood. A man can fairly readily, therefore, construct more than one dwelling, if separation of wives will make for greater domestic harmony, as may sometimes be the case — though some wives will prefer to share and keep each other company.

It is more difficult for a man who lives in the 'top camp' to secure a second house there for part of his family, because top-camp dwellings are costly, carpenter-built houses with plumbing and electricity. The number of new constructions per annum is restricted by the size of the budget available to the chief carpenter and his crew. There is therefore a long waiting list. A man qualifies for the waiting list by accumulating credits for work. It is a policy of the mission to find a job for everyone who wants one, the jobs available being in the farm-produce, frozen fish, lumber, building, maintenance and educational industries.

15. EDUCATION FOR MENSTRUATION AND CHILDBIRTH

The unmarried adolescent girls who recorded interviews had been prepared for menstruation a year or two ahead of time by their mothers, and they also knew something from the talk of other girls. In an earlier era, the first menses would have been negotiated with ceremonial body-painting and chants which today have fallen by the wayside of cultural change. A girl is still expected, however, to pay lip-service at least to the ancient custom of menstrual isolation. Formerly she was isolated under a woven conical mat where she rested and slept. She conformed to dietary restrictions, notably the avoidance of fish and shellfish. Educated girls today, away in the city at school, still are likely to obey the dietary rule, so as to play safe and avoid the risk of falling sick. There is no further adherence, however, to the old custom of concluding menstruation with a spiritual cleansing by being passed through the fumes of a smoky fire.

Boys and young adolescent males, at least those who talked to us, had negligible or inadequate knowledge of menstrual bleeding in girls. They confused it with bleeding resulting from early or initial intercourse with a boy.

When a girl goes to her early marriage, she knows about getting pregnant, but is, according to present custom, given no systematic preparation for childbirth until she experiences it at first hand. It is probable she will know that, whereas today the majority of women deliver in the hospital, in former times a woman in labor went in the bush with several older women, one of whom would get in front, the other in back, to hold and help her have the baby, delivered from a squatting position.

Fig. 2. Unsolicited drawing from a young Yolngu man, illustrating the traditional copulatory posture.

The squatting position is the one traditionally favored also for sexual intercourse. The man sits on the ground, legs outstretched, and the woman squats on his erect penis. This positioning was nicely illustrated unrequested, when a young man elected to include a sexual theme as one in a series of drawings (Fig. 2). Preliminary love play, especially manual, may precede coitus itself, but the information available on this topic was meager and difficult to obtain because of the language barrier in talking with older, experienced males.

Whatever today's boys know about delivery, they learn it unofficially from talk with a relative or other who is willing to disclose women's information. We found that neither boys nor girls got instruction from the school, church, hospital or other community institution in matters of sex education as it pertains to the biology of reproduction, the social and personal psychology of love and sex, contraception and family planning, childbirth and infant care, or sexual hygiene. This is a matter that deserves more systematic consideration and planning, especially with respect to rate of reproduction which is maintained at its present phenomenal 5 per cent level only on the basis of what is, in effect, a mission-dispensed equivalent of a family subsidy — which cannot be expected to continue forever. There is at present no problem of venereal disease in the community, though gonorrhea did once put in an appearance, returning with a man who had been visiting in Darwin.

At present there is also no issue in the community concerning miscegenation. There is one young child whose father is known to be a Melanesian from Fiji. He was a visitor to the mission. In the recent past a preschool child died whose father was said to be a Greek immigrant in Darwin, where the mother had been sent for health reasons. The only other specifiable genetic mixing is with the Macassar people from Indonesia: one of the most respected leaders among the village elders is the son of a Macassan trader and an Aboriginal mother.

Among teenaged boys and young men today there is a good deal of joking talk about the possibility of sexual relations with a white girl. There is in this talk the implication not only of status and prestige, but also that white girls, not being subject to the restrictions of the promise system, are more free to choose and more sexually proficient. Adolescent boys and young men assume that girls have a corresponding interest in white boys, but the girls do not reveal their secrets directly in the presence of males. In the presence of white men, the women scrupulously follow the avoidancy rules. They averted their gaze when meeting us. The younger generation of Aboriginal males expressed no misgivings about interracial marriage, which has been recorded at other missions and settlements, albeit infrequently.

16. PERFUNCTORY SEXUALITY IN WOMEN

Systems of human behavior, as already indicated, must be self-sustaining. Otherwise they disappear. Obviously then, the Yolngu polygamous promise system has so far been successful in the sense that a girl adjusts to copulating and breeding within it. Exactly how well she adjusts to it is difficult for a male investigator to ascertain, for the system imposes a taboo on a woman's talking about her sex life to a man. Most older women are bound by the taboo, some younger educated ones less so. There are some women who have a joyous sex life with their husbands. But not all the evidence is positive. There are today some young women who balk at the promise system and hold out in favor of a boy friend. There are a few also whose elderly husbands have died and who categorically have refused to be claimed by the deceased husband's brother, as the system prescribes. At least one of these women has, by her own admission, said goodbye to sexual intercourse forever. She wants no more than the four children she has. She professed no interest in contraception, should it become available at the local hospital, since she has decided on celibacy. Though she obeyed the taboo against talking of her sex life, there was not much doubt that it had been a joyless, perfunctory affair, with no experience of sexual climax ever.

This particular woman is not unique. Several others from among a group with chronic complaints of minor ailments (Bianchi et al., 1970) were reported to have said that they had abandoned sexual intercourse permanently, glad perhaps that a new and younger wife could take on the duties of satisfying the husband and having the pregnancies.

Until fairly recently, a girl who did not adjust to her marriage partner might look forward to the one great episodic outlet or escape, the kunapipi already mentioned. A major ceremony of song and dance celebrating a cycle of the mythical history of the people, kunapipi, was rather like carnival or mardi gras, being an acknowledged and customary time for the free exchange of sexual partners. Secret lovers could meet openly, and men without promise partners could have sex without fear of reprisals.

For a woman with a permanent grudge against the marriage system there was also, in times past, another outlet for her emotions. She could, especially as she got older, retaliate by railing at the younger men of her family group for their lack of manhood in not being diligent enough in the pursuit of a blood feud. Taunted into action, the men would take up the challenge and spear an alleged opponent, perhaps on the basis of no more evidence than the divinations of a witch-doctor. Thereby they became next on the cycle of retribution and would be speared themselves. This type of incitement to ritual murder nowadays seldom ends in actual killing. The most recent attempt was to kill a man at Yirrkala, because he in turn had been a killer. This socially disruptive feud remains still unresolved.

In a closed community as that of the Yolngu at Elcho, there is little anonymity. Everyone has something known about him. This information by hearsay extends the range of data from detailed sex-history interviews, obtained only from those who spoke English fluently enough. Combining these two sources of information, one has the impression that the sexual problems of Yolngu women were essentially the problems of sexual apathy, frigidity or joylessness, and of despair at having more children than their health, often chronically impaired by anemia caused by untreated hookworm, permitted them to cope with. There were no other ascertained instances of psychosexual pathology or sexual behavior disorders in females.

17. MEN'S SEXUALITY

The male counterpart of sexual apathy and frigidity in the female, namely apathy, impotence and/or premature ejaculation, did not present itself as a problem. To all intents and purposes, these complaints do not exist among Yolngu men, unless in association with pathological depression in rare cases. The men also did not complain about the burden of too many children. On the contrary, they were buoyantly aware of the fact that, thanks to the high birth rate and low mortality rate of life on the mission station, the Yolngu are no longer doomed to the threat of extinction that before World War II seemed so imminent. Men have no direct responsibility for child care. They spear large game, fish and birds for food, but most of what children eat today is, if not gathered by the women, supplied by the community kitchen of the mission. Fathers permit babies an indulgent amount of physical proximity when they are resting together with their infants, and they are solicitously attentive to them.

Among young teenaged boys there was some reported admission of masturbation, and some evasive evidence of talking and joking about it. Boys and young adolescents joked about using the glutinous sap from chewed leaf stalks of the *malwun* tree as a masturbatory lubricant. There was no overt evidence of masturbation among young men segregated from women on fishing trips or in lumber camps. White supervisors who knew the language reported overhearing no sexual bragging of the locker-room type and seeing no sexual horseplay.

Among adult men the reported incidence of any form of sexual behavior pathology was extremely rare. There were stories of one man from an adjacent settlement and now deceased, who buffooned at being a dog having intercourse with an actual dog. He was universally known as being a person who did not respond appropriately when spoken to: the same word is used for a deaf mute as for a person who is out of his mind. This man had no wife and no promise girl. His public display with the dog might be interpreted, therefore, both as a reproach to his people and a symptom of the insanity with which today he would be diagnosed.

Among adult men there was also a report of behavior that at first glance, though not when subject to closer scrutiny, might appear to be the psychopathology of transvestism. This behavior was considered to be prankish by those reporting it, especially in so far as a young man not only put on a woman's dress, but also filled out the breasts with wads of clothing. The prankster's purpose was to be able to rendezvous with his girl friend, and perhaps her female accomplices, after nightfall, according to a prearranged plan. From a distance and through the darkness, other people would see only a group of females together, and nothing more would be thought of it. The wolf in woman's clothing meanwhile had the perfect opportunity to sneak off into the shadows illicitly, with the lover otherwise forbidden to him.

There was no reported or observable incidence of effeminate homosexuality among grown men, nor of homosexual preference of partners among non-effeminate men. Sexual activity between two males was reported only in connection with prepuberty and adolescence. Young male informants had no more inhibition or shame in reporting this activity than any other play activity. Their game was one in which a partner, usually a younger boy, would acquiesce to taking a feminine coital position in interfemoral, but probably not anal or oral intercourse, for the reward of nothing more than being accepted by the older boys who held prestige in his eyes.

18. SEXUAL BEHAVIOR AND PETROL-SNIFFING

These older boys held prestige because they constituted a special group of gasoline-inhalers, identified on the island as 'petrol-sniffers' (Nurcombe et al., 1970), the local equivalents of American glue-sniffers. They used rags soaked with petrol, obtained from gas tanks of the few vehicles on the island or from the drips from the auto-fuel pump. They inhaled the fumes until they got intoxicated. This was the only known way of getting 'high', since there were no other aromatic hydrocarbons available, no plant intoxicants, and absolutely no alcoholic beverages within a hundred or more roadless miles. The technique of petrol-sniffing had been introduced into the area by Australian airmen stationed on the northern coast in the early 1940s when the Japanese were preparing for invasion.

From among 18 different tribal or clan groups, partially overlapping with the 19 different language groups, the 40-odd known petrol-sniffers, aged 7—26, but mostly teenagers, came from only five different tribal groups. Predominantly they were from the Galpu tribe and from the two tribes, Arramiri and Gumatj, with whom the Galpu preferentially intermarried. These groups, and especially the Galpu, had a history of cultural conservatism, as a compensation for defeat and expulsion from sacred totemic places early in the 20th century. The elders resisted modernization and the yielding up of their ancient traditions. In doing so they abdicated their responsibilities to their young people, who could not identify with the program of traditional ways of behaving that the old men wished to perpetuate. Simultaneously, the young people, having no mandate from their elders, could not identify with the program of modernization and Christianization as sponsored by the mission. Their solution was to escape their dilemma by putting together a program of their own. They found a very literal escape in the altered consciousness and toxic imagery of gasoline-inhalation. As one informant indicated, they might find a new courage to disobey the promise system and approach a girl, even breaking the totemic avoidancy rules. Another informant epitomized the entire issue in a trance-state dream: he was, he said, being pursued by a devil-spirit man who was half-black and half-white. That is, he was being pursued by his own black heritage plus the new white one. In the end he escaped them both.

The petrol-sniffers were the prime proponents of juvenile delinquency on the island, chiefly in the form of stealing food when they came back hungry from sniffing in the bush, and stealing for the sake of increasing their meager pocket money. Two petrol-sniffers, teenaged brothers, were the only two males recorded to have stepped out of line with female mission personnel: one was said to have a history of peeping and the other to have approached two young girls in play and an older woman in anger. His anger against this woman was because she condoned the refusal of his promise girl to finish her schooling so that she could go with him.

Another petrol-sniffer, a boy in early puberty, was a ring-leader of socially unacceptable behavior. One of the chief offenses in his record was that he had impersonated an elder and staged an unofficial circumcision ceremony for a younger boy. He and his friends circumcised the boy well enough, but they were too young to have knowledge of the proper ceremonial songs and dances to be performed, much to the chagrin of the elders who hastily arranged to perform them.

It is rather remarkable that the ascertainable examples of male sexual behavior that might be classed as disorder or misdemeanor were so few. They were almost exclusively manifested by the small group of the youths who had the monopoly of delinquency, stealing and petrol-sniffing.

19. GENDER IDENTITY AND SELF-IDENTITY

The three types of nonconformity, sniffing, stealing and sex, were manifested by boys and youths who were experiencing acutely and at first hand the incompatibility of what their fathers and tribal elders stood for, versus what their school teachers and others of the mission staff stood for. The adults were unable to work out a compromise. Those youths who were unable to take sides, completely rejecting either the Aboriginal old guard or the mission new, had no model on whom to develop their teenaged sense of masculine identity. They manifested this lack very directly in the way that they looked up to and followed rare visitors to the island, like the crews of supply ships; and in the way they adopted comic-strip nicknames like One-Eye-Jack (with illicit gambling overtones) and Dick the Surfie, inked on their arms or the backs of their shirts.

The primary identity problem confronting these youths was: what kind of man am I to be? It was not a sexual problem of whether one was a man or not. It is thus fascinating to speculate that, among the youths, one discovers the principle at work that, when one's total sense of identity is at stake, then one's sexual behavior may become disturbed, and not *vice versa*. Of course one could reverse the proposition, for the sake of argument, and propound such a hypothesis as that crowding into village living after nomadic spaciousness somehow, mysteriously, induces psychosexual maldevelopment, which in turn creates a broader disturbance of the whole sense of identity. There is no absolute rebuttal of such an argument. But it is known that not all village life, universally the world over, produces homosexual and other disturbed sexual and social behavior; and petrol-sniffing, when the fluid is available, is no more a specific product of village life than is drinking alcohol.

Despite the obstacles confronting Yolngu males as they grow up and differentiate a sense of identity, living and choosing between two worlds, the total frequency of ascertained psychosexual and sexual behavior disorders was low. Moreover, in each youth who manifested any degree of inappropriate sexual behavior, its extent was trivial and in no instance involved serious disturbance of the sense of gender identity as a male.

The same can be said of females, except for the high frequency of erotic inhibition and apathy towards intercourse in marriage. Though this problem is probably rather widespread and severe, it does not involve the sense of female gender identity per se. The females are, in fact, less involved in an identity problem than the males. The very circumstance of their being sexual chattels not only facilitates their erotic inhibition, but also makes women so unimportant that they have less to gain by fidelity to the old order of things than by allegiance to and acculturation in the new. There is symbolic significance in the fact that the girls' ceremony marking the first menstruation is no longer observed, whereas circumcision of the boys is still ceremonially very important. Educationally, the girls, like girls around the world, by and large are superior achievers to the boys. Their schooling is for them an avenue of escape from the serfdom of too early marriage into a career, and into even the remote, though possible chance of romantic falling in love and marriage outside the promise system. Girls, unlike boys, do not find an identity by escaping from both the old traditions and the new along a middle way of a self-selected tradition of delinquency and petrol-sniffing. The girls of this generation will become, as mothers, the Yolngu exponents of the new way as an acceptable ideal for their sons to follow.

20. TO EVADE PSYCHOSEXUAL PATHOLOGY

In the next generation or two, as the new tradition becomes consolidated in a more and more operational and viable compromise with the old, one of the many challenges for the Yolngu people will be to find a way of preserving their remarkable freedom from most of the psychopathologies of sexual behavior, and their virtually complete freedom from homosexuality and related disorders of gender identity. To this end, it will be almost essential for them to preserve, amongst other things, their present unprudish attitude to the normalcy of nudity and sexual play of young children. They will need preschool teachers, like the wise woman they have at present, who at rest periods remains unfazed when a small boy lying in proximity to a small girl unselfconsciously begins to make pelvic thrusting movements. This teacher can approach this behavior with the same equanimity as when a child wets his pants or sucks his thumb too much, making it neither an offense nor a display. That, by the standards extant in the U.S. and in most of Australia today, is no mean accomplishment.

The straightforward attitude of the Yolngu towards nudity and sex play in young children allows these children to grow up with a straightforward attitude towards sex differences, towards the proper meaning and eventual significance of the sex organs, and towards their own reproductive destiny and sense of identity as male or female. It is here that one may look for an explanation for the relative freedom, in Yolngu society, from sexual behavior disorders.

From the point of view of psychosexual theory, it does not so much matter what is considered masculine and what feminine in the Yolngu social order: what does matter is that the two are quite clearly differentiated. Children can easily grow up to develop a gender identity without any confusion as to their proper gender role, present or future. The restrictions and taboos they will encounter do not refer to the practice of their masculinity or femininity, but to the eligibility of the partner with whom they may practise it. In our own society we have both types of taboos. The Yolngu, especially in the case of women, are not completely free of sexual 'hang-ups'. The 'hang-ups' affect the frequency of sexuality, but not the way of expressing it (sexual intercourse) nor the sex of the partner (heterosexual) with whom to express it.

21. DICTATES OF CULTURAL CHANGE

As valuable as it will be for the Yolngu to retain their straightforward way with sex in young children, it will also be valuable, and indeed necessary, for their society to outgrow other features of its traditional nomadic culture which become outmoded in a settled community that is adapting to the surrounding world. Three things wrong with the culture were spontaneously enumerated by one of its more articulate members, the man who was still unable to claim his bride after seven years of paying to redeem her from her promise man. He named the fear of ghosts and devil-devils; shame and shyness associated with social activities for young people of both sexes combined (because of suspected illicit sexual connections thereby engendered); and the unfairness of polygamy and the promise system. These three are indeed challenging issues. If the society does not find solutions to them, it may well drift into being split asunder by social conflict.

Yet another issue to which the foregoing three are indirectly related is the economic one. Having decided to come in from the bush and the nomadic way of subsistence, the Yolngu have, like it or not, committed themselves to the economics of work-for-pay, even though, up to the present, the money they have been paid is the equivalent of pocket money. Most of what they have earned has been credit that goes toward housing, food and community services. Up to the present, the economic system has been essentially a communal one, paternalistically administered. It cannot remain that way, if the Yolngu are to be brought from their geographical isolation into the mainstream of Australian life. The transition to full participation in the Australian money economy is fraught with many adaptational dangers and pitfalls, but it cannot be postponed indefinitely on that account. The Yolngu themselves will rebel against the delay as they become more closely acquainted with a work-for-full-pay system in the vast bauxite (aluminum) mining enterprise now opening up 100 miles away. Consultation with specialists in human systems engineering would no doubt help to make the transition to a full money economy more effective and satisfying to all concerned, instead of haphazard and unjust.

The change to a work-for-pay instead of a work-for-services economy will have very direct repercussions on sex. The services rendered in return for work include the maternity service of the hospital — given without qualification to all pregnant women. This service, plus the free-meal service for all infants and the school children (and for the dependent aged also), is responsible for the high birth and survival rate of the Yolngu and therefore for their very survival as a people. Without these community services, no matter how high the birth rate, it would be so effectively counteracted by a high infant mortality rate that the Yolngu would again be threatened with extinction.

The change to a work-for-pay economy will make the polygamous system untenable. Formerly, under nomadic subsistence, polygamy worked well when two or more females were competitors for only one surviving male. It ceased to work well when, subsidized by the communal system, survival rates changed, so that too many males survive but are in too many cases so subordinate in status as to be assigned no sexual partner. Females all are assigned to a subordinate man's older brother(s) with priority status, and the younger brother left out.

No man, on his own pay check alone, will be able to guarantee the survival of all the children of two, three, four and five fertile wives, as their survival is now guaranteed under the communal system. A work-for-pay system will, therefore, help to bring about a more equitable and socially stabilizing distribution of sexual partners than currently exists.

22. CONCLUSION

At the outset of my Arnhem Land experience I had, with my colleagues, asked two questions. The first we could answer affirmatively: yes the infants do play at the movements of sexual intercourse without taboo or secrecy. The second question, regarding the effect in adulthood of this lack of prudery or taboo on infantile sex play, could not be answered so simply. The effect of sexual frankness in infancy is masked by the imposition, after the age of eight, of a complicated set of social rules that require a boy or a girl to set up avoidancy relationships with certain other boys or girls. These same rules also specify who might marry whom, and dictate that a girl must share her 'promise man' with other wives who usually are her sisters. Thus the Aboriginal society imposes limits, regulations or taboos on sexual expression that are as stringent as our own, if not more so — but they are different restrictions and are imposed at a different age in a child's development. These restrictions seem to have an adverse effect on a woman's sex life more than a man's in today's Aboriginal world, since many wives have joyless and perfunctory sexual relations with their husbands.

In the Aboriginal system is it not sex itself that is tabooed, but certain selections of the person with whom one may have it. This may be the key to the finding that there is very little or nothing at all in the way of abnormal sexual behavior, homosexuality, and the paraphilias, among the Arnhem Land people.

ACKNOWLEDGEMENTS

This research was supported by a grant from the Institute of Aboriginal Studies (Canberra, Australia), and by U.S.P.H.S. grant no. 5K3-HD-18635.

BIBLIOGRAPHY

Bianchi, G.N., McElwain, D.W. and Cawte, J.E. (1970) The dispensary syndrome in Australian Aborigines: origins of their bodily preoccupation and sick role behaviour. *Br. J. Med. Psychol.* 43: 375–382.

Nurcombe, B., Bianchi, G.N., Money, J. and Cawte, J.E. (1970) A hunger for stimuli: the psychosocial background of petrol inhalation. *Br. J. Med. Psychol.* 43: 367–374.

CHAPTER 39

Peking: the sexual revolution

JOHN MONEY

1. BOARDING SCHOOL ANALOGY

My interest in China was to discover what I could of a sexological nature, in 1974, and of the place of sex in the social scheme of things. I found out something, much less than I had wanted to, and it was not easy. The chief difficulty was to contact informants — in fact to be able to talk freely with any Chinese citizens, for they fear being monitored.

I heard China described, among diplomatic people, as being like a gigantic boarding school, with strictly enforced discipline. The more I experienced China, the more I could elaborate the analogy.

By analogy, the school was religiously owned and operated. It had a monistic theology, with no heresies tolerated. Dissidents who failed to tow the line were expelled and sent away, not so much for punishment as for long-term correctional training or thought reform. To obedient students, the principal and his administration were beneficent, but demanding. The basics of food, shelter, clothing, transportation (chiefly by bicycle), entertainment, and health care were assured and equally distributed. None was rich, and none poor, but some were powerful. Most favored status could be obtained only by adherence to the dogma, and by serving the church, preferably if one's parents or grandparents had not belonged to another religion. Within the hierarchy of power, there was much private squabbling behind the scenes as to who would be subservient, who dominant, and who would replace or succeed whom in power.

To prevent the contagion of heresy, the students of this gigantic school were severely restricted in their contacts with outsiders. Here the system had its greatest weakness, for it failed to be totally self-contained. It needed a certain amount of knowledge that only heretics from the outside could provide, namely, technological knowledge, and knowledge of foreign languages for commercial and technological exchange. To meet these needs, the system imported hand-picked scholars from the outside, in exchange for exporting

Handbook of Sexology, edited by J. Money and H. Musaph
© *Elsevier/North-Holland Biomedical Press, 1977*

to the outside hand-picked scholars of its own, who were presumably immune to heresy or defection.

A short-term visiting scholar like myself, whose presence was more or less fortuituous, was welcomed courteously and respectfully, but was accorded the status of visitor only, not of scholar. I was granted translator and escort service to visit museums, a farm commune, and the children's hospital in Peking, but not the university. Unobtrusively and courteously, my conversations with Chinese pediatricians were monitored, even though two of us might speak English with equal fluency. I learned that there was no precedent whereby visiting scholars might address an audience of Chinese students and colleagues. The etiquette toward guests was to give, not to receive. Nonetheless, I was left in no doubt that people, especially those who in an earlier era had fraternized with outsiders, were as frustrated as I was at not being able to talk unrestrictedly.

English-speaking Chinese were very guarded. They also needed to avoid being monitored. Nonetheless, there had been over the years, some exchanges of information. This was the basis of some of the sexological information I received at second hand from English-speaking foreigners.

2. SEXUAL IDEOLOGY

Another source of information was from reading — historical reading. I learned for the first time that the Ming period (1368—1644) was the great age of erotic open-mindedness, frankness and honesty. This was the golden age of erotica in Chinese art and literature. The Manchu conquerors of the Ching dynasty (1644—1912) were sexually prudish and suppressive. What once was legitimate now became illegal: it was copied or imitated and covertly circulated as pornography. Behind the facade of official respectability, male and female prostitution, juveniles included, flourished, especially at the ports. Men were paraphiliacally obsessed with 'the lotus', the bound, deformed foot (still seen daily in Peking in a small proportion of women older than forty), as a sexual fetish of ancient origin.

Without taking into account the history of prudery and erotic repressiveness in the Ching era, one cannot, I think, begin to understand the apparent sexual inertia of today's China. In the same vein, one can assert that repressive sexuality in today's America cannot be understood if one omits reference to Victorianism. Whereas Victorianism in the West is subject to revision (the so-called sexual revolution), there is no such anti-Victorianism in China. I did not uncover enough variables to be able to explain why.

Probably, there is no comprehensive and systematic official sexological ideology in China today. I had to rely on piecemeal information. I came across a slogan: "Making love is a mental disease that wastes time and energy," but I could not satisfy myself as to the extent or strength of its impact. It was clearly obvious to me, however, that there was little evidence of romantic love in parks and public places. On a landing of the back stairway of a department store, I happened upon a young couple descending, holding hands. They were as flustered as if I had seen them partly naked.

Not only is there no sex in Chinese movies, but also no romance. This is a safe statement to make for, in all of China, there are fewer than a dozen movies. Like the opera in our society, they are a form of entertainment to be seen over and over again. People learn them by heart. School children are taught the themes prior to seeing them on class time. Party committees of the commune, street or factory — everyone is under the jurisdiction of a local committee — wait their turn for blocks of seats allocated, very cheaply, to their people.

I saw the two movies made for the 25th Anniversary of the People's Republic of China — Battle South and North (at a special screening with English translation); and Bright Shining Star (at a local Chinese theater). Photographically, both were of the highest caliber, and dramatically highly effective. The dramatic action excluded all body contact except for killing. The reunion of a soldier with his mother, wife or child, after years of separation, was effected at arm's length. There was much facial emotion, but no embracing, kissing, or touching.

The same downplaying of romance and sexual love is typical of the contemporary Peking opera, each of which incorporates the marvelous and traditional operatic dance—acrobatics. I saw "Cuckoo Mountain."

When I made my official visit to a farm commune, the visit began with the standard welcome accorded to guests: green tea served in the reception room, while I was briefed on the history, statistics and activities of the commune. There is a family planning and birth control service in the health clinic, talk of which gave me an opening to ask a question for which there was not a rehearsed answer: What is the age at which young people begin their sex lives? The reply initially was a rehearsed statement about the marriage age: 25 for women and 28 for men, which happens to be about the same as in Japan, another over-populated country. In China, younger couples must wait, for housing, which is in short supply, is allocated by the local committee of the party only to the older couples.

I suggested that there must be many couples who cannot wait so long before beginning their sex lives and, somewhat to my surprise, was told: "Yes, many." I said that it seemed to be the same everywhere and did not push the inquiry further. Elsewhere I eventually discovered that if young people do begin their sex lives before marriage, they usually use birth control, most typically the pill. Limited family size is a major tenet of China's sexual ideology — preferably two children per couple. Contraception is free, and applicants do not have to be married to obtain it, according to a rare conversation of a Chinese woman with an Amercian woman. If an unmarried girl gets pregnant, her local political committee will probably put considerable pressure on her to have an abortion, which also is free, and not socially stigmatized. The campaign for limited population growth, according to my reading, has lowered the rate of reproduction significantly. It is counterrevolutionary to have too many children, and a social disgrace.

Another campaign with significant success is that for the eradication of V.D., which is now said to be all but nonexistent in China. The worst trouble spot is near the border of the People's Republic of Mongolia, where V.D. is not controlled.

3. SEXUAL PRACTICES

The ordinary Chinese couple has very limited sexual privacy. On the commune, I saw a typical house. It was made of mud plaster and brick, and adjoined many others that opened onto a maze of inner courtyards. It had two rooms, one of which served as an eating and living room. Each room had a raised sleeping deck at one end. The enclosed, empty space under each deck was heated by the fumes escaping from a mud-brick stove. Six to ten people could keep warm in their quilted sleeping rolls on this heated deck in the extremely cold, bone-dry, snowless Peking winter. How much sexual privacy a couple could expect on their sleeping deck would depend on the number and sex ratio of members of the household. For example, in a household without grandparents, a couple with two teenaged children of the same sex, could sleep the children in one room and themselves in the other. If one child was a boy, he would sleep alone, and the girl would share her parents' deck. I cannot make a definitive statement, but I have the impression, from second-hand sources, that marital sex in China is mostly a matter of procreational rather than recreational sex. That means that for the wife copulation is a rather perfunctory business, done as noiselessly as possible, and geared to the husband's ejaculation rather than to the orgasm of both partners.

I did not come across any information as to what constitutes normality in Chinese sexual ideology. I obtained no information about the status of oral sex. From reading, I learned that prostitution, formerly renowned especially in the seaport cities, had been abolished by shooting the pimps and madams, and sending the whores to thought-reform schools for vocational retraining. I did not see or learn of any evidence of prostitution in Peking, though admittedly my exposure was extremely limited. The same applies to homosexuality, both public or private.

Officially, homosexuality is not tolerated. In 'Prisoner of Mao' by Bao Ruo Wang (Jean Pasqualini) and Rudolph Chelminski (Coward, McCann & Geoghegan, Inc., New York, 1973), I read the account of how the barber in a detention camp, caught for a second homosexual offence, summarily had his blood and brains splattered over other inmates assembled to learn an object lesson.

At third hand, I learned that lesbianism occurs, apparently fairly frequently among young women who, after completing their high school education, do routine service among the peasants. In the countryside, they live segregated from their male colleagues. The original informants were a Chinese student and her mother. I obtained no report concerning the male dormitories. Similarly, I obtained no information on masturbation. My questions were evaded.

I had very few opportunities to look for sexual graffiti in public toilets. In a park which was renowned for foreign and Chinese tourists, and for local painters and photographers, I found two toilet wall drawings, both very faint, and both of female genitals exposed in the lithotomy position.

Concerning recreational sex and the casual encounter, my one informant was an English-speaking business man who had made multiple business trips to China. On one occasion he had met an English-speaking diplomatic employee and foreign resident of China, on the train out of Hong Kong. Later he visited her in her apartment in Peking, and stayed overnight. Back at his hotel, he was courteously given the information that his whereabouts had been monitored, that his behavior was unacceptable, and should not recur, if he wished to have his reentry visa renewed.

In the diplomatic compound, it was manifestly impossible for Chinese to fraternize with foreigners, on a casual and friendly basis, even to play tennis or to eat together. A sexual relationship was equally out of the question, so strict is the political monitoring of Chinese employees and visitors to foreign embassies.

For sex education in schools, my informant was an English-speaking foreign boy who attended a Chinese grade school. Reproduction was mentioned in biology, but there was no mention of human sexuality.

4. SEX AND MEDICINE

At the children's hospital in Peking, the two women doctors, a pediatrician and pathologist, assigned to be my hosts knew of half a dozen cases of the adrenogenital syndrome in female hermaphrodites. They had been referred to the hospital for metabolic regulation of salt loss. I obtained zero information on the criteria and principles of sex assignment and/or reassignment in local practice. Not rare sex problems, but the major infectious and endemic diseases, it was said, were the primary concern of Chinese pediatrics, though the hospital did have special units for relatively rare cardiac and kidney diseases, and for other specialty cases. It was like a large city hospital, slightly shabby, that I might have seen anywhere, except for the policy of combining modern medicine with traditional Chinese practice as in the acupuncture clinic and in the use of acupuncture analgesia for some surgical operations. Sexual health is not a concern of medicine today in China.

Many doctors are women. Woman's emancipation in contemporary China is of a magnitude unthinkable two generations ago. But there is not yet true equality, and the lack of it is especially notable in the higher echelons of political and economic power which are man's domain. Lower on the career ladder, women share with men. There are some exceptions I noted and could not explain: no women traffic police, and no military women assigned to city or diplomatic guard duty.

5. SEX AND CLOTHING

Just about everyone in Peking, male and female, young and old, military and civilian, wears the national uniform, the Mao suit, quilted in winter, of baggy cotton pants and jacket buttoned to the collar. The colors are drab green, grey-blue, and grey. A few elderly people wear the traditional black cotton pajama-like garments. The Mao suit uniform of high ranking officials is tailored, and of better quality cloth. Western style clothes are worn only by the tiny minority of foreigners. So also are conspicuous cosmetics.

Men's and women's uniforms differ in the side on which the jackets are buttoned, right for men and left for women, and in the fly on men's pants. At a distance one tells the difference between the sexes not by body shape, for the uniform is unisex in its bagginess, but by haircut. Man invariably have a short crewcut. Older women may wear their hair uncut in a bun, but the majority have it sheared straight at the neckline, mid-parted, and held off the eyes with a hairclip on each side.

Beneath the closed collar of the Mao jacket, it may be seen that many women wear a colorful blouse shirt, of which many can be seen in the well-stocked department stores. I heard it said that girls and women dress more colorfully at home. In public only toddlers are dressed colorfully. Some are snuggled inside a fancy animal costume. The kitten is popular, and the bunny with its big ears projecting from the hood. The uniform drabness of all the older children and adults, I heard it said, was a protection against being singled out as revisionist or potentially nonconformist politically. I met a Chinese student, a visiting foreigner, who had a modish, shaggy hair cut, Beatle style, wide-cuffed, tight pants and bright jacket. He encountered more curious, covert wonderment in public than I did — and understood the accompanying remarks, too!

The sum total of sex-related grooming and clothing differences in China is that they underplay erotic differences between the sexes, but they leave each sex quite readily recognizable, the juvenile years included. Sex differences are minimized, but they are not obliterated. Emancipation of the girl and the woman in China pertains chiefly to work roles and recreational roles. It has opened formerly all-male roles to females, though the most powerful roles in society are still a male monopoly.

To a much lesser extent, emancipation has opened formerly all-female roles to males. This incomplete emancipation from the old order of things could hardly have been otherwise, given the fact that the Chinese family system has not been much changed by the revolution. It is in the family that social formulas and stereotypes — in the present instance, sexually dimorphic formulas and stereotypes — are first imprinted in infancy and early child-hood. Then they become more or less indelible.

6. FAMILY TRADITION

Total social revolution can be achieved only by total revision of socialization in infancy. That total revision can be achieved only by abolishing traditional socialization in the family, which is an almost impossible task. Its impossibil ity lies in the fact that the majority of adults who were, as infants, socialized in a family cannot help but transmit the traditions they themselves were heir to. Thus the old traditions persist as tenaciously as does the native language of a minority group. A minority group can be persecuted and forced to relinquish its language, and so also family-life traditions can be destroyed, but only by going to the extreme of abolishing the traditional institution of the family. That presupposes power and a supply of ideologically trained personnel who could substitute a new tradition and a new institution in place of the old one. To abolish the family and replace it with a substitute institution among a population of eight hundred million Chinese people is a task of too great magnitude. The techniques of revolution are inadequate to permit success in such an undertaking at the present time. In contemporary China there is no evidence of any effort being expended in this direction. Nor is there the knowledge on which to base an attempt.

There are no departments of psychology or behavioral science in the uni-versities and research institutes, to the best of my knowledge. There are only departments of political philosophy, misnamed as social science, which are not empirical and research-oriented, but didactic only.

The spectacular success of China's revolution as a whole, as well as of its partial sexual revolution in particular, is the success of a monistic ideology, widespread power by edict, and deportation and thought reform (brain-washing) for all nonconformists. America's revolution, by contrast, was the success of pluralistic ideology, restricted power by edict plus heresies for all up to a certain point, and punitive incarceration for those who transgressed that certain point.

At the outset, American pluralism of ideology excluded sexual ideology. There was only one socially decreed sexual ideology to conform to. This ap-plied to dimorphism of both erotic and vocational sex roles. Today, after two hundred years, that monism is changing, and society is experiencing all the usual anguish, antagonism, and divisiveness of revolution, even though the sexual revolution does not involve guns and killing.

In China, monism is not changing. The sexual revolution has lost its momentum. It will probably get in motion again when the generation that was juvenile in the era of the Red Guards and the Cultural Revolution comes of age. They saw teenagers of the Red Guards claim some degree of sexual freedom, and they may in turn claim some of it for themselves.

7. SUMMARY

Human sexuality is a taboo subject in the People's Republic of China. The puritanical traditions of the Ching dynasty (1644—1912) have been incorporated into revolutionary doctrine, but not the subculture of licentiousness that disobeyed official Ching puritanism. Prostitution is no longer evident, and V.D. control has been very effective. Homosexuality and masturbation are not overtly discussed. Adolescent and young adult relationships are not sanctioned, but are known to occur. Birth-control information is freely available, as is abortion; both are available premaritally. It is counter-revolutionary, and a social disgrace to have too many children. The marriage age is late twenties for males, and middle twenties for females. An effective constraint on earlier marriage is the unavailability of housing, except by approval of a political committee. Though the emancipation of women has been of a magnitude unthinkable by pre-1949 standards, equal representation of the sexes, in the higher echelons of work and politics, is not yet evident.

CHAPTER 40

Divorce and remarriage:
trends and patterns in contemporary society

LYNN G. SMITH and JAMES R. SMITH

Since the early 1960s the rate of divorce has steadily increased in the U.S. and in most other countries that report divorce data to the Statistical Office of the United Nations. Particularly pronounced increases have been evident in the U.S.S.R. and in Scotland where rates doubled during the past decade (Vital Statistics, 1973). With few exceptions, marital dissolution is increasing on a worldwide basis.

Only 12% of the women in the U.S.A. born at the turn of the century and now in their seventies have ended their first marriage in divorce. Demographers project that 25—29% of women born 1940—44 (those currently in their early thirties) will experience divorce during their lifetime (Glick and Norton, 1973). Four-fifths of these young women are expected to remarry and of all American women now around 30 years of age, some 5—10% are expected to experience divorce at least twice in their lifetimes (Glick and Norton, 1973).

Divorce, traditionally most common in the early years of marriage, has become increasingly frequent among older married couples. In the U.S.A. divorces have more than doubled since 1960 among couples who have maintained relationships for periods of 15 years and longer ('The broken family,' 1973). The divorce rate among families with young children has also been climbing. One American child in seven is now being raised in a single-parent family (Dullea, 1974).

When divorce was less common, family sociologists sought to predict marital adjustment and explain marital dissolution on the basis of such variables as similarities or dissimilarities in the partners' backgrounds and conventional or nonconventional patterns of socialization and courtship. Studies of marital stability tended to emphasize mate selection as the principal basis for explaining happy or unhappy outcomes (Foote, 1956). Thus, Goode (1961), for example, in discussing family disorganization summarized a number of variables related to 'divorce proneness'. These variables included marriage at very young ages, short acquaintanceship before marriage, short or no

Handbook of Sexology, edited by J. Money and H. Musaph
© *Elsevier/North-Holland Biomedical Press, 1977*

engagement, marital unhappiness of parents, nonattendance at church, mixed religious faith, disapproval of the marriage, dissimilarity of background, and different definitions by spouses of their mutual roles.

While such variables as age at marriage and length of acquaintanceship are still relevant for predicting the relative outcome probabilities of various unions, a different level of analysis must be undertaken to account for the recent and continuing changes and trends in patterns of marital stability and instability which have been occurring on a global scale. Herein we will briefly explore the effects of industrialization on the course and content of family life and then consider some of the most recent developments in conceptions of growth, maturation, and adulthood which may be expected to further affect the evolution of marriage in economically developed countries.

Industrialization, urbanization, and the consequences of technological innovation are making themselves felt on an international basis as factors affecting, directly and indirectly, social life, family function, and the dynamics of marriage and divorce. The roles they play are different in different phases of socioeconomic development. In undeveloped countries they exist as future norms and future problems, trends yet to be conceived or anticipated; in developing countries they are emerging trends and blueprints for changes just beginning to be perceived as social problems; and in highly developed countries they represent extant and volatile current conditions, many of which appear to be beyond comprehension or control.

We do not intend to commit ourselves to a simplified version of either economic or cultural determinism by adopting such a perspective. Indeed, the intervention of such factors as scientific research and professional leadership, media influence, mass education, and public planning to anticipate the effects of industrialization upon family life and marital relations means that the shocks and traumas of change can be minimized, accommodated, and, in significant ways, ameliorated. Foreknowledge of change neither determines it nor makes it inevitable. But it does aid those who must undergo and cope with it. Our intent here, ultimately, is not only to describe trends but to post warnings and suggest that national and international planning should anticipate sweeping and dramatic changes in kinship and family systems, mate selection, and sexual mores and lifestyles among the peoples of the pre-industrial and transitional economies of the world.

1. SOCIOECONOMIC STRUCTURE: INDUSTRIALISM, URBANISM, AND TECHNOLOGICAL DEVELOPMENT

Due to scientific and technological developments, life expectancy in the U.S. has nearly doubled in the last century. A hundred years ago the average American lived 35—40 years; today 70 years is the norm (Francoeur, 1973). While marriage for life once involved a period of 15—20 years, today a life-time marriage may span a period of 50 years or more. Death does not part us as soon as it used to.

In generations past it was common for people to spend their whole lives in a single location. If they were to move they were not likely to move very far away. The individual and the family existed within relatively stable, cross-generational kinship and community networks. The pattern of 'here today, gone tomorrow' people, places and relationships was peculiar to specialized segments of the community such as military personnel, seasonal workers and entertainers. *

Through a combination of basic social forces, central among which are industrialization, urbanization, and technological innovations in transportation and communication, the modern family has become a nuclear unit. When one moves once every five years and fourteen times in one's lifetime, as the average American has been doing since 1948, one cannot take one's aunts and uncles, nieces and nephews along (American Families: Trends and Pressures, 1973). Institutionalized support systems, bureaucratically and impersonally operated, have arisen to take over many of the functions previously served by extended family, neighborhood networks and long-standing peer groups. In the search for a balance between mobility and stability the result is often dissatisfaction, disorientation and alienation.

Developments typical of increasing industrialization — falling age of marriage, rising life expectancy, decreasing number of children, and the growing absorption of women by the labor market — have been shown to correlate with a rise in divorce rates (Künzel, 1974). In a study of aggregate data from 28 European countries classified into two groups on the basis of their degree of industrialization, Künzel demonstrated that there are typical changes in the phases and content of the family cycle that result from industrialization, urbanization and a rise in the level of education in a country, changes which are relatively independent of time and culture but intimately associated with these socioeconomic processes. Künzel explains that in the course of industrialization functions are increasingly transferred out of the family and into other areas of society, that a separation of the private and the occupational spheres comes about, that increasing numbers of married women are employed outside the home, and that there is a continual reduction in birth rates with increasing industrialization. In the developing industrial countries of Europe there is a tendency for employed women to be recruited predominantly from the ranks of the unmarried; in highly industrialized countries over half of the employed women are married. In 1940 in the U.S. only 17% of the married women were gainfully employed; in 1974, 43% of all American wives were in the labor force (U.S. Dept. of Labor). With the growing independence acquired by women in the course of industrialization, Künzel concludes that divorce rates around the world will continue to rise. Regional and intra-national analysis reflect a similar trend. Data from Yugoslavia, where figures vary widely from region to region, indicate that divorce rates

---

* Useful perspectives on the subject may be found in Ellul (1964), Toffler (1970), Bennis and Slater (1968) and Lifton (1969).

tend to be higher in better-developed areas of the country than in less-developed areas (United Press International, 1975).

Increases in the rate of industrial development produce a world of truly dizzying proportions and mystifying relationships. Social relationships no longer turn so clearly on either physical propinquity or kinship. One's next-door neighbors may be strangers. The alienation of parents and children is by now a cliché. Yet media and education have put us in communication with the 'global village,' albeit one-way communication. Vast segments of the society are 'plugged in' to a common, if diverse, world culture, an environmental and ideological interdependence only vaguely understood. What happens in Athens or Saigon is known that evening in the most remote and rural areas of a vast proportion of the civilized world.

The ebb and flow of industrialization and social change produces a world in which intimate and interpersonal relationships take on the characteristics and reflect the dynamics of the whole. Even institutions become the victims of standardization, planned obsolescence, and routinization. Social relations are reduced to their component parts or roles, each of which is replaceable, interchangeable, or capable of therapeutic readjustment. Nothing lasts as long as it used to, not products or relationships; nothing, that is, except our lives which last longer than ever before. As Toffler has said, 'Serial marriage — a pattern of successive temporary marriages — is cut to order for the Age of Transience in which all man's relationships, all his ties with the environment, shrink in duration.'

2. THE CONCEPT OF ADULT DEVELOPMENT

In the midst of all this, with life spans lengthened and lived out in a series of temporary systems subject to an increasing rate of change, we are beginning to see that adulthood may be differentiated into developmental stages.

It was not until the 17th century, according to Aries (1962), that the modern idea of childhood as a distinct phase of life developed in Western thinking. The concept of adolescence as a life phase is of even more recent origin. The periods of childhood and adolescence have each been further divided into a series of more refined developmental stages. Our concept of adulthood is now yielding to an increased awareness that growth and development continue throughout the course of life (Erikson, 1959; Gould, 1972; Graves, 1974; Levinson et al., 1974).

The family life cycle has also become more protracted and is now seen to exhibit phases that are more and more clearly distinct from one another. Künzel (1974) reports that: "The various phases of the family cycle in the highly industrialized countries make plain how, with the passing of time, the role constellations of the marriage partners change several times and thus produce phases of differing stability, the phases without children and the times when the woman can engage in employment having a lower stability.

In agrarian countries and developing industrial countries [where the length of marriage tends to be shorter] . . ., the whole of the marriage has more or less the same content and tasks and . . . there is hardly any formation of phases that are clearly distinguishable from one another . . ."

In highly industrialized countries, varying phases of stability and instability succeed one another in the family cycle and these affect the divorce rates (Künzel, 1974). The issues around which these periods of stability and instability revolve vary with the levels of both individual development and socioeconomic status.

Maslow's conception of a hierarchy of basic human needs characterized by a dynamic interplay in which the 'lower' needs must be satisfied before the 'higher' needs emerge and command attention is useful here (Maslow, 1954, 1962). Maslow's need hierarchy spans five levels: physiological needs, safety and security needs, belongingness and love needs, self-esteem needs, and the need for self-actualization. These needs may be understood on both an individual and cultural level of evolution and development (Graves, 1974). One American researcher, for example, studied the sources of marital dissatisfaction among applicants for divorce and found that "spouses in middle-class marriages were more concerned with psychological and emotional interaction; while the lower-class partners saw as more salient in their lives financial problems and unstable physical actions of their partners" (Levinger, 1966). In another study (Kephart, 1954) concern with sexual incompatibility was found primarily among divorce applicants from the higher social strata. Thus, as Levinger (1965) points out, "Sexual gratification is one vital source of marital attraction, but its lack apparently is less keenly felt among spouses who have not achieved a satisfactory material standard of living."

In 1956 Nelson Foote prophetically suggested that successful marriage might come to be defined in terms of its potential for continued development. He pointed out that even then the kind of marriage in which stability most depends upon mutual development was on the increase. * The 1960s in the U.S. proved to be a decade in which the concept of adult development and growth throughout life, identified variously as self-actualization, consciousness raising, psychic liberation, and self-transcendence, gained notoriety and spawned the beginnings of many popular movements devoted to that process. The 'Third Force' humanistic psychology movement with its encounter and sensitivity training groups, the women's movement, the black liberation movement, the sexual freedom movement, all flew the banner of consciousness expansion and self-actualization. A revolution of rising expectations for marriage and interpersonal relations caught hold on the socioemotional level, following on the heels of national policies of economic expansionism. As Farson (1969) has explained, we now expect and demand

---

* This was part of the trend toward companionate marriage whose philosophical fundamentals had been analyzed a generation earlier by Bertrand Russell, Havelock Ellis, and Judge Ben Lindsey.

more and more from our relationships, interpersonally as well as materially.

Rollin (1971) has suggested that personal growth may be the biggest marriage killer of all. This is, of course, one of the reasons why early marriages are so often doomed. More individual growth and change occurs in the compressed period of late adolescence and early adulthood and thus more interpersonal adaptation is required. If growth is truly continued throughout adulthood, it may endanger a marriage at any point. Individuals grow at different rates and in different directions. Mutually compatible parallel change and growth between partners is by no means insured throughout the course of a long-term relationship. It used to be the husband who, in the course of higher education and career advancement, outgrew the wife who stayed at home. Recent and current conditions, however, are redressing the balance on this point.

3. AUTONOMY AND COMMITMENT: THE DILEMMA OF MODERN MARRIAGE

As industrialization continues women are presented with more and more challenges and opportunities outside the family and the home. Previously women had fewer alternatives and more restricted roles, both in and out of the home, and they largely contented themselves with their place, knowing no other. Many women who were reared and socialized according to traditional codes and roles are now seeking identity and autonomy in their relationships. Many of these relationships, however, were conceived and initiated at a time when role differentiation and status inequality were relatively unquestioned elements of marriage. Such new concerns cause strain and sometimes disintegration of the relationship. In the future more relationships will likely begin from a peer standing.

With the current shift toward equality between the sexes and less differentiation in sex roles, marriage is becoming more a relation of choice than necessity, more a relation of interdependent peers than symbiotic complements. This change in the role and status of women affects the bonding between male and female, husband and wife. The dependent status of the wife is altered. A sense of individuality and selfhood within a marital relationship becomes more important to the woman who has previously subordinated her needs to those of her husband and family. As a result, the whole power structure of marital relations is changing. And so are the motivational elements which draw people to marriage and sustain them in it.

More than ever in highly industrialized countries like the U.S. the dilemma in intimate relationships is how to be close yet free, free to be an individual and to grow as a separate person; independent yet connected. There is often conflict between one's commitment to another with its inevitable compromises and sacrifices, and the process of self-actualization. Each person needs a sense of community and relatedness but each also needs a sense of individuality and identity.

Recent research indicates that this is a problem for young cohabiting couples as well as older married folk. Macklin (1974), for example, found that the most common emotional problem reported by cohabiting college couples was "the tendency to become overinvolved: to feel overdependent on the relationship, with a subsequent loss of identity and a lack of opportunity to participate in other activities or to be with friends." Almost half of the cohabiting students reported that they occasionally felt trapped in their relationship.

The need for individuality and autonomous growth on the part of both partners places a new demand on the institution of marriage. It must now serve 'higher' and more subtle and complex needs. Women's drive for identity beyond marriage, family, and gender role leads to upsetting the balance of dominance and deference within the home and family. This necessitates a shift from patriarchal and materialistic conceptions of marriage to egalitarian and eupsychian models. The thesis proposed here concerns the personal status, identity and growth needs of both men and women. Men, who at first blush appear to be losing status and power by the changes in the roles of women, must redefine their needs for growth and identity as well. Paternalism, chauvinism, and masculine egotism are not conducive to self-actualization, and certainly do not contribute to companionship, effective communication between the sexes, or adult development in the interpersonal sphere. The ultimate advantage goes to both in terms of relationship potential but the changes involve threats and traumas for both women and men alike.

Both men and women have a basic need for relatedness and for autonomy. These needs are rarely found in perfect harmony either between or within individuals. Smith and Phillips (1971) explain that the themes of closeness and freedom are basically in conflict, just as are the desires to be dependent and to be independent. They suggest that the best way out is to allow the natural ebb and flow of closeness and distance to operate so that a relationship is a continuing balance between the two.

Such a balance extends also into the area of sex roles. While male and female are socialized along what are considered to be sex-appropriate lines, there is reason to believe that the fully mature individual of each sex transcends such channelization and achieves an individual androgynous balance of both 'masculine' and 'feminine' characteristics (Block, 1973; Rosenzweig, 1973). Shostrum (1972) argues that, "Just as in Gestalt psychology, the two sides of the coin, or figure and ground must always go together, so the individual derives his identity from the reconciliation and integration of the polarities within himself." Shostrum sees the expression and integration of polarities — strength and weakness, love and anger, dependence and independence, masculine and feminine — as basic to the process of self-actualization, the developing of the full potential of one's being. The balance between autonomy and relatedness becomes accentuated in this process and it is at this level that the divorce battles of families of the future will more and more be fought. Fluctuations in one's status from single to married to divorced to remarried reflect this shifting balance between the need for autonomy and the need for commitment. Economic scarcity, whether recession or depression, may, however, have a dampening effect on this trend as people seek stability over growth and change in times of economic hardship.

4. REMARRIAGE: COUPLING, UNCOUPLING, AND RECOUPLING

The divorce process generally results in an extensive reorganization of one's life — lifestyle, economics, relationships with others, and especially, in the individual's own self-concept (N.C.F.R., 1974). Hopes are smashed, shared dreams dissolved, dependencies left dangling, and the previous partners must face the traumatic process of separating out, psychologically and materially, from one of the most intimate unions social life has to offer. However amicable the agreement may be, almost no one gets divorced without some feelings of real or imagined loss and failure, and guilt. But wounds heal, and people grow and try to draw lessons from their past to aid them in the future.

As the divorce rate has risen, so has the remarriage rate. Data from the United States indicates that in 1969 approximately one out of every four marriages was a remarriage. This ratio varied widely from a high of 40% of all marriages in some states to a low of 15% in others (Vital Statistics, 1974). Remarriage rates were found to be highest at the younger ages, higher for men than for women, and higher for the divorced than the widowed (Vital Statistics, 1974). Further, most persons who remarry were found to do so in a relatively short period of time after their previous marriage was dissolved. A limited sampling of 15 states in 1969 showed that 50% of the previously divorced brides and grooms had remarried within slightly more than one year from the time of their divorce (Vital Statistics, 1974). These figures suggest the influence of a rebound effect which operates to ameliorate the presence of trauma and disorganization produced by divorce. Some, of course, simply divorce in order to remarry someone else. And every year in the U.S. there are 10,000 remarriages to the same person (Rollin, 1971).

What is different about second marriages? Most people in their second marriages will tell you that they try harder to make a go of it, that they really work at the relationship and take it less for granted. They know from experience that it can end and they know better what they are getting into when they choose to remarry. By the time most people remarry, they are older and know themselves better, both personally and professionally, than when they first married. They are more likely to have found themselves and less likely to look to the other person for support and definition. They have experienced both dependence and independence and theoretically stand a better chance of forming a truly mature relationship based on an appreciation of their interdependence. Yet among the middle and upper middle classes in the U.S.A., the divorce rate of remarriages is the same as for first marriages. One out of every three first marriages ends in divorce; the same is true of second marriages (Ramey, 1975). Third and fourth marriages are still relatively uncommon.

It is against our hopes and expectations that we compare our reality. When our expectations are unrealistic, reality cannot measure up. When we expect marriage to last a lifetime and the statistics show that there is a better and better chance that it will not, our expectations are out of line with our reality. Perhaps if we expected marriage to be a temporary association, perhaps tuned to our shifting phases of adult development as in Margaret Mead's concept of 'stage marriage,' uncoupling would be less traumatic and less subject to feelings of personal failure. A 'successful' marriage might then last through one, more than one, or all phases of a person's life.

Stability in marriage is a function of a variety of factors — only one of which is marital happiness (Hicks and Platt, 1970). Recent findings even suggest that marital stability may often be associated with low happiness (Hicks and Platt, 1970). Stability and permanence cannot remain our only criteria of success and failure and divorce rates our only measure. A new framework, a new philosophy, a new set of norms for evaluation and analysis is needed. In them the norms of candor, trust, communication, companionship and growth come to the fore and challenge the norms of stability, affluence, procreation, and productivity for relevance in explaining why people get married, divorced, and increasingly often, remarried.

5. SUMMARY

With few exceptions, marital dissolution is increasing on a worldwide basis. Divorce, traditionally most common in the early years of marriage has become increasingly frequent among older married couples and among couples with young children. One American child in seven is now being raised in a single-parent family. Macroanalysis is required to account for the changing patterns of marital stability and instability occuring on a global scale.

Industrialization alters the entire institutional, technical, and cultural framework of a society and in so doing influences the course and content of family life. With increasing industrialization, life expectancy rises, birth rates drop and families become smaller, kinship and community networks are fragmented, women are absorbed into the labor market, and the rate of divorce tends to increase. In highly industrialized countries the role constellations of the marriage partners change several times in the course of the family cycle and produce phases of differing stability and satisfaction. Growth and development continued throughout adulthood, in psychological as well as material terms, become increasingly important to both men and women in the move from patriarchal to egalitarian relationships. The need for individuality and autonomy on the part of both partners places a new demand and a new strain on the institution of marriage.

The swelling ranks of the divorced, however, do not indicate a rejection of the institution of marriage. Most who divorce remarry, and many do so in a relatively short period of time after the dissolution of their first marriage.

Professionals in health care, family counseling, and sex education in developing countries should anticipate social development and look ahead to the changes industrialization brings. Dislocation and adjustment may be inevitable, but alienation and misery are surely not. The mobility, the easing of sex segregation and gender specialization, the reduced emphasis on procreative roles and functions brings a whole new context and set of historical functions to the family. A pluralism of family forms and marital styles looms on the industrialized horizon (Sussman, 1971). Alternatives to procreation, subsistence, and monogamy, including serial, group, and eupsychian marriage, begin to emerge more clearly and can be expected to come closer to meeting human needs under conditions of rapid change and adjustment.

Marriage, and its institutionalized adjustment mechanisms, divorce and remarriage, serve modified ends, new functions, altered purposes, and less rigidly defined values in industrialized and urbanized social systems. A significant amount of 'future shock' may well be reduced by anticipating it, and meeting the challenge instead of allowing it to overwhelm the agencies and institutions which serve marital and familial needs. Marriage can become more fully humanized despite the industrialization and mechanization of the surrounding environment. It is neither necessary nor useful to view divorce and remarriage as a social scourge. They need to be seen as process adjustments which may well be functional and socially adaptive under industrial and urban circumstances.

BIBLIOGRAPHY

American Families: Trends and Pressures, 1973 (1974) Hearings before the Subcommittee on Children and Youth of the Committee on Labor and Public Welfare, United States Senate, Ninety-Third Congress. (U.S. Government Printing Office, Washington, D.C.)

Aries, P. (1962) *Centuries of Childhood: A Social History of Family Life.* (Knopf, New York.)

Bennis, W.G. and Slater, P. (1968) *The Temporary Society.* (Harper and Row, New York.)

Block, J.H. (1973) Conceptions of sex role: Some cross-cultural and longitudinal perspectives. *Am. Psychol.* 28 (6) 512—526.

The broken family: Divorce U.S. style. (1973) *Newsweek* March 12, 47—58.

Divorces: Analysis of changes, United States, 1969 (1973) *Vital and Health Statistics,* Ser. 21, No. 22. 58 pp.

Dullea, G. (1974) Single parent families, becoming an American way of life. *Honolulu Star-Bull.* December 11.

Ellul, J. (1964) *Technological Society.* (Knopf, New York.)

Erikson, E.H. (1959) Identity and the life cycle. *Psychol. Issues.* 1 (1).

Farson, R. (1969) Behavioral science prdicts and projects. In: (Farson, Stroup, Hauser and Wiener, Eds.) *The Future of the Family.* (Family Service Association of America, New York.)

Foote, N. (1956) Matching of husband and wife in phases of development. *Trans. World Congr. Sociol.* Vol. 4, 24—34.

Francoeur, R.T. (1973) Value systems and marital pluralism in a meta-primitive society. (Plenary address to the annual meeting of the National Council of Family Relations.)

Glick, P.C. and Norton, A.J. (1973) Perspectives on the recent upturn in divorce and remarriage. *Demography* 10 (3) 301—314.

Goode, Wm.J. (1961) Family disorganization. In: (R.K. Merton and R.A. Nisbet, Eds.) *Contemporary Social Problems*. (Harcourt Brace, New York.)

Goode, Wm.J. (1963) *World Revolution and Family Patterns*. (Free Press, Glencoe, Illinois.)

Goode, Wm.J. (1965) *Women in Divorce*. (Free Press, New York.)

Gould, R. (1972) Phases of adult life. *Am. J. Psychiat.* November.

Graves, C.W. (1974) Human nature prepares for a momentous leap. *The Futurist*, April, 72—87.

Hicks, M.W. and Platt, M. (1970) Marital happiness and stability: A review of the research in the sixties. *J. Marr. Fam.* 32 (4) 553—574.

Kephart, Wm. H. (1954) Some variables in cases of reported sexual maladjustment. *Marr. Fam. Living* 16 (August) 241—243.

Künzel, R. (1974) The connection between the family cycle and divorce rates: An analysis based on European data. *J. Marr. Fam.* M, 379—388.

Levinger, G. (1965) Marital cohesiveness and dissolution: An integrative review. *J. Marr. Fam.* 27 (February) 19—28.

Levinger, G. (1966) Sources of marital dissatisfaction among applicants for divorce. *Am. J. Orthopsychiat.* 36: 803—807.

Levinson, D.J., Darrow, C.M., Klein, E.B., Levinson, M.H. and McKee, B. (1974) The psychosocial development of men in early adulthood and the mid-life transition. In: (D.F. Ricks, A. Thomas and M. Roff, Eds.), *Life History Research in Psychopathology*. Vol. 3 (University of Minnesota Press) 243—258

Lifton, R.J. (1969) Protean man. In: *History and Human Survival*. (Random House, New York.)

Macklin, E.D. (1974) Cohabitation in college: Going very steady. *Psychol. Today* (November) 53—59.

Maslow, A.H. (1954) *Motivation and Personality*. (Harper & Bros., New York).

Maslow, A.H. (1962) *Toward a Psychology of Being*. (Van Nostrand, Princeton, N.J.)

National Council on Family Relations, Task Force on Divorce and Divorce Reform. (1975) Divorce and divorce reform. (October)

Olson, D.H. (1971) Marriage of the future: Revolutionary or evolutionary change? *Fam. Coord.* October.

Ramey, J.W. (1975) *Intimate lifestyles of the future*. (Symp. Current and Future Intimate Lifestyles, Connecticut College, New London.)

Remarriages, United States. (1974) *Vital and Health Statistics*, Ser. 21, No. 25.

Rollin, B. (1971) The American way of marriage: Remarriage. *Look* (September 21) 62—68.

Rosenzweig, S. (1973) Human sexual autonomy as an evolutionary attainment, anticipating proceptive sex choice and idiodynamic bisexuality. In: (J. Zubin and J. Money, Eds.). *Contemporary Sexual Behavior: Critical Issues in the 1970s* (Johns Hopkins University Press, Baltimore, Maryland.)

Shostrum, E. (1972) *Freedom to Be*. (Bantam, New York.)

Smith, G.W. and Phillips, A.I. (1971) *Couple Therapy*. (Collier, New York.)

Sussman, M.B. (1971) Family systems in the 1970's: analysis, policies, and programs. *The Annals*, July.

Toffler, A. (1970) *Future Shock*. (Random House, New York.)

United Press International (1975) Play house, then marry, Slavs told. *San Fransisco Sunday Examiner & Chronicle*. January 5.

CHAPTER 41

Today's changing sexual mores

ROGER W. LIBBY

In 1906 William Graham Sumner stated that mores could be equated with taboos on behaviors not to be engaged in rather than positive laws or guidelines to responsible behaviors. When speaking of sexual mores, Sumner observed: "The sex mores are one of the greatest and most important divisions of the mores. They cover the relations of men and women to each other before marriage and in marriage, with all the rights and duties of married and unmarried, respectively, to the rest of the society. The mores determine what marriage shall be, who may enter it, divorce, and all details of proper conduct in the family relation." (Sumner, 1906, p. 342).

Sumner acknowledged that positive laws replaced previously held negative mores in time, and that sex mores have traditionally differed for men and women due to the double standard of sexual morality.

Since mores have been conceived as regulations or taboos on behavior, sex mores define proper boundaries and symbolic motives and meanings of sexual behavior. Mores have been seen as controlling natural sexual desires, usually in relation to the boundaries of marriage or some form of cohabitation between the sexes. Reiss (1973) noted the importance of cross-cultural research on sexual attitudes and behavior to determine commonalities and differences between societies. Murdock's cross-cultural and historical study indicated that about 70% of 250 societies allowed premarital intercourse (Murdock, 1949). And yet, Christensen and Gregg (1970) reported that Danish college students' premarital * sexual attitudes and behavior were more permissive than American attitudes and behavior, and Christensen (1973) has also shown that extramarital attitudes and behavior are more permissive in Denmark. Similarly, Gallup (1973) surveyed American and European youth and found that while 23% of U.S. youth felt premarital intercourse should

---

* The term 'premarital' is used here to include sexual behavior before marriage. No assumption is made that marriage will occur or that all premarital sexual behavior is marriage-oriented. Nonmarital sexual expression is included in the use of premarital.

Handbook of Sexology, edited by J. Money and H. Musaph
© *Elsevier/North-Holland Biomedical Press, 1977*

be avoided under any circumstances, only 4% of Swedish, 6% of West German, 8% of Swiss, and 10% of French youth agreed with such a limitation. These generalizations are supported by Hertoft (1973) who observed that a permissive * attitude toward premarital coitus has been a tradition for some time in Scandinavia. However, Hertoft was careful to recognize that permissive sexual norms are only functional to the extent that a society has a social support system to affirm a positive expression of sexuality. Unlike much American research and speculation on possible adverse effects of premarital sexual experiences on marital adjustment, Hertoft (1973) stated that such a research question is not appropriate in Scandinavia where premarital experimentation is accepted and practiced without guilt.

It is probably true that most sexual behavior occurs in marriage, and also that most cultures emphasize marital sex as more appropriate than non-marital sex. Reiss provided an overview of sexual relationships in the following propositions: ". . . the more likely a sexual relationship is viewed as promoting and stabilizing marriage, the more likely that sexual relationship will be socially permitted; the more likely a relationship is viewed as disturbing to marriage, the more likely that it will be prohibited." (1973, p. 2).

Reiss also stated that males are given more sexual rights than females in most societies. While these generalizations have been supported by cross-cultural data over time, recent studies indicate that sexual mores are changing in America and in other countries (Scandinavia and England). The change is obvious on several levels — women are becoming more liberal in attitude and behavior, and sexual intercourse without definite marital plans has become more acceptable (the ad hoc marriage without legal sanction). Additionally, recent studies on sexually open marriages (Libby and Whitehurst, 1973; Smith and Smith, 1974) suggest that an increasing minority of Americans (and others probably) are experimenting with marriages in which spouses agree to some conditions where they may enter into sexual relationships beyond their marital sexual relationship (co-marital sex).

The Kinsey studies (1948, 1953) reported that if one experienced premarital coitus one was about twice as likely to enter into an extramarital liason. Thus, changing sexual standards in regard to sexual behavior prior to marriage and the behavioral enactment of these more liberal standards will likely increase the rates of extramarital and co-marital sex. This view is elaborated by Libby (1977).

Increased technological advancements such as birth control and the automobile have broadened the opportunity for multiple sexual relationships

---

* 'Permissiveness' is typically used to connote liberal attitudes and/or behavior with no reference to the context of the interpersonal relationship or the basis for the decision to have premarital intercourse. However, as Kirkendall and Libby (1966) have pointed out, when the quality of relationships is considered, a mutual decision to have premarital intercourse with positive consequences diverts attention from the act to the consequences and may not be 'permissive' in terms of the responsibility of the couple to the decision itself.

prior to and after marriage. Reiss (1973) stated that the most significant single change in the past fifty years is the 'legitimization of sexual choice.' People are now increasingly offered a choice of a sexual or marital life style rather than accepting a unimodal model of sexually exclusive marriage and premarital virginity. Attitudinal change was shown by Reiss (1973) when he compared his 1963 national sample with a 1970 national sample collected by Klassen and Levitt in America. Twenty-one percent of adults accepted premarital intercourse under some conditions in 1963, while 50% did so in 1970. If one can legitimately project a linear progression of increasing attitudinal permissiveness, sexual mores will continue to change. College students' attitudes have always been more permissive than parental (or adult) attitudes, and college students' premarital sexual attitudes and behavior have become more permissive, particularly among females (Luckey and Nass, 1969; Bell and Chaskes, 1970; Christensen and Gregg, 1970; Eshleman, 1972; Hunt, 1974).

On a reported behavior level, Zelnik and Kantner's (1972) national population study in America indicated that 46% of 19-year-old white women and 80% of 19-year-old black women reported premarital coitus. Since there really are no adequate baseline data to compare these proportions with in America (Schofield's 1965 British teenage study indicated considerably less premarital intercourse), it is difficult to discuss behavioral change as preceding or following attitudinal change. Using the Kinsey studies one can tell women born after 1900—1915 were considerably more likely to experience premarital coitus than women born prior to 1900. Reiss (1973) posited a 'consolidation process' where we have learned to change our attitudes and accept the previous behavioral changes by today's grandmothers in our current belief systems about premarital sex. The recent behavioral shift toward more female premarital coitus for more reasons with more men is another change in a permissive direction. There seems to be a close interaction and feedback between female attitudinal and behavioral change in a permissive direction, and the double standard of sexual morality seems to be slowly passing with these changes. The Women's Liberation movement has forced a re-evaluation of the legitimacy of female sexual expression apart from marital status or affectional levels; this social movement has resulted in changed attitudes as one crucial indicator of changing sexual mores.

1. SEXUAL LANGUAGE AND CHANGING MORES

Changing sexual attitudes, values and behavior are reflected in new words coined to describe emerging symbolic meanings and motives for sexual expression (such as 'co-marital' for open marriages with sexual freedom beyond the marital pair-bond). Arnold and Libby (1976) observed that cultural relativity of norms, mores and customs is described by the language in a culture. Since most of sexuality has been expressed through negative mores (regula-

tions and taboos), most sex-related concepts are also negative. The Sapir—
Whorf Hypothesis (Fearing, 1954) posits that language forms the parameters
of understanding and meaning about behavior in a culture. Language change
is reflected in emerging sexual life styles made possible through social change
from technology and social movements such as the Women's Movement and
a concern for population control (a shift from a pro-natalist to a non- or
limited reproductive mentality).

Language describes attitudes, values and mores. Behavior is socially
scripted so that we are like actors playing roles on a stage; there are different
scripts for particular cultures and subcultures. The symbolic exchange
(Libby and Carlson, 1973b) between sexual actors must first be related to
the self, and then to marriage or to some form of singlehood. Traditionally,
all sex mores and social scripts have been tied to marriage (terms such as premarital, marital, extramarital and postmarital). With the emergence of friendship, 'horniness' (or sexual desire) and other motives for sexual relationships, we will need to reconceptualize the symbolic motives and meanings
for sexual expression as they define different sexual life styles prior to qualifying our description of sexual attitudes and behavior with 'marriage' as a
linking concept. All coitus before marriage is not premarital since most sex
before marriage does not lead to marriage with that sexual partner. Much sex
prior to marriage involves single people meeting their needs for sexual pleasure, intimacy, ego-gratification, status, or the need to exploit another. To
attempt to tie all sexual expression to marriage is to overlook a broad range
of symbolic motives and consequences of sexual behavior.

2. SEX AND INTERPERSONAL RELATIONSHIPS

As was pointed out by Kirkendall and Libby (1966), sexual behavior must
be conceptualized within the context of interpersonal relationships —
whether there is trust, honesty, integrity, sensitivity and responsibility, or
whether there is game-playing and exploitation. The morality of sexual relations must go beyond whether a penis enters a vagina, so that the range of
symbolic motives of sexual expression can be understood as a part of a
holistic view of interpersonal relationships. Such an analysis leads to a
greater understanding of the nature of intimacy, and how sex may be used
to further or impede the growth of love. In relation to this, Pearlman (1974)
reported that high self-esteem college students of both sexes stated they had
more coital partners than those with low self-esteem. In contrast with the
findings of Reiss (1967), sexual involvements were not tied to degree of affection for either sex, indicating a continued trend toward a single of premarital sexual morality. Contrary to Reiss' prediction (1960), this shows an
increased acceptance of coitus with less affection over time. This latter finding is supported by female college students in studies by Bell and Chaskes
(1970), Christensen and Gregg (1970), Eshleman (1972), and Hunt (1974),

where less affection was seen as necessary to engage in intercourse prior to marriage than in the case of previous samples. From most data it appears that American college students are moving toward a more relaxed view of sexual expression which is reflected in their reported behavior — sexual behavior is not taken as seriously, nor is sex as limited in its motives and meanings. This also seems to be true of Danish college students (Christensen and Gregg, 1970).

The changes are explained in part by Libby and Carlson's theory (1973a), where portions of exchange and symbolic interaction theories were utilized to explain and predict the process of premarital sexual decision-making. Throughout the exchange process, variations in socialization background, definitions of the situation, perceptions of group versus individual profits, and variations in the values of the participants were related to decisions made about premarital sex. Following Turner (1970), consensual and accommodative decisions to have or not to have premarital intercourse were explored. Reference group theory was used to explain anticipatory socialization from peers, parents, the mass media and other sources. These groups were related to the socialization of an 'image' of oneself. It is obvious that one's sexual role identity and sexual activities are reflected in perceived profits from engaging in any given sexual activity. It appears from recent research that more women are perceiving rewards which extend beyond any costs, so they are having coitus prior to marriage with more men for more reasons, and that they are enjoying this. As Reiss (1973) indicated, the double standard is still with us, but it is passing, and this means that there are fewer negative sanctions to hinder the female's participation in nonmarital intercourse. This is part of the overall acceptance of female sexuality in America, and in cultures in contact with Western sexual mores.

One typology which seems to describe two ideal types of heterosexual interaction prior to and after marriage is the contrast between the traditional courtship—dating social script and the more flexible 'getting together' social script conceptualized in Table I.

As can be seen with the ideal types of scripts shown in Table I, the socialization of differing social scripts concerning heterosexual interaction begins in pre-adolescence and extends throughout life. Through resocialization from the mass media and various cogent reference groups, attitudes, behaviors and mores change. These changes can and often do produce conflicts between parents and their offspring. Regarding adolescent sexuality (Libby, 1974b), parents and their children are typically at odds with each other as to the meanings and appropriate expression of sexual behavior, resulting in a kind of 'generational chauvinism' (Sorensen, 1973) where both adults and adolescents take an authoritarian stance concerning each other's sexual values. In an intensive interview study of 250 randomly selected parents (Libby, 1970, 1971; Libby and Nass, 1971; Libby et al., 1974), attitudes about teenage sexual behavior and sex education in high schools were ascertained. It was typical for parents to refer to adolescents who were engaging in coitus as

Table I

SOCIAL SCRIPTS FOR SEXUAL RELATIONSHIPS *, SOME THOUGHTS

Age group	'Primrose path' of dating (untouchables)	Branching paths of 'getting together' (touchables)
5—6th grade	Structured heterosexual activities; spin-the-bottle type of activity; having a boy or girlfriend	Unstructured activities, with no real emphasis on marriage or relating to one member of the opposite sex
7—9th grade	Group dating and dating with parents as chaperone figures. Parents drive car, etc. Sneaking around with opposite sex	Less parental imposition of monogamous expectations. Nonpossessive relationships with no emphasis on dichotomy of sexual and nonsexual relationships
High School	Double and single-dating in cars with exclusive expectation once one dates a person a few times	'Getting together' rather than dating, with female initiating relationships as much as male, and with female paying for and picking up male in her car as much as he does
After High School	Work and continue monogamous dating, or dating with more than one person, or go to college and do same, or marry monogamously. Static, rigid role expectations for female and male	Emphasis on qualities in relationships as a basis for decision making about sex and other relationships and concerns
	Emphasis on physical levels of intimacy as a basis for sexual morality. Sex viewed as ownership, meeting one's needs, and as exclusive. If live together, it is exclusive sexually	Touching and sensuality encouraged. Sex only in mutually appropropriate and mutually discussed situations. Sex as one language in some relationships with a range of symbolic meanings — from mutual pleasure (or horniness!), friendship, to love (love not seen as exclusive but as multiple following Robert Rimmer in The Harrad Experiment, and other novels)
	Divorce, tolerate unhappy 'marriage,' or for a minority, live happily ever after in a sexually and emotionally exclusive monogamous marriage	If living together, relationship is sexually and emotionally nonexclusive
	Remarriage and divorce, or a repeat of the above (serial monogamy with 'cheating' on the side by both spouses)	Creative singlehood, or if marry, some kind of open arrangement, as in the following alternatives from Libby and Whitehurst, 1973
	Emphasis on the weakness of the participants in marriage when unhappiness or divorce occur, rather than question the monolithic image of marriage as 'the answer' for anyone who chooses to marry	A decision to be open or closed in various areas of marriage, with the ongoing process of renegotiation of the marital contract ... (marriage as a process)
	Disillusionment with marriage for many. Searching for the "good life," but confused as to how to find it. Conflict of images in the mass media and what the local min-	Various open marriages with comarital or satellite relationships viewed as supportive of the pair-bond rather than as a threat to it

Table I (Continued)

Age group	'Primrose path' of dating (untouchables)	Branching paths of 'getting together' (touchables)
	ister is preaching. Enter the therapist . . . who may or may not help . . . What next???	Swinging — from recreational to utopian
		Group marriage
		Communal living with or without sexual sharing
		Compartmentalized marriage — e.g., with a 'night off' from marriage
		If divorce, joy rather than sadness (creative divorce)
		SYNERGY: 1 + = more than 2. See O'Neill and O'Neill, *Open Marriage* (Avon paperback)

* It is not uncommon for those socialized in the traditional script to later decide to take on different roles and to adopt one of the emerging alternatives to the monogamous image or the cheating reality . . . so some switching back and forth between scripts prior to and after marriage(s) is common. The above are two ideal types on a continuum rather than actual dichotomies. However, many people still fit the traditional extreme of the 'primrose path.'

'children.' If the 'child' was engaging in intercourse, the parents were disapproving, and usually in a very chauvinist manner.

Parents are not the only chauvinists; the adolescents in Sorensen's (1973) study were often chauvinist in their attitudes toward parents and other adults. They often felt they knew more about sex than adults. The breakdown in generational communication about sex has resulted in generational chauvinism and a communication gap complete with hostilities, conflicts, deadly silence and evasiveness. Sociologically, there is a basic conflict between the courtship institution or dating, and the family. Reiss (1967) indicated that as one moves toward courtship and away from family control, and as one goes to college, one becomes more permissive in sexual attitudes and behavior. However, a more recent study by Libby (1974a) shows that perceived closeness to the sexual standards of one's mother but not father is far more predictive of variation in college students' sexual attitudes (both sexes) than is perceived closeness to the standards of peers or close friends. Therefore, the role of the mother still appears to limit the permissiveness of college student attitudes. Also contrary to Reiss' theory (1967), Libby (1974a) reported that degree of courtship involvement (current dating status) was not an important indicator of permissiveness of sexual attitudes.

Sex laws as indicators of sex mores

When considering changing sexual mores, we must include mention of the most formal level of social-sexual mores: sex laws. We should also consider sex laws in relation to actual sexual behavior. Even though sex laws are typically difficult to enforce, they serve as rough indicators of what the most conventional element of society considers to be sexually legitimate. Neither adults nor adolescents seem particularly concerned with sex laws as a guide to their own sexual values and behavior. Thus, whether sex prior to marriage is legal, or whether oral and genital sexual contacts are legal, people are prone to engage in these acts. The ad hoc living-together situation is one example of illegal sexual behavior in most states in America. Approximately 26—54% of college students have cohabited with the opposite sex (the higher percentages apply to seniors, Macklin, 1972; M. White, unpublished). It is likely that these estimates will go up in the future, as living together is becoming normative behavior depending on how one operationalizes living together (some college students maintain separate residences to make it appear to parents that they do not cohabit). Additionally, it appears that about a third of ad hoc arrangements do not involve a sexually exclusive commitment (Jen Huang, 1974). This forces a redefinition of ad hoc as well as legal marriage as something other than a legal sanction.

Premarital and nonmarital sexual attitudes and behavior

If one were to be strict about a definition of premarital or nonmarital sex, one would include a discussion of preadolescent sexual behavior, but this section will be limited to trends in the college years. Some of the college trends have already been referred to. And yet, an in-depth study of sexual decision-making and the symbolic exchange between sexual partners in adolescence and young adulthood has not yet been published. Even though a rough idea as to the degree of commitment and/or affection needed to engage in coitus is available, there still has been too much emphasis on description and percentages engaging in various sexual acts rather than on the development and testing of theory on the personal and social meanings of sexual behavior. We have yet to go far beyond Kinsey and his associates in the development of such in-depth, theoretically based studies. We are more precise in our prediction of premarital sexual attitudes (Reiss, 1973; Reiss and Miller, 1974), but an empirically based theory of sexual decision-making allowing for explanation and prediction of behavior is yet to be well developed. As in other areas of social psychology, sexual attitudes have not been very accurate predictors of sexual behavior. It is generally easier to predict attitudes than behavior. The major hope for relevant theory appears to lie in the work of Reiss and Miller (1974), Walsh and his colleagues (1974), Libby (1974a) and others working to refine Reiss' original (1967) theory of premarital permissiveness. Reiss' efforts to develop a theory applying to behavior as well as attitudes is commendable. Cross-cultural and longitudinal studies should provide a basis for generalizability of propositions concerning sexual attitudes and their relation to sexual behavior. It is likely that the inclusion of more social psychological and personality variables such as the nature of behavioral intentions, sexual fantasies and perceptions of reference group influences will lead to more predictive theory. The use of multiple regression techniques should allow for theory grounded in the data. A causal relationship between variables predictive of premarital sexual behavior can then be inferred (though never really proven). The reader is referred to Reiss and Miller (1974) for an elaboration on the emergence of a theory of heterosexual permissiveness. Libby and Carlson's (1973a) theory of sexual decision-making draws on earlier theoretical and empirical work by Skipper and Nass (1966), where the latter authors compared dating motives of student nurses and college men or interns. Men were primarily interested in recreational sex, while nurses were trying to improve their status by marrying an intern or other high-status male. And yet, the motives for sexual exchange were rarely verbalized between the actors in the dating situation. The student nurses were stereotyped as 'easy makes' by the males (double standard of sexual morality), but the student nurses did not accept this labeling process (rationalizations abounded among the nurses). Thus, the costs were high for the nurses and the relationships typically were short and numerous. It can be said that those in Skipper and Nass' sample were socialized into the traditional 'dating script' (see Table I). Since 1966 more college-aged youth seem to be developing a more flexible 'getting together' script of heterosexual relating.

The trends are fairly clear — females are enjoying sex more for more reasons with more men (Simon and Gagnon support the increased enjoyment during the first intercourse; 73% as compared with 46% of women in the 1953 Kinsey Report enjoyed the first coitus). Luckey and Nass' (1969) cross-cultural study supports the notion that women are more inclined to have nonmarital coitus with males other than their spouses-to-be than was evident in earlier data. Eshleman (1972) made some crucial distinctions which held in the Phillipines as well as in America. He reported that college students are most conservative in what they believe to be proper sexual behavior, more permissive in what they say they do, and most permissive in what they perceive others to be doing. As with Christensen and Gregg's (1970) cross-cultural, longitudinal study, a similar research design by Eshleman yielded the same generalization that the gap between premarital sexual attitudes and behavior is closing over time. And yet, females feel the need to cover up the extent of their sexual arousal and fantasies (Schmidt and Sigusch, 1970) after exposure to pornography (from the lack of cultural support to express such realities).

An increase in a variety of sexual practices and partners (such as engaging in oral-genital sex and more positions of intercourse) was noted by Hunt (1974) when compared with the earlier Kinsey Reports (1948, 1953). Reiss

(1973) stated that he suspected that about 70% of college women engage in coitus prior to marriage. This is supported by married college females (White, unpublished); 72% of wives and 85% of husbands stated they had engaged in premarital coitus. As Hunt (1974) concluded, it appears that premarital sexual intercourse in America will be all but universal within ten years. It seems that Americans are becoming more and more like Scandinavians in their sexual behavior, but it is not yet clear whether the symbolic meanings and motives are very similar in the two cultures. A recent economic recession in America and many other countries seems to have slowed the evolution of change in sexual behavior patterns, such that many college students are somewhat less concerned with having several sexual relationships at the same time, and more concerned with sheer survival economically and in terms of their advancement through college. This rather recent economic shift does not mean that the liberal trend in sexual attitudes and behavior has radically changed to a conservative trend, but it is probable that economics has affected the liberal trend for a short time at least. It is too early to tell definitively whether the liberal evolution of sexual attitudes and behavior has even slowed very dramatically.

Marital, extramarital, and co-marital sex

Unlike premarital sex, there is less obsession with marital sex; therefore there are fewer data to evaluate the realities of marital sexuality. As with existing data on premarital sex, the studies on marital sex are typically limited to a rather simplistic description of the frequencies of intercourse and of female orgasm, and a rough idea as to the perception of marital satisfaction. Most studies are based on samples which are 10—40 years old. As Carlson (1976) emphasizes, research has lacked a theoretical orientation. In contrast with the descriptive approach with general perceptual variables, Carlson (1976) utilized a structural role theory framework to focus on marital sexuality. In a conservative sample in Eastern Washington, Carlson found that both spouses viewed the initiation of sexual activity as husband-oriented. Husbands wanted a more equal sharing between wife and husband in the initiation of sex, but wives preferred the status quo. Following other research (Blood and Wolfe, 1960; Komarovsky, 1962; Clarke and Wallin, 1964), husbands believed that sex was less crucial to their wives than was indicated by the wives' responses.

Bell and Bell (1972) reported on 2372 married women (60% return of questionaires making generalizations somewhat tenuous to married women). They found that there was a close relationship between marital sexual frequency and personal happiness for married women, and that 66% said the frequency of coitus was 'about right'. Like Hunt (1974), Bell and Bell reported that the duration of coitus was longer than was true in the Kinsey studies (1948; 1953).

Christensen (1973) reported on a longitudinal, cross-cultural study of 'marital infidelity,' where he found that males were stronger than females on the double standard, while females were stronger on the single standard. This is counter to much of the research on premarital sexuality, as well as data on sexual semantics particular to one's sex. As with Kinsey and his associates' reports (1948, 1953), those with premarital sexual experience were most accepting of extramarital coitus, particularly in the more restrictive cultures. Carlson (1975) also found little support for extramarital relations, but it should be remembered that these studies made no distinction between adulterous behavior and co-marital sex approved by spouses.

Cuber and Harroff (1965) were pioneers in making distinctions between marital styles with various goals, ground rules and expectations about the sexual exclusiveness or openness of marriage. They indicated that many spouses in intrinsic-vital marriages sanctioned some kind of openness for sexual and emotional experimentation with others (although the term co-marital was not yet in vogue).

3. SUMMARY AND CONCLUSIONS

In this chapter on changing sexual mores, the definition of mores includes proscriptions as to the proper place of sexual expression in relation to marital status. It has been noted that sexual mores and laws have differed for men and women, with men having greater sexual freedom. Sexual mores as regulations and taboos on behavior have been in a state of flux, with women receiving increasing freedom to act out their sexual desires and fantasies with fewer negative social sanctions, in part due to the Women's Liberation Movement.

Cultural and subcultural variation in sexual mores over time have been noted; America has been moving toward a Scandinavian conception of the acceptance of nonmarital and premarital sexual behavior, and the gap between sexual attitudes and behavior has been closing. Most cultures have a vested interest in emphasizing marital sex as most appropriate but there has been an increasing acceptance of premarital, extramarital and co-marital sexual behavior. The legitimacy of choice of a sexual or marital life style has been one of the major changes in the sexual scene. These choices include open marriage, swinging, group marriage, communes, creative singlehood and other options as detailed in Libby and Whitehurst (1977).

Changing sexual mores are reflected in changing words to describe emerging symbolic motives and meanings for sex as a language in relationships. Conceptual clarification of the nature of sexual decision-making has been advanced by Libby and Carlson (1973b), Reiss and Miller (1974) and others. Kirkendall and Libby's (1966) emphasis on an interpersonal relationship context to study sexual expression is being more accepted in theory, research, and by those making decisions about sex. The social scripting of sexual relationships is changing, with a tendency to define heterosexual relating as 'getting together' instead of courtship and dating in the more traditional sense (see Table I). Adolescents and their parents have tended to be chauvinists toward each other's view of what is moral or responsible sexual behavior. However, contrary to Reiss' earlier theory (1967), Libby (1974a) has indicated the greater importance of the role of mother in influencing college students' sexual attitudes as compared with the lesser role of peers and close friends. Similarly, Libby (1974a) found that current dating or courtship status is no longer a crucial indicator of one's sexual attitudes.

Studies on sexual behavior are lacking in a sound theoretical basis to make sense of the data. We have not yet gone far beyond the simple description of Kinsey and his associates to study sexuality. Theory development remains as the crucial task for sex researchers. It is time to go beyond the descriptive relationships between global sociocultural variables, such as church attendance, to determine the social psychological and situational correlates of the sexual decision-making process as this process varies according to the array of emerging sexual life styles.

BIBLIOGRAPHY

Arnold, W. and Libby, R.W. (1976) Semantics of sex-related words. *Bull. Gen. Semantics.* 38—40.

Bell, R. and Chaskes, J.B. (1970) Premarital sexual experience among coeds, 1958, and 1968. *J. Marr. Fam.* 32: 31—34.

Bell, R. and Bell, P. (1972) Sexual satisfaction among married women. *Med. Aspects Hum. Sex.* 6: 136—146.

Blood, R. and Wolfe, D. (1960) *Husbands and Wives.* (Free Press, New York.)

Carlson, J. (1976) The sexual role. In: (I. Nye et al., Eds.) *Role Structure and Analysis of the Family*. (Sage, Los Angeles.)

Christensen, H. and Gregg, C. (1970) Changing sex norms in America and Scandinavia. *J. Marr. Fam.* 32: 616—627.

Christensen, H. (1973) Attitudes toward marital infidelity; a nine-culture sampling of university student opinion. *J. Comp. Fam. Stud.* 4: 197—214.

Clarke, A. and Wallin, P. (1964) The accuracy of husbands' and wives' reports on the frequency of marital coitus. *Populat. Stud.* 18: 165—173.

Cuber, J. and Harroff, P. (1965) *The Significant Americans.* (Appleton-Century, New York.)

Eshleman, J.R. (1972) A cross cultural analysis of sexual codes: beliefs, behavior, and the perception of others. (Paper presented at the National Council on Family Relations, Portland, Oregon.)

Fearing, F. (1954) An examination of the conceptions of Benjamin Whorf in the light of theories of perception and cognition. In: (H. Hoijer, Ed.), *Language in Culture.* (University of Chicago Press, Chicago) pp. 47—82.

Gallup, G. (1973) Attitudes of Americans on sex seen undergoing profound change. (Press Release.)

Hertoft, P. (1973) Some remarks on premarital sex. *Proc. WHO Symp.* (Oxford Univ. Press, New York.)

Hunt, M. (1974) *Sexual Behavior in the 1970s.* (Playboy Press, Chicago.)

Jen Huang, L. (1974) Some patterns of non-exclusive sexual relations among unmarried cohabiting couples. (Paper presented at The Midwest Sociological Society, Omaha, Nebraska.)

Kinsey, A.C., Pomeroy, W.B. and Martin, C.E. (1948) *Sexual Behavior in the Human Male*. (W.B. Saunders Co., Philadelphia, Pa.)

Kinsey, A.C., Pomeroy, W.B., Martin, C.E. and Gebhard, P.H. (1953) *Sexual Behavior in the Human Female*. (W.B. Saunders Co., Philadelphia, Pa.)

Kirkendall, L.A. and Libby, R.W. (1966) Interpersonal relationships crux of the sexual renaissance. *J. Soc. Issues* 22: 45—60.

Komarovsky, M. (1962) *Blue Collar Marriage*. (Random House, New York.)

Libby, R.W. (1970) Parental attitudes toward high school sex education programs. *Fam. Coord.* 19: 234—247.

Libby, R.W. (1971) Parental attitudes toward content in high school sex education programs: liberalism-traditionalism and demographic correlates. *Fam. Coord.* 20: 127 136.

Libby, R.W. (1974a) A multivariate test of reference group and role correlates of Reiss' premarital permissiveness theory. (Unpublished Ph.D. dissertation, Washington State University, Pullman, Washington.)

Libby, R.W. (1974b) Adolescent sexual attitudes and behavior. *J. Clin. Child Psychol.* 3: 36—42.

Libby, R.W. (1977) Extramarital and co-marital sex: a critique of the literature. In: (R. Libby and R. Whitehurst, Eds.). *Marriage and Alternatives: Exploring Intimate Relationships*. (Scott, Foresman, Glenview, Illinois) Ch. 6.

Libby, R.W. and Carlson, J. (1973a) A theoretical framework for premarital sexual decisions in the dyad. *Arch. Sex. Behav.* 2: 365—379.

Libby, R.W. and Carlson, J. (1973b) Sexual behavior as symbolic exchange: an integration of theory. (Paper presented at the Pacific Sociological Association, Scottsdale, Arizona.)

Libby, R.W. and Nass, G.D. (1971) Parental views on teenage sexual behavior. *J. Sex. Res.* 7: 226—236.

Libby, R.W. and Whitehurst, R.N.. (Eds.) (1973) *Renovating Marriage: Toward New Sexual Life Styles*. (Consensus Publishers, Inc., Danville, Calif.)

Libby, R.W. and Whitehurst, R.N. (Eds.). (1977) *Marriage and Alternatives: Exploring Intimate Relationships*. (Scott, Foresman, Glenview, Illinois.)

Libby, R.W., Acock, A. and Payne, D. (1974) Configurations of parental preferences concerning sources of sex education for adolescents. *Adolescence* 33: 73 80.

Luckey, E.B. and Nass, G.D. (1969) A comparison of sexual attitudes and behavior in an international sample. *J. Marr. Fam.* 31: 364—379.

Macklin, E. (1972) Heterosexual cohabitation among unmarried college students. *Fam. Coord.* 21: 463—473.

Murdock, G. (1949) *Social Structure*. (Macmillan, New York.)

Pearlman, D. (1974) Self-esteem and sexual permissiveness. *J. Marr. Fam.* 36: 470—474.

Reiss, I.L. (1960) *Premarital Sexual Standards in America*. (Free Press of Glencoe, Glencoe, Illinois.)

Reiss, I.L. (1967) *The Social Context of Premarital Sexual Permissiveness*. (Holt, Reinhart and Winston, Inc., New York.)

Reiss, I.L. (1973) Heterosexual relationship inside and outside of marriage. (General Learning Press, Module.)

Reiss, I.L. and Miller, B.C. (1974) *A Theoretical Analysis of Heterosexual Permissiveness*. (Technical Report No. II, Minnesota Family Study Center, University of Minnesota, Minneapolis, Minnesota.)

Rimmer, R. (1966) *The Harrad Experiment*. (Bantam Books, New York.)

Schmidt, G. and Sigusch, V. (1970) Sex differences in responses to psychosexual stimulation by films and slides. *J. Sex Res.* 6: 268—283.

Schofield, M. (1965) *The Sexual Behavior of Young People*. (Little, Brown and Co., Boston.)

Skipper, J.K. and Nass, G.D. (1966) Dating behavior: a framework for analysis and an illustration. *J. Marr. Fam.* 28: 412—421.

Smith, J.R. and Smith, L.G. (1974) *Beyond Monogramy: Recent Studies of Sexual Alternatives in Marriage*. (Johns Hopkins Press, Baltimore, Md.)

Sorensen, R.C. (1973) *Adolescent Sexuality in Contemporary America.* (World Publishing Co., New York.)

Sumner, W.G. (1906) *Folkways.* (Dover Publications, Inc., New York.)

Turner, R.H. (1970) *Family Interaction.* (John Wiley and Sons, New York.)

Walsh, R., Tolne, W., Leonard, W., Ferrell, M. and Bryant, D. (1974) An eight-year study of attitudes about sexual permissiveness. (Paper presented at the National Council on Family Relations, St. Louis, Missouri.)

Zelnik, M. and Kantner, J.F. (1972) Sexual experience of young unmarried women in the United States. *Soc. Sci. Res.* 1: 335—341.

SECTION VII

Regulation of procreation

Section coordinator: Christopher Tietze

CHAPTER 42

Introduction

CHRISTOPHER TIETZE

The human species possesses a truly awesome capacity to 'be fruitful and multiply.' While the probability of pregnancy resulting from a single unprotected coitus, timed at random during the menstrual cycle, has been estimated to be on the order of only 2—4%, the risk increases about 10-fold when coital frequency rises to a level of 2 to 3 times weekly. Given early first mating, continuing sexual activity, and a pattern of no or short breastfeeding, the 'average woman' would bear a dozen children during her life time. However, a variety of restraints, such as delayed marriage, early widowhood, and/or prolonged lactation, have kept the total fertility rate (number of live births per woman surviving to menopause) below 8 in most populations, historical and contemporary, with little or no recourse to specific measures of fertility control.

A large number of children, especially of sons, was and still is considered not only acceptable, but highly desirable in many agricultural and pastoral societies, where infant and child mortality is high. In modern industrial societies most couples prefer a small or moderate-size family, with two children increasingly emerging as the model norm. However, there are situations in all societies in which pregnancy and childbearing are considered inappropriate, condemned, and, on occasion, cruelly punished. Because for many persons prolonged abstention from coitus is a stressful experience, most societies have developed techniques designed to reduce the probability of coitus resulting in pregnancy or at least in live birth. In some societies these methods are rarely used, in others they are known to and practiced by most sexually active men and women. This section is concerned with the currently available methods of fertility control and their interaction with various aspects of sexual behavior.

Traditionally, fertility control practices have been categorized into contraception, sterilization, and abortion. Owing to the development of quasipermanent methods such as oral and, even more drastically, injectable contraceptives, the distinction between contraception and sterilization has become

Handbook of Sexology, edited by J. Money and H. Musaph
© *Elsevier/North-Holland Biomedical Press, 1977*

blurred in recent years; other new procedures, such as postcoital ingestion of estrogens and so-called 'menstrual regulation' have had a similar effect on the distinction between contraception and abortion. To a remarkable extent these imprecisions have been utilized for the resolution of conflicts between pressing personal or social needs and ideological stances vis-a-vis various methods of birth prevention.

Notwithstanding the limitations outlined in the preceding paragraph, the first two chapters of the section concern themselves, separately, with contraception (temporary and permanent, that is, sterilization) and induced abortion. This dichotomy reflects, in part, the professional preoccupations of the authors and also the presumed interests of different groups of readers. Bruce Shearer's chapter focuses on the technology of contraception; my own includes a relatively large amount of data on the legal, demographic, and public health aspects of abortion.

Because man is pre-eminently a 'zoon politikon', a social animal, the chapter by Patricia McCormick and her associates, dealing with the psychosocial aspects of fertility regulation, is a long one. The authors trace the interactions of sexual behavior, contraception, abortion, interpersonal relationships, social and economic pressure, and the resulting reproductive achievement through the life cycle, from the postpubertal period during which children are not yet desired to the premenopausal or later years of marriage when no additional children are wanted.

The final chapter takes us at least part of the way into the political arena. Women's involvement with most methods of fertility control is obviously close and has become closer in recent years with the increasing importance of procedures requiring action by or to women. Moreover, most of these procedures require — in fact or by law — the participation of a physician, who is more often than not a man. Women's growing consciousness of themselves as persons with claims to respect and self-determination, has created or perhaps more correctly stated, brought to light tensions in regard to sexual and reproductive attitudes and behavior. Emily Moore is a competant guide through this new area of concern.

CHAPTER 43

The status of technology for contraception

S. BRUCE SHEARER

1. CONTRACEPTION AND SOCIETY

As demographic and anthropological data clearly reveal, the practice of contraception is relatively recent in human societies (Himes, 1936). It is certainly true that for millions of years following the emergence of the human species pregnancy was quite commonly followed by lactational amenorrhea (and its associated infertility), and then by successive cycles of pregnancy and lactation from early puberty to the onset of menopause. In some areas of the world this is true even now. Under these 'natural' conditions, women menstruate only rarely; instead, new conception generally occurs at about the same time or even before menstruation recommences, near the end of the breast-feeding period following the last pregnancy (Short, 1974).

The first widespread practice of fertility control based on contraception (as opposed to infanticide, crude modes of abortion, and drastic tribal solutions to excess fertility) took place during the so-called 'demographic transition' in Europe beginning in the last half of the 18th century (Himes, 1936). Employing methods that had been invented thousands of years before, but had been used primarily by the wealthy and privileged, large numbers of couples throughout the entire population of Europe began actively to curb their natural fertility (Himes, 1936). The methods they used — coitus interruptus, 'absorbants' placed in the vagina, and or postcoital douching — were inadequate to permit the actual planning of families. These folk methods did, however, enable couples to substantially reduce the chance that any given coitus would result in conception. As a result, the birth rates for Europe as a whole declined sharply during the course of the 19th century (Hawley, 1950).

The popular practice of contraception occurred concomitantly with the industrialization of Europe and with the diffusion of the notion that each individual possesses the right — and should possess the capacity — to exert control over his or her biological life and human destiny. The folk methods of

Handbook of Sexology, edited by J. Money and H. Musaph
© *Elsevier/North-Holland Biomedical Press, 1977*

contraception clearly belied this right because of the very uncertain protection against pregnancy that they provided.

Over the course of the 19th century, couples began to demand a greater capacity for choice over their fertility through better birth control technology. It was this very public and widespread demand for more reliable methods of controlling fertility that ultimately stimulated the perfection of the diaphragm, the rubber condom, spermicides, cervical pessaries, cervical caps and methods of female sterilization during the 19th century (Himes, 1936; Langley, 1973) and the intrauterine device, vasectomy, and modern abortion techniques early in the 20th century (Langley, 1973).

It is abundantly clear from the literature of the period that the driving force behind the development of new birth-control technology was the desire to grant individuals greater control over one of the major economic and social features of their lives, their reproductive capacity (Himes, 1936; Langley, 1973). The idea that such improved technology might permit freer sexual interaction between men and women was generally regarded as a criminal, or at least immoral, concept, and most of the developers and proselytizers of the new technology took great pains to dissociate themselves from such thinking (Langley, 1973).

However, during the second half of the 20th century, these views of the role of contraception (and the resultant demands for better birth-control methods) underwent transformation. In industrialized countries at least, the new technology that had been developed as a result of the earlier impetus was widely available and utilized. The great goal of the early 1900s had been achieved: couples could, with only a modest margin of error, plan their family size while maintaining normal marital relations (Westoff et al., 1961). Attention shifted from the availability of birth-control technology to its quality.

A new set of public demands emerged, and with gathering momentum that has not yet lost its force, these demands stimulated organized efforts to develop new birth-control technology around a new set of goals. Primary among these goals has been effectiveness, convenience of use, and freedom from annoying side effects. The influence of these new priorities has been verified in numerous marketing and fertility surveys (Westoff et al., 1961; Wood et al., 1970; Campbell and Berelson, 1971) as well as by the users selection and rejection of the available fertility control methods (Westoff et al., 1961; Westoff, 1973).

These historical developments in contraception reflect events in industrialized countries, those of the West in particular. In other areas of the world, a demographic transition from high fertility to low fertility has not yet taken place. As a result, average family size remains double or triple that now common in Western countries, and most of the poorer, less industrialized nations are experiencing doublings of their populations every 20 to 40 years (Nortman, 1974). Until the last decade, the availability of contraceptive technology in most developing nations was very restricted. With the widespread introduction of national family planning programs over the last 20 years (Nortman, 1974; Mauldin, 1975), availability is rapidly increasing, but the high rates of fertility have thus far shown only a small tendency to decline (Mauldin, 1975).

This situation in developing countries has lead to greater emphasis on the development of new technologies (such as 6-month contraceptive injections or long-acting subdermal contraceptive implants) which will be easier to deliver through existing health and educational systems (Schearer, 1973; Segal, 1973; Tejuja, 1974). Since these systems are often weak and over-extended, it is thought that different technologies from those suitable in western countries will be required to meet this demand. On the other hand, as relatively few couples now practice family planning in these countries, even where modern fertility control methods are available (Nortman, 1974), the design of new methods with high appeal to such couples has become a prime objective (Schearer, 1973; Segal, 1973; Tejuja, 1974). As with ease of delivery, technologies that provide ease of use and appeal to users in developing countries are likely to be different from technologies which meet these same demands in more developed countries.

Hence, birth control technology is currently viewed from two overlapping but somewhat different perspectives — one based in the developed world and the other in the developing world. Indeed, largely in recognition of these differences, and of the single focus taken by most commercial efforts to develop new birth control methods, two major contraceptive development programs were launched early in the 1970s with the aim of providing new technology that will specifically meet the needs of developing countries (Barnes et al., 1974).

2. CONTRACEPTION AND THE INDIVIDUAL

Ideally, the different conceptualizations and expectations of birth-control technology in different parts of the world reflect the interests and views of the individual couples. Unfortunately, surveys of the opinions and attitudes of individual couples regarding their practice of contraception are usually not aimed at revealing why couples select one contraceptive method from all others (Mauldin, 1965). When they do, surveys attempt to classify the natural diversity of responses into a handful of categories, often preconceived and narrow in scope. As a result, one knows little, either in developed or developing countries, about the role of such factors as sexual attitude and behavior, personality type, health, family structure, or family economics on contraceptive choice (Fawcett, 1970). Only very recently have these dimensions of contraceptive use begun to receive attention; it is not even certain that adequate social science research techniques (not to mention sufficient sources of funds) are available to permit discrimination between the behavior and attitudes of individual couples.

Because information about the contraceptive practice of individuals (as opposed to populations) is sparse, there is a lack of knowledge about the performance of contraceptive methods among individuals (as opposed to populations). Like the information about the preferences and attitudes of individual couples toward contraceptive methods, the information about the effectiveness and side effects of the methods themselves comes from studies that average the practices and the fertility of large numbers of different couples (Tietze and Lewit, 1974; Faundes, 1975). The result is average pregnancy rates and average incidences of side effects, which fail, by wide margins in some cases, to inform a specific couple how likely it is that they will experience an unwanted pregnancy or unwelcome side effect.

Clinical studies of the performance of contraceptive methods increasingly seek to specify the biological, social, and economic features of the subgroups, that correlate with low or high pregnancy rates or varying incidences of side effects. For example, it has been reported that younger women and those who have borne fewer children are more likely to spontaneously expel an IUD from their uterus than are older, more parous women (Tietze and Lewit, 1970). The effectiveness of the diaphragm is also strongly correlated with the age of the users (Vessey and Wiggins, 1974).

One of the most revealing studies about the personal variables that influence the use of contraception was conducted by Ryder (1973) in the U.S. He used survey information to analyze the actual one-year pregnancy rates of couples after initiating contraception with a given method. Thus, he was able to obtain measures of the extended use-effectiveness of contraceptive methods; that is, the combination of the theoretical biological failure rate associated with the method and the failure rate resulting from a couple's failure to use this method correctly or their failure to use it at all. As other retrospective studies of both limited and extended use-effectiveness have shown (Ryder, 1973), the failure rates of contraceptive methods measured in this way are far higher than those measured in controlled clinical studies. In Ryder's study, for example, human oral contraceptive use was associated with 4 to 7% failures, as compared with 0.1 to 0.5% failures observed in large-scale studies of theoretical effectiveness (Advisory Committee on Obstetrics and Gynecology, 1969).

What is most illuminating about Ryder's findings, however, is the impact of a couple's intentions regarding their fertility on the actual effectiveness they experience when using any contraceptive method. Ryder found that couples who intended to delay their next pregnancy had almost twice as many contraceptive failures as those who intended to prevent further pregnancies. This differential effectiveness held true for all methods but was most pronounced for the intrauterine device, the condom, rhythm, and oral contraception. With the intrauterine device, three times as many failures occurred among those intending to delay pregnancy, presumably because they failed to use some other contraceptive method after the device had been expelled or removed.

In most instances, unfortunately, information about individual variables of this kind which influence the performance of contraceptive methods is not known. Since the same contraceptive method is usually very different in effectiveness and varies in the range and incidence of side effects among different classes of users, the average results that are now available for most methods cannot be taken as reliable predictors for any individual couple.

3. THE ASSESSMENT OF CONTRACEPTIVE PERFORMANCE

The limitations in our knowledge are not restricted to uncertainties about the dynamics of contraception for individual couples. It has only been within the last several years that a fully documented epidemiological picture of the less common side effects associated with the oral contraceptive pill has begun to emerge (Corfman, 1974; Oral Contraceptives and Health, 1974). Even now, this kind of comprehensive assessement is limited to western societies. In the case of intrauterine devices, the overall incidences of infrequent side effects, including deaths associated with IUD use, are a matter of gross estimation (Jennings, 1974). The only country with sufficient epidemiological data to make even such crude assessments possible is the United States. The situation is much the same regarding the effectiveness of contraceptive methods.

The causes for our lack of adequate knowledge of the performance of available fertility control technology are two-fold. Firstly, in the cases of rare side effects, large numbers of individuals must be carefully observed over long periods of time to obtain significant measures of their occurrence (Corfman, 1974). Since the resources required to conduct such epidemiological investigations are limited, so is our knowledge.

Secondly, the measurement of even frequent side effects in human populations is fraught with the difficulty of controlling the variables which affect human behavior and the difficulties in detecting the frequency of occurrence of the event being measured. A recent review of 22 large-scale clinical studies of the Dalkon Shield intrauterine device revealed differences in the measurement of the pregnancy rate of users. In the various studies it ranged from 0.5 to 7.8 pregnancies per 100 women after one year. Removal of the device by the physician took place in 2.7% of the initial group of women in one study and 28.7% in another. Removal rates fell within these two extremes in the other 20 studies (Schearer, 1976).

As these data demonstrate, it is impossible to make an exact measurement of the effectiveness or of the incidences of specific side effects of any contraceptive method. The performance of the contraceptive method varies substantially, depending on proficiency of the physician administering the method, the clinic where the study is being conducted, the age, marital status and other relevant background information about the people in the study. A host of other known and unknown factors that are, at most, only indirectly related to the contraceptive method itself may affect its performance (Jain, 1975; Snowden and Williams, 1975).

For these reasons, it is also impossible to compare reliably the performance of different contraceptive methods using the data obtained in separate studies. Only in instances where such data reveal extreme differences in contraceptive effectiveness, can it be concluded that the different contraceptive techniques, rather than the differences in the population or clinics studied are responsible.

Methodologies do exist, however, for obtaining accurate and reliable comparative data; they entail random-assignment and multiclinic comparative studies. Although costly and burdensome, such evaluations are now being initiated for testings of a growing number of new contraceptive methods (Jain, 1975; Schearer, 1976).

4. REVIEW OF AVAILABLE TECHNOLOGY

Excluding abortion there exist at present just a baker's dozen of methods for limiting fertility. If the ineffective folk method of postcoital douching is excluded, only 12 means for reliably controlling fertility are known. Their performance characteristics are summarized in the following sections.

Coitus interruptus or withdrawal (Sjöval, 1970)

At the time of imminent ejaculation during coitus, rapid withdrawal of the penis and deposition of the semen outside the vagina has been employed by men as a contraceptive technique since Biblical times. Coitus interruptus qualifies as one of the oldest contraceptive methods, and is practiced widely throughout the world even today.

The efficacy of the technique depends upon keeping the sperm from entering the female reproductive tract. Whether this can be achieved with complete effectiveness or not is uncertain, since it is known that even prior to ejaculation, the penis frequently discharges a small amount of fluid which may contain small numbers of spermatozoa (Masters and Johnson, 1964). It is certain that if withdrawal occurs too late and even part of the semen has been ejaculated into the vagina, pregnancy can occur (Eliasson and Lindholmer, 1972). Accidental deposition of the semen on the external genitals of the woman can also result in pregnancy if some of the seminal fluid finds its way into the vagina. Consequently, the margin for error is small, and the practice of coitus interruptus, especially on a routine basis, requires great commitment on the part of both partners. With such rigorous requirements for successful use, the reported pregnancy rates * for this method, between

---

* These and other pregnancy rates reported here represent the extreme values taken from published prospective clinical studies or retrospective fertility surveys. Yearly pregnancy rates are computed from such studies using different statistical procedures. Also, the

10% (Westoff et al., 1953) and 23% (Westoff et al,m 1961; Sjöval, 1970) are surprisingly low.

Historically, a wide variety of gynecological, urological, neurological, and psychiatric disorders hase been attributed to the practice of coitus interruptus. Masters and Johnson have demonstrated that a progression of complex physiological changes from early excitation through plateau and orgasm to final resolution occurs in the female during normal coitus (Masters and Johnson, 1964). These findings have led to new speculation that coitus interruptus might result in observable physiological consequences in women if orgasm is prematurely abridged by this form of birth control on a regular basis (Calderone, 1970). No objective data exist to justify claims concerning the consequences for male sexual performance or urological function. Of course, with any contraceptive method, particularly those directly connected with coitus, a complex interrelationship between the contraceptive method and the etiology and maintenance of various sexual disorders, such as impotence or frigidity, is not unusual.

The classical version of coitus interruptus is increasingly used as an adjunct to other methods rather than as a primary method in its own right and, because of its simplicity and freedom from side effects, it remains one of the most widely practised of all modes of contraception (Schearer, 1976).

In recent years there have been increasing numbers of popular reports documenting the use of oral and anal sexual practices for contraceptive purposes. Whether such embellishments of the conventional version of coitus interruptus have become adopted to any wide extent is unknown.

Rhythm methods (Ross and Piotrow, 1974)

Successful impregnation of a woman can take place from a few days before to up to a day or two after the release of the egg from the ovary, which generally occurs around 12 to 18 days after the start of the last menstruation. The rhythm method seeks to restrict coitus to those parts of the menstrual cycle before or after ovulation when conception cannot occur.

The time between ovulation and the onset of menses, and the time between menses and the next ovulation vary considerably between different women and from cycle to cycle in the same woman (Treloar, 1973). Three different techniques have been devised for estimating the time of ovulation in the practice of the rhythm method. These three variants are known as calendar rhythm, temperature rhythm, and cervical mucus rhythm, and they

---

number of users, the period over which they used the method, and a variety of other factors vary widely between studies. Consequently, the reported pregnancy rates cannot be regarded as firm measures of performance. Furthermore, since natural fertility rates are always less than 100% per year, the reported pregnancy rates do not directly reflect contraceptive effectiveness, but rather serve as indices useful for comparing different methods (Tietze and Lewit, 1970; Schearer, 1976).

differ widely both in the manner in which they attempt to predict ovulation and in their reliability as contraceptive methods.

(a) Calendar rhythm
Sometimes known as the Ogino—Knaus method because of the role these two researchers played during the 1930s in establishing this technique (Ross and Piotrow, 1974), this method seeks to estimate how many days after menstruation a woman is likely to have her next ovulation, as calculated from the length of her previous six or twelve menstrual cycles. In practice, this requires a woman to keep a precise record of the duration of her menstrual cycles for at least six months or a year in order to obtain the necessary data on her menstrual regularity. She uses these data to calculate when in her cycle ovulation is likely to occur and then allots additional days of coital abstinence to this time. The additional days of abstinence take into account variability in her cycles and the length of time sperm can remain fertile within the female reproductive tract following coitus (estimated to be 3 days). For a woman whose menstrual cycles vary in length from 26 to 31 days, these calculations yield a minimum of 13 days of midcycle abstinence each month. In fact, it is not unusual for some cycles, of even those women who menstruate regularly, to vary in length by more than four days (Johansson et al., 1972; Treloar, 1973). The amount of coital abstinence required for protection against pregnancy increases with the greater variability in cycle length. In women with relatively short, moderately variable cycles, so-called 'safe' coitus will be limited to a few days just before and after menstruation. For women with highly variable menstrual cycles, calendar rhythm is totally unfeasible.

Evidently, calendar rhythm can only be practiced by highly motivated couples who will and can perform and follow the calculations required by this method. Even so, the pregnancy rates for this method, which range from 14 to 47% (Ross and Piotrow, 1974), are among the highest of all contraceptive methods. In addition to the sociological factors which influence the use-effectiveness of this method, current evidence from clinical studies indicates a much greater variability in menstrual patterns, even among women who menstruate regularly, than had been previously suspected (Johansson et al., 1972; Treloar, 1973).

(b) Temperature rhythm
The observation that ovulation is accompanied by a slight rise in body temperature provided the means for development of a more reliable form of the rhythm method, temperature rhythm. Temperature rhythm relies on detection of ovulation by observation of a rise of $0.5-1.0°F$ in the basal body temperature. Because the shift is so slight and because pronounced variations in basal body temperature are common, women practicing temperature rhythm must observe and record their temperature daily on a graph. This allows nonspecific fluctuations in temperature to be distinguished from the

shift caused by ovulation. Since the ovulatory shift is observed only with basal body temperature (when the body is at complete rest), the user must take her temperature, either orally or rectally, in bed in the morning before initiating other activity.

Two alternate versions of temperature rhythm are practiced. In one case, coitus is permitted only three days after the temperature shift until the start of the next menses; that is, only during the last 10—12 days of each menstrual cycle. Alternatively, after using the calendar method to estimate which days are safe prior to ovulation, a couple may practice coitus during the first part of the cycle as well.

More than for any other form of rhythm, temperature rhythm proves successful if practiced by literate, highly motivated couples with a moderately high material standard of living. The pregnancy rates for the two versions of temperature rhythm are quite different, as might be expected from the poor performance of the calendar method alone. At best, a failure rate as low as 1% has been reported, rising to 19% when coitus is permitted during both parts of the cycle (Ross and Piotrow, 1974). It has been demonstrated that the use-effectiveness of temperature rhythm varies markedly with age, with pregnancy rates below 1% in women over the age of 35, but as high as 28% for women between 20 to 24 years of age (Doring, 1973; Marshall, 1973). It has also been shown that intentions regarding future childbearing affect the efficacy of rhythm (Ryder, 1973). From the overall clinical evidence, it appears that the strict version of temperature rhythm can be as effective a contraceptive method as an IUD, if it is used with scrupulous care by couples who have completed their desired family size. With younger or less-motivated couples, it is far less effective, yielding only slightly better results than the poorly effective calendar rhythm method.

Failures may occur with the temperature rhythm method because of illness, emotional tension, or even extended lack of sleep, all of which may produce spurious temperature shifts. The method cannot be used by lactating women until after they have resumed menstruation, and it is unsuitable for premenopausal women or early postpubertal women because of their menstrual irregularity and frequent lack of ovulation.

(c) Cervical mucus rhythm

Ovulation is known to be accompanied by many physiological changes other than the temperature shift. One of these, alterations in the quantity and characteristics of the mucus secreted by the cervix, has been utilized as the basis for a third kind of rhythm, known as cervical mucus rhythm, ovulation rhythm, or the Billings Method — after the discoverers (Billings and Billings, 1973). In this version of the rhythm method, a woman keeps track of changes in the amount, consistency, and appearance of mucus in her vagina during each day of her cycle. Coitus is permitted during any 'dry' days at the start of the cycle up until the first flow of cloudy, tacky mucus is observed. Then, coital abstinence is practiced during the 7—14 days that the secreted mucus gradually alters until it becomes more abundant and is slippery, stringy and clear. This marks the period of ovulation. Within the next few days, reversion of the mucus to its former cloudy appearance and tacky consistency signals the start of the 'safe' period which continues through the time of menstruation at the end of the cycle (Billings and Billings, 1973; Ross and Piotrow, 1974).

Thus far there have been almost no studies of the effectiveness of the cervical mucus method. In the two studies published to date, both undertaken by the discoverers of the technique, 32 unplanned pregnancies occurred among 226 Tongan couples who practiced the method for an average of about eight months. In Australia, five unplanned pregnancies occurred among 165 couples using the method for an average of 6.4 months (Billings and Billings, 1973). Together, these studies yield a yearly pregnancy rate of about 12%. With one exception, all of these failures were claimed to have been the result of improper use of the method. as judged by the discoverer.

Beyond the emotional stress that frequently accompanies the long periods of abstinence required by all forms of the rhythm method (Marshall and Rowe, 1972), there are no known hazards to the health of couples who practice rhythm. There is evidence, however, that pregnancies which result from contraceptive failures of the rhythm method are far more likely to be abnormal than are conceptions that occur among couples planning a pregnancy (Jongbloet, 1971; Orgebin-Crist, 1973). Prospective studies of rhythm users which seek to confirm or refute these potential side effects are currently under way (Ross and Piotrow, 1974).

Spermicides and diaphragm (Dickinson, 1970; Bernstein, 1974; Belsky, 1975)

Spermicides are creams, jellies, pastes, foams, or suppositories which are placed in the vagina prior to coitus in order that the sperm will be prevented from passing through the cervix and uterus to reach the unfertilized egg. They contain one or several chemical agents which destroy or immobilize sperm. Several products are commercially available, but in most instances their comparative performance is unknown. Creams made up of stearates and glycerine along with a surface-active spermicide (nonylphenoxypolyethoxyethanol) appear to be somewhat more effective than other preparations. However, limited clinical studies have indicated that there is an extremely wide range in performance among as well as between products (Belsky, 1975). Overall pregnancy rates reported in such studies have ranged from 2% to 36% (Ryder, 1973). Side effects reported in these studies have been limited to rare allergic reactions (Bernstein, 1974).

Combining spermicides with the use of a diaphragm increases the effectiveness of either used alone (Tietze and Lewit, 1967). The diaphragm, a flat, round device made of flexible rubber, is inserted across the posterior part of the vagina where it physically blocks the opening of the cervix (Dickinson,

1970). In a study by Vessey and Wiggins (1974), the use of the diaphragm with spermicidal jelly or cream was as effective as an IUD among confirmed users of this method although much lower use-effectiveness rates have been reported for other populations (Westoff et al., 1961; Tietze and Lewit, 1967; Vessey and Wiggins, 1974).

In spite of the extremely limited data on the performance of these two methods, they are widely used because of their freedom from systemic action and their easy reversibility. In 1970 in the United States, for example, 12% of all couples practising contraception used either spermicides alone or the diaphragm with spermicidal jelly or cream.

Condom (Dalsimer et al., 1973; Dumm et al., 1974)

The condom, an elastic, sac-like sheath used to cover the penis during coitus, retains the ejaculated semen, preventing its deposition in the vagina. Condoms are available in a variety of shapes, colors, sizes and materials. However, only two characteristics significantly influence performance of the condom: the thickness of the wall of the condom, and the material from which it is made. Both these characteristics are related to the strength, hence effectiveness of the condom, and to the physical sensations that the user and his partner experience. Color, size, and shape, including those designed to increase friction during intercourse, are believed to have primarily and perhaps solely a psychological impact (Matsumoto et al., 1972). Some condoms are manufactured with a lubricating substance on the outer surface for the purpose of facilitating coitus. All condoms are packed as tightly rolled rings which must be placed on the glans penis and then unrolled over the shaft of the erect penis prior to intromission.

Almost all modern condoms are made of latex rubber and meet national standards designed to minimize the possibility of rupture or leakage due to pinholes (Dumm et al., 1974). In addition to latex condoms, condoms made from the skin of lamb intestines are also manufactured and sold, primarily in the United States. These condoms cost about twice as much as latex rubber condoms, but allow for greater sensitivity during intercourse. The quality control procedures and standards for skin condoms are not as rigorous as those for latex rubber condoms (Dumm et al., 1974). Condoms are available without prescription in almost every country in the world from pharmacies and, in many cases, from other commercial outlets and family planning clinics as well.

If condoms are used correctly and consistently and all contraceptive failures are limited to those resulting from rupture of the device, pregnancy rates are in the range of 1—3%, as judged from clinical studies (Tietze, 1960; Peel, 1969; John, 1973). This low failure rate may be achieved under conditions of more general use, by strongly motivated couples (Peel, 1969, 1972; Glass et al., 1974). More commonly, however, pregnancy rates in studies of large populations have been 10—20% (Dumm et al., 1974).

As with the diaphragm or coitus interruptus, there is no risk to health associated with condom use. Indeed, if sexual contact is limited exclusively to that utilizing a condom, the transmission of venereal disease from one partner to another can probably be prevented (Dumm et al., 1974).

Intrauterine devices (Huber et al., 1975; Schearer, 1976)

Intrauterine devices (IUDs) made of metal, plastic or fiber, are inserted by way of the vagina and cervical canal into the uterine cavity, where they cause infertility. An IUD can be left in place for years or, to restore fertility, removed at any time. Of the 100 or more conventional IUDs that have been designed and developed, only three or four are widely used (Huber et al., 1975; Mishell, 1975). However, at least two dozen others are being employed locally around the world (Huber et al., 1975; Tietze and Lewit, 1970). In addition to these conventional IUDs, a completely new type of intrauterine device, the copper-releasing IUD, has been introduced. It releases minute amounts of copper into the uterus from wire or rings of copper that encircle the device (Tatum, 1974; Mishell, 1975). Unlike conventional IUDs, which can maintain their effectiveness indefinitely, the copper devices need to be replaced at regular intervals — every two to four years — in order to replenish the supply of copper. A long-acting model which may eliminate this requirement is under development (Tatum, 1974).

IUDs are generally better tolerated by women who have previously given birth compared to women who have never had a child. To minimize this drawback, many IUDs are manufactured in 2, 3 or even up to 5 different sizes (Huber et al., 1975), and physicians attempt to select the size most appropriate to the size of the woman's uterus. The newer copper devices, which are smaller than most conventional IUDs, are available in only one size, but they have been reported (Mishell, 1975) to be much better tolerated than are most other IUDs by younger women who have not had children. IUDs are generally inserted following a normal menstrual period or after an induced or spontaneous abortion but not immediately after childbirth, when they are more likely to be expelled.

The mode of action of conventional IUDs in women is not yet fully known, but the evidence clearly indicates that they involve only local action and do not entail systemic hormonal effects (Nygren and Johansson, 1973; Segal and Atkinson, 1973). Ovulation occurs normally (Nygren and Johansson, 1973) but one or several of the processes between fertilization of the egg and its development in the uterus are interrupted. Copper-bearing IUDs combine the mode of action of conventional IUDs with the added action of a locally released antifertility agent, copper metal. There is wide agreement that the effect is a local one and that no measurable amounts of copper are absorbed systemically (Middleton and Kennedy, 1975).

IUDs are generally regarded as less effective than oral contraceptives, but more effective than all other contraceptive methods (Jain, 1975). This conclusion is based on pregnancy rates obtained in large-scale clinical studies of various contraceptive methods. Under such conditions, roughly 1—5% of women using an IUD become pregnant each year (Huber et al., 1975), compared to only about 0.7—1.4% of women using oral contraceptives in such studies (Oral Contraceptives and Health, 1974).

While it is known that the largest proportion of contraceptive failures occur among women still bearing the IUD in utero, a significant number of failures do arise among women who experience an unnoticed expulsion of the device and who, therefore, fail to utilize alternative means of contracep tion (Tietze and Lewit, 1970). The occurrence of pregnancies when the device is in place is thought to be a consequence of the inherently limited biological effectiveness of this mode of contraception. Whether this limitation might be more pronounced in some categories of users than others, is unknown.

The three most common side-effects associated with IUDs result from the physical presence of the device in the uterus. One of these three, spontaneous expulsion of the IUD by the uterus, has no direct adverse effect on the woman, but may result in an accidental pregnancy if she fails to notice the expulsion. Unwanted pregnancies of this kind occur in 5—15% of the women who experience expulsions (Tietze and Lewit, 1974). Somewhere between 2 and 25% of IUD users spontaneously expel the device during the first year of use (Tietze and Lewit, 1970; Huber et al., 1975; Jain, 1975).

The other two most common side-effects of IUDs are excessive menstrual and intermenstrual bleeding and pain in the lower back and pelvic areas. Almost all women who are fitted with an IUD experience increased bleeding and pain immediately following the insertion of the device. Increased menstrual flow is a permanent feature of this mode of contraception for many users. Taken together these two side-effects cause somewhere between 3 and 25% of women to request removal of the device within the first year after insertion (Tietze and Lewit, 1970; Huber et al., 1975; Jain, 1975).

Relatively rare but potentially serious side-effects are associated with IUD use. Perforation of the uterus by the device has been observed somewhere between 3 to 30 times out of every 10,000 insertions (Tietze and Lewit, 1970; Anon, 1974; Mishell, 1975), depending on the type of IUD, the insertion procedure and the type of perforation. Perforations that result in a complete translocation of the IUD into the abdominal cavity, usually at the time of insertion of the device, may be without consequence. On the other hand, in rare cases, serious illness and death have been associated with complete IUD perforations of the uterus (Advisory Committee on Obstetrics and Gynecology, 1968).

The most serious, prevalent side-effect associated with IUD use is infection. The insertion of an IUD typically carries bacteria from the vagina into the uterus, resulting in a transient local infection of the uterus (Mishell et al., 1966). While this brief infection is completely eliminated in 30 days and causes no ill effects for the majority of IUD users (Mishell et al., 1966), in some cases it can apparently be sustained for longer periods and then flare into acute pelvic inflammatory disease, sometimes giving rise to serious complications which in extreme cases may result in death (Advisory Committee on Obstetrics and Gynecology, 1968; Jennings, 1974).

Among IUD users in recent years, an increase in the number of hospitalizations resulting from spontaneous abortions associated with infections has been reported (Jennings, 1974; Dreishpoon, 1975). The mortality incidence thus far is very low, in the range of 3 deaths per million IUD users (Jennings, 1974). In the event of an accidental pregnancy with the IUD in place, physicians and users have been advised to remove the IUD.

Other complications of pregnancy — spontaneous abortion, premature labor, premature rupture of the membranes, and hemorrhage — are also more frequent when an IUD is in utero during the gestation (Dreishpoon, 1975). Also, it is known that since the IUD is more effective in preventing normal uterine pregnancies than it is in preventing the rare pathological pregnancies which sometimes occur in the Fallopian tubes, ovaries, or abdomen, the proportion of these ectopic pregnancies compared to normal pregnancies is relatively high among IUD contraceptive failures (Mishell, 1975; Tietze and Lewit, 1970).

In the United States, it has been estimated that 1 to 10 deaths per million users per year are associated with IUDs; hospitalization rates are estimated to be about 1000 times higher (Jennings, 1974; Huber et al., 1975; Tyler and Kahn, 1975). When compared to similar risks associated with oral contraceptives or sterilization, the IUD is widely regarded as one of the safest methods of contraception (Jennings, 1974; Jain, 1975).

*Pharmacologic methods**

Conventional oral contraceptives act by preventing ovulation. They rely upon a combination of two hormones which exert the same action on the body as do the two natural sex hormones, estradiol and progesterone. The synthetic versions of these two hormones used in the pill are much more potent, and when administered daily, they cause the body to enter a hormonal state of artificial pregnancy in which no ovulation and no menstrual cycling take place. Regular monthly bleeding is artificially produced by the temporary interruption of pill-taking for seven days each month; as the hormone levels in the blood decline, the endometrial tissue lining the uterus is gradually sloughed off, resulting in the 'withdrawal bleeding' that gives oral contraceptive users the illusion of normal menstruation.

Many chemical variants of both natural sex hormones are known, and various of these are combined (or, in some contraceptive regimens, administered

---

* Advisory Committee on Obstetrics and Gynecology, 1969; Eckstein et al., 1972; Preston, 1972; Rice-Wray et al., 1973; Kuchera, 1974; Nor-Q.D., 1974; Oral Contraceptives and Health, 1974; Connell, 1975; Potts et al., 1975; Rinehart and Winter, 1975.

sequentially) to yield the different commercially marketed oral contraceptive products. All of these preparations are extremely effective as contraceptives, if taken regularly. Under conditions of actual use by large populations, however, effectiveness is less, with pregnancy rates as high as 7% in extended use-effectiveness studies in the U.S. (Ryder, 1973).

In recent years, products with much lower doses of one of the synthetic hormones, the estrogen component, have appeared. Termed low-dose combined oral contraceptives, these preparations block ovulation somewhat less effectively than do the conventional high-dose orals; consequently they are slightly less effective as contraceptives. The two regimens differ more widely in their control of menstrual bleeding. The low-dose preparations do not produce as reliable a withdrawal bleeding as do the conventional pills, and irregular bleeding patterns are, therefore, much more common among women taking the low-dose regimens (Preston, 1972).

The low-dose combined oral contraceptives were introduced largely because of the demonstrated association of the estrogenic component of conventional pills with a 4—8-fold higher death rate due to venous thrombosis or pulmonary embolism and a 7-fold higher rate of thrombotic strokes (Vessey, 1974). Very recently, 1 3—5-fold increase in the risk of coronary thrombosis has also been demonstrated to be associated with oral contraceptive use (Mann and Inman, 1975). Whether these increased risks of thromboembolic and cardiovascular diseases will be reduced as a result of the reduction in the amount of estrogen in these newer preparations is still unknown.

Other potentially serious side effects associated with oral contraceptives include gall bladder disease, occurring about twice as often among oral contraceptive users, and hypertension, occurring up to 2.5 times more frequently (Oral Contraceptives and Health, 1974). There appear to be strong genetic factors associated with some of these risks; hypertension, for example occurs much more frequently among black women taking the oral contraceptive, whereas there is a much higher incidence of thromboembolic disease among white oral contraceptive users. Urinary infections and certain skin problems also occur more frequently among white oral contraceptive users (1.5, and 2—4-fold increases, respectively (Oral Contraceptives and Health, 1974)), and a wide variety of changes in body metabolism are observed in conjunction with oral contraceptive use (Corfman, 1974). The significance and potential risks of most of these metabolic alterations remain unknown. Many subjective symptoms — headaches, vaginal discharge, depression, loss of libido — have also been reported by oral contraceptive users, but it is uncertain to what extent these reports reflect side-effects of the drug or non-specific placebo effects (Oral Contraceptives and Health, 1974). Although scanty menstruation occurs about 3 times more frequently, other menstrual disorders are about half as common among oral contraceptive users. Significant reductions in iron deficiency anemia, complaints of premenstrual syndrome, benign breast nodules, ovarian cysts, and acne are among other health benefits conferred by the conventional oral contraceptive (Oral Contraceptives and Health, 1974).

Retrospective studies from the U.S. suggest there may be an elevated risk of fetal abnormalities, in particular heart defects and limb reductions, among infants conceived as a result of oral contraceptive failure (Janerich et al., 1974). These preliminary findings suggest that such birth defects result from exposure of the fetus in utero to the progestational component of the oral contraceptive (Janerich et al., 1974).

The overall mortality rate associated with oral contraceptive use is estimated at 22—45 deaths per million users per year (Jennings, 1974; Huber et al., 1975; Mauldin, 1975). Hospitalizations related to contraceptive use are believed to be in the range of 0.5 to 1 hospitalization per 1000 users per year (Tyler and Kahn, 1975). Long-term studies comparing the experience of very large numbers of oral contraceptive users to matched groups of non-users are now confirming the low overall risk and generally high effectiveness associated with oral contraceptive drugs compared to other medications (Corfman, 1974; Oral Contraceptives and Health, 1974). While these studies are not yet of sufficient duration or magnitude to give information concerning rare or very long-term side effects, they do provide a new basis for reassurance about the relative safety of this widely used contraceptive method, as compared with pregnancy itself.

Within the past several years, two variants of the oral contraceptive have gained use in some countries. One of these is the mini-pill, or progestin-only pill, a daily regimen which delivers without interruption a low-dose of the progestational hormone alone. Ovulation is blocked in only some of the cycles, and contraception depends on additional, low-dose, antifertility actions of this hormone (Eckstein et al., 1972). Effectiveness is, therefore, lower than for conventional orals, and pregnancy rates are reported in the range of 2—4% (Nor-Q.D., 1974). The occasional occurrence of ovulation, the lack of administered estrogen, and the continuous administration schedule of the mini-pill all disrupt the kind of control of menstrual bleeding that the conventional orals provide. Irregular menstrual bleeding is also very common among mini-pill users (Eckstein et al., 1972; Nor-Q.D., 1974). Because of the lower dose of synthetic progestin and complete absence of estrogen, the mini-pill is thought to be associated with fewer side-effects. Studies of sufficient scope to demonstrate this assumption have not yet been conducted.

The second variant is a contraceptive injection administered either monthly, tri-monthly, or six-monthly. All three types of injection act by blocking ovulation in the same fashion as a conventional pill. The tri-monthly and six-monthly injections contain only a synthetic progestin, while the monthly injections also contain a synthetic estrogen in order to provide more regular menstrual patterns. All are highly effective, but the tri-monthly and six-monthly preparations are associated with very unpredictable, irregular menstrual bleeding patterns, which often change into extended intervals without menses in long-term users of this method (Rice-Wray et al., 1973; Rinehart and Winter, 1975).

The so-called post-coital pill consists of a very high dose of synthetic estrogen taken for five successive days beginning within 72 h after coitus. The estrogen blocks the implantation of the fertilized egg in the uterus. The method is highly effective if the therapy starts within the 72-h period (Kuchera, 1974). However, treatment is usually associated with nausea and vomiting, and the subsequent menstrual cycle is often irregular (Kuchera, 1971). If tho drug is taken too late to prevent implantation and a newly implanted female embryo is exposed to the administered hormone, there is a high risk that the fetus will develop a susceptibility to subsequent carcinoma of the vagina at puberty (Connell, 1975). For this reason, the post-coital pill is considered an emergency rather than routine contraceptive method, and if it fails, abortion is advised (Connell, 1975).

Vasectomy (Wortman and Piotrow, 1973c; Wortman, 1975)

Vasectomy, the cutting or blocking of the vas deferens so that sperm cannot be transported out of the testis, is perhaps the simplest known means of birth control. The conventional vasectomy procedure is completed in roughly ten minutes with little discomfort or riok to tho patient (Wortman and Piotrow, 1973c). Healing following this minor surgery is generally rapid and without complication, and after the residual sperm have been ejaculated, usually within 10 to 15 ejaculations, the semen thereafter remains permanently free of sperm (Wortman, 1975). As with female sterilization, vasectomy is slightly less than 100% effective because of failures during the surgery to identify and divide the correct anatomical structure, and because of the great capacity of the cut ends of the vas to come together and heal to reform an intact structure following surgery. In addition, unwitting duplication of the vasectomy on the same vas sometimes occurs. Other failures may result from unprotected coitus before there has been sufficient depletion of the residual sperm (Wortman, 1975).

The risks associated with the vasectomy procedure are low. Deaths have been reported only in one instance: of 62,000 men who underwent vasectomy at a family welfare festival in India in 1971, five subsequently died of tetanus. The death rate associated with vasectomy in general is certainly lower than that of 80 per million procedures, the figure calculated from this Indian experience. It appears to be negligible in developed countries (Wortman, 1975).

The reported occurrence of all complications, both major and minor, associated with vasectomies ranges widely from less than 0.1% to over 12.2% (see Wortman, 1975). Hematoma, infection, and epididymitis make up the bulk of these complications. Symptomatic sperm granuloma formation, either shortly postoperation or after an extended period of time, is the next most common complication (Schmidt, 1975; Wortman, 1975). In the vast majority of cases, treatment without hospitalization is successful in resolving the condition.

In recent years the techniques for surgical reversal of a vasectomy have been significantly improved, and in as many as 80—90% of men requesting re-anastomosis of the vas, sperm can be successfully restored to the ejaculate (Schmidt, 1975). In only about 30% of these successful cases do the sperm prove to be fertile. Consequently, vasectomy must still be regarded as a permanent sterilization procedure.

The cause for this impairment of fertility remains unknown, but it is widely thought to be associated with the appearance of antibodies to sperm in the blood of vasectomized men at some time after the procedure. Nonetheless, although it has been well established that different classes of sperm-agglutinating and sperm-immobilizing antibodies are produced as a result of vasectomy in about 50% of the cases (Ansbacher et al., 1975), no correlation between these antibodies and subsequent irreversibility of the sterilization or subsequent illness or pathology of any kind has yet been demonstrated (Ansbacher et al., 1975; Berendes and Crozier, 1975). Long-term, prospective studies of these issues in monkeys and men are continuing (Berendes and Crozier, 1975).

Recent findings from studies of this kind indicate that blood levels of the male sex hormone, testosterone, may increase significantly by the end of the first year following a vasectomy (Smith et al., 1975). The significance of these findings is as yet uncertain, but they clearly dispel previous concern that impaired libido resulting from decreased testosterone levels might be a side effect of vasectomy. While psychological sequelae are sometimes reported (Rodgers and Ziegler, 1974), there is no evidence that sexual performance is physiologically affected by vasectomy.

Female sterilization (Wortman and Piotrow, 1973a; Ross and Piotrow, 1974; Shepard, 1974)

In recent years, both the demand and the means for achieving female sterilization have sharply increased. Currently, six different techniques are available. Widespread clinical research to develop improved new methods is being conducted (Shepard, 1974; Schearer, 1976).

Traditionally, female sterilization for contraceptive purposes has been carried out by way of an incision through the abdomen in order to expose the Fallopian tubes, which are then severed, tied, or crushed. The ovaries and uterus are left intact, and sterilization occurs as a consequence of the damaged tubes which prevent both the ascent of sperm and the transport of the unfertilized egg from the ovary where it is produced to the uterus where gestation takes place. Eggs are released each month, but they degenerate in the upper reaches of the tubes without ever becoming fertilized.

This conventional tubal ligation procedure using the abdominal approach (laparotomy) is widely utilized for sterilization following an abortion, a delivery, or for nonpregnant women who elect to be sterilized. The procedure may also be carried out in conjunction with either delivery by Cesarean section or with late termination of pregnancy by hysterotomy (Presser, 1970; Edwards and Hakanson, 1973).

Effectiveness of the procedure ranges from 98 to 99.9% in published studies (Presser, 1970). However, since it entails major surgery, it is associated with a significant risk of death (about 250 deaths per million procedures) and morbidity (between 48 and 130 complications per thousand procedures), a hospital stay of several days, and with the resultant high cost. Although surgical repair of the tubes to restore fertility is sometimes attempted, the high expense, medical risks, and imperfect success rates all indicate that tubal ligation (as well as all other techniques of female sterilization) is essentially an irreversible method of fertility control (Presser, 1970).

In recent years, exposure of the Fallopian tubes by an incision through the rear wall of the vagina (culpotomy) has become an increasingly popular technique (Wortman and Piotrow, 1973a; Aguero et al., 1974). Tubal ligation achieved through this surgical approach is associated with about the same range of pregnancy rates as when the abdominal approach is used. Some women, however, are poor candidates for this procedure because the tubes may be more difficult to locate and to identify when exposed via the vaginal approach. Morbidity and mortality rates are about the same for the abdominal and vaginal procedures (Wortman and Piotrow, 1973a; Shepard, 1974).

Female sterilization can also be carried out by complete surgical removal of the uterus and cervix (hysterectomy), and this procedure can be undertaken via either the abdominal or vaginal approaches. Since the ovaries are left intact in such hysterectomy procedures, secondary sex features and sexual drive are not affected, although menstruation, of course, no longer occurs. The medical rationale for favoring hysterectomy instead of tubal ligation as a voluntary sterilization procedure for some women is based on the elevated incidence of uterine and cervical pathologies, particularly cancers, in older women. Removal of these organs at the time of sterilization eliminates this future risk (Van Nagell and Roddick, 1971). Although this rationale is controversial because of the radical nature of such surgery and the greater risks of mortality (between 1250 and 3000 deaths per million procedures; Ledger and Child, 1973; Shepard, 1974) and morbidity (generally reported at nearly 600 complications per thousand procedures, Shephard, 1974) associated with it, elective sterilization by hysterectomy, particularly by the vaginal approach, is widely practiced (Van Nagell and Roddick, 1971; Coulam and Pratt, 1973; Wilson et al., 1973; Bazley and Crisp, 1974; Shepard, 1974).

In order to simplify the surgical requirements of tubal ligation, two new techniques have been introduced within the past several years (Porter and Hulka, 1974; Wortman and Piotrow, 1973b). They rely on endoscopy, the direct visualization of structures inside the body with an optical instrument that is inserted into the body through either a small incision or through one of the body's orifices. For sterilization, a tube-like instrument is passed through two (or sometimes only one) small puncture hole(s) in either the abdomen (laparoscopy) or the vaginal wall (culdoscopy). The instrument's optical system and attachments permit the Fallopian tubes to be seen, grasped, and then either cut, tied, clipped or cauterized, all without a major surgical opening of the abdomen or vagina. As a result, the length of the hospital stay is reduced, and some of the discomforts and risks associated with other techniques of female sterilization are lessened. Although mortality risk is not much superior to the conventional procedures and effectiveness is somewhat lower, morbidity is considerably less (Shepard, 1974). Further improvement of these recently introduced laparoscopic and culdoscopic sterilization techniques is to be expected. It is unlikely, however, that these methods will ever become routine outpatient procedures available from most hospital clinics or specialists' offices. Notwithstanding their appeal and their use without general anesthesia under outpatient circumstances by some physicians, the technical sophistication of these procedures, the need for insufflation of the abdomen in the case of laparoscopy, the requirement for complex, costly instrumentation, and the inherent medical risks, all limit the settings in which these techniques can be successfully employed. Perhaps more than for any other fertility control technology, the efficacy and safety of laparoscopic and culdoscopic sterilization depend upon the technical proficiency of the physician who carried out these procedures (Wortman and Piotrow, 1973b).

Little is known about long-term side effects or complications which may occur after sterilization by any of these procedures. There have been reports of increased menstrual bleeding disorders, but carefully controlled studies have not been conducted (Shepard, 1974). As with male sterilization, psychological sequelae are known to occur in a small minority of women following surgery (Presser, 1970; Wortman and Piotrow, 1973a; Shepard, 1974).

BIBLIOGRAPHY

Advisory Committee on Obstetrics and Gynecology (1968) U.S. Food and Drug Administration, *Report on Intrauterine Devices*, (U.S. Government Printing Office, Washington, D.C.) 101 pp.

Advisory Committee on Obstetrics and Gynecology (1969) U.S. Food and Drug Administration, *Second Report on the Oral Contraceptives*, (U.S. Government Printing Office, Washington, D.C.) p. 14.

Aguero, O., Cardenas-Conde, L. and Rios-Simanca, J. (1974) Puerperal tubal ligation. In: (M.E. Schima, I. Lubell, J.E. Davis, E. Connell and D.W.K. Cotton, Eds.), *Advances in Voluntary Sterilization*. (American Elsevier Publishing Co., Inc., New York) pp. 30—35.

Anon., (1974) Copper T. IUD: Embedding common but not harmful. *Fam. Plann. Digest* 3: 8—9.

Ansbacher, R., Williams, B.S. and Mumford, D.M. (1975) Vas ligation: sperm antibodies. In: (J.J. Sciarra, C. Markland and J.J. Speidel, Eds.), *Control of Male Fertility*. (Harper and Row, New York) pp. 189—195.

Barnes, A.C., Schearer, B. and Segal, S.J. (1974) Contraceptive development. In: *Working Papers: Third Bellagio Conference on Population*, (The Rockefeller Foundation, New York) pp. 75—78.

Bazley, W.S. and Crisp, W.E. (1974) Postpartum hysterectomy for sterilization. *Am. J. Obstet. Gynecol.* 119: 139—149.

Belsky, R. (1975) Barrier methods: vaginal contraceptives, a time for reappraisal? *Popul. Rep.* Ser. H, No. 3, January, 20 pp.

Berendes, H.W. and Crozier, R. (1975) Vasectomy research program of the Center for Population Research. In: (J.J. Sciarra, C. Markland and J.J. Speidel, Eds.), *Control of Male Fertility.* (Harper and Row, New York) pp. 164—168.

Bernstein, G.S. (1974) Conventional methods of contraception: condom, diaphragm, and vaginal foam. *Clin. Obstet. Gynecol.* 17: 21—33.

Billings, J. and Billings, E.L. (1973) Determination of fertile and infertile days by the mucus pattern: development of the ovulation method. In: (W.A. Uricchio and M.K. Williams, Eds.), *Natural Family Planning.* (The Human Life Foundation, Washington, D.C.) pp. 149—163.

Calderone, M.S. (1970) Editor's note on coitus interruptus. In: (M.S. Calderone, Ed.), *Manual of Family Planning. and Contraceptive Practice.* (Williams and Wilkins Co., Baltimore) pp. 437—438.

Campbell, A.A. and Berelson, B. (1971) Contraceptive specifications: report of a workshop. *Stud. Fam. Plan.* 2: 14—19.

Connell, E.B. (1975) The pill revisited. *Fam. Plann. Perspect.* 7: 62—71.

Corfman, P.A. (1974) Coordinated studies of the effects of oral contraceptives. *Contraception* 9: 109—122.

Coulam, C.B. and Pratt, J.H. (1973) Vaginal hysterectomy: is previous pelvic operation a contraindication? *Am. J. Obstet. Gynecol.* 116: 252—260.

Dalsimer, I.A., Piotrow, P.T. and Dumm, J.J. (1973) Barrier methods: condom-an old method meets a new social need. *Popul. Rep.* Ser. H., No. 1, December, 20 pp.

Dickinson, R.L. (1970) The diaphragm. In: (M.S. Calderone, Ed.), *Manual of Family Planning and Contraceptive Practice.* (Williams and Wilkins, Co., Baltimore, Md.) pp. 351—367.

Doring, G.K. (1973) Detection of ovulation by the basal body temperature method. In: (W.A. Urrichio and M.K. Williams, Eds.), *Natural Family Planning.* (The Human Life Foundation, Washington, D.C.) pp. 171 180.

Dreishpoon, I.H. (1975) Complications of pregnancy with an intrauterine contraceptive device in situ. *Am. J. Obstet. Gynecol.* 121: 412—413.

Dumm, J.J., Piotrow, P.T. and Dalsimer, I.A. (1974) Barrier methods: the modern condom — quality product for effective contraception. *Popul. Rep.* Ser. H, No. 2, May, 15 pp.

Eckstein, P., Whitby, M., Fotherby, K., Butler, C., Mukherjee, T.K., Burnett, J.B.C., Richards, D.J. and Whitehead, T.P. (1972) Clinical and laboratory findings in a trial of norgestrel, a low-dose progestin-only contraceptive. *Br. Med. J.* 3: 195—200.

Edwards, L.A. and Hakanson, E.Y. (1973) Changing status of tubal sterilization: an evaluation of fourteen years' experience. *Am. J. Obstet. Gynecol.* 115: 347—353.

Eliasson, R. and Lindholmer, C. (1972) Distribution and properties of spermatozoa in different fractions of split ejaculates. *Fert. Steril.* 23: 252—256.

Faundes, A. (1975) Assessment of clinical testing methodology. *Contraception* 11: 363—394.

Fawcett, J.T. (1970) *Psychology and Population: Behavioral Research Issues in Fertility and Family Planning.* (The Population Council, New York) 149 pp.

Glass, R., Vessey, N. and Wiggins, P. (1974) Use-effectiveness of the condom in a selected family planning clinic population in the United Kindom. *Contraception* 10: 591—598.

Hawley, A.H. (1950) *Human Ecology.* (Ronald Press, New York) pp. 110—111.

Himes, N.E. (1936) *Medical History of Contraception.* (Williams and Wilkins, Co., Baltimore) 521 pp.

Huber, G., Piotrow, P.T., Orlans, R.B. and Kommer, G. (1975) Intrauterine devices: IUDs reassessed — a decade of experience. *Popul. Rep.* Ser. B., No. 2, January, 27 pp.

Jain, A.K. (1975) Safety and effectiveness of intrauterine devices. *Contraception* 11: 243—259.

Janerich, D.T., Piper, J.M. and Glebatis, D.M. (1974) Oral contraceptives and congenital limb-reduction defects. *New Engl. J. Med.* 291: 697—700.

Jennings, J. (1974) *Report of safety and efficacy of the Dalkon Shield and other IUDs.* Prepared by the ad hoc Obstetric-Gynecology Advisory Committee (to the U.S. Food and Drug Administration) October 29—30, 16 pp. (Mimeo).

Johansson, E.D.B., Larsson Cohn, E. and Gemzell, C. (1972) Monophasic basal body temperature in ovulatory menstrual cycles. *Am. J. Obstet. Gynecol.* 113: 933—937.

Jongbloet, P.H. (1971) Month of birth and gametopathy: An investigation into patients with Down's, Klinefelter's and Turner's syndrome. *Clin. Genet.* 2: 315—330.

John, A.P.K. (1973) Contraception in a practice community. *J. R. Coll. Gen. Pract.* 23: 665.

Kuchera, L.K. (1974) Postcoital contraception with diethylstilbestrol — updated. *Contraception* 10: 47—54.

Langley, L.L. (Ed.) (1973) *Contraception,* (Dowden, Hutchinson, and Ross, Inc., Stroudsberg, Pa.) 500 pp.

Ledger, W.J. and Child, M.A. (1973) The hospital care of patients undergoing hysterectomy: an analysis of 12,026 patients from the Professional Activity Study. *Am. J. Obstet. Gynecol.* 117: 423—433.

Mann, J.I. and Inman, W.H.W. (1975) Oral contraceptives and death from myocardial infarction. *Br. Med. J.* 2: 245—248.

Marshall, J. and Rowe, B. (1972) The effect of personal factors on the use of basal body temperature method of regulating births. *Fertil. Steril.* 23: 417—421.

Marshall, J.R. (1973) Prediction, detection and control of ovulation and overview. In: (W.A. Uricchio and M.K. Williams, Eds.) *Natural Family Planning.* (The Human Life Foundation, Washington, D.C.) pp. 135—145.

Masters, W.H. and Johnson, V.E. (1964) Sexual response: anatomy and physiology. In: (C.W. Lloyd, Ed.), *Human Reproduction and Sexual Behavior.* (Lea and Febiger, Philadelphia, Pa.) pp. 460—473.

Matsumoto, Y.S., Koizuma, A. and Nohara, T. (1972) Condom use in Japan. *Stud. Fam. Plann.* 3: 251—255.

Mauldin, W.P. (1965) Application of survey techniques to fertility studies. In: (M.C. Sheps and J.C. Ridley, Eds.), *Public Health and Population Change.* (University of Pittsburgh Press, Pittsburgh, Pa.) pp. 93—118.

Mauldin, W.P. (1975) Assessment of national family planning programs in developing countries. *Stud. Fam. Plann.* 6: 30—36.

Middleton, J.C. and Kennedy, M. (1975) The biological actions of endouterine copper. *Contraception* 11: 209—225.

Mishell, D.R., Jr., Bell, J.H., Good, R.G. and Moyer, D.L. (1966) The intrauterine device: A bacteriologic study of the endometrial cavity. *Am. J. Obstet. Gynecol.* 96: 119—126.

Mishell, D.R., Jr. (1975) Current analysis of the intrauterine device. *Fam. Plann. Perspect.* 7: 103—111.

Nortman, D. (1974) Population and family planning programs: a factbook. *Rep. Populat./Fam. Plann.* (2) December, 96 pp.

Nor-Q.D. (1974) Package Insert, Syntax Laboratories, Inc., Palo Alto, California.

Nygren, K.G. and Johansson, E.D.B. (1973) Premature onset of menstrual bleeding during ovulatory cycles in women with an intrauterine contraceptive device. *Am. J. Obstet. Gynecol.* 117: 971—975.

Oral Contraceptives and Health (1974) An Interim Report From the Oral Contraception Study of the Royal College of General Practitioners, (Pitman Publishing Co., New York) 100 pp.

Orgebin-Crist, M.C. (1973) Sperm age: effects on zygote development. In: (W.A. Uricchio and M.K. Williams, Eds.), *Natural Family Planning*. (The Human Life Foundation, Washington, D.C.) pp. 85—93.

Peel, J. (1969) A male-oriented fertility control experiment. *Practitioner* 202: 677—681.

Peel, J. (1972) The Hull family survey. II. Family planning in the first five years of marriage. *J. Bio-soc. Sci.* 4: 333—346.

Porter, C.W., Jr. and Hulka, J.F. (1974) Female sterilization in current clinical practice. *Fam. Plann. Perspect.* 0. 90 00.

Potts, M. van derVlugt, T., Piotrow, P.T., Gail, L.J. and Huber, S.C. (1975) Oral contraceptives: advantages of orals outweigh disadvantages. *Popul. Rep.* Ser. A (2) 33 pp.

Presser, H.B. (1970) Voluntary sterilization: a world view. *Rep. Popul./Fam. Plann.* 5, 36 pp.

Preston, S.N. (1972) A report of a collaborative dose-response clinical study of decreasing doses of combination oral contraceptives. *Contraception* 6: 17—35.

Rice-Wray, E., Gutierrez, J., Gorodovsky, J., Maqueo, M. and Goldzieher, J.W. (1973) Injectable contraceptives in family planning: clinical experience in 14,958 cycles. *Adv. Planned Parent.* 8: 103—113.

Rinehart, W. and Winter, J. (1975) Injectables and Implants: Injectable progestogens — officials debate but use increases. *Popul. Rep.* Ser. K, No. 1, March, 16 pp.

Rodgers, D.A. and Ziegler, F.J. (1974) Effects of surgical contraception on sexual behavior. In: (M.E. Schima, I. Lubell, J.E. Davis, E. Connell and D.W.K. Cotton, Eds.), *Advances in Voluntary Sterilization*. (American Elsevier Publishing Co., Inc., New York) pp. 161—166.

Ross, C. and Piotrow, P.T. (1974) Periodic abstinence: birth control without contraceptives. *Popul. Rep.* Ser. 1, No. 1, June, 20 pp.

Ryder, N. (1973) Contraceptive failure in the United States. *Fam. Plann. Perspect.* 5: 133—142.

Schearer, S.B. (1973) Tomorrow's contraception. In: (C.F. Westoff, Ed.), *Toward the End of Growth: Population in America.* (Prentice-Hall, Inc., Englewood Cliffs, N.J.) pp. 47—56.

Schearer, S.B. (1976) Contraceptive technology: current and future methods. *Rep. Popul./Fam. Plann.* (In press.)

Schmidt, S.S. (1975) Complication of vas surgery. In: (J.J. Sciarra, C. Markland and J.J. Speidel, Eds.), *Control of Male Fertility.* (Harper and Row, New York) pp. 78—88.

Segal, S.J. (1973) Population and biological man. In: (S.L. Kaplan and E. Kivy-Rosenberg, Eds.), *Ecology and the Quality of Life.* (Charles C. Thomas, Springfield, Illinois) pp. 49—55.

Segal, S.J. and Atkinson, L.E. (1973) Mechanism of contraceptive action of intrauterine foreign bodies. In: (R.O. Greep, Ed.), *Handbook of Physiology, Section 7, Vol. II, Part 2.* (Am. Physiol. Soc., Washington, D.C.) pp. 359—366.

Shepard, M.K. (1974) Female contraceptive sterilization. *Obstet. Gynecol. Surv.* 29: 739—787.

Short, R.V. (1974) Man, the changing animal. In: (E.M. Coutinho and F. Fuchs, Eds.), *Physiology and Genetics of Reproduction, Part A.* (Plenum Press, New York) pp. 3—15.

Sjövall, E. (1970) Coitus interruptus. In: (M.S. Calderone, Ed.), *Manual of Family Planning and Contraceptive Practice.* (Williams and Wilkins, Co., Baltimore) pp. 433—436.

Smith, K.D., Chowdhury, M. and Tcholakian, R.K. (1975) Endocrine effects of vasectomy in humans. In: (J.J. Sciarra, C. Markland and J.J. Speidel, Eds.), *Control of Male Fertility.* (Harper and Row, New York) pp. 169—176.

Snowden, R. and Williams, M. (1975) The United Kingdom Dalkon Shield trial: two years of observation. *Contraception* 11: 1—13.

Tatum, H.J. (1974) Copper-bearing intrauterine devices. *Clin. Obstet. Gynecol.* 17: 93—119.

Tejuja, S. (1974) Contraceptive testing in India: an editorial comment. *Contraception* 10: 335—336.

Tietze, C. (1960) *The Condom as a Contraceptive.* New York, National Committee on Maternal Health, Inc. Publication No. 5, 44 pp.

Tietze, C. and Lewit, S. (1967) Comparison of three contraceptive methods: diaphragm with jelly or cream, vaginal foam, and jelly/cream alone. *J. Sex. Res.* 3: 295—311.

Tietze, C. and Lewit, S. (1968) Statistical evaluation of contraceptive methods: use-effectiveness and extended use-effectiveness. *Demography* 5: 931—940.

Tietze, C. and Lewit, S. (1970) Evaluation of intrauterine devices: ninth progress report of the Cooperative Statistical Program. *Stud. Fam. Plann.* 1: 1—40.

Tietze, C. and Lewit, S. (1974) Statistical evaluation of contraceptive methods. *Clin. Obstet. Gynecol.* 17: 121—138.

Treloar, A.A. (1973) Variations in the human menstrual cycle. In: (W.A. Uricchio and M.K. Williams, Eds.), *Natural Family Planning.* (The Human Life Foundation, Washington, D.C.) pp. 64—71.

Tyler, C.W. and Kahn, H.S. (1975) Morbidity and mortality associated with the use of intrauterine devices in the United States and Puerto Rico. In: (F. Hefnawi and S.J. Segal, Eds.) *Analysis of Intrauterine Contraception.* (American Elsevier, New York) pp. 47—58.

Van Nagell, J.R., Jr. and Roddick, J.W., Jr. (1971) Vaginal hysterectomy as a sterilization procedure. *Am. J. Obstet. Gynecol.* 111: 703—707.

Vessey, M.P. (1974) Thromboembolism, cancer, and oral contraceptives. *Clin. Obstet. Gynecol.* 17: 65—78.

Vessey, M. and Wiggins, P. (1974) Use-effectiveness of the diaphragm in a selected family planning clinic population in the United Kingdom. *Contraception* 9: 15—21.

Westoff, D.F., Herrera, L.F. and Whelpton, P.K. (1953) Social and psychological factors affecting fertility. *Milbank Mem. Fund Quart.* 31: 291—357.

Westoff, C.F., Potter, R.G., Jr., Sagi, P.C. and Mishler, E.G. (1961) *Family Growth in Metropolitan America,* (Princeton University Press, Princeton, N.J.) 433 pp.

Westoff, C.F. (1973) Changes in contraceptive practices among married couples. In: (C.F. Westoff, Ed.), *Toward the End of Growth: Population in America.* (Prentice-Hall, Inc., Englewood Cliffs, N.J.) pp. 33—46.

Wilson, E.A., Dilts, P.V., Jr. and Simpson, T.J. (1973) Comparative morbidity of post-partum sterilization procedures. *Am. J. Obstet. Gynecol.* 115: 884—889.

Wood, C., Leeton, J., Downing, B., Matthews, J. and Williams, L. (1970) Emotional attitudes to contraceptive methods. *Contraception* 2: 113—126.

Wortman, J. (1975) Sterilization: vasectomy — what are the problems? *Popul. Rep.* Ser. D, No. 2, January, 15 pp.

Wortman, J. and Piotrow, P.T. (1973a) Sterilization: Colpotomy — the vaginal approach. *Popul. Rep.* Ser. C, No. 3, June, 15 pp.

Wortman, J. and Piotrow, P.T. (1973b) Sterilization: laparoscopic sterilization — II. What are the problems? *Popul. Rep.* Ser. C, No. 2, March, 10 pp.

Wortman, J. and Piotrow, P.T. (1973c) Sterilization: vasectomy — old and new techniques. *Popul. Rep.* Ser. D, No. 1, December, 20 pp.

CHAPTER 44

Induced abortion

CHRISTOPHER TIETZE

1. INTRODUCTION

Induced abortion is, and probably has been for centuries, the most widely used method of birth control throughout the world. In spite of strong condemnation by governments, religious bodies, and the medical profession in many countries, there can be little doubt that each year millions of women obtain abortions, legally or illegally, at their own initiative and, sometimes, at substantial expense, and at great personal risk to their life and health

Abortion is generally defined as the termination of pregnancy before the fetus has attained viability, that is, before it is capable of independent extra-uterine life. According to medical tradition, viability is reached after 28 weeks of gestation, estimated from the first day of the last menstrual period; this usually corresponds to a fetal weight of approximately 1000 g. This definition is based on the observation that infants weighing less than 1000 g have little chance of survival and that the mortality of infants above 1000 g declines rapidly with increasing weight.

Advances in the care of premature infants during recent years have led to a re-evaluation of the definition of viability. A few infants born at less than 24 weeks of gestation have been reported to have survived as have a few others weighing less than 600 g at birth. However, no well-documented case of survival of any infant born at less than 24 weeks of gestation and weighing less than 600 g was found by the U.S. National Commission for the Protection of Human Subjects of Biomedical and Behavioral Research (USDHEW, 1975). Hence, both the duration of pregnancy and the weight of the infant must be considered if viability is to be presumed.

The two major categories of abortions are: (1) induced, that is, brought about voluntarily with the intention to terminate pregnancy and (2) spontaneous, including all other abortions, even if an external cause is involved, such as injury or fever. This chapter, unless otherwise noted, deals with induced abortion only, both legal and illegal as defined by the laws of each country.

Handbook of Sexology, edited by J. Money and H. Musaph
© Elsevier/North-Holland Biomedical Press, 1977

Where abortions are illegal, they are frequently performed by unqualified persons under insanitary conditions, resulting in an increased risk of infection and other complications. This higher risk also applies to self-induced abortions, regardless of their legal status.

It is rarely possible to differentiate between spontaneous and induced abortion either clinically or at autopsy, unless there is evidence of manipulation such as injury to the cervix or perforation of the uterus or unless the woman herself, her family or the abortionist provide this information. Although physicians often diagnose septic abortions as induced, many induced abortions show no signs or symptoms of infection, whereas some spontaneous abortions do.

Additional diagnostic categories, such as imminent, inevitable, and incomplete abortion denote states in the abortive process. Once an abortion has been initiated, a woman may seek medical care at any stage in the process, although a knowledgeable woman may wait until she feels sure that the process is irreversible. Incomplete abortion is the most common diagnosis among women admitted to hospitals for aftercare, usually for postabortal bleeding caused by the retention of placental tissue.

2. LEGAL STATUS OF ABORTION

The worldwide legal status of induced abortion ranges from complete prohibition of abortion under any circumstances to elective abortion at the request of the pregnant woman (Kalis and David, 1974). As of late 1976 the situation can be summarized as follows: at least 8% of the world's population lives in countries where abortion is completely prohibited, and 15% in countries where it is permitted only to save the life of the pregnant woman. About 12% live in countries authorizing abortion on such broad medical grounds as a threat to the woman's health, as well as to her life, and sometimes also on eugenic and/or juridical grounds such as rape. Countries where social factors may be taken into consideration to justify termination of pregnancy account for 23% of the world's population, and those allowing elective abortions either for all women or for certain categories of women, defined in terms of parity and/or age, for 36%. No information is available for the remaining 6% of the world's population; it is likely that most of these people live in areas with restrictive abortion laws.

In most countries where abortion on request is permitted, it is limited to the first trimester of pregnancy; thereafter a specific indication is required. A few countries disallow termination of pregnancy within six months or one year of a prior induced abortion.

In many countries, abortion laws are not strictly enforced and, in most countries, some abortions on medical grounds are tolerated. In a few countries with restrictive laws, abortions can readily be obtained from physicians, without interference by the authorities, while in other countries, nonrestrictive laws are not implemented in all localities, with the result that abortion services are not available to women living in these localities.

Over the past ten years, 1967—76, several countries have liberalized their abortion laws to varying degrees, notably Austria, Canada, Denmark, Finland, France, G.F.R., G.D.R., Great Britain, India, Italy, the Republic of Korea, Singapore, Norway, Sweden, Tunisia and the United States. Four countries in eastern Europe have enacted more restrictive legislation during the last decade (Bulgaria, Czechoslavakia, Hungary and Romania).

3. INCIDENCE OF ABORTION

The widely used figure of 55 million pregnancies terminated legally and illegally each year by induced abortion throughout the world, published by the International Planned Parenthood Federation (IPPF, 1974), is an estimate of highly variable validity and has little or no statistical justification. According to the latest available data, legal abortions reported in countries with reasonably complete statistics, most of which appear in Table I, totaled about two million a year (Table I). This figure excludes the three countries with the presumably largest numbers of legal abortions: China, for which there are no statistics; the USSR, which has not published any since the 1930s; and Japan, which publishes annual data but where the reporting of legal abortions is believed to be grossly incomplete (Muramatsu, 1970).

Annual abortion rates in countries and localities where legal abortion has been available in recent years to all or most women have ranged from about 20 to 80 per 1000 women of reproductive age, conventionally defined as 15—44 years. The corresponding abortion ratios have ranged from about 300 to 1300 per 1000 live births. Efforts to estimate the incidence of illegal abortion have not been successful. Many respondents willing to be interviewed about their contraceptive practices are reluctant to reveal their experience with illegal, or even legal, abortion. The classic example of the failure of retrospective surveys to produce reliable data on abortions is the Hungarian Fertility and Family Planning Study of 1966, conducted a decade after the legalization of abortion in that country. In this study, the number of abortions reported for the years 1960—65 corresponded to about 55% of the number known to have been performed in that country's hospitals (Hungary: Demographic Research Institute, 1969). A realistic appraisal of what is known about human fecundity, spontaneous fetal losses, sexual and contraceptive behavior, and the efficacy of contraception as actually practiced, suggests strongly that no country has ever attained a birth rate as low as 15—20 per 1000 population without widespread recourse to induced abortion, legal or illegal. It is probable that the rates and ratios of illegal abortions in countries with restrictive abortion laws are of a similar order of magnitude as the rates and ratios of legal abortions in countries with comparable birth rates, comparable patterns of contraception, and nonrestrictive abortion laws.

Table I
Reported number of legal abortions, abortion rates, and abortion ratios; selected countries, 1970—74.

Area and year	Reported number of abortions [a]	Abortion rate per 1000 women, 15—44 yrs	Abortion ratio per 1000 live births [b]
Bulgaria			
1970	120,900	64.0	882
1971	132,700	70.4	944
1972	133,600	71.0	986
1973	115,400	61.3	799
1974	123,500	65.8	828 [c]
Canada [d]			
1971	37,700	8.1	105
1972	45,400	9.5	131
1973	48,700	10.0	145
Cuba [e]			
1970	70,500	40.3	279
1971	84,800	47,8	326
1972	100,000	55.7	388
1973	112,100	61.6	520
1974	131,500	71.3	640 [c]
Czechoslovakia			
1970	99,800	32.3	427
1971	97,300	31.4	398
1972	91,300	29.2	347
1973	81,200	25.6	287
Denmark			
1970	9,400	9.4	129
1971	11,200	11.1	148
1972	13,000	12.9	176
1973	16,500	16.3	231
1974	24,900	24.3	344
England and Wales [f]			
1970	76,000	8.1	96
1971	94,600	10.1	126
1972	108,600	11.5	158
1973	110,600	11.7	168
1974	109,400	11.5	176
Finland			
1970	14,800	13.8	241
1971	20,400	18.9	337
1972	22,200	20.4	384
1973	23,400	22.4	392
Hungary			
1970	192,300	83.5	1296
1971	187,400	81.3	1242
1972	179,000	77.5	1161
1973	169,600	73.5	1023
1974	102,600	44.6	518
GDR			
1973	110,800	32.2	626

Table I (continued)

Area and year	Reported number of abortions [a]	Abortion rate per 1000 women, 15—44 yrs	Abortion ratio per 1000 live births [b]
Norway			
1970	7900	10.9	123
1971	10,400	14.1	159
1972	12,200	16.4	192
Scotland [g]			
1970	5600	5.5	64
1971	6900	6.8	83
1972	8400	8.3	110
1973	8600	8.5	119
Singapore [h]			
1970	1900	4.1	42
1971	3300	6.3	69
1972	3700	7.4	75
1973	5100	9.8	110
1974	6600	12.3	149
Sweden			
1970	16,100	10.2	143
1971	19,300	12.2	171
1972	24,200	15.2	218
1973	26,000	16.3	237
1974	30,600	19.2	285
Tunisia [h]			
1970	2700	2.7	14
1971	3200	3.0	17
1972	4600	4.2	22
1973	6500	5.8	34
1974	12,400	10.7	NA
United States [i]			
1970	193,500	4.5	52
1971	485,800	11.2	140
1972	586,800	13.2	184
1973	742,500	16.5	239
1974	899,800	19.5	282

[a] Data for the most recent year may be preliminary (Tietze and Murstein, 1975).
[b] Six months later, unless otherwise noted.
[c] Ratio computed per 1000 live births during calender year.
[d] Including residents of Canada obtaining abortions in New York State.
[e] Abortions in government hospitals (no formal legalization).
[f] Residents only.
[g] Including residents of Scotland obtaining abortions in England and Wales.
[h] Abortions performed under the National Family Planning Program.
[i] 1970—72: Abortions reported to state health departments (United States: Center for Disease Control, 1976). 1973—4: Survey of providers of abortion services (Weinstock et al., 1976).

4. PERIOD OF GESTATION

One of the most important factors in the evaluation of morbidity and mortality associated with abortion is the period of gestation (Table II). The major distinction is customarily drawn between abortions in the first trimester and those in the second trimester, that is, between those performed at 12 weeks of gestation or earlier and those at 13 weeks or later. In practice, few abortions are performed after 20 weeks, even when not prohibited by law.

Among the countries for which statistics on legal abortions by period of gestation are available, the proportion of second trimester abortions was highest in Sweden, England and Wales, and the U.S.; much lower in Japan, which has no legal restrictions as to the period of gestation; and lowest in Czechoslovakia and Hungary where, as elsewhere in eastern Europe, second trimester abortions are generally permitted on medical indication only. The percentage of second trimester abortions is declining in all countries where it is still high, most dramatically in Sweden. This downward trend probably reflects: (1) a growing awareness among women and among physicians that abortion is more dangerous later in pregnancy than earlier, and (2) the increasing availability of abortion services.

Table II
Percent distribution of legal abortions by weeks of gestation: selected countries and years

Country and year	Percentage of legal abortions	
	≤ 12 weeks	≥ 13 weeks
Czechoslovakia		
1973	99.4	0.6
England and Wales		
1968	62.0	38.0
1973	81.9	18.1
Hungary		
1973	99.5	0.5
Japan		
1951 [a]	80.8	19.2
1974	96.8	3.2
Sweden		
1968	43.0	57.0
1974	86.7	13.3
United States [b]		
1971	79.9	20.1
1974	87.7	12.3

[a] Gestation reported in months: 3 or less, 4 or more.
[b] Estimate for 1971 based on data from 13 states reporting 66% of all reported abortions; estimate for 1974 based on 32 states and 62% of abortions.
Source: Tietze and Murstein, 1975 (updated).

Late abortions occur most frequently among women of low socioeconomic status and especially among women in the youngest age group. The strong inverse association between period of gestation and women's age probably reflects the inexperience of the very young in recognizing the symptoms of pregnancy, their unwillingness to accept the reality of their situation, their hesitation to confide in figures of authority, and their ignorance about where to seek advice and help. Economic considerations and, in many places, regulations prohibiting surgery on minors without parental consent also contribute to delays.

5. ABORTION PROCEDURES

The methods used by physicians for the termination of pregnancy can be conveniently grouped under three headings: (1) evacuation by instruments through the vaginal route, (2) stimulation of uterine contractions, and (3) major surgery.

Vaginal evacuation is the method of choice for the termination of pregnancy in the first trimester; in some countries, such as the United Kingdom, it is often used in the second trimester as well. The classical method is customarily referred to as dilatation and curettage (D & C). The procedure involves stretching the cervical canal by the insertion of a series of metal dilators, each slightly larger than the preceding one. When the canal has been sufficiently enlarged to permit the passage of instruments into the uterine cavity, the contents of the uterus are removed with a small ovum forceps, following which all remaining placental tissue is scraped out with a metal curette.

In recent years D & C has been progressively replaced by suction, also known as uterine aspiration. This method was first described in China in 1958, became popular in the USSR and other countries of eastern Europe during the early 1960s, and was introduced in Western Europe and the United States in 1966. After dilatation of the cervix, a metal or plastic cannula, either open-ended or with a lateral opening near its end, is inserted into the uterus to dislodge the products of conception from the uterine wall. This technique has been modified for use primarily in the early part of the first trimester. Dilatation may or may not be required. The cannula, developed by Karman, is made of flexible plastic and has two lateral openings on opposite sides; the purpose of this design is to permit the tip of the cannula to bend if it is pushed against the wall of the uterus, thus reducing the risk of perforation. After mobilization, the uterine contents are removed by an electric pump connected to the cannula by a flexible tube. Many gynecologists complete the procedure with a metal curette to make sure that no tissue remains; others believe that doing so increases the risk of perforation. In general, suction is considered to be simpler, quicker, and less traumatic than D & C. Both methods of vaginal evacuation are ordinarily performed under general anesthesia or under local anesthesia by paracervical block.

Menstrual regulation (MR), also known as endometrial aspiration, interception of pregnancy, or minisuction, is a variant of the suction procedure limited to the first two weeks after a missed menstrual period when pregnancy cannot yet be diagnosed reliably by either pelvic examination or currently available urine tests. As a rule, neither anesthesia nor dilatation is required. A flexible Karman cannula with a diameter of 4—5 mm is used for the removal of the uterine contents and the necessary vacuum is produced manually by a 50-ml syringe. While abortions early in the first trimester are associated with fewer complications than those performed a few weeks later, failure to terminate the pregnancy occurs more frequently. Moreover, many women who experience a delayed menstrual period are not pregnant, and it has been argued that there is no sound medical reason to expose these women to the admittedly small risks associated with MR, at least in situations where abortion is legal. In individual cases, however, there may be good psychological or social reasons for doing so.

During the second trimester of pregnancy, abortion is usually initiated by the stimulation of uterine contractions. One widely used method, especially in the United States, is the replacement of amniotic fluid by hypertonic salt solution. The uterus is tapped by means of a needle through the abdominal wall and a quantity of fluid, usually 200 ml, is withdrawn and replaced by an equal or larger amount of saline, without use of anesthesia. The fetal heartbeat usually disappears within one and a half hours. As a rule, labor starts 12 to 36 h after salt infusion, and the expulsion of the fetus and placenta is completed a few hours later. The physiologic mechanism by which this effect is produced is not fully understood.

A more recent method for the stimulation of uterine contractions is the intra-amniotic injection (without prior withdrawal of fluid) of prostaglandins in single or in repeated doses. The interval from injection to fetal expulsion tends to be shorter than with hypertonic saline. Other routes of application of prostaglandins, now under investigation, may be used in the first as well as in the second trimester of pregnancy.

The two major surgical procedures used for the termination of pregnancy are hysterotomy and hysterectomy, usually performed under general anesthesia. Hysterotomy is in essence a cesarean section at any stage of pregnancy before the fetus is viable. The uterus is usually approached by laparotomy, but up to the 16th week hysterotomy can also be performed by the vaginal route. Because the scar in the uterine wall following hysterotomy is thought to weaken the tissue and thus likely to cause rupture of the uterus at a later delivery, many physicians believe that all subsequent pregnancies will require cesarean section. For this reason, hysterotomy is usually combined with tubal sterilization.

Hysterectomy is a sterilizing procedure involving the removal of the uterus, but not of the ovaries, and is, therefore, not a castrating operation, as some ill-informed persons fear. Hysterectomy is often performed when the purpose of the operation is the removal of the uterus because of fibroid tumors as well as the termination of the pregnancy. Some gynecologists recommend hysterectomy in lieu of tubal sterilization in order to avoid possible later complications in an organ they consider nonfunctional. Hysterectomy can be achieved by either the abdominal or vaginal route.

Techniques used by lay persons to induce abortion, including self-abortion, range from spells and incantations through a variety of traditional medications, which tend to be ineffective and/or toxic, to grossly traumatizing procedures designed to damage or destroy the conceptus, leaving its expulsion to natural forces. The most widely used procedure is probably the insertion of such foreign bodies into the uterus as twigs, roots, metal rods, hooks, and rubber tubes. In some parts of the world, injection into the uterus of soapy water or some readily available household disinfectants has been reported.

6. COMPLICATIONS OF ABORTION

Induced abortion, at any period of gestation, exposes the woman to a risk of complications which can vary considerably, depending on the circumstances under which the abortion is performed. The severity of complications also varies widely from very minor complaints to the occasional fatal outcome.

Serious immediate complications are rare with legal abortions. They may include perforation of the uterus by one of the instruments used in vaginal evacuation, sometimes combined with injury to the intestines, or other organs; major hemorrhage, laceration of the cervix, severe disturbances of blood coagulation and hypernatremia associated with saline-induced abortions, water intoxication resulting from the use of high doses of oxytocin, and untoward effects of general or local anesthesia.

The most frequent delayed complications include retention of fragments of the placenta resulting in postabortal bleeding; infection, which may range from mild endometritis through more severe forms of pelvic inflammatory disease to generalized peritonitis and septicemia; and venous thrombophlebitis resulting in pulmonary embolism. Postabortal depression has been reported but is rare. Guilt feelings are usually of short duration whereas relief is a frequently noted psychological reaction.

Known late somatic complications or sequelae of induced abortion are sensitization of Rh-negative women by red blood cells from an Rh-positive fetus (preventable by injection of Rh immune globulin) and endometriosis in the scar tissue following hysterotomy. A third type of late complication, considered definite by some investigators but questioned by others (U.S.: National Academy of Sciences, 1975), is an increased risk in subsequent pregnancies of premature birth and neonatal mortality and of spontaneous abortion in the second trimester. These complications may be due to a 'combination of damage to the cervix at the time of dilatation and placental insufficiency resulting from too vigorous curettage of the basal layers of the endometrium' (Kleinman, 1972). Prospective studies, sponsored by the World Health Organization (WHO), have been initiated in several countries to provide more information on this important question. Secondary sterility and ectopic pregnancy can be the late results of pelvic infection, following self-induced abortions or abortions performed by unskilled operators. The role of legal abortion in the etiology of these conditions has not been established.

Some authors, including psychiatrists, have expressed the view that every abortion is a stressful experience involving major risks to mental health. Others have pointed out that most women undergoing abortion continue to lead essentially normal lives and that an adverse psychological reaction to an unwanted child may be far more common and more serious than the reaction to having an abortion. A WHO Scientific Group on Spontaneous and Induced Abortion states that 'there is no doubt that the termination of pregnancy may precipitate a serious psychoneurotic or even psychotic reaction in a susceptible individual.' (WHO, 1970). However, the report notes that emotional stress experienced by the woman may be more closely associated with such factors as the circumstances under which the abortion was performed, the period of gestation, the type of operation, and the attitudes of the woman's family and of the professionals involved in the abortion. With increasing acceptance of abortion, concern about its long-term effects on mental health appears to be diminishing.

The statistical evaluation of morbidity following abortion is made difficult by the fact that there are no generally accepted criteria of what constitutes a complication. The most comprehensive investigation of this type was undertaken in the United States under the Joint Program for the Study of Abortion (JPSA), sponsored by the Population Council (Tietze and Lewit, 1972). It involved the voluntary participation of the Obstetrics and Gynecology Departments of 60 teaching hospitals in 12 States and the District of Columbia and six abortion clinics not affiliated with hospitals. Reports on 73,000 patients aborted from mid-1970 to mid-1971, about one-seventh of all legal abortions in the United States during that year, were assembled and analyzed.

In this study all complications reported by the participating investigators were included in the analysis; each patient with more than one reported complication was counted only once. Because of the large number and wide geographic distribution of participating institutions, the total complication rates may represent the 'average' or 'typical' definition of 'complication' among American physicians performing legal abortions at the time of the investigation.

Major complications were defined by the JPSA on the basis of uniform criteria such as: unintended major surgery, hemorrhage requiring one or more blood transfusions, protracted fever; and in a small group of women individually classified, complications associated with roughly comparable risks of death, prolonged illness, or permanent functional impairment.

Complication rates reported by the JPSA were computed in two ways: from all known complications occurring in the total number of patients, and from complications reported on follow-up (10 or more days after abortion), where women attended clinics locally. The local follow-up rate therefore represents the maximum rate of complications.

In analyzing the complications of abortion, it is necessary to distinguish those attributable to the termination of pregnancy from those associated with pre-existing disease or with surgical procedures undertaken for other purposes, such as the removal of a uterus because of fibroid tumors or for

Table III
Total and major complications related to by gestation, abortion procedure and sterilization.

Gestation, abortion procedure	Total complications		Major complications	
	Total patients [c]	Local patients with FU [f]	Total patients [e]	Local patients with FU [f]
All patients				
12 weeks or less	5.2	7.8	0.6	1.1
13 weeks or more	22.2	26.1	2.2	3.0
All gestations	9.6	13.1	1.0	1.6
Patients without pre-existing complications or sterilizing operations:				
12 weeks or less	4.2	6.2	0.4	0.6
13 weeks or more	20.6	24.0	1.6	2.1
All gestations	8.4	11.1	0.7	1.0
Procedure:				
Suction [a,b]	4.2	6.1	0.4	0.6
D and C [a,b]	6.0	8.2	0.4	0.8
Saline [a,b]	23.4	27.2	1.7	2.4
Hysterotomy [a,c]	33.4	32.9	6.7	6.9
Hysterectomy [a]	49.9	50.4	14.3	15.6
Sterilization: [a,d]				
Done	14.0	16.9	2.8	3.5
Not done	4.2	6.1	0.4	0.6

[a] Patients without pre-existing complications.
[b] Without tubal sterilization.
[c] With tubal sterilization.
[d] Aborted by suction.
[e] Data obtained at time of abortion.
[f] Includes data from a follow-up examination (FU) at least 10 days after the abortion.
Source: Tietze and Lewit, 1972.

permanent sterility. Complication rates were computed not only for the aggregate of all patients, but also for presumably healthy women subject only to the risks associated with the abortion procedure itself.

As shown in Table III, the minimum estimate of the total complication rate, including all reported diagnoses and complaints, was 9.6 per 100 women and 13.1 per 100 local women with follow-up. Complication rates during the second trimester of pregnancy were 3—4 times as high as the rates during the first trimester. The pattern was similar for major complications. About 1 in 9 patients with any complications experienced a major complication. Compared with all patients, complication rates among the presumably healthy women, exposed to the risk of abortion only, were lower at each period of gestation. Rates of total and of major complications were lowest for abortions by suction, followed in ascending order by D & C, infusion of hypertonic saline solution, hysterotomy, and hysterectomy. For women aborted by suction, the risk of post-abortal complications was considerably increased when a tubal sterilization was performed concurrently with the abortion.

In 26 of the hospitals participating in JPSA for a full year, rates of total and major complications following abortion in the first trimester declined by approximately one-half. There was no decrease in complication rates of abortions during the second trimester, mainly by the saline method, in the same hospitals over the 1-year period.

7. MORTALITY DUE TO ABORTION

Mortality associated with legal abortion can no longer be evaluated on the basis of clinical studies because of the extremely low level to which it has declined. To obtain stable rates it is necessary to use statistics for large populations. Table IV shows such data, by weeks of gestation, for England and Wales and the United States during recent years. Because a substantial proportion of legal abortions in England are combined with surgical sterilization, which carries its own risks, the data from that country are limited to the abortions without sterilization. In the United States comparatively few abortions are combined with sterilization.

The outstanding finding in regard to mortality associated with legal abortion is the strong association between mortality and period of gestation. In the United States during 1972—74 the mortality ratio ranged from 0.4 per 100,000 legal abortions at 8 weeks or less to 17 per 100,000 for abortions at 16 weeks or more. In England and Wales during 1968—73 the pattern was similar, but the mortality ratio was higher at each period of gestation, probably reflecting the greater number of years covered by the statistics. Other factors contributing to the higher abortion mortality in England and Wales as compared with the United States are the more frequent use of hysterotomy and the greater average age of the women obtaining abortions.

Table IV
Number of legal abortions, number of deaths, and mortality per 100,000 abortions, by weeks of gestation: England and Wales, 1968—73, and United States, 1972—74.

Country and gestation	Legal abortions	Number of deaths	Ratio per 100,000
England and Wales [a]			
8 weeks or less	115,000	2	1.7
9—12 weeks	315,000	12	3.8
13—16 weeks	96,000	9	9.4
17 weeks or more	22,000	9	41
United States [b]			
8 weeks or less	851,000	3	0.4
9—10 weeks	658,000	13	2.0
11—12 weeks	374,000	12	3.2
13 15 weeks	146,000	12	8.2
16 weeks or more	200,000	34	17

[a] Abortions without sterilization (Kestelman, 1975).
[b] Estimate based on United States: Center for Disease Control (1976).

Abortion-related mortality may be compared appropriately with the risk associated with carrying a pregnancy to term. In the U.S., maternal mortality attributed to complications of pregnancy and childbirth, excluding abortion, had declined to 15 deaths per 100,000 live births in 1972—74. Most of these occurred late in pregnancy, during labor, or during the puerperal period. Adjustment to the age distribution of women obtaining legal abortions raises the maternal mortality ratio to about 17 per 100,000. The corresponding ratios for England and Wales in 1968—73 were 14 and 18, respectively. It would appear, then, that in both countries mortality was substantially lower with first-trimester abortion (1.5 per 1000 women in the U.S.) than with childbirth. Mortality with late abortion was comparable to that with childbirth in the U.S., but in England the mortality ratio was higher for late abortion than for childbirth.

It is generally recognized that mortality is much higher following abortions that are self-induced or induced by untrained persons than with those legally performed in hospitals and clinics. It is impossible, however, to quantify these higher risks, since mortality reflects not only the skill of the persons performing or initiating the illegal abortions, but also the availability, utilization, and quality of subsequent medical and hospital services in the event life-threatening complications develop.

8. EFFECTS OF LEGALIZATION OF ABORTION

Liberalization of abortion laws and policies has resulted in the substitution of legal abortions for illegal abortions and for unwanted births. Eradicating illegal abortions is primarily a matter of public health; preventing unwanted births has obvious demographic implications. Which of the two predominates depends on the situation in which legalization occurs.

If, prior to liberalization of the abortion law, the birth rate was low, as it usually is in developed countries, the incidence of illegal abortions was probably high, contraception was widely practiced, and unwanted births were comparatively infrequent. In this situation legalization of abortion produces a greater effect on public health than on population growth.

Because the transition from a restrictive, narrowly interpreted abortion law to a law providing for abortion on request was quite abrupt in New York City, it resulted in a rise in the number of legal abortions from a few hundred per year to almost 70,000 during the first year of the new law, and because the increment in the number of abortions from the first to the second year was far smaller than the corresponding decline in births six months later, it is possible to estimate the relative magnitude of the demographic and public health effects.

According to my own previously published analysis of the two-year experience in New York City it would appear that about 70% of the legal abortions of resident women replaced illegal abortions, while 30% replaced unwanted births, contributing about one-half to the decline in births from 1970 to 1972 (Tietze, 1973). The other half of the decline in births resulted from other factors — notably more general and more effective practice of contraception, including increasing acceptance of voluntary surgical sterilization by men and women. About 45% of the legal abortions among New York City residents were obtained by women who had never borne a child and almost 20% by women with only one prior birth; most of the births prevented by these abortions will probably be made up in later years. The ultimate demographic impact will perhaps be as little as 0.15 children per woman.

The public health effect of a non-restrictive abortion policy is most clearly reflected in a declining number of deaths attributable to abortion. In Hungary and Czechoslovakia, where policies were liberalized in the 1950's, reported mortality from abortion declined by 50 and 75%, respectively, in the course of a few years. No such declines occurred over the same period in other European countries where restrictive legislation remained in force. More recently, mortality from abortion has declined in England and Wales and in the U.S. after legal abortions became more available. Table V summarizes statistics for the U.S.

The number of abortion-related deaths declined from an annual average of 292 during the period 1958—62 to 158 in 1969, when access to abortion was limited to a few states, and subsequently to 48 in 1974, two years following the ruling of the Supreme Court invalidating restrictive abortion laws. The annual rate of decline during the earlier period averaged 6.6%, probably reflecting more effective contraception, fewer illegal abortions, and more successful treatment of complications. From 1969 to 1974 the number of

Table V
Deaths associated with abortion, by type of abortion: United States, 1958—73.

Year(s)	Type of abortion		
	Legal	Spontaneous or illegal	Total
1958—62	5	287	292
1963—67	4	218	222
1968	5	157	162
1969	4	154	158
1970	30	128	158
1971	46	86	132
1972	24	64	88
1973	26	30	56
1974	24	24	48

Source: Tietze, 1975 (updated).

deaths declined at an average annual rate of 21%. It is difficult not to link the acceleration of the downward trend to a replacement of illegal by legal abortions.

Deaths associated with spontaneous or illegal abortions declined even more rapidly in the United States from 1969 to 1974 than the overall mortality rate associated with abortion. Most of these deaths were associated with illegal, rather than spontaneous abortions. In the 1960s, a substantial proportion of illegal abortions in the United States were performed by physicians, including some highly experienced practitioners. This is no longer true. Women having illegal abortions in 1974 were probably the poorest and least educated and were most likely to obtain the services of unqualified practitioners or to attempt self-abortion. It is entirely possible that the mortality rate in illegal abortion is now higher, not lower, than it was 10 or 15 years ago. A change to a more restrictive abortion policy increases the number of illegal abortions and of associated deaths. In Romania, for example, the enactment of a restrictive abortion law in 1966 was followed by an increase in deaths due to abortion from 64 in 1965 to 364 in 1971. A change to a less restrictive abortion policy, however, reduced the number of illegal abortions, and consequently the mortality rate.

BIBLIOGRAPHY

Hungary. Demographic Research Institute (1969) *Survey Techniques in Fertility and Family Research: Experience in Hungary.* (Budapest) pp. 110—118.

IPPF (1974) International Planned Parenthood Federation. *Survey of World Needs in Family Planning.* (London.)

Kalis, M. and David, H.P. (1974) Abortion legislation: A summary international classification, 1974. In: (H.P. David, Ed.) *Abortion Research: International Experience.* (D.C. Heath, Lexington, Mass.) pp. 13—34.

Kestelman, P. (1975) Personal estimates, derived from OPCS published and unpublished data (October).

Kleinman, R.L. (Ed.) (1972) *Induced Abortion.* (IPPF, London.)

Muramatsu, M. (1970) An analysis of factors in fertility control in Japan. *Bull. Inst. Public Health* 19 (2) pp. 97—107.

Tietze, C. (1973) Two years' experience with a liberal abortion law: Its impact on fertility trends in New York City. *Fam. Plann. Perspect.* 5, no. 1 (Winter) pp. 36—41.

Tietze, C. (1975) Legalization of abortion, population growth and public health. *Fam. Plann. Perspect.* 7, no. 3 (May/June) pp. 123—127.

Tietze, C. and Lewit, S. (1972) Joint Program for the Study of Abortion (JPSA): Early medical complications of legal abortion. *Stud. Fam. Plann.* 3, no. 6 (June) pp. 97—122.

Tietze, C. and Murstein, M.C. (1975) Induced abortion: 1975 Factbook. *Rep. Popul./Fam. Plann.*, no. 14 (December).

U.S. Center for Disease Control (1976) *Abortion Surveillance 1974.* Atlanta (April).

USDHEW (1975) Office of the Secretary. "Protection of human subjects: fetuses, pregnant women, and in vitro fertilization." *Federal Register* 40, no. 154 (8 August), pp. 33, 526—533, 552.

U.S. National Academy of Sciences (1975) Institute of Medicine. *Legalized Abortion and the Public Health: Report of a Study by a Committee of the Institute of Medicine, May 1975.* Washington, D.C.: National Academy of Sciences (May).

Weinstock, E., Tietze, C., Jaffe, F.S. and Dryfoos, J.G. (1976) Abortion needs and services in the United States, 1974—1975. *Fam. Plann. Perspect.* 8, no. 2 (March/April) pp. 58—69.

WHO (1970) *Spontaneous and Induced Abortion.* Technical Report Series No. 461. (World Health Organization, Geneva.)

CHAPTER 45

Psychosocial aspects of fertility regulation

E. PATRICIA McCORMICK, RAYMOND L. JOHNSON,
HERBERT L. FRIEDMAN and HENRY P. DAVID

1. INTRODUCTION

Theoretical rationale

Throughout their fertile years, men and women are faced with many choices and alternative courses of action which will largely determine the success of their efforts to control fertility. The degree to which choices are based on realistic appraisals of benefits, costs, and consequences is held to be the keystone of healthy fertility-regulating decisions (Friedman, Johnson and David, unpublished).

Numerous academic and professional disciplines are involved in studying varied aspects of fertility regulation, including anthropology, demography, economics, medicine, public health, psychology, and sociology. While fertility regulation in vivo is the product of a complex of interacting forces, it is usually experienced on an individual level within a specific psychosocial environment. Understanding, predicting, and modifying fertility-regulating behavior requires analysis of environmental as well as personal forces synthesized within an individual. The process typically involves two people and is subject to change over the life cycle.

The couple

In studying fertility regulation, it is important to observe all aspects which may inhibit or facilitate reproduction, particularly expressed or unexpressed perceptions one partner may have about the other. For example, it appears that in many countries abortion is a topic about which men are less well informed than women, whereas contraceptive practices may be more openly discussed. However, the decision to terminate an unwanted pregnancy or the choice of a contraceptive is most probably determined by the joint estimates of the consequences to the couple (even in those instances where such judgments are made by one partner alone).

Handbook of Sexology, edited by J. Money and H. Musaph
© *Elsevier/North-Holland Biomedical Press, 1977*

While it is not always feasible to study both members of a couple at the same time, it is frequently possible to ascertain what each partner believes to be the perceptions of his or her spouse. Cross-sectional surveys of men and women yield less adequate and predictive information than simultaneous but separate interviews (by skilled and experienced interviewers) on the same fertility topic. Better understanding of the dynamics of fertility regulation is more likely to result from couple profiles than from profiles obtained separately from women and men.

The psychosocial model of fertility-regulating behavior, originally developed by Friedman and Kellerhals (Friedman, 1972), emphasizes the subjective assessment of the environment by the individual and the importance of the two partners in determining each other's decision. Extension of this model and its implications for research methodology have been summarized elsewhere (Friedman, 1974a; Friedman et al., 1976).

The life cycle

Biopsychosocial conditions of fertility tend to change throughout a person's or couple's life cycle. While numerous studies have reported on 'women at risk' or 'women in their fertile years', or focused on 'age and parity', emphasis has usually been on demographic rather than psychosocial or psycho-economic variables.

Miller (1972) and others have noted that there are recurrent hazard points in the sexual and procreational careers of women at which times the risk of unwanted pregnancy may be particularly high. For example, immediately after marriage the threat of out-of-wedlock pregnancy is removed and contraceptive vigilance may be more relaxed. In terms of the life cycle, the biopsychosocial 'fertility career' of most couples may be divided into three major phases, reviewed in the following sections of this chapter: (1) the postpubertal adolescent period prior to the stage at which children are desired; (2) the actual fertile years, usually in a stable partner relationship when children may be desired but preferably spaced at convenient times; and (3) the premenopausal or later years of marriage when children are no longer desired.

While it is sometimes difficult to determine the borders of these stages for each couple, it is possible to divide available literature on psychosocial aspects of fertility regulation into subsegments of the adolescent years, family building among young adults, and the constraints of later years of marriage. That is what we have tried to do in this review, focusing more on evolving psychosocial approaches than on specific methods of fertility regulation.

Chapter overview

In considering recent reports on adolescent sexuality in diverse cultures, it has become apparent that the age of initiation is decreasing and the extent of activity increasing, while the relationships continue to be limited, often to the intended spouse. Typically, research has focused on young women; partner perceptions have rarely been sought. The interaction between awareness of information on fertility regulation, practice of contraception, and resort to abortion appears to be complex, often influenced by a range of societal and personal psychological factors. The individual is further handicapped by the lack of ready access to effective contraception for many adolescents and unmarried younger women and the restrictions imposed by conservative medical practitioners in many parts of the world. At the same time, more attention is gradually being given to understanding the sociocultural and interpersonal context in which adolescents develop motivation and competence in contraceptive practice and the prevention of unwanted pregnancies.

Perhaps the most hopeful progress is among younger adult couples who are delaying marriage and effectively planning a smaller family. This section of our review takes a psychoeconomic perspective and suggests possible patterns of interaction between the costs and benefits of children which might account for the apparent changes in family size. It appears that there is an increasing expense associated or perceived to be associated with parenthood, especially when coupled with rising expectations for a better standard of living. If economic aspirations can lead to more rational fertility regulation as evidenced in the declining birthrates among younger married couples, then the tempo of family formation may be slowed by policies oriented to such psychoeconomic motivations.

Discussion of the later years in marriage, when most couples presumably wish to prevent additional childbirths, focuses largely on psychosocial aspects of fertility termination, either by vasectomy or female sterilization procedures. Advantages appear to outweigh disadvantages. A choice voluntarily and jointly made by both marital partners without outside pressure is likely to have generally positive consequences.

As noted on another occasion (Friedman, 1974b), individual and/or couple success in fertility regulation depends largely on motivation to delay or prevent childbirth and the implementation of that motivation. Motivation relates to social pressure, the stage in the couple's fertility career, degree of couple concordance and mutual understanding, perceived capability of controlling one's environment, and prior experience (and success) with any kind of planning. Given the right combination of ingredients, effective implementation of fertility regulation often becomes a question of community resources and availability of information, accessible services, and sensitive management of counseling needs.

As apparent from the number of co-authors, this chapter is the product of several hands, differing approaches, and diverse writing styles. It endeavors, however, to reflect a consistent approach rooted in our experience, continuing interaction, and exchange of ideas with colleagues in the U.S. and other lands.

In subsequent sections, available literature on psychosocial aspects of fertility regulation is reviewed in terms of actual behavior among adolescents (E.P. McCormick), young married adults (R.L. Johnson), and couples in later years of marriage (H.L. Friedman). One of us (H.P. David) prepared the introduction and overview. Everyone contributed to the editorial process.

2. ADOLESCENCE

Introduction

The regulation of fertility in adolescence is of growing concern to professionals in a variety of disciplines. Earlier initiation and increasing incidences of sexual activity, rising rates of out-of-wedlock births, the spread of venereal disease, and the increasing resolution of unwanted pregnancies by abortion have accelerated efforts toward better understanding. Recent research has focused on contributory factors and influences, the sociocultural context, and effective services and intervention measures appropriate to the needs of youth.

From a psychosocial perspective, adolescence is viewed as a transitional period preparatory to the assumption of adult sex roles and responsibilities. Until recently, successful completion of adolescence was characterized by biologic maturity, financial competence, and freedom to undertake the responsibilities of marriage and a family in a socially acceptable manner. While puberty now occurs earlier than in previous generations, financial self-sufficiency and sociological maturity are further delayed. Modern society's demand for increased education and technologic skills, particularly in the more developed countries, has tended to postpone marriage and family formation. The contemporary adolescent usually encounters a prolonged period of sexual awareness and need, often without means of socially acceptable gratification (Wolfish, 1973).

Regions and countries vary widely in the incidence of premarital sexual activity, problems associated with premarital conceptions, and the emphasis placed on fertility regulation in adolescence. In those nations where marriage traditionally follows closely upon puberty and laws against the extramarital loss of virginity are stringent (as, for example, in some lands of Africa and Asia where cultural traditions of Islam and Hinduism prevail), sexual permissiveness is uncommon and fertility regulation among unmarried adolescents of minimal concern. However, in countries predominantly Christian in religion and Judeo-Christian in ethos, changing trends in adolescent sexual behavior have stimulated more intensive approaches to fertility regulation (Llewellyn-Jones, 1974).

Fertility regulation among young and unmarried couples is influenced by a range of factors, often quite distinct from those encountered in later years and/or among married persons. The discussion that follows reviews selected major research findings, with primary reference to the U.S.

Sexual behavior in adolescence

Although evidence on the incidence of premarital sexual intercourse among teenagers is conflicting, most would agree that it is widespread. In recent years within the U.S., debate has arisen over trends in sexual behavior; some observers maintain that a virtual sexual revolution has occurred since the turn of this century (Ehrmann, 1964). Those who disagree point out that greater liberalization in sexual attitudes has not necessarily been accompanied by a corresponding change in behavior, particularly coital experience (Reiss, 1966; Osofsky, 1971).

Still others, in evaluating research findings, cite methodological limitations which preclude consensus; major restrictions in research design include lack of comparability between studies, restricted sampling on limited subpopulations, and the absence of standardized measures (Cannon and Long, 1971). Nonetheless, the most recent and reliable evidence suggests that the extent of premarital intercourse among teenagers is on the increase (Kantner and Zelnik, 1972).

Few research studies have involved probability samples of large populations, particularly among youth. A notable exception is the Kantner and Zelnik survey of 1971 involving a national sample of the 15–19-year-old female population living in U.S. households, providing perhaps the most valid and up-to-date estimate of the incidence of sexual intercourse among adolescents. Their report indicates the proportions who had experienced coitus increased within each age group from a level of 14% at age of 15 to 46% by age 19. Notable differences were observed, with the incidence in general greater among blacks, those of lower socioeconomic status, urban residents, those living in mother-headed households, and among less frequent churchgoers (Kantner and Zelnik, 1972).

Age at first coitus varied by race, with 75% of the never married, sexually experienced, black respondents having had intercourse before age 18, compared to 40% of the white subjects. The survey indicated also that premarital intercourse among women of both races was beginning at younger ages. It was estimated that a minimum of 3% of the women who were 19 in 1971 were likely to have had sexual intercourse by age 15, compared to 9% of those who were currently 15.

Sexual relationships were not indiscriminate. Three-fifths of the sexually experienced young women had only one partner ever, and half reported that they only had relations with the man they intended to marry. Frequency of intercourse was limited; approximately two-thirds of those with sexual experience had either had intercourse only once or twice, or not at all, in the month prior to the interview (Kantner and Zelnik, 1972).

Cross-cultural research on sexual behavior in adolescence, particularly large-scale research, is limited. Schofield's study of English youth represents a welcome exception, especially because it explores the sexual attitudes and behavior of both young men and women. The interviews were obtained with a random sample of 1873 unmarried teenagers between the ages of 15 and 19 living in London boroughs in 1965. About 30% of the older boys (17—19 years) had experienced sexual intercourse, compared to 11% of the younger boys (15—17 years); among the girls, the corresponding figures were 16% and 6%. Fewer than 1% of the boys or girls had experienced sexual intercourse before the age of 14. Projecting from study findings, it was predicted that by age 16, 14% of the boys and 5% of the girls will have had sexual relations. And by 18, a third of the boys and about 1 in 6 of the girls will have experienced heterosexual relations at least once. (A follow-up study 7 years later of a subsample of these respondents showed that the gap in sexual experience narrowed as the boys and girls reached adulthood. By the age of 21, 75% of the men and 71% of the women had experienced sexual intercourse). These estimates of sexual activity among the young women are substantially less than the incidence reported among their counterparts in the U.S. six years later (Schofield, 1965, 1973; Kantner and Zelnik, 1972).

A mid-1960 investigation of the sexual attitudes and behavior of both male and female college students in Canada, England, Germany, Norway and the U.S. (Luckey and Nass, 1969) revealed the highest proportion of coital experience reported by English respondents, 74.8% of the men and 62.8% of the women. The subjects with the least incidence of sexual intercourse were from Canada (among the female students) and from Germany (among the male students). Among these, the proportions having participated in coitus were 35.3% and 54.5% respectively. Men tended to be younger than women at age of first coitus, except for Canadian and English men who reported initial coitus at nearly the same age as Canadian and English women (17.5 years). This was also the lowest age indicated by respondents from any of the countries. While considerable variation existed in the sample in the reported number of coital partners, the majority of female students in all countries, except England, reported having either only one or two partners.

A comparison of three earlier Japanese surveys of high school and university students (1948, 1953, and 1960) indicates considerably less sexual activity among adolescents, although increases over time were evident (Asayama, 1975). Trends reflect a situation close to that in the U.S. and European countries.

Of particular bearing on fertility regulation in adolescence are the following observations derived from research findings: (1) although inconclusive, there is some evidence that the extent of sexual intercourse among adolescents is increasing; (2) at the same time, the age of initiation of coitus appears to be decreasing; (3) frequency of intercourse, as reported, usually does not exceed several times a month; and (4) sexual relationships tend to be limited to a few partners, often to the future intended spouse.

Contraceptive behavior in adolescence

Findings on the incidence of sexual experience in adolescence appear less congruent than the reports of contraceptive practice. Data have been derived from surveys on young women who are premaritally pregnant, those seeking contraceptive assistance or requesting pregnancy termination, and through more general surveys of adolescent sexual and contraceptive behavior. Typically, the perceptions of partners have not been surveyed.

Findings document that while many sexually experienced female adolescents have contracepted at some time, regular contraceptive use is considerably less frequent. (Furstenberg et al., 1969; Braestrup, 1971; Goldsmith et al., 1972; Kane and Lachenbruch, 1973; Kantner and Zelnik, 1973; Presser, 1974.) A New York survey of mothers having their first baby indicated that only 45% of the respondents aged 15—19 years had ever contracepted and less than 10% had used a method consistently during the month of conception even though the pregnancy was unintended (Presser, 1974). Data on unmarried mothers under the age of 21 in Copenhagen in 1968 corroborated these findings. Although a higher proportion, 67%, had ever contracepted, only a few had contracepted on the occasion when they became pregnant (Braestrup, 1971). A small study in North Carolina, comparing aborting and nonaborting pregnant young women, indicated that while the majority in both groups were noncontraceptors, those seeking abortion were somewhat more likely to have had contraceptive experience. However, the young women in both groups were equally desirous of avoiding a pregnancy (Kane and Lachenbruch, 1973). In another sample utilizing both aborting and nonaborting patients in 1971, drawn from 14 municipal hospitals in New York City, those patients seeking abortion were also contraceptive users to a greater extent than those whose pregnancies continued to term (Daily and Nicholas, 1972). A third comparison group was added to a study in California. A contraception group (never-pregnant young women seeking contraception), an abortion group, and a maternity group (residents in two maternity homes) comprised the study population. All of the young women were 17 years of age or younger and unwed. As in previous studies, those respondents seeking abortion were more contraceptively experienced than the nonaborting women in the maternity group. However, those who had never been pregnant and were seeking contraception had used contraceptives in the past to a greater extent than either of the other two groups of adolescents (Goldsmith et al., 1972).

More general investigations of the sexual and contraceptive experience of adolescents indicate that while most young women have used contraceptives at some time in the past, a minority are consistent users (Schofield, 1965; Bauman, 1970; Kantner and Zelnik, 1973). In general, the younger the women the less likely that contraceptives either have ever been used or used consistently (Daily and Nicholas, 1972; Settlage et al., 1973).

Where contraception is used, various methods tend to be tried, most often nonprescriptive and ineffective ones (Goldsmith et al., 1972). Some investigators, however, have found substantial resort to effective means. Accordingly, the method most recently used was either the pill or condom by nearly half of the 15—19-year-old sexually experienced never-married women in the

1971 national U.S. survey (Kantner and Zelnik, 1973). Somewhat higher percentages of past experience with these two methods were reported by young women seeking medical assistance in obtaining contraception for the first time from five family planning clinics in California. Over two-thirds, 70%, of the respondents indicated having used either the condom or pill in the past; all of the subjects were aged 17 or younger, unmarried, and never-pregnant (Settlage et al., 1973).

Noncontraception

Reasons for failure to contracept among adolescents are complex, not easily attributable to any one or several factors, and are most likely influenced by a mixture of situational, interpersonal, and intrapersonal considerations. It has been assumed that lack of knowledge is a major determinant of the failure to contracept. Two aspects particularly have been cited — lack of understanding of reproductive functioning and lack of knowledge about contraceptive measures themselves.

Ignorance about physiological aspects has been repeatedly documented (Furstenberg, 1971b; Presser, 1974). The period of greatest risk of conception during the menstrual cycle and the point after the menarche when pregnancy can occur are frequently misunderstood. The most common fallacy in the U.S. survey was that the period of greatest risk was right before, during, or after the menses (Kantner and Zelnik, 1972). This is particularly distressing considering the substantial numbers of young women who rely upon their 'safe period' to avoid pregnancy. Chance taking is common among those who fail to use contraception not only because they believe that it is the wrong time of the month to become pregnant, but also that they are too young or have sex too infrequently to conceive (Thiebaux, 1972; Kantner and Zelnik, 1973; Presser, 1974).

Knowledge of contraceptive measures is difficult to evaluate because it has so often been assessed solely by inquiring of respondents which methods are familiar to them. More often than not there is no attempt to appraise the depth and scope of knowledge the adolescent may possess about a contraceptive method, aspects that may be important in selection of a method and assurance of use. Such approaches have yielded estimates ranging from only approximately 50% of an adolescent study population in rural India who spontaneously mentioned even one contraceptive method with which they were acquainted, to nearly all study subjects in an urban U.S. project serving adolescents (Furstenberg, 1971a; Taylor, 1973). Ironically, young women often tend to be most aware of those forms of contraception to which they have the least access (Furstenberg, 1971a).

Regardless of facility of recall, adolescent contraceptive knowledge characteristically is limited and superficial. This is hardly surprising considering the circumstances under which such information is acquired. While casual conversations with friends, who are often equally misinformed, are a frequently cited source, health personnel, teachers, and parents are far less often the primary source of information (Schofield, 1965; Braestrup, 1971; Connell and Jacobson, 1971; Furstenberg, 1971a; Thiebaux, 1972; Presser, 1974).

The link between source of information and contraceptive use has been explained by Furstenberg (1971a). In his investigation of pregnant adolescents, not only was birth control more likely to have been used by girls from families in which contraception had been discussed but the mode of instruction as well had an effect. Where the mother counseled the girl to use a specific method, birth control was more likely to have been used. However, when instruction was extremely vague, contraceptive practice was hardly greater than if nothing at all had been said. In addition to providing specific information, another aspect of the mother—daughter communication was postulated as significant in promoting contraceptive use; in raising the issue of contraceptive use, a mother indicates her awareness that her daughter is sexually active. This revelation allows the girl to define sex less as a spontaneous and uncontrollable act and more as subject to planning and regulation (Furstenberg, 1971a).

The influence of communication has been inferred in the nature of the dyadic relationship. Kirkendall (1961), in an exploratory study of college men, categorized their heterosexual liaisons along a continuum of six levels according to the intensity and emotional attachment associated with the relationships. While contraception was not extensively used within any level, there was substantially more evidence of contraceptive use at the levels of deeper emotional involvement than within less committed relationships. These liaisons were characterized by more developed interpersonal communication, not only in the exchange of ideas and awareness of feelings and attitudes but also concerning the sexual relationship itself (Kirkendall, 1961). A similar conclusion was reached in a study of unmarried aborting women in the Netherlands; prior contraceptive use was more often associated with stable relationships with a possibility of marriage than in those with no fixed commitment (Van Emde Boas, 1965).

Abortion in adolescence

Although marked differences exist between and within countries, resort to induced abortion has been increasingly frequent among adolescents. Data available on legal abortion for 11 selected geographic areas indicate that the proportion of aborting women under age 20 has been increasing, reaching 22—29% in the U.S., England and Wales, Scotland, and Sweden, and almost 33% in the State of California (Tietze and Dawson, 1973). Trend data for the years 1967—71 in North Carolina reveal a younger abortion population each year, with the percentage under 20 increasing from 12.5% in 1967 to 33.7% in the period June—December 1971 (Howell, 1972). Major differences among countries are reflected in marital status. While in the U.S., Sweden, and England about 50% of the women having abortions have never been married, married women overwhelmingly predominate in the socialist countries of Eastern Europe such as, for example, Hungary and Czechoslovakia (Tietze and Dawson, 1973). Varied explanations have been suggested by David (1973).

Reasons for seeking an abortion reflect the point at which women find themselves in their personal and fertility careers, nearly always without the social, interpersonal, and material supports to cope with an unplanned and unwanted pregnancy. While the clause relating to the mental health of the women was (until recently) almost universally invoked among the young and unmarried as the major indication for the abortion, a review of the abortion situation in the United Kingdom (and also applicable in the United States) noted: "it is becoming increasingly recognized that there is no such danger of injury in the majority of these cases as the 'indication' is purely a social one" (Royal College of Obstetricians and Gynaecologists, 1972, p. 87). Elimination of hypocrisy on this point has meant that psychiatrists are now far less commonly consulted for their endorsement than previously. Other professionals concerned with abortion among the young have been directed to consider environmental and situational factors to understand motivations, and to develop more effective intervention strategies, introduce educational and counseling measures, and encourage primary prevention of unwanted pregnancy through efficient contraceptive use.

As may be expected, a major consequence of legal abortion among the young has been a decrease in out-of-wedlock births. The introduction of legal abortion on request in Hungary is credited with reducing the illegitimacy rate from 23.8 in 1954 to 10.1 in 1965; declines were similarly reported in Czechoslovakia and Poland during these same years (Cutright, 1972). The U.S., which witnessed a substantial annual increase in teenage illegitimacy during the last half of the 1960s, has thus far experienced a decline in the 1970s. The introduction of legal abortion was a major determinant, with illegitimacy among teenagers declining by 10% between 1970 and 1971 in states with liberalized laws but continuing to increase slightly in those where abortion was prohibited (Sklar and Berkov, 1974).

Programs to counsel abortion patients have focused primarily on assisting the young women in their decision making, identifying those most at risk for physical or psychological adverse reactions, lending emotional support, and providing contraceptive education and services (Cobliner et al., 1973). Professionals who deal with adolescents stress that the problems and circumstances which these young women encounter often differ from those of their older counterparts. The adolescent tends to seek termination of pregnancy later in her pregnancy than older women; she is often imprecise as to the exact duration of her pregnancy (this being more likely among younger women whose menstrual cycles may still be irregular) and she frequently approaches the experience with apprehensions intensified by lack of parental support, partner abandonment, limited financial resources, and fears associated with the pregnancy and abortion procedure itself (Hausknecht, 1972).

Studies indicate an inverse relationship between length of gestation and age at abortion, a finding which has potentially damaging physical and psychological consequences. Data from England and Wales, Japan, and the U.S. in 1970—71 showed the highest proportion of those aborting after the twelfth week of gestation in the under-20 age group in all countries (Tietze and Dawson, 1973). In New York State in the first 18 months of operation of the liberalized abortion law, approximately 43% of the young women aged 15 or less who presented themselves for termination of pregnancy, did so after 12 weeks' gestation. While the proportion decreased in the age group of 15—19 years, it remained at a worrisome 30%. In contrast, overall figures indicate that nearly 80% of all women seeking abortions in New York were less than 12 weeks' pregnant (Hausknecht, 1972).

While age of the adolescent appears to be strongly associated with delay in seeking abortion, other factors are also correlated. Among 443 applicants for abortion, those who were single and under 21 years of age and with no living children were more likely to apply for the abortion after their tenth week of pregnancy. While these variables themselves were interrelated, further analysis suggested that the effects of age, number of living children, and marital status were relatively independent and additive (Bracken and Swigar, 1971).

Such findings are particularly consequential for the teenager undergoing abortion, both from a physiological and psychological point of view. Somatic complication rates during the second trimester of pregnancy have been found to be 3—4 times as high as comparable rates during the first trimester (Tietze and Dawson, 1973). For the consideration of future fertility, potential long-range adverse complications are of greater consequence in the young girl than when they occur in the older woman who already has a family.

The adolescent's psychological reaction to abortion is probably complicated by a number of factors. While it has been observed repeatedly that adolescents tend to delay in booking abortion more than older women, studies of the psychological effects of abortion which include the stage of pregnancy and different abortion procedures as variables have been limited (Bracken and Swigar, 1971).

Any conclusion on the psychological effects of abortion among teenagers needs to be tentative. Research on the psychological effect of abortion among adolescents is subject to the same methodological limitation as assessments applied to their older counterparts. As has been astutely observed, rigorous analysis would require the study of suitable control groups matched according to decision-making and attitudes toward abortion, sexual activity, and use of contraception. The self-selection involved in abortion makes it unlikely if not impossible to obtain an unequivocal assessment of the nature and frequency of psychological sequelae of abortion (Tietze and Dawson, 1973).

While postabortion psychotherapy is infrequent, there is some evidence that abortion may be psychologically more stressful during the teenage years than in later years. A physician in an adolescent abortion clinic explains that: "With regard to emotional sequelae, there is a much greater sense of loss following abortion in teenage girls than in the 20—30-year-olds. Also the older adolescent (15—18) suffers a much greater reaction than does the very young girl aged 13 or 14. Pregnancy, although an accidental consequence, often fulfills some kind of need, and if the girl loses the pregnancy (and eventually the boy friend) the sense of loss at 6 months postabortively can be quite immense (Cowell, 1972).

However, it is the impression of many experienced with abortion patients that the majority do not need more than the counseling done by the gynecologist or counselor at the abortion clinic (Bridwel and Tinnin, 1972). Yet the motives and conflicts of younger adolescents (15—16 or younger) are most often quite different than those of older adolescents and approaches need to take account of these differences (Cowell, 1972; Cobliner et al., 1973).

Programmatic directions for fertility-regulation in adolescents

While adolescents have the greatest need for effective contraceptive information and services from a psychosocial, medical, and obstetrical viewpoint, they most often have the least access. In many areas of the U.S., birth-control information and contraception remain inaccessible for unmarried adolescents who are sexually active (Furstenberg, 1971b). In addition to substantial public disapproval, many practitioners within the medical profession have been reluctant to provide contraception, particularly without parental approval or where legal guidelines have been prohibitive or ambiguous. Within the U.S., unmarried teenagers are said to contribute to nearly twice the proportion of unintended fertility as they do to the proportion of total fertility. In spite of this, recent estimates suggest that 80% of the sexually active never-married women aged 15—19 not wanting a pregnancy are currently not receiving medically supervised contraceptive services. The most liberal projections conclude that not more than one-third of the teenagers in need of family planning services are now recipients of such services. There is a significant gap between estimated need and utilization of family planning services among unmarried adolescents in the U.S. (Morris, 1974).

Efforts to assure more responsible regulation of fertility in adolescence have tended, broadly, in two directions — toward increased education in sexuality and reproduction accompanied by greater accessibility of contraceptive and other fertility-regulating services. Unfortunately, these have too often not been initiated until the adolescent has come to the attention of medical and social services through the crisis of an unwanted pregnancy. Although support for such practices is gradually being eroded, a complex of legal and social factors have historically supported the delay in delivering these needed services as preventive rather than as correctional measures.

In the U.S., impetus for the development of programs to assist young persons has come through legislative revisions allowing medical personnel and educators greater latitude in conducting such programs without parental permission or surveillance, accompanied by the assurance of confidentiality to adolescents who seek these services. For several years, trends have reflected liberalizing laws and policies with regard to medical treatment of minors without parental consent, including treatment for contraception. Such trends have gained momentum with the more frequent passage of state laws allowing prescription of contraceptives to minors as well as more comprehensive family planning laws which do not specifically exclude minors (Pilpel and Wechsler, 1971). Similar developments in the extension of family planning services to the young are also evident in other countries (Royal College of Obstetricians and Gynaecologists, 1972; Wolfish, 1973).

Further, professional organizations are assuming responsibility for providing services, without necessarily espousing an advocacy position of any one approach to fertility regulation. The American College of Obstetricians and Gynecologists has gone on record opposing the legal barriers which restrict the physician in exercising his best judgment in prescribing contraceptives as well as those affecting the treatment of a minor who, though unemancipated, refuses to involve her parents. Other groups, such as the American Medical Association, the American Association of Planned Parenthood Physicians, and the American Academy of Pediatrics have endorsed similar positions. In England, the Royal College of Obstetricians and Gynaecologists has recommended the provision of a comprehensive contraceptive service equally available to the young and unmarried (Finkelstein, 1972; Pilpel and Wechsler, 1971; Royal College of Obstetricians and Gynaecologists, 1972).

While programmatic approaches for adolescents vary (some organized solely as family planning clinics and others integrated with multipurpose health facilities), certain components are common to most. Education, counseling, and a nonjudgmental milieu are emphasized within a structure that stresses individualization in the approach to the teenage contraceptor (Marinoff, 1972).

Conclusions on the effectiveness of fertility-regulating programs for adolescents are premature. Many have been designed to assist young women already faced with an unwanted pregnancy to resolve their dilemma and adopt an effective contraceptive regime on a postabortion or postpartum basis. Interpretation of the results of these programs is confounded by the effect of the pregnancy experience itself, making it difficult to evaluate the impact of the associated features of sympathetic counseling, sex education, and contraceptive assistance. Such studies do indicate, however, substantial increases in contraceptive knowledge and acceptance following exposure to these programs (Furstenberg, 1971b; Jorgensen, 1973; Klein, 1974; Lal et al., 1974; Rauh et al., 1969).

Lessons learned from these and other programs aimed at the primary

prevention of pregnancy suggest certain aspects warranting special consideration in program design. For one thing, it seems apparent that it is not enough
just to assure contraceptive availability and accessibility. A multidisciplinary
approach that incorporates a wide array of medical and social services, including health and nutritional information, educational and vocational counseling, along with exploration of sexual attitudes and contraceptive instruction, seems more assured of success. Secondly, clinics that dispense with the
formalities of appointments, include informal techniques such as 'rap' (discussion) sessions, and involve teenagers both in planning and participatory
roles as counselors and receptionists, have found wide appeal among adolescents (Marinoff, 1972; Caplan, 1973; Jorgensen, 1973; Reichelt and Werley,
1974).

It is being increasingly recognized that future program designs should give
more attention to the sociocultural and interpersonal context in which adolescents develop motivation and competence in contraceptive use. Particular
facets include exploration of the processes by which information and attitudes toward fertility regulation are acquired, including interaction with the
family, peer group, and community institutions. The virtually neglected area
of the role of the male partner, both in communication and adoption of
contraception among adolescents, seems likely to be remedied as efforts are
made to attract young men to educational and clinic programs. Ultimately,
the measure of success will be the extent to which primary prevention replaces the usual pattern of contraceptive adoption, secondary to the resolution of unwanted pregnancies.

3. CONTRACEPTION AND THE TEMPO OF FAMILY BUILDING
AMONG YOUNG ADULTS

Introduction

The shift in American values concerning child-centered family life can be
sensed from one's own reactions while watching a rerun of the movie, *Gone
With the Wind*. What was accepted as believable character motivation in the
1930s now seems a lavish parody of an oldtime soap opera. Sudden and profound character transformations and suicidal personal sacrifice are all explained and justified by the joyous experiences of being a parent. Rhett
Butler instantly gives up his racy cavalier ways to become a doting father,
while saintly Melanie Wilkes knowingly risks her life to bear beloved Ashley
a second child because 'birth renews life.' In contrast, the wicked willful-
ness and self-indulgence of Scarlet O'Hara is dramatized by her vow not to
have another child, despite Rhett's many pleas, because the burdens of
motherhood proved too confining to her life in Atlanta society and her business career at the sawmill. In one respect, however, *Gone With the Wind* was
prophetic of possible future trends. Neither the Butlers nor the Wilkes had
more than a single child.

More tangible evidence of the change in family values (at least as these values pertain to family size) is the decline in fertility rates observed in the U.S. during the past 15 years. And the continuation of this trend seems likely in view of recent reports of a massive and apparently quite sudden shift toward a preference for only two children among young wives aged 18—24. Ideal family size has also declined to fewer than three children among adults under 25, the lowest point observed since such data have been collected. These and other indicators of declining fertility led the Census Bureau to revise downward its long-run population forecasts (U.S. Bureau of the Census, 1972). Similar trends are being recorded in other countries. In Korea, more than half the married respondents in a recent survey believed that as many as three children impose a heavy financial burden on the family. Over 40% in Thailand agreed (Fawcett et al., 1974). Throughout the urban, industrialized regions of the world, family size values appear to be undergoing significant change among young adults.

The demographic importance of these values for the future stems from the fact that the more children a couple expects to have, the sooner the first child is born, and the larger the family tends to be (Moors, 1974). In this section, we will discuss this trend from a psychoeconomic standpoint and attempt to describe some possible patterns of interaction between the costs and benefits of children which could account for the apparent changes in family size values.

A skeptic's view

Some would cut short any discussion of the perceived trend by questioning its existence. For example, Blake (1974) urged caution in too readily accepting survey data on the preference for two-child families as evidence for a fundamental shift in family size values in the U.S. She suspected that the 'sudden massing' of responses in the two-child category between 1967 and 1972 was an ephemeral, not an enduring, change which could be attributed to a 'sudden wave' of antinatalist propaganda in recent years. Three main reasons were given for doubting that the currently stated birth expectations of young adults are reliable indicators of their future fertility behavior:

1. A family of 4 or 5 children is not considered 'too large' by most adults surveyed, even though the ideal family size is less than 3.

2. While there is a fondness (or at least tolerance) for the idea of large families, there is strong aversion to the ideas of voluntary childlessness or the one-child family.

3. The happiest time of married life is said to be the childbearing period, a finding which Blake interprets as meaning that 'for respondents of all ages, educational levels, and among Catholics and non-Catholics, children quite clearly make the marriage.'

These attitudes, Blake argued, are inconsistent with expressed preferences for two-child families. The current state of mind of young married couples concerning family size appears to contain too many dissonant elements to permit confident predictions about their future procreation. It is possible that young adults who now espouse the two-child ideal may later change their minds while there is still time to add to their families.

The positive values of parenthood

The pleasures which parents experience in raising their children are highly valued, as Fawcett (1974) and his colleagues have found in their cross-cultural investigation in five Asian countries and Hawaii. Three subgroups were sampled in each country (urban middle class, urban lower class and rural), where comparable data were collected from young couples who had at least one child. Husbands and wives were interviewed separately; altogether, more than 2500 individuals participated.

The economic utility of children, the researchers found, was a waning motivating factor for most parents, and persisted primarily in rural areas. Far more important were the psychological and emotional benefits. Among the most frequently mentioned advantages were:
— Happiness for the family as a group
— Happiness for the individual parent
— Companionship, avoidance of loneliness
— Play, fun with children; avoidance of boredom
— Pleasure from observing the growth and development of children (an important value to American parents especially)
— Help in old age
— Help in housework, family chores; practical help (most often mentioned by Philipino parents).

Children are highly valued, it seems, because they contribute to the psychological well-being of the parents and this role is not easily filled by other means. As Fawcett (1974) observed, 'There is no substitute for a child.' But it may not be necessary for a couple to bear and rear a large family in order to experience the psychological and emotional advantages of parenthood.

Blake (1974) implied that large families are intrinsically more satisfying in this respect when she argued that 'couples desiring two children will . . . almost inevitably need to be less emotionally oriented toward children than those for whom childbearing and child rearing comprise the major share of adult life.' This point is debatable, since it is at least equally likely that children in small families are closer emotionally to their parents and other family members. The possibility that the joys of parenthood do not depend on family size was reinforced by findings from Terhune's (1973) study of the fertility values of 310 married women in the U.S. As did Fawcett, Terhune found that American parents placed most value in the satisfaction of watching children grow up — in seeing their talents and abilities develop. But Terhune also reported that the rewards of raising children seem to vary only slightly with family size. Watching four children grow up may be substantially less than twice as satisfying as watching two achieve their maturity.

The negative values of parenthood

While the pleasures of parenthood may not continue to increase apace with an enlarging family, the costs certainly do keep climbing. Several recent investigators have expressed the view that parental consideration of the cost of children is the main determinant of procreation.

It has not been difficult for investigators to elicit direct confirmation of this hypothesis from respondents themselves. Peel (1970) for example, presented early findings of a projected longitudinal study of 20% of all marriages which took place in Hull, U.K., during late 1965 and early 1966. As is typically the case in such studies, the ideal family size was larger than the expected size (3.4 and 2.6, respectively). But Peel reported that most couples regarded two children as the maximum which they 'can afford to bring up properly' — to use the phrase which Peel said recurred ad nauseam in the interviews. People decide against having more children when they expect the added costs will exceed the added rewards. "Motivation is needed not to *have* children," Terhune (1973) suggested, "but to *stop* having them"; it is the burden of increasing costs which furnishes the necessary motive. In summarizing the findings of the value of the study of children, Fawcett concluded that: "For most people, it appears that childbearing is an activity characterized by ambivalence but with benefits clearly outweighing costs up to some number of children, at which parents try to stop having more. On the other hand, it may be that costs are simply accepted (or ignored) up to some threshold, after which costs come to play a major part in childbearing decisions." (Fawcett et al., 1974, pp. 17—18).

The idea of a threshold for family size has also been proposed by Namboodiri (1974), following his secondary analysis of data from the 1965 U.S. National Fertility Study. The level of the threshold for a particular couple is determined by demographic characteristics, and very few couples are content to remain below this threshold. But, once passed, social and economic background characteristics begin to discriminate couples who expect to have additional children from demographically similar couples who do not.

Blue print for a psychoeconomic model

A crude theoretical model of fertility regulation is beginning to emerge from the several studies cited above. The model consists of two variables: the benefits and costs of children (both experienced and expected). The benefits or reward function is relatively stable in two respects. It is not much affected by family size (at least above the two-child level) and, because it is essentially affective and interpersonal in nature, is not greatly influenced by events outside the family. The cost function, on the other hand, is more labile. A combination of economic and psychological factors, it increases with each additional child in a family and is sensitive to environmental conditions. Hence, while the costs of children may fluctuate considerably over time, the rewards are more or less constant. It is assumed that a married couple will tend to continue bearing children so long as the expected rewards are greater than the anticipated costs. But once the 'break even' point is approached the couple begins to exercise greater caution in adding to the family. For the sake of simplicity, the reward and cost functions are described here as being monotonic, but Terhune (1973) mentions the possibility that either or both functions might be curvilinear with respect to family size; psychological relationships often are. Terhune speculated, for example, that the benefits of companionship might be seen to increase with family size up to a point, after which a family might begin to break up into small cliques and warring factions.

The escalating costs of childrearing may also help to explain the sudden convergence on two children as the preferred family size. In the past, there tended to be a surplus of benefits over costs, even for fairly large families. But now the situation may be nearly reversed for many young couples, especially at the start of their married lives. It has been estimated that raising a child in the Unites States can easily cost $60,000 (Commission on Population Grown and the American Future, 1972). The effect of inflation alone will be to dramatically raise this figure. For example, the current average cost of four years of education in a private college is $31,000. When children now in their infancy have reached college age, the projected cost for four years is $98,000. Parents of a newborn infant would have to begin to regularly save $3250 annually for the next 18 years to accumulate funds sufficient to meet this educational expense (New York Times, March 13, 1975).

The rising costs of child rearing is also reflected in increasing child support payments in cases of divorce. The Family Law Court in Seattle, for example, recently adopted a new schedule which raised payments by 50%. An absent parent, with a net monthly income of $1000, must now pay $240 a month for the support of a single child, $350 for two, $420 for three, and $480 (nearly half the monthly income) for four children (New York Times, March 9, 1975).

Even though the rewards of parenthood continue (as they have always been) to be very real, they have remained relatively constant, while the costs of parenthood are continuing to rise — partly due to inflation, partly as a result of the increasingly higher standards which parents set for themselves in raising their children, and partly as a result of the extended period of dependence for children. It is not at all uncommon today for middle class parents to continue to support their offspring through college, graduate school, and the early years of marriage.

The following model, in its still formative stage, resembles an exploratory framework originally put forward to account for helping behavior (Schwartz, 1970) and later extended and refined to cover decision-making during family crises as when relatives were called upon to donate a kidney to someone in their family (Simmons et al., 1973). The framework was intended to explain two types of responses in situations which are norm-governed (for example when moral issues are seen to be involved): (1) A person will respond immediately, without hesitation or deliberation, whenever (s)he fully subscribes to the norm in question and accepts its personal relevance in the existing situation (or conversely, rejects the norm or denies its present relevance); (2) A person will delay responding when the norm is weak, uncertain in its applicability, or when the anticipated personal cost of compliance is burdensome. It is under these circumstances of postponement and delay that behavior can be said to involve a 'rational' weighing of costs and benefits.

Childbearing is norm-governed behavior. There are strong social expectations that everyone will become a parent (barring sterility or churchly calling) and raise at least two children. There is also consensus about the appropriate timing and spacing of births (Blake, 1974). While young couples may feel some ambivalence about enlarging their families, because of the costs involved, the strength of the childbearing norm is usually sufficient to override any temptation to avoid parenthood, or even to significantly delay pregnancies. Possibly for this reason, contraceptive use by young couples is often marked by half-hearted vigilance and 'unexpected' pregnancies are the result.

That the newly married couple is likely to be especially susceptible to ineffective contraceptive use was suggested by data from the 1970 National Fertility Study (Ryder, 1973). Couples who intended to delay a wanted pregnancy were generally less successful, whatever contraceptive they used, than couples who sought to prevent an unwanted pregnancy, and those women who were relatively young at the beginning of exposure to risk (that is, younger than the national average for any specific pregnancy order) were much more likely to fail than those who were older. Data were analyzed only for intervals between pregnancies or since the last pregnancy for which the couple used contraception. Intervals preceding a woman's first pregnancy were not included because the period of time she was at risk was unknown. Nevertheless, the intention of almost all newly married couples using contraceptives to postpone rather than prevent pregnancy would imply that this group may experience an especially high incidence of unexpected or unplanned births.

There is clinical support for this conjecture. From his experience interviewing women coming for abortion and prenatal care to the Stanford University Medical Center, Miller (1973) identified eight vulnerable stages in the sexual careers of women at which time they are especially susceptible to an unintended pregnancy. One of these hazard points occurs before or just after marriage, when contraceptive vigilance is commonly relaxed. Miller suggests that as the marriage date approaches, contraceptive vigilance tends to decline because the consequences of an unplanned pregnancy are not so grave.

A similar conclusion was reached by Ford and his colleagues (1971): ". . . among those women initially claiming contraceptive failure, true failures represent a smaller number than one might at first suspect. Upon further questioning, we have found that pregnancy often occurs in a contraceptive user after some change in life circumstance has aroused an unconscious motivation toward pregnancy."

Whether unconscious or not, there has been in the past an almost undeviating acquiescence to the childbearing norm. The depth of this acquiescence was impressively demonstrated by three generations of Minneapolis families studied by Hill and his associates (1970). In comparing the timing of the first birth among couples married about 1907, 1931, and 1953, it was found that the first child was born 1.67, 1.69, and 1.66 years after marriage, respectively, indicating to the investigators that 'all three generations married with hopes for children early in marriage.' It was in the spacing of subsequent births that significant differences began to appear. The second child, for example, was born to the grandparent generation (those married in the early 1900s) about 4.45 years after marriage, and 4.59 years after the marriage of couples who established their homes in the 1950s. Depression-era couples, however, postponed their second child until 5.27 years following marriage.

To summarize, the prevailing childbearing norm encourages young couples to begin having children soon after marriage, and does not condone attempts to unduly postpone the birth of the first child. The overwhelming compliance with this norm for generations in the U.S. (and elsewhere) is an index of its strength. As Epstein (1974) commented, 'In my generation, you went into having children somnambulistically. It was expected of you and you never questioned whether you wanted to be a parent."

Now, however, at least some couples are beginning to question the jurisdiction of this norm over their present life situations. There is growing sensitivity to the costs and sacrifices of parenthood and attention is being directed to the trade-offs which are involved; a couple may well decide to postpone the next pregnancy while a decision is being reached. Scarlet O'Hara's unromantic view of parenthood has gained respectability. It is under these circumstances that childbearing can be said to exhibit rational characteristics.

Costs and the tempo and family building

An important implication of the model is that the perceived cost of children influences the timing of births. Higher costs lead to postponement and, as has been found in the Netherlands, delayed births can substantially reduce the fertility rate. In his study of child spacing and family size, Moors (1974) concluded that about 40% of the decline in marital fertility for Dutch couples between 1958 and 1968 resulted from delaying pregnancies by means of contraception, rather than from reductions in family size values. Observed differences in the degree to which the timing of the first and second pregnancies was purposeful, led Moors to formulate a classification scheme of 6 family planning patterns, displayed below in Table I.

Between 1958 and 1968, Moors found a 3-fold increase in the number of

Table I
Timing patterns in family planning (from Moors, 1974).

No conception within an exposure period of at least 36 months without use of contraceptives			SUBFECUNDITY
Never used contraception and not intended to use contraception in the future			TRADITIONAL
Did use contraception or intends to use contraception	Unsuccessful planning of first pregnancy	No planning or unsuccessful planning of second pregnancy	HEDONISTIC
		More or less successful planning of the second pregnancy	REACTION
	More or less successful planning of the first pregnancy	First child wanted as soon as possible or successful planning of first pregnancy while a short interval was wanted	RATIONAL I
		Successful planning of the first pregnancy for at least 18 months exposure time	RATIONAL II

Dutch couples who used contraceptives to schedule the first pregnancy (the Rational II type) and a 50% decline in those who had never used contraceptives, nor intended to in the future (the Traditionalists).

A similar trend has been observed in the United States. In their analysis of the 1970 National Fertility Study, Rindfuss and Westoff (1974) found evidence that "it was approximately in the mid-1960s that increasing proportions of women began using contraception prior to their first pregnancy." Among the younger women in the sample, between 65 and 71% practiced contraception before becoming pregnant for the first time. As a general rule, the contraceptive users tended to marry later, were less likely to have a premarital pregnancy, and have their first child later than women who did not contracept before their initial pregnancy. White users had been married an average of 27 months at the end of their first pregnancy (thus meeting the criterion for Rational II types in Moors' classification), while white nonusers had been married 13 months. It was also clear that younger women are relying increasingly on the pill as their first contraceptive method.

Comparable findings come from a 1970—71 study of 350 recently married couples participating in the Hull Family Survery (Peel, 1972). One-half of the couples reported using contraception before the first pregnancy, and only 30% of all first pregnancies were found to be unplanned.

It is apparent that increasing numbers of young married couples are relying upon contraception to slow the tempo of family formation from the very beginning, thereby postponing the day when the full burdens and obligations of parenthood are assumed. But no matter how long delayed, the birth of the first child marks an abrupt transition.

The high cost of the first born and the psychoeconomic conditions for voluntary childlessness

One of the facts of life which can surprise unsuspecting young couples is that the heaviest costs of parenthood are incurred with the first birth. As Fawcett and his colleagues (1974) observed: "The major restrictions and change in life style occur with the birth of the first child and additional children have relatively slight impact . . . It is probably true that most people do not realize . . . the extent to which their future life course is determined by that event."

A major cost associated with the birth of the first child in the United States is residential relocation. The traditional American pattern has been for the couple to relocate from an apartment to a house (Hill et al., 1970). There is a strong preference in the U.S. for home ownership, rather than rental, and for the detached single family dwelling (Butler et al, 1969). Given the desire for small families and the roominess of the conventional house, subsequent additions to the family do not soon result in a crowded living space. As Hill and his collaborators (1970) noted: "The shift to parenthood for the first time requires more changes in the living quarters than the shift from one child to a two-child family and therefore is . . . [more] likely to precipitate a residential move."

Chevan (1971) concurs that "it is the first child who puts the greatest strain on available space."

Because of the high cost of beginning a family and the prevailing prejudice against the single child family, the young couple is usually confronted with the choice of having at least two children or none at all. This built-in constraint is one factor which may increase the incidence of childless marriages.

Blake (1974) could find no evidence in survey data that any "numerically important vaguard in our population" is choosing to remain childless. One reason this may be true is that, in the past, couples have tended to slip into childlessness, without overtly intending to do so. Veevers (1973) studied 52 urban, middle-class working women who were childless after at least five years of marriage and found that in two-thirds of the cases there was no explicit decision not to have children. The women and their husbands followed a pattern of decision by default, postponing parenthood until a more convenient time, which never came.

Bram (1974) studied a small group of white, educated, middle-class couples who had consciously chosen voluntary childlessness, at least at the time of the interviews. The decision appeared to be more often the wife's than the husband's, and was made on the grounds that having children would interfere with her professional aspirations, an egalitarian companionate marriage, and an unencumbered life style. The wife found ideological support for her choice in the women's movement but perceived her marriage as having had a major positive effect on her development as an individual.

While voluntary childlessness is no doubt an elitist position at this time, the seeds for its future growth are present in current attitudes. The recent Virginia Slims American Women's Opinion Poll (1974), in which a national quota sample of 3000 respondents participated, found that only 38% of young women (age 18—29) considered that having children was 'very important' to a good marriage. In contrast, 91% believed that being in love and being able to talk together about their feelings were very important. The substantial discounting of the role of children in a satisfying marriage is difficult to reconcile with Blake's (1974) contention that women strongly believe that children make a marriage. But Blake agreed that college-educated women feel some conflict concerning the issue. She noted that while these women are not willing to become advocates of childlessness, they are not as ready as other women to defend the virtues of parenthood. Instead, they straddle the fence.

Blake also suggested that the bleak prospect of a prolonged 'empty nest period,' following all the fun and excitement of raising children, might prompt couples to revise their intentions to have only two offspring and decide to have a third or more. However, a recent study by Campbell and his associates (1974) found that "the time of the empty nest turns out to be a time of fulfillment." The costs of raising small children are substantial and cause a great deal of strain for the parents, both in personal and economic terms. The pressure gradually subsides as the children mature, until they are old enough to leave home, when the parents are at last able to enjoy a relatively stress-free time by themselves. Once the nest is empty, however, parents still may not be able to begin building a nest egg for themselves. The high costs of sending the children to college may deplete family financial resources and many parents feel obligated to help their newlywed offspring purchase homes, automobiles, and major appliances. Perhaps cognizant of these seemingly unending financial commitments, the survey found that young (18—29) childless couples expressed greater overall contentment with married life than did their counterparts who were the parents of small children.

Conclusion

The rising costs of children are possibly forcing a reduction in family size, both observed and expected, and are altering spacing patterns by motivating couples to postpone births, perhaps indefinitely. Because the first child is, in many respects, the most costly to a couple, the timing of the first birth may come to be influenced by anticipated costs to a greater extent than has been true in the past. Significant delays in the initiation of childbearing can have a far-reaching demographic impact.

Coincident with the escalating costs of parenthood have been the development and diffusion of modern contraceptive methods. The effective use of contraceptives offers the couple a means of coping with costs by scheduling the births of children to avoid unexpected demands on limited family resources. But contraceptives may alter the conditions of choice for young couples in other respects, as well.

In his study of the general impact of technology on values, Mesthene (1968) concluded that technological innovation (of which the development of contraceptives is an important example) can restructure the hierarchy of a society's values in two ways:

1. the costs associated with a course of action may be either reduced or increased as the result of technological development, and . . .

2. goals which were unattainable prior to the innovation are brought within the realm of realistic choice.

Both types of impact may be expected on the hierarchy of family values. Easy access to inexpensive, effective contraception (in addition to the wide availability of abortion and simpler techniques of sterilization) have lessened the personal costs of trying to limit family size. When couples had to depend upon the rigors of sexual abstinence, coitus interruptus, or cumbersome and unreliable birth control devices to avoid pregnancy, the value of a small family was somewhat diminished.

But of greater significance is the freedom which young couples now have, as a result of contraception, to discover and experience facets of married life which were obscured by the ever-present demands of child rearing. The realization that childless marriages can be satisfying, together with the emphasis young people place on a companionate relationship, are indicators that a realignment in values is taking place: that husbands and wives need not wait till the Golden Years of retirement and the empty nest to share a life free of the demands and distractions of a growing family.

4. THE LATER YEARS IN MARRIAGE

Introduction

As previously noted, for most people throughout the world the fertile years are divided into three stages: (1) the early years when childbearing is possible, but not yet desired: (2) the middle years, when childbearing is a natural and expected part of life; and (3) the later fertile years when most couples no longer want to bear children. This is statistically the case. Age fertility schedules of all human populations ". . . rise smoothly from zero at an age in the teens to a single peak in the twenties or thirties, and then fall continuously to near zero in the forties and to zero not much above age 50" (Coale, 1972). Earlier sections of this chapter have discussed psychosocial and psychoeconomic aspects of the first two stages. What follows will endeavor to view factors which influence fertility-regulating behavior in the later years of marriage, with special emphasis on voluntary male or female sterilization for preventing future childbirths.

Successful contraception (Ryder, 1973) and early (in the gestation period) requests for pregnancy termination (Tietze and Dawson, 1973) are both positively correlated with age. The decline in childbearing with age undoubtedly has many reasons, including the following: a lowering of fecundity, an increase in spontaneous abortion, a decrease in the frequency of sexual relations, greater experience with contraceptives, more skill at detecting pregnancy earlier, greater experience with requesting and finding someone to induce an abortion, easier access to family planning services and supplies, fewer social taboos associated with birth prevention, and perhaps greater motivation not to have young children to raise. Techniques for spacing births, or simply for delaying the next childbirth until a decision about whether to have any more is made, include traditional and modern contraception and abortion, but do not include sterilization. For the couple, or individual, who decides against having any future children, male or female sterilization becomes a thinkable alternative. While there is often a possibility of reversal (some 40% of female sterilization and 20—40% of male; Hulka, 1972), the odds remain against a successful reversal leading to a pregnancy. For psychological and ethical purposes, the assumption must be made that the process is irreversible.

The problem

In spite of the fact that older couples are more successful at preventing births, there often remains a gap between wanting no more children and actually terminating childbearing. The data collected by Landis and Poffenberger (1972) on vasectomy patients suggest that the older couple who has experienced one unplanned pregnancy is more likely to be driven to vasectomy than the younger (but not very young) couples.

Both male and female sterilization is on the increase (Bumpass and Presser, 1972; Curt, 1973; Potts, 1973; McGarrah, 1974) which means that more and more there is an opportunity to choose method(s) with attendant advantages and disadvantages. Neither the factors which determine the choice of sterilization nor its likely psychological consequences have yet been well studied, but both questions are arousing increasing interest (David and Friedman, 1973; Rogers and Ziegler, 1973).

The advantages

The advantages of sterilization are clear and major: vasectomy, particularly, is a very safe and quick method which can be performed on an outpatient basis (Deys and Potts, 1972); both male and female methods are highly effective if done properly so that the problem of unwanted pregnancy is permanently solved; it is a one-time affair (and for some Catholics that may mean a one-time sin; Presser, 1973) rather than a repeated one as in the case of the pill or abortion; it can be kept secret; it should have minimal or no side effects; no skill or experience on the part of the patient is needed; because of its effectiveness it removes the fear of pregnancy as an inhibitor of sexual intercourse and sexual pleasure; and, finally, it eliminates the need for the use of contraceptives or abortion and their real or imagined unhealthy or unpleasant consequences.

The disadvantages

Despite these advantages there is resistance to sterilization for a variety of reasons. Some of it is historical, as in Europe and Israel where the use of sterilization as a genocidal weapon remains a strong memory. Resistance to male sterilization is generally stronger than to female sterilization. This appears to be especially true in Latin America (including Puerto Rico where female sterilization is well established) and among black Americans (Bumpass and Presser, 1972). Resistance by males to vasectomy is generally believed to be rooted in the idea that it is demasculinizing and this may threaten the male and female partners in different ways.

The major disadvantage of either method is its irreversibility. Where infant mortality is high or there is felt to be a possibility of a broken marriage while the partners are relatively young, either through death or separation, the permanence of the method is daunting because children may be wanted at a later date. The ease of getting a qualified practitioner to perform a sterilization is also quite variable, since the legal situations vary and costs differ from country to country. Sometimes, as in the Indian experience with vasectomy campaigns, incentives have been provided for clients, but generally the clients must find the funds themselves. Another problem with either male or female methods is the need for one partner to assume responsibility, a decision which has consequences of its own.

The major fears which have been identified as sometimes existing prior to vasectomy, or which may enter into the choice of this method, include: the fear of consequent sexual impotence, the fear of pain, and the fear of mutilation. Pond (1970) considers sterilization to be in fact multilating because ". . . something has gone on inside which leads to a loss of function." These fears are sometimes expressed or felt, not only by laymen who equate vasectomy with castration but by the medical profession who may exhibit considerable hostility toward the choice of vasectomy by their patients (Wolfers, 1970). It should be emphasized, however, that many who choose vasectomy have no such conscious fears (Lear, 1972).

Landis and Poffenberger (1972) suggest that men and women have different concerns with respect to vasectomy. Male respondents who had vasectomy performed (between 1956 and 1961 in the U.S.) said that their chief concerns were . . . "their fear of pain, fear that their sex drive might be affected, and concerns over the fact that they could have no more children in the future should they wish to. The men reported that their wives were most concerned about whether the operation would surely prevent conception, whether the husband might be promiscuous with other women, whether the wife might be blamed if the husband's masculinity was affected, or if the wife should later become pregnant." The predominant reason for the couple's choice of vasectomy over tubal ligation, as is usually the case, was that the procedure was easier and cheaper.

Female sterilization, while a more complicated procedure than vasectomy, is something which is often performed in conjunction with abortion or childbirth. It is a method which is growing in importance but it may also face difficulty because of a growing female resentment against taking sole responsibility for ending fertility. Perhaps the most common theme of all, which runs through the literature on family planning generally, is that the success is greater and consequent problems fewer when the husband and wife share in the decision (Rosario, 1970; Stokes and Dudley, 1972). This appears to be particularly true for the choice of sterilization as a method. Cushner (1974) considered ambivalence toward tubal ligation as an indication that the husband should be brought in to visit, to see whether perhaps the decision has been more his than hers. Dodds (1972) says that "the lack of complete agreement between husband and wife appears to be the most common cause of emotional problems following sterilization." He goes on to say that "preparing for and arriving at a decision to have sterilization performed can be one of the most cooperative ventures of a marriage. The decision to stop having children and the actions taken to fulfill this decision are perhaps even more important and require higher levels of cooperation than are needed to produce a child."

The consequences

In spite of the many fears cited, often by professionals in medicine, psychiatry, or psychology, the literature overwhelmingly shows the consequences of either male or female sterilization to be usually favorable or, at least, without negative consequences. It is true that the subject is difficult to study because of the self-selecting nature of the population and the frequent absence of base line measures prior to the procedures, but follow-up studies almost invariably show the vast majority pleased that they underwent the procedure (Wolfers, 1970; Black and Sclare, 1972; Ferber et al., 1972; Paniagua et al., 1972; Thompson and Baird, 1972).

Where problems do arise after sterilization, they usually seem to have been present previously, or the result of false expectations. As contraindications to these methods of ending fertility, Dodds (1972) suggests a checklist for the couple which provides a useful summary of what is known and also provides insight into conditions for optimal choice:

1. Is either of us afraid that the operation might change our feelings about ourselves, about each other, or about how other people regard us?

2. Are we likely to regret that we cannot have more children?
3. Do we both completely agree on the operation being done?
4. If one or more of our children died would we want to have more?
5. If the husband lost his wife through death or divorce and remarried would he want to father more children? And vice versa.
6. Are we expecting sterilization to solve marital problems?
7. If the pattern of our sexual relationship changes following sterilization are we both willing to make adjustments according to our partner's needs?

There are certain other problems which have been cited as potential difficulties following the choice of sterilization, such as the danger of one partner 'making the sacrifice' which will then be used in bargaining with the partner on other issues. Another problem might arise if sterilization frees the couple from a fear of pregnancy and thereby removes a rationalization for the avoidance of sexual relations. Sterilization may thus expose a more deep-rooted problem in the relationship itself. But, it should be emphasized that these are questions, not findings, and the evidence which exists suggests that a choice voluntarily made, with a minimum of outside pressure, by both partners in a marriage, is likely to have positive rather than negative consequences.

5. SUMMARY

With the deepening worldwide concern about present and future problems of population and its interaction with socioeconomic development, modifiability of fertility choice, motivation for fertility regulation, and effective implementation of service capabilities have become priorities for social science research. Our experience suggests that the primary unit of research be the couple and that populations for study be defined on the biopsychosocial dimension of fertility career stages.

A summary presentation of our theoretical rationale and an overview of the chapter precedes reviews of available literature on psychosocial (and/or psychoeconomic) aspects of fertility regulation among adolescents, young married adults, and couples in later years of marriage. While noting transnational and cross-cultural aspects, primary focus is on behavioral variables rather than technical aspects of fertility regulating.

BIBLIOGRAPHY

Asayama, S. (1975) Adolescent sex development and adult sex behavior in Japan. *J. Sex Res.* 11: 91—112.

Bauman, K.E. (1970) Selected aspects of the contraceptive practices of unmarried university students. *Am. J. Obstet. Gynecol.* 108: 203—209.

Black, W.P. and Sclare, A.B. (1972) Sterilization by tubal ligation — a follow-up study. In: (L. Lader, Ed.), *Foolproof Birth Control: Male and Female Sterilization*. (Beacon Press, Boston) pp. 159—169.

Blake, J. (1974) Can we believe recent data on birth expectations in the United States? *Demography* 11: 25—44.

Bracken, M.B. and Swigar, N.E. (1972) Factors associated with delay in seeking induced abortions. *Am. J. Obstet. Gynecol.* June 1, pp. 301—309.

Braestrup, A. (1971) Use of contraception by young mothers in Copenhagen. *J. Biosoc. Sci.* 3: 43—60.

Bram, S. (1974) *To Have or Have Not: A Social Psychological Study of Voluntarily Childless Couples, Parents-To-Be, and Parents.* (Unpublished doctoral dissertation, University of Michigan.)

Bridwell, N.W. and Tinnin, L.W. (1972) Abortion referral in a large college health service. *J. Am. Med. Women's Assoc.* 27: 430—431.

Bumpass, L.L. and Presser, H.B. (1972) Contraceptive sterilization in the U.S.: 1965 and 1970. *Demography* 9: 531—548.

Butler, G.W., Chapin, F.S., Jr., Hemmens, G.C., Kaiser, E.J., Stegman, M.A. and Weiss, S.F. (1969) *Moving Behavior and Residential Choice*. (Natl. Acad. Sci. Washington, D.C.)

Campbell, A., Converse, P. and Rodgers, W. (1974) *Childless Marriages*. (Institute for Social Research, Ann Arbor, Mich.)

Cannon, K.L. and Long, R. (1971) Premarital sexual behavior in the sixties. *J. Marr. Fam.* 33: 36—49.

Caplan, H.M. (1973) Teen rap session. In: (S. Lowit, Ed.), *Advances in Planned Parenthood*, Vol. 8, International Congress Series No. 271. (Excerpta Medica, Amsterdam) pp. 63—66.

Chevan, A. (1971) Family growth, household density, and moving. *Demography* 8: 451—458.

Coale, A.J. (1972) *The Growth and Structure of Human Population: A Mathematical Investigation*. (Princeton University Press, Princeton).

Cobliner, W.G., Schulman, H. and Romney, S.L. (1973) The termination of adolescent out-of-wedlock pregnancies and the prospects for their primary prevention. *Am. J. Obstet. Gynecol.* 115: 432—444.

Commission on Population Growth and the American Future (1972) *Population and the American Future*. (U.S. Government Printing Office, Washington, D.C.)

Connell, E.B. and Jacobson, L. (1971) Pregnancy, the teenager and sex education. *Am. J. Public Health* 61: 1840—1845.

Cowell, C.A. (1972) Problems of adolescent abortion. *Orthopanel* 14: 2—5.

Curt, J.N. (1973) Evidence relating to acceptability of sterilization: individual, social, legal, medical, religious and professional (The Puerto Rican Experience). Paper presented at the University of Puerto Rico, School of Public Health, February 1973.

Cushner, I.M. (1974) Counseling sterilization patients. *Orthopanel* 20: 6—11.

Cutright, P. (1972) Illegitimacy in the United States: 1920—1968. In: (C.F. Westoff and R. Parke, Jr., Eds.), *Demographic and Social Aspects of Population Growth*. Vol. 1 of Report of the Commission on Population Growth and the American Future (U.S. Govt. Printing Office, Wasington, D.C.) pp. 375—438.

Daily, E.F. and Nicholas, N. (1972) Use of conception control methods before pregnancies terminating in birth or a requested abortion in New York City municipal hospitals. *Am. J. Public Health* 62: 1544—1545.

David, H.P. (1973) Abortion trends in European socialist countries and in the United States. *Am. J. Orthopsychiat.* 43: 376—383.

David, H.P. and Friedman, H.L. (1973) Acceptability of contraceptive sterilization: Psychosocial research approaches. (Paper presented at the Workshop on Research in Behavioral Aspects of Research, NICHD, Bethesda, Maryland, June 1973.)

Deys, C.M. and Potts, D.M. (1972) Condoms and things. In: (G. Raspe and S. Bernhard,

Eds.), *Advances in the Biosciences 10. Schering Workshop on Contraception. The Masculine Gender*, Berlin, November-December 1972, (Pergamon Press, Oxford) pp. 287—297.

Dodds, D.J. (1972) Male or female sterilization? In: (L. Lader, Ed.), *Foolproof Birth Control: Male and Female Sterilization*, (Beacon Press, Boston) pp. 52—59.

Ehrmann, W. (1964) Marital and nonmarital sexual behavior. In: (H.T. Christensen, Ed.), *Handbook of Marriage and the Family*, (Rand McNally, Chicago) pp. 385—622.

Epstein, J. (1974) *Divorced in America*. (Dutton, New York.)

Fawcett, J.T., Arnold, F., Bulatao, R.A., Buripakdi, C., Chung, B.J., Iritani, T., Lee, S.J. and Wu, T-S. (1974) *The Value of Children in Asia and the United States: Comparative Perspectives*, Paper No. 32. (East-West Population Institute, Honolulu.)

Ferber, A.S., Tietze, C. and Lewit, S. (1972) Men with vasectomies: A study of medical, sexual, and psychosocial changes. In: (S. Lader, Ed.), *Foolproof Birth Control: Male and Female Sterilization*, (Beacon Press, Boston) pp. 110—130.

Finkelstein, R. (1972) Program for the sexually active teenager. *Pediat. Clin. North Am.* 19: 791—794.

Ford, C.V., Atkinson, R.M. and Bragonier, J.R. (1971) Therapeutic abortion: Who needs a psychiatrist? *Obstet. Gynecol.* 38: 206—213.

Friedman, H.L. (1972) An approach to psychosocial research in fertility behavior. (Paper presented at the International Conference on Contraception, Abortion, Sterilization, and Prostaglandins, Paris, France, May 1972.)

Friedman, H.L. (1974a) Fertility choice behavior: Some recommendations for research design. *Fam. Plann. Perspect.* 6: 184—185.

Friedman, H.L. (1974b) Individual factors in the prevention of childbirth: Transnational findings. (Paper prepared for presentation at the Seminar on Family Planning for Rural India, Allahabad Agricultural Institute, Allahabad, India, November 1974.)

Friedman, H.L., Johnson, R.L. and David, H.P. (1976) The dynamics of fertility choice behavior: A pattern for research. In: (S. Newman and V. Thompson, Eds.), *Population Research and Education*. (NICHD, Center for Population Research, Washington) In press.

Furstenberg, F.F., Jr., Gordis, L. and Markowitz, M. (1969) Birth control knowledge and attitudes among unmarried pregnant adolescents: A preliminary report. *J. Marr. Fam.* 31: 34—42.

Furstenberg, F.F., Jr. (1971a) Birth control experience among pregnant adolescents: The process of unplanned parenthood. *Soc. Problems* 18: 192—203.

Furstenberg, F.F., Jr. (1971b) Preventing unwanted pregnancies among adolescents. *J. Health Soc. Behav.* 12: 340—347.

Goldsmith, S., Gabrielson, M.O., Gabrielson, I., Mathews, V. and Potts, L. (1972) Teenagers, sex, and contraception. *Fam. Plann. Perspect.* 4 (1): 32—38.

Hausknecht, R.U. (1972) The termination of pregnancy in adolescent women. *Pediat. Clin. North Am.* 19: 803—810.

Hill, R., Foote, N., Aldous, Jr., Carlson, R. and Macdonald, R. (1970) *Family Development in Three Generations*. (Schenkman, Cambridge, Mass.)

Howell, E.M. (1972) *A Study of Reported Therapeutic Abortions in North Carolina*, State Board of Health Statistical Report Series. (North Carolina Department of Human Resources, Raleigh.)

Hulka, J.F. (1972) Voluntary sterilization: The role of physician and hospital. *Hosp. Prac.*, November 1972, pp. 119—125.

Jorgensen, V. (1973) One-year contraceptive follow-up of adolescent patients. *Am. J. Obstet. Gynecol.* 115: 484—486.

Kane, F.J., Jr. and Lachenbruch, P.A. (1973) Adolescent pregnancy: A study of aborters and non-aborters. *Am. J. Orthopsychiat.* 43: 796—803.

Kantner, J.F. and Zelnik, M. (1972) Sexual experience of young unmarried women in the United States. *Fam. Plann. Perspect.* 4 (4): 9—18.

Kantner, J.F. and Zelnik, M. (1973) Contraception and pregnancy: Experience of young unmarried women in the United States. *Fam. Plann. Perspect.* 5 (1): 21—35.

Kirkendall, L.A. (1961) *Premarital Intercourse and Interpersonal Relationships.* (Julian Press, New York.)

Klein, L. (1974) Early teenage pregnancy, contraception, and repeat pregnancy. *Am. J. Obstet. Gynecol.* 120: 249—256.

Lal, S., Lewis, S., Belsey, E.M. and Greer, H.S. (1974) Contraceptive practice before and after out-patient termination of pregnancy. *Fam. Plann.* 23 (1): 4—7.

Landis, J.T. and Poffenberger, T. (1972) Hesitations and worries of 330 couples choosing vasectomy for birth control. In: (L. Lader, Ed.), *Foolproof Birth Control: Male and Female Sterilization.* (Beacon Press, Boston) pp. 62—72.

Lear, H. (1972) Psychosocial characteristics of patients requesting vasectomy. *J. Urol.* 108: 767—769.

Llewellyn-Jones, D. (1974) *Human Reproduction and Society.* (Faber and Faber, London.)

Luckey, E.B. and Nass, G.D. (1969) A comparison of sexual attitudes and behavior in an international sample. *J. Marr. Fam.* 31: 364—379.

Marinoff, S.C. (1972) Contraception in adolescents. *Pediat. Clin. North Am.* 19: 791—794.

McGarrah, R.E., Jr. (1974) Voluntary female sterilization: Abuses, risks and guidelines. *Hastings Center Report* 4 (3): 5—7.

Mesthene, E.G. (1968) How technology will shape the future. *Science* 161: 135—143.

Miller, W.B. (1972) Personality and ego factors relative to family planning and population control. *Conference Proceedings: Psychological Measurement in the Study of Population Problems.* (Inst. Personality Assessment and Research, Univ. California, Berkeley.)

Miller, W.B. (1973) Psychological vulnerability to unwanted pregnancy. *Fam. Plann. Perspect.* 5: 199—201.

Moors, H.G. (1974) *Child Spacing and Family Size in the Netherlands.* (Netherlands Interuniversity Demographic Institute, Voorburg.)

Morris, L. (1974) Estimating the need for family planning services among unwed teenagers. *Fam. Plann. Perspect.* 6: 91—97.

Namboodiri, N.K' (1974) Which couples at given parities expect to have additional births? An exercise in discriminant analysis *Demography* 11. 45 55.

Osofsky, H.J. (1971) Adolescent sexual behavior current status and anticipated trends for the future. *Clin. Obstet. Gynecol.* 14: 393—409.

Paniagua, M.E., Tayback, M., Janer, J.L. and Vazquez, J.L. (1972) Medical and psychological sequelae of surgical sterilization of women. In: (L. Lader, Ed.), *Foolproof Birth Control: Male and Female Sterilization,* (Beacon Press, Boston) pp. 169—184.

Peel, J. (1970) The Hull family survey, I: The survey couples, 1966. *J. Biosoc. Sci.* 2: 45—70.

Peel, J. (1972) The Hull family survey, II: Family planning in the first five years of marriage. *J. Biosoc. Sci.* 4: 333—346.

Pilpel, H.F. and Wechsler, N.F. (1971) Birth control, teen-agers and the law: A new look, 1971. *Fam. Plann. Perspect.* 3 (3): 37—45.

Pond, D.A. (1970) Psychological aspects of sterilization. *Fam. Plann.* 20: 109—112.

Potts, M. (1973) Current status of sterilization in the world: Prevalence, incidence, who and where. (Paper presented at the Second International Conference on Voluntary Sterilization, Geneva, February-March 1973.)

Presser, H.B. (1973) Contraceptive sterilization as a grass roots response: A comparative view of the Puerto Rican and United States experience. (Paper presented at the Conference on Research on the Behavioral Aspects of Surgical Contraception, Center for Population Research, NICHD, Bethesda, Maryland, June 1973.)

652

Presser, H.B. (1974) Early motherhood: Ignorance or bliss? *Fam. Plann. Perspect.* 6 (1): 8—14.

Rauh, J.L., Johnson, L.B. and Burket, R.L. (1969) Family planning in an adolescent clinic. *Ohio's Health*, September 1969, pp. 1—13.

Reichelt, P.A. and Werley, H.H. (1975) A sex information program for sexually active teenagers. *J. Sch. Health* XLV (2) 100—107.

Reiss, I.L. (1966) The sexual renaissance: A summary and analysis. *J. Soc. Issues* 22: 123—137.

Rindfuss, R. and Westoff, C.F. (1974) The initiation of contraception. *Demography* 11: 75—87.

Rogers, D.A. and Ziegler, F.J. (1973) Psychological reactions to surgical contraception. In: (J.T. Fawcett, Ed.), *Psychological Perspectives on Population*, (Basic Books, New York) pp. 306—328.

Rosario, F.Z. (1970) *Husband-Wife Interaction and Family Planning Acceptance: A Survey of the Literature*, Working Paper No. 3. (East-West Center, Honolulu.)

Royal College of Obstetricians and Gynaecologists (1972) *Unplanned Pregnancy: Report of the Working Party*. (London.)

Ryder, N.B. (1973) Contraceptive failure in the United States. *Fam. Plann. Perspect.* 5: 133—142.

Schofield, M. (1965) *The Sexual Behavior of Young People*. (Little and Brown, Boston.)

Schofield, M. (1973) *The Sexual Behavior of Young Adults*. (Little and Brown, Boston.)

Schwartz, S.H. (1970) Moral decision making and behavior. In: (J. Macaulay and L. Berkovitz, Eds.), *Altruism and Helping Behavior*, (Academic Press, New York) pp. 127—141.

Settlage, D., Baroff, S. and Cooper, D. (1973) Sexual experience of younger teenage girls seeking contraceptive assistance for the first time. *Fam. Plann. Perspect.* 5: 223—226.

Simmons, R.G., Klein, S.D. and Thornton, K. (1973) The family member's decision to be a kidney transplant donor. *J. Comp. Fam. Stud.* 4: 88—115.

Sklar, J. and Berkov, B. (1974) Teenage family formation in postwar America. *Fam. Plann. Perspect.* 6: 80—90.

Stokes, C.S. and Dudley, C.J. (1972) Family planning and conjugal roles: Some further evidence. *Soc. Sci. Med.* 6: 157—161.

Taylor, E.M. (1973) Population growth, contraception, and the high school student in the rural Punjab. *Stud. Fam. Plann.* 4: 65—69.

Terhune, U.W. (1973) Fertility values: Why people stop having children. (Paper presented at the American Psychological Association Meeting, Montreal, August 1973.)

Thiebaux, H.J. (1972) Self-prescribed contraceptive education by the unwillingly pregnant. *Am. J. Public Health* 62: 689—694.

Thompson, B. and Baird, D. (1972) Follow-up of 186 sterilized women. In: (L. Lader, Ed.), *Foolproof Birth Control: Male and Female Sterilization.* (Beacon Press, Boston) pp. 142—159.

Tietze, C. and Dawson, D. (1973) Induced abortion: A factbook. *Rep. Popul./Fam. Plann.*, December 1973, No. 14.

United States Bureau of the Census (1972) *Birth Expectations and Fertility*, Current Population Report, Series P. 20, No. 240. (U.S. Government Printing Office, Washington, D.C.)

Van Emde Boas, C. (1965) The possibilities and limitations of instruction in the use of contraceptives. *Sex and Human Relations: Proceedings of the Fourth Conference of the Region for Europe, Near East, and Africa of the International Planned Parenthood Federation*, London, June 1964, International Congress Series No. 102, pp. 80—83.

Veevers, J.E. (1973) Voluntary childless wives: An exploratory study. *Sociol. Soc. Res.* 57: 356—366.

Virginia Slims American Women's Opinion Poll (1974) Vol. 3. (The Roper Organization, New York.)

Wolfers, H. (1970) Psychological aspects of vasectomy. *Br. Med. J.* 4: 297—300.

Wolfish, M.G. (1973) Adolescent sexuality: Counseling, contraception, pregnancy. *Clin. Pediat.* 12: 244—247.

CHAPTER 46

Fertility regulation: friend or foe of the female?

EMILY C. MOORE

1. WHAT DO WOMEN WANT?

When Sigmund Freud long ago asked "What do women want; my God, what do they want?" he must surely have known that the answers would vary as much for women as they would if the question were asked about men — differing according to cultural context, individual characteristics, stage in the life cycle, and a host of situational variables.

At the subsistence level, women's wants are strikingly similar to men's wants: food, shelter, clothing, and hope for the future for themselves and their children. Beyond the subsistence level, wants are elaborated and varied; often they include a desire for affection, recognition, sexual satisfaction, and varying degrees of autonomy and self-determination.

How shall we define 'want'? Is it something expressed by a respondent answering survey questions? Do women really 'want' contraception, abortion, sterilization, more children? Is it what they privately acknowledge and express to their closest associates, or what they 'know' privately only within themselves? Or does a 'want' lie even deeper than that, unacknowledged even by the individual herself? If we ask 'How many children do you want?' we have conveyed clearly that to want none at all is unacceptable in this context; we should not be surprised to find few or none volunteering 'zero' as a reply, but then have we really measured what the women 'want'?

Although women's goals may be similar to men's, their attainment is made infinitely more difficult by the overriding fact of reproduction. The periodic occurrence of a relatively disabling condition (generally followed by an extended period of culturally sanctioned responsibility for the outcome), at unpredictable intervals, has meant for the female at all times and in all places a relatively restricted role and a complex skein of disadvantages, only some of which stem directly from the fact of pregnancy. (That she is often honored or revered for the 'accomplishment' of childbirth does not negate the disability.)

Handbook of Sexology, edited by J. Money and H. Musaph
© *Elsevier/North-Holland Biomedical Press, 1977*

Control over this unpredictable and often disadvantageous event is such a crucial prerequisite to all other avenues to self-determination, that it can quickly be understood why the goal of 'reproductive autonomy' is prominent in women's liberation efforts, and why full and equal participation in social and political decision-making is not a realizable goal for women until they can determine whether and when they will be pregnant. 'Anatomy is destiny' only if a woman is unable to manipulate the consequences of her anatomical capabilities.

Let me hazard a generalization about 'what women want,' remembering that no generalization encompasses all women under all circumstances.

KAP surveys (knowledge—attitude—practice) from many countries indicate a widespread readiness on the part of the women surveyed to accept some form of fertility regulation. Although these surveys have methodological shortcomings (Cleland, 1973), they do indicate a clear, near-universal approval of the principle of fertility regulation.

To the casual observer, control over the reproductive function may seem an unquestionably straightforward positive goal for all women everywhere. Planned childbearing offers health benefits to the woman and her children; psychological benefits as she plans for the future, controls her destiny, refusing manipulation by Fate or others; and possible economic and social benefits as she is better able to take advantage of educational and occupational opportunities — assuming, of course, that they are offered, and assuming that greater numbers of children offer no economic advantage, as they may in agricultural work.

With all of these 'obvious' benefits to be derived from exercising pregnancy control, how can it be, then, that women have not massed at the doors of the family planning services? And how can it be that even those who have already experienced modern fertility control often do not continue to use the methods?

2. WHAT IS THE MATTER WITH THOSE WOMEN?

The judgmental expression so often encountered, suggesting that 'those women' don't know what's good for them, can be directed at different groups of women, and the distinction is an important one.

Those who use contraception 'well' (avoiding all unwanted pregnancies) are classified as Good Women. Those who use no methods of birth prevention are Bad Women. The women, however, who rely solely on abortion, or who resort to abortion when contraception fails, are alternately classified as 'Good' or 'Bad', depending on whether the classifier's criteria for 'Good' is complete avoidance of unwanted fertility, regardless of method, or only 'successful' use of pre-conception methods. Aborters may be seen either as unsuccessful contraceptors, risk-takers, poor planners, lacking an orientation to the future, or as successful, planful, birth-preventers. The personal judgmental biases of many writers and researchers are readily apparent according to the way they categorize 'success' and 'failure'.

The advantages of fertility control are so apparent to some, that their studies of women who 'fail' to take advantage of these modern miracles are replete with judgmental, culture-biased statements: "Why such a sizable portion of our population fails to exploit fully the apparent advantages to themselves of current contraceptive science is a question of fundamental social concern. . . . Women give unreasonable and inconsistent explanations as to why none of the various methods are utilizable." (Sandberg and Jacobs, 1971). *

The frequent references to women who 'fail' seldom note the additional possibilities of method failure, partner failure, or medical care system failure. What are some of the barriers — external, structural, as well as internal, individual — to the use of contraception?

Cultural and individual resistance to fertility control in general

At the outset, it should be clearly noted that the following are suggestions only, not all of which are supported by research data, others are possibly researchable hypotheses. Indeed, some of them are considered useless at best, or offensive at worst, by women who find the often far-fetched efforts to find out 'what's wrong' with noncontracepting women to be highly insulting.

External (social/cultural/situational) obstacles
Some of the reasons for collective resistance to fertility control are obvious: a pronatalist policy on the part of the government, rendering family planning services unavailable, or available only to the few with means; governmental policy of laissez faire or disinterest, with the same effect, religious opposition; poor distribution and publicity for those services which are available; peer group resistance to innovation, whether the innovation be technological (the mechanical aspects of a new 'gadget') or psychosocial (new notions of control over one's health and destiny). Resistance to innovation is certainly not confined to underdeveloped societies or 'backward' communities.

Internal (individual/psychological) obstacles
In addition to the obvious possibility that women do not practice optimal fertility regulation because it is unavailable to them, there are many reasons why women might not utilize services that are technically available to them.

---

* The same authors state categorically that "women [all women?] are ambivalent about pregnancy throughout most of their reproductive lives" and suggest that as legal abortion becomes more readily available, "hostile feminists" will increasingly rely solely on abortion for control of their fertility. (If disability insurance becomes available, do drivers drive more carelessly?)

What does 'available' mean if clinic hours are such that a poor woman must lose a day's pay in order to utilize the services? Or if the clinic is located where she cannot reach it by public transportation? Or if it is located close to home, but is actually too close for privacy? Or if there is no care for her children while she waits, often for many hours? Or if, once at the clinic or hospital, she finds the layout confusing, the staff condescending, the explanations unsatisfying, and the procedures humiliating? (I have seen IUDs being fitted in rows of women in the usual pelvic-exam, feet-in-the-stirrups position, with construction workers nearby casually peering in the window; doctors said the cubicles were too warm with curtains closed.) Are services really 'available' when they are strategically and psychologically out of reach?

Women in most cultures are taught from a very early age to keep their knees together. A pelvic examination contradicts a lifetime of training. The woman is supine, the doctor erect. She is semi-nude; he is fully clothed. She is female; usually the doctor is male. She lies in a position not designed for comfort or modesty, while a strange man puts his fingers into her vagina. The word 'embarrassment' is insufficient to convey the feelings of many women in such a situation which emphasizes in every possible way the relative powerlessness of her position. That the acquisition of a contraceptive is a step toward self-determination and a boost to self-esteem is unlikely to be uppermost on her mind at the time she is flat on her back with her feet in the air.

Apart from the characteristics of the family planning clinic — the staff composition (age, sex, ethnicity), staff attitudes, convenience and ambience and the women's own determination to overcome the embarrassment and confusion of the procedures, what other reasons are there that a woman might reject fertility control altogether, or at a particular time, when to an outside observer it might seem more in her interest to adopt it?

Self-determination and autonomy are goals shared by many women with most men; however, not all women are prepared even to contemplate such freedom. Many women have spent their lives with little scope for making decisions; confronted with the possibility of a genuinely important choice, some women are frightened and avoid taking action which might bring them freedom they fear.

There are women who will not use contraception because they think it is the partner's responsibility to do so. Some do not think the risk of pregnancy is worth the bother, risk, and expense of the measures necessary to avert it. Others do not want to give up their excuse for refusing intercourse. (This may be considered trivial by some, but for the woman with a vaginal phobia and a brutal, demanding husband, the plea of possible pregnancy may be her only tactic to minimize violent sexual approaches.)

And finally there are a host of reasons why women consciously or unconsciously do not control their fertility because they do not want it controlled — either ever, or at a particular point in time. Their objections may be religious, political (nation-building), or personal. Their desires for a child may be rational or irrational; it is too easy to judge what is 'sensible' for other persons to do.

Many of the possible explanations of why a woman may proceed with a pregnancy when others believe it not in her best interest include: punishing her parents/husband/boyfriend; forcing marriage or preventing divorce; proving she is adult; proving she is feminine; having a live 'doll' to care for and feel protective toward; locking herself into a lifestyle in which career and educational options are deliberately limited, and so on. Those who put forth such explanations seldom distinguish between a willingness to be pregnant (sufficient to prove femininity and upset her parents, if that be the aim) and willingness to bear a child (with more serious consequences than pregnancy begun but terminated). Rather than disparage these 'infantile' reasons for becoming pregnant, we should consider why females sometimes want to punish parents or partners, hurt themselves, assert their selfhood by acts of defiance, or prove they are feminine, and why they select pregnancy as the means toward these ends.

Collective and individual barriers to use of particular methods of fertility regulation

Embarrassment and shame   These may cause rejection either of fertility control in general, or of particular methods. A nonprescription method may be preferred by some not because of cost or convenience, but because 'the couple can use it without having to bring a third party, a doctor, for example, into their sexual life.' (International Research Associates, 1971).

In a doctor's office or clinic, embarrassment can be minimized by privacy in consultation, screens or curtains, presence of a female (the doctor herself or an assistant), and draping. (However, where 'verguenza' and 'pudor' are cultural factors, Scrimshaw (1973) recommends that draping be adopted where not yet in use to maximise modesty; in the U.S., customary draping is now seen as a symbol of discomfort with her body and some women now ask that it be discontinued.)

The pelvic exam and intimate contact by a male doctor are not the only sources of embarrassment for women in a clinic setting: consider also fear of appearing stupid if asked many questions; fear of revealing illiteracy if asked to fill out a form or to read something; fear of being 'found out' that she's had an abortion or that she's been masturbating (can the doctor tell just by looking into her?).

Even the druggist may be seen as a 'third party' and the cause of embarrassment: the report of the International Research Associates states that even in a relatively sophisticated sample of New York City young married couples, husbands were embarrassed to buy condoms ('he comes home with another toothbrush instead').

It is not only embarrassment relative to other people that affects use of certain methods. What sophisticated diaphragm-user has not felt slightly absurd, even when alone in the privacy of her own bathroom, when her jelly-smeared diaphragm shoots out of her hand and flies across the room? Some women may laugh, but other consider it revolting and begin finding excuses not to use the diaphragm again.

Preference for the condom over the diaphragm may be based on the condom's disposability — quickly removing the 'shameful evidence' may be a symbolic way of removing the shame; having to wash and use the diaphragm again means having to confront the 'shameful evidence' each time she opens her medicine cabinet.

For some, having to handle genitals (as with the condom, foam, and diaphragm) is too great an obstacle to overcome, especially in the presence of spouse/partner.

Guilt   In addition to shame and embarrassment, guilt may influence the selection of particular methods. The widespread adoption of sterilization by Puerto Rican women (by 1965, one third of the women of reproductive age had been sterilized: Presser, 1973) can partly be accounted for by the fact that a woman need confess her 'sin' only once, rather than weekly if she uses other 'forbidden' methods. For some Catholic women, pregnancy may be seen as appropriate punishment for their having used forbidden methods; the forgotten pill may be a way of 'settling' matters with the conscience.

Fear   Add to the above genuine fear with respect to some methods: for example, fear of harmful side-effects known or rumored to occur with the use of the pill or IUD; fear of surgery (procedure, hospital setting where people are 'sick', personnel) affecting the choice of abortion or sterilization; fear that family, employers, or friends will find out; fear of needles (if the blood test is done); fear of foreign bodies; fear that a condom will come off and be 'lost' inside her body, or that an IUD will migrate and pierce her heart or brain.

Many women fear their husbands' rejection should they become sterilized and 'less of a woman', particularly if the sterilization is accomplished by hysterectomy. One author, after noting a study in which seven of eleven women's husbands had in fact rejected them after hysterectomy, 'thereby fulfilling the pre-operative fantasies of loss of sexual desirability', goes on to say that 'sexual disturbances . . . following surgical sterilization, with or without hysterectomy . . . in most instances are not due to organic changes. Far more responsible are the irrational fears and beliefs' (Mathis, 1973). This author once heard a middle-class, urban American say to his wife, who had been sterilized, "What can you say about the subject? [unrelated to fertility] You're not a woman any more." Can other women's fears be termed 'irrational'?

Blood   There are cultural and individual reactions to changes in the amount of menstrual flow: an increase is painful, inconvenient, and alarming to many, particularly if the woman has not been forewarned. A decrease in blood can also be upsetting:where does the usual flow go? Is it 'backing up' inside of her? Breakthrough bleeding may disrupt sexual relations where coitus is taboo whenever the woman is bleeding.

Beauty   While fertility control may have cosmetic benefits for those who value a youthful figure, for some women there are more immediate cosmetic disadvantages. Would men adopt medication which caused facial discoloration and weight gain?

Planning/fatalism   In order to use the diaphragm or rhythm method successfully, methods requiring care, planning, and self-control, a woman must be convinced that by her own actions she can affect her future; for many women in many societies this is so patently untrue in nearly all other aspects of their lives that they have little reason to believe it could be true regarding fertility.

Since most societies emphasize curative medicine over preventive action, it should not be surprising that women are not interested in doing something about fertility until an unwanted condition appears; both men and women generally do not visit a doctor until they experience symptoms of disease. Why should women be better planners than other members of their society? Once the certainty of a pregnancy has been realized, she can undertake 'curative' action — such as induced abortion. [*]

Some women may feel that using any method which involves advance planning is an admission of sexual desire and sensuousness (Devereux, 1965). This may be a valued characteristic for some, but for others a cause for considerable embarrassment.

Teenagers have particular problems, affecting use or non-use of particular methods. Equipping herself with 'serious' methods such as the pill or IUD is an admission to herself, and to others, that she has begun and is planning for regular sexual contact. Where premarital intercourse is condemned, she may prefer to maintain a self-image as not-yet-active sexually, believing each act of coitus to have resulted from her being 'overcome' by the passion of the moment. Since she did not conceive after the first few experiences, she may think that there is little or no risk in continuing unprotected sex. The psychiatric literature may call this 'denial' — 'other women get pregnant, not me.' It could more simply be described as ignorance regarding the laws of probability. Even if the teenager obtains foam or a diaphragm, she may deliberately leave it at home to test her self-control.

---

* While the risk of illegal abortion is well-known to physicians and statisticians, it may be less apparent to women who can have many acquaintances who have undergone illegal abortions with no untoward effects, giving them reason to conclude that the procedure is safe. Post-conception methods have an obvious appeal since they parallel other types of curative medical care.

Family, medical influence In addition to many other internal barriers to adoption or consistent use of certain methods (messiness, association with prostitutes and VD, side-effects, cost, inconvenience, necessity for planning and control) there are external barriers as well — husbands and mothers-in-law, as well as physicians who advise for or against particular methods. Figa-Talamanca (1971) found among urban Italian women who had had illegal abortions many who had been advised by their physicians not to take the pill, and had not been advised on any alternate preventive method. Metzner and Golden (1967) found that removal of the IUD was more frequent in women who had been persuaded by their physicians to adopt it.

Rejecting male-controlled methods Variously called endometrial aspiration, early abortion, menstrual extraction, and menstrual regulation, this procedure has political implications for many women in America and Western Europe, who see it not solely as a convenient and relatively safe method of regulating their fertility, but also eliminating the intrusive third party (the medical establishment) when women perform it on each other. It is an assertion of their political right to handle and control their bodies. Gynecological self-help groups, when legally challenged on cervical examinations (preceding and ideologically linked with menstrual regulation), point out that women are now encouraged to examine their own breasts, so why not their own cervices? They explain why they do not call menstrual regulation 'abortion': "Menstrual extraction provides a mechanism by which all women can be the final determiners regarding the number of children we will or will not have, and the time and place of our periods. We find her [a hypothetical woman] now, three or four days late on her period. She does not want to be pregnant. Her group meets; she and they extract her period, at which point she is not pregnant. Was she or wasn't she? Who cares? She does not; the group does not . . . Menstrual extraction . . . is not an abortion. We are not being coy or cute. We simply are not concerned enough with the question of a possible fertilized egg to include it in our thinking. Menstrual extraction is menstrual extraction because our concern is our health . . . There is no need for medication, restraint of intercourse, severe discomfort, doctors' offices, cold and sterile gynecological tables, waiting or high costs." (Menstrual Extraction, 1974)

Contraceptive suitability There is growing interest in the question of 'contraceptive fit', or 'method acceptability'. I would urge two caveats; it is tempting to search for individual internal psychological barriers to use, missing an external explanation such as the husband forbidding contraceptive use or the fact that in a certain culture it is unthinkable to use a method that involves touching the genitals. It is incumbent upon us to look first for the external reason before probing for 'what's the matter with that woman.' Second, a more appropriate question to ask might be not 'what's the matter with that woman,' but 'what's the matter with the method, with the circumstances, and with the manner of its introduction?' It is now considered sensitive to try to 'fit' a method to the woman low in self-esteem, dependent or self-punishing (likely candidates for unplanned pregnancy); it is even more sensitive to ask what there is about the social context that causes so many women to be dependent and low in self-esteem.

3. THEY CAN'T HAVE IT BOTH WAYS

There was a time when male researchers in the laboratory developed methods of fertility regulation, and male physicians prescribed them to women in their clinics or offices. The Women's Movement and the Health Consumer Movement in the United States have converged, largely on the issues of abortion, contraception and sterilization, now encompassing other health issues as well (Moore, 1971). The counterattack says: "You women say you want better methods of contraception, yet claim you're guinea pigs when new methods are released for your use. You want control over your bodies, yet argue for research on male methods. Which is it going to be?"

Male versus female methods

With the exception of abortion, the only fertility regulating methods available until recently were 'male' methods: the condom and withdrawal. * Margaret Sanger emphasized the use of the only female preventive method then available, the diaphragm, as the means for women to gain control of their fertility. Now that the most effective, modern methods (the pill and IUD) are female methods, women protest that men should take equal responsibility (and risk) in preventing unwanted births. This is neither ambivalent nor inconsistent, if the position is fully understood: women approve continued research for improvement of female methods; single women and those who do not trust their partners continue to place primary reliance on female methods for their own protection; those in more stable unions hope for the development of male methods so that the risks and responsibilities can be more equitably shared. It is often difficult to remember that different women want different things, or that the same woman may require different things at various times in her life.

Women's agitation for more research on male methods is not, as often suggested, a hostile display of revenge. The position suggests that men should assume equal responsibility for procreation and its control, that males have a right to have effective methods available to them, that the question of method use should be open to negotiation between male and female, and that

---

* Withdrawal may affect the woman as much as or more than the man; since most males reach orgasm sooner than most females, if the male withdraws just prior to his own climax, many women never experience orgasm, which may explain why the very existence of female orgasm is denied or deemed "unseemly" in many cultures.

covert hostilities should not be expressed through contraceptive battles, but be resolved by open discussion. As long as the most effective methods are female, the door to discussion is effectively closed for most couples.

Who shall use which method, and when? Tensions may be expressed by the choice of contraception. The condom may be objectionable to the male, yet acceptable to the female because it slows his orgasm or because she objects to having semen in her vagina. Some couples may decide never to use it, and some may attempt to turn an objectionable aspect to pleasurable, incorporating its placement into foreplay. Or they may decide to alternate — six months for her on the pill, six months for him with the condom.

Who shall be sterilized? The question is complex, and the choice is rarely based only on relative risk to the male or female. Fears of castration, impotency or unmanning, unrelated to actual risk of organic damage, can affect the choice for vasectomy. Fears of loss of femininity and attractiveness, also unrelated to organic change, may influence the choice of tubal ligation. Although it is difficult for a woman to be sterilized without her husband's knowledge, men do obtain vasectomies without consulting their wives.

If the husband gets a vasectomy, the wife may view it as his way of 'checking up' on her (if she conceives, she will have some explaining to do). If the wife gets a tubal ligation, the husband may view it as her way to infidelity.

When a couple are divorced, the one who has been sterilized leaves the union disadvantaged or advantaged, dependent on the desire for more children.

Resentment may result when a couple discuss the alternatives of his vs. her sterilization; knowing that his is a safer procedure, she may be angry, openly or covertly, when the 'couple' finally settle on a sterilization for her.

One reporter, interviewing U.S. couples on their fertility desires, found hostilities erupting in his presence. 'What will you use after your family size is completed?" He: "Oh, we'll use the pill." She: "Probably vasectomy." He: "What do you mean, vasectomy? You never mentioned that before!" She: "What do you mean, we'll use the pill? I won't have my hormones messed over for twenty years!" The battle was on, apparently never having been discussed before the reporter's question prompted it.

The questions of control, power and powerlessness, are entwined with the choice of contraception. For example, the only way a woman can be sure she is protected is if the man wears a condom (visible to both of them) or if she uses a female method; trust between them must be substantial if she is to rely on his word that he is sterilized or that he will withdraw before ejaculation. If the woman uses contraception, her partner may increase his demands for sex, without a concomitant increase in his ability to satisfy her. On the other hand, she may demand sex more often than he desires; he may then feel his 'greater masculine sexuality' threatened (if he measures it in terms of coital frequency), or he may suspect her of satisfying her sexual demands with another partner. Thus, the removal of or reduction in fear of pregnancy may be threatening to either or both partners and may alter power relations between them.

"The one who uses contraceptives admits to being the 'sexier' of the two . . . the increasing use of feminine contraceptives has coincided historically with the acceptance of the idea that it is 'respectable' for women to have sexual needs. Large-scale female contraception in a Victorian climate is both psychologically and sociologically unthinkable" (Devereux, 1965). Yet, it may be in just such a repressive climate that some courageous women will find methods they can use without their husbands' knowledge.

Optimal risk-taking: guinea pigs and experimental methods

Both of the following are popular messages beamed at female contraceptors today: (1) women who have abortions are masochistic, self-destructive, 'risk-takers' because they 'failed' to use the most effective contraceptives; and (2) women should not heed the fear-mongers who proclaim the dangers of the pill, but should be willing to take this small risk (International Planned Parenthood Federation, IPPF News, 1974b), which after all is less than the risk of pregnancy. It is difficult for women to know just how risk-taking they must be in order to meet the approval of the many Judges with whom they come in contact. during enough to use a medication with several known, and many unproven but suggested dangerous side-effects, but not so daring that they expose themselves to the almost identical mortality risk of legally induced abortion (Tietze and Dawson, 1973).

Women do desire improvements in pre- and post-conception technology, but do not want to be subjected to dangerous, experimental methods. After the rats and the monkeys have been laboratory subjects, there comes a time when a human population must be tested. This is unavoidable. Women's response to well publicized pill scares, and well-publicized IUD scares, is simply that the same criteria for experimentation be applied to them as for men (That this is not necessarily the case, was illustrated at the Population Tribune in Bucharest, where a male researcher commented that male methods now being tested, seemingly with great success, are not yet considered suitable for general distribution because some of the experimental subjects complained of headaches and nausea — complaints which have clearly not prevented wide distribution of female methods.) While this may seem obvious, suspicion based on past experience, rooted in relative powerlessness in many dimensions of life (health care included), leads them to stress the need for informed consent, careful controls, meticulous monitoring, and more attention to safety than to public relations and profits for drug companies.

Resentment by women's groups of the manner in which the pill has been tested and marketed was found in New York (International Research Associates, 1971) to be not an isolated suspicion, but part of a general trend toward consumer demands for restraint in marketing drugs, and a generalized suspicion toward the medical profession and drug companies regarding untested chemicals and the profit motive:

"Although the pill has had the broadest appeal to those interviewed, many now have serious misgivings about its safety and are afraid to use it. It seems fair to say that these fears would generalize to any new, chemically oriented method. There is also some evidence to suggest that they have been enhanced by a growing sense of wariness about the extent to which consumer products, in general, are authorized for use without adequate testing, or without allowing adequate information to filter down to the user. . . . there is a tendency to be cautious about the extent to which 'official' or 'expert' endorsement of products which might involve the health of their consumers — including endorsement by medical authorities — can be accepted as sufficiently well-informed, or even as completely candid . . . Reservations of this sort have implications not just for acceptance of the pill, but also for acceptance of any future product in this field. . . . The fact that early assurance about its [the pill's] safety later fell so far short of expectations also helps to account for another suggestion in the data: there are important signals that announcements of any new, more 'ideal' approach to contraception, particularly a chemical one, will be met with increased caution, if not with deep distrust. . . . "While many feel they lack adequate knowledge of how even current methods work, there is also the feeling that experts cannot be depended on to know precisely what effects they may be setting into motion . . . some respondents point to the belief that medical opinion is divided, or uncertain, about methods currently available, and that products have been endorsed and distributed without adequate testing."

The extensive quotes above are from a survey not of radical feminists but of young white married couples in New York. The repeated emphasis on the finding of suspicion and distrust, stemming largely from misrepresentation of the safety of the pill, should not go unheeded.

The miracle methods: expectation and reality

One of the causes for current dissatisfaction with the medical establishment, and family planning promoters in particular, is the enormous publicity given in the 1960s to the pill and IUD, and the suggestion that with the introduction of these highly effective methods, perfect fertility control was now possible for all women. The U.S. Supreme Court, ruling that a state may deny disability benefits for pregnancy, described it as a 'voluntary' condition.

Yet no single method, including the pill and IUD, satisfies all the requirements (safety, effectiveness, aesthetic acceptability, and low cost) of the highly touted 'perfect' method. Women not only have differing needs and preferences, but may value effectiveness more or less at different stages in the life cycle. The choice of method or combination of methods involves trade-offs, compromises, a weighing of risks and advantages, all of which occur within medical, individual, couple, peer group, and cultural contexts.

Even an informed consumer may find it confusing to decide for or against using the pill. Against what shall she and her partner compare its risk: Pregnancy? * Abortion? Other contraceptive methods? What males are expected to risk? Or the promises of safety made to her by the deluge of articles in the popular press? (When reality proved different from expectation, it is no wonder that anger and resentment resulted.)

Relative risk is a complicated matter. Women's consumer groups are particularly annoyed when research focuses on the 'risk-taking' woman undergoing an abortion — research which would be unlikely if the subjects were males who 'failed' to fasten their auto safety belts on all occasions, thereby subjecting themselves to Willful Exposure to Unwanted Dismemberment (WEUD), ** or intelligent, educated business executives who smoke and fail to exercise properly, even after experiencing a heart attack: Willful Exposure to Unwanted Coronary (WEUC). **

If women had access to all methods — all forms of contraception, legal abortion, and sterilization — which very few do have, they would still have to weigh the following aspects (considering only three of many desirable characteristics):

Method	Effective	Safe	Coitus-independent
pill	ı		+
IUD	+		+
sterilization	+		+
condom		+	
diaphragm		+	
rhythm		+	
foam		+	

The safer methods are less effective, and the more effective are less safe. It is not surprising that some switch from method to method, sometimes despairing and giving up entirely. Given the present state of technology, is it realistic to expect that a single-method family planning program, or a single-method clinic, or a single-method doctor will suit all women, at all stages in their life cycle, and with all their varying needs and desires, taboos and fears?

What do women want? They want both male and female methods so that the choices are broader. They want access to the presently available methods, continued research on better methods, with the very highest standards of experimental safeguards. And they want not only the technology, but also a reason for greatly altering their life design. After reduced family size, then what: is a reduction in fertility worth it at the individual level?

---

* Mortality and morbidity risks from pregnancy are generally not salient in these considerations; it is the relative risks vs. advantages of the various fertility-regulating methods that are weighed. Pregnancy may be undesired, yet considered less negative than the physical or psychic strain of contraception or abortion.

** The reference is to WEUP (Willful Exposure to Unwanted Pregnancy). "Emotional factors may thwart the protective action of contraception." (Lehfeldt, 1959, 1965).

4. WOMEN'S ROLES AND FERTILITY

A great hoax of the century was the widely publicized notion that with the development of the IUD and the pill, women now had the liberating method by which they could control their fertility and hence their lives. "Now that women are free from unwanted childbearing, . . ." began many a popular article of the 1960s. The hoax was two-fold. In the first place, it was soon learned (though it took the popular magazines longer than individual women to discover) that neither the pill nor the IUD met all of these criteria, even though they were a marked improvement over other methods. In the second place, even if a woman found one of these methods acceptable, she found herself free to plan her pregnancies, but scarcely any more free to exercise a wide range of career and life-style options than she had been before.

Dixon (1970) noted that the pill permits women to have the children they want, and to stop when they want; it does not free them from social pressures for motherhood, nor from the constraints on a single or child-free life style, nor does the pill itself provide meaningful alternatives so that women will want fewer babies. She was now free from unplanned pregnancy, but what was she freed for? "The pill brings one form of emancipation, but it does not bring the other." (Dixon, 1970).

In our haste to introduce a measure which is presumed to be a means for improving individual lives, we may not realize that in so doing we also denigrate and downgrade the importance of the primary role performed by half of humanity. That the chief decision-makers and promotors of this measure are nearly always members of the other half of humanity cannot help but result in suspicion and resentment.

It is difficult to construct an analogy in which sex roles are reversed, but let us try. Suppose the male inhabitants of the imaginary Island of Canuvia (Moore, 1974) were primarily engaged in making many canoes; boys helped their fathers as they learned the craft; an adult male was not eligible for marriage if he could not make one. His status, prestige, satisfaction, and position in the community depended on his canoe-building. Then a plastic coating that would extend the life of the canoes was brought to Canuvia by a technical expert, making it no longer necessary to build so many. Stockpiling of excess canoes soon became a threat to the small island. The governing council of women met to decide what to do: should they ask the men to stop building canoes after they have made two? (What are the men to do, since they will be only 30 years old after completing two canoes and will have many more years of life ahead of them?) To postpone the onset of canoe-building? To build less frequently, say one every four years, instead of every two? And how shall they be persuaded to do this — by education, cash incentives, taxing those who over-produce, or forcefully sewing together the fingers of each man after he has completed two canoes? Consider, then, the feeling that many women have when they learn of yet another conference of all male, or nearly all male, delegates brought together to discuss the alternative ways of persuading/convincing/coercing women to 'retire' after creating two children, thereby greatly altering their life patterns, with little or no regard for new ways in which they may find satisfaction, gain community recognition, and occupy their time.

Not only would meetings of women be more likely to pay attention to the matter of alternative non-familial roles, but they are also more apt to consider personal and social obstacles to the optimal practice of fertility control often overlooked by males. For example, it is impossible to imagine a conference of thirteen females (and one male) * reaching the following conclusion: "the severe problems of fertility control in the United States are more likely to be solved by an easily obtainable, highly effective female method than by a highly effective and more acceptable male method." (Campbell and Berelson, 1971).

Thus, women must be considered not only as consumers (or users of fertility control methods), but also as providers, researchers, and policy-makers (deciding how the methods are to be promoted and what activities will replace child-bearing and rearing).

Wassertheil-Smoller and her colleagues (1973a) found that women obstetrician/gynecologists in New York State prescribed the pill post-abortion significantly less often than did their male counterparts. They also found that of the male physicians who routinely recommended the pill to post-abortion patients, only 24% had wives who used the pill themselves (Wassertheil-Smoller et al., 1973b).

Cowan (1973) refers to family planning program administrators as professionals who "see women as wombs to be deactivated rather than human lives to be fulfilled."

On February 25, 1974, "women delegates to the UN took over the General Assembly hall for a forum on women's roles in population and economic development but failed to muster much attention from the men who head the 135 UN delegations. [The reporter describes the event in terms of the women failing to muster attention, not of the men failing to attend.] Three hundred invitations went out, but only a dozen delegates turned up." (New York Times, 1974.) Other accounts of the same event noted that the few men who did attend gave audible expression to their amusement. Being taken seriously in population and development policy discussions is a first priority for women.

It is not only American feminists who call for a greater role for women in family planning decision-making and policy implementation. The prime minister of Singapore (Bloodworth, 1974) said in an interview:

"Family planning workers must include more women than men, because they can talk more frankly with the women and convince them [to limit their fertility]. The head of the

---

* A 1969 workshop called to explore the issue of involving social scientists working with biological scientists in the design of new contraceptives had just such a composition — only in reverse.

Family Planning Board is a lady doctor. I believe she carries much more weight with the women than would a male doctor."

A spokesman for the Family Planning Association of St. Lucia is quoted as follows:

"Women must now be involved not merely as acceptors of this or that contraceptive device or as passive tools or policy, but as makers of decisions and active participants in policies which profoundly affect their lives." (IPPF, 1974a)

Yet in the same issue of IPPF News, an executive decree in Argentina, forbidding the promotion of birth control by any means whatsoever, noting the low rate of population growth, points to:

"interests which are not Argentine, which seek to promote ways of life which are antagonistic to those which correspond with the destiny of a great country, discouraging the consolidation and expansion of the family unit, promoting birth control, deforming the fundamental maternal function of woman and, finally, distracting our youth from its natural duty as protagonists of the future of the fatherland." (IPPF News, 1974a)

Thus, women in some countries are still exhorted not to curtail their fertility, while in others the sanctions and rewards — political, religious, and cultural — which once worked to promote maximum fertility now reward lower fertility. To neither set of instructions do the women themselves have any meaningful input. Economist Charlotte Muller puts it this way:

"Historically, the demand for women's labor in specific expanding industries and at specific times helped to convert the life patterns, expectations and needs of women, and to provide a direct reward for fertility control. Women should not be surprised that their fertility is a variable in someone else's equation." (Muller, 1974)

If Freud, program administrators, policy-makers, and clinicians really want to know what women want, some women say they are prepared to provide some answers — undertaking roles in which they can decide what research shall be done, when and on whom the methods shall be tried, how and in what context (health programs, social and welfare programs) the methods shall be introduced and by whom, and what shall be the concurrent social measures affecting education, employment, etc. that will be undertaken to compensate for the diminished role of motherhood.

5. WHAT IS THE DOCTOR TO DO?

Recognizing differences among clients

The one-method program, clinic, or doctor is well known. It should be clear from the above that there is no single method which fits all women all of the time; discontinuation rates are bound to be substantial when all who pass through a service are expected to adopt the same method. While International Research Associates (1971) found among New York couples considerable distrust of 'experts,' medical and otherwise, they also found the opposite — total reliance on medical authority:

"because of the complexity of the issues involved in the choice of a birth control method . . . in their inability to make judgments about what method to choose a number of respondents look to the medical profession to make that choice for them."

The doctor would do well, therefore, to make an effort to distinguish among those women who (1) look to him/her to make the choice, (2) ask him/her for advice on the final selection, and (3) come to him/her for the method they have already chosen but which requires his/her intervention.

Promoting or inhibiting choice; value judgments in the clinical setting

It is not only in the matter of contraceptive choice that the physician's role can have a profound effect (sometimes welcome sometimes not) on the client's action. Fertility decisions can also be affected by the considerable influence of the physician, as when he/she comments, for example, that a woman will 'outgrow such a silly idea' when she makes known a desire to remain childless.

The physician as sociologist and psychologist

The doctor sees one patient at a time. Although these clients may be unrepresentative of a larger group of women, it is very tempting, and not uncommon for the physician to generalize to all women on the basis of the women in his/her practice. When he/she finds a recurring problem, or finds that in a single day women seem repeatedly to come in with similar reasons for non-use or poor use of contraception, it may be hard to resist making remarks (some of which may find their way into print) about how 'women do or don't because   ' Sociological perspective enables the physician to see just how typical or aberrant these commonalities really are.

Because it is the woman, and not her husband or partner, nor the larger society, nor the complex network of norms and sanctions that the doctor sees in the office, it is surely understandable that the most visible explanation for non-use of contraception lies with the woman. The doctor may, on the one hand, ignore individual differences and treat each patient as a uterus and not as a personality, or may go to the opposite extreme and play armchair psychologist, exploring the psyche of each women to explain her 'failure' to practice fertility control, declaring her fears, reservations, and side-effects as imaginary.

Before concluding why Ms. X did not use contraception, or why she used it and became pregnant anyway, the following thoughts should occur: perhaps the method itself failed, or was unacceptable; perhaps I did not explain it correctly; perhaps her husband or some other person objected to her using it; perhaps it is not an acceptable time for her to limit her fertility. Only

672

after these have been considered, should the amateur psychologist emerge and tinker with possibilities of parental rejection, proof of femininity, inability to plan, and so on. Before one considers oneself an expert on other people's innermost motivations, one should first consider a host of external influences and constraints.

If the doctor becomes impatient with the slow rate of adoption of optimal fertility control — by individual women and by whole nations — let him/her be reminded that the American Medical Association recommended in 1937 that birth control be taught in all medical schools. How long has it been until this recommendation was realized, and how many medical schools even now have no sex education?

Being a good patient; being a good doctor

"If I go to the doctor at the first sign of pain, he says I'm a hypochondriac; it's psychosomatic; I'm wasting his time. If I wait until the pain is severe, he scolds me for neglecting myself; I'm masochistic and self-destructive. How should I know the precise moment at which it is appropriate for me to consult a physician?"

It is difficult for many people, men and women, to be Good Patients. "How many questions shall I ask? If I ask none, he treats me like a child, doesn't tell me why I should take the medicine or what it will do, and I wonder if it's all right to mix the new pills with those I'm already taking. But if I ask too much, he gets angry and says 'I'm the doctor, you're the patient, trust me, just do as I say.' And each doctor is different — how am I to know how much questioning is appropriate?"

The doctor, in this age of consumerism, also has difficulties learning the appropriate role, and gauging the expectations of each client as she walks in the door. Some patients want authority, some want only a little advice, some want only the technical information and access to medicine that the doctor can provide. The doctor can expect growing numbers of patients who want to participate actively in their own care in the future.

6. CONCLUSION

Contraception has been both boon and bane to modern women. In some sense, the possibility of regulating their fertility is a most important advance for women, relieving them as it can of unintended and unwelcome childbearing; contraception, sterilization, and abortion combine to free many women from unpredictable and burdensome tyranny of their anatomies. Yet at the same time, the means to lower fertility do not provide the reasons for doing so; hence the pressure world-wide to combine increased participation of women in the decision-making process with continued improvements in the technology of contraception for women and men.

BIBLIOGRAPHY

Bloodworth, D. (1974) Lee Kuan Yew: Male chauvinism is to blame. International Planned Parenthood Federation. *People* 1: 10—14.

Campbell, A. and Berelson, B. (1971) Contraceptive specifications: Report on a Workshop. *Stud. Fam. Plann.* 4: 42—47.

Cleland, J. (1973) A critique of KAP studies and some suggestions for their improvement. *Stud. Fam. Plann.* 4: 42—47.

Cowan, R. (1971) Ecuador: Birth controlling the people. *Ramparts*, October.

Devereux, G. (1965) A psychoanalytic study of contraception. *J. Sex Res.* 1: 105—134.

Dixon, R.B. (1970) Hallelujah the Pill? *Transaction* 8: 44—49, 92.

Ehrenreich, B. and English, D. (1973) *Witches, Midwives, and Nurses — A History of Women Healers.* (The Feminist Press, New York.)

Figa-Talamanca, I. (1971) Social and psychological factors in the practice of induced abortion as a means of fertility control in an Italian population. *Genus*, 27: 99—266.

Ghali, F. and Gadalla, F. (1973) Fertility characteristics and family planning knowledge, attitudes, and practice in Baghdad, Iraq. *Stud. Fam. Plann.* 4: 143—145.

Heath, L.L., Roper, B.S. and King, C.D. (1974) A research note on children viewed as contributors to marital stability: The relationship to birth control use, ideal, and expected family size. *J. Marr. Fam.* 36: 304—306.

House, A. (1973) What contraceptive type are you? *Ms.*, March, 7—14.

IPPF News (1974a) St. Lucia in the public eye. July.

IPPF News (1974b) The estimated risk at the present time of using the pill is one that a properly informed woman should be happy to take. Report of the Royal College of General Practitioners, Britain. July.

International Research Associates (1971) In search of an ideal contraceptive technology: An exploratory study of attitudes. Prepared for the Population Council.

Landesman, R., Kaye, R.E. and Wilson, K.H. (1973) A two-man experience with the Copper T intra-uterine device. *Contraception* 7: 477—489.

Lehfeldt, H. (1959) Willful exposure to unwanted pregnancy. *Am. J. Obstet. Gynecol.* 78: 661—665.

Lehfeldt, H. (1965) Psychological aspects of planned parenthood. *J. Sex Res.* 1: 97—103.

Lennane, K.J. and Lennane, R.J. (1973) Alleged psychogenic disorders in women — A possible manifestation of sexual prejudice. *New Engl. J. Med.* 288: 288—292.

Mathis, J.L. (1970) Psychological aspects of surgery on reproductive organs. *J. Obstet. Gynecol. Neonatal Nurs.* 2: 50—54.

Menstrual Extraction (1974) The means to responsibly control our periods. *The Monthly Extract: An Irregular Periodical* 3: (New Moon Communications, Stamford, Connecticut.)

Metzner, R. and Golden, J. (1967) Psychological factors influencing female patients in the selection of contraceptive devices. *Fertil. Steril.* 18: 845—856.

Moore, E.C. (1971) Abortion, contraception, sterilization: the camel's nose. Paper presented at the annual meeting of the New England Psychological Association, New Haven, Connecticut, November 13. Shorter version published as S. Freud: My God, we've been telling you! *Fam. Plann. Perspect.* 1972, 4: 2—4.

Moore, E.C. (1974) The parable of the excess canoes, *Concerned Demography*, Special Issue on Women, 4: 8—10.

Moore-Cavar, E.C. (1974) *International Inventory of Information on Induced Abortion.* Columbia University: International Institute for the Study of Human Reproduction.

Muller, C. (1974) Feminism, society and fertility control. *Fam. Plann. Perspect.* 6: 68—72.

New York Times (1974) UN women disappointed by a small male turnout at forum. February 26.

Presser, H.B. (1973) *Sterilization and Fertility Decline in Puerto Rico*. Berkeley: University of California, Population Monograph Series No. 13. Available in Spanish from the Population Council.

Sandberg, E. and Jacobs, R. (1971) Psychology of the misuse & rejection of contraception. *Am. J. Obstet. Gynecol.* 110: 227—242.

Santee, B. (1974) Family planning clinics: Does "free" access mean "easy" access? Unpublished paper. Columbia University: International Institute for the Study of Human Reproduction.

Scrimshaw, S. (1973) *Lo de nosotras: Pudor and family planning clinics in a Latin American city*. Columbia University: International Institute for the Study of Human Reproduction.

Sharpe, J. (1972) The birth controllers. *Health Policy Advisory Center Bulletin* 40: 3—12.

Tietze, C. and Dawson, D. (1973) Induced Abortion: A Fact Book. New York: Population Council. Reports. Number 14.

Wassertheil-Smoller, S., Lerner, R.C., Arnold, C.B. and Heimrath, S.L. (1973a) New York State physicians and social context of abortion. *Am. J. Public Health* 63: 144—149.

Wassertheil-Smoller, S., Arnold, C.B., Lerner, R.C. and Heimrath, S.L. (1973b) Contraceptive practices of wives of obstetricians. *Am. J. Obstet. Gynecol.* 117: 709—715.

SECTION VIII

Pregnancy and childbirth

Section coordinator: Ary A. Haspels

CHAPTER 47

Introduction

ARY A. HASPELS

Prenatal instruction, preferably education from childhood on, can make a pregnancy part of the normal way of life.

Not so long ago multiple pregnancies were inevitably part of marriage and the lot of womanhood. Women continued to have children right into their forties. The 'natural' average without contraception amounted to 12.4 children! Nowadays pregnancies are becoming a rare event in the life of a woman in the developed countries. This may contribute to the reason why young women feel estranged to the idea of pregnancy and labor. The percentage of men and women in the Netherlands who do not want children at all, has risen from 1.5 to 9% in the last 10 years.

Sexual behavior may vary considerably during pregnancy. The woman undergoes important physical, hormonal and psychological changes. Many suffer loss of libido. However, we advocate that a satisfactory sexual relationship during pregnancy is important. Preparation for changing sexual behavior, for the delivery of the expectant mother and of the expectant father are of paramount importance.

Spontaneous birth control covers all those problems of chronic or episodic failure to get pregnant, including persistent sterility. It covers disturbances of implantation and tubal motility, as well as chronic miscarriages for whatever reason, and failures to get pregnant, secondary to sexual apathy and inertia, in either the male or the female. Medications may have a side effect of producing impotence in the male. Elective hysterectomy or surgically imposed hysterectomy can be considered a form of spontaneous birth control. Reduction of fertility is seen under conditions of starvation and emotional stress.

Postpartum problems can be avoided by good prenatal preparation. The question of resumption of sexual intercourse is an important one and should be a normal part of postpartum guidance as well as counseling on contraception.

Handbook of Sexology, edited by J. Money and H. Musaph
© *Elsevier/North-Holland Biomedical Press, 1977*

CHAPTER 48

Infertility: male and female

J. KREMER

1. MALE ASPECTS OF FERTILITY

Introduction

The male contribution towards creating a pregnancy depends, under normal circumstances, on two factors: the potential fertility of the semen and the ability to bring it into direct contact with the 'semen receptacle' in the female. This 'receptacle' is not, as was earlier supposed, the posterior fornix of the vagina but is the cervical 'mucus carpet' that covers the posterior lip of the portio. In this part we will discuss sperm transfer from semen into cervical mucus during and after coitus; the investigation of male fertility; semen characteristics important for fertility; faults in semen deposition; indications for testicular biopsy, and the treatment of male fertility disorders.

Sperm-transfer from semen into cervical mucus during and after coitus

The number of normal spermatozoa which mingle with the cervical mucus due to the thrusting movements of the penis during ejaculation and the number which pass through the contact area between semen and cervical mucus after ejaculation determine whether or not there will be conception. This number depends on the density of spermatozoa in the ejaculate, the percentage of spermatozoa with normal morphology and the ability of these spermatozoa to move from the one fluid (ejaculate) into the other (mucus). Because this 'crossing' does not have the help of any 'insuck' from the uterine cavity, apart from the density, it is primarily the percentage of motile spermatozoa and their forward speed that determine the number that will pass into the cervical mucus.

Although only one spermatozoon is sufficient for conception, to achieve a normal chance of this, probably several hundreds have to be present in the pars ampullaris tubae. Because large numbers get lost in the journey from the

Handbook of Sexology, edited by J. Money and H. Musaph
© *Elsevier/North-Holland Biomedical Press, 1977*

cervix to the pars ampullaris tubae, a 'surplus' is necessary in the cervical mucus. The minimum amount of this depends partly on the efficacy of the intrauterine sperm transport. Little is known about this but it is probably a passive transport brought by myometrial contractions (Blickman et al., 1970).

The investigation of male fertility

The above facts give the impression that procreative potential in the male can only be assessed by microscopic study of the cervical mucus after coitus. And indeed this test (the Sims—Huhner test) provides valuable information in this context. However, it is a mistake to believe that this test alone is sufficient to assess male fertility. Even when the physicochemical properties of the cervical mucus are optimal for sperm survival and when the Sims—Huhner test can be carried out within half an hour of coitus — which in practice is seldom possible — a low density or poor motility of the spermatozoa in the cervical mucus still means that no definite conclusions can be drawn about the potential fertility of the man. It should always be understood that these spermatozoa could be 'stragglers'. Most of the functional, fully developed spermatozoa could have already left the cervical mucus on their way to the tubes. As early as 5 minutes after intravaginal semen application, spermatozoa have been found in the female tubes (Fordney Settlage et al., 1973). Equally, however, when the Sims—Huhner test reveals many spermatozoa with good motility one still cannot conclude fertility is normal. It could be that the structure of the spermatozoa is abnormal, making conception impossible. A known, albeit rare, example is microstrongylospermia (Hellinga, 1949) where the heads of the spermatozoa show characteristic morphological abnormalities but they penetrate the cervical mucus well (Fig. 1).

The only true way to assess potential fertility in the male is by close examination and palpation of the genital organs and a careful analysis of as fresh a specimen of ejaculate as possible, collected in a small, clean dry, body-warm glass or plastic container, after a period of continence of 2—5 days. Before ejaculation the penis should be washed with water but no soap.

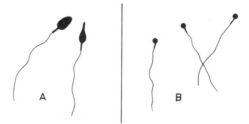

Fig. 1. (A) Normal spermatozoa (left front view, right side view). (B) Microstrongylospermia; all spermatozoa have small round heads. This semen is sterile.

As the ejaculate must not be allowed to mix with the contents of the vagina, the best way to obtain it is through stimulating the ejaculatory reflex by manual friction. Coitus interruptus is a less desirable method as the semen can be contaminated by vaginal contents. There is no point in investigating a few drops of semen taken from the vagina after coitus as this will also be mixed too greatly with vaginal contents. Neither should a rubber condom be used as sometimes the rubber contains spermicidal substances; one could, however, use a plastic condom such as the Milex seminal pouch (Milex products, Chicago, Illinois 60631). An ejaculate more than two hours old is not suitable for assessing fertility.

Semen characteristics important for fertility

Three characteristics are essential for potential fertility of an ejaculate; these are density, motility (percentage of motile spermatozoa and speed of motility) and morphology. Of these three qualities, motility is the most relevant to potential fertility. In the literature opinions differ as to what threshold values of these three characteristics are necessary to qualify an ejaculate as presumably normally fertile. This is understandable when one considers that a man's potential for achieving conception depends on the potential fertility of his partner. It is quite common to find a pregnancy where the quality of the semen would scarcely lead one to expect it. In such cases one need not necessarily assume that this pregnancy is due to some other male partner; it should also be taken into account that high fertility in the woman — and this is difficult to evaluate — may have compensated for deficient semen. To obtain some point of reference the American andrologist, MacLeod (1953), established three minimum values on the basis of semen analysis of more than 1000 men who had already proved their fertility. These values are: the ejaculate must contain at least 20 million spermatozoa per ml, of which, two hours after ejaculation, at least 40% should still have good progressive motility and 60% should show normal head formation in a stained sperm swab. If these qualifications are not fulfilled then there may be subfertility. If in at least five different ejaculates spaced out with at least a month between each one, close investigation reveals no spermatozoa then the man is sterile.

None of the methods used to establish these three semen characteristics gives the exact value. A sperm count made with a hemocytometer as it stands at the moment, seems to have a considerable margin of error. Determination of the percentage and speed of motility is usually done by estimation but even with a great deal of experience this method cannot give precise values. The assessment of morphology using fixed and stained spermatozoa is yet another method open to criticism. The fixing and staining can cause artefacts and, in addition to this, the criteria for normal and abnormal differ from one laboratory to the other.

Although the potential fertility of an ejaculate is highly dependent on the three characteristics mentioned above, two other properties should also be taken into account — the ejaculate volume and the sperm vitality. It appears that an ejaculate volume of less than 1 ml is too small for a normal chance of conception. This small amount of ejaculate presumably cannot form a sufficiently large contact-area with the 'mucus carpet' to allow good sperm penetration. Only a high sperm density can compensate for this shortcoming.

To determine sperm vitality, most investigators use a method based on the duration of sperm motility in the semen. However, this method is incorrect. The fluid from the prostate and vesicular glands forms an environment which, under physiological circumstances, is used for only a short time by the spermatozoa as a means of transport from the male to the female genital tract. This fluid is unsuitable for any long-term stay because here, at a temperature of 37°C, the spermatozoa usually lose their motility 10 to 15 h after ejaculation. The most physiological fluids to test sperm vitality are normal pre-ovulatory cervical mucus and blood serum. The latter is in biochemical composition more or less similar to tube secretions. The blood serum should be clear and free of sperm agglutinating activity. It can be stored for a prolonged period under deepfrozen conditions. Cervical mucus is less suitable for deepfreezing but can be stored in the refrigerator at 4°C for one week. We use the sperm penetration meter to carry out the vitality tests (Kremer, 1968). The capillary contains the penetration medium; the ejaculate is pipetted into a small semen reservoir adjacent to a slide (Fig. 2). From this semen reservoir the spermatozoa penetrate the medium in the capillary. In order to simulate physiological conditions as closely as possible the test is carried out at a temperature of 37°C. The motility of the spermatozoa in the capillary is determined at regular intervals by placing the sperm penetration meter under a microscope. Vitality may only be considered adequate if there are still motile spermatozoa to be seen after at least 24 h. If the semen is highly fertile, motile spermatozoa may still sometimes be found after 72 h or more (Kremer, 1968).

Faults in semen deposition

When, on the basis of the above test, the semen may be considered potentially fertile and the fertility tests on the female also indicate potential fertility,

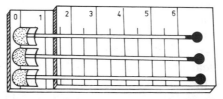

Fig. 2. Sperm penetration meter with 3 semen reservoirs. The apparatus has the sizes of a slide and can be examined under a microscope; the semen reservoirs are small enough to keep the contents if the apparatus is in a horizontal position. The glass capillaries can be filled with cervical mucus or other penetration fluids.

failure to achieve pregnancy may be caused by the inability of the male to deposit the ejaculate deep into the vagina. It is quite common to find a couple who have been married some years and are very keen to have children but who have never had effective coitus. The most common andrological causes of faulty coitus are inability to achieve and to maintain a good erection, inability to ejaculate in the vagina, and premature ejaculation. These abnormalities are the sole cause in around 6% of cases of unwanted childlessness.

Faulty coital technique can also be the cause that the semen is not delivered deep enough into the vagina. In our out-patient clinics for fertility disorders we have found that, when taking a coital history, even of both partners separately and helped by leading questions, the true state of affairs is not always given. Time and time again we are confronted with a negative or very poor Sims—Huhner test, with presumably normal semen and good ability to penetrate the cervical mucus. The latter can be concluded from a good result of the in vitro sperm penetration test by use of the sperm penetration meter, when the capillary tube is filled with cervical mucus (Fig. 2). When these results are discussed with the couple and detailed information is once again sought about coital technique, in a number of cases it has emerged that there has been no, or only partial penetration of the penis into the vagina.

Additionally, severe hypospadias or epispadias of the penis, especially the corporal or perineal forms, can be the cause of a discrepancy between in vivo and in vitro results of the sperm penetration test. In couples with impaired fertility it is, therefore, wrong to confine the investigations of the man to semen analysis alone. A directed coital history should also be taken and the male genital apparatus should be physically examined by inspection and palpation.

Indications for testicular biopsy

A testicular biopsy is rarely needed to evaluate male fertility, although occasionally it is required to differentiate between obstructive and spermatogenetic azoospermia. However, this differential diagnosis can often be done by careful palpation of the intrascrotal organs.

When the ductus deferens is nonpalpable on either side, the ejaculate volume is small (less than 2 ml) and the ejaculate pH is lower than 7, the diagnosis of obstructive azoospermia points to a bilateral regression of the Wolffian duct (Kremer, 1967). Small or flaccid testicles indicate spermatogenic azoospermia; there is no need for a testicular biopsy here. Neither is a testicular biopsy indicated in the case of oligospermia as the histological results of the material have no therapeutic consequences.

The only indication for a testicular biopsy is azoospermia without palpable abnormalities of the intrascrotal organs. But beforehand the couple should be informed of the low success rate of an anastomosis operation (5—10%) in cases of obstructive azoospermia.

The treatment of male fertility disorders

Apart from the often successful varicocele operations involving high ligation of the vena spermatica interna in men with subfertile semen, and the rarely successful anastomosis operations for obstructive azoospermia, most therapies recommended to improve semen quality rarely have any rational basis. They are mostly 'embarrassment' therapies that are resurrected from time to time in the hope that 'this time, in this man' they perhaps will help. The expensive and sometimes time-consuming injection courses with gonadotropic hormones are hardly ever successful (Kremer, 1965), and the same goes for clomiphene treatment which normally does more harm than good.

Therefore, in couples with impaired fertility due to subfertile sperm it makes much more sense to assist sperm transfer from the intravaginal ejaculate into the cervical mucus (utilizing the sperm). This can be achieved by giving coital instructions: penile penetration into the vagina against the portio, continuing intravaginal friction movements during ejaculation and stopping these movements after ejaculation, recommending that the woman remains lying on her back for half an hour afterwards, raising the vaginal pH before coitus (by the use of a baking soda douche, 2 tablespoons to a quart of water), increasing the mucus 'carpet' and decreasing the viscosity of the cervical mucus (by stimulating the endocervix with estrogen).

As compared with subfertility of the semen, the chances of achieving pregnancy are much greater when the problem is due to coital difficulty and the semen is potentially fertile. In a number of cases, an enlightening discussion with both partners is often enough to put things right. However, it is advisable to introduce a vaginal speculum in the presence of the man so that he can see for himself the female genital anatomy. It can also be very useful to give the man 'permission' to use manual help in coitus to bring the penis to the introitus vaginae.

Impotence, however, is a difficult problem. Psychiatric treatment is often disappointing. Homologous artificial insemination is usually the quickest way to achieve pregnancy. A skillful couple can, with suitable apparatus (for example, a long, 1-ml disposable tuberculin syringe) be taught auto-insemination. In most such instances of insemination the semen can be obtained by manual friction. In impotentia ejaculandi, however, this is not usually possible. In this situation an electro-vibrator will nearly always produce an ejaculate provided that the man involved has had emissions in sleep or on some other occasion (Fig. 3). I have used this method successfully in 32 couples. Even in three cases where there was a transverse lesion of the spinal cord, the electro-vibrator induced an ejaculate and auto-insemination produced a pregnancy. However, one condition for the success of homologous insemination by the doctor, or auto-insemination by the couple, is an ejaculate which is potentially fertile. Auto-insemination will have little chance of success with a subfertile ejaculate. Only after intracervical or intrauterine insemination by a special technique with the appropriate apparatus can a subfertile

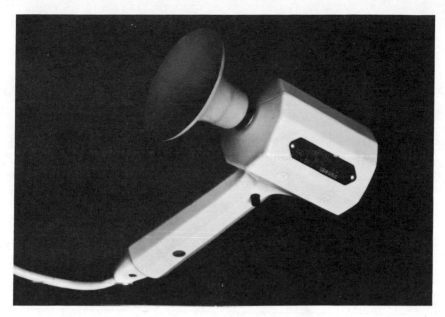

Fig. 3. Electro-vibrator used to induce the ejaculatory reflex.

ejaculate sometimes lead to a pregnancy. An intrauterine insemination rather often leads to a salpingitis or pelveo-peritonitis; one should never use more than 0.1 ml of a 'clean' ejaculate (Fig. 4).

From a psychiatric point of view there could be objections to homologous insemination in couples where the man is affected by impotentia coeundi as this could be an indication of a poor marital relationship and the doctor, by helping such a couple have a child, could be doing them a disservice. However, psychiatric opinion is divided on this matter. After an unsuccessful treatment for impotentia coeundi, sometimes the psychiatrist urges the gynecologist to carry out artificial insemination, or even donor insemination. Whilst, in impotentia coeundi, homologous insemination (Artificial Insemination with the Husband as donor, AIH) can bring about pregnancy if the sperm is fertile, with impotentia generandi heterologous or donor insemination (Artificial Insemination by a Donor, AID) is the only possibility. Impotentia generandi occurs with azoospermia and also when subfertility is so severe that in repeated Sims—Huhner tests, no motile spermatozoa are seen in the cervical mucus and the in vitro sperm penetration tests are also negative.

In the last decade therapeutic insemination, like adoption, has been continually on the increase. Both are symptomatic treatments for childlessness and are, in most cases of fertility disorders of andrological origin, the only means by which the couple can have children. This is because causal treatment of a fertility disorder in the male is seldom possible. It is very impor-

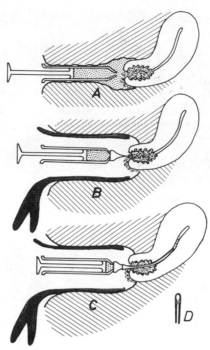

Fig. 4. Artificial insemination using a disposable, 1-ml tuberculin syringe, approximately 10 cm long. (A) Intravaginal method (2 ml semen). (B) Intracervical method (0.2 ml semen); flexible plastic canula max. length 2 cm and ext. diameter 0.6—0.8 mm. (C) Intrauterine method (0.1 ml semen); rubber canula (pediatric catheter) max. length 6 cm and ext. diameter 3 mm. (D) Tip of the rubber canula; the holes are some distance from the end.

tant to prepare the couple psychologically for these forms of parenthood.

The technique of AID is the same as that for AIH (Fig. 4). Personally I prefer the intracervical method because few sperm are required (max. 0.2 ml) and the woman can get up immediately after treatment. Therefore the treatment can be carried out in the consulting room.

The use of frozen semen for AID facilitates the organization scheme but reduces the success rate of 70% (with fresh semen) to 40%.

2. FEMALE ASPECTS OF FERTILITY

Introduction

When potentia coeundi and potentia generandi are sufficiently developed in the human male, the possibility to bring about an intrauterine pregnancy by means of cohabitation will depend on the following qualities in the female partner: vaginal receptivity to the penis; the hospitality of the pre-ovulatory cervical mucus to spermatozoa; transport possibility of the spermatozoa through the uterus; transport possibility of the spermatozoa through the tubes; the occurrence of ovulatory menstrual cycles; the existence of a tubal ovum-seizing mechanism; transport possibility of the ovum through infundibulum and pars ampullaris tubae; the ability of the oocyte to be fertilized; the ability of the tube to carry the fertilized ovum to the uterine cavity, the possibility of ovum nidation in the endometrium, and the absence of psychogenic infertility.

Vaginal receptivity to the penis

There is no, or scarcely any, likelihood of this receptivity in the case of vaginismus or pseudovaginismus. The fear of and resistance to coitus which occurs in vaginismus is due to psychoneurosis, often accompanied by phobias and symptoms of compulsion neurosis. Pseudovaginismus results from an organic abnormality of the vaginal introitus, causing pain when attempts are made to introduce the penis (Musaph, 1965). Vaginismus requires psychosexual treatment; this may cause the symptom to disappear, but the neurosis may otherwise remain. Pseudovaginismus can be relieved by surgery or by giving drugs to remove the pain.

The hospitality of the pre-ovulatory cervical mucus to spermatozoa

A few days before ovulation there is an increase in the production of cervical mucus brought about by an increase in estrogen production by the theca interna of the ripening follicle. This mucus production takes place mainly in the clefts and crypts of the endocervix and can amount to 0.5—1 ml per day. There are no glands in the endocervix (Fluhman, 1961). Because the production of water and electrolytes by the endocervix increases to a much greater extent relative to the organic constituents (mainly glycoproteins) the viscosity of the cervical mucus progressively decreases as ovulation approaches Some hours before ovulation, the external os of the cervix stands wide open and the clear, watery cervical mucus streams slowly over the posterior lip of the portio vaginalis into the vagina. When production is profuse the mucus may even descend to the vulva; the woman can pull this out like a long piece of thread and thus she can determine the day on which she ovulates. This threadability (fibrosity, elasticity, Spinnbarkeit) is one of the parameters of good estrogen stimulation of the endocervix (Cohen et al., 1951). Another is the fern test: a drop of cervical mucus is dried on a slide giving a fern-like structure which is particularly attractive when seen through the microscope (Fig. 5).

Cervical mucus which has been well stimulated by estrogen possesses a high degree of receptivity to sperm, provided that the pH lies between 7 and 8.5 (Moghissi et al., 1964). The 'mucus carpet' is usually acidic under the influence of the low vaginal pH (3.5—4, Masters and Johnson, 1966); the Dö-

Fig. 5. Fern test in cervical mucus (×200).

derlein's bacilli cause lactic acid to be formed from the glycogen of the vaginal epithelium. Sometimes, therefore, the pH of the 'mucus carpet' falls below the critical limit of 6.2. Here sperm motility more or less disappears completely. During coitus, however, the movements of the penis within the vagina cause the 'mucus carpet' to be mixed with the alkaline ejaculate. Consequently its pH increases sufficiently to maintain sperm motility. For some thirty minutes after intravaginal ejaculation the buffer action of the ejaculate remains sufficient to allow the active spermatozoa to cross from the so-called 'seminal pool' into the 'mucus carpet' (Fig. 2). After this no more sperm transfer takes place (Kremer, 1968). Therefore it is useless for a woman to remain lying on her back more than half an hour after coitus in order to increase the chance of pregnancy. From the 'mucus carpet' the spermatozoa swim into and through the cervical canal; passive sperm transport does not take place. 'Insuck' due to orgasm does not happen in the human species (Masters and Johnson, 1966).

Intracervical sperm transport is directional as a result of the structure of the cervical mucus, the framework of which consists of long filaments of glycoprotein molecules (Van Bruggen and Kremer, 1970). By reason of the slow release of the cervical mucus from the clefts and crypts to the lumen of the cervical canal during the pre-ovulatory phase, these glycoprotein filaments fall into two definite categories: those which lie against the convoluted wall of the cervical canal end up in the crypts and those which lie more towards the centre of the lumen, in a more or less parallel manner longitudinally along the canal. By this way sperms, swimming in the neighborhood of the longitudinal axis of the cervical canal reach the internal os of the cervix via the shortest route. This section can be covered within 5 min. (one of the facts to emerge from the investigations of Fordney Settlage and her colleagues (1973). This directional sperm transport can be demonstrated in vitro by sucking the pre-ovulatory cervical mucus up into the capillary of the spermatozoa penetration meter (Fig. 2). During the aspiration into the glass capillary, the long filaments of glycoprotein molecules are stretched longitudinally and come to lie more or less parallel to the wall of the glass capillary. Between the molecular filaments, 'channels' of an aqueous, isotonic solution containing electrolytes, proteins and glucose exist. These 'water channels' are utilized by the sperm to move forward.

Sperm which swim along the wall of the cervical canal mostly disappear into the clefts and crypts of the endocervix and form a reservoir from which regular ascents are made to higher parts of the genital tract. Here, under normal circumstances, they can maintain their motility for 48—72 h and sometimes even for as long as 5 to 6 days.

As early as a few hours after ovulation the production of cervical mucus begins to decrease; this is because of the antiestrogenic effect of progesterone from the corpus luteum. In particular, the production of water and electrolytes diminishes; the mucus therefore becomes tough and, due to the presence of many leucocytes, also becomes cloudy. The characteristic preovulatory structure is lost and thus sperm penetration and migration become severely impeded. In pathological circumstances this state of cervical hostility can also occur in the pre-ovulatory phase. Causes of this cervical hostility are: inadequate endocervical response to estrogen stimulation, progestagen therapy, and cervicitis. Sometimes there is no cervical mucus in the pre-ovulatory phase, this dry cervix can be the result of destruction of the endocervix by electro coagulation — a common treatment for a portio erosion. Because of the autonomic innervation of the endocervix, psychogenic causes are also not to be ruled out in cases of dry cervix.

Sometimes cervical hostility is caused by the presence of sperm agglutinins (immune antibodies) on the glycoprotein threads; they 'glue' the spermatozoa to the glycoprotein threads and change their progressive movement into a local movement. This so-called 'shaking phenomenon' also occurs when the semen contains sperm-agglutinins, localized on the spermatozoa; these spermatozoa 'glue' to the glycoprotein threads (Kremer and Jager, 1975).

Diagnosis of cervical mucus is made by viewing the cervix through a vaginal speculum. The pH of the 'mucus carpet' is measured in situ and then the ectocervical mucus is drawn into a 1-ml tuberculin syringe. A special thin electrode is used to assess the pH of the mucus in the endocervical canal (Kroeks, 1974). The endocervical mucus is drawn into a second syringe and the physicochemical properties of both fractions are determined in the laboratory. If coitus has taken place prior to this, both fractions are investigated under the microscope for spermatozoa (Sims—Huhner test or postcoital test). The chance to become pregnant will be greater if progressively moving spermatozoa, instead of only nonprogressively moving ones, are seen in the cervical mucus. The couples whose postcoital test shows no spermatozoa at all in the endocervical mucus have, on statistical grounds, the least chance to achieve a pregnancy (Kremer, 1975).

Cervical hostility requires adequate therapy. Sometimes chronic cervicitis will not respond fully to antibiotic therapy. Then curettage of the endocervix and electrocoagulation of the portio erosion (often present in cervicitis) are necessary. Estrogen given in the pre-ovulatory phase of the cycle seldom has effect in cases of cervical hostility; only when started early in the cycle and at high dosages can the cervical mucus be improved; but then, more often than not, cycle irregularity results. When cervical hostility is due to low endocervical mucus pH, alkaline douches used about an hour before coitus can sometimes be effective.

Transport possibility of the spermatozoa through the uterus

During the pre-ovulatory phase of the menstrual cycle, the influence of estrogen causes the internal os of the cervix to open, thus allowing the passage of sperm in the fluid of the cleft-formed uterine cavity. Progesterone causes the internal os to close again.

Little is known about sperm transport through the uterine cavity to the tubes. Fordney Settlage and her colleagues (1973) have demonstrated that within 5 min of the introduction of semen into the vagina, spermatozoa are found in the tubes. Since passage through the cervical canal can only be covered within 5 min by very quickly moving sperm, for the transport through the uterus and tubes only a few seconds are left. Moving X-ray studies have shown that myometrium contractions can drive a small amount of contrast fluid from the isthmus uteri into the pars ampullaris tubae in a few seconds (Kremer and Blickman, 1971). It is possible that intrauterine abnormalities or myometrium dysfunction may disturb sperm transport but this has not as yet been investigated.

Transport possibility of the spermatozoa through the tubes

As with the intrauterine variety, transtubal sperm transport is also probably a passive affair, effected by the contractions of the tube musculature. The same waves which drive the fluid containing the sperm from the isthmus uteri into one of the horns of the fundus, carry it along the musculature of the pars intramuralis and pars isthmica tubae (Kremer and Blickman, 1971); in this way the sperm travel from the isthmus uteri into the ampullae in 1 to 2 sec.

Disturbances in transtubal transport can be caused by disturbed tubal function or closure of its lumen. The latter can sometimes be corrected by surgery or hydrotubation.

The occurrence of ovulatory menstrual cycles

About 14 days before the start of menstruation, under normal physiological conditions, ovulation takes place; after which the graafian follicle forms the corpus luteum which produces estrogen and progesterone. Before this, the follicle produced only the estrogenic hormones (estrone, estradiol and estriol). Estrogen lowers the body temperature by 0.2—0.4°C and progesterone increases it by 0.2—0.5°C.

By recording her rectal temperature every morning at the same time before getting up, a woman can draw her basal body temperature curve and can thus work out in retrospect the day on which she ovulated. If she gets pregnant, this high temperature will remain high after the missed menstruation during a period of about 4 months.

A biphasic curve is not a definite indication of an ovulatory cycle as this can also occur with follicle atresia; then the luteal phase, however, is usually less than 10 days. On the other hand, a monophasic cycle is a very strong indication of an anovulatory cycle. Anovulatory cycles are usually irregular and hardly ever bring premenstrual tension or dysmenorrhea. Usually drugs are used to induce ovulation in women with an anovulatory cycle, the most commonly used being clomiphene and gonadotropic hormones. The disadvantage of these products is the risk of overstimulation, causing ovarian cysts or polyovulation. With the latter there is the risk of multiple pregnancy.

The existence of a tubal ovum-seizing mechanism

Under normal circumstances, after ovulation the oocyte is received into the infundibulum of the tube; the fimbriae 'seize' the ripe follicle. This ovum-seizing mechanism is considerably less important than was earlier thought. Metz (1974) showed that even a small fistula in the side of a tube where the fimbriated end is closed off is enough for the oocyte to be received. Furthermore, intrauterine pregnancies have been reported after bilateral salpingectomy, in cases where the tubes are blocked but there is a fistula opening in the scars of a previous caesarean section. Even after uterus extirpation pregnancies can occur. All this illustrates how relative a normal infundibulum and normal fimbriae are to the ovum-seizing mechanism.

Transport possibility of the ovum through infundibulum and pars ampullaris tubae

Transport of the oocyte through the infundibulum and the pars ampullaris tubae towards the isthmus is mainly achieved through the ciliated epithelium of the endosalpinx. The oocyte remains in the pars ampullaris for about 3 days. Segmental contractions of the myosalpinx move the oocyte to and fro in the pars ampullaris to give the greatest possible chance of contact with any sperm which may be present. For the first 24 h the oocyte is surrounded by the zona pellucida and by a covering of granulosa cells. Fertilization takes place during this period. After that, the granulosa cells disappear; the zona pellucida remains right up until nidation which takes place around 6 days after ovulation. Therefore the ovum cannot increase in volume although continuous cell division is taking place. Its diameter is about 0.14 mm, that is, 'the size of a tiny grain of dry sea-sand on a sheet of black paper' (Hartman, 1962). During its 3-day stay in the pars ampullaris tubae, the ovum derives its nutrition from the secretory products of the endosalpinx. It is not useful, therefore, to do a tubostomy to open up a tube which has been destroyed by inflammation and become a hydrosalpinx; in such a 'restored' tube there can be no normal development of the ovum. A salpinx is more than an open tube!

The ability of the oocyte to be fertilized

As opposed to spermatozoa, oocytes are not easily obtainable for morphological and functional investigation. It is, however, possible that in some cases of unexplained sterility the cause may be found in functional or anatomical changes in the oocyte which make it nonfertile.

The ability of the tube to carry the fertilized ovum to the uterine cavity

Trouble-free transtubal ovum transport depends not only on a clear and unimpeded passage but also on normal functioning of the epithelial cilia and the myosalpinx. The 'freedom of passage' can be established using hysterosalpingography in which an X-ray contrast medium is introduced into the uterine cavity via the cervical canal. However, the hysterosalpingogram cannot give any information about tubal function although abnormal filling can sometimes correctly indicate functional disorders. Laparoscopy gives a better indication of tubal function; a laparoscope introduced below the navel allows direct examination of the uterus and adnexa and at the same time the tubal passageways can be tested by injecting a colored fluid through the cervical canal to the uterine cavity, from where it will pass, via the tubes, into the abdominal cavity (chromotubation).

The possibility of ovum nidation in the endometrium

During the follicular phase there is proliferation of stroma cells and glandular epithelium in the endometrium. About the time of ovulation its thickness is about $\frac{1}{2}$ cm. The proliferation can be seen microscopically due to the presence of mitosis in the stroma and glandular epithelium. Because of the rapid division, the nuclei of the glandular epithelium do not lie on the same level, but lie more like those of squamous epithelium (pseudostratification). During the luteal phase, the influence of progesterone changes the proliferative endometrium into a secretory one; in the early luteal phase the appearance of glycogen maintains subnuclear vacuoles in the glandular epithelium; the midluteal phase is characterised by apical secretion and the late phase reveals exhausted glands while the stroma may sometimes show decidual changes.

Hormonal disorders and diseases of the endometrium may disturb nidation of the blastocyst. These abnormalities can be diagnosed histologically by taking an endometrial biopsy with a microcurette. The optimal time for this investigation is the late luteal phase. An endometrium which has not developed in tune with the cycle indicates luteal deficiency, either due to an insufficient corpus luteum or to decreased reactional capacity of the endometrium. The biopsy material should also always be examined for signs of inflammation especially tuberculosis — previously a very common cause of female sterility. There is still much diversity of opinion about the treatment of endometrial abnormalities — particularly those caused by luteal deficiency. It is possible that in some of these cases the luteal deficiency is the result of follicular atresia and there the treatment should be ovulation induction. But one should realize that signs of luteal deficiency in one or more cycles does not mean luteal deficiency during all the cycles. Affected women may be subfertile, but they need not be infertile. Therefore, one should be sceptical of the successes of luteal phase treatment by human chorionic gonadotropin, estrogen, or progestagen.

Psychogenic influences on fertility

Inability to have children is due in about 40% of childless couples to sterility or subfertility in the female and in about 40% to sterility or subfertility in the male. It is possible that subfertility in one partner can be counter-balanced by high fertility in the other. Subfertility in both partners, however, means an unfavorable fertility prognosis. In 20% of childless couples, fertility investigations in both partners do not reveal any abnormalities which would point to sterility or subfertility. This is the 'unexplained fertility disorder'. It is highly probable that in a percentage of these cases the cause is psychogenic, though little work has been done in this field. Probably, the autonomic nervous control of the female genital organs influences the chance to become pregnant unfavorably in women who strongly desire to have a child and who anxiously await each menstruation. These women often become pregnant during a period in which they do not expect it. The doctor can make use of this phenomenon by discontinuing established treatment for a short time; when the woman thinks that, because the treatment has been stopped, she is not likely to become pregnant at that particular time, then she often does! A pharmacological approach to these psychogenic causes for example, with tranquilizers, or adrenergic or cholinergic agents usually has no success.

BIBLIOGRAPHY

Blickman, J.R., Kremer, J. and Schepers, J.P. (1970) Over intra-uterien transport. *Ned. T. Geneesk.* 114: 1075.

Van Bruggen, E.F. and Kremer, J. (1970) Electron microscopy of bovine and human cervical mucus. *Int. J. Fertil.* 15: 50.

Cohen, M.R., Stein, I.F. and Kaye, B.M. (1951) Spinnbarkeit: A Characteristic of cervical mucus. *Fertil. Steril.* 2: 20.

Fluhman, C.F. (1961) *The Cervix and its Disease*, Vol. 3. (W.B. Saunders, Philadelphia.)

Fordney Settlage, D.S., Motoshima, M. and Tredway, D.R. (1973) Sperm transport from the external cervical os to the Fallopian tubes in women: a time and quantitation study. *Fertil. Steril.* 24: 655.

Hartman, C.G. (1962) *Science and the Safe Period* (Williams and Wilkins Co., Baltimore.)

Hellinga, G. (1949) *Het onderzoek by stoornissen in de mannelijke vruchtbaarheid.* (Acad. Proefschrift, Amsterdam.)

Kremer, J. (1965) Behandeling van verminderde mannelijke vruchtbaarheid met gonadotrope hormonen, in het bijzonder met HMG. *Ned. T. Geneesk.* 109: 888.

Kremer, J. (1967) Bilateral regression of the Wolffian duct, a little known but relatively frequent cause of obstructive azoospermia. *Ned. T. Geneesk.* 111: 2120.

Kremer, J. (1968) *The in vitro Spermatozoal Penetration Test in Fertility Investigations.* (Van Denderen, Groningen.)

Kremer, J. (1975) De betekenis van de Sims—Huhnertest voor de fertiliteitsprognose. *Ned. T. Geneesk.* 119: 1127.

Kremer, J. and Blickman, J.R. (1971) Filmdemonstration of the intra-uterine and intratubal transport of small quantities of radiographic contrast fluid. *Ned. T. Geneesk.* 115: 860.

Kremer, J. and Jager, S. (1976) The sperm-cervical mucus contact test; A preliminary report. *Fertil. Steril.* 27: 335.

Kroeks, M.V.A.M. (1974) pH-meting in situ bij het fertiliteitsonderzoek. *Ned. T. Geneesk.* 118: 1244.

MacLeod, J. and Gold, R.Z. (1953) The male factor in fertility and infertility. *Fertil. Steril.* 4: 10.

Masters, W.H. and Johnson, V.E. (1966) *Human Sexual Response.* (Churchill Ltd., London.)

Metz, K.G.P. (1974) Pregnancy after fimbriectomy. (Int. Congr. Fertil. Steril. Nov. 1—7, Buenos Aires.)

Moghissie, K.S., Dabech, D.D., Levine, J. and Neuhaus, O.W. (1964) Mechanism of sperm migration. *Fertil. Steril.* 15: 15.

Musaph, H. (1965) Vaginisme, een seksuologische beschouwing. (Erven F. Bohn, Haarlem.)

CHAPTER 49

Spontaneous or unwanted birth control of nonhormonal origin

ARY A. HASPELS

1. SURGICAL ETIOLOGY

Surgical removal of the ovaries, tubes or uterus seems too clear to mention as a cause of infertility, but it has happened that a doctor might accept a patient's word that the scar on her abdomen was due to an appendectomy only. In fact, an old-fashioned subtotal hysterectomy might have been done at the same time.

Amputation of the cervix

A history of cervical amputation may result in spontaneous birth control if subsequent pregnancies end in late abortions caused by cervical insufficiency.

Caesarean section

Delivery by means of Caesarean section is a well known cause of spontaneous birth control later on. The operation adversely affects subsequent fertility because of endometritis, tubal infection, and psychogenic restraint from coitus secondary to pain and high morbidity during the postoperative course compared with, for example, hysterectomy.

Dilatation and curettage

This common procedure may produce endometritis which may lead to ascending infection of the adnexa, subsequent scar-tissue, and unwanted birth control.

Salpingitis and appendicitis

Both varieties of inflammation may cause pelvic infections and subsequent scar tissue on tubal walls. The ovary and tubal relationship may be distorted

Handbook of Sexology, edited by J. Money and H. Musaph
© *Elsevier/North-Holland Biomedical Press, 1977*

by adhesions so that the ovum cannot be liberated, or if so, may not find entry into the tube.

Ovarian and tubal pathology

Tumor formation or cysts may produce torsion of the tubes. Large cysts may actually displace the ovary away from the tubes. Ovarian or tubal endometriosis prevent pregnancy.

2. CONGENITAL ANOMALIES

Congenital hypoplasia of the genitalia may occur on the basis of ovarian underdevelopment and hypofunction. In true infantilism all the sexual organs remain arrested at the infantile state in size and shape and do not further develop, with or without hormonal substitution therapy.

Vulva

Closure of the vulva is usually congenital. In rare occasions it may be due to inflammation or injury. Imperforate hymen is caused by a thickened and fibrous hymen that cannot be torn. The patient is not aware of this condition until first menstruation occurs. If it is not corrected, the menstrual blood accumulates behind the hymen, filling the vagina and eventually the uterus and even the tubes. Pregnancy subsequently is rare as the anatomy has usually been grossly impaired.

Vagina

A vaginal atresia is due to the lack of vaginal lumen formation in the Müllerian ducts during embryonic development. Often the uterus is also absent, while the ovaries are normal. A transverse vaginal septum or vaginal diaphragm produces infertility by acting as a conceptive barrier. The septum sometimes has a small opening so menstrual fluid can be released. The septum can be easily excised. A similar condition exists in the androgen-insensitivity (testicular feminizing) syndrome in phenotypic females.

Cervix and uterus

Atresia of the cervix is rare. At puberty, it may lead to an accumulation of blood in the uterus. Atresia of the uterus may be seen along with vaginal atresia. Making a good functioning vagina by using the labia (William's method) is usually very satisfactory.

3. OTHER GYNECOLOGIC PATHOLOGY CONNECTED WITH UNWANTED BIRTH CONTROL

Vulva

Vulvar pathology causing infertility includes acute and chronic inflammation, vulvar growths caused by elephantiasis and tumors. Inflammation may cause dyspareunia, secretions inimicable to fertility, or altered pH. Growths or distortions after infection may prevent semen entry or even coitus.

Infections of the vulva may be caused by *Trichomonas vaginalis*, *Monilia albicans* or maybe of venereal origin. Tuberculosis of the vulva is a rarity now. Vulvar growths include condylomata acuminata which are cauliflower-like tumors that vary from a small size to those that are spread over the entire vulva, entering the vagina. They become inflamed, ulcerated and very painful.

Vulvar cysts may be present in the Skenes glands, Bartholin glands or labia. Vulvar tumors can be benign fibromas, but may be malignant. The malignant tumors, however, are usually not present during the fertile period of life.

Vulvovaginal varicosis may follow pregnancy. In cases of phlebitis, varicosis may cause mechanical discomfort during coitus. Friction of the penis may produce painful hematomata.

Urethra

Prolapse of the urethral mucosa may lead to widening of the meatus due to stretching from childbirth. The meatus may be so large that coitus may mistakenly take place in the urethra causing pseudo-infertility.

Vagina

Apart from the vaginal infections mentioned above, mixed bacterial vaginitis may play a role in unwanted infertility. The causative organisms are usually staphylococci, streptococci, coli, herpes simplex, or the more common venereal infections. Vaginal infection may create an alkaline discharge. Chemical irritation of the vagina may be caused by lysol, bichloride of mercury, phenol or other corrosive agents used for douching.

Cervix

Disturbances of the pH of the cervical secretion decrease sperm activity and penetrability. Normally the pH varies from 8 to 9. Trauma to the cervix will damage the folds of the cervix and may cause closure and atresia due to scar tissue formation. Cervical causes of unwanted birth control include those changes produced by infections, changes in cervical tissue, and new growths.

Uterus

The uterus should be normally developed and free from significant pathology in order for pregnancy to occur and be maintained. Defects in the health, position or development of the uterus may result in early abortion. If this happens more than twice in a row it is called habitual abortion or chronic miscarriage. For example, chronic miscarriage is associated with infantile uterus.

Formerly it was thought that retroflexed uteri could cause infertility. In Indonesian women 80% of the uteri are in a retroflexed position. However, fertility in Indonesian women is normal. Most likely only retroflexed uteri with adhesions to the rectum may cause problems.

Uterine disease includes inflammation, hyperplasia, new growths, and the secondary effect of emotional disturbance. Inflammation of the uterus may be due to pathogenic organisms associated with gonorrhea or syphilis, to staphylococcus, streptococcus, and herpes simplex, and to rare infections namely tuberculosis, typhoid, diphtheria, or amoebiasis. Chronic endometritis, in its bacterial form, can be the end result of acute endometritis e.g. after nonmedical or self-induced abortions. It may lead to unwanted birth control because of scar tissue. If the walls of the uterus partly unite it is called the Asherman syndrome. Treatment is performed by careful dilation and currettage combined with placement of an intrauterine device for three months to let the endometrium regenerate. If total atrophy of the endometrium has occurred treatment is no longer possible. Secondary amenorrhea is a symptom which may point in this direction. Gynecologists who perform a diagnostic curettage, should be alerted to prevent endometrial changes. Some doctors like to scrape until the "grating sound" is heard. This is unnecessary, and may be hazardous, especially in curettage for abortions. If the uterus is scraped too deeply, the process will create a secondary hypertrophy, producing exuberant tissue that may act as a plug to the tube at the cornual region. Furthermore deep curettage may provoke a low-grade infection, causing disturbance of implantation.

The endometrium and its glands contain many ciliated cells. The cells help propogate the sperm upward. They aid in fixing the blastula so that implantation is facilitated. Destruction of the cilia is one of the reasons for unwanted infertility.

A growth in the uterus is always a threat to fertility, since such lesions disturb the shape, contour, cycle, epithelial integrity or openings to the tubes and cervix. Small benign tumors do not usually complicate implantation, nor pregnancy, and should be left alone. Enthusiasm for surgery is an understandable and sometimes a commendable trait in gynecologists. However, an opportunity to become a mother is a woman's right. Premature or extensive pelvic surgery is likely to destroy forever that possibility. For example, hysterectomy seems, at first, the logical treatment for fibroids of the uterus. The surgeon may forget that it is also a sterilizing operation, and that less radical procedures may be effective and preferable. This is a worthwhile decision if it means preservation of the pregnancy potential now, and postponement of sterilizing surgery until after the patient has completed her family.

The Fallopian tubes

A reasonable estimate of the tubal factor in infertility is 30 to 40%. Gynecologists may arrive at different incidence figures, but all agree that a tubal factor is the commonest cause of unwanted birth control. The tubes are normally so narrow that it takes very little infection to seal them off. Regardless of cause, if the lumen is blocked off, infertility results. Bacterial infections are caused by gonococcus, by tubercle bacillus, streptococci, coli bacilli, or staphylococci, as a result of unsterile instrumentation, or in connection with pelvic disease.

Tubal congestion may occur in any case in which there is interference with the blood supply of the tubes. This may result from torsion due to ovarian cysts, or from peritubal adhesions from a pelvic infection or from schistosomiasis of tubes or ovary.

Malignant tumors of the Fallopian tubes are rare, especially during the child-bearing age. Since the treatment is radical excision, there is no way of preventing infertility. Benign tumors include fibrous or glandular tissue. They are small and are imbedded in the walls of the tube. Tubal endometriosis is usually found in the interstitial position of the tube.

Ectopic pregnancy represents the danger of partial blockage of the tubes. Final results of Siegler's (1945) series showed that 29% of patients with an ectopic pregnancy were infertile after operation, 27% had repeated abortions and 3.5% had repeated ectopic pregnancies. Among 75% of these women, there was a history of prior pelvic operations and an inflammatory tubal condition or appendicitis.

Tubal motility has been studied by several investigators. They concluded that estrogen increased the rate, amplitude and tonus of tubal contractions, and that these changes are inhibited by progesterone (Rubin and Davids, 1940). Chang (1966) demonstrated that progesterone accelerated egg transport when given prior to ovulation, and delayed it when given after ovulation. Estrogen increased the rate of transport when administered either prior to, or after ovulation. This led Chang to postulate that progesterone normally counteracts the accelerating effect of estrogen for 3 to 4 days, after which estrogen resumes its hastening of ovum transport. Normal tubal transport and its timing seem to depend upon the appropriate ratio of estrogen and progesterone in the genital tract. On these principles, Haspels (1972) and Morris and van Wagenen (1966) based the introduction of postcoital estrogen as an interceptive to prevent pregnancy. Several other medications influence tubal motility, for example, pilocarpine has a stimulatory effect, which can be blocked by treatment with atropine. Epinephrine stimulates either the tonus or the contractions of the oviduct. Several pharmacologic agents influence tubal motility and may disturb, by increase or decrease of motility, the timing of the arrival of the conceptus in the uterus. The result may be spontaneous or unwanted birth control.

The ovaries

Endocrine syndromes may be associated with emotional attitudes and reactions in the patient. There is an intimate interweaving of sympathetic nervous system activity, emotional states and endocrine balance. Disease anywhere along this chain may disturb the endocrine balance enough to cause infertility.

Ovarian atrophy can be the result of pressure associated with large cysts. Follicular damage inevitably follows. One type of ovarian malposition is displacement of the ovary from its bed, with resultant menstrual and physical distress. Infertility may result because of the inability of the ovum to gain tubal access.

Inflammations of the ovary are usually secondary to pelvic and tubal infection. Ovarian growths show a wide variety and are usually associated with unwanted birth control.

4. CHRONIC ABORTION, PREMATURE LABOR

Spontaneous abortion may occur in about 15—20% of pregnancies. Abortion may be due to a variety of causes which may be grouped in these categories: external, surgical, medical, endocrine, obstetric and gynecologic.

External

The factors here include illegal abortions and traumata. Illegal abortion can cause damage of the cervix, especially in a nullipara, and lead to chronic miscarriages later on.

Surgical

Here the causes include any operations performed on the cervix or the abdomen, since these procedures may excite uterine contractions. Also in this category should be included those cases of women who have had frequent curettages before pregnancy, since this may result in scar tissue which leads to a poor implantation bed. Damage to the uterus associated with previous caesarean sections, hysterotomies and illegal abortions may also be responsible for premature termination of pregnancy.

Medical

Medical causes of chronic abortion include vitamin deficiencies, dietetic inadequacies, industrial poisonings, Rh-incompatibility and blood dyscrasia, as well as the effects of infectious diseases, exanthema, nephritis, diabetes, hypertension, heart disease, syphilis and malaria.

Endocrine

The endocrine apparatus is responsible for a certain proportion of miscarriages and spontaneous abortions. Factors here include imbalance of corpus luteum hormone control, and menstrual abnormalities due to thyroid, pituitary and other endocrine dysfunctions.

Obstetric and gynecologic

Finally the list must include a variety of obstetric and gynecologic factors: endometritis, fixed retroflexion of the uterus, uterine hyperirritability, tumors within the uterus, for example, fibroids, endometrial scars, and excessively small infantile uterus. There are a number of essentially obstetric causes of miscarriage or abortion, for example, disease of the placenta, abnormalities within the ovum, disturbances of the sperm—ovum combination, and some abnormal development inconsistent with viability of the fertilized egg.

5. DIET AND SPONTANEOUS BIRTH CONTROL — STARVATION

In sheep sterility can be caused by feeding them an improper diet. Autopsies done by Marshall (1905) revealed later a degeneration of Graafian follicles. Instead of continuing to develop, the follicle suffered retrogressive changes, resulting in shrivelling of the ovum with ultimate absorption of the entire follicle contents. Also in women oogenesis can be disturbed by undernourishment causing metabolic damage to the ovaries, leading to secondary amenorrhea and spontaneous birth control. These changes are usually reversible.

6. RÖNTGEN AND RADIUM AND SPONTANEOUS BIRTH CONTROL

Röntgen, radium or megavolt treatment, usually applied for malignancies or Hodgkin's disease, damage the function of the ovaries. Oogenesis is indefinitely stopped and the damage is irreversible.

7. WAR AND SPONTANEOUS BIRTH CONTROL

War generally decreases human fertility. This effect arises because of absence of many young men, causing a decrease in the frequency of coitus; death of many young men; grief and shock causing emotional imbalance with consequent physiologic and endocrine effects; biologic effect of disease, starvation, captivity, and unsanitary living conditions associated with heavy labor; and increase in venereal diseases.

Associated with the wartime pace of life is a pituitary depression with noxious effects on the ovaries. A high proportion of Dutch women in Japanese internment camps in Indonesia began to suffer from amenorrhea after the onset of their captivity. Sydenham (1946) mentioned that in the Stanley Camp at Hong Kong only 35% of the previously normal women menstruated regularly after their internment. The last world war brought a new threat to human productivity. According to Greenhill (1946) every pregnant woman within one kilometer of the Hiroshima atomic blast miscarried. Not only may one expect many miscarriages, but also a massive sterilization resulting from the newer and more potent atomic bombs under development.

8. PSYCHOGENIC DISTURBANCE OF OOGENESIS

Oogenesis is more likely to be disturbed by emotional stress situations than is spermatogenesis. Moderate stress may already lower oogenesis, as in a simple change of environment. Temporary anovulation and amenorrhea may be the result.

True vaginismus is of psychologic origin, and if not treated may lead to spontaneous birth control. Lack of interest in sexual intercourse, frigidity and anorgasmia are very rarely a life-long process, and do not typically disturb coitus to an extent that pregnancy is prevented.

9. IMPOTENCE IN THE MALE AND SPONTANEOUS BIRTH CONTROL

Organic causes are rare, about 2%. They can be due to pathologic changes of the penis — phimosis, hypospadias, or epispadias; to inflammations of the prostate, urethra or vesiculae seminales; to traumatic damage to the penis or its corpora cavernosa; to neurologic pathology as in tabes dorsalis, multiple sclerosis, and syringomyelia; and to damage in the spine of the spinal erection center. The diagnostic list further includes testicular hypoplasia or aplasia; diseases of the pituitary (Simmond's cachexia, acromegalia) dystrophia adiposo-genitalis; Frölich syndrome; diseases of the thyroid (Basedow's disease, myxedema); diabetes mellitus; and the adrenocortical deficiency, Addison's disease.

Secondary impotence may occasionally be seen after coronary infarction and after serious liver—kidney disease. Intoxication may lead to impotence e.g. arsenic, aniline and excess of hard drugs such as morphine, heroin and cocaine as well as LSD. Chronic alcoholism may have the same effect; and also drugs given for hypertension, such as reserpine and guanethidine sulfate; and tranquilizers, for example, diazepam.

Men who are operated on for prostatic hypertrophy should be coached not to expect impotence as inevitable. Impotence is more frequently seen after the perineal approach. For sexologic reasons, the suprapubic or transurethral operation is to be preferred. Psychogenic causes of impotence are far more frequent than the organic or functional causes.

BIBLIOGRAPHY

Chang, M.C. (1966) *Endocrinology* 79, 939.
Greenhill, J.P. (1946) *Yearbook Gynecol. Obstet.* (Chicago Year Book Publ.)
Haspels, A.A. (1972) I.P.P.F. Med. Bull. 6, nr. 2.
Marshall, F.H.A. (1905) *Proc. R. Soc. Biol.* 1: 29.
Morris, J.M. and van Wagenem, G. (1966) *Am. J. Obstet. Gynecol.* 96, 804.
Rubin, I.C. and Davids, A.M. (1940) *Endocrinology* 26, 523.
Siegler, S. (1045) *N.Y. State J Med.* 45, 1974.
Sydenham, A. (1946) *Br. Med. J.* 2, 159.

CHAPTER 50

Childbirth

HELEEN CRUL

1. BECOMING A PARENT

Preparation for childbirth

A couple faced for the first time with pregnancy, labor and future parenthood, have much to adjust to. Very little has been written about the emotional state of a man and woman who are about to become parents. This lack illustrates the necessity of a more thorough psychological guidance, which should give an answer to their questions and lighten their problems. Ideally this guidance should prepare them for the birth of their child and their new responsibilities. Especially the mentally well-adjusted couple can experience the birth of their child in a "sense of triumph and creation" and can look forward to being parents with a sense of confidence. Parental instruction, as it exists at the moment, is not much geared to giving psychological guidance. It tends to have a predominantly medical accent, whereby the personal problems, which are part and parcel of every pregnancy, are pushed into the background.

The mother role

Women nowadays enjoy an historically unprecedented freedom. They may choose to a large extent their education, job and friends, and it is accepted that they have the right to exchange opinion regarding such matters. This applies to a certain extent to marriage as well, but not to motherhood. Motherhood has a finality about it. One cannot separate oneself from one's child simply because one feels like it, neither can one change one's children. Except in cases of child abuse, motherhood presupposes absolute responsibility, and the total involvement demanded will leave little place for other interests. The realization of all this might heighten a woman's moments of doubt and uncertainty. The wide dissemination of information concerning contra-

Handbook of Sexology, edited by J. Money and H. Musaph
© *Elsevier/North-Holland Biomedical Press, 1977*

ceptives makes it all the more difficult for many women to see themselves playing the role of mother. Not so long ago multiple pregnancies were inevitably part of marriage and the lot of womanhood. Women continued to have children right into their forties. Young girls grew up in this atmosphere, continually confronted with pregnancy, birth and babies. It stood them in good stead for their own childbearing years. In the Netherlands and other European countries, pregnancy is becoming a rare event in the life of a woman, occuring twice, sometimes three, more rarely four times.

The father role

Pregnancy is becoming less and less something which just happens and more of a premeditated act, decided upon beforehand by a willing couple. Generally, the mutual decision of "We want a baby" ensures that the man, right from the very beginning, is psychologically involved. The less-defined barrier between male and female pursuits, the love relationship on which most modern marriages is based, and the isolation in which a family functions, separated from relatives, commits a man to his unborn child, and makes his support and devotion indispensible. This does not imply, however, that his capacity to fill the role of father is clearly defined by society. He may also, to a certain degree, be assailed by doubts as to his future role. He might be at a loss regarding those typical feminine accomplishments of pregnancy, labor and childcare. The new pressures which pregnancy makes upon him and the heavier responsibilities which come with it, might undermine his emotional confidence and make him dread the approaching labor.

The second half of pregnancy

The fifth and sixth months of pregnancy bring with them a steadily increasing acceptance of the pregnancy, and with it, a more positive attitude toward the baby. The pregnant mother is psychologically attuned to her condition. The baby has become a part of her body and of herself, and determines her outlook and her way of thinking. The second half of pregnancy is thus ideally the time for psychological advice regarding her relationship with her husband and family; her possible fear of labor and of not giving birth to a normal healthy infant; and her doubt about her ability to fulfill her forthcoming role. Frequently heard complaints are disinterest in sex and an emotionally labile and changing pattern in sleep rhythms and in behavior. These complaints are rarely mentioned in so many words to outsiders. It is difficult for someone outside her immediate family unit to penetrate the psychological state of the pregnant woman in the second half of pregnancy; neither does she expect outsiders to be interested in her problems. At the same time her life reaches a new depth of meaning which occupies her and belongs to her alone, no matter what happens in the outside world. The expectant mother during this phase turns inward.

Sexual behavior

Some pregnant women suffer loss of libido. The frequency of coitus may become considerably less, especially in the last three months, the reasons being physical awkwardness, less inclination, fear of injury to the fetus, and acting on a doctor's advice, as well as a feeling of being less physically attractive. Medically speaking, where a normal pregnancy is concerned, there would appear to be no reason to perpetuate the old belief of abstaining from intercourse during the last six weeks of pregnancy. Neither coitus nor orgasm endanger the onset of labor, nor do they have any influence on the birth-weight of the child, the duration of pregnancy, or the health of the baby.

A satisfactory sexual relationship during pregnancy is important, especially as it can help the couple to cope better with the stresses imposed upon them by the pregnancy. Most couples are too diffident or shy to ask their doctor or the midwife for advice. All too often the scanty advice given tends to be of a purely medical character and does little to help them cope with the problem involving physical awkwardness. A relaxed and satisfactory sexual relationship can be promoted by suggesting a change of position, to mention but one example, during intercourse and by assuring the couple that frequent or prolonged intercourse absolutely can do no harm. It is, of course, more difficult to dispel a woman's belief that she is physically unattractive, even if the husband does not share her opinion.

In our society, reproduction is dissociated from sexuality and a woman is looked upon primarily as a sexual symbol. Her sexual characteristics must ideally accentuate the sex image. In other words, to be desirable, she must be necessarily or preferrably young, slim and physically attractive. A woman's child-bearing attributes, where breasts and stomach are functional rather than decorative, certainly do not contribute to this societal ideal. A woman may have difficulty in accepting her pregnant body and even become depressed when she contemplates her changing shape. Another woman, by contrast, may be elated by her pregnant shape.

Natural childbirth

A group of people who find themselves in the same situation may offer an opportunity to learning how to cope with that same situation. A group, therefore, is most suitable in the setting up of an antenatal course. This intimate group serves as a support for its members, and offers them the opportunity to express more readily their feelings. The methods for the relief of pain in labor take a separate place within the framework of the antenatal course. Sometimes this subject is treated as the most important part of the course. There are numerous 'psychoprophylactic' methods for the relief of pain in childbirth. The method originally described by the English physician, G.D. Read has become widely popularized as natural, or prepared childbirth. In France, it is known as the Lamaze method (Vellay, 1959), and has become widely known through Lamaze's own films of natural childbirth at home with the father, and in some cases other children present. Another French physician, Le Boyer, advocates not only natural childbirth, but also a quiet and gentle delivery in soft light so that birth is not a trauma to the baby. Le Boyer rests the baby on the mother's abdomen before the cord is cut. There the mother can touch it, and the important process of mother—child pair bonding begins with no delay. Then the baby is bathed in warm water. The baby stays with the mother, instead of being separated in a nursery.

Read ventured three explanations for excessive pain during labor: social tradition regarding the pain of labor; suboptimal physical condition of the mother, and the mother's ignorance of how to cooperate in labor.

If the mother is anxious at the outset of labor, muscle tension and cramps will increase. If the vicious cycle of anxiety—tension—pain is broken, labor progresses more easily and with less pain.

Preparation for delivery

The subject of natural childbirth is still a matter of controversy. Its greatest disadvantage is that the mother may feel directly and solely responsible for her behavior during labor. One can understand the sense of personal failure and perhaps bitterness and disillusion, which a woman experiences when labor does not proceed either according to plan, or when waves of pain shatter any illusion of anticipated freedom from pain. The fact remains, however, that natural childbirth, especially if its promise of painlessness is not too stressed, does have several aspects which help towards a quicker labor and which are indispensible in preparation for childbirth. This applies especially to the following: dispelling of fears and anxieties about the unknown; the establishment of a good relationship of trust and confidence between doctor and patient; the learning of antenatal exercises designed to relax muscles; and the occurrence of the delivery in pleasant and quiet surroundings where the mother feels she is being helped by people in whom she trusts.

According to Read, the physical condition of the pregnant woman should receive special attention during the course of antenatal exercises. Read's method, in its insistence on instruction and enlightenment, and its training and guidance during the pregnancy, has its greatest reward in changing the mother's emotional and physical defenselessness to a feeling that she has some control over the forces working within her. A woman who has been coached ahead of time, and helped if necessary, by pain-killing drugs, can go through labor with the feeling that she is taking part in an act of creation. As such, her predominant emotion can be that of joy and achievement.

Preparation of the expectant father

Little is known of the father's experiences and feelings during his wife's pregnancy and labor. A couvade syndrome (Trethowan, 1968) has been described which takes on different forms in different parts of the world. In some cultures, for instance, it is known for the father to receive the care and attention normally reserved for the delivering mother, by taking to his bed, and undergoing all the motions of labor and childbirth. Milder forms of the couvade syndrome were observed in soldiers during the Second World War, who at the time of the wife's expected date of delivery, complained of temporary disorders such as nausea, abdominal pain, and reduction or increase in appetite. It is not often realized that, if unprepared, it can be very difficult to witness a delivery.

As a preparation for childbirth, an expectant mother in the Netherlands has the opportunity to choose between two instruction courses — a prenatal exercise course or a practical mothercraft course, which includes not only the care of the baby, but also how to take care of her health in pregnancy. A limited number of hospitals organize 'parents evenings' for the expectant couple, if delivery is to take place in a hospital. The expectant mother must take the initiative, however, to enroll in any of these courses. Such courses are sponsored by different organizations, and often the antenatal psychological guidance leaves a lot to be desired.

There is a growing tendency these days for the father also to be invited to attend these courses. He can thus gain satisfaction from learning how to assist the mother during her confinement. 'Husband coached childbirth' courses are a popular part of the Lamaze method in some American hospitals. The popularity of these courses has shown that many men are interested enough to participate in them. The medical staff of these hospitals organize a three month course for expectant fathers where, by means of diagrams, visual aids, lectures and practical demonstrations, the father is not only instructed to stand by his wife before, during, and after delivery, but, if necessary, to take over the management from the midwife, nurse, or doctor.

The prevention of stress and conflict

New parents may find that their work routine, household activity, interests and social obligations, not to mention their relationship with each other, are difficult to combine with having a baby. Tensions and conflicts arising from the situation may be avoided with proper preparation. Few parents seem to realize how disruptive to the peace and quiet of their home-life a baby can be, from the moment it is born. Not only that, but parents may be bound to the house more than ever, with limited alternative diversions. Taking care of a baby means that they may have less time for each other, and any conversation becomes centered more and more on the baby. Their role as parents may become a primary one, to the detriment of their relationship to each other, and their sexual life may have to take second place.

The so-called 'prevention program' puts forward practical ways of how to cope with and prevent these difficulties. Group discussion, theoretical and practical, deals with the responsibility of motherhood, the role of the father, contact with family and friends, and the relationship between work and motherhood, and also offers more practical tips to the expectant mother, such as not to lose interest in activities outside the home, to set aside some time for herself, and to organize her household routine. The father is advised to take a free week from work when his wife comes out of the hospital, and to devote one hour every day exclusively to the baby. Both parents are advised to cultivate friendship with other couples in a similar position, and to keep on the look-out for a good and reliable baby-sitter. It is also suggested that they plan a holiday for just the two of them when the baby is about 3 months old.

General advice

The following topics should be borne in mind when preparing expectant couples for the birth of their child:
— Assessment of the feelings, temperament, and dreams of the pregnant mothers may bring to light fear of labor, anxiety for the normality of the baby, and self-doubt in the mother's ability to live up to the expectations of motherhood.
— A pregnancy free of fear is almost unknown. The unknown, understandably, brings its share of fear and anxiety. Should this fear become continuous and threatening, and unable to be kept under control, then it becomes pathological.
— The absence of a good liason between the pregnant woman, her husband and her medical advisors makes all antenatal instruction and guidance worthless.
— The value of incidental discussions and of fragmentary information is short-lived. Verbal advice should be supplemented by written material and vice-versa. Visual aids in the form of slides, films and diagrams, and perhaps a guided tour of the labor room and the apparatus for administrating the inhalation analgesics, are all enlightening and of special value.
— Prenatal guidance which does not take into account the individual needs and character differences of the parents-to-be, is to be discouraged.

2. EXPERIENCE OF DELIVERY

Woman's heritage

"One has to experience it oneself to know what it is all about" women have often said. Yet it has often been men who have written about labor, who have concluded how painful it is, who interpreted woman's feelings, who established the rules of behavior during labor and who caused many a woman to privately protest and rebel — quite rightly in my opinion because the opposition also has a right to be heard, and no man has yet become pregnant. We have now, for the first time in history, a new generation of women, who are prepared to express their feelings and talk about their experiences, interpret them and draw their own conclusions from them. We also have a situation that up to a short time ago, was unthinkable, and that is the combination of mother as midwife, mother as physician, mother as writer, and mother as sociologist. Such power has to be reckoned with and taken seriously. The time has arrived where it is women who are re-defining the concept 'woman', who at the same time are eliminating false images and giving a clearer picture of the truth and are making their influence felt in areas where men have always considered themselves privileged.

My first delivery

"Be prepared; the first labor will take a long time." This sort of advice was repeatedly given to me. The same opinion also was held by my husband, Ben. I waited and waited for that first sign until one evening at eleven o'clock, just as I had got into bed, I felt something. I thought: "Oh! . . . Oh, it is about to begin!" Had I imagined it? I couldn't have, surely. A real contraction, pain from top to toe and then it was over. Silently, I crept under the blankets, happy with myself and yet perhaps a bit apprehensive as well. Despite being ten days overdue, it still came unexpectedly. A surprise for Ben who, on coming home half an hour later, found me doubled up in bed from another contraction! Kisses, tears and joy followed. tomorrow, perhaps we'll have a child. During the next hour, in between contractions, I carried on as usual. Soon after that, however, I had to give up what I was doing and sought the refuge of my bed. My own physician examined me to see how labor was progressing. "There is very little dilatation of the cervix" he said. "Try to sleep, it will take some time yet". The bedside clock showed one o'clock. Sleep . . . easier said than done! To preserve my energy for later I tried to stay still and relax. A thousand thoughts, all of them about babies, flitted through my mind.

At 3 a.m. I sought the comfortable armchair in the living-room. Between pains I tried to concentrate on the book, which I clutched in my hand. When the contractions start coming every 5 minutes, then its time to go to hospital, my gynecologist had said to me. Surely there was something wrong with me. These pains had been coming on for every five, then every three minutes for hours and hours and still the pains kept coming . . . I couldn't sleep, or sit, or walk, I could hardly relax anymore. If this is just the start and there is still a whole day ahead of me, I thought in despair, then it is much worse than I imagined! 4.45 a.m. Contractions every two minutes with hardly a pause between the waves of pain. I woke Ben. At first he looked unbelieving, then as realization dawned, there followed bewilderment and shock. It is true that first babies don't usually come this quickly. At least, in his personal experience, he had never seen anything like this before. I should have woken him much sooner, but how was I to know? Everyone had been so keen to remind me that the first labor takes ages . . .! I had heard stories of contractions that disappeared and stayed away for days, and what really registered in my mind, was that I mustn't go too early to hospital. At the same time I kept asking myself what would happen in the morning, as I had absolutely no idea the baby was about to be born.

5 a.m. Things start happening very quickly in rapid succession. Suddenly I feel a warm gush of water between my legs. The membranes had ruptured. I look down dismayed at all that wetness, whilst a very strong desire to 'push' comes over me. I pant, to suppress this inclination, something I had been taught in my antenatal relaxation class. Slippers on, coat over my nightdress and bag in hand, we walk down the four endless stairs of the apartment building, and nothing but contraction following contraction. The car sped through the darkness. Don't brake . . . please hurry . . . I can't keep it anymore! "Baby born in car" the paper headlines swam before my eyes. With horror I look down at the bristly car mat. "Carry on panting" is all I heard from my husband.

5.20 a.m. I see a dimly-lit delivery room and an overwhelming feeling of safety rushes over me; nothing can happen to me now. At last I could get on with it. I felt possessed by all sorts of primitive instincts which were gathering together to form an overpowering force inside me. I don't think, I don't feel, I push and I push, again and again. "I'll burst. I can't push any harder," I hear myself say in despair. I feel a floundering sensation between my legs. What? Has the baby arrived already? Why have I noticed so little of what's happening? I am completely perplexed . . . . Then I see a grey-pink besmeared creature, protesting loudly against the most difficult journey of her life. A daughter. Healthy. Everything in the right place. Much later I look at her properly. First there is Ben. I see the relief on his face and our hands entwine. Such happiness makes me tremble. Then we look at our child, Cathelyne, almost $6\frac{1}{2}$ pounds, a whole little person formed almost from nothing. . . . Goodness, she is still so strange! An hour later we are moved to the maternity ward, Ben walking beside us. "She has your nose" he says tenderly. Seldom have I felt so relieved, triumphant, so intensely happy . . . and so empty.

A unique experience

So much eludes one when one has gone through such an experience, and much of what is afterwards remembered tends to be distorted. It is later, sometimes a long time afterwards, that one remembers all sorts of details, some important, and some not so important. During my lying-in I realized only too well how marvellously brisk and smooth it had gone, and with a minimum of pain, too. Yet I could not stop thinking about it all. One day one has an enormous swollen abdomen and the next day it is gone, but one's mind and spirit cannot change so quickly! Before initiated into the 'Holy Rites of Motherhood' I always felt irritated by married women's chatter about childbirth. Now I can fully understand it and even find myself joining in, occasionally. Giving birth to a child is not only an unique human experience, but also so overwhelming, so gripping that in the first weeks afterwards one wonders if one has dreamt it all. The baby, tangible though it is, only enhances this state. That something so fragile and tiny, somethings so perfect and so magnificient could come out of one's body, I considered a miracle. Even after the birth of my second child — and this was quite different from the first — I pondered again.

Childbirth is dying a little. You don't know the day or the hour. A compelling primitive force suddenly takes possession, and one's body and spirit can but bow to its will. In more than one respect, one drifts completely alone in a sort of vacuum, stripped of human identity, seemingly touching the fringe of creation. It was for me a dramatic and enriching experience, one that has influenced my attitude towards life and death. I feel more bound to mother earth. I have as a woman been granted a gift, which men will never know.

The relief of pain in childbirth

During my first pregnancy I had decided that I was not going through labor without some form of pain depressant. This wish of mine would hardly arouse much surprise, or opposition, in Scandinavian or Anglo-Saxon countries, where pain relief methods are routinely used during labor. In The Netherlands, however, many doctors and obstetricians claim that labor is both a natural and normal process, for which a women is physically and biologically well equipped. They see no reason, therefore, why a labor which is progressing normally should give rise to much pain. To a certain degree this belief has been strengthened by the natural childbirth method. The system, whereby the mother gives birth in her own home under the supervision of the doctor or midwife, which was, and still is, customary in this country, is preeminently suitable to the psychological approach to pain as propagated by this method, but does not lend itself to the artificial methods of pain relief such as the administration of analgesics, or some form of anesthesia. These artificial methods can be safely applied only under hospital conditions, and one cannot expect a doctor, or midwife to use them in the home. Another factor is that Holland has lagged behind the Anglo-Saxon countries in the emergence of anesthesia as a speciality.

The individual experience of pain

Whenever I talk with women about their confinements, I am invariably struck by the discrepancies which exist between their descriptions of what they have felt, and what doctors have to say about it. I still think that it should be left to the woman herself to estimate the degree of pain, her ability to bear it, and to consider it her right to demand something to diminish that pain. My opinion is not changed by the fact that during my own first delivery two anesthetists stood by idle, and watched the baby being born quickly and almost painlessly. The same happened with the birth of my second child. It would be most unrealistic, however, to use one labor as a criterion to measure others. The really painless delivery occurs one per thousand, or even less, and as such is an exception to the general rule.

Anesthetists do not doubt that certain stages of labor can be so painful, that if experienced in another clinical situation the pain would certainly require their services. Pain is so terribly difficult to define. Give ten women the same stimulus of pain, and they'll all react to it differently. The subjective experience of pain is something highly individual, influenced by all manner of physical, mental and social factors. In some cases one can influence these factors and in so doing also alter the character of the pain. This, however, succeeds only partially in some cases and fails completely in others.

Some women do feel the pain of labor but find the physical sensation of pain overshadowed, overwhelmed as they are by the tremendous spiritual sensation of giving birth. This response can be encouraged and strengthened by the attitude of the husband and/or doctor. Others feel labor as painful, but what pulls them through is the knowledge that after some time it will be all over, and then they will hear and see the baby. Others can't see why they should suffer pain or lose control of themselves, finding it much worse than they ever expected. Their endurance to pain can be lowered either by a faulty mental buildup, or by the circumstances in which they find themselves.

The over-technical approach

The Dutch approach to obstetrics is typified by its mainly passive and patient, though guarded awaiting for nature to take its course. Labor is not induced, membranes not ruptured, and caesarian sections are only performed when there is a strict medical indication. From the social and the medical view-point, this outlook has indeed great advantages to offer the mother and the baby. Not without good reason, there exists in America a growing group of women who are protesting against the excessive technical approach to childbirth, claiming that such an attitude can be damaging to the child, as well as having a negative influence on the mental and physical well being of the mother. Very few people would go so far as to suggest that giving birth under general anesthetic is an ideal system. Yet, in America, the giving of a general anesthetic during labor has become routine, making life much easier for the obstetrician. The great disadvantage of this method is the unnecessary risk which every general anesthetic brings with it, and the exclusion of the mother from partaking in the birth of her child. Surely to a mother waking up from such an anesthetic, and to her husband, who only then may appear on the scene, there must be little difference as to whether she has just had a baby or had her appendix taken out; particularly if the baby has already been removed from the delivery room.

The birth of a child is one of the rare occasions in a lifetime where patience, waiting, pain and effort are rewarded with deep joy and a great sense of fulfillment. It is such a great pity if a couple cannot share the moment together.

Methods used in the control of pain

A woman should, through good management, and with due respect for her individual emotional needs be able to emerge from childbirth happy and with her self-respect intact. Methods for relief of pain in childbirth can be placed in 6 categories:
— The so-called 'psychological' methods such as the natural childbirth method of Read; the Russian, Pavlovian-derived psychoprophylactic method of Nicolajev with whom Lamaze studied; and hypnosis.
— The administration of tranquilizers which not only have a calming and sedating effect, but are also effective against pain.
— Morphine derivatives and inhalation analgesics for use during the phase of dilatation of the cervix.
— Infiltration anesthesia and pudendal block.
— Regional anesthesia, for example, caudal and epidural block, whereby the lower parts of the body are rendered insensible to pain.
— General anesthesia during expulsion of the fetus.
Psychological methods are effective in 10—20% of women. The woman undergoes a sort of hypnosis where pain is either stilled, or driven into the background. In 30—50% of all cases there is a slight degree of relief, but the rest are not helped by it at all. However, the trying out of one method, does not necessarily exclude the use of another one. Tranquilizers would appear to be effective in relieving pain in 70—80% of cases. Inhalation and regional anesthesia produce complete freedom from pain in 90% of cases.

As a result of a healthy mental and physical build-up during pregnancy, combined with the most suitable agents for the relief of pain, a woman can experience the birth of her child, not as a terrifying ordeal, but as a deeply rewarding, gratifying human experience, giving more depth to her feminine role.

Emancipation of women

A woman in the Western world is now at the cross-roads. Some degree of disillusion would seem to be her lot, no matter in which role she has been cast. A great step towards her emancipation has been the wide dissemination of information concerning reliable contraception. Thanks to this she may now choose to become or not to become pregnant. She can now regulate the number of children she bears, and she can plan her life in such a way that her talents and other personal qualities can be put to use other than solely in marriage and childbearing. It is not surprising to find that pregnan-

716

cy and motherhood are not held in high regard among some militant feminists when one considers how, for centuries, they have prevented women from
achieving equality with the male and prevented her from developing along-
side the male in nondomestic achievement. The greatest emphasis on the intellectual development of women only too often goes hand in hand with the
suggestion that her biological heritage — her ability to bear children — may
have a retarding effect on this development, making her despise her own nature. I deplore this attitude, because it is in the full exploitation of her mental and physical abilities that the multi-faceted potential of the female as
woman and as person comes into its own right. Surely this is what emancipation is all about; the ability and the freedom to choose and plan critically
whether to bear children, knowing that having children is only one of the
paths towards personal fulfillment. I am very conscious that being a mother
has been to me a tremendous source of emotional and intellectual satisfaction. I am glad that I have twice experienced pregnancy and labor, and I am
also glad that I can say now: "That's enough". These two statements may
appear contradictory, but they do not have to be, as many women may yet
discover for themselves.

BIBLIOGRAPHY

Bonica, J.J. (1972) *Obstetric Analgesia and Anaesthesia.* (Springer Verlag, Berlin.)
Boston Children's Medical Center (1972) *Pregnancy, Birth and the Newborn Baby.* (Dela-
corte Press, Seymour Laurens, New York.)
Crul, H. (1975) *Wij willen kinderen, voorlichtingsboek voor toekomstige ouders over
gezinsvorming, zwangerschap en de baby.* (Hollandia, Baarn.)
Friedan, B. (1963) *The Feminine Mystique.* (Norton, New York.)
Gill, K. (1974) Sociale verloskunde in New York, pars pro toto. *Huisarts en Wetenschap,*
17: 340—344.
Hobbs, L. (1970) *Love and Liberation.* (McGraw-Hill, New York.)
Janssen, M.C. (1968) *Zwangere en Kraamvrouw in Psychologisch Perspectief.* (Dekker
and Van de Vegt, Nijmegen-Utrecht.)
Kooy, G.A. (1973) De toekomst van het Westerse gezin. *T. Soc. Geneesk.* 51: 8—19.
Leboyer, F. (1975) *Birth Without Violence.* (Knopf, New York.)
Read, G.D. (1954) *Childbirth Without Fear.* (Heinemann, London.)
Solberg, D.A., Buttler, J. and Wagner, W.W. (1973) Sexual behavior in pregnancy. *N.
Engl. J. Med.* 288: 1098.
Sullerot, E. (1965) *Demain les Femmes.* (Laffont-Gonthier, Paris.)
Trethowan, W.H. (1968) The couvade syndrome — Some further observations. *J. Psycho-
som. Res.* 12: 107—115.
Vellay, P. (1959) *Childbirth Without Pain.* (Dutton, New York.)

CHAPTER 51

The postpartum period

ARY A. HASPELS

1. UNCOMPLICATED RECOVERY

Ambulation

Ambulation is permitted nowadays 12 h after a normal delivery. Also in uncomplicated cases a hospital diet is permissible from the beginning.

Urine

Urine retention complicating the postpartum period may occur in the patient with a normal delivery, but is more likely following an instrumental procedure. The constant desire to void, with urination of only small amounts, usually means urine retention or an overflow bladder. Also characteristically, the full bladder displaces the uterus out of the pelvis upwards. Abdominal palpation may reveal the uterus away from the midline and the fundus may reach the costal margin. If there is any doubt as to whether the patient is emptying her bladder, she should be catheterized once. Intermittent catheterization is thought to be less infectious than use of an indwelling catheter.

Emotional problems

In their preparation for childbirth, patients should be told that some emotional letdown is often experienced around the fourth postpartum day, so that when this happens it comes as no surprise. It must be regarded as normal part of the postpartum course. Tears without cause is a well known symptom, and the patient usually states that she can find no reason for her behavior and she tends to be apologetic. One might speculate that this is a state of emotional exhaustion following the successful completion of a new experience, but it happens to primipara and multipara alike. Reassuring the patient is usually enough. We have the impression that those emotional prob-

Handbook of Sexology, edited by J. Money and H. Musaph
© *Elsevier/North-Holland Biomedical Press, 1977*

lems have been less serious since early ambulation came in vogue. In previous times when patients were flat in bed for 7 days, emotional disturbances were as common as they are rare now. It is important that the patient does not feel inadequate as a mother.

Breast feeding and skin contact

Women who like to breast feed their baby should be expected to do so for three to six months. Only when the milk supply decreases or there is evidence of breast infection should the infant be placed on formula feedings.

In women who do not choose to breast feed, some use estrogen to suppress lactation. Without doubt these substances will prevent some engorgement with its associated discomfort which reaches its peak on the third postpartum day. The time-honored method of the breast binder is also effective. Postpartum estrogen increases the incidence of postpartum thrombosis.

Women who do not breast feed should hold their child to the bare breast while feeding. It is very important for the child to have warm skin contact with the mother.

Postpartum advice

Although patients are ambulatory from the first day after delivery, they should realize that a period of one or two weeks is required before they regain their strength sufficiently to take over their household duties in full.

Vaginal douches are not advised any more. Postnatal exercises to restore the tone of the abdomen and pelvic floor should be done daily for at least six weeks.

Sexual intercourse

A problem which is likely to be uppermost in a patient's mind, although one to which she may feel too reticent to confess, is the question of resumption of marital relations and how, for the meantime, to avoid further pregnancies. In the standard textbook on obstetrics one can still read that sexual intercourse is best postponed until after the postpartum check-up, which is customarily performed at the sixth to eighth postpartum week. Some authorities suggest a shorter time if it is congenial to the couple, especially to the woman.

The patient and her husband should receive clear information that ovulation and the menstrual periods may recur within 6 weeks postpartum in 25% of women, and within 12 weeks in 61%. Lactation tends to delay the onset of ovulation. It is a popular superstition that breast feeding prevents conception. At 12 weeks, about one third of lactating primiparas are menstruating as compared with 91% of nonlactating primiparas. They should realize that it is possible, however, to become pregnant before the menses reappear. The patient and her husband should, therefore, receive information about contraception methods and the resumption of sexual intercourse.

After a few weeks there need be no restriction with regard to intercourse, although some women are unlikely to be much interested. Young husbands should be warned that this is no unnatural phenomenon. The fear of conceiving straight away is very real, and may play a role. In patients who like to use the contraceptive pill we advise them to start 14 days postpartum. It is not necessary to wait to prescribe the pill until after the first period has re-established itself. Intrauterine devices have a higher expulsion rate if inserted before eight weeks at least. Good advice about other methods of contraception should be given to the non-pill users.

2. COMPLICATED RECOVERY

The complications of recovery from delivery are sufficiently rare that the reader is referred to special sources for information concerning them.

SECTION IX

On parenthood

Section coordinator: Niles Newton

CHAPTER 52

Introduction

NILES NEWTON

1. PARENTHOOD AS PART OF SEXUAL REPRODUCTION

Parenthood in relation to other broad aspects of sexuality

Where does parenthood fit into the broad spectrum of sexology? Viewed biologically, parenthood is an integral part of the continuum of sexual reproduction starting with fertilization and progressing without break until a new entity is produced which is capable of total independence. This may come at the time of egg laying, as it does in certain fishes and reptiles, or it may come later, after the young have been warmed, fed, and protected for a period after leaving the mother's body, as is frequent among birds and mammals. In man, reproductive processes extend far beyond the age of weaning if continued viability of the young is to be assured.

From the point of view of survival of some species, caretaking behavior is often as essential as coital behavior and usually requires much greater commitment of time and energy, since nurturance involves a series of repeated acts over days, weeks, months, or years.

This section will concentrate on this long end period of sexual reproduction in mammals — a period when there is bodily separation but continuing interactive bonds between mother and young, usually involving not only lactation, but also many other facets of care. At this time, too, other members of the social group often contribute much to the survival of the young, in various ways ranging from the sharing of food and warmth and protection against aggressors, to role-modeling complex modes of behavior.

To separate this end-period from all that has gone before leads to a narrowing of understanding. Repeatedly in the chapters of this section pregnancy and birth are also mentioned as significant precursors of parenthood.

Specific relationships between coitus, birth and breast-feeding

Indeed there are strong psychological similarities between all three interpersonal acts of reproduction, namely coitus, birth, and breast-feeding (New-

Handbook of Sexology, edited by J. Money and H. Musaph
© *Elsevier/North-Holland Biomedical Press, 1977*

ton, 1973; Baxter, 1974). They may share the following basic characteristics: (a) they are based in part on closely related neurohormonal reflexes, (b) they are sensitive to environmental stimuli, being easily inhibited in early stages, and (c) all three, under certain circumstances, may trigger caretaking or nurturant behavior (Newton, 1973).

The neurohormonal relationship of these three acts was dramatically demonstrated in a classic experiment by Debackere and colleagues (1961). They joined the circulatory systems of pairs of sheep, so that a ram was joined to a lactating ewe. The seminal vesicles and ampullae of the ram were massaged, often to the point of emission. After a minimum of thirty seconds, there often was a sharp rise of pressure in the udder of the connected ewe, indicating that the milk-ejection mechanism had been triggered by the blood of the sexually excited ram. Two ewes also had their jugular veins joined together combining their blood supply. The vagina of one member of the pair was distended with a balloon, simulating the dilation that occurs both during labor and during coitus. This stimulation in the vagina of one ewe often caused signs of milk ejection to occur in the other ewe.

Although the physiology of the neurohormonal reflexes involved in coitus, parturition and lactation are at present only fragmentarily understood, it appears that oxytocic substances are involved, and that quick conditioning and easy inhibition of the milk ejection reflex also apply to the fetus-ejection reflex and the sperm-transport reflexes in male and female (Newton et al., 1966a; Newton, 1973).

The contribution of the neurohormonal reproductive reflexes to species survival may be considerable. The milk-ejection reflex rapidly becomes conditioned to the offspring's cry or hungry snuffling. It is easily inhibited by distractions and fear (Ely and Peterson, 1941; Newton and Newton, 1948, 1950), thus helping to prevent milk stealing by other species or by inappropriate young of the same species.

The fetus-ejection reflex and its inhibition may increase the likelihood of labor being initiated in safe environments (Newton et al., 1966a, b, 1968a). Parturition is a time of maximal defenselessness of both female and young. The female with a fetus in her birth canal cannot move with normal efficiency and the newly emerged young are in a peak state of helplessness. Thus, the ability to regulate the emergence of the young according to environmental cues may be of key significance to survival.

Although information about the sperm-transport reflexes is fragmentary, it is known that environmental disturbance inhibits sexual functioning as well as milk ejection and fetus ejection, and that oxytocic substances in male blood may be in the same range as female levels (Rorie and Newton, 1964), despite the involvement of this hormone with lactation and labor. Just as is the case with milk ejection and fetus ejection, there is survival value in mechanisms that limit coitus to environmental situations that are relatively safe and protected, since a male and female engaged in coitus are not in a favorable position for fight or flight if danger threatens.

Another way the three interpersonal reproductive acts of coitus, birth, and breast-feeding are similar is that all three may trigger caretaking or nurturant behavior. The most usual human pattern is for males to protect and help to nourish women with whom they are cohabiting (Mead and Newton, 1967). Similarly, females who form long-term coital relationships with a male, usually engage in some nurturant activities toward them, such as cooking for them. The relationship between birth and lactation and nurturant behavior is still more clearly defined. The baby at birth triggers caretaking behavior. Lactation and other aspects of maternal behavior appear to be closely related.

2. THE RELATION OF LACTATION TO OTHER ASPECTS OF PARENTAL BEHAVIOR

Lactation not only has strong similarities with psychophysiological processes occurring at birth and during coitus but also appears to be intimately interwoven with certain other aspects of parental response. Early zoologists, who flourished in an era when they frequently saw breast-feeding in their homes, named the whole group of animals to which man belongs 'mammals' in honor of their unique mode of giving nourishment to the young.

Research data relating lactation to other aspects of behavior

Both experimental studies on animals and statistical studies in humans have found that lactation is related to some other aspects of parental behavior, but not others. Whether specific researchers are convinced that the relation of lactation to other aspects of maternal behavior is appreciable or negligible depends in large part on the nature of the data they have collected.

Animal investigators concentrating on such items of 'maternal behavior' as time spent in the nest, pup-licking, crouching over the young or speed of pup retrieval, report few differences between lactating females and controls (see following chapter by Rosenblatt). More major differences tend to appear when the mother must expend energy or sustain pain to get to the young. The lactating female may try harder to keep contact with the young (Nissen, 1930; Seward and Seward, 1940; Newton et al., 1968b; Gandelman et al., 1970; Bridges et al., 1972). Differences in direction or nature of aggression is also suggested in fragmentary research. Increased defense of the nest responses (Beniest-Noirot, 1958) and reduced aggressiveness in lactating females toward stranger pups (Richards, 1966) have been reported. Unfortunately, tests of drive to be with young or alterations in aggressiveness have not been frequently used in 'maternal behavior research', in spite of their significance for species survival.

In human work similar problems regarding type of data collected occur. Much of the research has involved token breast-feeding of the type currently practiced in the U.S. with limitation of sucking and body contact, and much supplementary feeding rather than the unrestricted lactation typical of most preliterate, historic, and traditional cultures (Newton, 1971). An added difficulty is that since human beings cannot be randomly assigned to breast- and bottle-feeding, and since it is known that personality and attitudes do determine feeding choice (Newton, 1955; Newton and Newton, 1967) no cause and effect relationships can clearly be demonstrated.

There have been a few studies involving systematic observations of behavior of lactating human mothers with their infants. Thoman and co-workers (1972) found that new mothers who talked to their infants the most during nursing on the second day after birth were likely to continue to breast-feed the longest. Bernal and Richards (1970) observed mothers feeding their babies on the second, third, eighth, ninth, and tenth days after birth. They found that the nursing mothers touched their babies more in other ways and also kept nipples in their babies' mouths longer than the bottle-feeding mothers. Newton and her colleagues (1975) studied postpartum mothers who had the choice of being near their babies 24 h a day, only during the daytime hours, or only during four feedings. Mothers electing to have the most contact with their infants more often chose to initiate breast-feeding.

Breast-feeding as part of childcare: historical and cross-cultural data

Historical and cross-cultural data reinforce the observational psychological data that breast-feeding appears to be related to some other aspects of infant care. Ryerson (1961) analyzed medical advice concerning child-rearing published between 1550 and 1900. Her sample is based on texts written in English or translated into English and after 1800 she relied solely on books published in America. The first texts recommended two years as the desirable weaning age, but as late as 1700 authors wrote with disapproval of nursing 4-year-olds, indicating that this practice was occurring. Wet-nursing, swaddling, rocking, and sleeping with the mother were in favor at this time. Gradually the average recommended weaning age decreased until it fell below one year by 1800. Along with this breast-feeding change came other major differences in child-care practices. Feeding schedules were first mentioned about 1725 and by 1850 and thereafter all medical authors studied recommended limiting feeding to scheduled times, thus indicating suckling restriction. Swaddling, rocking and sleeping with the mother decreased, and masturbation and sex play began to be mentioned — always with disapproval. The critical rapid change in infant care methods began about 1750, with the beginnings of the industrial revolution in England.

Breast-feeding customs are also closely related to some other infant care customs in traditional and preliterate cultures — so much so, in fact, that it is difficult to separate them. Mead and Newton (1967) have called this period the 'Transition Period' of parental care: "It involves a set of independent patterns, which include physical closeness to the mother by day and sleeping with the mother at night, soothing of all crying, prolonged and frequent sucking at the breast, and spacing of children so that maternal attention and energy are not quickly divided."

A biological base of this transition period behavior is suggested by the fact that it is found in widely scattered and diverse cultures in many parts of the world. Two examples, one from South America and the other from the Middle East, exemplify this parental pattern as it repeatedly recurs in the accounts of the peoples who still adhere to traditional ways.

Tichauer (1963) described the Aymara of Bolivia as follows: "Wherever the mother goes, even to a dance, the baby will go with her, little head close to hers and easily slung forward in front of her in case of need . . . No modesty is attached to nursing even in public places . . . At night the child sleeps next to his mother. This continues until he is about 2 years old or until the next child is born. Nursing has precedence over any other activity in which the mother may be engaged, such as selling her vegetables in the market, for instance, although she may be extremely anxious to make the sale."

Granqvist (1947) describing a traditional Jordan village indicates the same pattern of closeness in a totally different culture context and on the other side of the world. "Even after birth the mother and the child are closely connected for a long period. To be fed the baby requires its mother all the time for it must not be hungry. Both in everyday life and at festivals one can observe how, as soon as the little child cries or shows the least sign of restlessness, it is at once laid to the mother's breast. Very often a woman who is nursing a child has an opening in her dress over each breast and thus she can feed it at once. And she does it unhesitatingly in any place, at any time and very often."

The spacing of children is another component of the fully developed transition period, since full lactation tends to inhibit ovulation, thus assuring the infant additional months of undivided parental attention. Although planned parenthood groups have emphasized the use of nonlactational methods of birth spacing, a current statistical report from developing countries indicates that lactation is conferring 34,700,000 couple years of protection, as compared to 24,000,000 couple-years of protection obtained from all other contraceptive practices, including the contraceptive pill, the IUD, and sterilization (Rosa, 1975).

Transition period in relation to later parental behavior

Lactation among humans with a fully developed transition period lasts about 2 to 4 years (Ford, 1945; Ryerson, 1961). This helps to assure the mother's regular presence during the attachment period which is often considered of key importance to the later psychosocial development in humans (Bowlby, 1969, 1973; Ainsworth, 1973).

Even in nonhuman mammals, lactation may have psychological as well as nutritional function. An experiment done by Nováková (1966) is suggestive.

Male rats were weaned at 15, 16, 17, 25 and 30 days of postnatal life. Rate of elaboration of conditioned reflexes at 8 months and stability of memory traces at 12 months were studied. The 30-day weaned group elaborated conditioned reflexes more quickly and had firmer memory traces than any of the other groups. Those weaned as late as day 25 resembled the 15-day-old weanlings more than the 30-day-old weanlings.

It is possible that some mammals use lactation as a method of keeping the young sufficiently oriented to the mother so that social learning has a better possibility of taking place. The duration of lactation in the aquatic mammals suggests this. Marked differences exist in the duration of nursing. The mysticetes are simple grazers of the sea, whereas the odontocetes exhibit a complex social structure, cooperation in herding schools of fish, and a sophisticated navigational training. The mysticetes nurse 7 to 10.5 months, whereas the odontocetes nurse 18 to 25 months (Brodie, 1969).

In weighing the research studies reported in this section the reader needs to keep in mind whether they relate to the transition period when mother and young are still physiologically interacting or to the post-transition period. Much of the research being reported relates to studies after complete physiological separation. Even the landmark experiment on the development of attachment behavior in human mothers in the immediate postpartum period as described in Chapter 57 was conducted on non-breast-feeding mothers (Klaus et al., 1972).

Research concentration on the nonlactation period of parenthood is of special importance to our current culture in which even breast-fed infants are likely to get less than 10% of the number of breast-feedings they would receive in cultures that do not restrict breast-suckling. However, findings need to be generalized with caution since they represent conditions far from the mammalian biological base.

It is true that even in human societies with fully developed transition periods, the duration of parental behavior post-weaning far outweighs in duration parental behavior given during prolonged lactation, but it is also true that the early years are times of first impressions and most rapid psychological development. Their impact on what comes later is not fully known. Starting the mother—baby interaction without pleasurable breast-feeding may be psychophysiologically similar to starting marriage without pleasurable coitus.

3. PARENTHOOD IN OTHER PERSPECTIVES — OLD AND NEW ISSUES

The focus of the following chapters is on current issues and research frontiers. In each decade or generation new topics come to the fore and other approaches, often equally valid, recede from scientific interest for a while. In the next few paragraphs we will briefly mention some issues to round out the view of parenthood in terms of past classics and future possibilities as the cycle comes full circle.

Individual biological base of parenthood

Within the species, marked variations of parental behavior occur which in part may have a psychobiological base. Of particular concern may be individual genetically determined differences in parental behavior and neuro-hormonal reflex conditioning of a pervasive sort.

There is clear evidence that some aspects of maternal behavior vary not only with the species but with individual strain differences. In studying 4 different strains of rabbits, nine items of maternal behavior appeared to be regulated by genetic variations (Ross et al., 1963). These included fertility rate, milk production, cannibalism of young, scattering of young, times of building nest, location of nest, shape of the nest, lining of nest, maternal aggression toward laboratory attendants, and interest in the young. Data on mice indicate that one inbred strain handled their young more than another, and that genetically determined strain differences in whisker-eating and cannibalism also exist (Weimer and Fuller, 1966).

The extent that humans are subject to individual genetic cues underlying their parental behavior is an issue fraught with the same type of implications as the individual genetic cues involved in coital behavior and sexual interest. Mead (1935) seized on the biological possibilities when she vividly described the dilemma of a plump, soft, big-breasted Mundugumore woman, Kwenda by name, who had the misfortune of being born into a very aggressive society that praised tall, lithe, slender, unmotherly women. Kwenda loved children. She refused to throw away her first child when her husband requested it. Later when her husband refused to be reconciled with her, she had no more children but adopted a baby.

Another area almost totally unexplored is the psychobiological individualization of parental behavior through neurohormonal reflex learning. I first realized how easily these reflexes are conditioned when I began to drip milk whenever I saw a glass of milk. I had just returned home from six days in a maternity unit which had the custom of serving a glass of milk to the mothers just before bringing out the babies thus conditioning my milk ejection reflex. Many other stimuli besides sucking may trigger hormones controlling parental behavior. For instance body contact with pups appears to delay the return of estrus in rats that have had their nipples removed, suggesting hormonal reactions from skin contact (Zarrow et al., 1973).

Parenthood in broader social and psychological context

Parenthood is not only a function of sexuality or the family or the individual but its roots go broader and deeper than is sometimes recognized, and scholarship using this holistic approach has a long outstanding tradition.

Some of the early studies on small societies before they were merged or distorted by increasing contact with the complex world gave a view of parenthood in relation to the total culture which makes them perennial classics, especially when the recording anthropologists were interested in the mother-child and father-child relationships from infancy onward. Particularly notable in this regard is the work of Margaret Mead whose central themes of parenthood and reproduction are imbedded in a rich context of multifaceted cultural data (Mead, 1928, 1930, 1935, 1949) and those that followed her lead such as Beaglehole and Beaglehole (1938), DuBois (1944), Granqvist (1947), and Holmberg (1950). Even in Mead's more recent work there is a constant emphasis on behavior in relation to the much broader cultural context within which it stands (Mead, 1961, 1974).

Broader issues in parenthood and reproduction were also forcefully raised by those working in mental health and psychological fields and their classic contribution raises issues fundamental to understanding both the past and future of parental behavior. Classic works which helped to mold much future thinking included Benedek (1946), Wortis and co-workers (1947), Gorer (1955), Soddy (1955), Wolfenstein (1955), Tanner and Inhelder (1958), and Escalona and Heider (1959). More recent noteworthy additions to this holistic view are Soddy and Ahrenfeld (1965), and Levi (1975).

Another way of obtaining a broad view of parenthood is through the use of films which record less selectively than the alphabetical and number symbols picked by the scientific observer to describe an event. Classic films concerning issues in parenthood preserve the behavior for reevaluation and learning in a unique way (Bateson and Mead, 1952a,b,c,e; Fries and Woolf, 1946, 1952; Robertson, 1959; Spitz and Wolf, 1948, 1953a, 1953b). Recent notable additions are Stoney (1968) and Sorenson (1976).

The balance between parenthood and nonparenthood

Although this chapter and the succeeding chapters focus on parental behavior, recognition needs to be made of the fact that the survival of a mammalian species depends not only on the existence of parental behavior but also on the limitation of it. Unlimited fecundity, lactation without weaning and boundless energy expended on cleaning, warming, and protecting the young can, in excess, militate against the health of the parent or the next generation of young.

Both on the biological and cultural levels there are limits. These are biologically enforced through stress reactions which include infertility, reabsorption of the fetus, spontaneous abortion and stillbirth (Wilson, 1975). On the cultural level such limits are set through rules limiting coitus, coitus interruptus, and other contraceptive measures (Newton, 1968). Induced abortion, infanticide, and infant exposure and neglect are also recurrent human patterns.

Basically, survival dictates that the amount of time and energy that is spent on parenting be limited. A corollary is that the time and energy available need careful allotment to maximize efficiency. Herein lies some of the most debated issues in parenthood today. These have been made more intense by the fact that technology has short circuited age-old biological methods of population control and new cultural means have not yet been fully established.

A final word needs to be said about direct and indirect parenting behavior. The utility of altruistic behavior or helping with the well-being and survival with distant sharers of the gene pool has been emphasized by Wilson (1975). Caretaking behavior in a broader sense applies to far greater numbers of individuals than one's own children.

BIBLIOGRAPHY

Ainsworth, M.D.S. (1973) Development of infant-mother attachment. In: (B.M. Caldwell and H.N. Ricciuti, Eds.), *Review of Child Development Research*, Vol. III (University of Chicago Press, Chicago).

Bateson, G. and Mead, M. (1952a) *A Balinese Family.* (Character Formation in Different Cultures Series.) New York University Film Library, New York, 16 mm, 17 min, black and white, sound.

Bateson, G. and Mead, M. (1952b) *Childhood Rivalry in Bali and New Guinea.* (Character Formation in Different Cultures Series.) New York University Film Library, New York, 16 mm, 20 min, black and white, sound.

Bateson, G. and Mead, M. (1952c) *First Days in the Life of a New Guinea Baby.* (Character Formation in Different Cultures Series.) New York University Film Library, New York, 16 mm, 19 min, black and white, sound.

Bateson, G. and Mead, M. (1952d) *Karba's First Years.* (Character Formation in Different Cultures Series.) New York University Film Library, New York, 16 mm, 20 min, black and white, sound.

Bateson, G. and Mead, M. (1952e) *Trance and Dance in Bali.* (Character Formation in Different Cultures Series.) New York University Film Library, New York, 16 mm, 20 min, black and white, sound.

Baxter, S. (1974) Orgasm and labour in primiparae. *J. Psychosom. Res.* 18: 357—360.

Beaglehole, E. and Beaglehole, P. (1938) Ethnology of Pukapuka. *Bernice P. Bishop Mus. Bull. 150.* Honolulu.

Benedek, T. (1946) *Insight and Personality Adjustment.* (Ronald Press, New York.)

Beniest-Noirot, E. (1958) Analyse du comportement dit maternel chez la souris. *Cent. Natl. Rech. Sci. Monogr. Franc. Psychol.* No. 1. [as abstracted in] *Biology of the Laboratory Mouse.* (1966) (E.L. Green, Ed.), 2nd edn. (McGraw-Hill, New York) pp. 633—634.

Bernal, J. and Richards, P.M. (1970) Effect of bottle and breast-feeding on infant development. *J. Psychosom. Res.* 14: 247—252.

Bowlby, J. (1969) *Attachment and Loss: Attachment.* Vol. I. (Basic Books, New York).

Bowlby, J. (1973) *Attachment and Loss: Separation.* Vol. II. (Basic Books, New York).

Bridges, R., Zarrow, M.X., Gandelman, R. and Denenberg, V.H. (1972) Differences in maternal responsiveness between lactating and sensitized rats. *Dev. Psychobiol.* 5: 123—127.

Brodie, P.F. (1969) Duration of lactation in cetacea: an indicator of required learning? *Am. Mid. Nat.* 92: 312.

Debackere, M., Peeters, C. and Tuyttens, N. (1961) Reflex release of an oxytocic hormone by stimulation of genital organs of male and female sheep studied by cross-circulation technique. *J. Endocrinol.* 22: 321—334.

Du Bois, C. (1944) *The People of Alor.* (University of Minnesota Press, Minneapolis.)

Ely, F. and Petersen, W.E. (1941) Factors involved in the ejection of milk. *J. Dairy Sci.* 24: 211—223.

Escalona, S. and Heider, C.M. (1959) *Prediction and Outcome.* (Basic Books, New York.)

Ford, C.S. (1945) *A Comparative Study of Human Reproduction.* (Yale University Publ. Anthropol., No. 32, New Haven.)

Fries, M. and Woolf, P. (1946) *A Character Neurosis with Depressive and Compulsive Trends in the Making: Life History of Mary from Birth to Fifteen Years.* (Studies on Integrated Development: Interaction between Child and Environment.) New York Film Library, New York, 16 mm, 40 min, black and white, silent.

Fries, M. and Woolf, P.J. (1952) *Anna N.: Life History from Birth to Fifteen Years.* (Studies on Integrative Development: Interaction between Child and Development.) New York University Film Library, New York, 16 mm, 60 min, black and white, silent.

Gandelman, R., Zarrow, M.X. and Denenberg, V.H. (1970) Maternal behavior: differences between mother and virgin mice as a function of testing procedure. *Dev. Psychobiol.* 3: 207—214.

Gorer, G. (1955) *Exploring English Character.* (Cresset Press, London.)

Granqvist, H. (1947) *Birth and Childhood Among the Arabs: Studies in a Muhammadan Village in Palestine.* (Suderstrom, Helsinfors.)

Holmberg, A.R. (1950) *Nomads of the Long Bow: The Siriono of Eastern Bolivia.* (Publ. No. 10, Smithsonian Institute, Institute of Social Anthropology, Washington.)

Klaus, M.H., Jerauld, R., Kreger, N.C., McAlpine, W., Steffa, M. and Kennell, J.H. (1972) Maternal attachment: importance of the first postpartum days. *New Engl. J. Med.* 286: 460—463.

Levi, L. (Ed.) (1975) *Society, Stress and Disease. Vol. II Childhood and Adolescence.* (Oxford University Press, London.)

Mead, M. (1928) *Coming of Age in Samoa.* (William Morrow, New York.)

Mead, M. (1930) *Growing up in New Guinea.* (William Morrow, New York.)

Mead, M. (1935) *Sex and Temperament in Three Primitive Societies.* (William Morrow, New York.)

Mead, M. (1949) *Male and Female.* (William Morrow, New York.)

Mead, M. (1961) Cultural determinants of sexual behavior. In: (W.C. Young, Ed.), *Sex and Internal Secretions,* 3rd edn, Vol. 2 (Williams and Wilkins, Baltimore) pp. 1433—1479.

Mead, M. (1974) Adolescence in a changing world. *UNICEF News* 79: 3—11.

Mead, M. and Newton, N. (1967) Cultural patterning of perinatal behavior. In: (S.A. Richardson and A.F. Guttmacher, Eds.), *Childbearing: Its Social and Psychological Aspects,* (Williams and Wilkins, Baltimore) pp. 142—244.

Newton, M. and Newton, N. (1948) The let-down reflex in human lactation. *J. Pediatr.* 33: 693—704.

Newton, N. (1955) *Maternal Emotions: A Study of Women's Feeling Toward Menstruation, Pregnancy, Childbirth, Breast Feeding, Infant Care, and Other Aspects of Their Femininity.* (Hoeber, New York.)

Newton, N. (1968) Population limitation in cross-cultural perspective: 1. Patterns of contraception. *Lying In: J. Reprod. Med.* 1: 343—354.

Newton, N. (1971) Psychological differences between breast and bottle feeding. In: (D.B. Jelliffe, Ed.), *Symposium on uniqueness of human milk. Am. J. Clin. Nut.* 24: 993—1004.

Newton, N. (1973) Inter-relationships between sexual responsiveness, birth and breast feeding behavior. In: (J. Zubin and J. Money, Eds.), *Critical Issues in Contemporary Sexual Behavior,* (Johns Hopkins Press, Baltimore) pp. 77—98.

Newton, N., Foshee, D. and Newton, M. (1966a) Experimental inhibition of labor through environmental disturbance. *Obstet. Gynecol.* 27: 371—377.

Newton, N., Foshee, D. and Newton, M. (1966b) Parturient mice: effects of environment on labor. *Science* 151: 1560—1561.

Newton, N. and Newton, M. (1950) Relation of the let-down reflex to the ability to breast feed. *Pediatrics* 5: 726—733.

Newton, N. and Newton, M. (1967) Psychologic aspects of lactation. *New Engl. J. Med.* 277: 1179—1188.

Newton, N., Paschall, N., Melamed, A. and Ryan, E. (1975) Psychological and behavioral correlates of mother's choice of postpartum nearness to infant. *The Family: 4th Int. Congr. Psychosom. Obstet. Gynecol.* Tel Aviv, 1974 (Karger, Basle) pp. 389—393.

Newton, N., Peeler, D. and Newton, M. (1968a) The effects of disturbance on labor: an experiment using one hundred mice with dated pregnancies. *Am. J. Obstet. Gynecol.* 101: 1096—1102.

Newton, N., Peeler, D. and Rawlins, C. (1968b) Effect of lactation on maternal behavior in mice with comparative data on humans. *Lying In: J. Reprod. Med.* 1: 257—262.

Nissen, W.H. (1930) A study of maternal behavior in the white rat by means of the obstruction method. *J. Genet. Psychol.* 37: 377—393.

Nováková, V. (1966) Weaning of young rats: effect of time on behavior. *Science* 151: 475—476.

Richards, M.P.M. (1966) Maternal behavior in the golden hamster: responsiveness to young in virgin, pregnant and lactating females. *Anim. Behav.* 14: 310—313.

Robertson, J. (1959) *A Two-Year Old Goes to the Hospital.* Tavistock Clinic, London, 16 mm, 60 min, black and white, sound.

Rorie, D.K. and Newton, M. (1964) Oxytocic factors in the plasma of the human male. *Fertil. Steril.* 15: 135—142.

Rosa, F.W. (1975) Breast-feeding in family planning. *PAG Bull.* 5 (3) pp. 5—10.

Ross, S., Sawin, P., Zarrow, M.X. and Denenberg, V.H. (1963) Maternal behavior in the rabbit. In: (H.L. Rheinsold, Ed.), *Maternal Behavior in Mammals.* (John Wiley, New York) pp. 94—121.

Ryerson, A.J. (1961) Medical advice on child rearing, 1550—1900. *Harv. Educ. Rev.* 31: 302—323.

Seward, J.P. and Seward, G.H. (1940) Studies on the reproductive activities of the guinea pig: 1. Factors in maternal behavior. *J. Comp. Psychol.* 29: 1—24.

Soddy, K. (Ed.) (1955) *Mental Health and Infant Development,* 2 Vols, (Routledge and Kegan Paul, London).

Soddy, K. and Ahrenfeldt, R.H. (1965) *Mental Health in a Changing World.* (Tavistock, London.)

Sorenson, E.R. (1976) *The Edge of the Forest: Land, Childhood and Change in a New Guinea Proto-Agricultural Society.* (Smithsonian Institute Press, Washington, D.C.) in press.

Spitz, R. and Wolf, K.A. (1948) *The Smiling Response.* New York University Film Library, New York, 16 mm, 22 min, black and white, silent.

Spitz, R. and Wolf, K.A. (1953a) *Grief — A Peril in Infancy.* New York University Film Library, New York, 16 mm, 35 min, black and white, silent.

Spitz, R. and Wolf, K.A. (1953b) *Mother-Child Relations.* New York University Film Library, New York, 16 mm, 22 mm, black and white, silent.

Stoney, G. (1968) *Robin and Peter and Darryl: Three to the Hospital.* Center for Mass Communication, Irvington, 16 mm, 53 min, black and white, sound.

Tanner, J.M. and Inhelder, B. (1958) *Discussions on Child Development,* Vol. 3, (Tavistock, London).

Thoman, E.B., Leiderman, P.H. and Olson, J.P. (1972) Neonate-mother interaction during breast feeding. *Dev. Psychol.* 6: 110—118.

Tichauer, R. (1963) The Aymara children of Bolivia. *J. Pediat.* 62: 399—412.

Weimer, R.E. and Fuller, J.L. (1966) Patterns of behavior. In: *Biology of the Laboratory Mouse,* 2nd edn, (McGraw-Hill, New York) pp. 629—653.

Wilson, E.O. (1975) *Sociobiology.* (Harvard University Press, Cambridge.)

Wolfenstein, M. (1955) Fun morality: an analysis of recent American childtraining literature. In: (M. Mead and M. Wolfenstein, Eds.), *Childhood in Contemporary Cultures,*
(University of Chicago Press, Chicago) pp. 168—178.

Wortis, S.B., Batesen, G., Galt, W.E., Morris, H., Kinsey, A.C. and Young, W.C. (1947)
Physiological and psychological factors in sex behavior. *Ann. N.Y. Acad. Sci.* 47:
604—664.

Zarrow, M.X., Johnson, N.P., Denenberg, V.H. and Bryant, L.P. (1973) Maintenance of
lactation diestrum in the postpartum rat through tactile stimulation in the absence of
suckling. *Neuroendocrinology* 11: 150—155.

CHAPTER 53

Parental behavior in nonprimate mammals [*]

JAY S. ROSENBLATT

1. PATTERNS OF MATERNAL BEHAVIOR

Mammals exhibit a wide variety of patterns of maternal care but these patterns fall into two main classes (Lehrman, 1961; Rheingold, 1963; Rosenblatt, 1967; Ewer, 1968). Among species which produce altricial young (rats, mice, cats and dogs) the mother deposits her helpless young at a site she has established as the home. She remains with them at this site, and exhibits a regular routine of maternal care until the young begin to function independently. In herd and large migratory mammals (such as, sheep, goats, elk and deer) which produce precocial young, the offspring are able to follow the mother within a few days after birth, and except for a brief period after delivery, there is no fixed site to which mother and young return for feeding or other maternal care.

Species with altricial young

In the rat and cat — social and semi-solitary mammals, respectively — there are three periods in the mother—young relationship. The first period is characterized by almost complete dependence of the altricial young on maternal care. The mother initiates nursing, retrieving, anogenital licking, and nest-building or adoption of a home site, in response to stimuli from the young. The second period is characterized by the bilateral initiation of feeding, and by a gradual decline in nestbuilding or attachment to the home site; there is also a reduction in retrieving and in anogenital licking. During this period the young begin to approach the mother to initiate feeding and she assists them by adopting the nursing posture. Moreover, at this time the young begin to leave the nest or home site occasionally but they return shortly afterward.

---

[*] Throughout this chapter the term 'mammals' will be used to refer solely to nonprimate mammals.

Handbook of Sexology, edited by J. Money and H. Musaph
© *Elsevier/North-Holland Biomedical Press, 1977*

They begin to evade the mother's attempts to retrieve them to the nest or home site, and they do not require anogenital licking to eliminate. In the third period the young become even less dependent upon the mother. As they begin to feed themselves from other sources they suckle less from the mother. They no longer remain in the nest or home site and only return to it at times. In many species the young establish other sites where they tend to aggregate for sleeping and resting. The mother no longer retrieves them or licks them to stimulate elimination.

The process of weaning and breaking up of the family group progresses during this third period and at its end the young remain with the mother for only a short time. Their ability to live independently becomes fully established, often aided by food-getting techniques they have learned from the mother. During this last period of mother-young relationship there is a good deal of play and other social activity among the young, and between the young and the mother which contrasts sharply with the behavior exhibited during the period of intense maternal care and more closely resembles the behavior normally seen among juveniles and adults of the species.

Species with precocial young

Among ungulates, maternal behavior and development of the maternal—young relationship is adapted to the more advanced behavioral capacities of the newborn and to the usual grazing and migratory habits of the species. The period from parturition until the resumption of migration is relatively short and the young are soon able to follow the mother for short distances. Among these species, those that are social and live in herds, and those that are solitary and live in small family groups, the following reaction by the young as the mother moves is important to prevent separation of the young from the mother. Moreover, the mother must learn the characteristics of her offspring and recognize it as an individual before they rejoin the herd or mix with other mother—young pairs. The process of mutual attachment between the mother and her young occurs while they are in seclusion following parturition; it occurs rapidly for the mother over the first few hours and particularly during the first few minutes of postpartum licking of the newborn. In the offspring the process is more gradual but by the time the mother and young rejoin the herd it has advanced sufficiently for the young to recognize their own mothers, to follow them and to return to them for nursing.

2. BEHAVIORAL INTERACTIONS BETWEEN MOTHER AND YOUNG

Nursing

The actual behavior which occurs in the interaction of the mother with her young during the performance of maternal care varies considerably among different mammalian species and can only be understood with reference to the natural history of the species. For example among marsupials (Russell, 1973) the newborn attach to nipples within the pouch shortly after emerging and remain attached continuously for more than 9 months in some species. Among rats and other small rodent species, nursing is periodic but occurs at frequent intervals (several times an hour), while in the rabbit nursing occurs only once each day then only for a short period of 3 to 5 min. In tree shrews nursing occurs only briefly on alternate days, at 48-h intervals. The fur seal mother nurses her young frequently during the first week postpartum while she remains with them but then she begins to go to sea for long periods and the young are not nursed for intervals of 5 to 8 days while the mother is at sea.

Among ungulates in which the young can follow the mother while she feeds, nursing behavior is more uniform among different species and occurs at regular intervals. Espmark (1969) describes 4 to 6 maternal care periods per day as typical in the Roe deer during the first 40 days postpartum, increasing in duration from 20 min to nearly an hour over this period. During each care period the young nurse as frequencly as 6 times, soon after parturition but this declines to twice each care period at the end of the first month.

Retrieving

Retrieving in species with altricial young also varies among different species. It is absent in the rabbit where it is unlikely that the young will ever be found outside the burrow nest except at parturition — during which time they are often cannibalized by the mother rather than retrieved (Ross et al., 1963). Rats, mice, hamsters and many other rodents readily retrieve young that are outside the nest by picking them up in the mouth and carrying them back to the nest (Ewer, 1968). Among marsupial 'mice' the mother retrieves her young by lowering her body over them and allowing them to grasp her fur then she drags them back to the nest (Beach, 1939). Among kangaroos and other pouched marsupials the mother allows the young to reenter the pouch after they have left it and in this sense she retrieves them. In the streaked tenrec, an insectivore, the mother retrieves younger pups, but with older pups she employs her stridulating organ to produce a sound which enables the young to find her and return to her. Often she leads them back to the nest after they have returned to her (Eisenberg and Gould, 1970).

Among ungulates the mother herself serves as the 'home site' after the parturition site is abandoned soon after delivery. She 'retrieves' her young to her by sound and movement signals to which the young respond by returning to her side. The fur seal, upon returning to the rookery, exhibits an unique pattern of retrieval of her offspring whom she may not have seen for a week while she was at sea. She goes to the parturition site and there emits a loud highly individually distinct call to which all of the young, including her own, who has remained in the vicinity of its place of birth and early care, respond by approaching her. The mother then sniffs the pups' noses and she may reject more than 15 alien pups before she finds and accepts her own off-spring (Bartholomew, 1959). Obviously, in this species, the offspring are marked by an odor which is individually characteristic and which enables the mother to recognize her own young.

Nestbuilding and establishment of a home site

Nestbuilding and establishment of a home site are extremely varied among the mammals; they consist of nests built partially by plucking fur from the body as in the rabbit to the minimal activity of simply clearing a secluded area in the woods which is seen among elk (Altmann, 1963). Nestbuilding is, however, distinguished from other maternal behavior by being less immediate-ly depend upon stimulation from the young than on aspects of maternal be havior which are directed at the young themselves and more directly depen-dent upon the internal state of the mother. This is shown by the fact that in most species of mammals nestbuilding begins before the young are born and it is often completed when the young arrive. After the young appear they play a role in maintaining the mother's tendency to repair the nest or rebuild it since in the rat and several other small rodents, removal of the young after birth results in the gradual decline of nest repair by the mother.

Licking

Licking of the young is one of the most widespread forms of maternal be-havior among mammals and it is perhaps the earliest that appears in the mother—infant interaction. In many species it is the mother's first response to her newborn during delivery when it aids in removing the birth mem-branes and initiating respiration (Schneirla et al., 1963); it is obviously per-formed in response to the presence of birth fluids on the newborn and as an extension of the mother's licking of her own genital region during delivery (Rowell, 1961).

Defense of young

Equally varied among different mammals, and equally widespread, is some form of defense of the offspring, a behavior we have not yet included in maternal care. This varies from aggressive attack against any animal that in-trudes upon the nest or home site as found among rats and mice, to evasive actions that lead predators away from the nest, as seen among deer, elk and other ungulates, and a most unique behavior, found among tree shrews, in which the mother deposits an odor on the young, shortly after birth, which serves to repel males and, presumably, other predators, while she is away from the nest.

3. STIMULUS INTERACTIONS BETWEEN MOTHER AND YOUNG

Rodents

The behavioral interactions described above imply that there are stimulus interactions between the mother and her offspring which elicit maternal care and which affect the motivational condition of the mother. The responses of mothers to stimuli from their offspring have been studied in greater detail among rodents than in any other mammals. In those species (such as rats, mice and hamsters), the young produce ultrasonic vocalizations and these have been found to play an important role in eliciting maternal retrieving and nestbuilding (Zippelius and Schleidt, 1956; Noirot, 1972a). It has recently been shown, in fact, that maternal mice respond differently to the ultrasonic vocalizations that are emitted by pups when they are cold as compared to those emitted when pups are handled. They show nestbuilding behavior in response to the former vocalizations and chewing of nest material as well as retrieving in response to the latter (Noirot, 1972b, 1974). Licking and nursing behavior are performed in response to tactile and olfactory stimuli, among mice and probably among rats and other small mammals. In the cat retrieving is elicited by audible vocalizations from the kittens, and nursing and licking appear to be in response to olfactory and tactile stimuli, although visual stimuli cannot be ruled out in any of these forms of behavior.

It is likely that stimuli from the pups act in combination to elicit the appropriate maternal behavior — what Beach and Jaynes (1956) have labelled 'multisensory control' of maternal behavior. Eliminating any one sensory system (for example, vision or olfaction) does not block maternal behavior in lactating rats but eliminating two or more often prevents females from retrieving pups. Recently it has been shown that even ultrasonic vocalizations are more effective in eliciting retrieving in mice and rats if they are combined with olfactory stimuli from the pups. The olfactory stimuli arouse the females to retrieve while the ultrasonic vocalizations enable them to locate the pups (Smotherman et al., 1974).

A change in a female's responsiveness to stimuli from pups between the time she is undergoing estrous cycling and the time she gives birth must constitute an important aspect of what is referred to as maternal responsiveness. Among rats, nonpregnant females act differently towards a single pup than toward a small plastic toy. They approach and lick the former and bite the latter (Rosenblatt, 1975a), but when they are presented with a group of pups they show clear evidence of avoidance after sniffing the pups (Terkel and Rosenblatt, 1971). The odors of pups to a female that has not been pregnant and given birth appear to be distasteful since, if nonpregnant females are prevented from smelling the pups by being made partially anosmic with intranasal infusion of zinc sulfate or completely anosmic by sectioning of the olfactory tracts, they show no avoidance of pups and in fact exhibit maternal behavior after a few hours of exposure to them (Fleming and Rosenblatt, 1974b). Nonpregnant and nonlactating mice show a similar avoidance response to pups after sniffing them (Noirot, 1972b). After parturition, however, maternal rats and mice appear to be stimulated by the odors of the newborn to exhibit maternal behavior. To explain this change in the female's behavior it has been suggested either that the olfactory system is affected by hormones during pregnancy so that what was a distasteful stimulus becomes an attractive one, or the pups odors are masked at parturition by odors from the birth fluids to which females have become adapted during pregnancy as a result of licking the same fluids around the genital region, to which they respond positively (Birch, 1956).

Ungulates

Odors and perhaps taste play an important role in the maternal responsiveness of goats and sheep toward their newborn immediately after parturition (Hersher et al., 1963; Klopfer, 1971). Mothers that are not permitted to lick their newborn at parturition show a rapid loss of responsiveness to all kids or lambs; if they are permitted to lick their newborn for a brief period, they retain their responsiveness but they are not selectively responsive to their own offspring alone. Given a longer period of licking their newborn they retain their responsiveness and in addition they become selectively responsive to their own young, which is characteristic of these species. Various studies with these two species have shown the importance of early postpartum licking of the newborn for maternal responsiveness but these studies also indicate that by itself this early licking cannot sustain maternal responsiveness. Additional contact of a varied sort that may include nursing is also required to sustain maternal responsiveness and if females are separated from their offspring too soon after birth, even though the separation may be for only a few hours, there is the danger that upon its return to the mother, the offspring will not be accepted but will be butted away.

Observations suggest that mutual calling between the mother and offspring among many ungulate species plays an important role in the elicitation of maternal care (Espmark, 1971) but the mother also responds to olfactory stimuli and, like the fur seal, identifies her own offspring by its odor. During nursing tactile stimuli play an important role both in positioning the mother for nipple attachment and during sucking in inducing let-down of milk and further milk production. Visual interaction between the mother and young are very important in these largely visual animals: the mother looks to see if her young is nearby and if it is following her when she begins to move with the herd.

4. LACTATION AND MATERNAL BEHAVIOR

Lactation as basis for maternal behavior

Milk production and secretion are important features of maternal care among all mammals. It was formerly believed that intramammary pressure created by accumulated milk served as a drive stimulus for the performance of nursing behavior and even, perhaps, for maternal behavior as a whole. This has now been shown not to be the case since postpartum rats without mammary glands exhibit all features of maternal behavior including 'nursing' behavior (Moltz et al., 1967). Moreover, virgin rats and mice (including males of both species) exhibit maternal behavior, even though there mammary glands are undeveloped. In the rabbit where nursing occurs only once a day it is not emptying of the gland which counts as a nursing stimulus to the mother but rather the experience of nursing her young; and, if females are nursed while they are under an anesthetic, they will return to nurse again when they recover from the anesthetic even though their mammary glands contain very little milk (Findlay, 1970). It is not yet clear, however, whether the accumulation of milk in the mammary glands over 24 h does play some role in initiating nursing.

Stimulus basis of mammary gland development and lactation

Lactation is dependent upon suckling stimulation both for the production of milk, via the release of prolactin, adrenocortical and other hormones, and the release of milk from the alveolar and milk ducts, via oxytocin release and mechanical pressure (Cross and Harris, 1952). The relationship between lactation and maternal nursing, in the course of which pups apply suckling stimulation having the above effects, is therefore opposite to that which was proposed in the early days of the study of maternal behavior: lactation is dependent upon maternal behavior, rather than the reverse.

Self-licking during pregnancy

In the rat the relationship between nipple stimulation and lactation begins during pregnancy as shown by the effects which self-licking has upon mammary gland development (Roth and Rosenblatt, 1967, 1968). Pregnant females deprived of the opportunity to lick their nipples and genital region (by wide rubber collars worn around the neck) show poorly developed mammary glands that contain only 50% of the normal amount of milk secretory tissue and milk production (McMurtry and Anderson, 1971). The effective stimulus for the nipples is mechanical stimulation which is normally provided by self-licking, but which can be effectively imitated by stroking with soft brushes (Herrenkohl and Pfizenmaier-Campbell, 1976). Genital licking alone is as effective as nipple-licking in stimulating gland development during pregnancy (Whitworth, 1972).

Exteroceptive stimulation of lactation

After parturition suckling substitutes for self-licking and lactation is maintained. As maternal behavior continues, however, it has been shown that suckling need not occur for prolactin to be released and lactation to be maintained, at least for short periods. Stimuli from the pups, other than suckling itself, become capable of causing the release of lactation-producing hormones from the anterior pituitary gland (prolactin, ACTH, TSH and others) around the 14th day postpartum in nulliparous rats and by the 7th day in primiparous rats (Grosvenor and Mena, 1974). In rats, olfaction appears to be the most effective route through which the exteroceptive control of lactation is exerted in this way.

Decline of lactation

The stimulus control of lactation appears to change once again towards the end of the mother—young relationship. In part this results from the decrease in suckling by the young, which alters the responsiveness of the neuroendocrine mechanism underlying pituitary release of milk-producing hormones. There is an additional factor, however, which may prove even more important in this respect: the pups begin to exert an inhibitory effect on lactation. Although they continue to stimulate the release of lactation-promoting hormones they also inhibit the action of these hormones on the mammary gland (Grosvenor and Mena, 1974).

The relationship between lactation and maternal behavior has only been explored in depth among rodents. There is sufficient information from other species, however, to indicate that this relationship may vary with respect to underlying neuroendocrine mechanisms, the hormones involved, and the stimuli that are effective in different species.

5. HORMONAL BASIS OF MATERNAL BEHAVIOR

The hormonal basis of maternal behavior has been explored in only a small number of mammalian species confined entirely to rodents and lagomorphs. These studies have been based upon the justified assumption that since maternal behavior begins around parturition the hormones which stimulate it are likely to be those which are secreted at the termination of pregnancy. However, since hormone secretion at the end of pregnancy is not uniform among all mammals (Perry, 1972) it is unlikely that the hormones found effective in rodents and lagomorphs are likely to be the same ones that are effective in species with different patterns of endocrine secretion at the end of pregnancy.

Rabbit, mouse and hamster

In the rabbit, estrogen, progesterone and prolactin have been found to stimulate hair loosening and nestbuilding when given to females whose own ovaries and in some instances, pituitary glands, were removed. Hormones were administered according to a schedule which resembles the rise in estrogen and prolactin secretion and the decline in progesterone secretion which normally occurs just before parturition on the 32nd day after mating (Zarrow et al, 1971).

In the mouse, maternal nestbuilding begins around the 5th day of pregnancy (which lasts 19 days) when progesterone secretion increases. Lisk (1971) found that a combination of estrogen and progesterone given to ovariectomized females stimulated a similar increase in nestbuilding. The other components of maternal behavior (retrieving, 'nursing', and licking pups as well as nestbuilding) can be elicited from nonpregnant females simply by exposing them to young pups. Therefore it is difficult to study the hormonal induction of these maternal behaviors. However, Voci and Carlson (1973) found that prolactin implanted in the brain of a female mouse enhanced the maternal behavior exhibited to young pups.

The hamster has a short gestation period of 16 days and at the end there is a decline in both estrogen and progesterone concentrations in the blood when the female initiates nestbuilding and other maternal behavior at parturition. Richards (1969) was able to induce nestbuilding with subcutaneous implants of estrogen and progesterone pellets (with the possibility that prolactin was secreted endogenously) but the other components of maternal behavior were not exhibited.

Rat

Hormonal basis for the onset of maternal behavior

The rat has received the greatest amount of study with regard to the hormonal basis of maternal behavior. Gestation lasts 22—23 days and at the end of gestation there is a decline in the secretion of progesterone and a rise in both estrogen and prolactin secretion. By imitating this pattern of hormonal changes at the end of a prolonged period of estrogen and progesterone treatment (12—22 days; Moltz et al., 1970; Zarrow et al., 1971) all components of maternal behavior, not only nestbuilding, were elicited with short latencies of about 30—40 h in ovariectomized females.

Several studies by Terkel and Rosenblatt (1968, 1972) indicated, however, that a short period of exchange of blood between a new mother and a nonpregnant female was sufficient to induce maternal behavior in nonpregnant females. This led to a search for a hormone treatment of short duration that would be as effective as the hormone treatment of long duration described above. This has resulted in the discovery that a single injection of estrogen given to nonpregnant females that have been ovariectomized and hysterectomized can elicit maternal behavior in 24—48 h (Siegel and Rosenblatt, 1975).

Removal of the uterus, found to be necessary for the estrogen to be effective, poses two problems: what role does the presence of the uterus play in preventing the action of estrogen on maternal behavior, and, what happens to the uterus during later stages of pregnancy that enables estrogen to act without interference?

While estrogen elicits maternal behavior under the conditions described above we cannot conclude that it does so alone. Estrogen normally causes the release of prolactin from the pituitary gland, and it may be that both hormones are required to stimulate maternal behavior. One study showed that this is not the case (Zarrow et al., 1971) but further study is necessary before any conclusions can be drawn about the role of prolactin in the onset of maternal behavior.

Nonhormonal basis of maternal behavior
Although maternal behavior in the rat is normally stimulated by hormones shortly before parturition, it has been possible to elicit maternal behavior from nonpregnant females under conditions in which one can be fairly certain that hormones are not involved (Cosnier and Couturier, 1966; Rosenblatt, 1967). This is especially true among mice which exhibit maternal behavior within a few minutes of their exposure to pups (Noirot, 1972b). A longer period of exposure to pups is required for rats to exhibit maternal behavior which may vary from 2 days in small cages to 5—6 days in large cages (Terkel and Rosenblatt, 1971). The maternal behavior exhibited by nonpregnant females closely resembles the maternal behavior of lactating mothers, except, of course, for the lack of milk secretion; when such females are given foster pups of the same ages as those which lactating mothers are rearing, their behavior toward the pups at corresponding ages is hardly distinguishable from that of the lactating mothers. They act maternally towards them until the pups reach 14—18 days of age then they gradually decline in maternal behavior and withdrawal and rejection behaviors set in (Fleming and Rosenblatt, 1974b; Reisbick et al., 1975).

Relationship between hormonal and nonhormonal regulation of maternal behavior
There is no occasion under natural conditions when maternal behavior, nonhormonally induced, as described above, would play an exclusive role in inducing the onset of maternal behavior: pups could not survive during the period when the female was becoming maternal and, furthermore, such females do not lactate. Yet this behavior must bear some relationship to the normal behavior of the rat mother.

There is evidence that after hormones have acted to stimulate the onset of maternal behavior in the rat, they no longer play a role in the maintenance and decline of maternal behavior (Rosenblatt, 1975b). The pups themselves provide the stimulation which maintains maternal behavior and later causes it to decline. If pups are removed from lactating mothers shortly after delivery, there is a steady decline in maternal behavior over the next four days, after which it disappears (Rosenblatt, 1965).

This means that the regulation of maternal behavior changes around parturition from an hormonal mechanism to a nonhormonal mechanism. As the hormonal mechanism declines the nonhormonal mechanism becomes more firmly established, based upon the mother's contact with her offspring during which she receives the stimulation necessary to maintain her maternal behavior. Under most circumstances the transition between these two mechanisms or phases in the regulation of maternal behavior occurs smoothly and there is no outward sign that it is occurring. However it becomes apparent when contact between the mother and her young is subject to interference or when the mother is exposed to stressful outside influences, as frequently occurs in overcrowded populations of rats when the mother has to contend with intruders that evoke her aggressive behavior and often force her to interrupt her maternal behavior toward her pups. When rat mothers abandon their young or cannibalize them, it is almost always within the first three days after parturition; if the young survive the first three days they are likely to be reared to weaning because maternal behavior is less vulnerable to disruption once it has undergone the transition from hormonal to nonhormonal regulation. It is, however, most vulnerable to interference during this transition.

Generality of findings on the regulation of maternal behavior in the rat
As indicated earlier, one cannot generalize from the rat with respect to the hormonal basis of maternal behavior in other mammals. However, it may be possible to find that the transition from hormonal to nonhormonal regulation (based upon stimulation from offspring) of maternal behavior is a general phenomenon. Russell and Giles (1974) report that pouch cleaning, a particularly maternal activity in the Tammar wallaby which increases when the young climb into the pouch at birth, is dependent upon the presence of young for its maintenance. In the mouse there is a significant rise in nestbuilding after parturition which is maintained even after removal of the pituitary gland (Leblond, 1940). Among sheep and goats an early period of continuous contact with the young, immediately postpartum, is necessary for maternal behavior to be established, if it is interrupted by removing the young for several hours, maternal behavior appears to wane. In almost all species, even those in which mothers leave their offspring for prolonged periods as, for example, in the fur seal, the mother spends some period immediately postpartum in close contact with her young and this appears to be sufficient to subsequently maintain her maternal behavior toward them even during her long periods at sea when she does not receive stimulation from them. Species may differ in the rate at which hormonally stimulated maternal behavior wanes postpartum, and in the rate at which nonhormonally based maternal behavior is established. Moreover, depending on their species, mothers may require different kinds of stimulation to maintain maternal behavior postpartum, but a shift in the regulation of maternal behavior around parturition may be a general phenomenon in the organization of maternal behavior among mammals.

6. SUMMARY

Though patterns of parental behavior among nonprimate mammals vary according to the natural habits of the species, there are two broad patterns: species with altricial young, like the rat and mouse, have prolonged periods of maternal care that last until the young become capable of independent functioning. Species with precocial young like the goat and sheep, have a short period of maternal care during which time the young follow the mother as she moves with the herd or forages for food. Species with altricial young have a wider repertoire of maternal behavior, consisting of nursing, retrieving, nestbuilding, licking and defense of the young than do species with precocial young, which exhibit mainly nursing and defense of the young. The actual behavioral interactions comprising maternal care are extremely varied in different species. Similarly the stimuli which mediate interactions between mother and young vary in different species: among rodents tactile, olfactory, and ultrasonic vocalizations are important, while among ungulates, olfactory, auditory and visual stimuli are important. Lactation is closely related to maternal behavior and is dependent upon it for its maintenance. The stimulus regulation of lactation changes during the reproductive cycle from gestation through weaning.

The hormonal basis of nestbuilding varies among rabbits, mice, and hamsters; other aspects of maternal behavior have not been elicited by hormone intervention in these species. In the rat the hormonal basis of the onset of maternal behavior appears to be either estrogen or estrogen and prolactin. Postpartum maternal behavior is maintained by pup stimulation, and is nonhormonal. The decline of maternal behavior appears also not to be hormonal (but pup-stimulated). Shortly after parturition there is a transition from hormonal to nonhormonal regulation of maternal behavior in the rat. During this transition period the effects of hormonal stimulation wane, while the effects of pup stimulation increase. This is a vulnerable period in the maternal behavior cycle of the rat. It may be a general phenomenon among nonprimate mammals that there is a shift in the regulation of maternal behavior around parturition.

ACKNOWLEDGEMENT

This writing of this article and the research reported from the author's laboratory were supported by National Institute of Mental Health Research Grant MH 08604. Publication number 206 of the Institute of Animal Behavior, Rutgers — The State University.

BIBLIOGRAPHY

Altman, M. (1963) Naturalistic studies of maternal care in moose and elk. In: (H.L. Rheingold, Ed.), *Maternal Behavior in Mammals.* (Wiley, New York) pp. 203—253.

Bartholomew, G.A. (1959) Mother-young relations and the maturation of pup behaviour in the Alaska fur seal. *Anim. Behav.* 7: 163—171.

Beach, F.A. (1939) Maternal behavior of the pouchless marsupial Marmosa cinerea. *J. Mammal.* 20: 315—322.

Beach, F.A. and Jaynes, J. (1956) Studies of maternal retrieving in rats. III. Sensory cues involved in the lactating female's response to her young. *Behaviour* 10: 104—125.

Birch, H.G. (1956) Sources of order in the maternal behavior of animals. *Am. J. Orthopsychiat.* 26: 279—284.

Cross, B.A. and Harris, G.W. (1952) The role of the neurohypophysis in the milk-ejection reflex. *J. Endocrinol.* 8: 148—161.

Eisenberg, J.F. and Gould, E. (1070) *The Tenrecs: A Study in Mammalian Behavior and Evolution.* Smithsonian Contributions to Zoology, No. 27 (Smithsonian Institution Press, Washington, D.C.).

Espmark, Y. (1969) Mother-young relations and development of behaviour in Roe deer. *Viltevy (Swedish Wildlife)* 6: 461—540.

Espmark, Y. (1971) Individual recognition by voice in reindeer mother-young relationship. Field observations and playback experiments. *Behaviour* 40: 295—301.

Ewer, R.F. (1968) *Ethology of Mammals.* (Plenum Press, New York.)

Findlay, A.L.R. (1970) Nursing behavior and the condition of the mammary gland in the rabbit. *J. Comp. Physiol. Psychol.* 69: 115—118.

Fleming, A.S. and Rosenblatt, J.S. (1974a) Olfactory regulation of maternal behavior in rats: II. Effects of peripherally induced anosmia and lesions of the lateral olfactory tract in pup-induced virgins. *J. Comp. Physiol. Psychol.* 86: 233—246.

Fleming, A.S. and Rosenblatt, J.S. (1974b) Maternal behavior in the lactating and virgin female rat. *J. Comp. Physiol. Psychol.* 86— 957—972.

Grosvenor, C.E. and Mena, F. (1974) Neural and hormonal control of milk secretion and milk ejection. *Lactation, Volume 1 The Mammary Gland: Development and Maintenance*, (Academic Press, New York) pp. 227—276.

Herrenkohl, L.R. and Pfizenmaier-Campbell, C. (1976) Mechanical stimulation of mammary gland development in virgin and pregnant rats. *Horm. Behav.* (In press).

Hersher, L., Richmond, J.B. and Moore, A.U. (1963) Maternal behavior in sheep and goats. In. (II.L. Rheingold, Ed.), *Maternal Behavior in Mammals.* (Wiley, New York) pp. 203—232.

Klopfer, P.H. (1971) Mother love: what turns it on? *Am. Sci.* 59: 404—407.

Leblond, C.P. (1940) Nervous and hormonal factors in the maternal behavior of the mouse. *J. Genet. Psychol.* 57: 327—344.

Lehrman, D.S. (1961) Hormonal regulation of parental behavior in birds and infrahuman mammals. In: (W.C. Young, Ed.), *Sex and Internal Secretions*, 3rd edn, (Williams and Wilkins, Baltimore) pp. 1268—1382.

Lisk, R.D. (1971) Oestrogen and progresterone synergism and elicitation of maternal nestbuilding in the mouse (*Mus musculus*). *Anim. Behav.* 19: 606—610.

McMurtry, J.P. and Anderson, R.R. (1971) Prevention of self-licking on mammary gland development in pregnant rats. *Proc. Soc. Exp. Biol. Med.* 137: 354—356.

Moltz, H., Geller, D. and Levin, R. (1967) Maternal behavior in the totally mammectomized rat. *J. Comp. Physiol. Psychol.* 64: 225—229.

Moltz, H., Lubin, M., Leon, M. and Numan, M. (1970) Hormonal induction of maternal behavior in the ovariectomized nulliparous rat. *Physiol. Behav.* 5: 1373—1377.

Noirot, E. (1972a) Ultrasounds and maternal behavior in small rodents. *Dev. Psychobiol.* 5: 371—387.

Noirot, E. (1972b) The onset of maternal behavior in rats, hamsters and mice: A selective review. In: (D.S. Lehrman, R.A. Hinde and E. Shaw, Eds.) *Advances in the Study of Behavior*, Vol. 4 (Academic Press, New York) pp. 107—145.

Noirot, E. (1974) Nest-building by the virgin female mouse exposed to ultrasound from inaccessible pups. *Anim. Behav.* 22: 410—420.

Perry, J.S. (1972) *Control of Parturition.* Proc. XIth Symp. Soc. Stud. Fertil., Nottingham, July 1971. *J. Reprod. Fertil.,* suppl. 16, (Blackwell Scientific Publications, London).

Reisbick, S., Rosenblatt, J.S. and Mayer, A.B. (1975) Decline of maternal behavior in the virgin and lactating rat. *J. Comp. Physiol. Psychol.* 89: 722—732.

Rheingold, H. (1963) *Maternal Behavior in Mammals.* (Wiley, New York.)

Richards, M.P.M. (1969) Effects of oestrogen and progesterone on nest building in the golden hamster. *Anim. Behav.* 17: 356—361.

Rosenblatt, J.S. (1965) The basis of synchrony in the behavioral interaction between the mother and her offspring in the laboratory rat. In: (B.M. Foss, Ed.), *Determinants of Infant Behaviour III.* (Methuen, London) pp. 3—41.

Rosenblatt, J.S. (1967) Nonhormonal basis of maternal behavior in the rat. *Science* 156: 1512—1514.

Rosenblatt, J.S. (1975a) Selective retrieving by maternal and nonmaternal female rats. *J. Comp. Physiol. Psychol.* 88: 678—686.

Rosenblatt, J.S. (1975b) Prepartum and postpartum regulation of maternal behavior in the rat. In: *Parent—Infant Interaction.* Ciba Foundat. Symp. 33, 17—37.

Ross, S., Sawin, P.B., Zarrow, M.X. and Denenberg, V.H. (1963) Maternal behavior in the rabbit. In: (H.L. Rheingold, Ed.), *Maternal Behavior in Mammals.* (Wiley, New York) pp. 94—121.

Roth, L.L. and Rosenblatt, J.S. (1967) Changes in self-licking during pregnancy in the rat. *J. Comp. Physiol. Psychol.* 63: 397—400.

Roth, L.L. and Rosenblatt, J.S. (1968) Self-licking and mammary development during pregnancy in the rat. *J. Endocrinol.* 42: 363—378.

Rowell, T.E. (1961) The family group in the golden hamster: its formation and break-up. *Behaviour* 17: 83—94.

Russell, E.M. (1973) Mother-young relations and early behavioural development in the marsupials Macropus eugenii and Megaleia rufa. *Z. Tierpsychol.* 33: 163—203.

Russell, E.M. and Giles, D.C. (1974) The effects of young in the pouch on pouch cleaning in the Tammar wallaby, Macropus eugenii Desmarest (Marsupiala). *Behaviour* 51: 19—37.

Siegel, H.I. and Rosenblatt, J.S. (1975) Estrogen-induced maternal behavior in hysterectomized-ovariectomized virgin rats. *Physiol. Behav.* 14: 465—471.

Schneirla, T.C., Rosenblatt, J.S. and Tobach, E. (1963) Maternal behavior in the cat. In: (H.L. Rheingold, Ed.), *Maternal Behavior in Mammals,* (Wiley, New York) pp. 122—168.

Smotherman, W.P., Bell, R.W., Starzec, J. and Elias, J. (1974) Maternal responses to infant vocalizations and olfactory cues in rats and mice. *Behav. Biol.* 12: 55—66.

Terkel, J. and Rosenblatt, J.S. (1968) Maternal behavior induced by maternal blood plasma injected into virgin rats. *J. Comp. Physiol. Psychol.* 65: 479—482.

Terkel, J. and Rosenblatt, J.S. (1971) Aspects of nonhormonal maternal behavior in the rat. *Horm. Behav.* 2: 161—171.

Terkel, J. and Rosenblatt, J.S. (1972) Humoral factors underlying maternal behavior at parturition: cross transfusion between freely moving rats. *J. Comp. Physiol. Psychol.* 80: 365—371.

Voci, V.E. and Carlson, N.R. (1973) Enhancement of maternal behavior and nestbuilding following systemic and diencephalic administration of prolactin and progesterone in the mouse. *J. Comp. Physiol.* 83: 388—393.

Whitworth, N. (1972) *Relationships between Patterns of Grooming, Endocrine Function and Mammary Gland Development in the Pregnant Rat.* (Unpublished doctoral dissertation, Rutgers University.)

Zarrow, M.S., Gandelman, R. and Denenberg, V.H. (1971) Prolactin: Is it an essential hormone for maternal behavior in the mammal? *Horm. Behav.* 2: 343—354.

Zippelius, H.M. and Schleidt, W.H. (1956) Ultraschall-laute bei jungen mausen. *Naturwissenschaften* 43: 508.

CHAPTER 54

Parental behavior in nonhuman primates

G. MITCHELL

1. INTRODUCTION

The more than 200 species of nonhuman primates display a variety of male and female parental behavior. For example, the mother tree shrew (a borderline form between insectivores and primates) directs very little care toward her two newborn infants, nursing her infants only once every 48 h (Martin, 1966). At the other extreme are female chimpanzees which display nurturant behavior toward their young throughout several years of their infancy and into their adulthood.

With regard to adult male care the male rhesus monkey (*Macaca mulatta*) is described as being generally indifferent and/or hostile toward young infants much of the time. At the other extreme, the male titi monkey (*Callicebus moloch*) holds and carries the infant at virtually all times except when it is being nursed. When nursing terminates, the infant titi monkey climbs to the mother's shoulders, from which it moves to the male or is removed by the male (Mason, 1966). Hence, parental behavior, by male or female primates, ranges from indifference to continual nurturance.

This chapter is a condensed review of the current information on male and female care within the primate order. Most of the experimental information included will concern macaques (particularly *Macaca mulatta*), but observational data from other species will also be presented in order to give the reader a better appreciation of the potential for variability in nonhuman primate parenthood.

2. ONTOGENY OF SEX DIFFERENCES RELATED TO PARENTHOOD

Prenatal influences

Prenatal hormone levels definitely establish sexuality in nonhuman primates, and androgen is the critical substance determining the external expression of

Handbook of Sexology, edited by J. Money and H. Musaph
© *Elsevier/North-Holland Biomedical Press, 1977*

morphological sex. In the rhesus monkey, when androgen is present at the correct time in embryological development (and in the right amounts), the genitals develop in a masculine form regardless of genetic sex. When androgen is absent, every individual develops in a feminine form, regardless of genetic sex (Goy, 1966).

Even more importantly, for our purposes, the developing nervous system also undergoes psychosexual differentiation under the control of androgen. The effect of early androgen is on behavior, not just on the gonad itself. Moreover, early androgen controls the expression of behavior patterns appearing later in life which are not immediately related to reproduction, although they may be sex-related. It is highly probable that later parental behavior is strongly influenced by prenatal androgens which have exerted their organizing effects years before (Goy, 1966).

Infant sex differences

There are at least three aspects of infant nonhuman primate behavior which consistently differ between the sexes. These are: social threat, play initiation, and rough play. Males display each of these at rates far exceeding normal females (Goy, 1966; Harlow, 1965). These differences are not dependent upon androgens during infancy or during the juvenile period; they refer back to prenatal androgens.

It is probably at least partly because of these inborn sex differences that the mother's relation with the male infant is usually different from her relation to the female infant. Mothers have more passive contact with female infants and restrain and retrieve them more frequently than they restrain males. Mothers of males, on the other hand, withdraw from, play with, and present to their infants more than do mothers of females. Male infants bite their mothers more than do female infants. Probably as a result of inherent differences in activity and aggressiveness, male infants are punished more than are females.

In the rhesus it appears that it is in the second three months of the infant's life that the sex of the infant most obviously affects parental behavior. In our laboratory we have a somewhat oversimplified description of sex differences during this period of the rhesus infant's life. We characterize mothers of males as 'punishers', mothers of females as 'protectors', male infants as 'doers', and female infants as 'watchers'. The mother plays a role in prompting a greater independence and activity in male infants (Mitchell and Brandt, 1970). The social systems thus subtly support the built-in biological basis of sex differences. Culture complements, rather than competes with, biology (see Mitchell, 1968a; Jensen et al., 1966; Mitchell and Brandt, 1970). However, as we shall see later, biological social systems in primates are flexible. There is potential, for example, among primate parents of both sexes to compensate for the absence of the other parent.

Pre-adolescent sex differences

Older juveniles and pre-adolescents display parental-like behavior toward small infants on occasion. In the wild, pre-adolescent female baboons, rhesus, langurs, and vervets show 'maternal' behavior toward infants (Lancaster, 1971). Juvenile and pre-adolescent female vervets are very attracted to young infants and appear to 'learn' maternal behavior by interacting with infants long before they themselves are sexually mature. Play mothering contributes to the survival of the infant, who is protected by animals other than the mother and who may be adopted if orphaned. Play mothering also contributes to the development of maternal and, to a lesser extent, to paternal behavior patterns.

Vervet female primates, for example, show maternal behavior toward infants 4 months of age and younger; after 4 months, the infants become objects eliciting play behavior. In contrast to females, young male vervets in the wild have little to do with infants. They usually spend time play fighting with each other while females are caring for infants. However, if the infants themselves become socially playful, male juveniles show interest and play with them (Lancaster, 1971).

Laboratory studies of pre-adolescent male and female care of infants reveal the same sex differences as those discussed by Lancaster. Both male and female rhesus monkey pre-adolescents display parental like care prior to puberty. However, the females show four times as much positive social behavior toward infants as do males, and the males show 10 times as much hostility (Chamove et al., 1967). Males of this age do show some affection for infants but it is awkward and often rough. Male infants both elicit and emit more aggressive behavior from pre-adolescents than do female infants. However, they also elicit and emit more play. If an infant is isolate-reared and paired with a pre-adolescent, less parental-like care will be directed toward it (Brandt and Mitchell, 1973). If pre-adolescent—infant pairs are separated, the infant goes into a separation distress syndrome resembling that seen when it is separated from its mother, particularly if the dyad is a heterosexual one (Maple et al., 1975).

3. ADULT FEMALE CARE

The rhesus female

Parturition

In the wild, rhesus monkey births usually occur in the spring. The female actually delivers away from the rest of her group, but prior to parturition the female may display heterosexual activity and some aggression. These changes have been partly attributed to increases in estrogen at this time.

In *Macaca mulatta* (the rhesus), night delivery, squatting, straining on bushes, genital exploration, licking, and placenta eating are common. Most laboratory deliveries take 2—3 h (following a gestation period of 160—180 days). The range in my own laboratory was from about 15 min to 5 h with the longest labors occurring in primiparous (inexperienced) females and/or in abnormal deliveries (Brandt and Mitchell, 1971). Mothers rarely vocalized during delivery. Eighty-five percent of them ate the placenta following its delivery (Mitchell and Brandt, 1976).

There is no prolonged rest period for the rhesus mother following delivery and she does not appear to be weakened by the birth. If another adult female is present she often grooms the mother in labor and threatens others. Sometimes the attending mother will attempt to kidnap the neonate. Occasionally she succeeds (Mitchell and Brandt, 1976).

Maternal experience

Primiparous (inexperienced) females have longer and more difficult deliveries than do multiparous females, and they are usually awkward and anxious during and following delivery (Brandt and Mitchell, 1971; Seay, 1966). Normally socialized primiparous mothers are anxious. They look, threaten, fear grimace and lipsmack (an appeasement gesture) at other monkeys and at human observers more frequently than do experienced mothers. In addition, the inexperienced mothers stroke or pet and restrain their infants more than do multiparous mothers. Normally socialized, experienced mothers begin to punish-bite and reject their infants at an earlier age and more frequently than do normal inexperienced mothers (Mitchell and Stevens, 1969; Mitchell and Brandt, 1970).

These differences relating to maternal age and experience in normal monkey mothers are real but are relatively subtle when compared to differences between isolate-reared multipara and primipara.

Seay and colleagues (1964) were the first to demonstrate that rhesus females reared in social isolation for the first 18 months of life become inadequate, indifferent, or brutal mothers as adults. Rejection and punishment are essentially nonexistent in normally reared primiparous mothers during the first 3 months of the infants' life. Yet, all of Seay's abnormal mothers were inadequate and many were violent and abusive during the first month of their infants' lives. When punishment appears in normal mothers, primipara or multipara, the form of the punishment is much different from the brutal rejections seen in primiparous, isolate-reared mothers. The youngest primiparous, motherless mothers were usually the most brutal (Arling et al., 1969; Arling and Harlow, 1967).

For Harlow's 'motherless mothers' who have given birth to a second infant, the story is very different. These abnormal, isolate-reared mothers definitely treated their second and third infants much better than they had treated their first. Multiparous (older and wiser) isolate-reared rhesus mothers are neither brutal nor indifferent (Arling et al., 1969). In fact, some of the multiparous, motherless mothers were actually overprotective, even when they had been excessively brutal toward their first infant.

In summary, in rhesus monkey mothers, there is more behavioral variability between inexperienced or young mothers than between experienced or older mothers, and this variability seems to be related most directly to the socioemotional histories of the mothers. For *Homo sapiens*, clinicians have long believed that there is a strong correlation between early experience and later maternal behavior, but the relation between this and birth order has not been closely examined (Mitchell and Schroers, 1973).

Mother—infant separation

Both mother and infant monkeys protest intensely when they are separated from one another. In the infant, this protest is in the form of vocalizations — screeches and coos in the rhesus. In the mother, there are fewer vocalizations but many more facial expressions (Brandt et al., 1972).

The behavior of the primate mother changes in a predictable way at separation, while separated, and at reunion. *Macaca nemestrina* and *Macaca mulatta* adult females become more active and vocal at separation (Simons et al., 1968), and their activity and response vocalizations increase during presentations of infant calls. This is true even in nonmothers (Erwin, 1974).

At separation, mothers react initially with agitation and, eighteen days after separation, they appear to be depressed. At about two months after separation, all of the measures suggesting depression return to preseparation levels (Jensen, 1968; Simons et al., 1968). The depression seen in macaque mothers is more subtle and not as severe as that seen in their infants following separation (Rosenblum and Kaufman, 1968; Mitchell, 1970). Repeated forced separations from the infant can have long-term effects on the mother. Mothers which had experienced brief, repeated, and forced separations from their infants throughout the first eight months exhibited a stronger preference for their own infants than did control mothers. Mother—infant pairs in the laboratory which observe a separation but which are not themselves separated show an increase in mother—infant physical contact. The observing mothers also show an increase in 'coo' vocalizations while witnessing the separation (Mitchell, 1970).

Variability in maternal care

All the data presented above were in reference to macaques. However, most of the differences regarding parity, effects of social isolation, and separation can be generalized to the female care of other nonhuman primate species. Even the birth process differs very little from prosimian to monkey to ape (Brandt and Mitchell, 1971). The complexity of maternal behavior observed does seem to be greater in the apes, however. For example, chimpanzee mothers have been known to administer mouth-to-mouth resuscitation to newborn infants that were not breathing (W. Lemmon, personal communication). We have never seen a monkey do this, nor have we read of others who have seen them.

4. ADULT MALE CARE

Variability in male care

In the primate order, there is far greater variability in male care than in female care (Mitchell et al., 1974). In some species of New World monkeys, such as *Callicebus moloch*, *Aotus trivirgatus* and *Cebuella pygmaea*, the father assumes almost the entire burden of infant care. The mother's only contact with her baby occurs during nursing and during short periods of cleaning the infant. In Hanuman langur troops, on the other hand, a new leader may attack and systematically kill infants. Still other monkey males, like the patas, show no apparent direct social interaction with infants (Mitchell, 1969). Even within a species, we have found that males interact with infants in a variety of ways. The next few sections will serve as an example of the potential for flexibility in male care.

The rhesus male

Parturition
In group situations, adult males show very little interest in newborn infants (Rowell et al., 1964). However, in my laboratory, we have witnessed and filmed two complete births where an adult male rhesus monkey was present alone in the same cage with the delivering female. The adult males showed a great deal of interest.

In one of these deliveries, a fully adult, wild-born male had been housed with a pregnant, feral, multiparous female for a few weeks prior to parturition. Fifteen minutes before the actual delivery, the male sat quietly but appeared to be somewhat disturbed. He scratched himself and yawned repeatedly. During the labor he approached, looked at, sniffed, and groomed the delivering female. He threatened away human observers if they approached the cage and bit himself four times during approaches by observers. He watched the actual delivery intently from a distance of only two feet and looked intently at the infant after it was born.

The female's response to this was primarily one of withdrawal from the male. When she withdrew she fear grimaced and/or mildly threatened the male.

Another male, socially reared in the laboratory and only $3\frac{1}{2}$ years old, was present at the birth of an infant for which he was the biological father. The female was also $3\frac{1}{2}$ years old and was primiparous. The young pair had been housed together from conception through birth. Prior to delivery the male had an erection, attempted to mount and thrusted at the female's back. He continually pushed the female's posterior into a different position so that he could see the infant emerge. Following delivery the female groomed the male after which he again tried to mount her. He was obviously sexually aroused. Next, the male continually approached and tried to touch and/or take the baby. The female withdrew and would not let him. The male managed to get the infant's head and pull on it twice. He did not appear to be threatening the mother or infant, but one hour after delivery he injured the infant on the head, and we separated him from the mother and her newborn.

Male care in the wild

There is little positive social interaction in the relations between free-ranging adult male and infant rhesus monkeys. Adult rhesis males in North India are usually 'neutral or indifferent' toward infants and juveniles (Southwick et al., 1964). Adult males in the wild frequently attack but only rarely associate peacefully with infants (Southwick et al., 1965; Lindburg, 1971).

Male rhesus sometimes defend infants from attack or threaten other animals while sitting near infants, but peaceful physical contact in the wild between males and infants is rare. Lindburg (1971) only twice saw males carrying infants or juveniles during 900 h of observation, and on only two occasions did he see an adult male play with an infant. Kaufmann (1967) also saw very few positive adult male—infant interactions on Cayo Santiago, Puerto Rico.

Male care in the laboratory

Experiments in my laboratory, wherein infant rhesus are removed from their mothers and paired alone with adult males, have shown that, while adult male rhesus monkeys rarely display parental behavior in the wild, they are certainly capable of doing so when given the opportunity in the laboratory. Moreover, male care is not merely maternal behavior adopted by an adult male. Rhesus male care differs significantly from maternalism in at least four ways: (1) There is much more ventral—ventral contact in adult female—infant attachment; (2) adult male—infant attachment apparently increases over time while maternal—infant attachment decreases with time; (3) a normal adult male monkey protects his infant by moving toward the threat while the mother retrieves her infant and withdraws; and (4) most importantly, adult males play more frequently and intensely with their infants than do rhesus mothers (Redican and Mitchell, 1974; Mitchell et al., 1974). Both male care and female care are effective in raising socially and physically healthy rhesus monkeys, even without benefit of contact with other animals.

Isolate-reared adult males

There is evidence that the infant monkey may be regarded as a special social stimulus to others of its own species. While age-mate aggression increases with age, infant-directed hostility declines (Mitchell, 1968b; Arling et al., 1969). Pairing older isolate-reared adult males with infants was therefore not as dangerous as one would expect given the data on brutal isolate-reared rhesus mothers.

In my laboratory, we removed infant rhesus monkeys from their mothers at one month of age and paired them with fully mature isolation-reared adult males. Initially, these bizarre and abnormal males did not protect their infants and appeared to be arbitrarily, though not excessively, aggressive toward them. Eventually, however, they did protect their infants and, more importantly, they came to groom and play with them. The infants did not imitate any of the bizarre behaviors of their isolate male cagemates and they did not suffer any severe trauma or social deprivation. Surprisingly, adult male isolates, whom we might expect to be at least inferior if not dangerous 'fathers', can function quite successfully as socializers for rhesus infants (Mitchell et al., 1974; Gomber and Mitchell, 1974).

Male—infant separation

Just as in the case of mother—infant separation, there is protest on the part of both parties when a socially reared adult male is separated from the infant he has reared. The socially reared adult males often react violently, usually by pacing and attempting to remove the barrier separating them from the infants. Finally, in some cases, the males bite themselves repeatedly, inflicting superficial and sometimes even severe wounds. The infants respond with many distress calls and by postures. When the dyads are reunited they usually immediately cling to each other and then resume play. There is no question that strong attachments have been built up (Mitchell et al., 1974).

When the infants who had been reared by isolate adult males are separated from their abnormal parents they also display marked and sometimes violent protest. There are many distress calls, and one little female infant repeatedly threw herself against the barrier separating her from her bizarre caretaker (Gomber, unpublished). Obviously, she had strong affection for him.

5. DIFFERENCES BETWEEN MALE AND FEMALE CARE

As stated above, rhesus male care in adult—infant dyads differs from rhesus female care, primarily in that there is a greater amount of play and less ventral contact in male—infant pairs (Redican and Mitchell, 1974). The quality of play between the adult males and their adopted infants is very intense.

Infants in social groups play very often with peers and very rarely with adults of either sex. In the absence of peers, intense and frequent play does not develop in mother—infant dyads; it does develop in the adult male—infant pairs.

These results point to a greater potential for parental plasticity in the behavior of adult males as opposed to adult females. Because of the male's wide range of modifiability he is a resource to the group. The mother, in contrast, provides stability and reliability for the social attachment and protection of infants. The female, by virtue of this stability, is also probably less vulnerable to environmental insult. This, of course, is good for the well-being of the infant.

What our studies of parental care have taught us is that there is a surprising potential for behavioral change in the primate. Within the primate order there are greater species differences in male care than in female care. Adult male monkeys who almost never interact with infants in the wild will adopt and rear them in the laboratory. And, finally, even isolated-reared adult males are capable of rearing well-adjusted infants. Normal rhesus males, let alone social isolates, are 'not supposed to' show positive parental behavior. They do. With the primates, at least, it is risky to make assertions concerning what an animal will or will not do.

6. SUMMARY

This chapter is a condensed review of the current information on sex differences in parental care in the primate order, with emphasis on the species *Macaca mulatta*.

Prenatal androgens establish sexuality and later sex-related behavior, including perhaps, parental behavior. The tendencies for male infants and juveniles to play and threaten are apparently a consequence of both prenatal hormonal 'priming' and differential maternal care. These male tendencies apparently carry over into parental behavior, since adult male primates, at least rhesus monkeys, tend to play more with infants than do adult female primates. There is also more variability in primate male parental care than in primate female parental care.

ACKNOWLEDGEMENTS

The inspiration, encouragement and intellectual support I have received while researching parental behavior have come entirely from my three children — Jody Lynn, Lisa Deanna, and Gary David.

Some of the research reported herein was supported by NIH grants MH 22253, HD 04335 and RR 00169.

BIBLIOGRAPHY

Arling, G.L. and Harlow, H.F. (1967) Effects of social deprivation on maternal behavior of rhesus monkeys. *J. Comp. Physiol. Psychol.* 64: 371—378.

Arling, G.L., Ruppenthal, G.C. and Mitchell, G. (1969) Aggressive behavior of eight-year-old nulliparous isolate female monkeys. *Anim. Behav.* 17: 109—113.

Brandt, E.M., Baysinger, C. and Mitchell, G. (1972) Separation from rearing environment in mother-reared and isolation-reared rhesus monkeys (*Macaca mulatta*). *Int. J. Psychobiol.* 2: 193—204.

Brandt, E.M. and Mitchell, G. (1973) Pairing preadolescents with infants (*Macacca mulatta*). *Dev. Psychol.* 8 (1) 14—19.

Brandt, E.M. and Mitchell, G. (1971) Parturition in primates: Behavior related to birth. In: (L.A. Rosenblum, Ed.), *Primate Behavior: Developments in Field and Laboratory Research.* Vol. II Academic Press, New York pp. 177—223.

Chamove, A., Harlow, H.F. and Mitchell, G. (1967) Sex differences in the infant-directed behavior of preadolescent rhesus monkeys. *Child Dev.* 38: 329—335.

Erwin, J. (1974) Responses of rhesus monkeys to separation vocalizations of a conspecific infant. *Percept. Mot. Skills* 39: 179—185.

Gomber, J. and Mitchell, G. (1974) Preliminary report on adult male isolation-reared rhesus monkeys caged with infants. *Dev. Psychol.* 9: 419.

Goy, R.W. (1966) Role of androgens in the establishment and regulation of behavioral sex differences in mammals. *J. Anim. Sci.* 25: 21—31.

Harlow, H.F. (1965) Sexual behavior in the rhesus monkey. In: (F.A. Beach, Ed.), *Sex and Behavior.* (John Wiley and Sons, New York) p. 234.

Jensen, G.D. (1968) Reaction of monkey mothers to long-term separation from their infants. *Psychonomic Sci.* 11 (5) 171—172.

Jensen, G.D., Bobbitt, R.A. and Gordon, B.N. (1966) Sex differences in social interaction between infant monkeys and their mothers. In: (J. Wortis, Ed.), *Recent Advances in Biological Psychiatry*, Vol. 9 (Plenum, New York) pp. 283—293.

Jost, A. (1953) Problems of fetal endocrinology: the gonadal and hypophyseal hormones. *Recent Prog. Horm. Res.* 8: 379—418.

Kaufmann, J.H. (1967) Social relations of adult males in a free-ranging band of rhesus monkeys. In: (S. Altmann, Ed.), *Social Communication Among Primates*, (University of Chicago Press, Chicago) pp. 73—98.

Lancaster, J.B. (1971) Play mothering: The relations between juvenile females and young infants among free-ranging vervet monkeys *(Cercopithecus aethiops)*. *Fol. Primatol.* 15: 161—182.

Lindburg, D.G. (1971) The rhesus monkey in North India: An ecological and behavioral study. In: (L.A. Rosenblum, Ed.), *Primate behavior: Developments in field and laboratory research.* Vol. II (Academic Press, New York) pp. 1—106.

Maple, T., Brandt, E.M. and Mitchell, G. (1975) Separation of preadolescents from infants *(Macaca mulatta)*. *Primates* 16 (2) 141—153.

Martin, R.D. (1966) Tree shew: Unique reproductive mechanism of systematic importance. *Science* 152: 1402—1404.

Mason, W.A. (1966) Social organization of the South American monkey, *Callicebus moloch*: A preliminary report. *Tulane Stud. Zool.* 13: 23—28.

Mitchell, G. (1970) Abnormal behavior in primates. In: (L.A. Rosenblum, Ed.), *Primate Behavior: Developments in Field and Laboratory Research.* Vol. I (Academic Press, New York) pp. 195—249.

Mitchell, G. (1968a) Attachment differences in male and female infant monkeys. *Child Dev.* 39: 611—620.

Mitchell, G. (1968b) Persistent behavior pathology in rhesus monkeys following early social isolation. *Folia Primatol.* 8: 132—147.

Mitchell, G. (1969) Paternalistic behavior in primates. *Psychol. Bull.* 71: 399—417.

Mitchell, G. and Brandt, E.M. (1975) Behavior of the female rhesus monkey during birth. In: (G. Bourne, Ed.), *The Rhesus Monkey.* (Academic Press, New York) Vol. 2 pp. 231—244.

Mitchell, G. and Brandt, E.M. (1970) Behavioral differences related to experience of mother and sex of infant in the rhesus monkey. *Dev. Psychol.* 3: 149.

Mitchell, G., Redican, W.K. and Gomber, J. (1974) Lesson from a primate: Males can raise babies. *Psychol. Today* 7 (11) 63—68.

Mitchell, G. and Schroers, L. (1973) Birth order and parental experience in monkeys and man. In: (H.W. Reese, Ed.), *Advances in Child Development and Behavior.* Vol. 8 (Academic Press, New York) pp. 159—184.

Mitchell, G. and Stevens, C.W. (1969) Primiparous and multiparous monkey mothers in a mildly stressful social situation: First three months. *Dev. Psychobiol.* 1: 280—286.

Redican, W.K. and Mitchell, G. (1974) Play between adult male and infant rhesus monkeys. *Am. Zool.* 14: 295—302.

Rosenblum, L.A. and Kaufmann, I.C. (1968) Variations in infant development and response to maternal loss in monkeys. *Am. J. Orthopsychiat.* 38 (3) 418—426.

Rowell, T.E., Hinde, R.A. and Spencer-Booth, Y. (1964) "Aunt" and infant interactions in captive rhesus monkeys. *Anim. Behav.* 12: 219—226.

Seay, B.M. (1966) Maternal behavior in primiparous and multiparous rhesus monkeys *Fol. Primatol.* 4, 146—168.

Seay, B.M., Alexander, B.K. and Harlow, A.F. (1964) Maternal behavior of socially deprived rhesus monkeys. *J. Abnorm. Soc. Psychol.* 39: 345—354.

Simons, R.C., Bobbitt, R.A. and Jensen, G.D. (1968) Mother monkeys' (*Macaca nemestrina*) responses to infant vocalizations. *Percept. Mot. Skills* 27: 3—10.

Southwick, C.H., Beg, M.A. and Siddiqi, M.R. (1965) Rhesus monkeys in North India. In: (I. DeVore, Ed.), *Primate Behavior.* (Holt, Rinehart and Winston, New York) pp. 11—159.

CHAPTER 55

Human parental behavior: an anthropological view

LUCILE F. NEWMAN

1. CULTURE, STRUCTURE AND ANTHROPOLOGICAL PERSPECTIVES

Anthropologists have concerned themselves with the modes by which biological parenthood and generational difference are shaped and tempered by social (customary) usage. Certain aspects of family life may be described as virtually universal, and definitive of the human condition. These include the coupling of individuals for procreative purposes who have themselves been subject to parenting; the bearing of children who are immature at birth and require some kind of caretaking; the growth and development of children until they themselves are of reproductive age, and may begin the cycle again. In what way, however, and in what context this cycle is enacted is subject to a wide range of cultural influences.

The study of anthropology has often served to question by extensive comparison the received notions, the standard accepted ideas of social analysis. In this review of anthropological perspectives on parenthood, the concept of family, what is expected of parental behavior in different contexts, how the family is integrated in the larger social fabric are all examined with the intention of broadening and enlarging the available definitions of these terms and ideas. Human parental behavior will be viewed here from multiple perspectives. Some of these focus on parental behavior as emerging from biological bases; some are developmental and emphasize parents as the first socializing force in the life of each individual; and some perceive parenthood as a part of the generational aspect of kinship. All of these perspectives reinforce the hypothesis that not only is parenting (including care-giving, nurturance, protection and sensory stimulation) important to the health and survival of each individual, but that because of its role in the transmission of culture, it is also crucial to the persistence and continuity of both species and societies. In short, parenthood means something important to all peoples, but it does not mean the same thing to all peoples.

Those who share common meanings are said to participate in a common

Handbook of Sexology, edited by J. Money and H. Musaph
© *Elsevier/North-Holland Biomedical Press, 1977*

culture. Some definitions of culture emphasize behavioral aspects. Linton described the common denominator of culture as those patterns and rules of behavior that are learned, shared and transmitted (Linton, in Kroeber and Kluckhohn, 1960). Clifford Geertz in describing culture emphasizes its symbolic aspects. "It is through culture patterns, ordered clusters of significant symbols, that man makes sense of the events through which he lives. The study of culture, the accumulated totality of such patterns is thus the study of the machinery individuals and groups of individuals employ to orient themselves in a world otherwise opaque" (1973: 563). Both definitions emphasize the ordering of human existence and the transmission of modes of ordering into distinctive and recognizable patterns.

The study of kinship has emphasized the importance of social structure — the ordered and enduring relation of parts to a whole, and social organization, the interrelations of those parts to each other (Firth, 1951: 30). It has been noted that the underlying social organization of kinship creates to a certain extent the interactive context of the family — the expectable content of relationships, indeed the form and quality of parent—child relations. It is, for example, expectable that parenthood is perceived and experienced differently under different structural conditions, that is, the nuclear family consisting of mother, father, and children, may require a concentration of all parental roles and responsibilities in two people, as contrasted with the extended family of three or more generations where there are multiple parental figures. The universal human experience of being born into an already existing social order, and the rich variety of patterns of particular cultures emphasize the role of parents as transmitters of culture. For each individual the social order is not quite a totally received system but rather is experienced as an habituation to a particular parental interpretation of culture. It may be said, then, that anthropologists explore the content and quality of relations both generational and parental.

In order to present an integrated view of anthropological perspectives on human parental behavior, three key perspectives are introduced with a few examples from the extensive literature of each. They include: family formation and biological parenthood, a biological and demographic perspective; kinship, the structural perspective that is the unique contribution of anthropology to the study of generations; and family interaction and the culture of parenthood, an interdisciplinary perspective stressing socialization.

2. FAMILY FORMATION AND BIOLOGICAL PARENTHOOD

Family formation

Every society has explicit rules about who may marry whom, and when a family may be formed and under what circumstances. These rules differ widely. Family formation may be accomplished through extended family decision, as in arranged marriage, or through decision of the individuals involved as in the so-called 'love match' of the Western world. In many societies, marriages are arranged by professional 'go-betweens' or by elder members of the families involved who investigate family backgrounds, personalities, economic status, and generally strive for the best possible 'match' of families. Marriage under these circumstances may be seen as an alliance between kinship groups and of significance to entire families rather than only to the couple who are being married. It is often said that marriage is too important a decision to be left to young people. Arranged marriages maintain culturally condoned parenthood patterns, serve a eugenic function, and perpetuate control of reproduction by family elders.

Where marriage is made by open and free choice of individuals, it may occur because of pregnancy, or the first pregnancy may result from the formation of a family for procreative purposes. In either case, it is often characterized by homogamy (marrying a person like oneself in ethnic origin, socio-economic status, education, and religious orientation; Bell, 1967). Both of these practices result in an essential endogamy, marrying within one's own group, and a resulting subcultural homogeneity. While the biological possibility of an open universal gene pool could exist, it is in fact limited by cultural norms that promote persistence of particular social groups and homogeneity within them (Newman, 1972). The negative proof may be seen in many societies in laws of 'miscegenation', or marriage with the wrong person, however culturally defined, and in the cultural sanctions associated with the stigma of the 'misbegotten' (again, however culturally defined). These are terms that denote that the cultural norms for family formation have not been conformed to.

Birth control

Not only does the world at this time not experience an open gene pool, it also does not express its full reproductive capability. While parenthood seems to be popular (world population is growing at 2.05% per year) population growth is not as great as the biological potential for human reproduction would allow, but is and has been limited through social, cultural, and psychological constraints as well as through natural hazards.

Not all people at all times are in a culturally appropriate situation for parenthood. Sexual behavior for reproductive purposes and for pleasure have been separated in many societies. The Aztecs had in the first millenium A.D., different goddesses for sexual pleasure and for reproduction, with concomitant differences in birth-control methods for what were perceived as different functions (Quezada, 1975).

Norman E. Himes in the classic *Medical History of Contraception* demonstrated the near universality of some form of family limitation dating as far back as the Egyptian papyrus of 1850 B.C. and in the more modern era representing all continents (1963: 59). Anthropologists (c.f. Devereux, 1955;

Ford, 1964; Polgar, 1968; Newman, 1972) have extended the scope of this understanding and shown further that parenthood is not determined solely by biological drives but has been sought or avoided, that is, controlled through culturally sanctioned means ranging from abstinence to abortion, according to the desires for parenthood of the individuals or their families.

Birth and neonatal dependence

Characteristic of the human species and central to the origins of culture is the relative immaturity of the newborn human and its dependence on human caretakers for its very survival. As Berger and Luckman have noted in *The Social Construction of Reality*, the human organism develops biologically after it is born, particularly during the first year of life. Central nervous system development takes place in a social situation: "... The developing human being not only interrelates with a particular natural environment, but with a specific cultural and social order, which is mediated to him by the significant others who have charge of him. Not only is the survival of the human infant dependent upon certain social arrangements, the direction of his organismic development is socially determined" (1966: 48). To become human, then, is to live in society. To objectify experience separate from its social milieu is to miss its essential humanity.

Comparative studies, using the natural laboratory afforded by common humanity and cultural diversity, make it possible to study the biological requirements of birth and neonatal dependence as contrasted with those practices mandated by cultural usage. Mead and Newton (1967) have used the references from the Human Relations Area Files on marriage, family formation, birth practices and social recognition of birth. They have reviewed variations in cultural usage on the theme of biological requirements, and found that cross-cultural comparison provides not only a range for each aspect of birth behavior but also that it is possible to gain from these variations insights applicable to one's own practice. "Cross-cultural materials break through the crust of habituation in a way of viewing human beings whether or not any item of behavior can be appropriately incorporated, as such, into our own repertoire, the knowledge that at least one group of human beings, surviving for generations under starkly difficult conditions, has used a practice or has taken account of a potentiality which we have not considered valuable to us. For example, the Manus of the Admiralty Islands place the crying neonate, cord uncut, facing the mother, in the belief that sight and sound together will facilitate delivering the placenta. This raises the question of whether the sight of the neonate, as well as the sound of its crying is involved in a biological releasing mechanism which should be taken into account in planning delivery style" (1967: 143).

The importance of early interaction in development of attachment and of adaptation of mother and infant to each other have been recognized by many investigators, particularly Trause, Kennell and Klaus, the authors of

Chapter 57. These studies suggest caretaker and neonate as an interactive system with growth, development and attachment as interdependent processes.

It has long been known that impaired early interaction can have deleterious effects on development of personality. John Bowlby in *Maternal Care and Mental Health* (1952) devised the negative concept of 'maternal deprivation,' suggesting the pathogenic effect on infants of extended separation from mother or chief caretaker. The discussion was continued with a second volume edited by Mary D. Ainsworth, entitled *Deprivation of Maternal Care: A Reassessment of Its Effects* (1962). Margaret Mead in this volume questioned the universal necessity of single caretakers, instinctiveness of maternal behavior, and the separation of parental behavior from the cultural context of any society. "In short, the accumulated evidence from primitive societies suggests that at a very early stage in human history, traditional modes of behavior were evolved which were related not to any immediate instinctive pattern of neonatal mother—child relationship ... but rather to other parts of the learned behavior of the particular people, their mode of life, means of transport, type of shelter, system of kinship organization, methods of economic exchange, and beliefs about the soul and the cosmos" (1962: 53).

Prevalent terms, 'maternal deprivation', 'the absent father', used in investigation of the dynamics of family interaction suggest a stronger past identification of mother—child than of parent—child or father—child bonds. An attempt to rectify this imbalance was made by Andry (1962) through the suggestion that impaired father-child interaction may be a determining factor in juvenile delinquency.

An example of the generalizing or spreading of parental responsibility and involvement between mother and father is found in the behavior called 'couvade'. This term refers to traditional male behavior parallel to or identical with that of the female during pregnancy or birth. It may take forms ranging from simulated childbed to mutual acceptance of food taboos or limiting of activity (Newman, 1966: 153—154). Malinowski wrote in *Sex and Repression in Savage Society*, "It is of high biological value for the human family to consist of both father and mother; if the traditional proximity between father and child, if all such customs aim at drawing a man's attention to his offspring, then the couvade which makes man simulate the birth pangs and illness of maternity is of great value and provides the necessary stimulus and expression for paternal tendencies" (1927: 215). The emphasis in this book on parental behavior reflects this concern also as research moves from centering on mother-child alone to the complex and multiple relationships among parents and children (c.f. also Parent—Infant Interaction, 1975).

Comparative studies: the nuclear triad

The role of the newborn infant in the family may be analyzed in terms of a 'nuclear triad' defined by the two parents and their offspring.

This heuristic device is used not to limit the perception of the new member but rather to hold constant that which is biologically given (parents and child) so as to be able to view comparatively that which is of cultural origin.

An example of the use of this device in describing family dynamics is found in Caudill and Plath's '*Who Sleeps by Whom*', in which they note the social significance of sleeping arrangements in Japan and the United States. They concluded that sleeping arrangements in Japanese families "tend to blur the distinctions between interdependence more than the separateness of individuals, and to underplay ... the potentiality for the growth of conjugal intimacy between husband and wife in sexual and other matters in favor of a more general family cohesion" (1966: 363). Sleeping arrangements symbolize certain rules of social organization. The American mother prepares for birth by making ready a new bed for the expected child. The nexus of strength for the American nuclear triad is centered in the husband—wife relation, and generational separation (the 'generation gap') is expressed by the structural phenomenon of sleeping arrangements of mother and father separate from child. Under similar circumstances the Asian Indian mother prepares a new bed for her husband for the duration of the time of her concentration on and feeding of the newborn when mother and infant sleep together. The Indian nuclear triad stresses the mother—child bond and reflects a lineage identity of continuity though time rather than an age-graded identity of each generation with each.

3.KINSHIP

A second anthropological perspective on parenthood may be seen in the structural approach of classic kinship studies. The importance of the large literature of kinship studies to this review is the extent to which it has demonstrated, through the analysis of social structure, the economic, political, ecological, in short, nonfamilial origins of kinship organization, as well as reliance of the quality of role relationships on kinship structure.

A kinship system is defined by Radcliffe-Brown (1952) as denoting descent from a common ancestor (putative or known), a common territory or coresidence, and recognized rights and duties expressed through distinctive modes of behavior. The study of kinship systems has enabled comparison of seemingly disparate customs and practices, some of which focus on parent— child and some family—society relationships.

Parent—child

One of the most significant of kinship phenomena for the study of parent-hood has to do with the locus of authority within the family — not individual families, but the expectable norm of family dynamics in a particular society.

Margaret Park Redfield in *'The American Family, Consensus and Freedom'* has described the western nuclear family structure. "The American family — parents and children — appears on the surface as a simple conjugal type with no important or formal connections with remoter kin, no rituals of ancestor worship . . . and no intricate economic ties. It is a small compact group of two generations, bound together by ties of affection and functioning to care for the young, until they reach years of maturity and can repeat for themselves the process of family rearing" (1946: 175). The nuclear family in American society is characterized by mobility and fragility (the national divorce rate was 10.5 per 1000 marriages in 1974 [U.S. Dept. of Commerce, 1975]. While family members are recognized and ties maintained, the residential family most often is made up of those who are in the process of raising children. Thus the nuclear family focuses authority (and conflict) on the parents, who are expected to share authority in terms of decision-making and to take full responsibility for early socialization of their children. Where there is a single parent the responsibility is still further focused on the one person. Parent—child interaction in the nuclear family is intense and all encompassing, authority total but limited in time, and not necessarily located in a particular place.

Irawati Karve, describing kinship in India has reflected on the family. "[An] important factor in Indian life is the family, and by family is meant here the joint family . . . A joint family is a group of people who generally live under the same roof, who eat food cooked in one kitchen, who hold property in common, participate in common family worship and are related to one another as some particular type of kindred . . . A joint family has always an ancestral seat or locality" (1965: 8—9). Karve has noted that in North Indian society, characterized by the patrilineal joint family household, a patrilineage is made up of a male head and his sons and grandchildren. With early marriage and young parents, the parental functions of reproduction and socialization were separated,with procreation and caretaking carried out by biological parents, and responsibility for socialization and authority resting with the grandparental generation. Major decisions, such as those relating to discipline, schooling and marriage, were made by grandparents. The joint family, grounded in lineage and place may persist for generations. Parent—child interaction is focused on caretaking with authority diffused among multiple adults.

Some variations in family structure have been described. The nuclear and joint family described above rest on marriage as a base. A classic challenge to the definition of family based on marriage and the alliance of two families came from Kathleen Gough's study of the matrilineal Nayars of South India. For this warrior caste, households were made up of one family — a matrilineage, a woman and her children, her daughters and their children, and their brothers. The *taravad* or ancestral home, built on a courtyard, permitted separate quarters for sections of the family, but they functioned as a unit. Marriage, while it existed in ritual form, was not expressed through residence, but through visiting. The father—child relationship was known and warm and supportive, but the mother's brother wielded authority in important matters. The father lived with his sisters, over whose children he had authority (1959).

Challenged by the Freudian postulation of oedipal conflict in the family based on biological parenthood, Bronislaw Malinowski hypothesized that if the family was patrilineal (characterized by a unilineal descent system reckoned through males) an oedipal conflict might well be universal with the opposite sex parent, but that if the family system was matrilineal (reckoned through females) it would not, because the oedipal conflict arose not from biology but from authority. Working in the Trobriand Islands in a matrilineal society, he found a family structure in which lineage, land, inheritance and title were passed from mother to daughter with the mother's brother as the key authority figure in the family. Along with this, expressed through myth and ritual ceremonials, through joking relationships, avoidances, and other stylized forms of interaction, he found the tensions of oedipal conflict between mother's brother and sister's children.

"Thus the building up of the sentiments, the conflicts and maladjustments which this implies, depend largely upon the sociological mechanism which works in a given society. The main aspects of this mechanism are the regulation of infantile sexuality, the incest taboos, exogamy, the apportionment of authority and the type of household organization. In this perhaps lies the main contribution of the present memoir. We have been able to indicate the relation between biological, psychological and sociological factors. We have developed a theory of the plasticity of instincts under culture and of the transformation of instinctive response into cultural adjustment" (Malinowski, 1959: 189).

From these few examples, it may be seen that the content and quality of parent—child interaction may not be assumed as universal and biologically based, but are subject to modification and adaptation to particular cultural configurations through which biological reality is expressed.

Family—society

Part of the contribution of anthropological studies to the understanding of society concerns extrafamilial functions of kinship organization. That is, for every society the particular social arrangements accomplish ends beyond the provision of nurturing and socializing for the next generation. Some of these may be divided arbitrarily into economic and political functions (although such divisions are necessarily distorting). They all promote cohesion within and between social groups and barriers or exclusion from other societies. They also provide mechanisms for sustaining that cohesion or exclusion. All have been adaptive for the survival of communities as well as families.

Marriage preferences and prohibitions affect recruitment for parenthood and the composition and expectations of the extended family. In North India, Karve describes arranged marriage based on certain preferences including caste endogamy (marrying within the caste group) and village exogamy (marrying a person from outside the natal village) in conjunction with a patrilineal structure in which males remain with the family home and females move out of their natal villages to the husband's home. What this means in terms of family interaction is that parents are perceived not as equals nor as even very much alike. Fathers are long-term residents and mothers are outsiders to the family with strong allegiances to another village. Authority and power rest firmly with the males, but particularly with older males. The young woman as a newcomer and a stranger changes status with age and motherhood arriving at a position of influence in the family only as her sons become mature. Male and female children for the same reasons are treated differently. The young girl is perceived as a sojourner in her own family because she has no claim on the family home and because she will leave it at an early age. The life experiences for male and female children are then quite different, as are their roles in later life.

Implications for Indian society as a whole are great. One can view, as did William Rowe, North India as a vast network of marriage relations with marriage ties spreading within caste groupings in all directions. Other villages are known by a designation that this is a village to which we are related by marriage (Rowe, 1960). Every child then, while living in one village, has allegiances in another and a separate set of relatives. Trading ties follow marriage ties, and economic bonds with these villages are important. Arrangement of marriages is, under these circumstances, a social and economic function carried on by elders. Ties between villages are strengthened with each succeeding marriage. Kinship in India then serves an integrative function between villages and as a barrier between castes.

Such extensive networks provide closed but geographically dispersed groupings that may be exploited for economic and political purposes.

4. FAMILY INTERACTION AND THE CULTURE OF PARENTHOOD

Cross-cultural comparison of societies suggests certain characteristics of social organization relating to parenthood. Some of these may be described as follows: (1) Continuity of social systems through formalized kinship structure, domestic arrangements and resulting socialization of the young and transmission of culture; (2) solidarity manifested by ritual and symbolic behavior, including reciprocity as a process strengthening the social networks thus established. Such comparisons have centered on the family-in-society rather than on parenthood as such and have illuminated variations in interactional processes and what may be termed 'the culture of parenthood' in various societies. Beside the maintenance of continuity and solidarity, family interaction is also characterized by (3) rules that are learned, shared, and transmitted, and sanctioned through legitimation.

Before noting these characteristics promoting social equilibrium in parenting — continuity, solidarity, rules and legitimacy — it is necessary to emphasize that social analysis must be of groups not of individuals, that each individual life is characterized by a unique biographical situation, that differences in genotype and phenotype, differences in age, circumstances, relationship of parents all serve the ontogenetic function — the differentiation of one person from another person. Before proceeding with commonalities in cultural experience it is necessary to invoke Kluckhohn's dictum that man is in some ways like all other men, in some ways like some other men, in some ways like no other man (1953: 53).

Continuity

The phylogenetic function of continuity is maintained through kinship structures described in the last section, symbolized by name, title, land, place; and through domestic arrangements deriving from these structures. A particular family may be in residence for only a generation as in the Western nuclear family or it may last for centuries in the same residence. Domestic arrangements vary, but all enable socialization of children to a particular way of life and assure a continuance of the social system through time. Socialization, taking place through both education and habituation, includes the transmission of culture — the learning of language and its cognitive implications, habituation to a value system, what should be done and how it should be done. It refers to formal instruction and to manners and mores. As the first and most significant socializing force, parents teach language, their own language, and tend to continue the values that were taught to them.

The culture of parenthood in each society is made up in part of the results of parenthood as a developmental stage of adulthood. The importance of (especially) the first child in adult identity is demonstrated in many ways. In some societies the unmarried woman never achieves adult status; the man without children is treated as a perennial adolescent. More positively, in certain societies adult names change to refer to the first child. The practice of teknonymy in Bali is the use of the first child's name to designate the adult, as Mother-of-so-and-so, Father-of-so-and-so. The birth of the first child constitutes a major status change for the parents marked symbolically by their change in name and the implication of continuity.

Solidarity

Solidarity is first suggested by the very definition of a family. It is manifested by ritual and ceremonial behavior, marking of life-cycle events —

birth, coming of age, schooling, marriage, death — all social events noted in the larger society as well as within the family. One of the ways of maintaining solidarity is through mutually reinforcing recognition and acknowledgement of common destiny which can be symbolized not only through ritual behavior but also through reciprocity.

Reciprocity, described most eloquently by Marcel Mauss in *The Gift*, refers to the set of mutual obligations set in motion by gift-giving and repayment or counter gift-giving. The depth of obligation may be perceived by thinking in one's own society of the social implications of refusal of a gift. Mauss notes "it is easy to find a large number of facts on the obligation to receive. A clan, household, association or guest are constrained to demand hospitality, to receive presents, to barter or to make blood and marriage alliances. The Dayaks have even developed a whole set of customs based on the obligation to partake of any meal at which one is present or which one has seen in preparation.

"The obligation to give is no less important . . . To refuse to give, or to fail to invite, is, like refusing to accept, the equivalent of a declaration of war; it is a refusal of friendship and intercourse" (1954: 10). Times of special importance for families are for many societies times at which reciprocity is most in evidence — those marking the life cycle of family members. Mauss refers to the mutual obligations as a spiritual bond that maintains and intensifies relationships among families and clans. In many societies there is key involvement of women in constant preparation for and carrying out of reciprocal gift giving throughout the network of families made up of lineage members and relatives by alliance (marriage). In others, reciprocal solidarity is maintained by male sharing of products of the hunt or catch. In any case, a family may be said to have been formed when a young couple takes on a part of the obligation of reciprocal giving within the larger community themselves.

Rules of interaction

The most dramatic and cross-culturally constant rules of interaction between parents and children are those governing the incest taboo, the prohibition against sexual relations between close relatives other than the married pair in a family. Definitions of the incest taboo are as varied as their social contexts, but the existence of such rules is consistent and explicit, sometimes codified in law, sometimes legitimized solely by custom, always strongly sanctioned. Lest it be assumed that some kind of cosmic genetic knowledge dictates the rules to avoid excessive inbreeding it should be noted that the incest taboo is extended in many societies to kin by marriage, to adoptive and even to fictive kin, and that in some societies, social differentiation is made between cross and parallel cousins (who would be genetically similar). "In effect, the incest taboo establishes bounded groups in complementary relationship to each other" (Mead, 1968: 115). That is, rules for appropriateness of interaction within families actually serve the function of identifying the boundaries of extrafamilial groups. They have to do with the family-in-society, defining those groups that are marriageable and with whom certain kinds of alliances may be made, and those with whom relationship is too close for marriage.

In terms of family dynamics, the incest taboo remains as a prohibition on sexual relations between parents and children and between siblings. Certain outstanding exceptions have existed — in the ancient royal families of Hawaii, of the Incas, of Egypt, or the Azande of West Africa, where leadership and blood lines were kept intact; in Mormon communities in America until outlawed; under certain ritual and emotionally highly charged circumstances in other societies. The taboo is not always maintained despite strong feelings about it described as 'grisly horror' by Murdock (1949), by Freud (1919) as 'uncanny' (that which is familiar and repressed). Weinberg (1955) in *Incest Behavior* surveyed and interviewed two hundred families identified as practicing incest and found them characterized by a strong degree of alienation, disorganization and family disintegration. The incest taboo, whatever its origins, is close to a universal cultural rule despite its abrogations which are special and its infractions which are few. The principle of exogamy, or marriage outside the primary group, expressed through the incest taboo finds its counterpart in the principle of legitimacy, the social recognition and sanction of family formation and reproduction. Legitimation is most often carried out through legal or customary contract and validated through ceremony including reciprocal gift-giving or through exchanges of goods or money known as dowry or brideprice. The alliance of families thus accomplished provides for each child a dual genetic and social heritage acknowledged in the larger community as right and acceptable.

Family interaction is subject to external sanctions as well as internal rules. Striking differences appear in how parents and children interact, their mutual expectations and the cultural expression of these. However, the intense affective content of parent—child relationships and the seriousness of the resulting responsibilities attest to its importance in all societies.

5. SUMMARY

Anthropological perspectives emphasize parenthood as inextricable from the social system in which it is found, expressing as well as demonstrating the societies' values. Observations about family formation and biological parenthood suggest that mankind maintains a controlled gene pool — in no known era has human reproduction been random, resulting in a totally open gene pool — and that mankind does not generally express fully its potential reproductive capacity. Families are formed according to rules that are explicit in each society.

Kinship studies have analyzed the structure of society influencing parent—

child relations and some of the nonfamilial origins and functions of kinship organization. Those described have been economic and political but the possibilities are many.

Family interaction and the culture of parenthood through certain practices, demonstrate the transmission of values and cognitive structure as well as mutual socialization.

The multiple perspectives of biology, structure, and interaction suggest some of the complex interrelations set in motion by the initiation of parenthood, not only in the caretaking and nurturance required by infant immaturity and dependence, but also in its role in the transmission of culture and maintenance of continuity in society.

BIBLIOGRAPHY

Ainsworth, M. (1962) The effects of maternal deprivation: a review of findings and controversy in the context of research strategy. *Deprivation of Maternal Care: A Reassessment of its Effects.* Public Health Papers, No. 14 (World Health Organization, Geneva).

Andry, R.G. (1962) Paternal and maternal roles and delinquency. *Deprivation of Maternal Care: A Reassessment of Its Effects.* Public Health Papers, No. 14, (World Health Organization, Geneva).

Anthony, M.D. and Benedek, T. (Eds.) (1970) *Parenthood: Its Psychology and Psychopathology.* (Little, Brown and Co., Boston.)

Bell, R. (1967) *Marriage and Family Interaction.* Revised edn, (Dorsey Press, Homewood, Illinois).

Berger, P. and Luckmann, T. (1966) *The Social Construction of Reality.* (Anchor Books, Doubleday and Co., Inc., New York.)

Bowlby, J. (1952) Maternal care and mental health. *World Health Organization Monograph Series,* No. 2 (Geneva).

Caudill, W. and Plath, D. (1974) Who sleeps by whom. In: (R. Levine, Ed.), *Culture and Personality, 1974.* (Aldine Publishing Co., Chicago.)

Devereux, G. (1955) *A Study of Abortion in Primitive Societies: A Typological Distributional and Dynamic Analysis of the Prevention of Birth in 400 Preindustrial Societies.* (Julian Press, New York.)

Firth, R. (1951) *Elements of Social Organization.* (Watts and Co., London.)

Ford, C. (1964) *A Comparative Study of Human Reproduction.* Publ. Anthropol., No. 32, Yale Univ. (Reprinted from 1945 edn by the Human Relations Area Files Press.)

Freud, S. (orig. 1913, 1959) *Totem and Taboo.* Vol. 13, pages ix-162. In: *The Standard Edition of the Complete Psychological Works of Sigmund Freud.* (Macmillan Press, New York.)

Geertz, C. (1973) *The Interpretation of Cultures.* (Basic Books, New York.)

Gough, K. (1959) The Nayers and the definition of marriage. *J. R. Anthropol. Inst.* 89: 23-34.

Himes, N. (1963) *Medical History of Contraception.* (Gamut Press, New York.)

Karve, I. (1965) *Kinship Organization in India.* (Asia Publishing House, Bombay.)

Kluckhohn, C. and Murray, H. (1953) *Personality in Nature, Society and Culture.* (Alfred A. Knopf, New York.)

Kroeber, A.L. and Kluckhohn, C. (1960) *Culture.* (Vintage Books, New York.)

Malinowski, B. (1957) *Sex and Repression in Savage Society.* 3rd edn (Meredian Books, New York.)

774

Mauss, M. (1954) *The Gift*. Translated by Ian Cunnison, introduction by E.E. Evans-Pritchard. (Cohen and West, London.)

Mead, M. (1962) A cultural anthropologist's approach to maternal deprivation. *Deprivation of Maternal Care: A Reassessment of its Effects*. Public Health Papers, No. 14. (World Health Organization, Geneva.)

Mead, M. (1968) Incest. *International Encyclopedia of Social Sciences*. (Macmillan Company and The Free Press, New York.)

Mead, M. and Newton, N. (1967) Cultural patterning of perinatal behavior. In: (S. Richardson and A. Guttmacher, Eds.), *Childbearing: Its Social and Psychological Aspects*. (Williams and Wilkins Co., Baltimore.)

Murdock, G. (1949) *Social Structure*. (Macmillan, New York.)

Newman, L. (1972) *Birth control: an anthropological view*. (Addison-Wesley Modular Publications No. 27, Reading, Mass.)

Newman, L. (1966) The couvade: a reply to Kupferer. *Am. Anthropol.* 68 (1) 153—156.

Parent-Infant Interaction (1975) Ciba Foundation Symposium 33. (Associated Scientific Publishers, Amsterdam.)

Polgar, S. (1968) Cultural aspects of natality regulation techniques. *Proc. 8th Int. Congr. Anthropol. Ethnol. Sci.* 3 (Tokyo and Kyoto, Japan.)

Quezada, N. (1975) Metodos anticonceptivos y abortivos tradicionales. *Anal. Antropol.* 12: 223—242. Mexico.

Radcliffe-Brown, A. (1952) *Structure and Function in Primitive Society*. (The Free Press, Glencoe, Illinois.)

Redfield, M.P. (1946) The American family, consensus and freedom. *Am. J. Sociol.* 52: 175—83.

Rowe, W.L. (1960) The marriage network and structural change in a north Indian community. *Southwest. J. Anthropol.* 16: 299—311.

United Nations (1971) *Statistical Yearbook, 1970*. (Statistical Office of the U.N., Dep. Econ. Soc. Affairs, New York.)

United States Department of Commerce, Bureau of the Census (1975) *Statistical Abstract of The United States: 1974*. (Government Printing Office, Washington, D.C.).

Vogel, E. (1963) *Japan's New Middle Class*. (University of California Press, Berkeley.)

Weinberg, S. (1955) *Incest Behavior*. (Citadel Press, New York.)

CHAPTER 56

Correlates of human parental behavior: a review

EVELYN B. THOMAN and ELISE GAULIN-KREMER

1. PARENTING AS A RESEARCH VARIABLE

Definition of parenting

The term parenting may refer to the feeding, burping, or bathing of a young infant, to playing peek-a-boo with a one-year-old or Monopoly with a 12-year-old, or to discussing the relative disadvantages of smoking pot or tobacco with a teenager. The commonalities among these diverse forms of behavior are: (a) they are social interactions with an offspring whether biologically related or not, and (b) they reflect the conceptions and values of the parents as to the nature of children and the aims of childrearing. The broad generality of these two statements reflects the fact that parenting is a major component of human behavior that is both complex and diverse. The problem of defining, delimiting and describing parental behavior is not yet surmounted despite the plethora of research.

Strategies used in the study of parenting

There have been two major approaches to the description of parental behavior, both in the method of data collection and in the type of data obtained. Over the years, interviews or questionnaires have been the most common source of information for research. Recently, however, there has been an emphasis on a second approach involving direct observation. This has often taken the form of bringing mother and child into the laboratory, setting up a 'naturalistic' type of situation, and observing the behavior that occurs. Even more recently, an emphasis on naturalistic observations has led to the use of observations of the parent and child in the home.

The data obtained from the interview—questionnaire approach have taken the form of rating scales. By means of these scales, underlying commonalities or themes in diverse forms of parental behavior are abstracted along global

Handbook of Sexology, edited by J. Money and H. Musaph
© *Elsevier/North-Holland Biomedical Press, 1977*

dimensions, such as acceptance—rejection, permissiveness—restrictiveness, and sensitivity—insensitivity. Observational data may also be condensed into ratings, or may be code-recorded to yield frequencies and/or durations of specific observed behavior. The type of data collected depends in part on the research question posed. Detailed behavioral descriptions derived from direct observation are increasingly recognized as being necessary to answer certain types of question.

It is clear that with either type of strategy, the data obtained will be influenced by the theoretical concepts and framework of the researcher. This is most evident in the selection of variables to be rated. Direct observation, however, while perhaps more easily objectified, is still selective and is influenced by the researcher's theoretical framework. Decisions must be made as to the level of description desired and the actual examples of behavior to record from the ongoing sequences which constitute the interactive process.

Variations in viewing of parental behavior

Parental behavior in research has been subdivided and classified as constituting independent, dependent, and correlating variables. When used as an independent variable, parental behavior is viewed as having an effect on the development of the child. This area of research is a very old one and not of central concern for the present chapter. The present focus is on the determinants or the correlates of parenting behavior. It is only with animals that it is possible to study in a rigorous manner the factors that may affect parenting, such as the number of offspring in a litter of rats, the presence or absence of various environmental conditions, or variations in manipulated hormone levels of the mother. Among human beings, it is generally possible only to identify those factors which co-exist with variations in specified types of parental behavior. These correlates of parental behavior may vary with respect to their presumptive role as determinants. Some of the major correlates that have been the subject of research interest will be described.

2. CORRELATES OF PARENTAL BEHAVIOR: SOME RESEARCH FINDINGS

Parental variables which have been most extensively studied as correlates of parental behavior to date include: social class, parental values and attitudes, sex of the parents, personality characteristics, parity of the mother and physiological status. Variables of the child include sex, age, birth order and behavioral characteristics. Typically, these correlates of parental behavior have been studied in isolation; although, as will be emphasized repeatedly, it has become increasingly evident that these variables interact complexly in their relations to variations in parental behavior.

Socioeconomic status of the family

Many studies have demonstrated that the parents' socioeconomic status, as indicated by their educational level, profession and/or income is related to qualitative differences in parental attitudes and behavior. Researchers have been intensively concerned with parental expressions of love or affection, and with the means parents use for controlling their offspring's behavior. For example, Busse and Busse (1972) found that paternal education was positively correlated with the amount of expressed love. Bayley and Shaeffer (1960) found that higher status mothers were more permissive and warm, especially with male children. However, there are contradictory findings in which no differences were found between social classes in parental acceptance and affection (Kagan and Freeman, 1963; Becker and Krug, 1965; Radin, 1972).

With respect to control of the child's behavior, punishment has often been studied. Kohn (1969) found that working-class mothers were more likely to use physical punishment than middle-class mothers. Bronfenbrenner (1958) reviewed a number of studies suggesting greater reliance on physical punishment among working-class parents and on withdrawal of love among middle-class families as a means of control. The complexities here are suggested by various interactions. Kohn (1969) found that middle-class mothers tended to refrain from punishing sons, but punished daughters for certain infractions.

Becker and Krug (1965) found that greater authoritarian control was exerted in the lower income classes, especially with respect to sexuality, aggression and lying. Social classes differ not only with respect to the kind of control used, but also the conditions under which control is exerted, and the sex of the child who elicits controlling behavior.

Additional studies differentiate the middle and lower social classes by indicating that the middle class parents provide more interactive stimulation (Kagan and Tulkin, 1971; Tulkin and Kagan, 1972); they are more concerned with independence and achievement in their children (Prothro, 1966; Kohn and Schooler, 1969; Tulkin and Cohler, 1973); they are less demanding of role conformity (Kohn, 1969); and they are also less directive and intrusive than the lower-class parents (Minton et al., 1971).

Social class differences may affect both the quality and content of interaction. Lower-class parents have been characterized as emphasizing status contingencies, role conformity and the immediate consequences of actions; whereas higher-class parents emphasize person rather than status orientation and the intention of actions (Hess and Shipman, 1965; Kohn, 1969; Kohn and Schooler, 1969; Kogan and Wimberger, 1969). The content of interaction also seems to differ; minimal class differences seem to exist in affective aspects of interaction, with larger differences in verbal and cognitive stimulation. Higher-class parents have been characterized as providing more verbal stimulation and more complex verbalizations, allowing infants more freedom to explore and have access to objects, and as offering the child more alternatives of thought and action (Hess and Shipman, 1965; Levine et al., 1967; Tulkin and Kagan, 1972).

Clearly, qualitative differences have been attributed to class status with respect to parenting behavior. The picture is not a clear one, however. Many findings are derived from questionnaires and interviews, and the relationship between data obtained in this manner and the actual behavior of parents is a major issue (Caldwell, 1964; Moss, 1965; Tulkin and Cohler, 1973). Furthermore, differences among the social classes today may or may not persist into the future. As already indicated even the behavior of individual parents at one age of the child is not the behavior of those parents at another age. Prothro (1966), in a cross-cultural study, reported that no necessary relationship exists between permissiveness in infancy and in childhood. Clearly parents' values and expectations for their children are influenced by their education and social status, and these values are reflected in their parental behavior, but expressions of values take very complex form. Furthermore, there are large variations in parental behavior within social classes (Tulkin and Kagan, 1972), as well as temporal, cultural, subcultural and geographic differences within each class (Richards, 1971). Thus, it is difficult to derive implications from the findings of variation associated with social class.

Maternal characteristics related to parenting behavior

Parity of the mother or birth order of the child
A vast literature exists which examines the differences among children as a function of their birth order and compares the behavior of the mother toward children in different ordinal positions.

Most studies comparing the behavior of parents toward children in different ordinal position have relied on retrospective responses either of the parents or of the child. Relatively few studies have observed actual interactions between parents and children of differing birth order. Mothers are reported to be less warm and more restrictive and coersive toward first born (Lasko, 1954). Mothers of second and later-born children allow more self-demand feeding in infancy, more permissiveness in nursing and weaning, and provide less bedtime nurturance; they also reported less anxiety about their own skills and the health and welfare of their children (Sears, 1950). Mothers of first borns were found to be more affectionately demonstrative than mothers of later borns; however, when the mothers of first-born children discovered their child was failing at a task, they showed a significant decrement in verbal support and demonstrative love not found with mothers of second-born children (Hilton, 1967). One review concluded that parents of first children pay more attention, talk and interact more, are more directive in achievement and responsibility, and show more inconsistency of training; the mother is likely to show more interference, more extreme affect, and more inconsistency (Hilton, 1968). Rothbart (1971) found that mothers gave more complex technical explanations to, and exhibited greater pressure for achievement of first borns, and exhibited greater anxious intrusiveness toward them. The effect of the mother's parity also interacts with the sex of the child. Samson (1962) suggests the first born receives more independence and responsibility, but that the training is more intense and earlier for the first-born female than male.

In a series of studies involving direct observation of mothers feeding their infants during the first three days of life, recordings were made of the frequency and duration of the behavior of mother and infant (Thoman et al., 1970b, 1971, 1972). Whether breast- or bottle-feeding, primiparous mothers spent longer at the feeding and interrupted it more frequently for burping or other nonfeeding activities. In general, the results strongly suggested that the primiparous mother is less sensitive to the cues shown by the infant during the feeding interaction. The data depict characteristics of primiparous and multiparous mothers that are similar to those reported in studies of parents with older children.

Parity of the mother clearly correlates with differing parental practices, and these differences seem to span the child's development. An amazing number of studies have been made which have served to catalog the numerous ways in which children of different birth order and mothers of differing parity vary in their behavior. This is somewhat surprising in view of the fact that the term 'parity,' as a variable, has so little explanatory value. Yet to be identified are the component variables of parity related to the behavior differences observed: a mother's previous experience in child care, her changes in physiology with successive pregnancies, and her maturational changes with age may each be significant variables that account for differences in behavior related to maternal parity. These factors have yet to be explored.

Maternal personality characteristics
Another maternal characteristic related to parenting is the personality of the mother, including expressions of anxiety. Davids (1968) rated women on anxiety levels during the third trimester of pregnancy. In those who showed high levels of anxiety, significantly more negative child-rearing attitudes were evident at eight months postpartum; on a questionnaire more hostility in control was expressed, and less favorable ratings were received on an observed mother—infant interaction. Caldwell and collaborators (1963) found that differences in mothering behavior related to the basic personality structure of the women. Moss and co-workers (1969) found that if mothers were rated high on animation and expressiveness in the last trimester of pregnancy, they were later found to show more affectionate stimulation to their male infant and more distal stimulation to the female infant. Maternal psychological characteristics, attitudes and ideas about infants, assessed pre- and postnatally, are significantly related to maternal practices (Moss et al., 1967; Moss and Robson, 1968; Tulkin and Cohler, 1973).

The problem of relating individual or personality characteristics of women to their parenting behavior remains as difficult as the problems of measuring personality characteristics and of measuring parental behavior. It would be expected that a mother's personality would be expressed in her parenting behavior, but the difficulties in measurement are seen in the extreme in this issue.

Physiological and psychological changes accompanying maternity

A major correlate of maternal behavior, one which presumably acts in a causal way, is the mother's physiological status, primarily in hormone levels changing with pregnancy, parturition and lactation. In animals, relations between maternal behavior and hormones have been explored extensively. With human mothers it is extremely difficult to isolate variables, even as correlates, without numerous confounding factors that can either exaggerate or conceal effective variables. For example, in a series of studies using rats, Thoman and collaborators (Thoman et al., 1968, 1970a) found that during lactation the maternal animal was buffered against a variety of stressors. Then, in an attempt to extend these findings by means of a comparative study of human mothers (Thoman, unpublished), measures of adrenal-cortisol levels were obtained from mothers 6-weeks postpartum preceding and following a controlled social stress. Multiparous and primiparous, breast- and bottle-feeding mothers, with 10 subjects in each group were included in this study. As predicted, the multiparous, nursing mothers showed markedly lower cortisol levels than primiparous or nonnursing mothers. However, the groups were highly variable and the differences did not reach significance.

Newton and colleagues (1968) reported differences in behaviors of nursing and nonnursing mothers. It is not possible to identify the degree to which these differences were related to physiological differences in the mothers or to experiential correlates. As Bernal and Richards (1970) point out, there are a variety of conditions that may be associated with whether the mother chooses to breast- or bottle-feed her infant. Nevertheless there is a variety of differences in maternal reactions among those mothers who breast feed and those who bottle feed their infants. Newton (1971) reviewed these findings. She noted that the differences are associated not only with whether or not the mother breast feeds, but also whether or not the feeding is simply a 'token' approach to breast feeding, or whether breast feeding occurs in an unrestricted manner for the baby. She found that breast feeding mothers maintained more body contact with their infants, were more accepting of sexual interest on the part of the children, and indicated more interest in the exchange of affection.

The studies just described are of special interest because they are concerned with the effects of breast and bottle feeding on the mother rather than on the infant. Typically, researchers concerned with the mode of feeding have asked questions about the infant: Does breast feeding provide better nutrition? Does breast feeding provide a better psychological experience for the infant? While the answers to these questions are important ones, they will not provide a complete picture of the significance of the way in which a mother feeds her infant. It is now clear that the experience of breast feeding and the physiological changes that accompany lactation may have significant consequences for the mother's behavior. These will, of course, find expression in the mother—infant relationship which will, in turn, affect the infant. But the point of emphasis here is that the mother is also a subject of direct interest, not just of concern because she is a mediator of effects for the child.

The father as a partner in parenting

Until very recently, the father has been largely neglected in research. Currently, as fathers are apparently taking a greater part in the caretaking activities of their young, researchers are beginning to turn their attention to their role and to the characteristics of their parenting activities. The importance of the father's role is emphasized by a recent study (Kotelchuck, 1973) in which infants aged 6—21 months were observed in an experiment involving the parents and a stranger. The results suggested that infants form an active, close relationship with the father during the first two years and did not support the idea of a uniquely important mother—child relationship. The children indicated contentment with either parent, a similarity of responses to them, and a large amount of interaction with both parents.

From a survey of anthropology studies Howells (1970) concluded that fathering constitutes an important element in child nurturing in most societies and that the father's participation in child care is greater than is generally acknowledged. Furthermore, the concern in the literature with the absent father implies that he plays an important role when he is present.

Parke and co-workers (Parke et al., 1972; Parke and O'Leary, 1975) have studied father—infant interaction during the newborn period. In a population of well-educated middle-class families they found a high degree of participation of the father in child care from the very earliest days. When the father and mother were together, the father tended to hold and rock the baby more than the mother. On all other measures, the father was just as likely to interact with the baby as the mother. When the mother was not present, the father was even more likely to touch and rock the baby. When together, both parents smiled more at the infant than when only one parent was present; the mother and father had a mutually interactive effect on their parent—infant interaction.

Studies of maternal and paternal interactions with older children have identified differences in the behavior of the two parents in structured situations (Osofsky and O'Connell, 1972; Rothbart and Maccoby, 1966). However, many differences between mothers and fathers were a function of each parent's and the child's sex. Kohn (1969) found that among middle class parents each parent tended to be more supportive of the child of the parent's own sex. Sears and co-workers (1957) report that fathers take a more active role in disciplining male children, with female children being disciplined primarily by their mother.

The child as a correlate for parental behavior

Sex of the child
The only characteristic of the child that has received a significant amount of attention is that of sex. In many studies, differences were found in parental behavior as a function of the child's sex, even where the subjects were parents of very young infants. For example, Thoman and co-workers (1972) found that primiparous mothers of newborn infant girls talked, smiled and stimulated them more than mothers of newborn infant boys during a feeding on the second day of life. Consistent with these findings are several studies in which mothers of females ranging in age from three months to $2\frac{1}{2}$ years provided more verbal stimulation than mothers of males (Levine et al., 1967; Goldberg and Lewis, 1969; Halverson and Waldrop, 1970; Lewis, 1972).

At older ages sex differences have been found in disciplinary measures. Primarily the differences are not in terms of quantity of discipline but the nature of the discipline, which is more likely to be in the form of withdrawal of affection for girls and physical punishment for boys (Sears et al., 1957). Furthermore, girls and boys may be punished for different kinds of violations (Kagan and Freeman, 1963; Kohn, 1969). In general, as suggested by Olley (1971) and Goldberg and Lewis (1969), parental behavior is designed to contribute to the shaping of sex-appropriate behavior. However, differences may also be in response to sex differences in the offspring's behavior; behavioral sex differences have been documented as early as the neonatal period (reviews by Olley, 1971; Korner, 1974).

Age of the child
The age of a child obviously influences parental behavior, but this variable has rarely been an object of study. A limited age-span is generally used for each study, and few longitudinal studies of parental behavior have been carried out. It should be noted, however, that where longitudinal information is available, parental behavior has not necessarily been found to be consistent over ages (Lasko, 1964; Prothro, 1966).

Korner (1974) suggested that maternal interventions and stimulation are geared to the infant's maturing sensory and behavioral systems and that with age, maturational changes in the infant evoke modifications in maternal behavior. Complementary changes in infant's and mother's behavior over the first few months have been described (Moss, 1967; Moss and Robson, 1968).

Abnormality in the child
The effect of an abnormal infant on parental behavior has received attention in recent years. Parental anxiety and rejection of a child has been the most frequently found consequence of physical abnormalities or of behavioral disorders in children. For example, Brazelton (1961) describes a difficult infant who presented an extreme, 'unreachable' state, beginning in the neonatal period, and he depicts how the infant's characteristics deleteriously influ-

enced the mother's reaction producing feeling of guilt and inadequacy in the mother. Prechtl (1963) interviewed mothers of infants with minimal brain damage (hyperexcitability syndrome). He found that mothers of aberrant infants felt that their 'mishandling' of the infant was to blame rather than the infant's characteristics, and they indicated a greater rejection of their infants than mothers of normal children. Shaheen and co-workers (1968) studied a group of failure-to-thrive infants under two years of age. A large percent of these children were either of low birth weight or premature, and were perceived by the parents as being damaged at birth or developmentally slow. Klein and Stern (1971) provided evidence that abnormality in the child predisposes to battering. They found that low birth weight, mental retardation, severe illness and early maternal—infant separation tend to coincide and to predispose to battering. Chavez and colleagues (1974) found that when nutritional supplements were provided to malnourished infants, the infant's behavior was changed to the extent that he initiated a different behavioral pattern and interaction within the family. The nourished children were able to elicit more responses, more praise, more verbal interaction, more rewards and more attention from both the father and mother.

Individual differences among normal children
The studies described above clearly indicate that general characteristics of children have consequences for parental behavior. Children show wide variations in their pattern of behavior from the time of birth. Korner (1974) has reviewed evidence for individual differences among newborns in characteristics which are likely to effect mother—infant interaction, including irritability, soothability, wakefulness, alertness and sensory responsiveness. However, relatively little research has focused on the effects of the individual characteristics of a child on his caretakers' behavior. A rather dramatic illustration of the potency of these effects is a case study by Yarrow (1963) describing two infants of the same age and sex, cared for at the same time by a foster mother. She showed markedly different behavior in every dimension of her maternal care except routine physical care toward the two infants. Differences in maternal treatment were related to individual characteristics of the infants eliciting very different feelings and behavior from the mother. Yarrow and co-workers (1971) studied the behavior of nursery school caretakers who had been given very specific role training. Nevertheless, their behavior, both positive and negative, and whether initiated by the adult or solicited by the child, were highly variable among children and systematically related to child characteristics of dependency, aggressive and friendly peer interactions, positive behavior toward the caretaker, and the sex of the child.

3. CONCLUDING REMARKS

Many factors are related to variations in parenting: parents are influenced by their social millieu; their own emotional states, anxieties and attitudes; the mother's physiology; and characteristics of the child. Although our overview of parenting studies included only a sampling from the extensive literature, those described were selected as being representative of the current status of research on parenting.

The picture of parenting is far from complete. Additional variables are yet to be explored; and most of the variables that have been studied have been examined only at limited age ranges of the child. Even more, many of the sociocultural variables studied will require continuous cataloging of correlates because the observed relationships are time-bound. For example, in our western culture, attitudes toward control of the child's behavior have changed over the past twenty years. Among all social classes physical punishment is less accepted as a means of control. Likewise, attitudes towards breast- and bottle-feeding of infants have shifted within the various social classes. Before 1930 and through the 1940s bottle feeding was more accepted among the middle class and breast feeding among the lower class (Garland and Rich, 1930; Havighurst and Davis, 1955); but subsequently there was a trend toward an increased frequency of breast feeding among the educated classes of mothers (Boek et al., 1957; Sears et al., 1957; Salber and Feinleib, 1966). As another example, notions on the nature of sex roles are currently undergoing a shift towards less differentiation of the expectations of girls and boys. Thus, while it is possible to conclude that culture and social class are major variables influencing parenting behavior it is not possible to make enduring generalizations with respect to the ways in which specific parental behavior will be affected by these variables.

Several studies in recent years suggest that a new view of parenting is emerging. These studies are based on the premise that analysis of neither the parent's nor the child's behavior alone can depict the behavior of either in all of its complexity. The parent is viewed as a member of a dyadic system including the child, for whom interaction is an ongoing process, as it is for the child, with continual mutual modification of behavior of each member by the other. A very clear exposition of this view is presented by Rosenthal (1973). As she points out, a number of researchers have been proponents of the interactional view of parenting, but very few have undertaken to cope with the complexities of such study. Early efforts in this direction include: a study of 'dyadic gazing' by Robson and co-workers (1969); studies of mother—infant interaction by Lewis (1972) and by Yarrow and colleagues (1972). Rosenthal (1973) points out that these studies are not truly interactional in nature because analyses are concerned with the simultaneity of occurrence of the behavior of mother and infant, rather than with attempting to depict mutual interaction over time. A truly interactional approach requires sequential analyses of behavioral events, probably based on the Markovian model or some extension of this model.

The study of sequencing of mother and infant behavior precludes the use of procedures involving indirect methods of obtaining data, including interviews, questionnaires and rating scales. It becomes necessary to find procedures by which actual behavior of parents and children are recorded. From defined behavior sequences, it is then possible to identify patterns of interaction for individual mother and infant pairs (Thoman, 1975). With an interactional approach, new questions about the correlates of parenting behavior are asked, for example: (1) What is the role of the parent in the interactive system? (2) How does the parent—child interaction influence the parent's behavior? (3) How does the parent—child interaction influence the child's development? (4) How does the parent contribute to a synchrony in this interactive system by perceiving the cues of the child and responding to the child's communications? and (5) How does an individual interaction develop as a function of the role played by the parent and the child? A whole range of questions about communication, both verbal and nonverbal, now become relevant. To the extent that the search for answers to these questions is effective, it may eventually be possible to reveal how parenting behavior affects and is affected by the child's behavior, developmentally. Here lies a promise of generalization about parenting that may, to some degree, be free of time, place, and culture.

4. SUMMARY

Parenting is a major component of human behavior which can be viewed as both an independent and a dependent variable. Parenting has been studied by means of interviews, questionnaires, and direct observation in both controlled and naturalistic situations. The major variables that have been found to vary with characteristics of parental behavior include: the socioeconomic status of the family, and the mother's personality, parity, and physiological status. The physiological changes associated with breast-feeding have been found to be related to the mother's responsiveness to her infant, her husband, and to other people.

In recent years, the father's role has received greater research attention, along with a growing tendency for fathers to participate in the caretaking activities of their children, at least in our western culture.

A major modifier of parenting behavior is the child. The sex as well as the age of the child are general factors that influence parenting behavior. In addition, the individual characteristics of any child, including physical or behavioral abnormalities, are recognized as a major source of influence on parental behavior.

In studies of parenting at the present time, there is a growing emphasis on interaction between both parents and the child, with the interaction considered as a system which is psychobiological in nature and characterized by an ongoing process of mutual modification. Within such a framework, an analysis of either the parental or the child's behavior alone cannot account for the developing behavior of either member of the dyad (or triad). The interactional emphasis has been accompanied by a growing interest in naturalistic observations of parents and children as a means of describing the qualities of the relationship, or system. This view assumes that the characteristics of the interactive system must be depicted if one is to understand either the process of parenting itself or the influence of parenting on the development of the child.

BIBLIOGRAPHY

Bagley, N. and Schaefer, E. (1960) Relationships between socioeconomic variables and behavior of mothers toward young children. *J. Gen. Psychol.* 96: 61—77.

Becker, W. and Krug, R. (1965) Parent attitude research instrument: Research review. *Child Dev.* 36: 329—365.

Boek, W.E., Lawson, E.D., Yankauer, A. and Sussman, M.M. (1957) *Social Class, Maternal Health and Child Care.* Dittoed publication. (New York State Department of Health, Albany) p. 103.

Brazelton, T. (1961) Psychophysiologic reactions in the neonate I. Value of observation of the neonate. *J. Pediat.* 58: 508—512.

Bronfenbrenner, U. (1958) Socialization and social class through time and space. In: (E. Maccoby, Ed.), *Readings in Social Psychology.* (Holt, Rinehart and Winston, New York).

Brown, F., Lieberman, J., Winston, J. and Pleshette, N. (1960) Studies in choice of infant feeding by primiparas. *Psychosom. Med.* 22: 421—429.

Busse, T.V. and Busse, P. (1972) Negro parental behavior and social class variables. *J. Genet. Psychol.* 120: 287—294.

Caldwell, B. (1964) Effects of infant care. In: (M. Hoffman and L. Hoffman, Eds.), *Review of Child Development Research,* Vol. 1. (Russell Sage Foundation, New York).

Caldwell, B., Herscher, L., Lipton, E., Richmond, J., Stern, G., Eddy, E., Drachman, R. and Rothman, A. (1963) Mother-infant interaction in monomatric and polymatric families. *Am. J. Orthopsychiat.* 33: 653—664.

Chavez, A., Martinez, C. and Yaschire, T. (1974) Nutrition, behavioral development and mother-child interaction in young rural children. (Symposium on Effects of Nutrition on Maternal-Infant Interaction, Atlantic City, April.)

Davids, A. (1968) A research design for studying maternal emotionality before child birth and after social interaction with the child. *Merrill-Palmer Quart.* 14 (4) 345—354.

Garland, J. and Rich, M.B. (1930) Duration of breast feeding: Comparative study. *New Engl. J. Med.* 203: 1279—1282.

Goldberg, S. and Lewis, M. (1969) Play behavior in the year-old infant: early sex differences. *Child Dev.* 40: 21—31.

Halverson, C. and Waldrop, M. (1970) Maternal behavior toward own and other preschool children: The problem of "ownness." *Child Dev.* 40 (3) 839—845.

Havighurst, R. and Davis, W. (1955) Comparison of Chicago and Harvard studies of social class differences in childrearing. *Am. Social Rev.* 20: 438—442.

Hess, R. and Shipman, V. (1965) Early experience and socialization of cognitive modes in children. *Child Dev.* 36: 869—886.

Hilton, I. (1967) Differences in behavior of mothers toward first and later-born children. *J. Pers. Soc. Psychol.* 7: 282—290.

Hilton, I; (1968) Dependent first born and how he grew. Paper presented at Am. Psych. Assoc., San Francisco.

Howells, J. (1970) Fallacies in child care II. That fathering is unimportant. *Acta Paedopsychiat.* 37 (2/3) 46—55.

Kagan, T. and Freeman, M. (1963) Relation of childhood intelligence, maternal behaviors and social class to behavior during adolescence. *Child Dev.* 34: 899—911.

Kagan, J. and Tulkin, S. (1971) Social class differences in child rearing during the first year. In: (H. Schaffer, Ed.), *Origins of Human Social Relations*. (Academic Press, London.)

Klein, M. and Stern, L. (1971) Low birth weight and the battered child syndrome. *Am. J. Dis. Child*. 122: 15—18.

Kohn, M. (1969) *Class and conformity: A study of values*. (Dorsey Press, Homewood, Illinois.)

Kohn, M. and Schooler, C. (1969) Class, occupation and orientation. *Am. Soc. Rev*. 34: 659—678.

Kogan, K. and Wimberger, H. (1969) Interaction patterns in disadvantaged families. *J. Clin. Psychol*. 25: 347—352.

Kornor, A. (1074) Effect of infant's state, level of arousal, sex and ontogenetic stage on the caregiver. In: (M; Lewis and L. Rosenblum, Eds.), *Effect of the Infant on its Caregiver*. (John Woley, New York.)

Kotelchuck, M. (1973) Nature of infant's behavior to his father. (Paper presented at Soc. Res. Child Dev., Philadelphia.)

Lasko, J. (1964) Parent behavior toward first and second children. *Genet. Psychol. Monogr*. 49: 97—137.

Levine, J., Fishman, C. and Kagan, J. (1967) Sex of child and social class as determinants of maternal behavior. (Paper presented at Soc. Res. Child Dev, New York.)

Lewis, M. (1972) State as an infant-environment interaction: analysis of mother-infant behavior as a function of sex. *Merrill-Palmer Quart*. 18: 95—121.

Minton, C., Kagan, J. and Levine, J. (1971) Maternal control and obedience in the 2-year old. *Child Dev*. 42: 1873—1894.

Moss, H. (1965) Methodological issues in studying mother-infant interaction. *Am. J. Orthopsychiat*. 35: 482—486.

Moss, H. and Robson, K. (1968) Maternal influences in early social visual behavior. *Child Dev* 39: 401—408.

Moss, H., Robson, K. and Pederson, F. (1969) Determinants of maternal stimulation of infants and consequences of treatment for later reactions to strangers. *Dev. Psychol*. 1: 239—246.

Moss, H., Ryder, R. and Robson, K. (1967) Relationship between preparental variables assessed at newlywed stage and later maternal behaviors. (Paper presented at Soc. Res. Child Dev., New York.)

Newton, N. (1971) Psychologic differences between breast and bottle feeding. *Am. J. Clin. Nutr*. 24: 993—1004.

Newton, N., Peeler, D. and Rawlins, C. (1968) Effect of lactation on maternal behavior in mice with comparative data on humans. *Lying-In: J. Reprod. Med*. 1: 257—262.

Olley, J. (1971) Sex differences in human behavior in first year of life. *Peabody Papers in Human Development*, Vol. 1.

Osofsky, J. and O'Connell, E. (1972) Parent-child interaction: daughters effects upon mothers' and fathers' behavior. *Dev. Psychol*. 7: 157—168.

Parke, R. and O'Leary, S. (1975) Father-mother-infant interaction in the newborn period: Some findings, some observations and some unresolved issues. In: (K. Riefel and J. Meacham, Eds.), *The Developing Individual in a Changing World, Vol. II. Social and Environmental Issues*. (Mouton, The Hague).

Parke, R., O'Leary, S. and West, S. (1972) Mother-father-newborn interaction: effects of maternal medication, labor and sex of infant. *Proc. 80th Annu. Conv., APA*, 85—86.

Prechtl, H.F.R. (1963) Mother-child interaction in babies with minimal brain damage. In: (B. Foss, Ed.), *Determinants of Infant Behavior, Vol. II*. (Methuen, London.)

Prothro, E. (1966) Socialization and social class in a transitional society. *Child Dev*. 37: 219—228.

Radin, N. (1972) Father-child interaction and intellectual functioning of 4-year-old boys. *Dev. Psychol*. 6 (2) 353—361.

Richards, M. (1971) Comment on social context of mother-infant interaction. In: (H. Schaffer, Ed.), *Origin of Human Social Relations*. (Academic Press, London.)

Rosenthal, M.K. (1973) The study of infant-environment interaction: Some comments on trends and methodologies. *J. Child Psychol. Psychiat.* 14: 301—317.

Rothbart, M. (1971) Birth order and mother-child interaction in an achievement situation. *J. Pers. Soc. Psychol.* 17 (2) 113—120.

Rothbart, M. and Maccoby, E. (1966) Parents' differential reactions to sons and daughters. *J. Pers. Soc. Psychol.* 4: 237—243.

Salber, E.J. and Feinleib, M. (1966) Breast feeding in Boston. *Pediatrics* 37: 299—303.

Sampson, E. (1962) Birth order, need achievement and conformity. *J. Abn. Soc. Psychol.* 64: 155—159.

Sears, R. (1950) Ordinal position in family as a psychological variable. *Am. Soc. Rev.* 15: 397—401.

Sears, A., Maccoby, E. and Levine, H. (1957) *Patterns of Child Rearing*. (Row and Peterson, New York.)

Shaheen, E., Alexander, D., Truskowsky, M. and Arberto, G. (1968) Failure to thrive — a retrospective profile. *Clin. Pediat.* 7: 255—261.

Thoman, E. (1975) How a rejecting baby may affect mother-infant synchrony. Ciba Foundat. Symp. 33, *Parent-Infant Interaction*. (Elsevier, Amsterdam.)

Thoman, E., Barnett, C. and Leiderman, P. (1971) Feeding behaviors of newborn infants as a function of parity of the mother. *Child Dev.* 42: 1471—1483.

Thoman, E., Conner, R. and Levine, S. (1970a) Lactation suppresses adrenal corticosteroid activity and aggressiveness in rats. *J. Comp. Physiol. Psychol.* 70: 364—369.

Thoman, E., Leiderman, P. and Olson, J. (1972) Neonate-mother interaction during breast feeding. *Dev. Psychol.* 6 (1) 110—118.

Thoman, E., Wetzel, A. and Levine, S. (1968) Lactation prevents disruption of temperature regulation and suppresses adrenocortical activity in rats. *Commun. Behav. Biol. A.* 2: 165—171.

Thoman, E., Turner, A., Leiderman, H. and Barnett, C. (1970b) Neonate-mother interaction: effects of parity on feeding behavior. *Child Dev.* 41: 1103—1111.

Tulkin, S. and Cohler, B. (1973) Childbearing attitudes and mother-child interaction in the first year of life. *Merrill-Palmer Quart.* 19: 95—106.

Tulkin, S. and Kagan, J. (1972) Mother-child interaction in the first year of life. *Child Dev.* 43: 31—41.

Yarrow, L. (1963) Research in dimensions of early maternal care. *Merill-Palmer Quart.* 9: 101—114.

Yarrow, L., Rubenstein, J.L., Pedersen, F.A. and Jankowski, J. (1972) Dimensions of early stimulation: differential effects on infant development. *Merill-Palmer Quart.* 18: 205—218.

Yarrow, M., Waxler, C. and Scott, P. (1971) Child effects on adult behavior. *Dev. Psychol.* 5: 300—311.

CHAPTER 57

Parental attachment behavior

MARY ANNE TRAUSE, JOHN KENNELL and MARSHALL KLAUS

> You can't pay anyone to do what a mother will do for free
> *Russian proverb*

Much of the richness of life comes from close relationships or attachments to other people. Early in life the infant develops an attachment to one individual, most often the mother. The characteristics of subsequent relationships will be strongly influenced by the quality and strength of this initial one. An attachment can be defined as an affectional bond between two individuals which endures through time and space and serves to join them together emotionally. An attachment of this type is an unique relationship, so that it is not unusual for an individual to have fewer than ten throughout his lifetime. It is useful to differentiate human attachments according to the individuals involved so that one may focus on the specific characteristics and functions of each relationship.

Perhaps the strongest affectional tie in the human is that of the mother to her child. This relationship has two unique characteristics in that before delivery the infant exists within the mother's body and after delivery it is utterly dependent upon her for its survival. Why do most mothers make the sacrifices necessary to care for an infant day after day; changing dirty diapers and giving feedings in the middle of the night when they may be tired and exhausted? How do they develop such a powerful bond to a tiny infant who at first sleeps for hours on end and only awakes to cry, eat, burp and fall asleep again?

Although the development of the attachment of an infant to its mother has been widely investigated in the past three decades starting with the publications of Spitz and Bowlby, the tie of a mother to her infant has only recently been the focus of study. Still newer has been the scientific interest in the father and his relationship to his newborn child. Nonetheless, studies and observations from a variety of sources now make it possible to fit together a

Handbook of Sexology, edited by J. Money and H. Musaph
© *Elsevier/North-Holland Biomedical Press, 1977*

Table I
Steps in Attachment (from Kennell and Klaus, 1971).

Planning the pregnancy	Birth
Confirming the pregnancy	Hearing the Baby
Accepting the pregnancy	Seeing the Baby
Fetal movement	Looking "en face" at the Baby
Accepting the fetus as an individual	Touching and holding the Baby
	Caretaking

tentative model of how affectional bonds between the human mother and her infant develop. It is also possible to identify factors that may alter or distort this process either temporarily or permanently. Some of the time periods which are apparently crucial are shown in Table I. The development of mother-to-infant rather than father-to-infant attachment will be the central focus of this chapter since more data are available for them from both clinical observations and controlled studies. Information relating to the father—infant bond will be presented parenthetically.

1. PREGNANCY

During pregnancy, a woman experiences two types of developmental changes at the same time: (1) physical and emotional changes within herself, and (2) the growth of the fetus in her uterus. How she feels about these changes will vary widely according to whether the pregnancy was planned, whether she is married, whether she is living with the father, whether she has other children and, if so, their ages, whether she is working or wants to work, her memories of her childhood and how she feels about her parents (Boston Women's Health Book Collective, 1971). For most women, pregnancy is a time of change and of strong emotions which are sometimes positive, other times negative and frequently ambivalent. With the realization that she will soon have a baby, particularly if it is her first, the woman must adapt to a dramatic change in her life as she changes from an individual responsible primarily for herself to a parent responsible for the life and well-being of a child. There will also be changes in her relationship with the father when she has to divide her time and attention between two people.

Caplan (1960) considers pregnancy to be a developmental crisis involving two particular adaptive tasks.

Acceptance of the pregnancy

During the first stage of pregnancy a woman must come to terms with the knowledge that she will be a mother. When they first realize they are pregnant, many women have mixed feelings because of a large number of considerations ranging from a change in their familiar patterns to more serious matters such as economic and housing hardships or interpersonal difficulties. This initial stage, as outlined by Bibring and co-workers (1961) is the mother's identification of the growing fetus as an 'integral part of herself'.

Perception of the fetus as a separate individual

The second stage involves a growing awareness of the baby in the uterus as a separate individual, usually starting with the sensation of fetal movement (quickening), a remarkably powerful event. During this period the woman must begin to change her concept of the fetus from a part of herself to a living baby who will soon be a separate individual. Bibring and co-workers (1961) believe that this realization prepares the woman for delivery and physical separation from her child. This preparedness in turn lays the foundation for a relationship to the child.

After quickening, a woman will usually begin to have fantasies about what the baby will be like, attributing some human personality characteristics to him/her and developing a sense of attachment and value toward him/her. At this time, further acceptance of the pregnancy and marked changes in attitude toward the fetus may be observed. Unplanned, unwanted infants may seem more acceptable. Objectively, there will usually be some outward evidence of the mother's preparation by such actions as the purchase of clothes or a crib, the selection of a name, and the re-arrangement of space to accommodate a baby.

Cohen (1966) pointed out that any stress (such as moving to a new geographic area, marital infidelity, death of a close friend or relative, previous abortions or loss of previous children) which leaves the mother feeling unloved, or unsupported, or causes her concern about the health and survival of her baby or herself may delay preparation for the infant and retard bond formation. After the first trimester, behavior suggesting rejection of pregnancy includes preoccupation with physical appearance with negative self-perception, excessive emotional withdrawal or mood swings, excessive physical complaints, absence of response to quickening, or lack of any preparatory behavior during the last trimester.

2. DELIVERY

The few data available for this period suggest that mothers who remain relaxed during labor, and who cooperate and have good rapport with those caring for them are more apt to be pleased with their infants at the first sight (Newton and Newton, 1962). Unconsciousness during delivery does not cause the mother to reject her infant in an obvious manner as has been observed in some animals. However, Helfer reports (personal communication) there is a ten-fold increase in child abuse after delivery by Caesarian section as compared with vaginal deliveries.

We have recently begun to study home deliveries in California by means of videotapes and discussion with a perceptive midwife (Raven Lang, personal communication) who has made naturalistic observations during fifty-two home deliveries. In sharp contrast to the woman who gives birth in the hospital, a woman delivering at home with this midwife appears to be in control. She chooses both the room in the house and the location within the room where she would like the birth to take place as well as the close friends who will be present to share this experience with her. She is an active participant during her labor and delivery rather than a passive patient. Immediately after delivery, she appears to be in a remarkable state of ecstacy. In fact many mothers have reported they had sensations similar to orgasm at the time of delivery. The exuberance is contagious and the observers share the festive mood of unreserved elation after the delivery. They offer congratulations and provide grooming and other comforts to the mother. Striking in the films is the observers' intense interest in the infant, especially in the first 15—20 min of life. Although controlled studies have not yet been done to test the effects of this experience on the mother—infant relationship, it seems clear that the conditions surrounding delivery greatly affect the mother's initial mood and interaction with her infant.

3. AFTER DELIVERY

Recently considerable attention has been devoted to the events of a relatively short period of time — the first minutes and hours immediately after delivery. This focus has been stimulated in part by detailed observations of animal mothers. As in other aspects of neonatology, animal models have provided a valuable starting point. They have suggested important variables for studies of the behavior of human mothers. Very useful have been the observations of species-specific maternal behavior patterns of nesting, exploring, grooming, and retrieving. Nature has not left the survival of a species to chance, but has instead provided intricate mechanisms which trigger maternal behavior in females during and after delivery and thus insure the care of their young.

Species-specific behavior and early reciprocal interaction

After delivery the human mother shows a characteristic behavior pattern, as do mothers of other animal species. Filmed observations made an average of 5.3 h after delivery show that a mother presented with her nude, full-term infant begins with fingertip touching of the infant's extremities. Within a few minutes she proceeds to massage, with encompassing palm contact of the infant's trunk (Klaus et al., 1970). Mothers of premature infants also follow a small portion of this sequence but proceed at a much slower rate. When mothers are given their fully clothed infants, according to Rubin (1963), it takes several days for them to move to palmar stroking of the trunk. We have observed that fathers go through some of the same routine. In contrast, Raven Lang has observed that during home deliveries where the mother rather than a doctor has been in control, she cradles her infant in her arms immediately after its birth and begins touching its face with her fingertips. Thus, there is fragmentary evidence that human mothers engage in a species-specific sequence of touching behavior when first meeting their infants, even though the speed of this sequence is modified by environmental conditions.

A strong interest in eye-to-eye contact has been expressed by mothers of both full-term and premature infants. When the words of mothers who had been presented their infants in privacy were taped, 70% of the statements referred to the eyes. The mothers said, "Let me see your eyes," and "Open your eyes and I'll know you love me." Robson (1967) has suggested that eye-to-eye contact appears to elicit maternal caregiving responses. Mothers seem to try hard to look 'en face' at their infants, that is to keep their faces aligned so that their eyes are in the same vertical plane of rotation as the eyes of the baby as shown by the mother on the left in Fig. 1. Complementing the mother's interest in the infant's eyes is the early functional

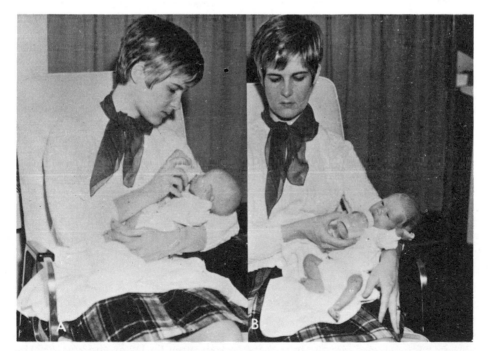

Fig. 1. A posed mother shows two different caretaking positions. (A) Infant is held in close contact (cuddling), mother is looking at infant 'en face', and milk is in the tip of the nipple. (B) Infant's trunk is held away from mother, mother is looking at infant but not 'en face', and there is no milk in the tip of the nipple. (From Klaus and Kennell, 1970.)

development of the infant's visual pathways. The infant is alert, active, and able to follow visually during the first hour of life (Brazelton et al., 1966) if maternal sedation has been limited and the administration of silver nitrate has been delayed.

If we are correct in our hypothesis that this type of looking at and touching is a species-specific behavior for the human, nature has provided a way of insuring continued contact between mothers and their newborns while the infants are helpless. A parturient mother already has had nine months of contact with her child since she has carried it in her uterus during pregnancy. During that period she has undergone physiological and psychological changes that have fostered her expectation and anticipation of the birth of her baby. She has become attached to the image of the baby she would deliver. Then with labor and delivery came an intense experience with maternal exertion, exhaustion, and the physical separation of mother and child. Yet with the mother's strong desire to touch and see her child, nature has provided for the immediate and essential reunion of the two. The alert newborn rewards his mother for her efforts by following her with its eyes and in this way, maintaining their interaction, kindling the tired mother's fascination with her baby.

Condon and Sander (1974) showed that young infants in the first days of life entrain and move in rhythm to human speech. Thus the normal neonate appears equipped to follow its mother with its eyes and move in tune to her words. Lind and his associates in Stockholm have shown that a surprising change in blood flow to the breast occurs when the mother hears the cries of her own infant (Lind et al., 1973). These intricate interactions have focused our attention on the cascade of interlocking sensory patterns that quickly develop between mother and infant in the first hours of life.

There is suggestive evidence that many of these early interactions also take place between the father and his newborn child. Parke (1974) in particular, has demonstrated that when fathers were given the opportunity to be alone with their newborns, they spent almost exactly the same amount of time as the mothers holding, touching, and looking at them.

In his work with a mother and her 3 month-old twins, Stern (1971) observed that the pattern of interaction between a mother and her child has a characteristic rhythm. Intricate interchanges occur within a period of a few seconds. And when these interactions were repeatedly out of phase, such as when one partner looked away just as the other looked toward, many aspects of the relationship between the two individuals were disturbed. Our observations suggest that this intricate interplay of mother and infant together, which may or may not be in phase, is first initiated in the immediate postpartum period. As Brazelton and his colleagues (1974) have stated, "This interdependency of rhythms seems to be at the root of their 'attachment' as well as communication." Thus, it seems important that the two have privacy in the first hours of life in which to become attuned to each other.

On the basis of our observations and the reports of parents, we believe that every mother has a task to perform during this postpartum period to look at and 'take in' her real live wiggling baby and reconcile the fantasy of the infant she imagined with the specific one she actually delivered. Many cultures recognize this need by providing the mother with a 'doula', or 'aunt' who mothers her and relieves her of other responsibilities so that she can devote herself completely to this task (Raphael, 1973).

Maternal sensitive period

There is evidence that when mothers are separated from their babies during the first hours after delivery, they have difficulty forming an attachment. Studies of mothers of premature infants who spent their first weeks of life in neonatal intensive care nurseries highlight this problem. In those nurseries where the mothers are not allowed to visit, doctors find that mothers temporarily forget they have babies and find reasons to put off taking them home. The evidence that a disproportionately high number of prematures is found among both battered children and among children with failure-to-thrive syndrome adds further weight to the hypothesis that separation of mother and her baby may disrupt normal attachment processes and result in disastrous consequences. Although only about 7—8% of live births are premature each year, as many as 25—41% of reported infants with failure to thrive and 23—31% of battered infants have been prematures (Fanaroff et al., 1972).

In a large number of animal species it has been found that separation of mother and baby immediately after birth can severely distort mothering behavior. If the goat, for example, is separated from her kid immediately after delivery for one hour she is likely to butt it away when it is returned. If however, a separation of similar duration begins five minutes after delivery, the dam will re-accept her kid upon reunion and allow it to nurse (Klopfer, 1971). Thus, there appears to be a sensitive period in the first minutes of life during which any alteration in the normal pattern of interaction can result in aberrant subsequent mothering behavior.

A few studies have focused on the possibility of a sensitive early period in the human mother. Observations at Stanford and in our own unit have been made with mothers of prematures, half of whom were permitted into the nursery in the first hours and half of whom could not come in until the twentieth day. At Case Western Reserve University mothers who had early contact with their infants looked at them significantly more than late contact mothers during a filmed feeding at the time of discharge. Furthermore, preliminary data on the IQs of these two groups of children at forty-two months indicate that children in the early contact group scored significantly higher (mean = 99) than did children in the late contact group (mean = 85). Strikingly, a significant correlation was found between IQ at 42 months and the amount of time women looked at their babies during the one-month filmed feeding (r = 0.71). This is consistent with our hypothesis that early contact affects aspects of maternal behavior which may have significance for the child's later development. At Stanford, when those separated from their premature babies from 3 to 12 weeks were compared with mothers of prematures permitted early contact, there were more divorces (5 compared to 1) and more infants relinquished (2 compared to 0) in the group of mothers with prolonged separation (Leifer et al., 1972).

In a tightly controlled study of 28 primiparous mothers and their full-term infants, half the mothers were given one hour of extra contact in the first 3 h after birth and 15 extra hours of contact with their infants in the first three days of life. The mothers who had early and extended contact were more likely to stand near their infants and watch during the physical exam, show significantly more soothing behavior, engage in more eye-to-eye contact and fondling during feeding, and were more reluctant to leave their infants with someone else at one month than were mothers not given the extended contact experience (Klaus et al., 1972). At one year the two groups of mothers were again significantly different. Extended contact mothers spent more time near the table assisting the physician and soothing the infants while he examined their babies, and they reported themselves to be more preoccupied with the baby when they went out (Kennell et al., 1974). At two years, when the linguistic behaviors of the two groups of mothers while speaking to their children were compared, extended contact mothers used twice as many questions, more words per proposition, fewer content words, more adjectives and fewer commands than did the controls (Ringler et al., 1975). It is impressive evidence for a sensitive maternal period that just sixteen extra hours of contact in the first three days of life had such far-reaching effects.

Studies of the effects of rooming-in have also confirmed the importance of the early postnatal period. At Duke University a number of years ago, an increase in breast feeding and a reduction in anxious phone calls was found when rooming-in was instituted (McBryde, 1951). In Sweden, mothers randomly assigned to rooming-in arrangements were more confident and felt more competent in caregiving and thought they would need less help in caring for their infants at home than non-rooming-in mothers. They also appeared to be more sensitive to the crying of their own infants than were mothers who did not have the rooming-in experience (Greenberg et al., 1973). In an interesting and significant observation of fathers, Lind (personal communication) noted that paternal caregiving was markedly increased in the first three months of life when the father was asked to undress the infant twice and to establish eye-to-eye contact with it during the first three days of life.

In our neonatal intensive care nursery we have noticed that some of the effects of separation can be overcome when the parents are brought into the nursery and encouraged to participate in early caretaking responsibilities such as diapering, feeding and cleaning their babies, as well as in procedures that aid the survival or progress of the baby, such as tactile stimulation to prevent apneic episodes. Even more important has been the observation that a mother seems to develop a particularly close attachment when she perceives her infant as actually seeing her, hearing her voice, rousing or quieting with her touch and in other ways being able to receive and communicate messages of distress or pleasure to her. On the basis of the limited evidence available at this time, it seems to be essential for the mother and child to begin interacting during the maternal sensitive period. When the child or mother is sick during this time, everything points to the value of special efforts to bring them together.

4. SUMMARY

In summary, it appears that mothers, and probably fathers, go through a number of steps while becoming attached to their babies. These steps may not be very different from those that occur when a man and woman fall in love and develop an affectionate attachment. First, there seems to be a readiness to fall in love, a period during young adulthood for the not-yet-married and during pregnancy for the not-yet-parent when one dreams of the person to appear in the future. An image develops of what he or she will be like. The young man dreams of his future mate as a woman with certain physical characteristics and temperamental traits and the young woman dreams of her future child as a boy or girl who will look and act in certain ways.

When the baby finally is delivered, the young parent is very excited and aware of this new being. He or she 'takes it in' visually and probably also through the senses of touch, hearing and smell. She touches its extremities first, then moves her hands to encompass its body. She goes through predictable patterns of behavior in getting to know her child; she gazes at it with prolonged staring as lovers gaze at each other. The acquaintance process may again be similar to the young couple's sequence of first holding hands, then desiring more intimate or bodily contact. For both pairs, the early period of interaction seems to be a time when emotions are at a peak and when each partner is especially sensitive and responsive to the other. If the two are separated at this time, many of the initial interactions which serve to lock the two together are interrupted and it seems, for the mother at least, that the future course of the relationship is somehow disturbed.

Further research is needed to substantiate our findings about the development of maternal, and paternal attachment. The hypotheses which we believe to be most fruitful for study include: (1) there is species-specific behavior in the human parent upon first encountering his or her newborn baby; (2) there is a sensitive period in the human parent immediately following birth when an affectional bond begins to develop; (3) the development of parental attachment must be fostered by the infant. If the infant does not somehow respond to the parent in a way that he or she can perceive and appreciate, the parent may have difficulty in forming an attachment, and (4) prolonged interruptions in parent—child contact during this sensitive period are likely to alter the subsequent development of the attachment bond.

Since the newborn baby is utterly dependent upon its parents for survival and optimal development, it is essential to understand the process of attachment as it develops from the first moments after the child is born. Although we have only a beginning understanding of this complex phenomenon, those responsible for the care of mothers and infants would be wise to re-evaluate hospital procedures that interfere with early, sustained mother—infant contact, to consider measures to promote a mother's contact with her nude infant, and to help her appreciate the range of sensory and motor responses of her neonate.

ACKNOWLEDGEMENTS

This work was supported by the Department of HEW Health Services and Mental Health Administration, Maternal and Child Health and Crippled Children's Services, the Educational Foundation of America, the Grant Foundation and the Research Corporation.

BIBLIOGRAPHY

Bibring, G.L., Dwyer, T.F., Huntington, D.S. and Valenstein, A.F. (1961) A study of the psychological processes in pregnancy and of the earliest mother-child relationship. *Psychoanal. Stud. Child.* 16: 9—23.

Boston Women's Health Book Collective (1971) *Our Bodies, Ourselves.* (Simon and Schuster, New York.)

Bowlby, J. (1958) The nature of the child's tie to his mother. *Int. J. Psychoanal.* 39: 350—373.

Brazelton, T.B., School, M. and Rabey, J. (1966) Visual responses in the newborn. *Pediatrics* 37: 284—290.

Brazelton, T.B., Koslowski, B. and Main, M. (1974) The origins of reciprocity — the early mother-infant interaction. In: (M. Lewis and L. Rosenblum, Eds.), *The Effect of the Infant on its Caregiver,* Vol. 1, (John Wiley & Sons, New York) pp. 49—76.

Caplan, G. (1960) *Emotional Implications of Pregnancy and Influences on Family Relationships in the Healthy Child.* (Harvard University Press, Cambridge.)

Cohen, R. (1966) Some maladaptive syndromes of pregnancy and the puerperium. *Obstet. Gynecol.* 27: 562—570.

Condon, W. and Sander, L. (1974) Neonate movement is synchronized with adult speech: interactional participation and language acquisition. *Science* 183: 99—101.

Fanaroff, A.A., Kennell, J.H. and Klaus, M.H. (1972) Follow-up of low birthweight infants — the predictive value of maternal visiting patterns. *Pediatrics* 49: 287—290.

Greenberg, M., Rosenberg, I. and Lind, J. (1973) First mothers rooming-in with their newborns: its impact upon the mother. *Am. J. Orthopsychiat.* 43: 783—788.

Kennell, J.H., Jerauld, R., Wolfe, H., Chesler, D., Kreger, N., McAlpine, W., Steffa, M. and Klaus, M.H. (1974) Maternal behavior one year after early and extended post-partum contact. *Dev. Med. Child Neurol.* 16: 172—179.

Kennell, J.H. and Klaus, M.H. (1971) Care of the mother of the high-risk infant. *Clin. Obstet. Gynecol.* 14: 926—954.

Klaus, M.H., Jerauld, R., Kreger, N., McAlpine, W., Steffa, M. and Kennell, J.H. (1972) Maternal attachment — importance of the first post-partum days. *New Engl. J. Med.* 286: 460—463.

Klaus, M.H. and Kennell, J.H. (1970) Mothers separated from their newborn infants. *Pediat. Clin. North Am.* 17: 1015—1037.

Klaus, M.H., Kennell, J.H., Plumb, N. and Zuehlke, S. (1970) Human maternal behavior at the first contact with her young. *Pediatrics* 46: 187—192.

Klopfer, P. (1971) Mother love: What turns it on? *Am. Sci.* 49: 404—407.

Leifer, A., Leiderman, P., Barnett, C. and Williams, J. (1972) Effects of mother-infant separation on maternal attachment behavior. *Child Dev.* 43: 1203—1218.

Lind, J., Vuorenkoski, V. and Wasz-Hockert, O. (1973) The effect of cry stimulus on the temperature of the lactating breast primipara: a thermagraphic study. In: (N. Morris, Ed.), *Psychosomatic Medicine in Obstetrics and Gynaecology.* (S. Karger, Basle) pp. 293—295.

McBryde, A. (1951) Compulsory rooming-in in the ward and private newborn service at Duke Hospital. *J. Am. Med. Assoc.* 145: 625—628.

Newton, N. and Newton, M. (1962) Mothers' reactions to their newborn babies. *J. Am. Med. Assoc.* 181: 206—211.

Parke, R. (1974) Family interaction in the newborn period: some findings, some observations, and some unresolved issues. In: (K. Riegel and J. Meacham, Eds), *Proc. Int. Soc. Stud. Behav. Dev.*

Raphael, D. (1973) *The Tender Gift: Breastfeeding.* (Prentice-Hall, Inc., Englewood Cliffs, N.J.)

Ringler, N.M., Kennell, J.H., Jarvella, R., Navojosky, B. and Klaus, M.H. (1975) Mother-to-child speech at 2 years — effects of early postnatal contact. *Behav. Pediat.* 86: 141—144.

Robson, K. (1967) The role of eye-to-eye contact in maternal-infant attachment. *J. Child Psychol. Psychiat.* 8: 13—25.

Rubin, R. (1963) Maternal touch. *Nursing Outlook* November: 828—831.

Spitz, R. (1945) Hospitalism: an inquiry into the genesis of psychiatric conditions in early childhood. *Psychoanal. Stu. Child* 1: 53—74.

Stern, D. (1971) A micro-analysis of mother-infant interaction. *J. Am. Acad. Child Psychiat.* 10: 510—517.

CHAPTER 58

What the future holds

MARGARET MEAD

The basic research reported in this section is drawn mainly from experimental and some natural history observation of mammals, nonhuman primates, cultural studies of ethnological literature based on relatively isolated and homogeneous cultures, and very limited culture-bound studies in modern industrialized societies. I wish to deal specifically with some of the implications for medical practice in its widest sense, including hospital practice, community practice, preventive medicine, mental health and the redesigning of various kinds of medical services for adolescents, young parents, parents of school age and adolescent children and grandparents. All of these are likely to become important components of our changing styles of medical practice (Mead, 1971).

In studies of animal behavior it is the disturbed behavior of caged animals which relates more directly to the exigencies of human living today than does the observed behavior of animals in the wild. For research purposes, information on the potentialities of human beings for attachment behavior, the formation in infancy of the precursors of appropriate mating and parental behavior, and the greater flexibility of parental behavior in males than in females, are all highly valuable. But for practice in this generation, it is necessary to stress that data obtained from the observance of homogenous species, or of mothers and fathers in primitive or traditional societies, may be less useful in providing immediate guidelines.

Among animals in the wild and members of most societies in the past, individuals are reared in such a way as to assure that the offspring will reproduce the behavior appropriate to their species or their culture. Today, however, young people live in a different world from that in which their parents were reared, so that we have to approach young parents of first babies (primiparae) as individuals who have only partially learned, if indeed they have learned anything at all, of the culture-specific behavior of the past. Young mothers and fathers will in all probability never have seen a birth, never held a neonate, and have very little knowledge of the course of infant

Handbook of Sexology, edited by J. Money and H. Musaph
© *Elsevier/North-Holland Biomedical Press, 1977*

development. Each step in prenatal preparation has to be treated as a new experience in which the instructions given on diet, sex during pregnancy, care of the breasts, conduct of breast or bottle feeding, appropriate degree of stimulation for the infant, have to be far more complete than they would have been two generations ago, when instructions were left to the current culture patterns as embodied in the current practice and the child-rearing literature of the period.

Because of the degree of urbanization and migration that has gone on since World War II, virtually no assumptions can be made about a group of parturient women in a maternity ward as to past experience or present models of maternal behavior. The role of the maternity ward has been transformed from the provision of physical safety for mother and child — and today, the inclusion of the father in the physical experience of birth — to a brief episode of tremendous potential importance in the life experience of parents, perhaps as significant as the imprinting period in nonhuman creatures. Every step in the process as the mother holds her baby for the first time, as she relates to the other mothers in the hospital, and as she takes over more care of her child, and the way the new father is or is not included, becomes a rehearsal for the whole parental role.

The extreme susceptibility of new mothers, which has been likened to imprinting, provides an opportunity for the establishment of new patterns. However, it is also an extreme hazard because the kind of reinforcement traditionally received from other members of the same society may be entirely lacking. It has been observed that the presence of one assured competent mother in a group of new mothers can set a good pattern, while one dominating but poor mother can set a bad one. The prenatal clinic, the obstetrical ward, the postnatal clinic are therefore endowed with a far greater responsibility than has been true in the past, even in areas where maternal and child care are attempting to introduce radically new patterns of behavior. The mothers who gather at a clinic in Africa or New Guinea come as a group who know each other, reinforce the behavior which brings them there and will continue to reinforce it afterwards. In modern cities, the women who attend a clinic, or share a week of their lives in an obstetrical ward may never have seen each other and will in all probability never see each other again.

There are, it is true, heroic attempts being made to provide these isolated women with some kind of social reinforcement (Raphael, 1973), but at the present time it is necessary to assume the lack of cultural tradition, the isolation from other women of the preceding and present generation, and the lack of experience of the mother. Her susceptibility provides an opportunity to make the most of this very brief period.

As the months of parenthood go on and the parents have to deal with the individuality of their child and its development through the stages that they themselves passed through long ago under exceedingly different circumstances, it will again be necessary to arrange situations in clinics and community institutions for pattern setting for the different phases — weaning, toilet training, first motor activity with the dangers to the child and to complex funishings, the hazardous urban environment, talking (with the great variety of individual verbal sequences and differential responses of the unaccustomed mother), separation by daycare center, nursery school or kindergarten. These are all crises for parents and occasions of readjustment of the parent—child relationship for which today's parents have no proper precedent or early preparation.

The crises of puberty and adolescence are occurring earlier each decade so that parents are disoriented not only from the contrast and lack of parallels between their own adolescence and that of their children, but by the actual physical maturity of their children. If grandparents are within reach of the parents, they are likely to be even more startled and disoriented by the emotionally immature but physically mature adolescent. Today's adolescents have an increasingly high degree of vulnerability, so that physicians and health workers should be prepared for adolescents to establish temporary peer-group styles for their own protection which may further complicate the tasks of parents, educators and physicians. Precocious and premature sex relationships for young people who are emotionally unprepared for them, teenage pregnancy, and the changing availability of contraceptives and abortion all make the relationships between parents and adolescent children more difficult.

Another parental crisis arises when the first grandchild is born, and the mother—daughter relationship is reactivated, sometimes plunging the new grandmother into difficulties, sometimes making it difficult for the new mother to relate to her infant. All of these crises are also a function of where the grandmother is in her reproductive life — whether she is still menstruating and possibly still able to have a child, whether in the midst of the menopause and facing an end to reproductivity, or whether she is long past the menopause.

Parenthood as an active part of human sexuality does not cease when the baby is taken home from the hospital, nor when a child is weaned, nor when it becomes self-sufficient, as the emphasis in these previous chapters might seem to imply (Benedek, 1946). It is a potentially active condition all through life, and at each stage in life the lack of consistent cultural patterns is important. Domesticated animals are also subject to the irregularities and irrelevancies of unrelated forms of animal breeding and care, which introduce the same kind of inconsistencies into their lives as are introduced by cultural change into the lives of contemporary human beings.

The discussions in the previous chapters might suggest that the most socially beneficial course would be to strengthen the ties of the biological parents to their offspring at the moment when each of them is most susceptible and capable of forming new habits. But it is necessary also to consider the high rate of divorce today and the possibility that parents of both sexes have to form ties to a child for whom they become responsible after that child is too old to evoke the types of maternal and paternal behavior which can be evoked soon after birth. Biologically, the susceptibilities of the new mother to the infant's cry, to its lips on the nipple, to the sight of its eyes, and the firm pressure of the grasping reflex on the father's hand, may be seen as ways of establishing bonding, as discussed in Chapter 57 on parental attachment behavior, by Trause, Kennell and Klaus. But we also need to investigate the relationship between having been exposed to the optimum neonatal bonding behavior and ability to generalize parental behavior beyond one's own biological offspring.

In some respects, in fact, we can regard the establishment of paternity as a social refinement upon the male's response to small dependent creatures. Paternity was unknown until a reasonably recent period in human history, and it is, of course, still inferential (Montague, 1937). The establishment of specific behavior in a given human male in response to the children born to him by a woman with whom he lived conjugally undoubtedly preceded by thousands of years the attribution of physical paternity. Today the establishment of specific and intense human fatherhood due to a combination of a knowledge of heredity and participation in the pregnancy, birth process and immediate neonatal care of the child, has reestablished the closeness of ties between father and child which had been eroded through long periods of human history by arbitrary divisions of labor between the sexes and styles of social stratification.

With the increase in divorce and the large number of children who will grow up in homes in which only one parent is related to them biologically, a new question needs to be asked. Can the experience of fatherhood of a particular self-procreated child, or motherhood of own offspring, intensify and stabilize parental response so that their responses to other children, step, adoptive or fictive, will be more satisfactory? Is a woman who has breastfed her child more maternal towards other children? David Levy once outlined the life experiences and physiological characteristics which inclined women to be overprotective — early interest in children, an experience of failing to conceive or loss of a child, abundant menstrual flow, a wide areola, et cetera (Levy, 1938). It would be similarly valuable to explore the way in which men and women today can learn to be parental and so to provide better parenting of step and foster children.

In thus directing our education for parenthood towards the establishment of firm bonds between parent and child, it is also necessary to consider the household in which parenthood is enacted as the basic unit, rather than the biological family, which may have been broken by separation, death or divorce. It is particularly important that the incest taboo be fully supported by a recognition that it is not a reflection of the possibility of genetic damage from inbreeding, but rather a sociologically useful way of protecting children during their immaturity from the sexual advances of adults, and protecting parents from sexual temptations from the budding sexuality of their children (Mead, 1968).

So the establishment of parenthood may be seen as presenting new and challenging tasks to the medical professions concerned with the reproduction and survival of human beings — public health, maternal and child health, pediatrics, obstetrics, geriatrics, psychiatry and community psychiatry. Parenthood will require continuous redefinition and the invention of new forms of social reinforcement for types of behavior that are neither firmly rooted in unmodified biologically given responses, nor supported by coherent cultural and social arrangements.

BIBLIOGRAPHY

Benedek, T. (1946) *Insight and Personality Adjustment.* (Ronald Press, New York.)
Levy, D. (1938) Maternal overprotection. *Psychiatry* 1: 561—591.
Mead, M. (1968) Incest. In: (D.L. Sills, Ed.), *International Encyclopedia of the Social Sciences,* Vol. 7 (Macmillan and Free Press, New York) pp. 115—122.
Mead, M. (1971) Childbirth in a changing world. In: The Boston Children's Medical Center, *Pregnancy, Birth and the Newborn Baby.* (Delacourte Press, Boston) pp. 40—61.
Montague, A. (1937) *Coming into Being Among the Australian Aborigines.* (Routledge, London.)
Raphael, D. (1973) *The Tender Gift: Breastfeeding.* (Prentice Hall, New Jersey.)

SECTION X

Geriatric sexual relationships

Section coordinator: Pieter A. van Keep

CHAPTER 59

Introduction

PIETER A. VAN KEEP

"Physicians know very little about old age." This was Cornaro speaking 450 years ago. In 1923, Hall echoed this observation in the same words, adding that "A man is not as old as his heart and arteries, as was once thought, but as his endocrine glands."

Endocrinology is now about a century old. Freeman (in Gitman, 1967) states that the birth of endocrinology took place on 1st June 1889, the day that Brown-Sequard stood before an audience at the *Société de Biologie* in Paris and, to quote Selye, reported "a truly astonishing degree of regeneration" after having treated himself with subcutaneous injections of Pasteur-filtered aqueous dog testis suspension. After describing improvement in urination and defecation and in muscle strength, Brown-Séquard hinted that his sexual capacity had also been rejuvenated: "I can also report that other capacities, not lost but diminished, were noticeably improved." Seventy-two years old at the time, Brown-Séquard died five years later.

Easy to trace as a red thread, as it runs through the history of endocrinology, is the long search for possibilities to prevent ageing. The decrease of gonadal function, with evidence of marked progression of ageing, led to the intuitive hypothesis that this was cause and effect. Behind this search, though in most cases unmentioned, was the search for ways to maintain sexual activity at a youthful level.

We know that hopes quickly to find in endocrinology the secret of eternal sexual vigor and youth were in vain. Yet it is easy to understand why this line of thought was pursued so long. Apart from the alleged cause and effect, apart from the social importance of the goal if it could be achieved, and apart from the personal expectations of investigators, there were indeed other promising findings in endocrinology — findings which showed that a failing function of endocrine glands could be compensated for completely by means of hormone substitution.

This section contains two chapters dealing with the involution of the gonads, in men and in woman, respectively. One chapter deals with sexual

Handbook of Sexology, edited by J. Money and H. Musaph
© *Elsevier/North-Holland Biomedical Press, 1977*

activity in the ageing man and another with sexual activity in the ageing woman.

Data concerning the sexual activity of old people are difficult to come by. Tentative explanations of this are found in the following pages. Little is known of frequency of intercourse, masturbation, nightly ejaculations or other sexuality in old people, and virtually nothing is known about those aspects of sexuality that, because they are more emotional than concrete, are more difficult to measure — such things as touch, love and fantasy. Yet these aspects may increase in importance and significance when libido decreases.

Practically all the findings presented here refer to heterosexuality. No substantial research has been done on homosexuality in later life, an area definitely in need of further exploration (Hendrix, 1972).

No space was available for sex crimes and old age. Gebhard (1967) has stated that it is a misconception that old people are relatively often involved in certain sex crimes. This is confirmed by Allersma (1970), who found that in the Netherlands less than 6% of all sex crimes were committed by people more than 60 years of age. Most of these were committed by ageing men and often involved minors, who can be more easily forced or seduced than adult women. Gebhard finds that the socially weaker old men are overrepresented in the group of ageing sex offenders and that alcohol abuse often plays a role. The beginning impairment of psychic functions due to degenerative vascular disease may also be involved in such criminal offenses as it sometimes is in those cases of exhibitionism which first manifest at a late age.

The few sex crimes committed by women in this elderly group involved their actions in cases of illegal interruptions of pregnancy. Levin (1965) observes that the elderly female is usually given greater permission to obtain satisfaction of libido by means of bodily contact with children, either through sleeping arrangements or otherwise, whereas elderly males are apt to be considered perverted in either a heterosexual or homosexual direction if they seek such contacts.

There are quite a number of blank areas in the knowledge of sexuality and ageing, a situation which needs to be corrected, not only because proper and effective counseling requires more accurate knowledge, but also because the growing population, in both relative and absolute numbers, of ageing people deserves more attention (Berezin, 1968).

BIBLIOGRAPHY

Allersma, J. (1970) Bejaarden en criminaliteit. *Ned. T. Criminol.* 12: 69—85 (Cit. Hendrix).

Berezin, M.A. (1968) Sex and Old Age, A Review of the Literature. *J. Geriat. Psychiat.* 2: 131—149.

Brown-Séquard, (1889) Expérience démontrant la puissance dynamogénique chez l'homme d'un liquide extrait de testicules d'animaux. *Arch. Physiol. Norm. Pathol.* p. 651—658.

Gebhard, P.M. (1967) Normal and criminal sexual behaviour at older ages. In: *Sexualität in Wort und Bild*. Beit. Sexualforsch. 41: 83—87 (Cit. Hendrix).

Gitman, L. (Ed.)(1967) *Endocrines and Ageing*. (Charles C. Thomas, Springfield, Illinois.)

Hendrix, H. (1972) *Bejaarden en Sexualiteit*. Literatuurrapport (Zeist, N.I.S.S.O., The Netherlands).

Levin, S. (1965) Some comments on the distribution of narcissistic and object libido in the aged. *Int. J. Psycho-Anal.* 46: 200—208 (Cit. Berezin).

CHAPTER 60

Sexual activity in the ageing male

CLYDE E. MARTIN

1. INTRODUCTION

The frequency with which males engage in sexual activity is known to be affected by age, marital status, potency, and physical and emotional health. However, the more general question of why males of comparable age vary widely in frequency of sexual expression and why the sexual vigor of the male declines with age have rarely been subject to systematic inquiry.

Several investigators dealing with observations on humans have considered level of sexual functioning as a dependent variable in relation to factors other than age. In the studies by Kinsey and his co-workers (Kinsey et al., 1948), sexual frequencies at various ages were related to marital status, social class, age at puberty, rural—urban background, and religious characteristics. Of particular interest was the finding of an inverse relationship between age at puberty and sexual frequency. Pfeiffer and Davis (1972), using a multiple regression analysis, considered various social, attitudinal, and health-related variables as possible correlates of degrees of sexual enjoyment, sexual interest, and coital frequency in a series of older subjects. Among males, in addition to age, such factors as health status, social class, life satisfaction, and a physical function rating were significantly associated with frequency of coitus. Hellerstein and Friedman (1969) reported that among normal coronary-prone males, sexual frequency varied in relation to level of income and physical fitness. Johnson (1974) cited evidence suggesting that taller men have coital activity more frequently than shorter men.

The following analysis was undertaken in an effort to identify experiential, physical and physiological correlates of frequency of sexual activity among males of comparable age. A premise of the study was that significant correlates so identified may be indicative of processes which contribute to the decline in male sexual vigor that accompanies ageing.

Handbook of Sexology, edited by J. Money and H. Musaph
© *Elsevier/North-Holland Biomedical Press, 1977*

2. MATERIALS AND METHODS

The 628 subjects interviewed for the study were members of the Baltimore Longitudinal Study of Ageing. Participants in the program return to the Gerontology Research Center at 12 to 24 month intervals for $2\frac{1}{2}$ days of testing. Study members are typically white, married, urban residents of the Washington—Baltimore area, varying from 20 to 95 years of age. At entry into the study, 76% of the subjects had a college degree, 87% were identified with professional, technical, and managerial occupations, 83% rated their economic status as comfortable or better, and 92% judged their health as good or excellent.

At each visit, participants receive a physical examination before undergoing a variety of procedures to assess aspects of physiological, biochemical, and psychological function.

Interviews concerning history of marriage and sexual activity followed a predetermined sequence of questions that had been memorized by the interviewer along with the various codes needed to record responses. Cooperation was excellent, with only 2.1% of subjects declining interviews.

Close attention was given to determining the presence or absence of coitus, masturbation, nocturnal emission, and homosexual activity in the adult life history and, when present, their respective ages at onset, duration in time, and frequencies of occurrence in relation to age and marital condition (for details, see Martin, 1975). These frequencies, usually expressed in terms of times per week, per month, or per year, were then converted into the number of sexual events falling into each five-year interval of age between age 20 and the time of report. In the present analysis, only that quantity of total sexual activity calculated for the last five-year interval prior to interview was used in relating sexual frequency to age and in correlating sexual frequency with various experiential, physical and physiological attributes, being thus limited to information subject to recent recall.

3. FREQUENCY OF SEXUAL ACTIVITY AND AGE

Table I summarizes the mean and median frequencies of coital and total sexual activity calculated for each five-year interval of age. Means generally exceed medians because the distributions at each age tend to be skewed toward the higher frequencies. As Fig. 1 illustrates, coitus comprises an increasing portion of total activity until 30—34 years of age, at which time the several measures tend to converge and fall together at a remarkably constant rate into the late sixties. The absence of a further decline over the three oldest intervals may best be explained by the above-average health status of this older group of men. Ratios between the number of coital to total events averaged over individuals indicate that coitus constituted about 48% of total activity at ages 20—24 and thereafter averaged 80—90% of total sexual activity.

Table I

Mean and median frequencies of coital and total sexual activity reported for the five-year age-interval preceding interviews.

Age inter-vals	Number of subjects	Coital activity				Total sexual activity			
		5-Year *		Weekly		5-Year *		Weekly	
		Mean	Median	Mean	Median	Mean	Median	Mean	Median
20—24	26	294	276	1.1	1.1	551	518	2.1	2.0
25—29	38	502	501	1.9	1.9	581	555	2.2	2.1
30—34	32	566	557	2.2	2.1	602	605	2.3	2.3
35—39	63	427	400	1.6	1.5	482	460	1.8	1.8
40—44	72	418	380	1.6	1.5	458	419	1.8	1.6
45—49	88	328	267	1.3	1.0	356	289	1.4	1.1
50—54	79	263	250	1.0	1.0	309	260	1.2	1.0
55—59	62	233	172	0.9	0.7	259	177	1.0	0.7
60—64	44	180	157	0.7	0.6	204	173	0.8	0.7
65—69	68	94	60	0.4	0.2	112	66	0.4	0.2
70—74	31	107	70	0.4	0.3	123	110	0.5	0.4
75—79	25	76	30	0.3	0.1	102	63	0.4	0.2

* Average number of sexual events reported as having occurred during each 5-year inter-val of age by respondents whose ages at interview fall within the next older age interval. Weekly averages were obtained by dividing the 5-year average frequencies by 260, the number of weeks in a 5-year period.

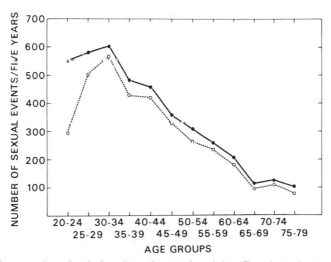

Fig. 1. Mean frequencies of coital and total sexual activity. Based on the number of coital (dotted line) and total sexual events (solid line) reported for the last 5-year age interval preceding interviews. Slopes were drawn to connect mean values for each age interval.

The frequencies of Table I may well represent optimum levels of sexual functioning for males in their middle and later years of life. The respondents generally enjoy good health, are relatively free of financial worry, and report unusually stable and satisfactory patterns of marriage. The importance of health, adequate income, and marriage for the retention and maintenance of sexual functioning in middle and later life seems by now to be well-established (Newman and Nichols, 1960; Pfeiffer et al., 1969).

The median frequencies of total sexual activity per week shown in Table I, compare favorably with similar data reported by Kinsey and his associates (1948). Specifically, over 10 age-intervals available for comparison, present medians differ by an average of 11% from those reported in the earlier study. However, present means at younger ages fall well below those previously reported. Since reports of high frequencies have little effect on the median while increasing the size of the mean, it is clear that the Kinsey data included proportionately more reports of high rates of sexual activity than were obtained in the present study. Whether this disparity between the two studies reflects the greater sexual conservatism of present respondents or the effect of long-term memory on estimated frequencies of activity in the earlier study is not readily apparent.

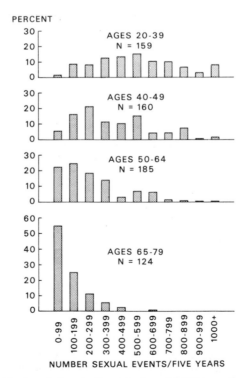

Fig. 2. Individual variation in frequencies of total sexual activity by age.

To correlate the frequencies of total sexual activity in Table I with experiential, physical and physiological attributes, an eight-year criterion period was used. Increasing the number of observations thus improved estimates of the attribute, enhanced sample size, and excluded from consideration subjects interviewed at first or second visit who lacked observations for the attribute falling into the criterion period. These data were then grouped into larger age categories for computing coefficients of correlation.

Fig. 2 describes the effect of age on the sexual frequencies obtained with respect to range of variation and skewness of distribution.

4. SEXUAL FREQUENCY AND BEHAVIORAL VARIABLES

In Table II, various behavioral variables derived from the interview are related to sexual frequencies for the age interval preceding interviews, ordered according to the correlation coefficients obtained for the 20—39-year-old group.

Factors appearing as significant correlates of level of sexual functioning are of interest in a number of respects. Both age at first coitus and SACWAM (sum of Subject's Age at first Coitus and Wife's Age at Marriage) appear to be of importance as indicators of the time of onset of regular coital activity. Thus early coital onset is seen to be conducive to elevated levels of sexual performance. Moreover, age at first coitus and number of coital partners prior to report are highly corrlated in the present data ($r = -0.65$), accounting for the appearance of the latter variable as a significant correlate. The time of onset of coitus appears to have no lasting effect on sexual frequencies past 40 years of age, judging from the low correlations observed among older age groups.

The three remaining measures in Table II are seen to vary in predictive value with respect to sexual frequency among older subjects. The degree of correlation between the maximum number of coital events in any week of marriage and sexual frequency, observed for ages 20—39, largely disappears at older ages, whereas the correlation between customary frequency of coitus in early marriage and total frequency continues to hold to 64 years of age. Since the data on customary frequency of coitus in early marriage enter into the calculation of total activity for the 20—39 age group, the correlation of 0.614 undoubtedly overstates the actual degree of association.

Retrospective data pertaining to earlier frequencies of total sexual activity were combined to derive a measure of the total number of sexual events reported for the twenty-year interval between 20 and 40 years of age. This variable is seen to be significantly related to the sexual frequencies obtained for all subsequent age groups. The finding is in accord with the concept that individual males are likely to maintain relatively high or low frequencies of sexual activity throughout most of their adult lives. This predisposition on the part of males to exhibit characteristic levels of sexual performance over

Table II
Behavioral characteristics correlated with frequency of total sexual activity, by broad age groups.

Characteristic	Age groups							
	Number of subjects				Correlation coefficients			
	20—39	40—49	50—64	65—79	20—39	40—49	50—64	65—79
Age first married	141	157	184	124	—0.101	—0.035	0.056	0.045
Age first coitus	155	159	185	123	—0.192 [d]	—0.084	—0.028	—0.004
SACWAM [a]	141	157	184	123	—0.235 [e]	—0.115	—0.069	0.040
No. coital partners	159	159	185	124	0.268 [e]	0.045	—0.017	0.036
Maximum no. coital events/wk [b]	141	157	184	123	0.387 [e]	0.109	0.120	0.159
Frequency coitus, early marriage [c]	141	156	184	120	0.614 [e]	0.309 [e]	0.365 [e]	0.161
Total sex activity, ages 20—40	—	159	185	107	—	0.498 [e]	0.403 [e]	0.196 [d]

[a] Sum of subject's age at first coitus and wife's age at marriage.
[b] In response to the question, "During the marriage, what was the greatest number of times intercourse ever occurred in any single week of marriage . . . ever as often as 5 times in seven days, every day for a week, or more frequently?" Despite the limited alternatives presented, the data obtained are well distributed between 1 and 21 times per week, with a concentration of cases at 5, 7 and 10 times per week.
[c] In response to the question, "In the first year or two of marriage, what was the customary frequency of intercourse?" Question immediately follows the one above.
[d] $P < 0.05$.
[e] $P < 0.01$.

long periods of time has been noted by other investigators (Newman and Nichols, 1960; Masters and Johnson, 1966; Pfeiffer and Davis, 1972).

Beyond the behavioral variables considered in Table II, various experiential factors were related to sexual frequencies by age. However, the general absence of significant correlations in this endeavor have precluded presentation of these data in detail. Briefly, frequency of total sexual activity at all levels of age was found to be independent of the following: religiosity of the subject, religiosity of the parents, economic status of the parental home, extent of harmonious relationships within the parental home, number of times intoxicated prior to interview, current hours of sleep, present amount of physical activity as reported by questionnaire, and scores obtained on the Cornell Medical Index. This latter finding was unexpected in that the Cornell Medical Index questionnaire was designed to measure symptoms indicative of current health status (Brodman et al., 1949; Gordon et al., 1959).

5. SEXUAL FREQUENCY AND PHYSICAL ATTRIBUTES

Except in the realm of endocrine research, there are few guides to investigation with reference to physical or physiological factors that may be of importance for sexual functioning. Thus, the measures selected for analysis in Tables III and IV represent choices which appeared to be of promise in this endeavor.

Height, for example, is found to be unrelated to sexual frequency at each age in Table III, in contrast to Johnson's (1974) evidence of a positive relationship between height and coital frequency among middle-age and older males. However, since both height and coital frequency are inversely related to age, and the Johnson data were not controlled for age, the reported association is likely to be a spurious finding.

Except for the one significant correlation between chest circumference and sexual frequency at ages 65—79, none of the physical attributes reviewed in Table III appear to be of importance for sexual functioning. Nevertheless, the observation that weight, abdominal circumference, and percent body fat are positively related to sexual frequency in the oldest age group suggests that retained body weight may be favorable to the retention of sexual vigor in late age.

6. SEXUAL FREQUENCY AND PHYSIOLOGICAL FUNCTION

In Table IV, a heterogenous array of physiological characteristics are related to frequency of total sexual activity by age. Since most variables achieving significance do so for age group 65—79, all were ranked according to the coefficients of correlation obtained for that age.

Clearly, none of the attributes considered are significantly associated with

Table III
Physical characteristics of subjects correlated with frequency of total sexual activity, by broad age groups.

Characteristic	Age groups							
	Number of subjects				Correlation coefficients			
	20–39	40–49	50–64	65–79	20–39	40–49	50–64	65–79
Grip strength, left hand	117	143	155	96	0.100	0.002	0.033	−0.004
Height	140	156	180	121	−0.057	−0.157	0.090	0.045
Lean body weight	102	123	139	95	−0.098	−0.004	−0.069	0.064
Prostatic size [a]	139	156	179	120	−0.058	−0.056	0.023	0.067
Angle of erection [b]	155	152	176	105	0.090	−0.034	0.048	0.123
Weight	140	156	180	121	0.022	0.020	0.053	0.170
Abdominal circumference	102	123	140	95	−0.087	0.031	0.071	0.197
Percent body fat	102	123	139	95	0.054	0.031	0.106	0.201
Chest circumference	102	124	140	94	−0.014	0.016	0.085	0.269 [c]

[a] Prostate rated as to size (5 categories) during the physical examination at each visit.
[b] In response to the question, "When you are standing and have an erection, is the penis carried at the horizontal, above the horizontal, or below the horizontal?" As asked, the question suggests three choices of response. However, by illustrating all possible angles, information was elicited falling into five response categories.
[c] $P < 0.01$.

Table IV
Physiological characteristics of subjects correlated with frequency of total sexual activity, by broad age groups.

Characteristic	Age groups							
	Number of subjects				Correlation coefficients			
	20—39	40—49	50—64	65—79	20—39	40—49	50—64	65—79
Serum triglycerides	133	147	165	116	−0.117	0.006	0.232 [b]	−0.018
Basal pulse rate	139	155	174	119	−0.103	0.035	0.101	0.039
Creatinine excretion	136	155	173	119	0.030	−0.005	0.016	0.043
Basal diastolic BP	139	155	174	119	0.012	0.021	0.067	0.091
Basal systolic BP	139	155	174	119	−0.048	0.063	−0.020	0.097
Hematocrit	139	156	180	119	0.131	−0.072	−0.014	−0.104
Hemoglobin	138	156	179	121	0.140	−0.048	0.003	−0.142
Vital capacity	133	154	177	118	−0.006	−0.095	0.000	0.157
FEV$_1$	132	149	175	113	0.039	0.014	0.025	0.181
Max. breathing capacity	136	154	180	121	0.125	−0.018	0.062	0.210 [a]
Basal metabolic rate	133	151	169	116	0.031	0.218 [b]	0.085	0.221 [a]
Serum cholesterol	138	156	179	120	−0.017	0.091	−0.024	−0.235 [a]
Basal O$_2$ consumption	133	152	170	117	0.002	0.124	0.080	0.265 [b]

[a] $P < 0.05$.
[b] $P < 0.01$.
BP = blood pressure; FEV$_1$ = forced expiratory volume at 1 second.

sexual frequency irrespective of age. Moreover, the correlations found between sexual frequency and serum triglycerides at ages 50—64 and basal metabolic rate at aged 40—49, although significant, fail to be replicated for adjacent age groups and must, therefore, be regarded as being of chance occurrence.

There is, however, reason to believe that the relatively modest but significant correlations found at ages 65—79 between sexual frequency and such factors as maximum breathing capacity, basal metabolic rate, level of serum cholesterol, and oxygen consumption are valid indicators of the importance of physical well-being as a condition of continuing sexual activity in old age.

In their study of normal coronary-prone men of middle age undergoing a program of physical conditioning, Hellerstein and Friedman (1969) found that as physical condition improved, frequency of sexual activity tended to increase at the same time that level of serum cholesterol declined. Their observation suggests that levels of sexual activity and serum cholesterol vary inversely according to degree of physical well-being, an interpretation consistent with the negative relationship found between these two variable in Table IV.

In sum, the evidence suggesting that weight retention in later life may be favorable to sexual functioning, the finding that several measures of pulmonary function and basal metabolism are significant correlates of sexual frequency in late age, and the observations of other investigators that demonstrate how oxygen consumption and serum cholesterol may relate to sexual vigor in old age, all suggest that physical well-being is an important determinant of sexual responsiveness and activity at an advanced age.

7. DISCUSSION AND SUMMARY

Since the wide dissemination of the Kinsey data on sexual ageing, present evidence that frequencies of coital and total sexual activity steadily decline over most years of the male life span is by now a familiar finding. It is nonetheless reassuring that new evidence based on information subject to recent recall shows a high degree of correspondence with the frequencies reported in the earlier study which included much information based on long-term memory.

The initial premise that factors found to be important correlates of individual differences in level of sexual activity may implicate processes responsible for sexual ageing in the male has not been realized. The concept may still be a useful guide to this kind of investigation, although the present failure to discover major correlates that are not dependent on age precludes such efforts at interpretation. Nonetheless, the finding that coital frequency in early marriage and the quantity of sexual activity reported for the 20 to 40-year age period are significantly related to sexual frequencies after 40 years of age, is consistent with the observation that males tend to maintain comparatively high or low levels of activity over many years of their lives. Why these patterns exist, however, is subject to differing interpretations. According to Masters and Johnson "The most important factor in the maintenance of effective sexuality for the ageing male is consistency of active sexual expression. When the male is stimulated to high sexual output during his formative years and a similar tenor of activity is established for the 31—40-year age range, his middle-aged and involutional years usually are marked by constantly recurring physiologic evidence of maintained sexuality."

The above interpretation is obviously based on the assumption that individual differences in frequency of sexual activity in early life are situational in origin and their persistence over time explained by reinforcement theory. Males, however, inherit or are born with numerous characteristics, some of which may account for differences in sexual responsiveness and motivation. The finding that sexual frequency and age at puberty are inversely related (Kinsey et al., 1948) is suggestive of a biological factor in this variation. It is also the author's impression from well over a thousand interviews that males who are ordinarily comfortable with coitus once a week or less are quite unlikely to ever increase their rate of activity to, say, five times a week or more, except under extraordinary circumstances and then for only a limited span of time. Moreover, Phoenix and his associates (Phoenix et al., 1967), in their review of hormonal and genetic factors in mammalian sexual behavior, conclude that a direct relationship has been established between the action of the gonadal hormones and the display of sexual behavior in all laboratory and domestic animals studied. They further conclude that the vigor or level of sexual behavior characteristic of the individual is clearly regulated by genetic mechanisms and, in particular, that the frequency and duration measures commonly employed in laboratory investigation are highly heritable. At present, it is well to recognize that the character of social environments, interpersonal relationships and the sexual rewards attendant upon individual initiative are of undoubted importance for male sexual functioning throughout the life span. Nonetheless, these factors alone seem insufficient to explain why some males are satisfied with sexual activity once a month while others are interested in and capable of daily sexual activity.

The present attempt to identify correlates of level of sexual functioning has met with limited success at the two extremes of age. Age at coital onset, which ordinarily coincides with the onset of regular coital activity, is apparently related to sexual frequency prior to the onset of middle age. It is not clear, however, why age at initial coitus bears this relationship to sexual frequency. Males who are most pressed for sexual expression may be more likely to become coitally active at an early age. But it is also true that coital involvement facilitates and increases perception of opportunities for frequent coitus.

At the other extreme of age, the appearance of greater maximum breathing capacity and basal metabolic rate, and lower levels of serum cholesterol in association with more frequent sexual activity after age 65, suggest that physical well-being is conducive to the retention of sexual vigor in late age. The concept of physical well-being is, however, not well defined and the use of the term here is for want of a more suitable expression.

In fact, problems concerning proper terminology arise in other contexts. For example, it was previously observed in the discussion of Fig. 1 that the pattern of a steady decline in mean frequencies of sexual activity with age was no longer apparent at ages 65—79, and that the absence of a continuing decline was attributable to the above-average health status of older respondents. Similarly, Pfeiffer and associates (1969), who followed 20 men, initially averaging 68 years of age, for a 10-year period and found no appreciable loss of sexual interest during that time, attributed this maintenance of sexual interest to the fact that their subjects were the survivors of a larger sample and were, therefore, biologically advantaged. In general, the resort to such terms as physical well-being, physical fitness, superior health status and biological advantage reflects a lack of precise information. Perhaps continued effort to discover factors related to level of sexual functioning among older men will provide better information from which to develop an understanding of the processes that contribute to sexual vigor in old age.

ACKNOWLEDGEMENTS

The author is indebted to Arthur H. Norris, Reubin Andres and Nathan W. Shock for the use of data collected under their supervision.

BIBLIOGRAPHY

Brodman, K., Erdmann, A.J., Jr., Lorge, I. and Wolff, H.G. (1949) The Cornell Medical Index: an adjunct to medical interview. *J. Am. Med. Assoc.* 140: 530—534.

Gordon, C., Emerson, A.R. and Simpson, J. (1959) The Cornell Medical Index questionnaire as a measure of health in socio-medical research. *J. Gerontol.* 14: 305—308.

Hellerstein, H.K. and Friedman, E.H. (1969) Sexual activity and the postcoronary patient. *Med. Aspects. Hum. Sex.* 3: 70—96.

Johnson, H.J. (1974) *Executive Life-Styles.* (Thomas Y. Crowell, New York.)

Kinsey, A.C., Pomeroy, W.B. and Martin, C.E. (1948) *Sexual Behavior in the Human Male.* (W.B. Saunders, Philadelphia.)

Martin, C.E. (1975) Marital and sexual factors in relation to age, disease, and longevity. In: (R.D. Wirt, G. Winokur and M. Roff, Eds.). *Life History Research in Psychopathology.* Vol. IV (University of Minnesota Press, Minneapolis).

Masters, W.H. and Johnson, V.E. (1966) *Human Sexual Response.* (Little and Brown, Boston.)

Newman, G. and Nichols, C.R. (1960) Sexual activities and attitudes in older persons. *J. Am. Med. Assoc.* 173: 33—35.

Pfeiffer, E., Verwoerdt, A. and Wang, H. (1969) The natural history of sexual behavior in a biologically advantaged group of aged individuals. *J. Gerontol.* 24: 193—198.

Pfeiffer, E. and Davis, G.C. (1972) Determinants of sexual behavior in middle and old age. *J. Amer. Geriat. Soc.* 20: 151—158.

Phoenix, C.H., Goy, R.W. and Young, W.C. (1967) Sexual behavior: general aspects. In: (L. Martini and W.F. Ganong, Eds.), *Neuroendocrinology: Volume II* (Academic Press, New York.)

CHAPTER 61

Sex and the involution of the genitals in the ageing male

K.D. VOIGT and H. SCHMIDT

1. INTRODUCTION

Age-dependent involution of the human testes has interested scientists since the 19th century when the famous French physiologist, Brown-Séquard, reported on his self-experiments; he had injected himself with extracts of testes and believed he experienced a second youth. Brown-Séquard was followed by Steinach who in 1920 published enthusiastic self-observations which he related to a self-implantation of a monkey glands' (testes). We know today that the belief that people could avoid ageing by these or other endocrinological procedures is illusory (for historical literature, see Voigt and Schmidt, 1968). However, the reports did promote research on various aspects of testicular ageing.

As the testes are the main source of testosterone, the most important androgenic hormone secreted, studies on the hormonal aspects of ageing in the male must predominantly concern the male gonads and their function. The adrenal gland also produces androgens, though the biological activity of these compounds is comparatively weak and their peripheral conversion to more active androgenic hormones does not play a significant role under physiological conditions. As it has also been shown that this organ does not undergo age-dependent changes, its role in the ageing man need not be discussed any further. The gonadotropic function of the pituitary gland, however, must also be taken into consideration as its function may influence the hormonal status in the ageing male. This chapter will, therefore, deal with the question of whether there really exists in the ageing man an involution of sex organs leading to changes of the hormonal situation and of sexual behavior.

Handbook of Sexology, edited by J. Money and H. Musaph
© *Elsevier/North-Holland Biomedical Press, 1977*

2. MORPHOLOGY OF THE AGEING TESTES

Macroscopic observations reveal small or no changes of the ageing testes. The testicular weight is only slightly reduced; when atrophic testes are excluded, virtually no weight change at all occurs with age (Rössle and Roulet, 1932; Olesen, 1948; Tillinger, 1957).

Spermatogenic apparatus

Slight reductions of testis weight in senescence must be attributed mainly to disorders of the spermatogenic apparatus which in general, however, is maintained intact until old age. This has been proven by histological examinations of the testicular tissue as well as by sperm counts in the seminal fluid (Nowakowski and Schmidt, 1959).

Leydig cells

The androgen-producing interstitial cells — the Leydig cells — contribute to the testis volume by only about 12%. A limited involution of this system therefore should not significantly affect testis weight. Histological investigations give a better insight into the problem. When Leydig cells are counted in relation to the seminiferous tubules of the testes, a continuous decrease is found with advancing age (Tillinger, 1957). Thus the mean values in the third decade of life are 5 Leydig cells per tubule, whereas in the eighth decade only 3 Leydig cells per tubule are counted. The lipid content of the Leydig cells, which has been considered as a parameter of their functional state, decreases continuously from the fourth decade of life onwards (Lynch and Scott, 1952).

3. ANDROGEN PRODUCTION IN MAN AS RELATED TO AGE

Rate of testosterone synthesis in testicular tissue

Testosterone synthesis in older men seems to be reduced. When incubating human testicular tissue with radioactive pregnenolone — a precursor of androgen — Axelrod (1965) showed that the reaction speed of certain steps in the biosynthesis of the hormone was slowed down in older testes. However, these in vitro findings cannot be related directly to testosterone values produced under in vivo conditions.

Testosterone concentration in the spermatic vein blood

Hollander and Hollander (1958) determined testosterone concentrations in spermatic vein blood of 20 men of different ages. A decrease in its concentration with increasing age was evident. With regard to its significance under physiological conditions, an interpretation of the findings is difficult. Only 3 men younger than 40 years of age have been studied, whereas most of the men in the older group suffered from a carcinoma of the prostate and had been treated with estrogen.

Testosterone production rates

By infusing of constant rates of labeled testosterone, one can calculate its daily production rate in blood; by definition it comprises the total amount of testosterone occurring in blood during 24 h. It includes the testosterone secreted directly by the testes and the testosterone being produced by the adrenals, as well as the testosterone which has been converted from other steroidal compounds by peripheral organs as, for instance, the liver. Kent and Acone (1965) found mean values of testosterone production rates of 7.6 mg/24 h in 5 men aged from 21 to 34 years, and of 4.4 mg/24 h in 6 men aged from 66 to 86 years.

4. CHANGES OF SEX STEROID KINETICS AND METABOLISM IN OLD AGE

Testosterone levels in blood plasma

Table I gives a survey of the data of the literature on testosterone concentrations in male blood plasma in relation to age. Although these values have been found using different methods, this table shows that a significant decrease in blood testosterone concentration does not occur before the seventh decade of life. Furthermore, it is evident that the drop noted is not very dramatic. From this observation one might be tempted to conclude that no physiological androgen deficit exists in males up to the sixtieth year of age. This conclusion cannot, however, be substantiated. For reasons to be discussed later, it is evident that the total testosterone concentration in blood plasma can be taken as a true parameter neither of testosterone production nor of testosterone available for androgenic action.

Testosterone binding in blood and the apparently free testosterone concentration (AFTC)

In blood, testosterone is attached to various plasma proteins. Regarding physicochemical characteristics, it is bound with high affinity but low capacity to a specific protein, the so-called sex-hormone-binding globulin (SHBG). Other binding proteins like the cortisol-binding globulin (CBG), and especially serum albumin, demonstrate a low affinity but a high capacity for androgen. When using equilibrium dialysis in vitro as a special technique, a

Table I
Testosterone concentrations in male plasma in relation to age.

Age (years)	N	Mean value (ng/100 ml)	Range or standard deviation	Authors and method
20—29	13	635	190	Kent and Acone, 1965; double isotope
30—39	11	560	190	derivative technique
40—49	8	470	90	
50—59	9	590	200	
60—69	12	590	180	
70—79	10	650	170	
80—93	5	280	130	
16—43	10	650	170	Coppage and Cooner, 1965; double iso-
46—92	19	500	180	tope derivative technique
18—35	21	740	290	Frick, 1969; competitive protein binding
>60	68	435	250	
20—30	34	616	280—1205	Vermeulen et al., 1972; gas chromatog-
30—40	22	634	350—1010	raphy
40—50	24	640	255—1025	
50—60	10	582	255— 950	
60—70	12	462	120— 870	
70—80	30	373	38— 850	
80—90	23	245	28— 390	
20—60	19	742	34	Nieschlag et al., 1973a; radioimmuno-
61—90	16	607	38	assay
22—61	50	545	315— 965	Doerr and Pirke, 1973; competitive
67—90	34	459	231— 849	protein binding
<50	30	492	440— 550	Rubens et al., 1974; radioimmunoassay
>65	30	281	247— 320	

small part of testosterone seems not to be bound to a protein. For physico-chemical reasons, however, it is doubtful whether free testosterone really occurs under in vivo conditions; nevertheless the free hormone is a good parameter for the easily accessible testosterone and therefore called "apparently free testosterone concentration" (AFTC). It is probable that the AFTC plays a dominant role in all biological mechanisms mediated by testosterone, that is, in androgenic action and in regulation of androgen production via a negative feedback mechanism through the hypothalamus and the pituitary gland, as well as in testosterone metabolism. The amount of physiologically available testosterone, then, will depend not only upon its concentration in the peripheral blood but also upon the SHBG level, so the higher it be, the more testosterone would be bound to it and thus the less would be found in the form of the free biologically active hormone. Determinations of SHBG concentrations, of the amounts of testosterone bound with high affinity and of the AFTC are therefore of special interest for the interpretation of the biological significance of testosterone blood concentrations in old age. Vermeulen and co-workers (1972) observed increasing mean values of SHBG capacity with advancing age. In a group of men 20—50 years old the mean value was 5.2×10^{-8} M; it increased to more than 6.5 in the age group 50—70 years and to 8.2 in the 70—90-year-old men. Doerr and Pirke (1973) reported identical results. Concomitantly, the AFTC fraction decreases with advancing age. In a more recent study, Rubens and associates (1974) found a highly significant drop in the AFTC from 10.6 ng/100 ml in men younger than 50 years to 3.6 ng/100 ml in men older than 65 years. By means of a differential dissociation technique, Horst and co-workers (1974) studied the specific testosterone and 5α-dihydrotestosterone binding under in vivo conditions. As may be seen from Table II, the binding of 5α-dihydrotestosterone exceeds the binding of testosterone in all groups. For both androgens an age dependency in the binding to SHBG was found. The higher binding of testosterone and 5α-dihydrotestosterone in patients with benign prostatic hypertrophy may possibly be related to the higher average age of this group.

Metabolic clearance rates

The knowledge of the metabolic clearance rates, that is, the speed at which a substance leaves the circulation, gives the basis for the determination of blood production rates. Studies of Kent and Acone (1965) demonstrated that in young men testosterone is eliminated from blood at a significantly faster rate than in old men. Two interpretations could explain the phenom-

Table II
Percent binding under various clinical conditions of testosterone and 5α-dihydrotestosterone (DHT) to SHBG (x = mean age, n = number of volunteers).

Clinical status	Age range (years)	SHBG-bound testosterone * (%)	SHBG-bound DHT * (%)	Testosterone * (ng/ml)
Normal males (n = 17)	30—35 x = 33	4.3 ± 1.4	54.8 ± 7.6	9.2 ± 2.2
Normal males (n = 12)	42—67 x = 54	8.5 ± 3.1	60.2 ± 10.7	5.0 ± 3.3
bph (n = 12)	62—85 x = 74	16.3 ± 5.6	76.1 ± 18.0	7.0 ± 5.4
Prostatic cancer estrogen treated (n = 7)	49—82 x = 65	47.2 ± 10.8	90.1 ± 14.0	3.1 ± 1.1

* Figures are expressed as mean ± SD.

enon: one could presume that with advancing age testosterone metabolism in testosterone metabolizing organs such as the liver and kidney is more and more delayed, a purely hypothetical assumption. The bulk of the data speaks for this second possibility: owing to the age-dependent increase in specific testosterone binding in senescence, smaller amounts of AFTC are found, thus limiting the rate of free testosterone entering into metabolizing and excreting organs.

Testosterone excretion in urine

Testosterone is excreted in urine mainly as glucuronide. The excretion rate correlates positively with the testosterone production rate and the metabolic clearance rate. For clinical purposes, the examination of testosterone excretion has proved to be a good parameter for the total androgenic potency of the organism. Testosterone values in urine (see Table III) show a distinct relation to age (Morer-Fargas and Nowakowski, 1965; Schmidt, 1968). Urinary testosterone values increase from puberty to reach highest values in the age group of 25—30 years. From then onwards a continuous decrease of the mean values occurs until the seventh decade of life. In even older men, no further drop can be observed. In men the age-dependent decline of androgen production as well as of intrinsic androgen effects are reflected best by the testosterone excretion values. One must take into consideration, however, that age-dependent changes in androgen binding and metabolism might interfere.

Changes in metabolic pathways of androgens

Without going into details it may be stated that, according to findings of Vermeulen and co-workers (1972), testosterone metabolism in male senescence is characterized by a relative decrease in 5α-reduced metabolites in

Table III
Testosterone excretion in urine of normal males (Schmidt, 1968)

Age (years)	N	Mean value (μg/24 h)	Standard deviation
14—20	11	35.9	5.3
21—25	11	60.5	11.9
26—30	7	88.8	23.0
31—35	10	71.2	22.1
36—40	9	56.3	15.5
41—50	14	51.4	13.9
51—60	9	39.9	7.5
61—70	15	29.3	8.1
71—82	16	31.4	10.2

favor of 5β-reduced compounds, the latter possessing no biological activity at all. Furthermore, a relative decrease in 17β-androstanediol occurs. Both changes suggest an impaired testosterone metabolism in target organs, that is, organs which are susceptible to androgenic action. The reason for this could be a decrease in the content and/or the activity of androgen-metabolizing enzymes and in specific androgen receptor proteins in target organs. The metabolic patterns observed are similar to those found in normal women (Mauvais-Jarvis, 1967; Mauvais-Jarvis et al., 1968), in hypogonadal men (Horton and Tait, 1966) and also to those of men treated with estrogens (Vermeulen et al., 1971). It is tempting to presume a correlation between the similarity in metabolite patterns observed in these various conditions and the reduced concentration of AFTC which is found in all of them.

Estrogen in blood and urine

A further factor which may explain female features in older men is the estrogen level in blood and urine. While parameters of androgen production decrease with advancing age, no reduction of estrogen excretion — whether measured by bioassay (Pincus et al., 1954) or by chemical methods (Kaufmann, 1968) — has been found. This results in an age-dependent increase of the estrogen/androgen ratio in urine. Estrogen levels in blood of different age groups have recently been determined by radioimmunoassay. Nieschlag and co-workers (1973a,b) found a two-fold increase of estrone and of estradiol concentrations in blood when comparing young men to men in their seventh decade. Rubens and associates (1974) obtained a smaller but also significant increase of both estrone and estradiol concentrations in blood when a group of men older than 65 years was compared to men younger than 50 years. This led to a highly significant increase of the estradiol/testosterone ratio in blood from 0.32 to 0.75. An increase of estradiol concentrations in blood in relation to advancing age was also reported by Doerr and Pirke (1973). Under physiological conditions, estrogen in both plasma and urine originate only in part from direct testicular secretion, estrone also being secreted by the adrenal cortex. Moreover, a considerable portion of both estrogens is derived from the peripheral conversion of the testicular androgens testosterone and androstenedione. The increased estradiol levels in the presence of decreased testosterone concentrations suggests an increased peripheral conversion of androgens to estrogens. This is supported by a positive correlation between testosterone and estradiol levels in elderly men (Rubens et al., 1974).

5. PITUITARY—TESTICULAR RELATIONSHIP IN OLD AGE

Testicular function is induced and maintained by pituitary gonadotropins: the follicle-stimulating hormone (FSH) stimulates mainly the spermatogenic apparatus, whereas the luteinizing hormone (LH) influences the Leydig cell function (androgen production and secretion). Reduced androgen formation in older men might therefore be due to a primary testicular involvement or to a diminished stimulation of the gonads by the pituitary.

Gonadotropin in urine and blood

The question whether the plasma levels of total gonadotropins and the urinary excretion of these protein hormones demonstrate an age dependence has been investigated by several authors (for literature see Apostolakis and Voigt, 1965; Schmidt, 1971). In both biological fluids a small increase in total gonadotropin activity as determined by bioassay techniques was observed; the increase in individual cases exceeding the normal range of younger people only slightly, however. Recent investigations on plasma LH and FSH levels have been performed by means of radioimmunological methods. Thus Nieschlag and co-workers (1973a,b) found a mean LH value of 9.0 mU/ml in a group of men aged 20—60 years which increased to a value of 13.1 mU/ml in men between 60 and 90 years. The FSH levels did not show any changes. Rubens and co-workers (1974) also found a highly significant increase of LH content in blood plasma, the mean value rising from 13.0 mU/ml to 24.1 mU/ml when a group of younger men (less than 60 years) was compared to older men (more than 60 years). Contrary to the findings of Nieschlag and his colleagues, however, significant increases in the FSH blood levels in the older group were also found. In our laboratory (Steins et al., 1975) the same age-dependent increase of LH has been obtained. FSH concentration showed a small but significant increase. Furthermore, patients with prostatic carcinoma demonstrated significantly lower LH concentrations in blood than probands from a normal test group of the same age range. In summary, blood and urine levels in gonadotropins tend to rise with increasing age, the changes being far less dramatic in males than in females, however. Furthermore, chronic diseases not involving endocrine glands may influence blood gonadotropin and/or testosterone levels.

Response of testicular testosterone secretion to exogenous gonadotropin administration

Human chorionic gonadotropic (hCG), which contains LH and FSH activity, is able to stimulate testicular testosterone output when injected intramuscularly for three days. It results in an increase of testosterone levels in blood and of testosterone excretion in urine. The extent of the testicular response to the exogenous gonadotropin may be regarded as a test for the functional capacity of the gonads. In previous investigations (Apostolakis, 1966, Apostolakis et al., 1968) in which 3000 IU of hCG were administered daily for 3 days to male volunteers, an increase of testosterone excretion values was seen. This was in a group of younger men (<30 years) from 75γ to 152γ/24 h and in a group of older men (>50 years) from 51γ to 107γ/24 h. Using about the same stimulation techniques, Nieschlag and co-workers (1973b) and Long-cope (1973), as well as Rubens and co-workers (1974), also found a decreased but still remarkable secretory capacity of testes in old men.

Response of pituitary gonadotropin secretion to LH-RH stimulation

Pituitary gonadotropic function can be studied by measuring blood gonado-tropin levels after injection of LH-RH (luteinizing hormone-releasing hor-mone). The test gives some information on the gonadotropic capacity of the pituitary gland. By using this test in elderly men, Rubens and co-workers (1974) could demonstrate an even stronger pituitary response of LH and of FSH secretion to LH-RH injection as seen in younger men. Two conclusions may be drawn from the results: (1) the full capacity of pituitary gonadotro-pic function is maintained in old men; and (2) the reduced testicular func-tion in this period of life occurs in spite of the increased gonadotropin secre-tion. It must be taken into consideration that in the old man LH-RH output from the hypothalamus might not be adequate to cope with the lowered cir-culating androgen levels, that is, that a drop in hypothalamic sensitivity might be responsible for changes in the hormonal feedback mechanism. It is not clear whether peripheral factors, such as a high estrogen level, may play a role in this respect.

6. INVOLUTION OF ANDROGEN TARGET ORGANS

With advancing age there is a very slow and gradual regression of androgen-dependent sexual organs such as the penis and scrotum and of sexual hair growth. Beginning with the fifth decade of life, the prostate gland under-goes characteristic microscopic changes starting with an atrophy of single lobules and a diminution of the secretory activity of the epithelial cells. The final result is a complete atrophy of acini and of muscle fibers (Moore, 1952). The microscopic picture thus allows one to distinguish a presenile phase from a senile phase of the involutionary process of the prostate. Mor-phological age-dependent changes of other accessory sex glands are less well established. The function of the seminal vesicles may be correlated to the fructose content of the seminal plasma originating from the gland. Its con-centration in seminal fluid decreases continuously with advancing age (No-wakowski and Schmidt, 1959). Signs of lacking androgen effects may also be observed at the spermatogenic apparatus of the testes: basal membranes of the tubuli contorti are target organs of androgen. Thickening and hyalinosis of these membranes occurring in advanced age may be attributed to weaken-ing androgen effects. Decrease of consistency of the testes as well as dimin-ished motility of spermatozoa are further characteristic signs of advancing age (Schirren, 1973).

7. SENSIBILITY OF ANDROGEN TARGET ORGANS

It could be that age-dependent involution of male sex organs is due only to the reduced amounts of testosterone available. Clinical observations, however, suggest that there are additional mechanisms of target organ 'ageing': fructose concentration in seminal fluid and sexual hair growth are reduced in old age. In many younger men suffering from hypogonadism these symptoms of androgen insufficiency are easily treated by exogenous testosterone. In the old man, testosterone administration has little or no effect on the symptoms (Weller, 1970). Recent investigations have brought new knowledge on the mechanism of androgen action on its target organs: testosterone is converted within the target organ to 5α-dihydrotestosterone by the enzyme 5α-reductase. 5α-dihydrotestosterone is bound to specific receptors and transferred into the cell nucleus where it acts mainly on RNA—protein synthesis (for detailed literature, see Tamm and Voigt, 1971). Limitation of any step in the reaction sequence would explain the lowered androgen sensibility at a molecular level. It is known from experiments with rats that androgen receptors in prostate are reduced in older animals (Shain, 1973). Only few data are available on human beings. Wilson (1971) demonstrated a reduced conversion of testosterone to 5α-dihydrotestosterone by the human prepuce with advancing age.

A short comment should be given on a typical disease of elderly men which probably is hormone dependent and which is not found in experimental animals. This disease, benign prostate hypertrophy (bhp), is very common in men over 40 years and may have an impact on sexual behavior. In spite of the fact that its pathogenesis remains open, changes in androgen uptake and metabolism have been reported in patients with this disease (for detailed literature, see Siiteri and Wilson, 1970; Becker et al., 1975). Whether or not androgen binding is also concerned remains to be investigated. The loss of sensitivity for testosterone in target organs could also play a role in sexual behavior of older men, for it may be that not only genital organs, but also sexual centers in the brain, are affected.

8. DISORDERS OF SEXUAL BEHAVIOR ASSOCIATED WITH GENERAL SYMPTOMS IN THE AGEING MAN — 'MALE CLIMACTERIC'

In men in the fifth or sixth decade of life, a syndrome often occurs which comprises psychological as well as neurovegetative phenomena. Diminished or complete loss of libido and/or disturbances of sexual potency may be reported. Long ago, before exact analyses of individual androgen status were possible, the syndrome was characterized as 'male climacteric' because of its striking similarity to the female climacteric and to symptoms observed in male castrates. Good therapeutic results from testosterone administration have been claimed.

Although individuals complaining from the symptoms have been examined carefully by means of modern analytical methods which allow an exact judgement of androgen status, it remains doubtful whether the syndrome is directly associated with this, that is, whether it really originates from the decreased androgenicity in old age. In our studies (Schmidt, 1971) urinary testosterone excretion was determined in 40 men aged 45—55 years who complained of these symptoms. In only two cases was the testosterone excretion rate below the normal range. One could conclude, then, that the drop in androgen production observed in patients with 'male climacteric' was not greater than that in normal elderly men of the same age, that is, not more pronounced than the physiological decrease of androgen concentration with advancing age. As compared to the situation in women, the fall in androgen production in men seems to occur less suddenly than that of ovarian hormones in the female climacteric. In men, therefore, the secondary reactions to functional gonadal involution do not occur in such a dramatic and pronounced way, and normally the 'climacteric' symptoms do not become manifest. The changes in the psychological situation of the ageing man seem to play a more important role for the genesis of the syndrome than do hormonal factors.

9. SEXUAL ACTIVITY IN THE AGEING MAN IN RELATION TO HORMONAL STATUS

There is no doubt that sexual activity decreases with advancing age. The largest body of statistical material concerning the phenomenon has been presented by Kinsey and his colleagues (1948) comprising data on 14,000 men of different ages. The study showed that there exists a nearly linear decrease of weekly sexual intercourse or ejaculations between the twentieth and sixtieth years of age. See, however, the preceding chapter, by Martin. As has been discussed in the preceding paragraphs, this is roughly in accordance with some age-dependent parameters of the endocrine function of the gonads and of the findings in secondary sexual organs. One might, therefore, assume that sexual activity is related to endogenous androgen effects, in both young and old men. However, the assumption has not as yet been proven. For a definitive answer, one would have to correlate sexual activity in individual cases with different parameters of androgen production and action; at the same time, such a study should take the man's psychosocial relationships into consideration, because these surely play a very important role also in his sexual behavior.

10. SUMMARY

Macroscopically, only slight reduction of the weight of testes occurs with advancing age. The spermatogenic apparatus remains intact and consequently

836

sperm counts are rather unaffected until senescence. The Leydig cells, being the source of androgen, reduce in number and demonstrate microscopic signs of decreased function in old men. In vitro examinations show a diminished capacity of testicular tissue to synthesize testosterone. In vivo, its testosterone secretion seems to fall and testosterone concentrations in spermatic vein blood decrease, as was confirmed by the determination of testosterone production rates. Testosterone levels in peripheral blood, however, do not show significantly decreasing values before the seventh decade of life. The difference between fall in production rates and normal blood concentration of testosterone may be explained by changes in its metabolic clearance rate, the latter probably depending to a greater extent on specific testosterone binding in blood. While the concentration of this protein rises with advancing age, the apparently free testosterone concentration (AFTC) diminishes at the same pace. The AFTC seems to correlate better with the androgenicity of the organism than does the total testosterone concentration in plasma. The same holds true for testosterone excretion rates, which also demonstrate a striking drop with advancing age. Furthermore, the androgen metabolite pattern in men approaches that found in women. While androgen levels drop, estrogen excretion in urine remains constant. In blood plasma, estrogen concentrations rise, resulting in a significant increase of estrogen/androgen ratio. As a reaction to the primary functional failure of testicular androgen production in elderly men, pituitary gonadotropins in blood go up moderately. The testosterone secretion of older men's testes in reaction to an additional pituitary stimulus is reduced but not abolished, whereas pituitary gonadotropic reaction to hypothalamic stimuli is not decreased; the hypothalamic reaction to lowered androgen levels, however, seems to be inadequate. Along with advancing age and decreased androgen stimulation, secondary sexual organs and characteristics undergo a slow involution. A diminished androgen sensibility of androgen-dependent sex organs is found in old age. Ageing men often develop unspecific symptoms associated with disorders of sexual behavior, a syndrome designated as 'male climacteric'. It is doubtful as to whether this syndrome is related to reduced androgen levels and/or effects. During life, there exists a general parallelism of sexual activity and androgen effectiveness. However, studies providing evidence to support the concept of a direct correlation of the two have not yet been performed.

BIBLIOGRAPHY

Apostolakis, M. (1966) Konferenz über die Physiologie der menschlichen Fortpflanzung. *Klin. Wochenschr.* 45: 439—448.
Apostolakis, M. and Voigt, K.D. (1965) *Gonadotropine.* (Georg Thieme Verlag, Stuttgart.)
Apostolakis, M., Tamm, J. and Voigt, K.D. (1968) The effects of HCG in cyproterone-treated male subjects. In: (J. Tamm, Ed.) *Testosterone.* (Georg Thieme Verlag, Stuttgart) pp: 156—161.

Axelrod, L.R. (1965) Metabolic patterns of steroid biosynthesis in young and aged human testes. *Biochim. Biophys. Acta.* 97: 551—556.

Becker, H., Horst, H.-J., Krieg, M., Steins, P. and Voigt, K.D. (1975) Uptake, metabolism and binding of various androgens in human prostatic tissue: In vivo and in vitro studies. *J. Steroid Biochem.* 6: 447—452.

Coppage, W.S. and Cooner, A.E. (1965) Testosterone in human plasma. *New Engl. J. Med.* 273: 902—907.

Doerr, P. and Pirke, K.M. (1973) Influence of male senescence on plasma oestradiol, testosterone and binding capacity of testosterone-binding globulin. *Acta Endocrinol.* suppl. 177: 123.

Frick, J. (1969) Darstellung einer Methode ("competitive protein binding") zur Bestimmung des Testosteronspiegels im Plasma und Studie über den Testosteronmetabolismus beim Mann über 60 Jahre. *Urol. Int.* 24: 481—501.

Hollander, N. and Hollander, V.P. (1958) The microdetermination of testosterone in human spermatic vein blood. *J. Clin. Endocrinol.* 18: 966—971.

Horst, H.-J., Becker, H. and Voigt, K.D. (1974) The determination in human males of specific testosterone and 5α-dihydrotestosterone binding to sex hormone binding globulin by a differential dissociation technique. *Steroids* 23: 833—844.

Horton, R. and Tait, J.F. (1966) Androstenedione production and interconversion rates measured in peripheral blood and studies on the possible site of its conversion to testosterone. *J. Clin. Invest.* 45: 301—313.

Kaufmann, J. (1968) Untersuchungen zur kausalen Genese der Prostatahypertrophie. *Z. Urol.* 61: 229—250.

Kent, J.R. and Acone, A.B. (1965) Plasma testosterone levels and aging in males. *Proc. 2nd Symp. Steroid Hormones, Ghent.* (Excerpta Medica Foundation, Amsterdam.) pp: 31—35.

Kinsey, A.C., Pomeroy, W.B. and Martin, C.E. (1948) *Sexual Behavior in the Human Male* (W.B. Saunders Co., Philadelphia-London.)

Longcope, C. (1973) The effect of human chorionic gonadotropin on plasma steroid levels in young and old men. *Steroids* 21: 583—592.

Lynch, K.M. and Scott, W.W. (1952) The Sertoli cell as related to age of man on experimental alternation of the pituitary gonad axis in the animal. *Fertil. Steril.* 3: 35—48.

Mauvais-Jarvis, P. (1967) Etude du métabolisme 17-beta-hydroxylé de la testosterone en fonction de la différenciation sexuelle humaine. *C.R. Hebd. Séances Acad. Sci.* (Paris) 262: 2753—2756.

Mauvais-Jarvis, P., Floch, H.H. and Berovici, J.P. (1968) Studies on testosterone metabolism in human subjects with normal and pathological sexual differentiation. *J. Clin. Endocrinol.* 28: 460—471.

Moore, R.A. (1952) *Cowdry's Problems of Aging.* (Williams and Wilkins Co., Baltimore.)

Morer-Fargas, F. and Nowakowski, H. (1965) Die Testosteronausscheidung im Harn von männlichen Individuen. *Acta Endocrinol.* 49: 443—452.

Nieschlag, E., Kley, K.H., Wiegelmann, W., Solbach, H.G. and Krüskemper, H.L. (1973a) Lebensalter und endokrine Funktion der Testes des erwachsenen Mannes. *D. Med. Wochenschr.* 98: 1281—1284.

Nieschlag, E., Lley, K.H. and Wiegelmann, W. (1973b) Age dependence of the endocrine testicular function in adult men. *Acta Endocrinol.* suppl. 177: 122.

Nowakowski, H. and Schmidt, H. (1959) Die Hodenveränderungen beim alternden Mann und deren klinische Bedeutung. *Schweiz. Med. Wochenschr.* 89: 1204—1226.

Olesen, H. (1948) *Morfologiske Sperma- og testisundersogelser.* (Munksgaard, Copenhagen.)

Pincus, G., Romanoff, L.P. and Carlo, J. (1954) The excretion of urinary steroids by men and women of various ages. *J. Gerontol.* 9: 113—132.

Rössle, R. and Roulet, F. (1932) *Mass und Zahl in der Pathologie.* (Springer, Berlin.)

Rubens, R., Dhont, M. and Vermeulen, A. (1974) Further studies on Leydig cell function in old age. *J. Clin. Endocrinol.* 39: 40—45.

Schirren, C. (1973) Zur Therapie männlicher Fertilitätsstörungen und des Klimakterium virile. *Fortschr. Med.* 91: 1123—1130.

Schmidt, H. (1968) Testosteronausscheidung bei männlichen Personen unter normalen und pathologischen Bedingungen. *Acta Endocrinol.* suppl. 128: 7—64.

Schmidt, H. (1971) Der Einfluss des Alterns auf die endokrinen Funktionen des Mannes. *Symp. Dtsch. Ges. Endokrinol.* 17: (Springer, Berlin) pp. 165—174.

Shain, S.A. (1973) Prostatic receptors and the aging phenomenon. In: (Goland, M., Ed.) *Symposium on the Normal and Abnormal Growth of the Prostate.* (Charles C. Thomas, Springfield, Ill.) pp. 712—730.

Siiteri, P.K. and Wilson, J.D. (1970) Dihydrotestosterone in prostatic hypertrophy. I. The formation and content of dihydrotestosterone in the hypertrophic prostate of man. *J. Clin. Invest.* 49: 1737—1745.

Steins, P., Hornung, D., Lindenmeyer, D. and Theile, L. (1975) Biological and radioimmunological determinations of pituitary hormones, especially prolactin, in patients with prostatic carcinoma. *21. Symp. Dtsch. Ges. Endokrinol. Acta Endocrinol.* suppl. 193: 68.

Tamm, J. and Voigt, K.D. (1971) Einige klinisch relevante Ergebnisse der neueren Androgenforschung. *Schweiz. Med. Wochenschr.* 101: 1078—1083.

Tillinger, K.G. (1957) The steroid production of the testicles and its relation to number and morphology of Leydig cells. *Acta Endocrinol.* suppl. 30: 1—192.

Vermeulen, A., Stoica, T. and Verdonck, L. (1971) The apparent free testosterone concentration, an index of androgenicity. *J. Clin. Endocrinol.* 33: 759—767.

Vermeulen, A., Rubens, R. and Verdonck, L. (1972) Testosterone secretion and metabolism in male senescence. *J. Clin. Endocrinol.* 34: 730—735.

Voigt, K.D. and Schmidt, H. (1968) *Sexualhormone* (Rowohlt Taschenbuch Verlag GmbH, Reinbek bei Hamburg.)

Weller, O. (1970) Alternsvorgänge an der männlichen Keimdrüse und das Klimakterium virile. *Fortschr. Med.* 91: 1123—1130.

Wilson, J.D. (1971) Testosterone metabolism in skin. *17 Symp. Dtsch. Ges. Endokrinol.* (Springer Verlag, Berlin.) pp: 11—18.

CHAPTER 62

Sexual relations in the ageing female

PIETER A. VAN KEEP and ANN GREGORY

1. INTRODUCTION

Little is known of the effect of ageing on the sexual capacities of the human female or on the pattern of female sexual interest and activity with advancing age. Partially because the studies of sex in the ageing woman are more complicated, they are far fewer than those of the ageing man.

The gathering of biological data in sufficient amounts to be of statistical significance will require some years as well as the cooperation of ageing women in greater numbers than have previously participated in such studies. It will also require development of new measurement techniques. The occurrence of regular penile erections during sleep, for example, has been recorded in the ageing male, while no comparable observations are available for study of female sex arousal during sleep and dreams because no proven measuring devices have been devised for them. Even awake, erection and ejaculation are easier to identify and record than are female arousal and orgasm and, in addition, a considerable portion of the female's sexual activity does not result in orgasm.

Thus one is dependent in large part on clinical impressions and subjects' responses to interviews. Though these provide some information on the measure of sexual interest and activity, the results are highly influenced by the emotional quality of the interview and the replies of the subjects influenced greatly by many social factors.

The embarrassment of both parties, when an interviewer pries into the sex life of an elderly woman, especially if the interviewer be a young male and the elderly woman unmarried, often poses serious limitations (Pfeiffer, 1970). The difficulties are probably compounded by identification of the female interviewer with her own mother, recalling her own emotion-charged experience of learning that her mother indulged in sexual intercourse with her father, and makes the interview seem linked to a violation of the incest taboo.

Handbook of Sexology, edited by J. Money and H. Musaph
© Elsevier/North-Holland Biomedical Press, 1977

Reciprocally, the inexperienced young male may identify the older woman with his mother and experience displaced incest embarrassment.

2. EFFECTS OF AGEING

Just as health and physical activity, while age-related, vary widely in ageing individuals, so do sexual responsiveness and activity. The human female ages slowly, and to a relatively small extent with respect to sexuality, however, and no time limit is drawn on her sexuality by the advancing years. Kinsey and his co-workers (1953) reported, for example, the case of a woman of 90 who responded regularly to masturbation.

Typically, a woman's highest frequency of eroticism seems to come between 25 and 30 years of age, remaining on a pleateau for about 20 years before beginning a gradual decline sometime after the end of her reproductive period. There is no sharp drop in sexual capacity, though typically sexual interest and activity, if not actively reinforced, may show decline after a woman has reached 55 to 65 years of age. However, there is great variation among women, with strong social as well as biological factors influencing sexual behavior as they age.

The Duke longitudinal studies, subjects of which entered the study at around 60 years of age (Pfeiffer et al., 1969) found women in general showing lower levels of sexual interest and activity than men of like age. Pfeiffer hypothesized that throughout life women, at least those reared in the Western mores may exhibit lower levels of sexual interest and activity than do men, or an earlier decline may have taken place before the subjects entered the study at around 60 years of age, or both. He suggested the possibility of an added factor: the psychological impact of the clearly demarcated climacteric of women may be perceived by at least some of them to mean their sexual life is over with at the end of their reproductive capacity.

Declines in the incidence and frequency of marital coitus are not evidence that the female ages in her sexual capacity; it is rather the male's ageing and loss of capacity which is reflected in her decline (Kinsey et al., 1953). The fact that more age-related decline in sexual interest is found among married than among unmarried women is probably related to this 'ageing husband factor' (Verwoerdt et al., 1969). Sexual activities such as masturbation and nocturnal dreams to orgasm, being largely a solo matter, should provide a better measure of decline in sexual interest and capacity with ageing. In these activities, the frequencies in women were shown to rise gradually, remaining more or less at a maximum level until, again, decline begins to become apparent at around 55 years.

Christenson and Gagnon (1965) gathered data from women aged 50 to 90, covering six areas of sexual behavior: coitus, petting, masturbation, nocturnal sex dreams, homosexual contacts and contacts with animals. At age 50, they found 87.5% of the married women having coitus on an average of once a week. By 60 years, this had dropped to 70% and by age 65 it was 50%. Among these same married women, masturbation (from 30% at 50 to 25% at 65) and nocturnal sex dreams to orgasm (27% at age 50 and 19% at 65) remained fairly constant.

Of the no longer married women, 37% were having postmarital coitus at age 50, though this dropped sharply in the next decade. A compensatory activity for these women was masturbation, with incidence double that for women still married.

Sexual activity in their later study of 71 never-married women also clearly showed ageing effects by 55 years (Christenson and Johnson, 1973). At age 45, about half of the subjects reported they were masturbating to orgasm, a third having heterosexual coitus, and slightly fewer than a fifth having sex dreams to orgasm, while two subjects were reaching climax with some regularity in a homosexual relationship.

By age 50, the incidence of masturbation had dropped only 5%, the number reporting coitus from a third to a quarter, and sex dreams had risen slightly. But by age 55, incidence and frequency of all sexual activities showed clear-cut ageing effects. Among the reduced sample of 14 remaining at 60 years of age, three still practised masturbation and one engaged in coitus (twice yearly), while none reported experiencing sex dreams.

Comparison of the previously married group with the never-married group (Christenson and Johnson, 1973), showed the ageing effect to be similar, though the levels of sexual activity differed between the two groups. The postmarital sexual outlets were more extensive, usually in both incidence and frequency than those reported for never-married women. In fact, the sex histories of a third of the never-married group gave so little evidence of the development of erotic interests that the ageing factor could not be traced, while the remaining two-thirds reported active sexual behavior of varying types and levels. In their women subjects, ageing from 60 to 92, Verwoerdt and co-workers (1969) also found the incidence of sexual activity in unmarried women to be very low, though the difference between the two groups in sexual interest was much smaller.

3. PRESENCE OF A PARTNER

The ageing woman's sexual activity and interest depend heavily upon the availability to her of a societally sanctioned, sexually capable partner.

Regardless of involutional changes in the reproductive organs, the ageing human female is fully capable of sexual performance at orgasmic response levels, particularly if she is regularly exposed to effective sexual stimulation (Masters and Johnson, 1966). With advancing age, however, fewer and fewer women have a sexual partner available and, among those who do, the husband is often older than his wife.

In contrast to unmarried men who maintain sexual activity and interest at levels roughly similar to those of married men, nonmarried women differ substantially from married women in the later years of life.

At age 50, for example, Christenson and Gagnon (1965) found 87.5% of the married women in their sample having coitus on an average of once a week, while only 37% of the postmarital group were having coitus, though the incidence of masturbation among the no longer married women (60%) was double that for the still married women (30%). Among the never married (Christenson and Johnson, 1973), almost half were virgins who had never experienced orgasm from any source. These virgin spinsters also reported a much higher degree of religious devoutness than the remainder of the sample. Of the eight never-married subjects with extensive homosexual histories, all reported heterosexual experience in coitus as well, and none had continued homosexual activity into their 50s.

In these later years, however, it was the never-married women who reported a higher frequency of masturbation, the formerly married showing a higher rate of coitus during their postmarital period — possibly due to a selective process of marriage in terms of potential sexuality or a higher degree of social skill in developing contacts with eligible male partners.

4. DURATION OF MARRIAGE

The mean frequency of marital coitus, as well as the frequency and extent of satisfaction involved, is probably negatively correlated with the duration of marriage. Personal clinical case histories as well as data from the studies of Kinsey and his co-workers support this assumption. Kinsey found the frequency of marital coitus in the female usually reaches its maximum in the first year or two after marriage, after which it declines at a constant rate from a median of 2.8 times per week at 20 years to 1.5 at 40 years of age and 0.6 by the age of 60 (see table 93 in Kinsey et al., 1953).

In the later years of an enduring marriage, the monotony of the sexual behavior pattern and of the same partner seems to contribute to decreasing interest of the male in marital coitus. In questionnaires (Pfeiffer and Davis, 1972), 35 men and 97 women gave reasons for ceasing to have sexual relations. The women overwhelmingly attributed responsibility for stopping to their husbands, while men generally attributed the responsibility to themselves, confirming earlier findings that in a marriage it is generally the man who determines whether sexual relations continue or cease.

As in other areas of their lives, the elderly couple tend to adhere to the norms of their own youth, one of which, for the present generation of aged, was disapprobation of sex for the elderly. Thus, feelings of guilt and shame may inhibit the sex life of the elderly woman, especially if the couple is living in the home of their children.

Another negative influence on sexual activity with long duration of marriage is probably a change in attitude of the woman. In her youth, though her sexuality gave her a certain power over her husband, withholding her favors presented considerable risk since he could easily be tempted to seek his satisfaction elsewhere. In later years, however, this competitive factor is probably absent, or at least less important. Finding it difficult to become enthusiastic, however, she may, out of habit or longstanding practice, allow him intercourse while discouraging or refusing the variations which might stimulate him to more satisfactory and pleasurable sexual experience.

5. EARLIER LEVELS OF PLEASURE AND PERFORMANCE

In women, as well as in men, there is a certain consistency in life style in that those women strongly motivated to sexual experience when younger tend to continue to be so in old age. Particularly in woman, however, it is not just the frequency but the satisfaction obtained from sexual relations in earlier years which is especially important to her as it relates to her continuing sexual interest and activity.

The capacity for sexual performance at orgasmic response levels seems to be a strong factor in the desire of a woman to continue having intercourse even after marriage ends and this capacity seems to continue into the later years, if she is exposed regularly to effective sexual stimulation.

6. IMPACT OF THE MENOPAUSE

Folklore competes with findings on the immediate impact of the menopause on a woman's erotic interest and practice, but there is no evidence that the hormonal changes around the time of the menopause have any direct influence on a woman's libido. It is rare to have complaints of frigidity beginning all of a sudden with the menopause and, as at any age level, such sudden complaints are generally attached to a host of other complaints about family and marriage. If a woman does find her sexual interest waning in the postmenopausal period, the cause very likely lies in life-history factors or the influence of the fatigue, vaginal atrophy and other symptoms of the climacteric.

There is in fact no reason why the menopause itself should blunt a woman's sexual capacity, performance or drive, especially since the symptoms which may indirectly affect her sexuality are amenable to hormonal and other treatment.

Masters and Johnson have confirmed that there is a slight slowing of the orgasmic reaction time in postmenopausal women. This does not appear to interfere with normal sexual enjoyment, however, rather to enhance it, at least in some cases. It is not unusual for a postmenopausal woman to indicate she is receiving increased pleasure from sexual activity (Lieberman, in Goldfarb et al., 1970).

Much of a woman's sexual desire and satisfaction during this period, however, depends upon her self-evaluation in terms of the menopuase. Confronted with the reality of physiological change manifested not only by general overall body changes, but also specifically with alterations and cessation of her menstrual cycle clearly indicating the end of her childbearing period of life, the middle-aged woman may interpret this as a threat to her sense of femininity or her role as a marital partner. If she views the end of her fertility as the end of her sexuality, the menopause will have a decidedly negative effect upon her sexual interest and activity.

Some report an upsurge in sexuality in the postmenopausal period which is usually attributed to the woman's view of the menopause as an end to the limitations imposed upon her by childbearing and an end to her fears of pregnancy. Our own findings show, however, that this upsurge is not the case for any large group of women, suggesting that the reports are anecdotal and casuistic. We found differences in levels of pleasure between women of different socioeconomic levels, though frequency of intercourse was found to decrease gradually from before the menopause and on into the postmenopausal period in women of both higher and lower social classes (Van Keep and Kellerhals, 1974). While the pleasure derived from intercourse followed a similar frequency gradient in women of the higher socioeconomic level, it dropped suddenly at the time of the menopause in women at the lower socioeconomic level.

Some psychiatrists report the development of freer or even aberrant types of sexual behavior in menopausal women. Oral-genital activity previously abstained from and, in women with no normal sexual outlet available, the development or increase of masturbatory activity are reported by Lieberman (Goldfarb et al., 1970) to be frequent in middle-aged women. Also, emergence of homosexual activities or tendencies towards utilizing domestic animals for erotic purposes are common among single women around the time of the menopause, according to Lieberman.

Reports of such changes are not common among medical authors, though aberrant behavior could occasionally be a result of the administration of androgen-containing preparations, used by some in treatment of menopausal symptoms. In any case, it seems likely that a far higher rate of atypical sexual behavior might be found among psychiatric patients than among others, though there is no conclusive evidence one way or the other.

Her interpretation of the menopause as it relates directly to ageing may on occasion propel a woman into increased sexual activity, sometimes extramarital and with a younger man, in an effort to deny the inevitable or seemingly to make the most of the time left to her, or simply to celebrate the new freedom of middle age.

By the time of the menopause, if the infidelity statistics are correct, many women will have had the experience of sharing their husbands, and maybe of nearly losing their marriages, which must affect their view of themselves as sexual partners. The woman who feels her menopause represents the end of her sexuality may turn her husband away, leaving him to prove his continued sexual competence in an extramarital affair.

In addition to fatigue and other nervous system symptoms of the climacteric, the most obvious and common complaint to interfere, often painfully, with the enjoyment of sexual intercourse, is the vaginal atrophy resulting from the estrogen deficiency that follows the menopause. The widely accepted treatment for this problem, as for the other symptoms reflecting hormonal changes, is estrogen replacement therapy.

Though hormone administration is not known to have a direct effect on the libido of the menopausal woman, it does have indirect effects by allevia tion of climacteric complaints, especially (a) easing the mechanics of intercourse to make it pleasurable instead of painful by rejuvenating the vagina and vulva and leading to better secretions and lubrication; (b) providing relief from the subjective climacteric complaints such as hot flushes, sweating, dizziness, nervous irritability, depression, insomnia, headache and other symptoms which tend to have a negative effect on her sexual responsiveness (Lauritzen, in Van Keep and Lauritzen, 1973, p. 15); (c) relief from the depression and destruction of self-image which often accompany the climacteric; innumerable clinical observations indicate beneficial effects, not only for physical symptoms, but also for emotional components such as anxiety, tension, mood depression and irritability (Kopera, in Van Keep and Lauritzen, 1973, p. 125) and (d) the fact that a woman is under medical supervision removes anxiety and her doctor's concern to relieve any discomfort or pain associated with intercourse serves in fact as an encouragement to sexual activity.

7. GYNECOLOGICAL PROBLEMS IN AGEING WOMEN

Some gynecological diseases also affect sexuality in the postmenopausal woman. Most commonly, it is infection that makes intercourse painful and unenjoyable enough for the woman to try to avoid it.

Surgical removal of carcinoma of the cervix can cause considerable damage. Even if the tumor is detected at an early stage, therapy may be followed by vaginal stenosis, requiring prompt use of dilator and estrogen therapy if the woman is to resume enjoyable sexual activity.

Physicians and surgeons sometimes create sexual problems in the middle-aged woman, as for instance in surgery for vaginal repair. In his zeal to make a new virgin-type introitus for a husband whose erection might not be quite as firm and strong as it used to be, the gynecologist may create a problem which both husband and wife are too embarrassed to report (Daly in Goldfarb et al. 1970).

Many seemingly unrelated surgical procedures can affect her libido, but often they interfere only because the woman believes they will. The psychological trauma accompanying gynecological surgery often interferes with the

846

woman's sexual activity or enjoyment of coitus, even when there is no reason for the operation to do so, because not rarely the patient is not told what the implications of surgery may or may not be for her sex life. Surgery for carcinoma of the cervix, for example, can leave her fearful that sexual activity may damage her or bring about a recurrence of the disease. Such fears are usually dispelled as soon as the woman is able to resume normal sex life, which she may need encouragement to do as soon as it is medically advisable. However, if she believes her ovaries or uterus are the locus of her libido, and when they are gone so is her sexuality, she may indeed function less well sexually after either hysterectomy or oopherectomy.

Whatever the nature of the surgical intervention in the ageing woman, counseling of the patient with regard to her sex life is advisble, even if it means the doctor must overcome his own inhibitions to do so.

BIBLIOGRAPHY

Christenson, C.V. and Gagnon, J.H. (1965) Sexual behavior in a group of older women. *J. Gerontol.* 20 (3): 351—356.
Christenson, C.V. and Johnson, A.B. (1973) Sexual patterns in a group of older never-married women. *J. Geriat. Psychiat.* VI (1) 80—98.
Goldfarb, A.F. (moderator), Daly, M.J., Lieberman, D. and Reed, D.M. (1970) Roundtable: Sex and the menopause. *Med. Aspects Hum. Sex.* 4 (11): 64 ff.
Kinsey, A.C., Pomeroy, W.B., Martin, C.E. and Gebhard, P.H. (1953) *Sexual Behavior in the Human Female.* (W.B. Saunders Co., Philadelphia and London.)
Masters, W.H. and Johnson, V.E. (1966) *Human Sexual Response.* (Little, Brown and Co., Boston.)
Pfeiffer, E. (1970) Sex in old age. *N. C. J. Ment. Health* 4 (1): 34—42.
Pfeiffer, E. and Davis, G.C. (1972) Determinants of sexual behavior in middle and old age. *J. Am. Geriat. Soc.* 20 (4): 151—158.
Pfeiffer, E., Verwoerdt, A. and Wang, H.S. (1969) The natural history of sexual behavior in a biologically advantaged group of aged individuals. *J. Gerontol.* 24: 193—198.
Van Keep, P.A. and Kellerhals, J. (1974) Die älterwerdende Frau. *Therapiewoche* 45: 5170—5194.
Van Keep, P.A. and Lauritzen, C. (eds.) (1973) *Ageing and Estrogens.* Proc. Workshop Conference Geneva, Oct. 5—6, 1972. International Health Foundation (S. Karger, Basle).
Verwoerdt, A., Pfeiffer, E. and Wang, H.S. (1969) Sexual behavior in senescence II. Patterns of sexual activity and interest. *Geriatrics* 24: 137—154.

CHAPTER 63

Pathology and involution of the genitals in the ageing female

C. LAURITZEN and P. MÜLLER

1. INTRODUCTION

The female genitalia undergo a climacteric involution, a regression beginning some years before the menopause and continuing to become increasingly apparent on through the 5—10 years following the menopause. The main cause of this involution is known to be the decreasing estrogen production of the ageing ovaries. However, it is not known to what degree the decreasing supply of the other ovarian hormones such as progesterone and androstenedione and of the androgenic and estrogenic hormones produced by the female adrenals (directly or by peripheral conversion) may participate in this regression process. The role of natural ageing in the involution of the female organs is also not clearly delimited.

The role of hormones

The symptoms of ovarian sexual hormone deficiency are easily understood when the physiological effects of sexual hormones on the target organs are considered: estrogen promotes the growth of the uterus, increasing its length, the thickness of the uterine muscular wall and the total weight of the organ. In addition, estrogen increases tone and contractility of the myometrium and stimulates the mucus secretion from the cervical glands. With the exception of estriol, estrogen causes proliferation of the endometrium and, together with progesterone, affects its secretory transformation. It stimulates endothelial proliferation in the Fallopian tubes and proliferation of the vaginal epithelium, which shows an increase of mitoses. Also, the proliferation and desquamation of the superficial cells of the vaginal epithelium are stimulated. Moreover, the blood flow through the target organs is intensified by the estrogen effect via a histamine and acetylcholine liberation. Also, the epidermis of the vulva is proliferated by estrogen. The turgor of these organs is increased through extracellular sodium and water retention (Diczfalusy and Lauritzen, 1961).

Handbook of Sexology, edited by J. Money and H. Musaph
© *Elsevier/North-Holland Biomedical Press, 1977*

In physiologic amounts, progesterone is functionally synergistic to estrogen. The physiologic role of androgen on the female genital organs is less well understood. Androgenic anabolic action on tissue may play a permissive role, especially in the absence of estrogen, and it may exert a proliferative effect on the vaginal epithelium. Moreover, androgen influences the size of the clitoris and labia majora and the growth of pubic hair. It may cause virilization and act antagonistically to estrogen, but only in unphysiologically high doses.

Hormone production

Typically, the internal secretion of the ovaries begins to decrease after the age of forty. First, the mean estrogen production declines; then, in the second half of the age decade of the forties, the progesterone of the corpus luteum decreases or fails because often the cycle is anovulatory. The corticosteroid function of the adrenal cortex remains normal for a long time following the menopause. However, as shown in Table I, the production and excretion of androstenedione and dehydroepiandrosterone decreases when the senium begins (60—65 years). Androstenedione, the main C_{19}-steroid, is produced at a rate of 1—2 mg per day and is peripherally converted to estrone at a rate of about 2%, which is in turn converted partly to estradiol-17β (MacDonald et al., 1969; Longcope, 1971). The percentage of conversion to one or other estrogen may increase slightly with increasing age, especially in conjunction with certain conditions such as adipositas or endometrial carcinoma. Most probably, estrogen is not produced directly by the adrenals in significant amounts in these later years (see Table II).

In menstrually cyclic women, the main estrogen secreted by the ovary is estradiol-17β, which is produced at a rate of about 100—800 μg per day according to the stage of the cycle. This estrogen production decreases to a rate of less than 100 μg per day, at the time of menopause and even less thereafter. Because the adrenal sex-steroid secretion consists mostly of an-

Table I
Decrease of 17-oxosteroids with age

Stage of life	17-oxo-steroids	Andro-sterone	Etio-cholanolone	Dehydro-epiandro-sterone
Normal cyclic women, N = 10 Mean (range)	9.9 (4.9—17.6)	4.2 (2.5—5.9)	3.3 (1.7—5.3)	1.8 (0.5—3.2)
Menopause, N = 10 Mean (range)	7.8 (2.1—11.0)	3.4 (1.0—5.2)	2.8 (1.0—3.2)	1.1 (0.2—1.5)
Senium, N = 10 Mean (range)	3.3 (1.6—6.0)	1.4 (0.4—2.5)	1.2 (0.8—2.3)	0.3 (0.1—0.7)

Table II
Production and conversion rate of estrone and androstenedione in postmenopausal women

Production rate of estrone (nearly exclusively extraglandular from androstenedione)	40—120 µg/day
Production rate of androstenedione	
— in postmenopausal women	1.62—2.16 mg/day
— in cyclical women	3.4 mg/day
Conversion rate: androstenedione → estrone	
— in postmenopausal women	1.7 (1.3—2.0) %
— in women with endometrial carcinoma	3.1 (2.1 6.0) %

Sources: Horton and Tait, 1966; Hausknecht and Gusberg, 1969; MacDonald et al., 1969, 1971; Longcope, 1971.

drostenedione, which is converted to estrone, the predominating estrogens circulating in the plasma of postmenopausal women are estrone as such or in the form of estrone sulfate (Rader et al., 1973; Table III).

It is well known that the affinity of the binding protein receptor of the target cell to estrone is lower than to estradiol-17β. Also estriol, the main metabolite among the primary estrogens, may replace estradiol-17β at the site of binding only when present in higher doses. This estrogen and its epimeres (16- and 17-epi-estriol) exert no appreciable effect on the endometrium; their stimulative action is directed mostly on the cervix and the vagina.

Table III
Estrogens in the postmenopause and senium

	Estrogen excretion (µg/24 h)			
	Estrone	Estradiol-17β	Estriol	Total
Urinary				
2 months following hysterectomy	3.5	3.0	1.8	8.3
2 months following X-ray castration	2.8	2.4	1.8	7.0
Spontaneous post-menopause				
9 years	1.5	0.6	5.0	7.1 *
15 years	0.8	0.3	3.6	4.7
Plasma	Estrogen concentration (pg/ml)			
Spontaneous postmenopause				
5— 8 years	44	10	3.7	58
20—20 years	40	14	3.0	57
>20 years	33	11	3.0	47

* No endometrial stimulation will occur below a level of 10 µg/24 h.

2. REGRESSIVE CHANGES OF THE TARGET ORGANS

Physiological regressive changes

The decrease and final loss of ovarian steroid hormones causes reduction of growth, proliferation and active hyperemia in the target organs. The skin of the vulva loses its turgor and elasticity and becomes thinner. The subcutaneous fat vanishes; the labia majora and the clitoris become smaller, retracting to the surface level of the vulva, and glandular secretions diminish. These atrophic changes also affect the perineum and the anus, the epithelium becoming dry and thinner, and fissures may form. The vagina shrinks as a result of the estrogen deficiency and the introitus gapes due to loss of elasticity. The urethral outlet may be drawn backward and upward, increasing the size of its opening, producing urethral ectropion and leading to incontinence of urine. Atrophic cystitis may occur.

The vaginal epithelium, which is the most sensitive indicator of the estrogenic proliferative effect, deteriorates and is easily bruised and irritated. It is pale, but may become red from inflammation and subepithelial bleedings. Discomfort due to burning sensations or itching can be quite intense. The vaginal secretion becomes scanty, the pH will increase to alkaline with the result that Döderlein's bacilli disappear (Table IV).

Table IV
Vaginal smear in the postmenopause (from Stoll and Ledermair, 1960).

Duration of postmenopause years	High proliferation (estrogen) (%)	Medium proliferation (%)	Atrophy (%)	Total
2—10	21	55	24	599
>11	14	49	37	512

Table V
Atrophy of the estrogen target organs in ageing females.

	Age (years)	Frequency (%)	Literature
Atrophy of the vulva	<55	15	McLaren, 1941
	>66	66	
Vaginal atrophy, kraurosis vaginae	>55	33	
	>66	94	
Descensus vaginae et uteri	<48	4—16	Krokefors, 1960
	>48	12—36	
Decrease of breast volume	60	40—50	Goldfarb, 1969

Table VI
Findings of endometrial histology of 60 uteri in postmenopausal women who died of
internal diseases (from McBride, 1957).

Histological finding	Frequency (%)
Atrophy	65
Cystic glands	20
Endometrial polyps	15
Hyperplasia	0

The absence of estrogenic protection leads to further bacterial invasion. The atrophic smear is characterized by almost 100% basal cells with basophilic stain. Numerous polymorphonuclear leukocytes and some lymphocytes are present. The muscles, ligaments and fascia of the pelvic floor deteriorate and changes of these structures may predispose to descensus uteri et vaginae and even to prolapse of the inner genitalia. The frequency of atrophic changes in older women is shown in Table V. The uterus shrinks because of loss of fluid and transformation of the myometrium into fibrous tissue. Eventually, existing myomas are reduced in size because of the decreasing blood supply. In all patients, the endometrium will show a progression of atrophy as the estrogenic stimulation declines (Table VI). If the cervical canal becomes too narrow, a scrometra by retention of uterine fluid may occur (Labhart, 1953; Oliven, 1955; Herrick, 1957).

The breasts also undergo regressive changes: the lobules disappear, the tubuli collapse, the subcutaneous fat may increase or decrease and the breast tissues are converted into subareolar structures which are intermixed with connective tissues. Finally the breasts become flat and pendulous.

Other effects of estrogen withdrawal may include loss of hair from the pubic region and the scalp, atrophy of the skin and loss of feminine bodily habitus and obesity, all of which result in a loss of sexual attractiveness. The preponderance of androgen may cause hirsutism, defeminization or even slight virilization.

3. PATHOLOGICAL CHANGES OF THE VULVA

Kraurosis vulvae

This is a progressive sclerosing atrophy of marked degree, resulting in stenosis of the vaginal orifice and effacement of the labia minora and clitoris. The vulvar skin is thin, dry, shiny, depigmented and yellowish-white in color. The tension of the tissue and the disturbance of its metabolism creates excoriations and annoying pruritus, intertrigo and sometimes eczema (Cockerell and Knox, 1962).

Leukoplakia

A localized leukoplakia will not infrequently develop upon the kraurosis vulvae. Its occurrence is of particular significance as a possible precursor of vulvar carcinoma. Chronic inflammatory and hypotrophic processes involve the epidermis and subepithelial tissues. These may occur as a single spot or as multiple discrete processes, finally as a general lesion involving clitoris, prepuce, labia minora, posterior commissure, perineum and perianal areas. The lesion shows a gray—white color and a thickening to an almost asbestos-like appearance. Fissures and ulcerations are common. The histologic picture includes hyperkeratosis, increase in the stratum granulosum, acanthosis, lymphatic infiltration of the subcutis and destruction of elastic fibers of the corium (Labhart, 1953).

Lichen sclerosis and atrophia of the vulva

Lichenification is a secondary change of kraurosis vulvae which may be provoked by prolonged scratching. It is commonly seen in patients with persistent pruritus vulvae. The skin is thickened and has a leathery appearance in which the normal markings are accentuated. When moisture is present, the lesion assumes a grayish-white, soggy appearance. Hyperkeratosis, parakeratosis, acanthosis and prolongation of the rete pegs can be distinguished histologically. The subepithelial elastic fibers are not destroyed. These changes may be the basis of different forms of vulvitis.

The decrease of the ovarian hormones has an important effect upon the vaginal epithelium: mitosis rate, proliferation, metabolism and blood perfusion of the tissues are reduced. This, of course, favors atrophic and inflammatory changes.

Kraurosis vaginae

This term means the shrinking of the vaginal wall, especially in the upper third of the vagina, so that the caliber of the vaginal channel is narrowed and the fornices vaginae are shortened. Behind the kraurosis of these fornices the portio uteri may be very flat and even become unrecognizable through the stenosed vagina. The rugae become less prominent and the epithelium is thin and pale rather than rosy. Kraurotic vaginal tissue is highly vulnerable during coitus or other manipulations (Grimmer, 1975).

Like any other membrane-lined body cavity, the vagina normally harbors many different pathogenic bacteria in the quiescent state. It is therefore only natural that the progressive decrease in the resistence of the mucus membrane as the result of estrogen deficiency should lead to bacterial inflammation.

Senile vaginitis

The clinical picture of senile vaginitis is quite characteristic. The vagina is narrowed, especially near the apex, making visualization of the cervix difficult. The thin epithelium is covered with numerous small petechial hemorrhages. In some areas these have coalesced with a breakdown of the superficial epithelia in the formation of small ulcerations. The mucus membrane around the hemorrhages and the denuded areas exhibits marked palor and an almost complete absence of the rugae. A thin, pale, malodoros and irritating discharge is usually present. Infection with *Trichomonas vaginalis* is not infrequently superimposed upon senile vaginitis. Almost any type of bacterial organism may be involved and the infection is often mixed. If the condition advances, attempts at regenerative repair may lead to the formation of adhesions, which are at first flimsy and break easily, but eventually they become firm and fibrous and may occlude a part of the vagina. Senile vaginitis may lead to postmenopausal bleeding, and is, in fact, one of the commonest causes of such bleedings. In the milder forms, a pinkish discharge may result from the denuded areas, while in the advanced state rupture of one of the adhesions as a consequence of trauma may result in profuse hemorrhage. Rupture of one of these adhesions may extend into the broad ligamentum causing direct injury of uterine vessels.

The histological picture of vaginitis is characterized by a thin superficial epithelium, often broken at some point by ulceration. In the submucosa, a diffuse infiltration of both polymorphonuclear leukocytes and lymphocytes is found. The stroma is edematous. Correspondingly, the smear from the postmenopausal vaginitis shows cells typical of complete atrophy with a gross influx of polymorphonuclear leukocytes (Labhart, 1953).

4. SEXUAL REACTIONS IN THE ELDERLY WOMAN

Regular sexual relations, for example, once or twice a week, may be a help in the adjustment to old age and in maintaining self-identity, social contact and joy of life, but may also add to the maintenance of good genital conditions. Normal lubrication, orgastic widening of the vagina and contraction of the orgastic manchette can occur in spite of slight atrophy of the vaginal epithelium. In older women with high grade atrophy and without regular sexual contact, the hyperemic phenomenon ('sex skin') of the vulva does not develop when orgasm occurs. Lubrication following sexual stimulus will be diminished and delayed, occurring only after 1—5 min instead of after 15—30 sec as in young women. So will the enlargement and extension of the vagina as a reaction to increasing sexual excitement. Elevation of the uterus during the plateau phase is less marked in older women. If uterine atrophy is present, orgastic contraction can be painful. The orgasmic phase is typically reduced in duration (Masters and Johnson, 1966).

Problems of intercourse resulting from the physiologic and pathologic atrophy of the female genitalia

Atrophy of the vulva and shrinkage of the introitus (Labhart stenosis) may produce difficulties in introducing the penis into the vagina and may even restrict orogenital contact. The postmenopausal woman may complain of dryness and soreness, itching, burning, pains and even lesions of the introitus. Nothing is known concerning a possible decrease in the sensibility of the clitoris, but touching an atrophic clitoris, which is no longer protected by the now retracted prepuce, may cause unpleasant or even painful sensations (Bieren, 1963). Lubrication of the vagina may be of itching and burning quality, and the dryness and lack of coital lubrication may lead to discomfort and dyspareunia. The enlargement of the vagina in orgasm cannot take place in atrophic vaginitis, and from the atrophic and inflamed vaginal wall bloody discharge and even bleeding during or after coitus may occur. Kraurosis can cause lesions of the vagina resulting in profuse bleedings. Ectropion urethrae can be worsened by coitus; urinary incontinence may occur during coitus and urinary urge follow it. Colpitis atrophicans and its complaints are certainly aggravated by intercourse. Of course, superinfection of *Trichomonas* or of various bacteria, which can be transmitted by coitus, deteriorates an already existing vaginitis.

The manifold complaints caused by the atrophy of the vulva and the vagina described above may cause not only practical difficulties in coitus, but also psychic problems. When sexual relations are avoided because of the pain and difficulties caused by contact, an aversion to intercourse may result.

Preventive therapy of involutional changes

The only logical preventive therapy of all involutional changes of the breasts and genitalia and the related pathological changes and complaints is estrogen substitution therapy, which should begin at or shortly before the time of menopause because of the declining estrogen level after the age of forty. However, only about 30% of all patients go to the doctor with their climacteric complaints or its sequelae and only half of these will be treated with estrogens. Prophylactic medication consists of the administration of natural estrogens, as for instance conjugated estrogens, 1.25 mg per day for 21 days. Thereafter an interval of one week without therapy or with reduced doses only is recommended. Also estradiol valerate, 2 mg per day, may be given in the first years. If periodic uterine bleeding is still wanted, progestogens may be added in the second half of the cycle. A third possibility is the use of estriol, which does not cause endometrial proliferation, and can therefore be given continuously in a dose of 1—2 mg daily without fear of causing uterine withdrawal bleedings. If no signs of overdosage occur, estriol can be administered without an interval in the fourth week. Although estrogen—androgen preparations are very effective also with regard to libido which is enhanced by androgen therapy, such therapy has disadvantages. The possible consequences of cumulative and excessive androgen medication — deepening of the voice, hirsutism and virilization — must be discussed with the patient.

Estrogen therapy should be a prolonged treatment, continued indefinitely as long as it makes sense to do so. Although estrogen per se has no effect on libido or orgasm, it does have a psychotonic effect. Moreover, estrogen therapy creates a feeling of well-being which, together with the absence of genital and extragenital symptoms, will lead to more satisfactory sexual contacts.

Local administration of estrogen in vaginal cream, foam or suppositories is also helpful, though it is preferable to give the benefit of estrogen to the whole organism.

The maintenance of an eutrophic state of the genitalia and of a healthy psychic condition may preserve sexual interest and ability far into old age.

Curative therapy in involutional changes

If regressive changes or even pathological changes such as with kraurosis vulvae, lichen sclerosis et atrophia, kraurosis vaginae, colpitis atrophicans or cystitis atrophicans are present, logically a therapy with estrogens is indicated (Simon, 1961; Slunsky, 1963; Rütte and Delnon, 1965; Dapunt et al., 1971). This medication will not only remove complaints but restore normality and sexual ability before neurotic fixation occurs (Table VII). Although this therapy can be performed by local application of estrogens (Korte, 1973), local therapy is for the most part only supplemental. In addition, estrogens should be administered orally or parenterally to increase the effectiveness of the tharapy (Wenner and Hauser, 1959; Kupperman, 1959; Hauser et al., 1961; Bieren, 1963; Joswig-Priewe et al., 1973). The same preparations and dosages are to be used as mentioned for prophylactic medication. Injection of estradiol esters, which exert a prolonged effect, is recommended only if the uterus has been removed.

In most cases, long-term therapy with estrogens will improve and finally normalize the regressive and pathological changes of estrogen deficiency and increase such physiological reactions as lubrication, muscle tone and distensibility of the vagina (Masters and Johnson, 1966; Lauritzen, 1970, 1971, 1974).

Contraindications for estrogen therapy are few and of no widespread prac-

Table VII
Treatment results of atrophic changes in the urogenital organs with conjugated estrogens 1.25 mg per day after 6 months (563 patients).

	Disappearance of symptoms (%)	Amelioration (%)	No change (%)
Colpitis senilis	89	11	0
Kraurosis vaginae with dyspareunia	73	27	0
Kraurosis vulvae with pruritus	68	21	11
Ectropion urethrae	100	0	0
Atrophic urethrocystitis	81	19	0
Urinary stress incontinence I°	37	45	18

tical importance, namely, severe liver damage and thromboembolic episodes in the woman's medical history. Significant side effects of the estrogen therapy are not to be expected.

BIBLIOGRAPHY

Bieren, R.E. (1963) Painful Sex in Women. *Sexology* 30: 88.
Cockerell, E.G. and Knox, I.N. (1962) Dermatologic diseases of the vulva. *Am. J. Obstet. Gynecol.* 81: 537.
Dapunt, O., Födisch, H.J. and Zeiger, J. (1971) Lichen sclerosus et atrophicus mit genitaler und extragenitaler Lokalisation. *Geburthshilfe Frauenheilk.* 31: 661.
Diczfalusy, E. and Lauritzen, C. (1961) *Oestrogene beim Menschen.* (Springer, Berlin— Göttingen—Heidelberg.)
Goldfarb, A.F. (1969) The climacteric and some of its problems. *Geriatrics* 24: 107.
Grimmer, H. (1975) *Gut- und bösartige Erkrankungen der Vulva.* (Grosse Verlag, Berlin.)
Hauser, G.A., Müller, Th., Valaer, M., Erb, H., Obiri, J.A., Remen, U. and Vanäänen, P. (1961). Der Zusammenhang zwischen gynäkologischen Krankheiten und dem Menopausenalter. *Gynaecologia* (Basel) 152: 270.
Hausknecht, R.U. and Gusberg, S.B. (1969) Estrogen metabolism at high risk for endometrial carcinoma. *Am. J. Obstet. Gynaecol.* 105: 1161.
Herrick, E.H. (1957) Sex changes in ageing. *Sexology* 24: 248.
Horton, R. and Tait, J.E. (1966) Estrogen production rates. *J. Clin. Invest.* 45: 301.
Joswig-Priewe, H., Joswig, E.H. and Otto, K. (1973) Orale Oestrioltherapie bei Kolpitis senilis. *Z. Allgemeinmed.* 49: 633.
Korte, W. (1973) Indikationen und Praxis intravaginaler Östrogen-Therapie mit Dienoestrol-Ortho-Vaginalcreme. *Fortschr. Med.* 91: 921.
Krokefors, E. (1960) *Alter, Geburtenzahl und gynäkologische Krankheiten.* (M. Liitos Bogtryckeri, Helsingfors.)
Kupperman, H.S. (1959) Hormonal aspects of frigidity. *Quart. Rev. Surg. Obstet. Gynecol.* 16: 254.
Labhart, A. (1953) Die Erkrankungen der äusseren Geschlechtsorgane. Die Erkrankungen der Scheide. In: (Seitz, L. and Amreich, A.J., Eds.) *Biologie und Pathologie des Weibes.* Band IV. (Wien, Urban & Schwarzenberg, Berlin.)
Lauritzen, C. (1971) Das Klimakterium der Frau. *Med. Klin.* 66: 1255.
Lauritzen, C. (1970) Das Klimakterium, Physiologie, Pathophysiologie, Diagnose, Differentialdiagnose und Therapie. *Tägliche Praxis* 11: 91.
Lauritzen, C. (1974) Grundlegende Daten über das Klimakterium und seine Beschwerden. *Therapiewoche* 24: 5161.
Longcope, C. (1971) Metabolic clearance and blood production rate of estrogens in postmenopausal women. *Am. J. Obstet. Gynecol.* 111: 778.
MacDonald, P.C., Grodin, J.M. and Siiteri, P.K. (1969) The utilization of plasma androstenedione for estrone in women. *Prog. Endocrinol.* (Excerpta Medica Foundation, Amsterdam) p. 770.
MacDonald, P.C., Grodin, J.M. and Siiteri, P.K. (1971) Dynamics of androgen and oestrogen secretion. In: (D.T. Baird and J.A. Strong, Eds.) *Control of Gonadal Steroid Secretion.* (Edinburgh University Press, Edinburgh) pp. 158—174.
Masters, W.H. and Johnson, V.E. (1966) *Human Sexual Response.* (Little, Brown and Co., Boston.)
McBride, J.M. (1957) Oestrogen excretion levels in normal postmenopausal women. *J. Clin. Endocrinol. Metab.* 17: 1440.

McLaren, H.C. (1941) The normal menopause. *J. Obstet. Gynaecol. Br. Emp.* 48: 1.

Oliven, J.F. (1955) *Sexual Hygiene and Pathology.* (Lippincott, Philadelphia.)

Rader, M.D., Flickinger, G.L., Villa, G.O. de, Mikuta, J.J. and Mikhail, G. (1973) Plasma estrogens in postmenopausal women. *Am. J. Obstet. Gynecol.* 116: 1069.

Rütte, B. von and Delnon, J. (1965) Die Urethritis atrophicans der Frau. *Helv. Clin. Acta* 32: 484.

Simon, M.J. (1961) Cystalgie de la Ménopause et Oestriol. *Press Méd.* 69: 1301.

Slunsky, R. (1963) Das Ovestin als konservative Behandlungsmethode der funktionellen Harninkontinenz. *Z. Geburtshilfe Gynäkol.* 160: 91.

Stoll, P. and Ledermair, O. (1960) Funktionelle Zytologie in der Postmenopause. *Geburtshilfe Frauenheilk.* 20: 263.

Wenner, R. and Hauser, G.A. (1960) Neurovegetative Untersuchungen und Therapieergebnisse bei klimakterischen Frauen. *Arch. Gynäkol.* 193: 58.

SECTION XI

Psychosexual impairment

Section coordinator: Dennis Friedman

CHAPTER 64

Introduction

DENNIS FRIEDMAN

Psychosexual impairment implies that there is an inadequacy of the ability to experience pleasurable sensations mainly but not exclusively in the genital organs. The inadequacy may be subjective with little or no interference with sexual performance and may apply to any partner, or it may be selective. Even when lack of warm feelings for the partner exists, performance may be normal but the 'loved' object exists only for the purpose of self-gratification. More overt manifestations of inadequacy are recognized in the two major failures of sexual communication in both sexes, namely erective impotence and vaginismus. These two disorders represent an extreme position on a continuum at the other end of which is the occasional missed orgasm or transient erective or ejaculatory impotence. They represent the inability to consummate the sexual act and must be considered pathological.

The problem may present itself with pain or dysfunction in the clinic of the gynecologist, endocrinologist or neurologist, and patients may risk finding themselves in the 'no man's land' of 'no abnormality diagnosed' and be excluded from the possibility of appropriate help. When eventual psychiatric referral is made, it may have taken place only after investigation of a symptom by radiography, endoscopy or even laparotomy. This may make an understanding of the psychopathologic determinants of the problem difficult through psychotherapy, since the emphasis placed on somatic manifestations reinforces them as a defense against such understanding.

The diagnosis of psychosexual impairment does not have a firm basis, if assumptions made by earlier investigators are accepted uncritically. For example the assertion that so-called vaginal orgasm is a sine qua non of female sexual maturity would at one time have implied that all those women who experience either pleasurable feelings during intercourse without orgasm, or who experience so-called clitoral orgasm only, are inadequate. There is also the danger that the cultural expectations of the so-called 'liberated' woman may cause her to aim for a goal which is out of her reach. Failure to achieve it results in disappointment, and resentment. Such envious

Handbook of Sexology, edited by J. Money and H. Musaph
© *Elsevier/North-Holland Biomedical Press, 1977*

attitudes may lead her wrongly to consider herself as sexually inadequate.

Reduction in sexual activity may be considered to be normal under some circumstances. Pregnancy may temporarily satisfy the procreative urge, and if coitus has been directed solely towards achieving this aim then there will be a reduction in sexual interest and activity. On the other hand increased activity by either partner may result from freedom from the fear of an unwanted pregnancy. While some women may suffer some slight reduction in endocrine activity after the menopause with a possible effect upon the erotic component of sexuality, the affectionate component will compensate for this, as may also the release from fear of another pregnancy.

It is possible that in the male too much emphasis has been placed in the past on dominance. Nonetheless, the current swing away from such a concept in the cause of socioeconomic equality may prove threatening to some men, and must be taken into account when considering potency in a society in which man sees himself as either competing with powerful rivals, or being encouraged into a 'unisex' status. The latter may rob him of his penis's symbolic meanings such as sturdiness, uprightness and penetrating power, and may render him impotent through the intervention of high performance anxiety.

A male whose partner becomes unattractive to him as a result of domestic or other reasons, or who has turned away from her to another may not necessarily be regarded as suffering from sexual inadequacy, if the new partner evokes a normal sexual response in him.

Inadequacy in both sexes should be considered pathological if it occurs with every partner, or when other partnerships are required outside the marital one in order to act out nonintegrated feelings of jealousy, greed, envy and hate.

Finally, inadequacy should be suspected as paradoxically underlying symptoms such as promiscuous overactivity accompanied by flirtatiousness and seductive behavior as is found in nymphomania and satyriasis. Inadequacy may also underly the so-called sexual deviations or paraphilias.

CHAPTER 65

Psychoandrology

DENNIS FRIEDMAN

In order to understand the psychological factors concerned with sexual arousal and its physical manifestation in the genitalia, it would be helpful to consider first the physiology of erection and ejaculation, and to follow this by a discussion of sexual feelings and the psychological factors which may modify or inhibit them.

1. PHYSIOLOGICAL ASPECTS OF NORMAL MALE SEXUAL FUNCTION

Erection is a vascular phenomenon which is dependent on the integrity of the blood and nerve supply to the penis. Tumescence results from constriction of the superficial and deep dorsal veins and dilatation of the terminal branches of the internal pudendal arteries which allows blood to flow into the three cylindrical masses of erectile tissue called the corpora cavernosa and the corpus spongiosum. This tissue, while flaccid, contains very little blood and is in a collapsed state. The vascular spaces fill up with blood following either physical or psychic stimuli.

The motor pathways involved are the sacral component of the craniosacral system (S 2 3 4), the nervi erigentes: a center for reflex erection also exists in the spinal cord.

Ejaculation is a reflex phenomenon consisting of two distinct actions, emission and expulsion. Sensory end organs are located in the glans penis and impulses from there are transmitted centrally via the internal pudendal nerves.

During the first stage of ejaculation (emission), sudden contraction of the smooth muscles of the internal genital organs expels seminal fluid into the urethra. This is accompanied by peristaltic contractions of the testes, epididymis and the vas deferens. At the same time the secretions of the seminal vesicles, prostate and bulbo-urethral glands pass into the urethra following

Handbook of Sexology, edited by J. Money and H. Musaph
© *Elsevier/North-Holland Biomedical Press, 1977*

similar contractions. In the second stage the bulbo-cavernosus muscle (which is skeletal) contracts and ejaculation takes place as the seminal fluid is expelled from the urethra to the exterior. Afferent impulses, arising mainly from the glans penis, pass to the spinal cord. The final efferent pathway of the reflex arc causing ejaculation results from increased neural activity transmitted via the internal pudendal nerves. The impulses that provoke ejaculation are parasympathetic and an ejaculatory center integrating the reflexes is present in the lumbosacral region of the spinal cord.

Responsiveness of the target organ is dependent upon an adequate level of circulating testosterone. The production of androgen by the testis depends on hormones produced by the hypophysis (pituitary) gland. Those concerned with gonadal activity are the follicle-stimulating hormone (FSH), and luteinizing hormone or interstitial-cell-stimulating hormone (LH or ICSH). FSH in conjunction with LH leads to proliferation of the seminiferous tubules, whereas LH (ICSH) stimulates the Leydig cells to secrete androgen. A negative feedback regulation also exists between the pars distalis (the anterior pituitary) of the adenohypophysis and the gonads. The organic factors concerned both in hormone production and the disorders, congenital, surgical and medical, which may affect the target glands will be considered elsewhere.

2. PHYSIOLOGICAL ASPECTS OF IMPAIRED MALE SEXUAL FUNCTION

Although coitus may be performed satisfactorily, sexual feelings may be diminished or may even be absent altogether. Libido is a word commonly used to describe sexual feelings; its original psychoanalytic meaning has undergone many changes, not only in Freud's own writings over a period of forty years, but also in those of his contemporaries and successors. When used in this text it will be taken to mean sexual desire which is expressed with the genitals and experienced both peripherally and centrally. The assessment of such feeling is subjective. Satisfaction may well be expressed by the coital partner if there is an ability to maintain an erection for an indefinite period, but only he will know that this is due to his inability to experience the high level of arousal needed for ejaculation to occur. His performance is measured objectively and may be rated highly, but his 'libido' rated subjectively is low.

Low libido, whatever the cause, leads to impotence, which may be either erective or ejaculatory. Erective impotence is considered to be psychogenic if the patient states that erection either occurs on awakening or is associated with dreams throughout the night, or if successful masturbation with ejaculation is achieved.

Organic factors

Although organic factors do cause impotence they account for less than an estimated 10% of all cases and, other than in diabetes, a patient who says that he has difficulty in obtaining or maintaining an erection with a sexual partner is likely to be suffering from psychogenic impotence. Local genital causes are easily excluded by the history and confirmed by examination. Klinefelter's syndrome (XXY sex chromosome constitution) usually presents as infertility and the condition can be recognized by the associated eunuchoid body build, gynecomastia, hypospermia and small testes. Primary neurological disorders which feature impotence typically have it as a late symptom, and obvious physical signs in the central nervous system will usually be present. Impotence may be the presenting symptom in endocrine disorders such as diabetes mellitus or pituitary dysfunction.

Other than alcohol, drugs which interfere with sexual performance tend to do so by inhibiting ejaculation and thus may reduce arousal levels. Drugs used in psychiatry are most often incriminated, such as thioridozine, amphetamine, chlordiazepoxide, tricyclic antidepressants, monoamine oxidase inhibitors and reserpine. Since impotent males are often depressed or anxious an enquiry into what other doctors have prescribed is important, since therapy may be perpetuating the disorder.

Decreased frequency of intercourse and failure of ejaculation may also be present if the patient is being treated for hypertension with drugs such as guanethedine or alpha-methyldopa.

There is no evidence for the common clinical assertion that obesity in the absence of endocrine disease can cause erective impotence.

A sudden reduction in sexual activity occurring in males between the ages of 55 and 65 may be associated with mild testicular atrophy and when accompanied by loss of libido, depression, irritability, hot flushes, lapses of recent memory and impotence, constitutes the symptoms of the male menopause or climacterium virile (Montgomery and Welbourn, 1975).

However, spontaneous testicular deficiency severe enough to produce symptoms is a rare occurrence. For the diagnosis to be confirmed there should be a low level of testosterone in the blood plasma and a raised urinary gonadotropin output. In most patients whose principal complaint is impotence there is an underlying emotional disturbance. Androgen therapy in these circumstances is valueless and provided there is no reason to suspect organic disease, treatment is directed towards reducing and eliminating the stress factors present in the causal situations.

3. PSYCHOLOGICAL ASPECTS OF NORMAL MALE SEXUAL FUNCTION

Bowlby (1953) refers to feelings of loss of love and security experienced by the infant at the breast and the serious disorders that may arise as a consequence. Later, weaning also carries with it emotional overtones associated in adult life with separation anxieties. Observations made on young infants reveal a range of behavior which seems to be a direct reaction to their mother's attitudes to them. From the moment of birth the infant is exposed to stimuli which evoke responses in him. It is observed that when he is hungry, cold or uncomfortable, he reacts with anger. When he has been fed and made comfortable he experiences his environment with contentment and satisfaction. The source of this repertoire of feeling is his mother and more specifically, the breast. As the infant grows older he makes attempts to resolve his mixed feelings for the mother in a number of ways which permit integration of the hostility and the love.

If he has been unable to resolve his aggression towards her he may continue his attack upon surrogate mothers when he grows up. He will be particularly prone to 'falling in love' as his unconscious recognizes qualities which remind him of his primary love; while 'in love' he will experience his love objects as 'idealized', (having all the qualities which he would have chosen in his mother had he been given the opportunity). Such a relationship excludes negative feelings which will only become apparent to him later. He must learn to integrate the opposing feelings acquired in infancy so that he will not feel the need to act them out as an adult. Hostile attitudes to women may take various forms including erective or ejaculatory impotence, and serve to prevent pleasurable sexual responses in them.

Classical psychoanalysis looks to the gradual development of the adult sexual instinct seeking expression through the genital organs out of successive contributions from the component instincts (oral, anal and phallic) which represent particular erotogenic zones. The energy of the sexual instincts is called libido. Libido could become 'fixated' at one or other of the stages of development if an instinct was prematurely satisfied, or if there was a repression of libido later on, then it would flow back to one of the fixation points, breaking through in the form of a symptom. The form of the neurotic illness would be determined by where the fixation point happened to be; thus the cause of neurotic illness is looked for in the individual's developmental history.

Therefore, it is postulated that every adult who is blocked in his sexuality falls back on infantile sexuality as a substitute. Pregenital and infantile attitudes are of course incompatible with sexual maturity that is, genitality, and failure to achieve coitus in an adult heterosexual relationship is inevitable.

Fenichel (1945) points out that Freud did not limit himself to recognizing that human sexuality results from impulses and actions which lead to sexual intercourse. He recognized above all the field of infantile sexuality which he described in his Three Essays on the Theory of Sexuality (1905).

4. PSYCHOLOGICAL ASPECTS OF IMPAIRED MALE SEXUAL FUNCTION

Introduction

Impotence may be interpreted as arising from the patient's ambivalence and the inability to experience the penis as a loving extension of himself in the same way as he could not appreciate the breast as a loving extension of his mother. Paradoxically the more he 'loves' his partner the more reluctant he is to offer the bad feeding organ which he sees in his fantasy as destructive.

Impotence based on this stage of psychosexual development probably accounts for erective difficulties, while later on urethral sadism will tend to account for difficulties in ejaculation. In the analysis of patients with the latter problem, the fear is invariably expressed that if he allows himself to ejaculate inside the vagina he will soil her by urinating instead.

The anal stage may be recalled with its underlying aggression when making debasing or sadistic attacks upon a partner. In adult life the individual may experience himself as empty and worthless recognizing only the nonvalued introjected parts of himself. This lack of self-esteem may lead him into greedy competition with others and an insatiable desire to overpower and replace them. The desire may be so overwhelming that projection once again is resorted to, resulting in feeling threatened by other men experienced as more powerful and therefore frightening (women are contemptuously devalued or seduced and are therefore not a threat), or an omnipotent defense is assumed which thinly covers the symptoms of his impotence.

Clinical approach to patients with psychogenic impotence

Coital anxiety
Coital anxiety is present in all patients with ejaculatio praecox (premature ejaculation) and all others suffering from psychogenic erective impotence other than those in whom coldness and underlying hostility is a feature of the personality. Where anxiety is a causal factor the patient usually complains of a fear of failure, or of being unable to live up to either his own or his partner's expectations, or of ageing.

An excessive concern for virility may be cultural or may be a reflection of perfectionistic attitudes common in the obsessional personality.

Sexual responsiveness
The young male with ejaculatio praecox and impotentia erigendi (erective impotence) who is prevented from successfully carrying out the sexual act is invariably sexually responsive, that is, he tends to masturbate to orgasm frequently with heterosexual fantasy, has nocturnal emissions accompanying erotic dreams and responds with erection to sexual stimuli, provided coitus is not expected by his partner or is situationally impossible. Patients such as these are classified by Cooper (1969) as 'early onset' impotence who suffer from 'coital anxiety' which he defines as related temporarily to the act of coitus but not to other life situations or events. This he contrasts with the sexual apathy of insidious 'late onset' impotence in which sexual interest and performance declines over a number of years. Indifference to the sexual demands of a frustrated partner leads eventually to anxiety which he sees as consequential, as opposed to 'early onset' impotence where the anxiety is in large measure causal.

Factors causing coital anxiety are based on (i) the relationship that the patient has with his partner to which his loss of sexual interest may be a reaction or (ii) factors within himself. Coital anxiety will lead to either premature ejaculation (ejaculatio praecox) or erective impotence (impotentia erigendi).

Premature ejaculation
Premature ejaculation, which is always psychogenic, is often normally present in the young male whose anxiety to succeed in his first sexual encounters provokes such a degree of sympathetic overactivity that hyperarousal with immediate ejaculation occurs. A sympathetic understanding and a non-demanding partner will go a long way towards restoration of his self-confidence. Severe forms are recognized in which ejaculation will take place even in response to a minor sexual stimulus such as kissing.

The condition should be considered pathological only if it is persistent, and if it occurs in the presence of a sympathetic partner. With the passage of time premature ejaculation may lead to erective difficulty. The latter will be a defense against ejaculating too quickly, with the patient believing that ejaculation will not occur in the absence of erection. The defense being neurotic may itself break down and some patients describe the ability to ejaculate without erection. There may be a history of withdrawal being practised to avoid conception which will cause anxiety about ejaculation and lead to an excessive concern about timing.

The patient may have certain character traits such as impulsiveness which will encourage him to be too hasty, and which will prevent him from taking a considered attitude to any problem. Lack of consideration is a step only to indifference and one further step leads to hostility.

In the psychopathology of patients with this disorder, the relationship with the mother has been predominantly a hostile one, acted out in all subsequent relationships with dependency, greed and dissatisfaction as the main ingredients.

Ejaculatory impotence
The inability to ejaculate within the vagina while maintaining an erection almost indefinitely both during foreplay and after penetration is a disorder that dates from the first coitus. It may not be considered a problem (and in fact his often multiorgasmic partner may regard it as a virtue) until children are wanted. For this reason it is sometimes called conceptive impotence. It is not due to coital anxiety, since it does not respond to anxiety-reducing techniques but may relate to a developmental fixation in which the infant's fantasies allow him to attack and soil the mother he experiences as nonloving, with his urine.

During the analysis of patients with ejaculatory impotence hostile attitudes to women become apparent. In some cases there may be a somatic manifestation of the anxieties evoked by these early learned attitudes in frequency of micturition, as he attempts to 'pour out his troubles'. Masturbation has often been resorted to in infancy and continues in adult life directed towards self-love and comfort.

Character traits associated with the anal stage of psychosexual development include meanness, difficulty completing tasks so that the finished product cannot be judged (dissatisfaction with products), obstinacy and reluctance to throw anything away.

Erective impotence

Primary erective impotence   Coital anxiety and a low level of sexual arousability leads to acute onset erective impotence. Erection fails to occur at the time of the first coital attempt and at all subsequent attempts. Concern about performance not only in the sexual situation but also in other areas of behavior is present. The patients feels himself to be inadequate in many life situations or he may have over-compensated by acquiring an omnipotent defense against his anxieties. Character traits such as boastfulness, lying, exaggeration and arrogance may be present.

The sexual energy may be sublimated into other activities such as sculpture and painting or competitiveness, particularly in sport.

Secondary erective impotence   This is the term used to describe sudden or gradual loss of potency after a long period of sexual success. The patient, usually married and in middle-age, may give a history of having failed 'out of the blue' on one occasion. This could well have been due to fatigue or alcohol. He reacts with anxiety to the idea of failing again.

The behavioral point of view (Meyer and Chesser, 1970) postulates that secondary erective impotence is the result of an acute and reversible reaction to a stressful situation. It is often possible to trace the condition to anxiety resulting from aversive conditioning. A previous experience of sexual failure, pain, criticism or guilt and anxiety may be sufficient to condition an anxiety response to subsequent attempts to have intercourse.

Meyer and Chesser state that more profound aversive conditioning has been established as a result of punishment and conflict experienced in relationships in those whose impotence is accompanied by evidence of other neurotic disturbances. This, they claim, could result in the acquisition of alternative consummatory responses such as homosexuality or a total suppression of overt sexual activity. In a study of 19 consecutive patients presenting with both erective and ejaculatory impotence, Friedman, (1968) concludes that anxiety seems to be the immediate and precipitating factor of impotence whatever sociological or psychopathological factors may underly it. The patient either is frightened of failing in the sexual act or is afraid of women generally. Such a situation which leads to a learned or conditioned fear of, or distaste for sexual intercourse may arise in childhood. The mother may bully the child to such an extent whenever he shows an interest in sex that he either surrenders and shows none at all, or he may be diverted to homosexuality (Allen, 1962).

Friedman (1968) further suggests that conditioning induced in this way is a learned fear which can be associated with the sexual attitudes of the parent, perhaps fear of venereal disease or pregnancy or even of impotence itself.

The male climacteric

Patients who present with impotence as a symptom in middle-age tend to express a fear of failure which may be rationalized by implying that advancing age is a causative factor. There is no doubt that in many males sexual vigor declines with advancing age with reduction in orgasmic frequency but there are certainly no physiological reasons why impotence should occur more frequently as age advances, providing sexual activity continues. Elderly men who have intercourse infrequently or are obliged to abstain for a long period may find that they are incapable of coitus when they wish to resume. The habitual component seems to become increasingly important with advancing age, probably due to the gradual waning of endocrine function, more apparent after a long spell of inactivity. It is particularly noted when the heightened expectations of a postmenopausal partner freed from the risk of unwanted pregnancy leads to impotence, when her own earlier anxieties had caused both of them to avoid coitus for long periods.

Sexual apathy

A disinterest in coitus associated with difficulty in arousal may be present at any age, and if so is associated with an underlying personality difficulty. Intercourse is infrequent and in extreme forms the patient may wish to give up any attempt at it. When latent homosexuality is an underlying feature, apart from lacking sexual interest, the personality may be a warm, concerned one. If the onset is in middle age apathy may be secondary to a loss of sexual interest in the marital partner. Psychological ageing will as stated above lead to a progressive decline in interest unless the effects of old age are delayed, as in all other areas of behavior, by activity.

Nonconsummation of marriage

Nonconsummation of marriage may occur as accompanying ejaculatio praecox or more usually primary erective impotence. The inability to penetrate is an extension of these disorders with grave consequences to the marriage. Help is sought early, often initiated by the nonimpotent partner, and if treatment is unsuccessful increasing sexual disappointment on her part tends to lead to separation and divorce.

Some impotent patients report that little anxiety is experienced during foreplay and erection is maintained until an attempt is made to penetrate. In such cases a masturbatory relationship satisfies an infantile wish for gratification, reassurance and above all, comfort, and constitutes acting out behavior aimed at warding off anxiety. The components of this anxiety include a greedy narcissistic arrogance which leaves no room for the giving of warmth or concern.

Personality disorders and psychosis
Impotence may be the manifestation of a severe personality disorder or a functional psychosis.

The schizoid personality can be associated with a denial of all feeling and the patient claims that no form of sexual activity is of interest to him, including masturbation. In coital activity, feelings may be experienced at a low level and may include 'anesthetic orgasm'. Arousal, associated with inadequate performance, may be intermittent.

Coldness is present in all areas of behavior. For example, the schizoid personality has great difficulty in 'feeling' and it has led to such patients being classified as suffering from 'constitutional impotence', the implication being that there is a genetic factor to account for such lack of feeling. There is, however, no evidence for this. Such patients have some features of the sociopathic personality in that the abnormality has been present throughout life and character traits are present such as coldness, distrust, aloofness and insincerity. Other features of sociopathy may or may not be present in obsessive—compulsive neurosis.

A morbid preoccupation of a more generalized nature may be present with physical appearance as a feature of the disorder. A preoccupation with hair loss or the shape of the nose often conceals sexual inadequacy. Attention should be directed towards the underlying obsessive—compulsive personality disorder. A fear of passing urine in a public lavatory may relate to an obsessional concern that the penis functions poorly. Concern about its appearance is usually not present so that in other situations nudity in the presence of other men does not cause embarrassment, but the fear that someone may witness micturition or indeed hear the splashing of urine in the toilet bowl (since such patients are obliged to use a cubicle) provokes an anxiety response with inhibition of urination.

Obsessionality often represents a defense against feelings of losing control. The fantasy is that there is a destructiveness internally which must be kept inside to avoid damaging a loved partner.

Mention should be made of the illnesses characterized by mood change present in depression and hypomania (or mania). Depression has as a dominant characteristic a feeling tone ranging from sadness to despair. Physiological function, thinking and all forms of activity become retarded, including sexual activity.

Hypomania which is characterized by overelation carries with it a heightened libido as one of the features of the illness. Sexual omnipotence, as in all other forms of overactivity may be regarded as a defense against impotence.

The tendency to a flattening of the affect, for example, in schizophrenia leads the patient to show an inability to respond emotionally in an appropriate manner to those whom he loves. Impotence may become an ingredient of this illness but the patient will seldom present with it; the other symptoms of the illness (schizophrenia) will be more in evidence.

5. SUMMARY

Psychosexual inadequacy is described in terms of erective and ejaculatory difficulty with particular reference to the physiology of both normal and impaired sexual function. Mention is made of organic factors which should be considered before a diagnosis of psychogenic impotence is made. In the absence of a severe personality disorder or a functional psychosis, anxiety in the coital situation based on fears of failing, ageing or of the inability to live up to partner expectation is the central factor involved in impaired performance.

BIBLIOGRAPHY

Allen, C. (1962) *Textbook of Psychosexual Disorders.* Oxford University Press, London.
Bowlby, J. (1953) *Child care and the growth of love.* (Penguin edn, London.)
Cooper, A.J. (1969) A clinical study of 'coital anxiety' in male potency disorders. *J. Psychosom. Res.* 13: 144—147.
Fenichel, O. (1945) *The Psychoanalytic Theory of Neurosis.* (W.W. Norton and Company, Inc., New York.)
Freud, S. (1905) *Three Essays on the Theory of Sexuality.* (Hogarth Press, London) 7: 125.
Freud, S. (1940) *An Outline of Psychoanalysis.* Ch. III Mind and the Development of the Sexual Function. (Hogarth Press, London) 23: 152.
Friedman, D. (1968) The treatment of impotence by Brietal relaxation therapy. *Behav. Res. Ther.* 6: 257—261.
Meyer, V. and Chesser, E.S. (1970) *Behaviour Therapy in Clinical Psychiatry.* (Penguin Books Ltd., England.)
Montgomery, D.A.D. and Welbourn, R.B. (1975) *Medical and Surgical Endocrinology.* (Edward Arnold, London.)

CHAPTER 66

Frigidity or hypogyneismus

HERMAN MUSAPH and GEORGE ABRAHAM

1. OPERATIONAL DEFINITION OF FRIGIDITY

Studying the extensive literature on the concept of frigidity in women it becomes clear that the content of the concept differs greatly (Kleegman, 1959; Cooper, 1969, 1970). Therefore we assert that this concept is insufficiently described since the word frigidity may have at least three different meanings, operationally stated as follows.

Frigidity as inability to experience sexual responses

Sexual responses may be by autostimulation or allostimulation. On hearing the case history one learns that the woman has never in her life experienced any feeling of sexual stimulation in any area of her body. At the same time it appears from her story that she never feels moved by an erotic or sexual approach. It soon becomes clear that in a great many cases one is dealing with patients whose own sexuality is repressed because it frightens them. This is a neurotic mechanism. Usually there exists a life-time amnesia for sexual experiences during infancy or early childhood. This amnesia can be removed by various strategies, such as narcoanalysis. Such a woman appears to be no longer symptomatic for frigidity after a successful treatment, unless a relapse should occur. One may not succeed in tracing adverse symptoms of sexual experience in the emotional life of her past. That does not permit one to conclude they never existed.

It is known from clinical psychiatry that those with mainly hysteric personality structures show a pathological defense against affects in general and sexual feelings in particular. In the anamneses of those few who recover from such a pathology, one can show that sexual experience is possible. But in most of the cases of such psychiatric pathology one can observe that the mechanism of infantile amnesia, present in normal human beings, is generalized with regard to, for example, infantile masturbation. An incapacity to experi-

Handbook of Sexology, edited by J. Money and H. Musaph
© *Elsevier/North-Holland Biomedical Press, 1977*

ence sexual feelings is always part and parcel of the incapacity of experiencing a lasting communicative feeling as part of normal attachment behavior.

Defenses against sexual feelings can be found in serious psychiatric disorders other than the hysteric — for example, schizophrenia, manic and depressive psychoses, severe forms of mental deficiency and so on. Here too, one can assert that frigidity in this sense is a symptom of the underlying psychiatric disturbance.

Frigidity as hyposexuality in women

This concept is a widespread one. One may refer to a woman as frigid if she can only be sexually aroused with great difficulty. Her frigidity concerns her entire personality, convincing both her and those around her that she is generally incapable of experiencing intense feelings.

Everybody, often including the woman herself, believes that she is emotionally impoverished. Sometimes there is a total absence of desire; sometimes the desire is poorly present. Many women with an even temper, an even level of reaction and an even pattern of behavior, belong to this group. Large variations in affect and behavior are absent, which not always points to a poorness of affect. Their partners may be very happy with a wife who represents a stabilizing factor in the family. These women are often amazed about the strength of sexual feeling in others and also in their sexual partner. One can only speak of frigidity if one accepts the criterion of the stronger feeling partner as an absolute and correct one. The construct validity of such an approach seems to us to be an unscientific one.

Frigidity as anorgasmia

This concept one finds almost everywhere in the world of laymen. One talks about a frigid woman if she is not orgastic. It is a common mistake to assume that in the female orgasm the same feelings and behavior pattern appear as in the orgasm of the male partner. The pattern of feeling and behavior of the orgastic man is used as a criterion for the woman. Needless to say such a concept is nonsense. Elsewhere in this book these problems are largely dealt with.

2. HYPOGYNEISMUS

The concept of frigidity has no construct validity. There exists too broad a spectrum between on the one hand the lack of any sexual feeling and on the other anorgasmia with its extensive problems. Complete absence of sexual feeling would be seen as an expression of total sexual repression. Also the concept of 'insufficient sexual experience' is too vague and requires further elaboration. Each case must be considered separately within a more detailed framework.

In clinical practice we never diagnose a case of frigidity. At the most frigidity is a signal to us to seek more information. Moreover there is a lack of a reliable methodology to quantify sexual feelings. The danger of over-generalization is immense, for in the mind of the patients frigidity has several meanings; and it cannot be detached from the thinking model of the investigator.

We think it better therefore not to use the term frigidity in scientific papers and we propose the term *hypogyneismus*. Furthermore we prefer the term hypogyneismus to frigidity because of the denigrating meaning of the latter.

3. THE SIGNAL FUNCTION OF HYPOGYNEISMUS IN WOMEN

Hypogyneismus is the inability of a woman to experience psychosexual satisfaction in an otherwise adequate situation.

We drop the criterion of achieving 'orgasm', for many women have what they report as a satisfactory sexual relationship with a partner without having an orgasm. Using the term 'psychosexual' we try to emphasize the emotional and not only the physiological side of the sexual experience. We are aware of the fact that putting the term 'adequate situation' seems rather vague. But in our opinion — as elaborated hereafter — the partner is of utmost importance in determining the psychosexual reaction pattern of the woman in a given situation.

There are many causes of hypogyneismus. We never consider it as an illness per se, nor as a syndrome, seldom as a symptom. In our opinion we have mostly to consider hypogyneismus as a signal. One must be on the alert to the possibility of the etiology being psychogenic (Musaph, 1965).

Hypogyneismus may be manifest in several symptoms, as general erotic apathy, lack of lubrication of the vagina, spasm of the musculus constrictor cunni (vaginismus), painful intercourse and failure of orgasm which may be situation-specific or generalized. Pain can be caused by dryness of the vagina, by spasm of the muscles, and in neurotics by transposition of sexual feelings in pain. Furthermore coital pain (dyspareunia) can occur during intercourse or afterwards. This delayed pain is the painful experience of change in blood flow of the vagina when the excitation phase is waning.

Some women react normally with lubrication, erection of the clitoris and the labia minora and with involuntary contractions of the vagina as long as the penis does not penetrate. They are suffering from a penetration phobia, which is always of neurotic nature. One cannot understand this penetration phobia without investigating the fantasies underlying it in each particular woman. Sometimes the penetration phobia is person-bound (selective), sometimes it is present with every partner (see Chapter 71 by John Money).

4. HYPOGYNEISMUS IN NORMAL WOMEN

The seismographic function of hypogyneismus

There are women who react with hypogyneismus because they are involved in an emotional conflict situation with a key figure outside the marriage. This causes a disturbance in the relationship with the marital partner. A classical example of this situation is an ongoing conflict with the woman's father or mother. As a result she is too preoccupied and not able to enjoy intercourse. She may also be preoccupied with problems of her own family. There are a great many examples from various situations in which the emotional center lies outside the relationship with her partner, but where nevertheless the affective earthquake is registered within the sexual relationship.

The partner as trigger of hypogyneismus

Cases of hypogyneismus which are related to a particular partner (selective hypogyneismus) are well known. This can be recognized by the attitude of the partner, who functions as an inadequate lover. Here too an emotional conflict situation concerning the partner can express itself in an hypogyneismus. For many women a conciliatory coitus (which for the man means an enjoyable experience at the end of a quarrel) may be impossible. Often she is unable, although she would like to overcome her feelings of continuing resentment. This attitude can lead to a negative reaction to the man and a conditioned response which may result in a lasting hypogyneismus.

The situation as trigger of hypogyneismus

A volatile, prohibitive or secret sexual relationship can cause a very strong tension, which accumulates and finds its discharge in an intense orgasm of a degree until that time unknown. But the same situation can be also the cause of not daring to give oneself totally to the partner. As a result the hypogyneismus can come into being, which can start to lead a continuing life of its own. Undoubtedly unresolved guilt feelings play a role. It is a well-known phenomenon that there are women who are orgastic only during the holidays, or vice versa. Here the anxiety of being disturbed plays a role, anxiety which certainly has infantile roots.

The victims of emancipation

A consequence of emancipation of woman may be hypogyneismus in normal women. One of the more unfavorable side-effects of emancipation is the man's attitude that his wife ought to have an orgasm similar to his. He takes as criteria for the sexual behavior of his partner the same form and expression of excitation, of orgasm (ejaculation of lubrication fluid), and of relaxation. He also expects that her orgasm should occur simultaneously with his. If these demands are not realized, the man feels himself to be an incompetent or insufficient sexual partner. The woman may acquiesce. A therapeutic approach in which this view is shown to be incorrect can be of great help. The masculinization of female sexuality, one of the sexual prejudices of our time, continually gives the woman the feeling that she has not fulfilled herself. It is a typical example of conditioning in the direction of hypogyneismus. To a lesser extent the same can be said of the man's feelings that he has to give up his initiative. The woman should play the role of initiator at least to the same extent. If this role is against her nature a hypogyneismus can come into being. Within a framework of a wrongly understood emancipation a feeling of guilt can be aroused in one or both partners if there is an unspoken demand that both partners should respond equally and with the same degree of sexual activity.

In nonmarried couples some girls may suffer from permissive premarital standards. They feel a moral obligation to have intercourse and to be orgastic with the boyfriend, in order not to be looked down upon by their contemporaries. Many adolescents are so anxious to have intercourse, that it becomes an impulsion. When carried out, it may or may not relieve them of their anxiety. One can consider this impulsion as a symptom of an age-determined experimentation phase of sexual development based on cultural expectations. In most cases these adolescents spontaneously resolve their hypogyneismus and become normally responsive and orgasmic. In such cases, hypogyneismus can be regarded as a temporary phenomenon in a normal human being.

BIBLIOGRAPHY

Cooper, A.J. (1969) Some personality factors in frigidity. *J. Psychosom. Res.*, 13, 149—155.

Cooper, A.J. (1970) Frigidity, treatment and short-term prognosis. *J. Psychosom. Res.*, 14, 133—147.

Kleegman, S.J. (1959) Frigidity in women. *Quart. Rev. Surg. Obstet. Gynecol.*, 16, 243—248.

Musaph, H. (1965) *Vaginisme.* (Erven Bohn, Haarlem, The Netherlands.)

CHAPTER 67

Psychogynology

DENNIS FRIEDMAN

Editors' note:

It is possible for two people to be having sex and to have an erotic response culminating in an orgasm which is nonetheless much less complete and much less satisfying than might otherwise be the case. What is missing is a complete sense of involvement with one another — complete abandonment and complete commitment — in the presence of which the orgasm becomes more intense, profound, pervasive and all-engrossing.

It is a feminine experience of an ecstatic, altered state of consciousness. People have struggled since time immemorial to find words to differentiate these two types of experience associated with orgasm, the lesser and the greater. Some people say it is the difference between sex with love and affection versus purely physical sex. Psychoanalysts in traditional theory have labelled the differentiation as clitoral versus vaginal orgasm. The basis of their terminology lies in the fact that it is easy to get a clitoral orgasm by automanipulation, whereas the most intense orgasm of all usually is associated with a partner.

The modern point of view is that it is metaphorical and not anatomical to talk about the difference between clitoral and vaginal orgasm. In actual fact it is possible for an orgasm to be triggered from the nipples, a fact to which many nursing mothers can testify. It is also possible, as some women know, for an orgasm to be triggered from other sensitive erotic zones and even, in rare cases, to be triggered from imagery in the mind.

There is a tradition, especially in psychiatric sexology, to equate the so-called clitoral orgasm with frigidity, in that it is considered in some degree to be a failure of the sexual response. This tradition is spurious. Failure of sexual response to qualify as frigidity represents failure to achieve orgasm, even though some erotic pleasure may be experienced. There are different types and degrees of erotic failure. The term frigidity is nowadays considered too broad and general, and also too stigmatized to do justice to the actual phe-

Handbook of Sexology, edited by J. Money and H. Musaph
© *Elsevier/North-Holland Biomedical Press, 1977*

nomenology. It is for this reason that the term hypogneismus is prefered.

Dr Friedman, in the following chapter, outlines some of the antecedents or etiological factors in failures of the sexual response in women.

1. THE INTERNAL THREAT

Psychodynamic considerations

Difficulties similar to those surrounding the definition of frigidity (Chapter 67) arise when consideration is given to the emotional background to the problem of psychogynology.

The classical psychoanalytic view of frigidity summarized by Abraham (1920) in his paper on the female castration complex, postulates that the Oedipal conflict and its nonresolution lead to a wish to revenge herself on the father by castrating him with the body cavity in which her biting hostility now resides. He points out that vaginismus from a practical point of view subserves repressed fantasies not only of castration but also the wish to rob the man of his penis by retaining it.

It is commonly found in the analysis of women who experience their husbands as parent figures that early memories relate to episodes in which a penis is seen as threatening and frightening. The feeling that the penis is threatening or that by taking it into herself she may damage or destroy it, arises out of fantasies acquired during early infancy with the mother and reinforced later by an unsatisfactory love affair with the father. In adult life these early attitudes are reinforced still further, either by avoidance or by repeated aversive responses.

However, Fisher (1973) reviewed the recent literature looking for a correlation between limited sexual responsiveness and psychological maladjustment. He found very little to support this commonly asserted speculation. He concluded that "the might of the empirical evidence favors the view that one can be seriously maladjusted and even schizophrenic and still enjoy a normal amount of sexual responsivity".

Frigidity as a defense

Some women are sexually anesthetic because they are unable to cope with feelings experienced by the ego as overwhelming, rather similar to a denial of grief after a particularly painful loss. In this case the assumption of frigidity becomes a defense against such feelings.

One patient with vaginismus and dyspareunia, felt that penetration could not take place because she said 'it felt as if there was something inside the vagina which was hard and immovable and seemed like a piece of concrete.' It was clearly demonstrable that this was not so since she was eventually able to introduce a large dilator. However, the idea that she had within her an unyielding piece of stone instead of feelings was linked to stony-hearted attitudes learnt during an unhappy childhood with a cold mother, and with a father who had died when she was nine. These attitudes had to be maintained to protect her against giving way to what she imagined would be uncontrollable feelings for others, particularly men. Her block of concrete, her frigidity, was her way of defending herself against emotion which had never been reciprocated.

2. THE EXTERNAL THREAT

Most patients complaining of frigidity are usually unaware that there are factors arising out of their past which account for their problem. They say that for reasons unknown to them, their partner's sexual approach causes extreme anxiety. They may attempt to rationalize this by relating it to marriage, childbirth, pain, increased domestic responsibility and tiredness, or even that they no longer love him. These women, who are usually married, may have put their sexuality to the test in extramarital relationships where similar reactions may have been experienced. Foreplay may be pleasurable in some women, but coitus is not. Others only become aroused after ejaculation has taken place so that penetration is no longer possible, the small penis being nonthreatening.

The appearance of the penis may cause revulsion and they avoid looking at it. It may not be touched and coitus is only permitted when precoital caressing is carried out only by the husband. Pleasurable feelings may occur but rapidly wane if he demands her active participation.

Pleasure may be gained by demeaning and debasing her partner sexually either by making insatiable demands on him and not reciprocating or by acting out sado-masochistic fantasies.

Fear of pregnancy and venereal disease

Anxiety caused by a fear of an unwanted pregnancy in a woman who has little confidence in contraception or in whom religious prohibitions preclude the use of contraceptives leads to frigidity directed towards an avoidance of coitus. It may be found in young girls before marriage or in older women whose urge to procreate has either been satisfied or is nonexistent. With the advent of effective contraception, fear of venereal disease because of its increased incidence in the population is encountered more frequently.

Denial of pleasure

A prudish upbringing in which sexual relationships have been looked upon as 'dirty' other than for procreation, leading to a strict observance of the Biblical injunction 'thou shalt be fruitful and multiply' * may provoke a distaste for coitus at times other than ovulation. The patient is usually unaware that her behavior resembles that of those mammals where coitus in confined to estrus.

Inadequate stimulation

Lack of sexual responsiveness may be secondary to a faulty contraceptive technique such as coitus interruptus or failure of the partner to be aware of her needs.

Furthermore, reduction in potency in the male due to either erective or ejaculatory difficulty may have led so often to disappointment that no further response may be expected until the impotence is successfully treated. It should be borne in mind that she may knowingly or not be maintaining her partner in an impotent state in which case a change in his sexual status will be unlikely to increase her responses.

3. DEPRESSION

Depression, whether the feeling tone is one of sadness or despair, usually leads to a loss of interest in sexual activity. Linford Rees (1967) sums up the symptoms by stating that depressive illnesses affect the whole organism: feelings, energy drive, thinking, bodily functions, personality and interests.

It would be expected that sexual energy and feelings would be reduced in direct relationship to the degree of depression. If the disorder remains untreated disturbances of menstruation including amenorrhea are common.

4. PERSONALITY DISORDER

The inability to experience warm feelings may be a feature of the schizoid sociopathic and hysterical personality.

Often performance may be normal but no feeling is shown to the partner. Greedy, insatiable demands are made, leading to promiscuity and unfaithfulness. The hysterical personality is highly labile, suggestible and seductive and is usually hostile to men.

Latent homosexuality

A hostile attachment to a mother experienced as nongiving and therefore expendable may lead to a homosexual potentiality as the adult seeks to renew a relationship with her, since the primary relationship was unsatisfying. At

---

* Genesis Ch. I.22

the same time she acts out her hostility to the 'motherly' partner she has selected by denying and rejecting what he offers her. Overt homosexuality may be absent but masturbation fantasies may relate to oral sexuality or lesbian acts with the patient sometimes playing the role of onlooker. Such fantasies represent a wish to return to the first homosexual relationship, that is, the one with the mother.

Occasionally satisfactory coitus may only take place with a male partner if another woman is present as an onlooker. Clearly the other woman is being 'left out'; the patient is this way retaliates against the mother who in the past had 'left her out'. Hostile dependency is being acted out with homosexuality as a feature. Sometimes arousal occurs when her partner has coitus with another woman in her presence, thus allowing her to enjoy curiosity which is represented by the child's fantasized conception of the parents having intercourse.

5. ORGANIC FACTORS

Introductory comments

The affectionate responses of a loved woman to her spouse are never reduced by organic disease. Erotic responses, however, are entirely dependent on the integrity of the endocrine system.

Sexual satisfaction in the human female in contrast to the lower mammals will occur irrespective of hormonal variations. Masters and Johnson (1966) have shown that postmenopausal women can continue sexual activity over many years. Although our sexual experience of each other is largely psychological rather than endocrinological, nevertheless localisation of feeling in the genitalia, notably the clitoris and vaginal introitus depends on at least some sex-steroid being available.

Studies have been reported on from the Sloan—Kettering Institute (1959) by Waxenberg and co-workers on the changes in the sexual lives of women who have undergone bilateral oophorectomy and adrenalectomy for the relief of hormone-dependent breast cancers. Therapy consists of removing both ovaries and both adrenals and in some cases the pituitary, which deprives the patient of any source of androgen. It is known that exogenous androgens when used in a variety of disorders in women provoke an increase in sexual desire, sensitivity and awareness. Estrogens on the other hand have the opposite effect, a fact to which some women taking the contraceptive pill will testify. Depriving women of androgens caused over 90% of a series of 29 women who preoperatively were sexually active to either reduce or stop completely all sexual activity. Of course these patients were being operated on for the palliation of metastatic breast cancer and could hardly be regarded as being in the full vigor of their lives. However, some of the cases reported or recorded dreams over a period of a few weeks postoperatively in which erotic feelings became progressively weaker, but which were replaced by dreams relating to closeness to a man with features indicating a need for reassuring and protective support. Androgens therefore seem to be connected with erotic sensation and have nothing to do with the affectionate, supportive (anaclitic) component of sexuality.

Dyspareunia

Dyspareunia is a symptom meaning that coitus is painful, which may be psychosomatic or organic in origin. The pain may be in the introitus or may only occur on deep penetration.

Superficial causes
These may easily be excluded by examination. Coital pain is a common problem with which gynecologists are confronted. Superficial or introital dyspareunia is caused by congenital malformations of the lower genital tract, faulty repair to the pelvic floor or perinium resulting in scarring and contraction, and operations for prolapse resulting in difficulty in penile penetration.
Other disorders include acute vulvitis or vaginitis, an infected Bartholin's cyst, kraurosis vulvae or lichen sclerosus et atrophicus and urethral caruncle.

Deep causes
Pain may only be felt on deep penetration, either at once or some hours after coitus has taken place. If the latter, the cause is always psychosomatic. Immediate pain is due to disorders in the ovaries or uterus, a retroverted uterus with one or both ovaries prolapsed into the pouch of Douglas and endometriosis. Severe or chronic constipation with large fecal masses in the bowel may cause pain as may bowel lesions such as Crohn's disease (regional ileitis) or spastic colon and finally chronic salpingo-oophoritis or any uterine tumor or ovarian cyst, particularly if prolapse has occurred.

6. DRUGS

Many drugs used in psychiatry reduce sexual responsiveness either because of a direct sedative effect or because orgasm is delayed or inhibited altogether due to anticholinergic effects. Such drugs include the monoamine oxidase inhibitors, tricyclic antidepressants, phenothiazines, particularly thioridazine, chlordiazepoxide and amphetamines.
Alcohol is small amounts nay be a mild aphrodisiac, but in beyond the optimum dose, responses are reduced.

7. ENDOCRINE DISORDERS

There are a number of disorders which reduce androgen production other than surgical ablation of the ovaries, suprarenals and pituitary. In the pituitary, tumors in the anterior lobe interfere with the production of follicle-stimulating hormone (FSH) and luteinizing hormone (LH) which control the production of female hormone and the menstrual cycle. Frigidity, although a symptom, is seldom an early one and evidence of hypofunctional syndromes is to be found elsewhere. The hypofunctional disorders include dystrophia adiposa genitalis in which tumor or cyst compresses the pituitary gland cells resulting in defective growth and sexual development, and a general hypo-function of the anterior lobe leading to dwarfism and infantilism in children and to sex disturbances in adults. Complete obliteration of sexual drive re-sults from total pituitary deficiency following surgical hypophysectomy.

8. OTHER ORGANIC CAUSES

Other disorders which will affect erotic responses are diabetes, lupus erythe-matosus and the collagenoses, partly because of the reduction in blood sup-ply to the clitoris due to obliterative endarteritis. Neurological lesions involv-ing the spinal cord as well as multiple sclerosis will present with erotic dys-function as well as the more obvious symptoms of the disorder.

BIBLIOGRAPHY

Abraham, K. (1920) Manifestations of the female castration complex. *Selected Papers of Karl Abraham*, 1954 (Basic Books, New York).

Fisher, S. (1973) *The Female Orgasm*. (Allen Lane, London) pp. 14—21.

Linford Rees, W.L. (1967) *A Short Textbook of Psychiatry*. (English Universities Press, London) p. 176.

Masters, W.H. and Johnson, V.E. (1966) *Human Sexual Response*. (Churchill, London.)

Waxenberg, S.E., Drellich, M.G. and Sutherland, A.M. (1959) The role of hormones in human behaviour. I. Changes in female sexuality after adrenalectomy. *J. Clin. Endocrinol.* 19: 193—202.

CHAPTER 68

Sexuality during pregnancy and postpartum frigidity

WILLY PASINI

1. INTRODUCTION

At the Congress of Psychosomatic Gynecology in London, 1971, among hundreds of communications, Miraglia (1966) gave an interesting account of erotic dreams during pregnancy, but not a single one treated sexuality in the pregnant women. The published data of Kinsey (1970) on female sexuality also did not take into consideration sexuality during pregnancy. Simon's report (1972) mentions it only in a marginal way.

However, there exists a recent French text from Gondonneau and Garnier (1973) which reflects very well the psychological and physiological point of view in the matter.

In psychoanalytical literature, we find again the same difficulties and observe a large scale of psychodynamic hypotheses on the actual experience of sexuality and maternity, which are the two poles of the woman's development, and are not simply physiological facts (Langer, 1951; Kestenberg, 1956; Dolto, 1967; Racamier, 1967). However, almost no study treats actual experience of sexuality and love in the pregnant woman.

In the literature of strict psychosomatic orientation, one finds some information in the Czech studies of Cernoch and Bartova (Bartova et al., 1969) which are first of all devoted to sexual behavior, though not to its psychological significance. American researches give interesting details, especially the booklet of Israel and Rubin (1967) and Solberg's (1973) research on interviews with 226 women just after childbirth. These studies showed that sexual activity decreased progressively from the moment the women knew they were pregnant. Not only desire and satisfaction, but also substitutive activities changed, and this confirms the hypothesis that emotional factors have an influence on sexual life during pregnancy. On the other hand, no relation was discovered between sexuality and prematurity.

I will mention the only work bringing new information either from a clinical or an experimental point of view, Masters and Johnson's (1966)

Handbook of Sexology, edited by J. Money and H. Musaph
© *Elsevier/North-Holland Biomedical Press, 1977*

research published in their first book 'Human Sexual Response', Ch. 10. These authors found a decrease of sexuality during the first trimester which was first of all due to psychological disturbances. Then followed an important increase of sexuality in all parameters in the second trimester, which was especially due to favorable physiological conditions, namely the pelvic vaso-congestion. In the third trimester, a decrease of sexuality was observed, mainly due to physical disturbances and to psychological concentration on the baby about to be born. This attitude persisted in the postpartum period until resumption of sexual intercourse which was sometimes painful, and sometimes unsatisfactory regarding desire and pleasure. Masters and Johnson (1966) found that negative reactions appeared more frequently in the primiparae, and that generally advice given by doctors was either inadequate or too restrictive.

A recent book published in the U.S. (Howells, 1972) contains more than 590 pages and mentions nearly every topic concerning obstetrics and psychosomatic perinatology except one, namely the relationship between sexuality and pregnancy. This confirms what I said at the International Congress of Psychosomatic Medicine (Morris, 1972) three years ago, namely that we face a taboo which involves not only the woman and the couple, but also the gynecologist—obstetrician and medical literature. A bibliographic research undertaken together with the Kinsey Institute (1970) showed only a dozen articles on the subject, in spite of its great social importance and the deep emotional tonality attached to the convergence of these two aspects of human nature: maternity and sexuality.

It can even be said that there is almost more information in the anthropological than the psychological and psychodynamic literature, not to mention the literature on gynecology and obstetrics.

2. ETHNOLOGICAL AND ANTHROPOLOGICAL FACTORS

From an ethnological point of view, valuable information was given by Ford and Beach (1951) who described some copulating prohibitions in numerous primitive societies, this being allegedly a way to protect the fetus. For instance, the Mourgines relate intercourse in pregnancy to bearing still-born children, and infantile mortality among them is high enough to explain this anxiety for the unborn child. One has to admit that sexuality during pregnancy has been liable to numerous moral and hygienic restrictions, on the assumption that the procreative purpose was directly bound to the survival of the race. For this reason, the other aspects of sexuality (source of pleasure, privileged means of communication between the couple, basis of personal identity) were put aside. In other primitive societies, the attitude has been more moderate; among the Crow Indian for instance, the wife has to refuse coitus only from the very moment she perceives the movements of the baby.

Other societies such as the Ifugas and the Tanalas, do not impose any restriction. Gebhard, director of the Kinsey Institute, told me that in the Azanda tribe in Africa, one considers that the father's sperm is necessary for the growth of the embryo. Therefore, sexual relations during pregnancy are indicated and encouraged (Gebhard, personal communication).

From an anthropological point of view, there is a wide margin regarding postpartum restrictions, varying from the second week to the eighth month, but the idea of this limitation is probably for anticonceptional purposes.

In the animal kingdom, sexual behavior during pregnancy is generally irregular and unpredictable, but mostly there is no copulation during this period. In the chimpanzee, for instance, Yerkes (1939) mentioned that sexual intercourse during pregnancy is sporadic and the female does not always agree to it. She seems to be accommodating in order not to have to fight with the male, but this is not an indication of her sexual desire.

3. PSYCHOLOGICAL FACTORS DURING PREGNANCY

One hundred women were interviewed after childbirth at the Maternity of Geneva (Pasini, 1974). We observed that their sexual behavior changed considerably during this period and in a significantly different way at three-month intervals. It diminished progressively as pregnancy proceeded, and we did not notice the increase Masters and Johnson pointed out after the first trimester. Sexual desire, satisfaction and frequency presented no important difference.

Sexuality improved in women whose sexual relations in the past had been changeable, while those who had satisfactory relations noticed few modifications. About half our sample mentioned substitutive sexual activities which acted favorably for the couple, and especially in women considered psychically normal; 25% of the women indicated compensatory erotic dreams during the last months.

The social variables we took into consideration did not present significant correlates. As a whole, we observed that the foreigners who are, in our sample, mostly Catholic and of low social and intellectual level, presented the largest differences, either for the best or for the worst. These changes were often influenced by a very 'folkloric' knowledge of pregnancy. Swiss women had the steadiest behavior, and a progressive decrease of sexuality appeared especially in the Protestants. In fact, religious denomination influenced less than religious practice, for the practising women were unsatisfied with their sexuality during the second and the third trimesters.

Whether the pregnancy was self-willed or accidental had little importance. We discussed the ambiguity of the notion of the pregnancy wish which cannot be reduced to a rigid alternative.

Parity affected sexuality as mentioned by Masters and Johnson (1966): for the primiparae sexuality declined, and for the multiparae it improved, especially after the three first months.

Physical condition had a great influence on sexual behavior, particularly on frequency. We mostly noticed the bad influence of asthenia, obesity, aches and vomiting, and in 10% of the cases, the threat of spontaneous abortion or premature birth led indirectly to psychological fears.

The psychic state affected sexuality too. The well-balanced women were steady, while the sex life improved in patients whom pregnancy made happy. The women who reacted negatively mentioned that sexuality was badly affected from the beginning, while those who were anxious for the baby reduced their sexual performance during the last weeks.

The male partners seemed to have an influence too. Half of them decided on their own will or with their wife's agreement to reduce the frequency of sexual acts; they showed real or imaginary fears concerning injury to the fetus, just as their wives did. The psychological changes towards the woman were generally positive: 62 husbands became more understanding and full of attention, while 7 had negative reactions. There is, therefore, no direct relation between a diminution in sexual intercourse and a deterioration of the emotional bond with the husband during pregnancy.

The gynecologist seemed to be inadequately informed on sexology and his role was insufficient and inferior to our expectations: $\frac{1}{3}$ only gave some advice, and the dialogue between physician and patient was often uneasy. In addition, the literature seemed too vague. Patients benefited from the preparation for painless childbirth (28 positive reactions). We could prove the significant correlation between their degree of information and their sexual satisfaction.

The intellectual level was clinically estimated and it also affected the sexual behavior. At either extreme, the more and less intelligent women showed the greatest change, either for medical reasons or through magic fears.

The psychiatric antecedents were epidemiologically evaluated; their influence on sexual intercourse during this period was below our clinical impressions. This is due to the fact that, in our clinical interview, some women had different or even opposite reactions which neutralized one another statistically. Few sexual modifications appeared in well-balanced women and, if they existed, they resulted from objective reasons as, for example, the risk of abortion. The anxious and phobic patients very often feared, mainly in fancy, to spoil the fetus, and therefore reduced sexuality. The childish and rather hysteric ones reacted in a contradictory way. Those who realized their fulfillment in pregnancy and childbearing were satisfied, while the narcissistic ones were less satisfied for esthetic reasons, and their libido fell. Finally, the obsessionals with virilistic tendencies avoided thinking of sexuality, devoting themselves to motherhood.

To conclude, this inquiry confirms the fact that there are not only somatic effects on sexuality during pregnancy, but also confirms all the linked psychoemotional aspects. As few medical surveys have been made in this field, we are convinced that a taboo, involving either the gynecologist or his patient, still exists. Masters and Johnson (1966) threw more light on this area and we ourselves have tried to extend it to a psychological and emotional dimension.

In our opinion, the best prophylaxis in this field would be thorough and systematic information for both the couple and the practitioner.

4. PSYCHOLOGICAL FACTORS IN THE POSTPARTUM PERIOD

Postpartum frigidity is a disorder that occurs frequently, according to the opinion of the gynecologist, and to the complaints of the patients (Chapter 67). Its definition is easy to understand if we refer to a chronological criterion, but it is more difficult to appreciate when we try to analyze the significance of the symptom and its multiple etiopathogenesis. It seems to be more accurate to speak of 'maladjustment' in the postpartum period, because we observe whether there is a decrease of the desire or a failure to resume sexual intercourse, or vaginismus, or especially momentary dyspareunia which arises before or together with frigidity. Among the etiopathogenic factors, one can take into consideration elements arising from pregnancy, childbirth and the postpartum. Among the factors relating to pregnancy, the conflict between maternity and sexuality may arise again, as these two roles are either complementary or in opposition in the same person. Their coexistence during this period is sometimes problematic and the woman does not realize this fact and complain of it while she is pregnant; her interest is mainly concentrated on the expected baby. But this intrapsychic conflict, which can also be relational with concomitant frigidity, can arise when anxiety due to pregnancy, delivery and baby is allayed.

First of all, we must not neglect the conditioning pregnancy can introduce into the sexual life of traditional couples. The physical modifications during this period, sometimes the change of position in sexual intercourse, the six weeks' abstention the gynecologist often advises, can act for the worst in couples who experience sexuality in a 'mechanical' way.

Among the psychological and psychopathological factors in the postpartum period, it is necessary to point out the fear, and even the obsession, of an undesired new pregnancy. Breast feeding which is generally wanted by most women, can be worried about by others who confuse the maternal and erotic function of their breast.

The increase of postpartum depression on the second and the third day can involve and explain a sexual pathology. Moreover, when the parents are disappointed by the sex of the baby, this fact can also influence sexual behavior.

The alteration of the roles during pregnancy (maternal role and conjugal role) can be stronger in the postpartum period and lead to negative behavior in the husband. Sometimes, if he does not aid his wife in the household or requests sexual relations too early, this may provoke a hostile reaction in the wife toward her husband and which she compensates for by her concentration on the baby.

Somatic factors in the postpartum period

Among postpartum factors, we have to mention somatic factors, in particular episiotomy, which can bring about painful reactions when sexual relations begin again. Masters and Johnson (1966) mention asthenia and a slower vascularization of the pelvic organs.

An eventual endocrine pathogenesis has been mentioned by many practitioners who used to consider the hormonal disorder in postpartum responsible for the lack of sexual desire after childbirth.

5. CONCLUSIONS

From these lines, it appears that the possible causes of postpartum sexual dysfunctions are numerous, and that the first step in therapy is to define the exact irritant thorn; this necessitates a psychological understanding of the woman and of the couple. At the same time, it is important not to neglect the gynecological aspect, in order that no somatic factor may heighten this difficult psychological situation. It will also be advisable to have an interview with the partner; sometimes a single consultation will be necessary, other times therapy of the couple will start. In general, if sexual pathology is only reactional and contingent, supportive psychotherapy will be sufficient. However, the more exploratory therapies will be reserved for those cases in which postpartum sexual dysfunctions depend on an underlying psychopathology.

6. SUMMARY

In medical and psychoanalytical literature, almost no study treats sexuality in the pregnant woman. Only Masters and Johnson (1965) give new information on this subject in their book 'Human Sexual Response'. They find a decrease of sexuality in the first and third trimesters of pregnancy, and an important increase in the second trimester. The author compares Masters and Johnson's observations with the results of an inquiry made in the Maternity of Geneva (Pasini, 1974) where 100 women were interviewed after childbirth. After having analyzed the psychological factors which influence sexuality during pregnancy, the author explains those which affect the post-delivery period, and especially frigidity.

BIBLIOGRAPHY

Bartova, D., Kolarova, J., Zuel, K., Spott, F. and Jicinska, M. (1969) Sexual life of women in pregnancy. *Ceska Gynekol.* 34, 560—562.
Dolto, F. (1967) Genèse du sentiment maternel, éclairage psychanalytique. *Bull. Off. Soc. Fr. Psycho-Prophylaxie Obstét.* 32, 43—55.

Ford, C. and Beach, F. (1951) *Patterns of Sexual Behavior.* (Harper, New York.)

Gondonneau, J. and Garnier, G. (1973) *La Sexualité de la Femme Enceinte.* (Balland, Paris.)

Howells, J. (1972) *Modern Perspectives in Psycho-obstetrics.* (Brunner/Mazel, New York.)

Israel, L. and Rubin, I. (1967) Sexual relations during pregnancy and the post-delivery period. *SIECUS Study Guide* No. 6. (New York.)

Kestenberg, J.S. (1956) On the development of maternal feelings in early childhood. *The Psychoanalytic Study of the Child.* vol. XI, 257—289.

Kinsey, A., Pomeroy, W., Martin, C. and Gebhard, P. (1970) *Sexual Behavior in the Human Female.* (Pocket Book, New York.)

Langer, M. (1951) *Maternidad y sexo.* (Editorial Nova, Buenos Aires.)

Masters, W. and Johnson, V. (1966) *Human Sexual Response.* (Little, Brown and Co., Boston.)

Miraglia, F. (1966) Observations sur les rêves pendant la grossesse. *Bulletin Officiel de la Société Internationale de Psycho-Prophylaxie Obstétricale.* T. VIII, 2, 77—85.

Morris, N. (Ed.) (1972) *Psychosomatic Medicine in Obstetrics and Gynaecology.* 3rd Int. Congr. (Karger, Basel.)

Pasini, W. (1974) *Sexualité et Gynécologie Psychosomatique.* (Masson, Paris.)

Racamier, P. (1967) Troubles de la sexualité féminine et du sens maternel. *Bull. Off. Soc. Fr. Psycho-Prophylaxie Obstét.*, No. 32, 3—41.

Simon, P. (1972) *Rapport sur le comportement sexuel des Français.* (René Julliard/Pierre Charron, Paris.)

Solberg, A. (1973) Sexual behavior in pregnancy. *New Engl. J. Med.* 288, 1098—1103.

Yerkes, R.M. (1939) Sexual behavior in the chimpanzee. *Hum. Biol.* 2, 78—110.

CHAPTER 69

Unconsummated and partially consummated marriage as sources of procreative failure

WILLY PASINI

1. INTRODUCTORY COMMENTS

The frequency of unconsummated marriage is difficult to establish as many couples do not consult the physician. Nevertheless, Kinsey (1953) notices in an inquiry made with a large number of cases, that about 2% of the couples of an age to copulate do not consummate sexual intercourse. Other studies in the U.S. state that at least 5% of the cases of sterility are in fact due to nonconsummation (Stallworthy, 1948; Malleson, 1954; Sturgis, 1957).

Traditional opinion, according to which unconsummated marriages are divided into two groups, those of feminine origin and those of male origin, is now out of date, because in 75% of cases the principal indispensable element in establishing the diagnosis and the therapy lies in the couple's dynamic interaction. The most efficient short therapy is, in my opinion, that which considers the couple taken as a whole. This point of view has been emphasized by Masters and Johnson (1970) in the U.S. and by French specialists (Michel-Wolfromm, 1954) who call it hymenology. This kind of therapy which I have adopted to cure 82 couples who had not consummated their marriage, seems to combine the advantages presented by psychoanalysis and conditioning techniques.

First I shall briefly mention some forms of male inadequacy and vaginismus—dyspareunia in the woman, these two disturbances being the principal causes of unconsummated marriages.

2. IMPOTENCE

Impotence can be provoked by a lack of desire, the marriage having been celebrated for social reasons and only with a reproductive aim; in these cases, the prognosis is poor. Other manifestations, such as premature ejaculation with inadequate erection, are more common. These cases have a better

Handbook of Sexology, edited by J. Money and H. Musaph
© *Elsevier/North-Holland Biomedical Press, 1977*

prognosis, as well as another disorder which is rather frequent, a dissociated sexual erection: sexual desire and excitability are normal, but penetration makes the shy and anxious husbands afraid due to fantasies of the toothed vagina (vagina dentata).

3. DYSPAREUNIA AND VAGINISMUS

Regarding the woman, except for a few absolute refusals to try sexual intercourse, one finds mostly dyspareunia and/or vaginismus. Dyspareunia means painful coitus. It may be superficial or deep, and in 50 to 80% of the cases it has organic components. When dyspareunia is psychological, it sometimes has a hysteric significance of secondary benefit, but in most cases it expresses a strong hostility towards men and sexuality in general. These women are often obsessional and in my opinion, the prognosis is poor. The cases of vaginismus are completely different and the type of personality is mostly hystero-phobic; in these patients, libido is intact, but a reflex of fright prevents them from accomplishing the sexual act.

By vaginismus is meant an involuntary reflex contraction of the constrictor muscle of the vagina (muscularis constrictor cunni). In rare cases, this disturbance is of retention and not at penetration. It is in fact not painful, and libido is often intact, I have especially pointed out this difference, which may seem artificial, because it is essential for psychodynamic understanding. However, clinically, vaginismus and dyspareunia are often superimposed, because penetration, in spite of muscle contractions, provokes pain, and dyspareunia induces muscle contractions as a reflex of defence.

The frequency of vaginismus is of 1 to 2%, and the underlying fundamental fantasy is of the aggressive and sadistic type. In frigidity one often finds a disturbance of erotic drive, but in vaginismus we are faced with a pathology of aggressive instinct. For a long time, especially in the U.S., the psychological approach to vaginismus has been neglected as diagnosis and therapy were only organic, although organic troubles are present only in 2 to 5% of the cases.

4. THERAPEUTIC CONSIDERATIONS

Abraham (1956) was the first physician to have started a form of short psychotherapy to cure vaginismus, but she did not use a local technique in addition. In Europe, Balin (1958) in London, developed fifteen years ago a combined technique, that is, one of local relaxation and woman's psychological understanding. Balint's observations have been summarized by Friedman (1962) in his book 'Virgin Wives'. He describes three types of women, namely:
(a) 'The Sleeping Beauty': an infantile woman who lives with her husband in

a fraternal relationship. These couples depend on their parents and remain eternal students.

(b) 'Brunhilde': sexuality is experienced as a battle of the sexes with fear that femininity might be a sign of weakness and passivity, and

(c) 'The Queen-Bee': these women want to have a child from their husband but refuse sexuality. Sexual intercourse is 'dirty' and 'mortifying', and is considered to be an unpleasant necessity in order to become pregnant.

More recently, Michel-Wolfromm (1954) in France began to study not women and men separately, but the psychology of the couple. She mentions that the partner is not chosen by accident, and that often husbands of women with vaginismus are very shy and less aggressive, and their wives are either mannish or infantile.

In the study of Friedman and Balint quoted by Friedman (1970), only 25% of the husbands were interviewed, and this fact had no influence on the prognosis; nevertheless, the husbands' potency was disturbed from the beginning in half of the cases, and 13% of the men became impotent after the successful treatment of the wife. These negative reactions especially justify treating the couple as a whole.

Case histories from the unit of sexology in Geneva were based on 82 couples: two-thirds of them consulted for a sexual problem and the others in order to have a child. The prognosis is not different for the two groups. In 75% of the cases, the relational aspect of the couple was so primary that it was necessary to treat husband and wife together. They came from once to ten times, and 88% of them succeeded in consummating their marriage which, for some of them, had not been consummated for 15 years!

For the slight and not too severe cases, realistic information on the physiology of the sexual act has a proper therapeutic function. This prevents shame and sadistic fantasies. It is useful to speak openly and precisely of technique and positions in sexual intercourse. But in severe cases, sexuality is experienced as mutual destruction and fragmentation which go far beyond the fear of penetration. This is often the case for those of borderline or psychotic personality, and therapy is required to attain a new balance, and to permit consummation of the marriage.

In general, the fundamental problem of these couples lies in badly integrated aggression; important changes of libido are observed more rarely.

The therapeutic choice depends on a good psychodynamic evaluation of the causes of vaginismus and its 'economy' in the psychology of the woman and of the couple. I am more and more inclined to use a short or intensive therapy, both somatic and psychological in nature.

The principle consists in provoking a voluntary misunderstanding, when, at the first stage, the physician asks the woman to massage her vagina for two minutes, three times a day, in order to make it supple; if the patient is inhibited, this is already progress. At this stage, one does not take into consideration the fact that estrogens in the jelly could render the muscles of the vagina more supple; but by these means one helps the woman to get a better corporeal scheme, because she has a constant fantasy that she is 'too narrow down there'. Therefore, if one tells her abruptly that it is because she dare not touch herself and ask that she tries to do it, she will never accept, for this contact is inhibiting. If one uses the kind of medical expedient mentioned (massaging the vagina to get it supple), the woman will gradually re-integrate the body schema of this region. The technique at this step may vary: one can use a finger-stall, an anesthetic cream, a bougie, or a personal vibrator; but the best way is to take a mirror in order to correct the distorted picture the woman has of her genital organs. This phase corresponds more or less to the Anglo-Saxon 'stretching' which Friedman (1962) describes in 'Virgin Wives'.

The second step consists of letting the partner do this massage in order to give it a relational setting. He will begin with his finger; this, as a rule, temporarily increases the inhibition, the actual experience of which has to be verbalized by the couple together and with the therapist. In the third phase, if progress is adequate, the husband or partner will try with his penis, but in a special position; the woman will be astride the man and therefore be able to control penetration and stop it if it is painful.

This technique has allowed a cure rate of 88% in unconsummated marriages the origin of which was specifically feminine or relational. When cure is not possible, there is typically an underlying psychiatric disturbance. In cases where, in addition to vaginismus, dyspareunia exists associated with strong aggressive tendencies towards the partner, one directs the woman or the couple to a psychotherapist.

Regarding symptoms, follow-up is extremely positive after a year, and many women have become pregnant. However, for neurotic personalities, the psychological significance of vaginismus has changed, and these patients may present later with phobia of delivery or other phobias. For these cases thorough psychotherapy has been necessary.

The more the relational aspect is in evidence, the more the husband needs to be psychologically supported; his anxiety must be calmed from the beginning and he should be considered as a collaborator indispensable to the success of the enterprise. Thus, it will be possible to avoid part of the conflict between husband and therapist, in which the latter is experienced in fantasy as the father or the mythical rival, which explains most of the cases of male impotence after dilatation of the woman under narcosis.

In order to ensure the best possible success in this kind of therapy, the physician must be made aware of his own excessive impulse to cure, and of his tendency to get rid of the more unpleasant couples. He should overcome his own voyeuristic tendencies when he is called upon to deal with the intimate life of the couple. When he ceases to believe in miracles, but is convinced that his intervention will have a therapeutic value, he will be in a good position to treat vaginismus and unconsummated marriage.

5. SUMMARY

According to American inquiries, 2% of marriages are not consummated, but this percentage is difficult to estimate because most such couples do not consult the physician.

The principal causes of nonconsummation are impotence, dyspareunia and vaginismus. In the author's opinion, the best therapy is that which considers the couple taken as a whole because the problem is mostly relational. Relationship therapy, adopted in Geneva, has had an 88% success rate in 82 couples who had not consummated their marriage. Husband and wife are treated together, each member of the couple being the therapist of the other, and they are told precisely about technique and positions in sexual intercourse.

BIBLIOGRAPHY

Abraham, H.C. (1956) A contribution to the problem of female sexuality. *Int. J. Psycho-Anal.*, 37, 351, 30.

Friedman, L.J. (1962) *Virgin Wives.* (Tavistock Publications, London.)

Friedman, L.J. (1970) Unconsummated marriages. *Med. Aspects Hum. Sex.*, No. 5, vol. IV, 16—29.

Kinsey, A. (1953) *Sexual Behavior in the Human Female.* (W.B. Saunders Co., Phildelphia/London.)

Malleson, J. (1954) Sex problems in marriage with particular reference to coital discomfort and the unconsummated marriage. *Practitioner*, 172, 389.

Masters, J. and Johnson, V. (1970) *Human Sexual Inadequacy.* (Little, Brown and Co., Boston.)

Michel-Wolfromm, H. (1954) Causes et traitement du vaginisme. *Rev. Fr. Gynécol. Obstét.*, 49, 30.

Stallworthy, M. (1948) Facts and fantasy in the study of female infertility. *J. Obstet. Gynaecol.*, 55, 171—180.

Sturgis, S. (1957) Routine psychiatric interviews in a sterility investigation. *Fertil. Steril.* 8 (6) 521—526.

CHAPTER 70

Genital pain and sexuality

MYRIAM DE SENARCLENS

1. WOMAN AND PAIN

To evoke pleasure and ignore pain is to forget one of the fundamental truths of human nature, the bipolarity of all feelings and sensations, the alternation of suffering and joy.

This concept is epitomized in the feminine condition, though by no means exclusive to that sex. For a woman the road to maturity is paved with a series of experiences which must be overcome before she can acquire her true identity and reach the fulfillment of her genitality.

The one constant in the successive stages of a woman's life is that they are all painful experiences which may be transformed into sources of pleasure provided they are mastered with success. It is for this reason that woman's destiny is marked from the outset by a kind of anticipation of suffering, intensified still further by her traditional submission to man.

The genital system of the small girl cannot be isolated from the world of her emotions of which it is a faithful mirror. Certain frustrations in early life and the unsatisfactory integration of specific physiological phases are known to be expressed in terms of pain: the oedipus complex is felt as pain; there is pain at the arrival of menstrual blood during puberty with all its attendant fantasies of wounding or impurity; and there may be pain too at the time of defloration, although this varies according to the cultural context and is tending to disappear. At a later stage, the experience of pregnancy and the contractions of childbirth, feared as a source of suffering, test the caliber of the mother-to-be; she will meet the experience of childbirth with success but may at the same time show masochistic tendencies as if profoundly marked by the words of the Bible: "In sorrow thou shalt bring forth children".

In this way the pelvis, seat of femininity and eroticism, will become for certain patients a favorite instrument of expression, giving rise to all kinds of affects such as guilt feelings and a need for punishment, which may or may

Handbook of Sexology, edited by J. Money and H. Musaph
© *Elsevier/North-Holland Biomedical Press, 1977*

not be conscious, every time they are subsequently confronted by difficulties or experience desires they are ashamed to confess.

2. GYNECOLOGY AND PAIN

The gynecological clinic is a pre-eminently ambiguous field. It is particularly difficult to define the normality or abnormality of the genital organs with their anatomical variations and cyclical and fluctuating mechanisms. Moreover the doctor is only interested in them if they are injured or painful but not as a potential source of pleasure. What happens is that the gynecologist, conditioned by a sort of mental habit, only too common in medicine, always looks for a somatic explanation when pain is felt in the lower abdomen. Conversely he is not in the least concerned if the same organs are painless or numb and characterized more by a distortion or an absence of erotic reaction. The misunderstanding may become serious when the organs are painful for emotional reasons, without being structurally affected; this is the case with the kind of pelvic pain known as psychogenic, which is purely functional or 'sine materia'. The gynecologist normally refuses to analyse the trouble, the field of the emotions being steadfastly ignored as likely to prove too distressing. This tendency to adopt a different approach towards the genital—organic as a possible seat of pain and the sexual—functional as a source of pleasure is not one of the most surprising paradoxes in the field of medicine. In point of fact it is impossible to draw a line between pain and pleasure since the two sensations may be simultaneous, intermingled and linked always by a common phenomenon, emotion, which underlies the whole range of reactions from suffering to joy, by way of anguish or indifference.

This discovery may have serious consequences since it calls into question the traditional form of gynecological practice. The age of the 'exclusive mechanism of the pelvis' has gone, at both theoretical and clinical levels. Everything has taken on another dimension, especially the principle of differential diagnosis, which now appears out of date and needs replacing by an understanding of the patient as a whole (without omitting modern techniques of investigation).

From this point of view physical suffering appears not only as a signal of alarm, a defense of the organism against aggression, which can easily be assimilated to a specific clinical symptom, but at the same time betrays an indefinable feeling of malaise. Whether the suffering is functional or associated with an anatomical lesion, the emotions which cause or accompany it belong to the patient, alone, and there is no way of measuring their intensity.

3. PSYCHOPHYSIOLOGY

Whether the pain originates in a transposition of affects to the corporal plane or conversely in unbearable physical sensations which give rise to emotion in the patient, it constitutes a language which has its source not only in time but at all levels of the subconscious. Such a language is not easy to interpret.

In the work 'Neuropsychologie de la Douleur' (Neuropsychology of Pain) by Quarti and Renaud (1972), the following important concepts are noted:

(1) Pain always corresponds with the upsetting of a balance which the cell membrane is unable to regain . . .

(2) Pain is a special sensory mode in that the role of the peripheral receptors does not appear to be essential. A pain which is 'sine materia' can be equally intense and possess all the neurophysiological characteristics of a pain transmitted through the receptors from a tangible lesion.

(3) Any functional pain may give rise to vascular reflexes which may complicate the pain in either a functional or a physical mode.

(4) The difference between an agreeable erotic sensation and pain is often a question of degree. Protopathic sensitivity makes it possible to feel either voluptuous or painful sensations from external objects or from the body. During a single stimulation the patient may pass from one sensation to the other.

(5) In the course of work connected with painful experiences, one is led to envisage the integration of pain into the physical and psychic self and its direct participation in the constant remodelling of the corporal schema.

These neurophysiological concepts provide a basis for a large number of clinical or psychodynamic observations. Engel (1962) is of the opinion that pain may be associated with sexual development and even experienced as pleasure at the time of erotic climax. Here we come face to face with the world of sadomasochism and touch upon the limits of perversion. Some people prefer to experience pain rather than sexual pleasure which exists essentially at the level of fantasy (de Senarclens, 1973, 1974).

Thus the pain felt depends not only on the threshold of sensitivity in the presence of a lesion but may often reflect the memory of emotional impressions which ontologically go back a long way. This means that in the case of woman one must take into account the psychological and somatic events which have marked her during the course of development and which have determined the image she has formed of her body and especially her sexual organs. Sometimes the organs are looked upon as being bad, either because they are painful or on the contrary because they are lacking in feeling, and patients may become so worried they are rendered incapable of realizing their aspirations in the social or emotional field. In this case it would be useless to expect the woman to make an immediate connection between the pain she feels and the underlying conflicts which are often at the origin of sexual dysfunction. What happens is that the pain succeeds in invading the personality of the patient so completely that all her psychic energy is concentrated on integrating the suffering and cannot be distracted by any other stimulus. The woman who falls victim to a disorder of this kind seems to be able to do nothing but suffer and even to obtain a kind of pleasure from her suffering, in addition to the benefit derived from the treatment she is given. It matters little whether the painful experience is the memory of a genital lesion which has healed, the expression of an unresolved conflict, or some existential frustration, since it reveals the weakness of certain personalities which, unable to erect effective defenses, give way to a steady emotional impoverishment.

It seems that the psychopathological models which include pain apply equally to sexual disorders (emotional immaturity, conversion hysteria, defense reactions, depression); the psychodynamic mechanisms involved in both types of disorder appear to be similar, giving rise on the one hand to somatization and on the other hand to sexual disorder, but in both cases serving to maintain a kind of homeostasis.

4. SYNDROMES

Exploration of the emotional context of patients suffering from genital pain often reveals the trace of former deprivation or problems of adaptation, besides a connection between the genital symptoms and certain sexual disorders which the woman in question would rather not discuss. The connection is particularly clear in the case of vaginismus and dyspareunia since these are both initially painful disorders, the former often preceded by a history of dysmenorrhea, and the latter sometimes alternating with crises of cystalgia or vulvar pruritus.

Vaginismus

Vaginismus, the inability of the woman to accept union, is nearly always attributed by her or by the couple to an unsuccessful attempt at intromission rendered painful as a result of some physical malformation; usually it is not until the first attempts at intercourse have failed that the patient, initially full of confidence, begins to be overwhelmed by the anguish of penetration, the fear of being lacerated, which reveals that she has a false picture of her own body.

Dyspareunia

Dyspareunia, whether it appears in a healthy patient or after the healing of a pelvic infection of which the painful memory still persists, is not caused only by the pathological organic conditions which are apparently responsible, but involves other personal factors. The symptom often affects patients involved in marital strife so that sometimes it appears as an expression of indifference, but more often of a claim which is being made on the attention of the partner. In both cases it is necessary to establish whether the suffering is accompanied by pleasure or sexual insensibility.

Coital or postcoital pain is often described as a simple pain without any mention of the underlying sexual difficulties. An organic diagnosis is not likely to resolve the sexual problem although the somatic act in itself, the treatment of a lesion if it really exists, may provide a good way of starting to help and can sometimes create a favorable atmosphere in which to get patients to relax or relieve them of their feelings of guilt.

Cystalgia, pruritis and vulvovaginitis

Other genital symptoms are full of significance for the sexual field, although the connection between pleasure and pain is less clear-cut than in the cases already discussed. Cystalgia in young married women is too seldom recognized for what it is — in a context of sexual initiation or during the first erotic emotions — and wrongly treated as a primary urinary infection. In the same way, pruritus or vulvovaginitis, with or without leukorrhea, are seldom lacking in overtones at the personal level. In the case of the young woman, pruritus has a quality of hope in the search for erotic fulfillment. Later, for the menopausal or postmenopausal woman, inflammation or pain of the vulva is nearly always a symptom of despair, whether it occurs after a bereavement, on the desertion of a loved one or at the departure of the children. Musaph (1969) postulates repression of emotions of rage and aggression in the conflict linked with pruritus. This type of patient shows an intolerance towards solitude and is incapable of discharging or mastering her too intense aggression.

Pruritus, whether accompanied by hope or despair, undoubtedly betrays the incapacity of the patient to live in the present moment and acquires overtones of masochism and self-punishment.

Mastodynia

Mention must also be made of mastodynia since there is no question that it belongs in the sexual field. Even if the direct cause is a hormonal disorder, psychosomatic teaching shows that emotional disturbances may be the source of the glandular imbalance involved; pain in the breast is laden with erotic evocations, and may even be accompanied by the fear of death, but it is also to be found in an atmosphere of frustration or desertion, as if the patient's entire emotional energy had been compromised by the indifference or absence of the partner.

Pelvic and lumbar pain

Lastly, pelvic and lumbar pain involves complex psychosomatic factors which, without being specific, are made up of both former and current experiences. During puberty the adolescent girl lives through marked bodily changes especially at the onset of menstruation which symbolizes her budding genitality and provides a hint of future motherhood. In this way there is often a history of dysmenorrhea and other types of pain accompanying the development of a sexuality which is both desired and unknown, sometimes even hated and feared. The impact of sex on manifestations of pain in the young woman on the threshold of life is clearer still; in the early stages of marriage, pelvic pain often betrays an unstable emotional state, the awakening of intrapsychic conflicts, and difficulties of conjugal and sexual adaptation. Young wives who remain firmly attached to their mother and take pleasure in an attitude of dependence and passivity often betray in their complaints a feeling of being misunderstood and sometimes the presence of forbidden desires; pain thus becomes meaningful in relation to the personality of the woman, to certain events in her history and to the image she has formed of her own body.

For this reason the dialogue between gynecologist and patient has a specific quality, sex always being invoked implicitly when the woman offers her body for investigation and when, through her physical problems, she is really seeking for understanding of the intimate feelings she is incapable of putting into words.

5. CONCLUSION

Pain, desire, frigidity and pleasure — in spite of their fundamental difference, these affects are undoubtedly related and may sometimes be interchangeable. This relationship is illustrated commonly, and often in the form of a caricature, in the field of gynecology: pleasure in pain, indifference in desire, pain without pleasure or pleasure without desire, these many possibilities well express all the hazards and contradictions of feminine emotions and sensory reactions. From pain suffered to pain sought for, there are numerous stages which form part of the psychobiological development of a woman whose masochistic tendencies can be explained by the complexity of her ontogenesis.

Although pain is primarily a sensory phenomenon, it is only given its true meaning by the emotion which accompanies it. Early deprivation, disorders occurring during maturation and unfavorable environmental conditions may lead to sexual dysfunctions after having given rise to disorders experienced as pain. In other words pain and pleasure are constantly coupled like the two scales of a single balance.

The ratio between affectivity and integrity at the pelvic level in the acquisition of sexual fulfillment, together with alteration of the data as a result of pain linked closely or remotely to the sexual function, represent a field of study which has so far been little explored.

BIBLIOGRAPHY

Engel, G.L. (1962) *Psychological Development in Health and Disease*. (Saunders, Philadelphia.)

Musaph, H. (1969) Aggression and symptom formation in dermatology. *J. Psychosom. Res.* 13: 257—264.

Quarti, C. and Renaud, J. (1972) *Neuropsychologie de la douleur.* (Herman, Paris.)

Senarclens, M. de (1973) Douleur génitale et problèmes sexuels chez la femme. *Med. Hyg.* 31: 1758—9.

Senarclens, M. de (1974) Pratique gynécologique et sexualité: de la douleur au plaisir. In: *Introduction à la Sexologie Médicale.* Ch. XIII. (Payot, Paris.)

CHAPTER 71

Hypersexuality in male and female

DENNIS FRIEDMAN

1. INTRODUCTION

The use of the word hypersexuality implies a degree of sexual activity which is in excess of the normal but this requires a normal standard of comparison. However, there are such wide variations even within one culture such as our own, that we may find ourselves postulating a normal standard which in fact is attained by only a very small proportion of the population.

It would seem to me that rather than look for so-called normal standards in any given population it would be more useful to consider any change in an individual's pattern of sexual behavior. Generally speaking the explanation for such behavior may be found in the psyche, although there are some rare cerebral lesions which can cause hypersexuality.

Definition

Hypersexuality is defined as a change in the sexual activity of an individual which is in excess of what either partner had come to expect from the other. The definition relates only to so-called mature activity conducted at the genital level; deviations from the 'normal' for that individual being excluded. Excessive promiscuous sexual activity is known as nymphomania in women and satyriasis in men.

2. NYMPHOMANIA

Nymphomania is a term commonly misused in the English language. It is popularly believed to relate to an insatiable demand for sexual intercourse in a woman heavily endowed with physical attributes attractive to a male. This would be the definition put forward by a layman and is incomplete. It is necessary to look into the background of the woman whose adult sexual needs are so insatiable that no one man may ever satisfy them.

Handbook of Sexology, edited by J. Money and H. Musaph
© *Elsevier/North-Holland Biomedical Press, 1977*

Those who suffer from this disorder have had early life experiences in which they have learnt to hold themselves in low esteem. A sense of internal emptiness causes them to continually strive to satisfy appetites which never leave them fulfilled. Their sexual gluttony may be matched by gastronomic excesses. A woman whose marriage was breaking down because of frigidity with her husband and her excessive sexual demands elsewhere always felt hungry during her therapy. Indeed it was quite common for her to bring food, usually oranges and eat them during the session. 'I cannot expect you to feed me' she would say. Her acting out of the transference was evidence from this patient of how much she both wanted a feed from me, accepted that she would have to feed herself and at the same time was afraid of recognizing her wishes because of her fears of rejection. She was also asking me whether I thought she was worth feeding.

In addition to low self-esteem and greed the nymphomanic woman is jealous of other women, seeing them as rivals. Arising out of this is competitiveness which is often exhibited in clothing and personal appearance. She looks for admiration, approval and acceptance from her 'sisters' to counter the guilt that arises out of her hostile feelings towards them.

She is often an older child in a large family who has been displaced on several occasions by the birth of other siblings. She may model herself on what she believes to be the preferred child and the preferred gender. If this should be male she may become a 'tom-boy' using denial of femininity as a defense against her wish for it. In the tom-boy, the nymphomanic or the desperate need to be loved has been replaced by, or sublimated in physical activity often relating to an interest in the grooming and riding of horses. The horse in the dreams and fantasies of women symbolizes the penis. To be 'in love' with one's horse (a condition almost unknown in males other than in homosexuals) implies an attraction to strength, power, sturdiness and an upright quality like the best qualities of masculinity; yet she causes him to 'eat out of her hand'. In this way she remains in charge introjecting within her the source of love, the penis or its earliest equivalent, the breast.

The clue to nymphomania lies in her wish to be the loved child but accompanied by the fear that this was not so. The earliest memories of such women embrace rejection as a central theme. One patient's earliest memory was being met by her mother at the age of about five years, from school. The school was at the top of a hill and she would start to walk down the hill to 'meet her mother half way'. She recalled running into a doorway to hide from a barking dog which had frightened her. Her mother panicked because she thought she had run away or had an accident and smacked her out of relief when she found her.

In this memory there may be seen firstly, the apparently uphill struggle of the mother to meet her child half-way, in itself something not accomplished easily. Secondly, the barking dog and the fear evoked by the possibility of being bitten (the projection of her own hostility?) and thirdly, being smacked. Early memories whether fact or fantasy represent memories of earlier emotions and cover events which cannot be recalled.

For a child to obtain the love she knows to be her birthright she may have to seduce her mother into giving it. Seduction is a mode of behavior designed to trick the giver into being loving. Similar behavior occurs in adult life.

Seductiveness

When seductive behavior is displayed, underlying frigidity should be suspected. The emphasis placed on appearances and sexual cues are directly proportional to the absence of such apparently attractive qualities internally. Seduction is a technique used by children to obtain from a parent, usually the mother, by subterfuge that which should be theirs by right. The technique is self-reinforcing, each time that it is used successfully to provoke the response, namely love which rewards the user. Nevertheless such love is not given freely and the child that uses seductive behavior does not feel loved. The 'feed' obtained in this way is not therefore a satisfying one given willingly and freely. The adult who has learnt to be loved only in this way must have ever more frequent feeds to be fulfilled. No one individual may satisfy such needs and frequent and short-lived relationships take place. The adult comes to believe that seduction apparently replaces the 'empty' breast of an earlier stage of development with a full one; a dangerous illusion which cannot be sustained. Using similar methods in adult life she soon finds what at first seemed to be a genuine relationship becoming nothing more than her unhappy concept of the primary love.

Seductive behavior is a common factor to be found in those women whose neurosis presents as a phobia. The phobia itself is a defense against both hostility and sexual anxiety and is related to the mother. The nonsatisfying mother in such disorders has provoked such a degree of hostility that to keep it internalized becomes intolerable. By projecting it into external situations which then although threatening can nevertheless be avoided, the patient hopes to avoid the consequences of her own anger, namely the sense of internal disintegration, destructiveness and depression that her own angry feelings may cause. At the same time, sexual feelings, both erotic and affectionate have been blocked and negated by hostility until the sexual awakening that marriage brings. Such dammed up impulses now become frightening and in the interests of the marriage 'frigidity' must be assumed. This coldness is a defense against hypersexuality. The fear of 'falling', of 'reaching a point of no return', of 'going too far then panicking' represents a wish (socially impossible) to let go of the feelings so long repressed. The only possible way out is in the taboo extramarital partnership which in the phobic patient her frigidity is a defense against.

Extramarital partnership

An outlet for eroticism, either per se, or preceded by the earlier component of sexuality namely affection (falling in love) and then followed by focal sexuality is achieved by having two partners. There is no difference in the psychopathology between the sexes since the second partner reflects an example of the 'splitting' that has already taken place in infancy in the ambivalent reaction to the mother. The marital partner at first may fulfill all loving needs. However, since it is not possible for any relationship to have love as its sole component, and if the primary relationship has included a good deal of hate, then as the marriage becomes more of a committing and enclosing one and early memories of involved relationships with their ambivalent feelings are exposed, then another partner is needed to invest with the idealized love. This turning away can take place at any time but is most likely when the partner in fantasy becomes a surrogate mother.

The role of the marital partner changes as the first child is born. This of course makes the wife a mother in her own right and makes it easier to react to her using the 'as if' principle, that is, as if she were his mother. Role change varies with time since it is related to the time of onset of hostile feelings to the individual's mother. This may not have taken place until after (say) the second child was born if the patient himself was the first-born. Feelings of envy and jealousy are inherent in the extramarital partnership since the original mother and now the surrogate is perceived as preferring a sibling or the father. For this reason a married woman with children may be chosen as a partner in order that she may attack the rival parent with whom she is in competition.

Gebhard (1970) reported that in urban America about half of the married men and a quarter of the married women have extramarital experiences up to the age of 40. There is no reason to suspect that urban America is atypical, in this respect. He points to a statistical correspondence between premarital and extramarital relationships; women with premarital experience tending more frequently to have extramarital contacts. He attributes this to the fact that these women are more sexually responsive and have a more liberal attitude towards sex. He concludes that 'the extramarital relationship can be an enriching experience, or can lead to difficulties, but it can also be an affair without consequence, depending on the people and circumstances concerned'. This, of course, includes all possible combinations. Therapy is only sought when difficulties are encountered.

3. SATYRIASIS

There is very little difference in the psychopathology of sexually hyperactive males and their female counterparts. They have both remained attached to the mother, experiencing the relationship as one in which they were insufficiently loved. Because their sense of emptiness is still present they are unable to separate from the source of the feed. In their state of perpetual undernourishment they must greedily take in whatever love they can from whatever source. Because of the feeling of being unloved, they may act out their hostility to women by a contemptuous rejection of tenderness and warmth offered them. Their arrogant self-insuffiency makes it difficult for them to be involved in any giving transaction. Frequent reassurances are required that they are lovable, potent and superior, none of which qualities they feel they possess. Reassurances never relieve them of their feelings of inadequacy, both sociointellectual and sexual, and they must move on to a fresh source of reassurance frequently. Since their attachment to the breast arises out of hostility to it for depriving them, little affection is shown for their sexual partners whom they tend to debase and denigrate. Another factor may be the need to find an outlet for erotic feeling to avoid coming up against the incest barrier which is completely detached from the anaclitic, that is warm, supportive affectionate object-choice. There are thus features of anal-sadistic eroticism in their sexual behavior.

Since the behavior of the Don Juan is due to his oedipus complex and is archaic in nature he is concerned only with erotic satisfaction and is usually little interested in the personality of his objects. One category of object relationships that is especially important is that of pseudosexuality (Fenichel, 1945). Sexual acts serve such defensive purposes as the contradictions of so-called perverse sexual goals by stressing the normal ones, by denying inhibition or by combating anxieties and guilt feelings, usually by satisfying a need for reassurance through narcissistic gains.

4. EXCESSIVE DEMAND OF ONE PARTNER UPON THE OTHER

In women

Women who feel unlovable may have insatiable appetites. The sexual appetite is temporarily satisfied by coitus with either the marital partner, or if he does not live up to her expectations, with one or more extramarital partners. If he is experienced as an idealized parent the hostility inherent in the symbiotic relationship binds her to him. If he is acting out his child/mother needs with her the relationship will be mutually comforting and will survive. Because hostility is a factor, envy of the partner's penis leads to jealousy and suspicion. Frequent coitus becomes both a test of his concern and tenderness and also a wish for the feeding organ to be emptied out and sucked dry, thus depriving imagined rivals of it. If mutuality is absent without each colluding in the other's neurotic greed, such a demanding relationship exhausts the partnership which then requires further symptoms as defenses against the separation anxieties, notably travel phobias which thinly veil the attachment and dependency on the other.

Because the unconscious recognizes immediately unfulfilled needs in another, 'Falling in love' (the neurotic acting out of the need), while replicating the primary love accounts for patients with similar symptoms being married to each other. When one arrives at maturity, the other's symptoms are then exposed and illness results.

In men

Men also use coitus as a 'comfort' and may experience it as a means of warding off anxiety in the same way as masturbation is used for this purpose from infancy onwards. Gratification with a partner is seldom 'giving' when excessive, but rather represents a relationship with the projected feminine parts of himself. This relationship with 'part-objects' is totally masturbatory and also 'feeding'. Oral sexuality is a common feature of the relationship as he uses his penis to feed the projected oral part of himself. One partner may seldom satisfy him and his masochistic acting out is repeated with stereotypes.

Once again the dependency is linked with hostility and the guilt resulting from his violent, often murderous feelings, is seldom reduced for long by his attempts to inflict suffering on himself or his marital partner whom he experiences as the 'bad' and 'nonfeeding' component of the breast.

Hypersexuality as a defense against anxiety
During wartime the exaggerated sexual behavior of troops is a well-known phenomenon. Visiting a brothel is a prominent activity of many soldiers while on leave and can be understood in terms of a defense against fear. On active service, troops may have difficulty in controlling their sexual impulses if they are being encouraged to express their aggressive ones, and consequently violent sexual acts such as rape are not infrequent occurrences.

5. HYPERSEXUALITY IN THE AFFECTIVE DISORDERS

If a diminution of libido has been a feature of the depressive phase of a manic depressive psychosis then increased sexual activity may be one of the earliest symptoms of a swing into hypomania. Coitus which had previously taken place on rare occasions with little or no enthusiasm may suddenly change with intercourse being demanded up to four or five times daily. The condition tends to be recognized more usually in males than females, probably because cultural factors tend to condition males to assume the active role in sexual behavior.

6. HYPERSEXUALITY DUE TO ORGANIC BRAIN LESIONS

Cerebral cortical lesions may lead to abnormal sexual behavior. Evidence for this has been found in animals. The Klüver-Bucy syndrome is a disorder in which a temporal lobe lesion leads to hypersexuality. Changes in sexual behavior similar to that described in animals by Klüver and Bucy (1939) have been shown to occur in temporal lobe lesions in humans, particularly in the organic dementias (Pearce and Miller, 1973).

The poor impulse control of epileptics either during the aura preceding the seizure or during the state of post-epileptic automatism may also lead to exaggerated sexual activity.

7. SUMMARY

Increased sexual activity in excess of the individual's usual behavior is described in terms of the organic and psychodynamic factors which may induce it.

Brain lesions are briefly mentioned, but attention is focused on those events in early life which lead individuals of either sex to experience themselves as deprived of maternal love. A hostile retaliation acted out in adult life with a partner chosen as a 'provider' is described in terms of a demanding greediness under the headings nymphomania and satyriasis.

An unsatisfactory primary love is also shown to lead either to extramarital partnerships, or within the marriage to excessive demands by the dependent partner upon the other.

BIBLIOGRAPHY

Fenichel, C. (1945) *The Psychoanalytic Theory of Neurosis*. (Norton, New York.)
Gebhard, P.H. (1970) Studies in the sexuality of women, In: *The Sexuality of Women*, Vol. I (Andre Deutsch, London) pp. 31—33.
Klüver, H. and Bucy, P.C. (1939) Preliminary analysis of functions of the temporal lobes in monkeys, *Arch. Neurol. Psychiat.* 42: 979—1000.
Pearce, J. and Miller, E. (1973) *Clinical Aspects of Dementia*. (Bailliere, Tyndall, London.)

CHAPTER 72

Paraphilias

JOIIN MONEY

1. PAIR-BONDING

Sexual or erotic pair-bonding takes place between two human beings in three phases: proception, acception, and conception. Problems or disabilities in the sexual relationship between a couple may occur singly or severally in these three phases (Table I).

Proception

The two components of proception are the solicitant and the attractant. Either partner may solicit the other, or both may do so reciprocally. Similarly, either partner attracts the other, or both may do so simultaneously. Solicitation is usually affected initially by means of appeal to the sense of sight through the use of postures and gestures — so-called eye-talk and body-talk

Table I
Three phases of eroticism and sexuality.

	Activity	Organs	Disorders
Proception	Solicitation, attraction, courtship	Eyes, nose, skin	Gender transpositions; paraphilias of inclusion or displacement; apathy
Acception	Erection, lubrication, copulation	Mouth, genitals, anus	Hypophilias, hyperphilias
Conception	Pregnancy, delivery, childcare	Internal reproductive, mammary	Sterility, anovulation, miscarriage, nonlactation

Handbook of Sexology, edited by J. Money and H. Musaph
© *Elsevier/North-Holland Biomedical Press, 1977*

— augmented possibly with cosmetics and adornment that signify erotic intention.

Solicitation may be effected also through the sense of smell, either from prepared perfumes or from natural body odors or pheromones. Additionally, tone of voice may be the medium of appeal; or the appeal may be made directly, or obliquely, through words and their meaning, especially after close proximity has been established. Close proximity also permits appeal through the skin senses of touch, pressure and temperature.

Solicitation fails if the solicited partner is not reciprocally in a proceptive phase, for then the signals of solicitation fail to be attractive to him or her. There is no single explanation for such failure. It may be temporary or long-term, that is reversible or persistent. It may be specific to a particular partner only, or systematic, as a manifestation of general erotic inertia.

The proceptive phase may pass into the acceptive phase in the course of minutes or hours, as is typically the case when two established partners have a repeat erotic engagement. Or it may be protected over weeks, months or even years, as is typically the case in a courtship or love affair prior to the transition to the copulatory phase. In the male, the culmination of acception is putting in (insertion, or injection). In the female, it is taking in (reception or intrajection). Reciprocally, the two-way culmination of acception in coitus, copulation or intercourse represents what may be called ambijection.

Acception

The unreceptive male or female may be not only indifferent to the solicitation of the partner, but may actively rebuff and reject her or him. Nonetheless, it is a fact that, in the case of the woman, but not of the man, copulation can take place even when the person is unconscious. Likewise, a paraplegic woman, unable to move or feel from the waist down can be passively positioned for the gymnastics of copulation (or of donor insemination), and may carry a pregnancy to term. It is, however, a misnomer to equate normal female receptivity with passivity. The properly receptive woman is, in actuality, a very active partner in copulation. Her proper state of receptivity, like the state of erectivity in the male, is dependent on appropriate stimulation of the autonomic and central nervous systems.

It is a misnomer to equate active or aggressive sexuality with male insertivity, to the exclusion of female participant receptivity. The one imperative of male insertivity is not activity or aggression, but penile erection. Getting an erection is not simply a matter of either activity or aggression. In fact, a man's penis gets or receives an erection only upon appropriate stimulation from the autonomic and the central nervous systems. Ejaculation, and resultant conception, can be accomplished even if the male does nothing more than be receptive to the thrusting of an aggressive pelvis and the sliding, rubbing, squeezing and clasping movements of an active, participating vagina.

If the male is inhibited, or resists, or is indifferent to the solicitation of the female, and fails to get an erection, then copulatory insertion cannot be achieved. The unconscious male cannot copulate. The paraplegic male may get a reflex erection, by way of a spinal reflex arc disconnected from the brain, but it is extremely difficult for his partner to use it for proper copulation — and conception is in most instances ruled out, as paraplegic testes become infertile secondarily to loss of proper temperature regulation.

In the popular imagination, the copulative phase of eroticism is linked with animal lust, physical relief, moral indulgence, sensual appetite, and carnal pleasure. The proceptive phase, by contrast, is popularly linked with romantic love, lyrical beauty, moral sentiment, sensuous tenderness, and devoted affection. The proceptive phase is love above the belt, and the copulative phase, sex below the belt.

Negative evaluation of the proceptive phase is seldom voiced. Evaluation of the copulative phase is, customarily ambivalent: in the folkways, it is either tabooed, reprehensible and dirty (so save it for the one you love!) or sacrosanct, licensed, and pure (but don't do it, for restraint is better!). Each ambivalent alternative is restrictive, rather than openly affirmative. Transition from the proceptive to the copulative phase may, therefore, be very difficult. For many people, a true unity is never achieved. They cannot graduate from sex above the belt to sex below it.

Conception

In human eroticism, the conceptive phase usually is a sequel to the proceptive and copulative phases, though not invariably so. It is known from cases of rape, and from the practice of donor insemination from the sperm bank, that conception may occur without the prior phases of proception and copulation.

On the other side of the coin, in the human species, conception and parenthood do not inevitably follow proception and copulation. Among human beings, proception and copulation are not hormonally enchained to ovulation and the estrous or the menstrual cycle, as is the case in most other mammals, especially nonprimates. Fertile human adults may and do solicit, attract and copulate during the woman's nonovulatory, infertile phase of the menstrual cycle, and they do so with mutual erotic gratification. Similarly, in the early postpubertal years of adolescence, some if not all young people pass through a phase of adolescent sterility, so-called, during which they are developmentally capable of proception, or courtship, and of infertile copulation.

It goes without saying that conception does not invariably lead to the delivery of a live birth, especially if the social and legal climate permits abortion. Likewise, delivery does not invariably lead to the continuance of parenthood, for a mother may decide on adoption; or a father may not have bothered to ascertain paternity, or may deny it.

In general, however, it appears that falling in love is the part of nature's reproductive scheme that gets a couple pair-bonded in courtship and copulation, ready for conception and parenthood. When the baby is delivered, the pair-bond enlarges into a three-bond. Mother and baby become bonded at the time of delivery and immediately thereafter. The ideal way for the father to be included, as a member of a threesome, is for him to be present at the delivery and to become himself bonded to the baby, at the same time as the bond between him and his wife is strengthened by the joint enterprise of the delivery. Otherwise the trio could become divided into two plus one, the pair-bond of the prior love affair broken, instead of enlarged.

With or without a baby, the pair-bond of a love affair does not exist forever in its original state and intensity. At a maximum, its natural lifetime is about two years — long enough for solicitation, copulation and conception all to have run their course to delivery, and for the pair-bond to have metamorphosed into a three-bond. The three-bond of parenthood is less hectic than the pair-bond of the love affair. The turmoil of love yields to the tranquility of erotic affection. Proception becomes a prelude to copulation, not a protracted period of courtship, and copulation becomes a very happy event that, repeated under normal conditions of maturation and aging, becomes increasingly more gratifying.

The three-way bonding process may be repeated with the birth of each subsequent child. In the human species, however, there is no guarantee that it will be renewed, or even that it will take place with the first baby. Conception does not automatically rectify defects or impairments of proception and copulation. Nor can correction of such defects or impairments automatically be guaranteed by switching to a new partner and a new love affair.

2. HYPO-, HYPER- AND PARAPHILIA

The problems of human sexuality, in each of its three phases, may be classified into too little, too much, or too peculiar. In each case, the problem may be either harmless or noxious, personally or societally. Conventionally, such problems have been considered as an individual's problems. Only recently have they more correctly been regarded as problems of a partnership. The differential diagnosis requires that one establish whether a problem is one involving gymnastic incompetency in sexual technique primarily on an anatomic or physiologic basis; or whether the primary disorder pertains to the imagery of erotic arousal, with secondary gymnastic incompetence. The latter is more common. One of its most frequent manifestations is phasic dyssynchrony between partners in the build-up and transition from proception to acception. That is to say, one partner may be either too fast or too slow in making the transition, or may be unable to complete the transition, either in imagery or participation, from sex above the belt to sex below the belt. In some couples, each partner may be unable to make the transition.

Hypophilia

The hypophilias are the sexual dysfunctions, deficiencies or disorders which, under the tutelage of Masters and Johnson, have recently become the domain of dual sex therapy. In both sexes, hypophilia includes sexual inertia or apathy, and anorgasmia. Formerly these conditions were scarcely recognized in the male, and in the female were subsumed under the single label, frigidity. Anorgasmia, according to the available evidence is more common in the female than the male. Sexual apathy or inertia is probably under-reported in the male, and could be equal frequency in both sexes.

In the male, hypophilia manifests itself also, possibly as a phobic or apprehensive reaction to the sex organs of the partner, as pre-ejaculatory impotence or impotence following premature ejaculation. In the female, the corresponding phobic hypophilias are failure of vaginal lubrication; and vaginismus or premature vaginal spasm, with or without concomitant pain (dyspareunia), plus failure of the expected clonic action of the vaginal muscles that precedes and leads to orgasm.

Hyperphilia

The hyperphilias have not, to date, been given much prominence in sexual medicine. Partly, the idea of hyperphilia has been treated with covert envy as a joke, deplored as a willful depravity, pitied as a brain syndrome, or reclassified as a compulsion associated with a paraphilia. Taxonomically, the joking attitude is perpetuated in the very words, nymphomania and satyriasis. Minus the joking, it is known that some women who elect prostitution as a career do not, in the erotic sense, enjoy copulating with their customers, but only in the compulsive sense of proving that they can do it. The same applies, vice versa, to some of their customers, and also to some male prostitutes and some of their customers.

It is also known that some husbands and, possibly, some wives put excessive copulatory demands on the partner — excessive as judged by the partner's personal criterion, and by copulatory statistics.

Rarely it happens that excessive sexual solicitation or acception may be associated with a temporal lobe brain tumor or a presenile deteriorative brain condition, notably Pick's disease. Brain changes may be associated also with sexual hypofunction. The relationship of brain dysfunction to either hyposexual or hypersexual function and/or expression is still largely conjectural. Hyperphilia is, for the most part, terra incognita, deficient in both fact and theory at the present time.

Priapism, or unremitting erection of the penis — more rarely of an enlarged clitoris — is not an authentic form of hyperphilia, though it may seem so for the few hours until it becomes excruciatingly painful. Priapism is a manifestation of a vascular disorder in which the veins of the penis fail to empty the engorged corpora cavernosa of the blood responsible for erection.

Paraphilia

Etymologically, philia means love, and para- means beside, near, beyond, and hence amiss. Popularly, paraphilias are known as bizarre or kinky sex. Legally they are defined as perversions and, in some jurisdictional statutes, as crimes against nature. The term, perversion is current also in medicine, especially psychiatry. Along with the term deviation, perversion is, however, falling into disuse. Both terms imply an absolute standard that has been perverted or deviated from, whereas in modern scientific medicine it is known that no such absolute standard exists. The term, paraphilia, is less judgmental in its connotation, and is therefore scientifically preferable. It does not, however circumvent the issue of whether a particular type of sexual behavior is harmless or harmful, either to the person, the partner, or society at large.

As a working rule, it may be said that a person's sexual behavior is harmful if it inpinges on another's right of privacy so as to endanger life, health and well being; or if it endangers the life, health and well being of the self. This rule clearly disqualifies such paraphilias as lust murder, a masochistic stage-management of one's own murder, erotic self-strangulation, noxious sadistic or masochistic wounding, and a rape or other traumatic erotic participation by edict rather than consent.

By its very nature, this pragmatic rule of consent and nontrauma is clearcut and easy to apply at the extremes of the spectrum rather than in the interdeterminate mid-zone. In times past, moralistic law-makers attempted to formulate absolute standards. Today it is evident that, in its moralizing absolutism, the law has failed. In the paraphiliac mid-zone, the noxiousness of a sexual practice to the partner is relative, not absolute. Each case must be evaluated on its own merit. For example, when a grandfather fondles his own beloved grandchild while sleeping in the same bed, the act is not incestuous in the same sense as when a visiting uncle forces his screaming, terrified, new pubertal niece to copulate with him.

A paraphilia does not, at first hand, seem abnormal to the person who has it, except that he or she can, at second hand, comprehend it to be so by the criterion of the law or the public mores. Thus the paraphiliac and his critics both can agree that, justifiably or not, there are limits to what people regard as publicly acceptable in sexual behavior. Historically, the criteria have changed. Masturbation was once considered a paraphilia (a perversion), but it is no longer. Likewise, oral sex. Cousin marriages rate as incest in some societies, but are prescribed in others. Genital stimulation in some societies is a legitimate method of calming and comforting an infant in distress, whereas in other societies it is a criminal offence, pedophilia. Beating and subjugating a wife into obedience, erotic and otherwise, is legally proper in some societies, whereas in others it is sadism, and cause for divorce, if not punishment of the assaulter.

Because there are only ideologies, not absolute standards as to what is allowable erotically between partners, there are also only ideologies as to what is not allowable. Ideology also determines who may or may not be partners. To complicate this relativism even more, it is a fact of nature that we human beings, as a species, do not have the masculinity or femininity of our gender identity fully programmed or preordained before we are born. The differentiation of gender identity as masculine, feminine, or mixed is largely programmed after birth, in the years of infancy and early childhood.

In its narrower sense of eroticism, the dichotomy of masculine versus feminine has its origins in the early postnatal years of the differentiation of gender identity as masculine versus feminine. Contrary to popular scientific and public misconception, gender identity is primarily differentiated, as is now known from various studies of intersexuality and related anomalies, not in prenatal life, but in the postnatal years of infancy and childhood. In this respect, the differentiation and development of gender identity resembles the development of native language. More precisely, it resembles the development and differentiation of bilingualism.

In gender identity differentiation, the duality of bilingualism has its counterpart in the duality of identification and complementation. Identification is a familiar concept. In the context of gender, it denotes the scheme of social learning whereby a child assimilates the example of persons of the same sex, especially the parent of the same sex. Complementation is not a familiar concept in the context of gender. It denotes the application of the identification schema in interaction with persons of the opposite sex, especially the parent of the opposite sex. It can be shaped directly by the opposite-sexed model, even when an identification model is represented in absentia.

Once the schemas of identification and complementation have been engrained into the brain/mind, the private experience of gender identity (manifested to the observer as gender role) becomes fixed. Regardless of whether it has differentiated as masculine, feminine, or ambivalent, it becomes as indelible as though programmed by the genes or hormones. The irreducible basics of sex differences are those that relate to procreation: men impregnate, and women menstruate, gestate and lactate. This basic sex difference is, by reason of the sexual taboo in our own society's cultural tradition, made covert in the sex education of our children. In consequence, children are rendered entitled to infer that the fundamentals of sex difference are the visible physique and optional sex-coded traditions of language, dress, work and play, and not the coital and procreative imperative of the sex organs.

In the early developmental years, it is possible for the identification and complementation schemas to become scrambled and confused. Such confusion is especially likely to be engendered if parents are themselves self-contradictory or at cross purposes regarding sex coding of roles, and ambivalent about their own genital sexuality. Then it is possible for the identification and complementation schemas to become transposed, partially or completely.

3. TRANSPOSITIONS OF GENDER IDENTITY

Table II specifies six points in a continuum of gender identity transpositions. The complete and chronic transexual has a compulsion to live erotically and in all other respects in the sex incongruent with his or her genital anatomy of birth. The transvestite's compulsion is a fetishistic addiction to the clothes of the other sex, and to impersonating the other sex, but on an episodic, not a full-time basis. Transvestism in young adulthood, in some cases, is prodromal to transexualism in middle life. Fetishistic, addictive transvestism is found only in males.

The sex coding of work has prehistorical origins in the division of labor on the basis of sex differences in procreation. In the twentieth century era of increased longevity, labor-saving devices, and contraception, the sex-coding of work roles is arbitrary. Men and women may equally well be reared to each other's work.

Effeminate male homosexuality and virilistic female lesbianism are usually chronic as life styles. They are not so complete a transposition as is transexualism, for they do not involve a compulsion for sex reassignment. Nonetheless, the dividing line is sometimes elusive.

Bisexualism may occur in an individual as a more or less persistent alternation of partners of either sex. It may also occur phasically. Thus, there are some ethnic cultures that prescribe a phase of homosexuality in adolescence before graduating to adult heterosexuality.

Sex-coding of play mirrors sex-coding of work and, in the present day and age, is arbitrary. The old rules are being discarded, so that the sexes share the same play, allowing for individual differences in physique and strength.

Transpositions of work and play are not generally classified as having anything to do with psychopathology. It has long been a tradition, however, to classify homosexuality and bisexuality as pathology. In an earlier era they were classified as heresy and treason. Today, they are classified, like left-handedness, as optional life styles. They are not pathological, per se, though they may, like heterosexuality, be associated with other psychopathology which requires therapy. Transvestism and transexualism both usually lead to so much personal distress as to require some form of therapeutic support. Some transvestites respond to a course of psychotherapy, or to a course of antiandrogen therapy with counseling. For transexuals, the only consistently effective form of therapy is, after the preliminary two-year, real-life test, sur-

Table II
Gender-role/identity transpositions.

	Total	Partial	Trivial
Chronic	Transexualism	Homosexualism	Sex-coded work and legal status
Episodic	Transvestism	Bisexualism	Sex-coded play, manners and grooming

gical sex reassignment. Hormonal and cosmetic reassignment accompanies the real-life test of social, vocational and economic reassignment.

4. PARAPHILIAS

The gender-identity transpositions of homosexuality, bisexuality, transvestism, and transexualism are not usually classified as paraphilias, partly because of the stigma thereby implied. Logically, however, they could be classified as the gender transposition paraphilias. Then they would be separated from the other, larger group, namely, the paraphilias of intrusion or displacement. The pathognomonic characteristic of all the paraphilias is that, for a given individual, erotic arousal is dependent on the imagery or an erotic fantasy that differs from the pertaining strictly to a consenting erotic partner of the opposite sex. For example, in fetishism, a man may be nonarousable by a woman unless she is wearing rubber training pants. The rubber fetish intrudes upon or displaces the image of the partner, herself, as the sole agent for effecting erotic arousal.

A paraphilia may be playful and benign, and easily incorporated into a couple's erotic play, to the enjoyment of both. At the other extreme, a paraphilia may be noxious and traumatic to the partner. An extreme example would be the amputation paraphilia of a man whose erotic arousal or turn-on is dependent on the amputated stump of his partner's leg, so that he puts great pressure on her to agree to infliction of a leg wound that will require amputation. The same man may have a compulsion to get his own limb amputated.

There is no fixed dividing line between the benign and the pathological paraphilias. Pragmatically, one may draw the dividing line thus: a paraphilia is pathological when, in the absence of consensual agreement between a couple, one partner enforces the enactment of his or her own sexual fantasy on the partner. Thus, a man's penis may be unable to become erect, except when he is urinated on by his partner. With a urophiliac partner, the fantasy can become a nontraumatic consensual game. With a urophobic partner, by contrast, the fantasy becomes a traumatic ordeal.

A few forms of paraphilia are always noxious, for example, those which compulsively require the sadistic imposition of force on an unwilling victim, as in enforced pedophilia, lust murder and rape. Conversely, masochism is a paraphilia which compulsively requires oneself to be the victim of enforced sex and painful injury. A masochist may stage manage his erotic partners into murdering him.

Some forms of paraphilia are borderline with respect to their danger to the partner. In our society, for example, large numbers of people feel threatened by a voyeur (peeping Tom), an exhibitionist, or an obscene telephone caller. Voyeurism and exhibitionism cannot exist, however, in a society in which people are not threatened, shocked, frightened, or surprised by being seen nude, or by seeing a nude male. Similarly, if people are not frightened by vernacular erotic talk, the obscene phone caller has no potential audience whose panic excites him.

In the meantime the sexual taboos of our society do allow some paraphiliacs to be erroneously stigmatized as dangerous, while others are unequivocally dangerous. These become known as sex offenders. They are subject to arrest and the threat of harsh and prolonged punishment. These are the paraphiliacs who can benefit from a program of combined counseling and antiandrogen therapy (see Chapter 102 by Money and Daléry).

Table III gives a list of paraphilias. They all share in common the characteristic that the image of erotic arousal intrudes upon and displaces the erotic image of the partner. It thus effects a social distancing. The paraphiliac image may also be counterphobic, that is to say, it once was negatively stigmatized, and has become positively eroticized. By most people it is avoided as repulsive. Typically, the paraphiliac image is partly or peripherally associated with the sex organs or some other facet of eroticism. Thus a fetish commonly has something to do with the sight, smell or feel of the opposite sex. Sadism and masochism have something to do with erotic conquest, but with an added excess of injury and pain.

Despite individual differences, and in view of the fact that a paraphilia is engendered by social conditioning, it is remarkable that the various paraphilias are basically consistent over time, place and generations, among strangers who have had no change of indoctrinating one another. A priori, it might appear that anything could become conditioned to be sexually arousing image. But such is not the case. Apparently, there are phyletically determined limits as to what human activities can become associated with erotic arousal. For example, in subhuman primates, the mother keeps the infant clean by licking off its feces and urine. Thus, here is a phyletic mechanism which, under appropriate circumstances, may be enlisted in the service of erotic arousal. By contrast, there is also a phyletic mechanism for licking the newborn and eating the afterbirth. In pathological circumstances, the young themselves may also be eaten. But there is no paraphilia corresponding to cannibalism of the neonate.

Table III
A listing of inclusion or displacement paraphilias

Apotemnophilia	Lust murder	Sadism
Coprophilia	Masochism	Scoptophilia
Exhibitionism	Mysophilia	Telephone scatologia
Erotic strangulation suicide	Narratophilia	Troilism
Fetishism	Necrophilia	Urophilia or Undinism
Frotteurism	Pedophilia	Voyeurism or Peeping Tomism
Gerontophilia	Pictophilia	Zoophilia
Kleptomania	Rape	
Klismaphilia	Self-strangulation	

A paraphilia does not generate itself in a vacuum. The ordinary rules of conditioning and reinforcement learning apply. Thus, a mother who is sexually aroused by diapering her infant may so successfully eroticize diapering for the infant that in infancy he develops a fetish for diapers and safety pins which becomes erotically full blown at puberty.

Paraphilias are more common in males than females. In fact, the female paraphilias appear to be chiefly either tactile fetishistic, masochistic, or kleptomaniac. Male paraphilias include these three, as well as all the visual-image paraphilias. This sex difference may well derive from a basic sex difference, probably fetal—hormonal in origin, which decrees that the threshold for visual erotic arousal is lower in the male than the female. That is to say, the long-distance imagery of the eyes more readily arouses the male than the female to initiate a sexual advance, whereas the female is somewhat more dependent on the intimacy of the sense of touch.

The content of the image of sexual arousal in the male is not preordained at birth. Routinely, it is expected that the image of the opposite sex will become the image of erotic arousal. However, this image may be displaced or intruded upon by an atypical, idiosyncratic or bizarre image which becomes persistent, engrained or imprinted. For example, a boy at age four masturbates. His mother punishes him by having his older sister hold him down while she ceremonially threatens with a carving knife to amputate his penis, should she catch him doing it again. In teenage, this boy's spontaneous erotic fantasies are of sadism against himself or a female partner. He resists putting them into practice, and a more covert fantasy emerges, namely, consensual sex with a male.

Fantasy images of a paraphiliac nature frequently are a covert factor in the hypophiliac dysfunctions, for example, impotence.

5. SUMMARY

Sexual or erotic pair-bonding in human beings manifests itself in three phases: proception or solicitation; acception or copulation; and conception or parenthood. Dysfunctions of the erotic partnership may occur at each phase, singly or severally, and are classifiable as hypo-, hyper-, and parafunctions. Paraphilias manifest themselves primarily insofar as the image of erotic arousal deviates from that conventionally expected on the criterion of species procreation. There are paraphilias of transposition, in which there is some degree of masculine—feminine transposition; and paraphilias of inclusion or displacement in which the imagery of erotic arousal includes an atypical or bizarre component without which erotic arousal is incomplete or nonexistent. The inclusion paraphilias in women are rare and limited to tactile fetishism, masochism and kleptomania. In males they involve predominantly visual imagery, but also olfactory and tactile. The inclusion paraphilias intrude a barrier or distancing effect between the paraphiliac and his/her partner, insofar as the image of the partner herself (or himself) is insufficient for complete erotic arousal and performance. In many instances the inclusion paraphilias are counterphobic, giving positive value to otherwise negatively stigmatized behavior. They may be harmless and playful, especially when engaged in by consenting adults; or noxious and indefensible, especially when enforced on an unwilling partner or when necessitating injury, homicide or suicide. The noxious paraphilias in males may be treated, with some promise of success, with antiandrogen combined with counseling.

ACKNOWLEDGEMENTS

This work was supported by USPHS Grant no. HD-00325 and by funds from the Grant Foundation, New York.

Sexual problems of the chronically impaired: selected syndromes

Section coordinator: John Money

CHAPTER 73

Introduction

JOHN MONEY

The sexual system of the body in both its reproductive and erotic aspects is like the respiratory, the circulatory, the endocrine or any other system of the body, for they are all interlinked, and all pervade one another. The sexual system has its upper reaches in the brain, and its lower reaches in the groin. It can function without the legs and arms, but without them is impaired. Thus, any deformity, disorder, disease or injury that afflicts the body thereby impairs, in some degree, the sexual system. The extent of the impairment, it goes without saying, is extremely variable. A record of all the permutations and combinations could in the future constitute a volume in itself. Today the record is incomplete, for it is not part of the tradition of medicine to be systematic in obtaining data on the sexological functions of even those syndromes which have a primary effect on a patient's personal sex life.

Stricken by a permanently disabling, but not mortal disease, a patient wants to know, early in the recovery period, how to predict the future of his or her sex life. For most syndromes, there are usually very few professionals with sufficient knowledge to make a good prediction.

For this Handbook, it would have been easy to get a catalogue of syndromes which adversely affect genital functioning. It proved extraordinarily more difficult to find authors who could not only catalogue the syndromes, but also give authentic information regarding the sex lives of affected patients. To illustrate: one would like to know, in a systematic, statistical, and nonanecdotal way about the sex lives of men with Peyronie's disease, or women with the Stein—Leventhal syndrome. The facts simply are not readily at hand. There is not even a readily available, authenticated body of knowledge from which to make probability predictions on the outcome of prostatectomy on a man's sex life; or of hysterectomy on a woman's sex life.

Undoubtedly, somewhere on earth, there is an expert in the sexology of a particular syndrome which is not represented in this Handbook. With no international organization of sexologists in the present day and age, it was

Handbook of Sexology, edited by J. Money and H. Musaph
© *Elsevier/North-Holland Biomedical Press, 1977*

not possible to locate such people. This section of the Handbook presents, therefore, in only four chapters, a sample of what the future can be expected to supply more completely. Supplemental information on other syndromes will be found in chapters dealing with endocrine and heramphroditic disorders.

CHAPTER 74

The handicapped: recreational sex and procreational responsibility

WARREN R. JOHNSON

Recreational and procreational sex are treated here as quite separate matters which need no longer confuse important issues by being confused with each other.

The sexually repressive attitudes of the Western (Christian—puritan) tradition have tended to be seen in intensified form as applied to the handicapped. Not only has sex for pleasure been viewed as intrinsically evil, but also it has been viewed as a cause of innumerable health problems and handicaps. Masturbation in particular has been blamed for an incredible number of physical and mental disorders. It has been denounced as both the cause and the effect of mental retardation and 'derangement' as well as of moral collapse of entire societies. Fornication and sodomy have been presumed guilty of damage to personal health and vigor and also in the larger scheme of things, to the moral fiber of societies. The one really legitimate excuse for sexual fulfillment being for procreational purposes within marriage, there has seemed no reasonable basis for any form of sexual expression on the part of the handicapped.

In recent years a new attitude toward 'special' groups generally has been emerging, and this has begun to include a new attitude toward their sexuality. Workers in the field of mental retardation have taken the lead in attempting to spell out the sexual rights and responsibilities of those they serve; but their basic position would seem to have application to special groups generally, including the physically and mentally handicapped, the chronically ill, and the aging. Focus here is upon the mentally handicapped, but implications may be obvious for special group members generally. (For a more general treatment of sex education and counseling of special groups, see Johnson, 1975.)

1. RECREATIONAL SEX

Traditionally, there has been but one view concerning recreational sexual in-

Handbook of Sexology, edited by J. Money and H. Musaph
© *Elsevier/North-Holland Biomedical Press, 1977*

terest of the handicapped: eliminate it. Now there are three possibilities: eliminate, tolerate or cultivate it. 'Eliminate' continues, without doubt, to be the prominent view. Certainly it is the only publically respectable one. However 'tolerate' and 'cultivate' are now viable even though minority views. All are considered briefly here.

Eliminate sexual interest

Little need be said about this view because virtually everyone who has worked with the handicapped (and children) has been taught, directly or indirectly, that this is the only tolerable view. When sexual interest does occur, it is, in effect, handicap heaped on handicap. Any effort, be it by diversion or relentless frontal attack, has been deemed justified. For example, the sterilization laws adopted by most of the U.S. early in this century are presumably aimed at preventing the mentally handicapped from reproducing. However, they actually got their start not as a eugenic measure but as a futile medical effort to stop masturbation among sex-segregated, permanently institutionalized retardates (Guttmacher, 1959);

The moral—religious aspect of this view has had enormous implications for the lives of the handicapped who, being more subject to close scrutiny than others, have been more prone to 'getting caught' in sexual activity. The traditional moral model of sexuality requires that only virginity is good, therefore all sexual activity is bad, as are those who engage in it. Not only have the handicapped been made to feel bad as persons for manifesting any sexual interest, but also their parents have been made to consider the possibility of their own, perhaps sexual, transgression as causative factors in their offsprings' disorders ("What have I done to deserve this?").

Tolerate sexual interest

This view has been becoming visible as something to be taken into account in very recent years. It reflects: (1) a widespread change in attitude towards recreational sex, sex for fun and pleasure having become acceptable forms of human behavior even to many major religious groups — at least within marriage; and (2) the widespread change in attitude toward the handicapped who are increasingly viewed as card-carrying members of the human race with rights accorded to others simply because they are human — and responsibilities somehow to be balanced with the rights (A.A.M.D., 1972).

The growing numbers of persons who feel compelled to tolerate sexual interest of the retarded as one of their human rights, are beginning to argue for accommodating it as well. They call for realistic teaching of 'time and place' for sexual gratification, but also for providing appropriate times and places for such activities. They speak up for teaching masturbation, petting and intercourse techniques as needed, for VD and contraception education and services, voluntary sterilization, back-up abortion, and for realistic marriage and parenthood counseling.

Holders of this view have emerged from virtually zero visibility to sizable, often outspoken, proportions today. Little has been said as yet about the implications of sexual tolerance for sex-integrated institutional arrangements or services to be provided by paid male as well as female partners.

Cultivate sexual interest

Proponents of this view hold that sexual enjoyment is potentially one of life's great experiences and that it therefore should be cultivated like any other gratifying talent — such as talents for art, music or sports. It is argued that the handicapped are especially justified in cultivating whatever talent they possess, sexual or otherwise, as partial compensation for their limited resources for full living.

Improbable as it might seem, this view is now not encountered only occasionally, but is also of the essence of a program for paraplegics and quadriplegics in a major American medical school. * The idea will doubtless spread to other special groups including the mentally handicapped. Implications for appropriate sex instruction, for use of especially trained, paid sex partners, and for possible legal complications have received very limited attention.

2. PROCREATIONAL RESPONSIBILITY

Procreational responsibility of the mentally handicapped may best be viewed within the framework of procreational and child-rearing responsibility generally. Population and eugenic considerations aside, there are a number of important factors which, if appreciated, tend to make parenthood unattractive, in part because under present circumstances it is unmanageable. A few of these factors are considered here briefly. Each bears directly upon what today is considered 'responsible' parenthood. For important historical perspective concerning the evolution of what has been considered responsible parenthood in the Western tradition, see Demause (1974).

In the first place, parenthood is enormously expensive, estimates in the early '70s putting in the cost at between fifty and one hundred thousand dollars, depending on economic level, educational level to be achieved, and so on. Moreover, this expenditure is entirely without tangible return on the dollar, children having lost their historical function as family workers or fighters, and as sickness and old age insurance.

Then, there are the enormous demands upon the time and energy, particularly of mothers, whose working hours and emotional involvement exceed those any employer would dare require. The impact of all this on living patterns of parents, including upon their recreational sex lives, is not easily imagined by the uninitiated. Moreover, parents who would be responsible go

---

* Department of Physical Medicine, University of Minnesota Medical School. The film *Touching* (Multimedia Center, San Francisco) portrays the spirit of this program in action.

beyond mere nurturing to all manner of environment-enriching activities, learning readiness and other school-supportive experiences.

In addition to all of this, the responsible parent understands children and knows what limits to set for them, how and when to discipline them, how to 'rap' with them, and so forth. This insight is somehow acquired despite lack of formal training in the fragmentary child psychology that does exist today, or in understanding of the importance of body contact, of disciplined body movement and play, or in awareness that children in this society, at least, normally pass through virtually every known psychopathology as they grow up. Parents, indoctrinated to believe their children will be sexless creatures and 'innocent', are then forced from the beginning to deal, somehow, with obvious sexual manifestations in their self-exploration and play.

Environments are not designed to take into account the nature of children, for example, their size, interests and developmental needs, or even their basic health and safety, with risks attached to all manner of things, from toys and clothing to damaging foods, automobile traffic and environmental poisoning. This is, by design, not a children's world anywhere near as much as it is, for example, the automobile's world. All this may in some strange sense be all to the good; but it certainly makes for difficult parenting.

Procreational responsibility, implying as it must responsible parenthood, would seem within reach of the mentally handicapped only under very special conditions which rarely exist. Wealth, or an extended family situation, may permit the absorbing of major parental responsibilities by trained employees or close, concerned family members. Some modern societies, for example, Cuba, China and Russia, officially attempt to involve the state in all child-rearing. In Russia, the mentally retarded commonly marry and may have children; but they are maintained in special colonies under the close supervision of profession people who see to their welfare and training (R. Lurie, personal communication, 1966). Responsibility thus being assured by appropriate support, procreation by at least some of the mentally handicapped apparently is seen as posing no serious threat either to the parents or to society.

In most countries, as in the U.S., there is no such systematic support. Occasionally here, one encounters reports of retarded persons functioning adequately as parents (Mattinson, 1970). But as with a 'successful' quadriplegic parent, it is invariably found that very special support as from family members and social workers accounts for the necessary compensations. On their own, mentally retarded parents are no more able to provide intellectual enrichment than a quadriplegic is able to change diapers.

3. CONCLUSION

In spite of widespread cultural conditioning to the contrary, there would no longer seem to be compelling reasons why sex should not be included among potential recreational resources available to those mentally handicapped who desire it. On the other hand, the circumstances of child rearing are such that people generally, let alone the mentally handicapped, are hard put to meet reasonable criteria of procreative responsibility. Except under extraordinary conditions of, for example, wealth or extended family, where close and continuous support and supervision are available, it is difficult to see how the mentally handicapped can hope to assume responsibility for procreative acts.

Recreational and procreational sex need to be very clearly distinguished in the minds of both the mentally handicapped and those who work with them. The fact that they usually are not so distinguished strongly suggests the need for intense education and counseling in this respect. The topics obviously needed for inclusion are: marriage; parenthood; and alternatives to parenthood (including opportunities for associating with children without having them); counterpropagandizing the idea that it is necessary to produce children to prove personal worth; sexual intercourse and sex without intercourse; contraception (including voluntary sterilization); masturbation; homosexuality; and venereal disease.

1. SUMMARY

Recreational and procreational sex are distinguishable and essentially different matters. Traditionally repressive attitudes have tended to be applied in intensified form to the handicapped; but there are newly emerging attitudes towards both sex and 'special' groups.

With regard to recreational sex of the mentally handicapped, there are now three options: prevent it; tolerate and perhaps accommodate it; and cultivate it like other talents. Although the first option, to prevent, is still evidently the most widely held view, the other two now have their supporters, especially the second, to tolerate and perhaps to accommodate.

Generally speaking, procreational responsibility implies responsibility for child rearing, and such responsibility entails very considerable commitment of money, time, energy and emotional and intellectual involvement. Among the handicapped, 'successful' parenting is possible among only the rich, or among members of certain extended families — both of which constitute small, minority groups. The mentally handicapped would seem especially hard pressed to qualify for 'responsible' parenthood by the usual standards.

There is an urgent need for sex education and counseling which will help the mentally handicapped and those who serve them, to the end that rational decisions may be made concerning recreational and procreational sex.

BIBLIOGRAPHY

American Association on Mental Deficiency (1972) *Proc. Conf. Sexual Rights and Responsibility of the Mentally Retarded.* (October, 1972).

Demause, L. (1974) The evolution of childhood. *Hist. Childh. Quart. (J. Psychohist.)* 1: 503—575.

Guttmacher, A. (1959) *Babies By Choice or By Chance.* (Doubleday, New York.)

Johnson, W.R. (1975) *Sex Education and Counselling of Special Groups: The Physically and Mentally Handicapped, Ill and Elderly.* (Charles C. Thomas, Springfield, Illinois.)

Mattinson, J. (1970) *Marriage and Mental Handicap.* (University of Pittsburgh Press, Pittsburgh.)

CHAPTER 75

Psychosexual problems of the motor-disabled

K. HESLINGA

1. IS THERE A REAL PROBLEM?

Often the question is asked: Do we make the handicapped restless by speaking about sexuality? Do we rouse expectations that we cannot meet? We see an analogy with the problem of the aborigines in very primitive cultures, of whom it is said that we had better leave them alone, because they are so happy in their present conditions.

Many handicapped persons were in great distress about their sexuality before it became a more or less permitted topic of discussion. From personal conversations and letters it appears clearly that there was and is much suffering in this respect. It is very healthy for people to be able to speak freely about their deepest desires. The tensions that can be seen now, were hidden and bottled up in the past.

The following recent case notes reveal some actual problems.

A young mother wrote that several years ago she had undergone an operation on her back and had been left an invalid. "Since my back operation, we have never resumed intercourse with one another. I feel very isolated since this has been omitted. The doctor doesn't know what advice to give me. Our marriage will go to pieces before long".

A man writes that there has been no sexual intercourse in his marriage for as long as 13 years. "When the wife you profess to love lies moaning with pain, any enjoyment either of you might have soon vanishes. The everlasting "No!" rings in my ears from one year's end to another."

An 18-year-old youth with progressive muscular dystrophy has been confined for a long time already in a center for those with chronic diseases. He knows that his condition will grow steadily worse; his sexual desires are strong and constantly torment him. His arms are too weak for him to try masturbation. He had a private room and on one occasion asked a young nurse who came to attend to him in the evenings to do it for him. She was highly indignant and immediately reported what had happened to the nurse in charge. The consequence was that he had to stay in the big ward from then on. This punishment served as a warning to other 'immoral' persons.

Handbook of Sexology, edited by J. Money and H. Musaph
© *Elsevier/North-Holland Biomedical Press, 1977*

"I am writing this letter under a pseudonym out of discretion. When you become disabled you might just as well write your sex life off. A patient in the ward here was caught flirting with a nurse and was immediately discharged by the medical director. Out he went: minus legs and minus rehabilitation!"

A 25-year-old physically handicapped woman wrote: "Nobody imagines that a girl in a wheelchair is pining for love. People say that I am not unattractive and that I have an affectionate nature. I am a very emotional person and am so keen to be happy. Whenever I see a man, my impulse is to get up and fly to him if I could. I am longing for love. How can I keep it to myself? I have never seen a naked man, or pictures of an erect penis or sexual intercourse, although I should very much like to see it sometime. I feel deprived both mentally and physically. I hope that what I am saying doesn't sound crude, I don't mean to be indelicate. It must be marvellous to make love with a man who cares for you. I have no idea how I can obtain information on the subject to read. We are so dependent on others, and there is no privacy for me at home. Those who are not handicapped can do things to suit themselves. Would you please let me have your telephone number, and allow me to ring you up one day?"

There are many groups among the motor-handicapped. The situation of a person born with severe cerebral palsy is quite different from that of the 35-year-old man who suffers from a spinal cord transection as a consequence of a road accident. The former runs the risk of an abnormal psychosexual development; the latter must readjust himself, which may or may not be a simpler task. Apart from the moment that the handicap starts, there is the question of the specific disease.

2. ORGANIC VERSUS SOCIAL PROBLEM

Many obstacles that the handicapped meet on their way to sexuality are not caused by their organic inadequacy, but by the attitudes prevailing in their culture. The prejudiced public looks upon the disabled as dependent children, who appeal for help all the time, and who are chained to their homes. The degree of helplessness is often exaggerated. Their intelligence is underestimated. They produce feelings of anxiety in others. The public at large has ambivalent feelings towards both the handicapped and sexuality. The combination of handicap and sex results in a 'multiplication' of ambivalences. The sexuality of the severely handicapped is not accepted. The intimate relations of disabled people are seen as disgusting and as something to be prohibited. The handicapped are often seen as sexless, innocent and impotent. The situation of the severely handicapped implies a lack of freedom. Whereas the nonhandicapped can decide independently, the handicapped need the cooperation or the permission of others. It is necessary that the attitudes in most cultures change in such a way that there are no stricter moral demands for a handicapped than for the average person.

3. CHILDHOOD, ADOLESCENCE AND ADULTHOOD

Parents of handicapped children often have ambivalent feelings towards them. On the surface one sees indulgence and overprotection. On a deeper level there is guilt and aggression. For a full sex life, the ability to establish and maintain human relations is important. This ability is first learnt in the fundamental interaction with the parents. An unhealthy relation in early life will give problems later on, especially with respect to sexuality. The mixed feelings of parents combined with the general prejudice towards the sexuality of the handicapped result in a bad climate for sex education.

The relative immobility of handicapped young people and the attitudes at home make it extremely difficult for them to become emotionally independent of their parents. 'Dating' and choice of books are not free. Another obstacle to relational learning is the lack of contacts with children of the same age. Integrated schooling and stimulating contacts with nonhandicapped children of both sexes are of great importance. Social skills should be taught by training and discussion. The children who grow up in an institute live in a predominantly feminine world. The necessity of making identification models should not be forgotten. Sex education and instruction are very important. Nothing should be left out because of misguided feelings of pity. The adolescent should receive information about his sexual possibilities and genetic status. Individual talks are desirable. Sexual development is also more difficult. Curiosity in sex play is excluded.

Institutional staff are mostly unmarried and traditional. They need special lessons on sex education. Their attitudes should be changed systematically. Contact with parents about this is relevant. Staff and other people ought to realize that kindness and love are not synonymous. Young people are kept to think that failures in romance and love are due to their handicap.

Sexuality is neglected in the process of rehabilitation. There are favorable exceptions, for example, a young man in a rehabilitation center was allowed to make love to his fiancée and attained an erection after three months of training. The technical difficulties for men are greater than for equally handicapped women. Getting an erection or an ejaculation is for the male more complicated than receiving the partner is for the female. For the woman, childbirth is often possible. However, there is a rather large group of handicapped women who appear to be uninterested in sex itself, yet they still need company. Attitudes play a great role. The handicapped woman especially experiences her body as ugly.

For many people it is extremely hard to deviate from normative patterns and ideals. In some cases the female partner must lie on top of the disabled man. Other couples have an oral-genital satisfaction. In both cases these activities may be felt to be abnormal. Sometimes the woman must be very active to sustain the man's reflex erection. It is practical to start and maintain sexual relationships once the handicapped person can perform daily living skills. Mobility and a telephone are desirable, too.

4. SEXUAL AIDS

Many handicapped persons have a need to release their bodily sexual tension. Some can help themselves by masturbation. This is impossible when the arms are too weak or paralysed. Therefore sexual aids are used, such as a variety of dildoes or prosthetic penises, artificial vaginas, and penis-shaped vibrators for women. Of these aids, only the electromechanical vibrators prove to be effective in stimulating both male and female subjects to orgasm. They have certain disadvantages. They are noisy, bulky, need to be switched on by someone else, or have batteries that run down. Research is needed to produce a compliant, electronic "technological partner". It may be a good thing to combine physical stimulation with the presentation of visual stimulation, for example, erotic pictures and films, or literature. Though the relational approach should dominate, the substitute of self-stimulation is a necessity for many lonely people.

We have some experience in the use of an artificial penis with vibrating top, in cases of impotency. Some spine-injured men can't satisfy their partners with their penis. The male and female partner derive much satisfaction from using a vibrating artificial penis, which is attached to the man. Psychologically he has the feeling of being potent again. The female often prefers this method to satisfaction by mouth or hand.

5. MARRIAGE AND PROCREATION

In our culture sex is most regular in marriages. Many handicapped people long for matrimony. Experience shows that marrying a severely handicapped person gives many problems. This should not be done in a hurry. Advisory committees can be of great use. More and more frequently we see that the partners live together for a certain period to discover if a day-to-day relationship is possible. Some marry, others stop the experiment. Marriages between two handicapped persons are also on the increase. The decision of having children is a very difficult one. It is not only a question of genetics. Mostly the problem is whether a child can grow up happily. This depends on many circumstances.

6. MORAL AND SOCIAL ASPECTS

Ethical matters connected with handicaps are under discussion, now that the handicapped claim to have a right to sexuality. Some people think it wise to abstain, and to lead a celibate life.

Circumstances are changing at a breath-taking rate. This means that the translation of fundamental norms into temporary standards goes on all the time, which has a confusing effect. Among the problems with which one is confronted nowadays is that of two severely handicapped people who cannot perform coitus without help. Should a third person help them? A person with paralysed arms cannot masturbate, but needs it very much. Should another person help him manually or by applying a vibrating device? Patients want to read erotic literature. Can the nurse provide them with it? A disabled man wants to visit a prostitute, as is done by nonhandicapped people. Can somebody else make this contact possible?

Most problems are produced by the helplessness of the handicapped. Where others are free to decide for themselves, the disabled need a second person for the performance of a certain act. This poses many difficulties for the workers in rehabilitation centers. It is clear that rehabilitation workers should never be under pressure to do things that conflict with their consciences. The solution of many problems is made difficult by the all-or-nothing standard in the relationships between men and women. Relationships which involve gradations are uncommon. Thus, people think it strange, if a woman who only likes a handicapped man, but does not love him, allows him to see or kiss her breasts. Sometimes, the moral problems for the second person disappear through social measures.

Handicapped people are often concentrated in large communities. This is done for reasons of economy and efficiency. This results in a loss of privacy. It will be clear that patients who start a sexual relation inside a center are in a difficult position. Handicapped people must often get or recover sexual self-confidence. The fear of discovery and interruption may prevent a successful sexual experimentation.

A disabled person who lives in a service flat could have far more freedom without causing moral problems for other people. Yet, a system of flats and visiting nurses and attendants is expensive.

If one wants personal relationships one must be able to meet people. As many houses, public buildings, and institutionalized activities as possible should be accessible to handicapped people. This should be regulated by law.

7. WAYS OF HELPING

Medical rehabilition specialists can help patients with advice, drugs and operations. Social experts can organize discussion-groups of varying compositions. Experience has taught that one had best start at the top of an organization. A good order of discussion is the Board, the administration, the medical and other specialists, the supervizing personnel, the nurses, the patients. There are many other possibilities: parents and staff, adolescents and parents; handicapped and nonhandicapped people; married and unmarried patients, and so on.

There is a great need for visiting counselors. They can be chosen from various professions but should have knowledge of handicaps, social work, marriage and sex problems. Family guidance bureaus have an important task with respect to handicapped people. Some of them should specialize in the handicapped. In The Netherlands there are some specialized bureaus where handicapped people do not only find a sexologist, but can also consult a rehabilitation specialist.

BIBLIOGRAPHY

Heslinga, K., Verkuyl, A. and Schellen, A.M.C.M. (1973) *Not Made of Stone — The Sexuality of Handicapped People.* (Noordhoff-Stafleu, Leiden, The Netherlands.)

Heslinga, K. (1972) Mentioning the unmentionable. *World Med.* 7: 17—19.

Heslinga, K. and Hooft, F. van 't (1968) Sex education of blind-born children. *New Outlook for the Blind* 62: 15—21.

'Touching'. Film made by the University of Minnesote (Multimedia Center, San Francisco).

CHAPTER 76

Some neuromotor syndromes and their sexual consequences

A. VERKUYL

1. FOUR ASPECTS OF SEXUALITY

Psychological and relationship aspect

In defects which are congenital or acquired when very young, too much attention may be paid at an early age to the body and its infirmities. The parents and other educators may focus too much on a child's physical make-up. This must exert a great influence on any child's relationship with his or her body.

Sexuality has a strong physical aspect, but when it takes an undisturbed course the person is completely integrated with his body. The more refractory the body is, the more the accent falls upon that body, and this is often a great hindrance to enjoyment.

In all of us there resides a primitive aversion from and defense against a disfigured, incomplete, and maimed body. We feel ashamed of this aversion, and nurse guilty feelings about it, which form a poor basis for one's love life.

The attractiveness of a person consists to a great extent in the physique, but also to a great extent in body movement: demeanor, gestures, walk, facial expression. In the physically handicapped the expressive movements, bearing and walk are often imperfectly controlled, and this can hinder a relationship. On closer acquaintance, the psychological aspects in the relationship between two people are mainly accentuated, but when love-making comes into the picture the physical impediment can get in the way once more.

Gonadal aspect

The aspects of the sex organs themselves further divides into functional, hormonal and germinal parts, that is, ability to perform the sexual act, ability to procreate, and genetic quality of the spermatozoa and ova.

Handbook of Sexology, edited by J. Money and H. Musaph
© *Elsevier/North-Holland Biomedical Press, 1977*

Neuromuscular aspect

Certain of the bodily organs must be intact as a prerequisite for coitus and its preliminaries, for other sexual activities and for masturbation. Not only the sense organs, but also the central, peripheral and vegetative nervous systems have a part to play. It may easily be imagined that disturbances in the muscles and joints, paralyses, spastic conditions, numbness, fixed positions, and abnormal postures have their effect on sexual life. This effect can show itself in several different ways, as is seen in the following.

Aspect of exertion

What is the strength of the heart and lungs and how does the blood pressure react during love-making? The question of danger to life and health is self-explanatory here: can coitus, pregnancy and childbearing aggravate the condition, or even endanger life?

2. TRANSVERSE LESIONS

Transverse lesions may result in paraplegia (paralysis of both legs) and quadriplegia (paralysis of arms and legs). A transverse lesion is an interruption in the continuity of the ascending and descending nerve fibers in the spinal cord at a specified level. A transverse lesion can hit the central cord from the neck down to the level of the medullary cone and cauda equina (the final, expanded part of the spinal marrow). Such a lesion may be complete, almost complete or incomplete. The origin is mainly traumatic but there are numerous causes: congenital defects, inflammations, tumors or disturbances in the blood supply.

Some psychological remarks

A transverse lesion normally affects someone who is healthy and is psychologically not different from the average individual. Of course, there are also individuals who are neurotic or psychotic, including depressive (transverse lesions resulting from suicide attempts are not unusual). In reaction to the onset of the lesion, the patient goes through several stages as a rule: denial (it cannot be true!), rebellion, realization, acceptance. Very many patients remain in one of these stages permanently, or (occasionally) regress to earlier attitudes. All of the young and adult sufferers from paraplegia, and quadriplegia, are eager to know if sexual life is possible or not.

Physical consequences of a complete lesion

Paralysis below the level of the injury, in the beginning, is always flaccid, at a later stage it can become spastic. The reflex pathways below the level of the lesion mostly remain intact, but the paralysis stays flaccid if the reflex pathways themselves have been severed, and also in injuries affecting the medullary cone and/or the cauda equina. The paralysis can also be partly flaccid and partly spastic.

All the qualities of feeling below the level of the lesion vanish; the senses of touch and pain, as well as the deep sensibility disappear.

Vegetative troubles constitute a very complicated subject. The chief consequences are these:

(a) Bladder function troubles are manifest as incontinence. In the acute phase there is a weak bladder, which, if the correct measures are not adopted, can lead to leaking and dribbling. Where the lesions are situated higher than the medullary cone, reflex contractions of the bladder muscle usually occur after several weeks, which lead, more or less, to emptying of the bladder. If a set procedure is adopted, this reflex can be used to achieve a socially acceptable condition; by patting the abdomen or taking other measures, the reflex is stimulated at the most suitable times. When the lesion affects the cone and/or the cauda equina, a relaxed bladder exists permanently, which can only be emptied more or less completely by external pressure on and off the abdomen wall. A satisfactory condition is seldom achieved in this way. In the case of a bladder reflex, a urine bag is often not necessary or only so in certain circumstances. With a relaxed bladder, a urine bag cannot be avoided. Unfortunately there is still no completely reliable urine bag for women, although considerable advance has been made recently. With skill and patience one is usually successful in obtaining a satisfactory urine bag for men. Incontinence can pose a serious threat to marriage and in sex life.

(b) There are comparable, but more easily treated disorders of rectal function.

(c) Disorders of blood circulation, blood supply and pressure, of respiration and of metabolism, lead, among other things, to fragile bones.

Complications include bedsores, infections of the bladder, renal calculi and so on.

Disturbances of the male genital functions in complete lesions

Erection
The erection normally has a strong psychological component, much stronger in fact than its reflex component, which is usually of subordinate significance. The reflex component is lost if there is an interruption in the reflex path (the parasympathetic center in the sacral marrow, especially S2, S3, S4).

Vasomotor fibers are closely involved in the swelling of the corpora cavernosa, and secretory fibers in the secretion of the prostatic fluid which accompanies the spermatozoa.

When the reflex pathway is intact, as in a lesion above the sacral marrow, a reflex erection is possible. When the transverse lesion is complete, a psychogenic erection is out of the question.

948

Seminal emission and ejaculation
The seminal emission is a reflex. The spermatozoa travel from the smooth muscle of the seminal vesicles, ampullae of the testicular duct, and prostate gland, and are delivered to the posterior urethra. The center which regulates this process lies in the lateral horn of the thoracolumbar marrow. The ejaculation reflex follows. The spermatozoa are propelled from the seminal vesicles, ampulla, and prostate gland. The same applies here, too, that damage to the reflex path concerned will upset the reflex.

Orgasm
The orgasm, closely linked with ejaculation, is an overpowering excitement which takes possession of the entire man. The participation of the whole central nervous system is required for this, especially an intact sensibility. With loss of the experience of orgasm, there can be diminished urgency of orgasmic feeling or drive, which varies from one patient to another. A phantom orgasm may be dreamed.

Spermatogenesis
The nerve supply to the gonads, in this case the testes, arises from the lowermost thoracic segments. In all probability damage is often sustained by the seminiferous tubules in connection with irregularities of temperature control in the testes (the normal temperature of the testes is below body temperature). Besides, inflammations quite often occur in the epididymis or less frequently in the testicle. Hormone secretion is usually normal.

Recapitulation
— There are no psychogenic erections in complete lesions.
— Where sensibility is lacking, no orgasm is possible.
— However, if the reflex path is intact, a tactile reflex erection may occur, sometimes of short duration, sometimes to the extent of priapism (protracted erection).
— When the lesion is lower down, the emission and ejaculation reflexes are very disturbed. With lesions which are higher up, they are intact. The centers for these two functions, however, lie at different levels.
— Backflow of the semen into the bladder (retrospermia) is repeatedly seen in those lesions which are low down.
— In addition, sometimes there is an enormous systolic and diastolic hypertension at the time of attempted coitus.

Some general remarks
Of the sexual functions, orgasm and ejaculation are more vulnerable than erection and are lost more frequently. This is strikingly demonstrated in the following tabulation:

Sexual function in 6 Series comprising 1206 Patients

Erection	77%
Coitus	35%
Ejaculation	10%
Progeny	3.4%

Erection is more frequent with higher lesion, but maintenance of ejaculation is possible with a lower level lesion.

Sexual function is much better with a partial cord lesion than with complete transection (erection in 26% of patients with complete lesion against in 90% of those with incomplete lesions of the lower motor neurones; ejaculation in 18% of persons with complete lesions of the lower motor neurones against 70% in those with incomplete lesions).

Disturbances in the female genital function

In the woman, disturbances are not likely to be so radical. Infection is less frequent, hypothermia does not affect the germinal function, and there is not the same dependence on good reflex coordination. In the first stage, immediately after the transverse lesion, there is amenorrhea for 6—8 months. The menstruation which then follows is only irregular and is attended with smaller blood loss than normal. The libido may or may not appear affected; sometimes a woman says it is increased. Orgasm rarely if ever occurs. At a later stage, the capability for conception is practically normal. Pregnancy has repeatedly been recorded. Good control of the blood pressure and kidney function is required. The confinement must take place in a clinic, with a doctor who specialises in rehabilitation on call. Beds must be made up very carefully, with a look-out for possible bedsores.

During parturition, labor is normal and generally painless. When the lesion is low down, the woman can assist expulsion by bearing down in unison with it; when the lesion is high, there are often troublesome spasms or cramps of the pelvic muscles. In the case of higher lesions, artificial assistance, for example, vacuum extraction and/or narcosis are frequently required. After the delivery, prolapse sometimes occurs when the lesions are low.

Adolescence and erotic partnership

The above outline mainly affects the physical aspect; we are well aware of the psychological angles.

Puberty usually starts at the normal time. Sometimes the patient is retarded in growth. Not much is accurately known about the psychosexual development in puberty of children with transverse lesions.

In adolescence one is less anxious about progeniture than about masturbation and the possibility of satisfying a partner. If the sex organs have completely lost their feeling, the patient often obtains gratification from sexy pictures or reading matter. Many patients, both men and women, suffering from transverse lesions, who are unable to manage coitus and/or an orgasm still achieve satisfaction by getting as close as they can to one another, with complete acceptance of one another, with a feeling of love and a mutual search for ways to express that love, showing affection and gaining a sense of security. Erogenous zones are often successfully found in places where these either do not normally occur or are usually much weaker. Since there is frequently an oversensitive, hyperpathic zone above the segmental level of the lesion, it is not unusual that this is also heightened in an erogenous sense. It often happens that when this zone is caressed lovingly, sensual feelings are aroused. In the woman, but also in the man, the area surrounding the nipples can become strongly erogenous in this way.

One must not underestimate the seriousness and the vexatiousness of the impossibility of obtaining sexual relaxation and erotic release. When the hormones are functioning normally and the libido is present, then the sexual drive can assert itself strongly, especially in the early years of life. Handicapped people whose arms are powerless are not able to masturbate or achieve a state of relaxation, unless helped by a partner.

How to offer assistance

Psychotherapy, the technique of which depends on the personality structure of the patient, is very helpful. People can learn to accept and to love their handicapped body. This is a condition for the acceptance that a lover can love you completely. Sometimes mechanical help is necessary. Sometimes you can help people with indications about their positioning; but most important is if you can teach people that their sexuality is not synonymous with coitus or masturbation! It is also a means of expression of two individual personalities and of merging them in symbolic and physical feelings of tenderness, respect and concern for each other and their pleasure.

3. SPINA BIFIDA

Spina bifida means a splitting of the vertebral arches, so that the spinal canal is open. This term is loosely used collectively to refer to conditions varying from an invisible to an obtrusive and externally visible 'open spine'.

Closed, hidden, or occult spina bifida is a condition which occurs fairly often but has little or no consequences. The vertebral arch is open, the spinal cord and its nerves are not affected. No impediment exists to marriage and sexual relations. A connection between occult spina bifida and bed-wetting is quite often assumed, but has never been proved. The skin covering the area is often very hirsute. There is a somewhat greater chance than normal of progeny with the same, or a worse, interference with the closure.

Sometimes a sac is seen, filled with cerebrospinal fluid. This mostly has no serious consequences, but often the cauda equina and/or a part of the spinal cord are a part of the meningomyelocele sac, and then mild to very serious neurological consequences are present: incontinence, pareses or paralysis of the legs, loss of sensitivity of the skin, and misshaped hipjoints and/or feet. Disturbances in the sexual sphere in people with meningomyelocele may occur, their seriousness depending on the seriousness of the damage sustained by the medulla or the cauda equina.

In a male it may happen that erections can be excited by reflex action, namely when the lowermost part of the medulla remains intact; while an orgasm can or cannot be brought about, depending on whether or not sensation is still intact, and on the extent to which the medulla is damaged. Sometimes seminal emission takes place without an erection. There is seldom a complete emission; usually the semen is found in the bladder after expulsion (retrospermia). Fatherhood is very rare. The libido can vary from slight to normal: on a few occasions we have observed complete absence of libido and of spontaneous development of secondary sex characters such as beard growth and breaking of the voice. Motherhood is possible. The confinement is generally painless during labor. Artificial aids are quite often required. Prolapse is not infrequent after parturition. The kidneys and their ducts need special care during pregnancy.

If it is undesirable for a patient with spina bifida to become pregnant, for example, owing to severe incontinence and/or defective kidney function, a contraceptive is required. The decision whether it is generally desirable that patients with meningomyelocele should become parents is an ethical one. Many medical authorities are opposed to the idea.

Remarks

Patients with spina bifida often suffer also from hydrocephalus to a greater or lesser degree. Sometimes this has no particular effect on their ability to move freely, but sometimes, in fact, the effect is substantial, for example, a certain measure of spasticity. Often the intelligence remains intact, but sometimes not. There may be an obvious muscular clumsiness, which is frequently associated with fine powers of conversation. They and others may be led to overestimate their full intellectual capability on the basis of verbal ability alone. Patients with spina bifida can display all possible aberrations, such as those also found in transverse lesions: contractures, bedsores, and bladder infections. Spina bifida is not uncommon: 1 to 2 in every thousand live births. Formerly nearly all of these children would die early, but nowadays a good many of them survive. Marriage is still rare, as are social opportunities for romance and sexual expression.

How to offer assistance

First, one has to be aware that this condition is congenital, with all its consequences: hospitalization, overprotection, never having been taught to appreciate one's body, ambivalence of the parents; very poor possibilities for social contacts, and immobilization. From the neuromuscular and also the sexual point of view, see the remarks about transverse lesions.

4. ENCEPHALOPATHIA INFANTILIS

The term 'spastic children' is employed, almost exclusively in everyday speech, quite ignorantly. It is incorrect as the majority of the sufferers are usually adults, and spasticity is only one of their symptoms. Properly, a distinction should be drawn between a spastic, an athetotic and an atactic form. In all three forms, the disability is peripartal or perinatal (arising before, during or shortly after birth), and afflicts an individual who is in the process of development. The consequences for the motor system, psyche, perception, learning ability, social development, sense organs, and emotional control, are many, some of which are indicated in the following.

Spasticity

Tonus in certain muscles is increased. It is chiefly the muscles which oppose gravity which are affected most often. These muscles oppose extension. There is a danger that fixed postures will be adopted, due to the increased tonus when at rest, and that contractures will result.

Primitive reflexes, which would otherwise disappear during the first few months of life, can remain in operation. Examples of these are neck and labyrinth reflexes, in which, when the head changes position, the extremities involuntarily stretch or bend; and fear reflexes, which can also persist for a long time.

Though a 'spastic' child is born without contractures, these can appear in the course of time; much less often with good, and much more often with insufficient treatment. Disorientation towards the individual's own body schema, and towards the outside world, in varying degrees may or may not involve the sense organs, perception, cognition, and the integration of cognitional experience.

Difficulties with eating and chewing and slight or serious impediments in the speech may also be present.

The intelligence can range from very low to normal or high. Ordinary tests of IQ, especially in those which measure performance, are inadequate.

In addition to the contractures mentioned, (sub)luxations of the hips, scolioses, and stunted growth can appear as complications. The 'spastic' form presents in various guises. Thus there is a hemiplegic form, with unilateral paralysis in which the opposite side remains intact; and a diplegic form (Little's disease) in which all four limbs are affected, the legs more so than the arms.

Recapitulation

One sees the following symptoms: a striking uniformity of movement and gesture, which nearly always leads us to prognosticate the same reactions (including psychic ones); spasticity, which gets worse on display of emotion, and can give rise to involuntary postures. There is an enormous variation, from very light encephalopathy (minor brain damage) to very pitiful affliction, with powerful spasms and a tendency to adopt one forced position. Intelligence can vary from very high to extreme feeble-mindedness. To a certain extent there is no paralellism between the gravity of the physical changes and the intelligence, although the very worst forms are nearly always associated with a quite low IQ. Where there are serious motor disturbances and a good intellect, the individual is often deeply conscious of his insufficiency.

Sexual difficulties in males

Owing to home taboos, lack of privacy and the regimen of an institution, but also to mere mechanical impossibility, manual masturbation is often out of the question. Some men discover other masturbatory methods, by managing to rub the parts without using their hands, or by venturing to get someone to help them. Sometimes there is the problem that violent spasms can occur before, during and after masturbation.

Rather frequently there are mechanical and emotional factors which hinder intercourse. These factors seldom make coitus impossible, but heavy spasms, especially those which affect the legs, and adductor spasms, can do so most effectively. If Valium (5–10 mg, 1 or 2 h before coitus) does not help, nor does physiotherapy, surgical intervention may be indicated.

In the male, emotional reactions can ruin erotic effectiveness and cause the body to become cramped. Premature cominal emission is not unusual. Spasms may constitute a mechanical, and fear of failure a psychological impediment. Libido, erection, potency, and semen are usually normal in themselves, except in the quite serious forms.

Sexual difficulties in females

Most 'spastic' girls seldom meet young men. Generally speaking, 'spastic' children become conservative; they have a tendency to become introverted. Emotional immaturing is subtly reinforced, and childish behavior is noticeable. By contrast, hormone secretion, the menses and the libido are normal.

Particularly in recent years, a growing trend towards matrimony has become noticeable in this group. Marriage and parenthood are quite often regarded as status symbols. Spastic people can become fathers and mothers, and although a limited genetic factor can be present, this is not a contraindication for matrimony.

It will be clear from the foregoing remarks on personality traits, that in this group progressive ideas must be broached with caution. The impression is gaining acceptance that, if adult spastics meet in clubs, and thus in groups, the group will provide an emotional base on which new opinions and increased social maturity can ground themselves.

Athetosis

In contrast to the 'spastic' form, the peripartal brain damage in the athetotic form is not in the cortex, but is located in the centers deep in the brain. These have, among other things, to do with the beginning and ending of movements and smoothness of action. Posture, carriage and movement are under the influence of these centers. The condition may occur as a sequel to perinatal lesions, and also to Rh blood group incompatibility between the parents. It is quite often combined with the spastic form.

Striking variations are encountered in this group:

(a) Movements which eventually reach their target, but tend to overshoot the mark and deviate from their fixed course.

(b) Very exaggerated movements, sometimes of the whole body, but especially of the face, which are present when the actions are deliberate. Often the mere intention of doing something is quite sufficient to release this surge of movement.

(c) Speech disturbances which are more or less serious, and not based on lack of understanding of the verbal symbols, or on a disorganization of 'internal' speech, but on poor coordination of all the organs and muscles which are involved in speech.

(d) Poor ability, and often inability, to walk.

(e) Frequent auditory impairment.

(f) Intelligence which is usually little or not at all affected.

(g) Pleasant, friendly, and extrovert disposition.

Owing to their uncontrolled movements and their poor speech, people with athetosis are often thought to be imbecile or deranged. They are often delayed in establishing independence. Their emotions exert a great influence on the spasms, and above all on their uncoordinated movements. Athetosis sometimes prevents both masturbation and coitus, while the libido is certainly present. Personally we only know of a few married patients with athetosis. They enjoy a happy married and sex life. The literature on this point is scarce.

5. HEMIPLEGIA = UNILATERAL PARALYSIS

The causes can be: congenital defects (see also encephalopathia); thrombosis cerebri; brain hemorrhage (or stroke or apoplexy); insufficient brain circulation; and embolism.

When the hemiplegia patient is youthful, the condition closely compares with that of the 'spastic'. This is just as true of the physical sexual development, which is mostly normal, as it is of the psychosexual development. The psychological consequences, however, are usually not nearly as serious, and the intelligence is less often affected. In adolescents and adults difficulties are quite often apparent. After the initial crisis, the first weeks following the onset of hemiplegia, there is often a renewed desire for intercourse in the man; it also arises in the wife, even if this is only for proof of her husband's love. The condition of the blood pressure, heart and blood vessels may induce the doctor to recommend caution. It is precisely in these cases, in which the emotions can rise very high, that coitus demands considerable effort. It is often advisable for the sexes to reverse their positions, for more relaxed forms of bodily contact to be tried, and for tranquilizers to be used.

Difficulties can arise through:

(a) The very frequent impotence, above all at the beginning, but also later on (psychological and/or physical)
(b) Premature emission of semen (ejaculatio praecox)
(c) The 'impossible' posture due to the unilateral nature of the paralysis
(d) The emotional reactions of the paralyzed person (and also indeed of the partner)
(e) The incontinence which sometimes exists (above all in women)
(f) The heightened reflexes and occasional contractures on the paralyzed side
(g) The aversion felt by the partner for the distorted body
(h) The noticeable difficulties in communication attending right-sided hemiplegia owing to speech disturbances (aphasia). Coitus is then often used as a means of communication, or 'communing'.

People suffering from hemiplegia can become fathers or mothers. There are no hormone imbalances, nor faults in spermatogenesis. Much attention should be paid to the basic discomfort. Much attention should be paid to the partner!

6. PROGRESSIVE MUSCULAR DYSTROPHY

The official name is dystrophia musculorum progressiva. This is a progressive disease of the voluntary muscles in which heredity plays a part, in many cases. In some forms of the disease, this part is not easy to recognize, in other forms it is obvious. It is just as well to state that, after much research, the following data have been obtained.

Genetics

In two thirds of cases, genetic causes cannot be demonstrated clearly.

There is a sex-linked (X-chromosome) recessive genetic form in which symptoms begin early in young children, before the third year. The mother, although not affected herself, is a carrier, and transmits the disease. Death usually supervenes between the 20th and 25th year. Of the male children of the mother, 50% have a chance of being afflicted with the disease.

There is also, however, a much more benign form of the sex-linked type, in which symptoms begin between the 12th and 25th year, and may run its course between the 25th and 30th year. So, offspring may be produced and the gene be passed down through the female line. A daughter in this line of descent is a carrier, therefore, and if she later bears children, then there is once more a 50% chance that these will have the defect.

There is an autosomal recessive genetic form in men and women, with symptoms beginning between the 2nd and 40th year. Quite often the parents are blood relatives.

There is an autosomal dominant form, arising in both sexes due to direct inheritance, hence not by-passing a generation. Symptoms commence between the 7th and 25th year. Often the progress is benign.

Marriage

In all cases of muscular dystrophy when marriage is being contemplated, expert advice is required both from a neurologist who is a specialist in this branch, and from a geneticist. This applies also to healthy women from families in which the men are affected by the disease.

Apart from heredity, a problem which can be by-passed by contraception or early abortion, it is necessary that the young people who are diseased are made aware of the prognosis. However, medical ethics become involved here. May the doctor in charge inform the partner? Yes, but only with the consent of the patient or of the carrier of the genetic factor. The greatest possible frankness between the two young people is essential. Not much is known regarding the presence or absence of sexual problems in various forms of muscular dystrophy.

Hormones

The following remarks apply to the so-called Duchenne form. Although in former years an endocrine etiology was proposed, it was later abandoned. It was adopted because people were struck by such symptoms as delayed puberty and the appearance of typical testicular atrophy.

It is well known that hormone disturbances can intervene during the course of the illness. The excretion of the gonadotropin FSH (follicle-stimulating hormone) in the 24-h urine is normal to slightly reduced, and the same applies to the excretion of 17-ketosteroids. Should the patient deteriorate at the beginning of puberty, in the usual way, it is not advisable to treat the testicular hypofunction with testosterone therapy, for virilizing anabolic measures have a deleterious effect on the illness. These factors tell against the use of remedies which one might like to prescribe as stimulants for the libido or potency.

The heart

The heart muscles are often involved, resulting in irregular cardiac action, dyspnoea, tachycardia and angina pectoris after exertion. Faulty cardiac action is rather frequently the cause of death; and it will be obvious that coitus can impose such a strain on the weakened muscular action that it will prove just too much for the defective heart. Of course, it is a personal ethical decision as to how one will risk dying , in coitus or otherwise.

Intellect, relationship and marriage

The infantile form of muscular dystrophy is often associated with oligophrenia, which appears at an early stage but does not get worse as the muscular weakness increases. Fatherhood and motherhood are out of the question in serious cases afflicting early childhood. The psychosexual development is usually disrupted, but sometimes development is normal, and so are sexual relations, and the ability to have children, to whom the disorder may be passed. It may seriously be considered that all patients who suffer from any form of progressive muscular dystrophy have a duty to refrain from procreation. Included are those apparently isolated cases where there are no demonstrable genetic factors. Expert advice must be sought in every instance. In marriages between relatives advice should always be given to avoid procreation. It is completely feasible to undertake an investigation of this kind, which can be completed in a few days, and will give decisive answers as to the form of heredity in 80% of cases.

Coitus and pregnancy in noninfantile forms

Although atrophy of the testes and slight hormonal disturbances often appear, it is known that many sufferers can achieve a normal sex life. The muscular weakness, the contractures, the scoliosis, and the heart weakness can be inhibiting factors. Similar considerations apply to pregnancy and childbearing. Pregnancy can impose a heavy strain when the muscular weakness is great, and where there is abnormal lordosis and malformed feet. Childbearing may have to be artificially assisted at delivery owing to poor muscular action. The function of the heart requires careful watching, and is sometimes a contraindication for pregnancy.

7. DIABETES MELLITUS

There is a strong genetic component in diabetes, and because so many diabetics are now able to remain alive and in good shape, the number of cases of the disease is on the increase. Relatively much is known concerning the influence of diabetes on sexual function, the fertility index and pregnancy. In spite of the fact that diabetes is one of the best controlled diseases in many countries, it must be observed that diabetes is viewed with suspicion by the sexologist and gynecologist. Regardless of good supervision, disabilities do show themselves in serious diabetes rather frequently, especially in the man. Trophic disturbances affect spermiogenesis and, therefore, will reduce sperm formation. Difficulties with erection and ejaculation due to diabetic polyneuritis may also be mentioned, and are mostly irreversible. So-called frigidity is not rare in the diabetic woman. Retrograde ejaculation is a well-known feature of male diabetes, and the disease can lead to vulvovaginitis in women, sometimes with dyspareunia. Although formerly the diabetic was often completely sterile, nowadays this is much less frequently the fact. Actually, diabetic women often have a serious obstetric case history, with infertility due to miscarriages or partus immaturus, and intrauterine death. Large babies are a problem during delivery, and there is more chance of the infants suffering brain damage, due among other things to these difficult births. Diabetes must be counted among those diseases which, in spite of optimum treatment, can lead to sterility, and gonadal and obstetric troubles. A pregnancy requires very stringent control by the gynecologist, in consultation with the internist. The dangers which threaten are: toxicosis; increased chance of intrauterine death, especially during the last weeks of pregnancy; and difficult births due to large, overweight babies, for which reason inductions are often performed at 36—38 weeks.

Contraceptive methods require careful consideration as diabetes can be greatly unsettled by oral contraceptives.

CHAPTER 77

Sexual behavior and the cardiac patient

NATHANIEL N. WAGNER

1. INTRODUCTION

The sexual aspect is an important part of life for most people, including those persons with cardiac illness, though, unfortunately, it is all too often neglected when it concerns the heart patient.

The sexual sphere has particular importance for the cardiac patient in that the feelings of anxiety, fear of death and a sense of impotence often, if not always, generalize to the sexual area. The cardiac patient often believes that a person with a heart condition should not, or cannot, perform sexually and the general fear of being impotent to face the continuing problems of life is symbolized in sexual impotence.

There are at least two reasons for the traditional neglect of the sexual aspects of life for cardiac patients. First, older persons no longer in the reproductive years are often not considered as sexual beings. Traditionally, their sexual needs — along with those of other nonreproductive groups such as the mentally retarded, the physically handicapped, the homosexual and the adolescent — have been ignored by medicine.

Second, the heart patient is a sick person and sickness and sexuality are considered incompatible. Clearly someone who is critically ill may not be interested in sex. But medicine and nursing have also denied sexuality to persons with chronic illness which might not be incompatible with certain kinds of sexual behavior, for example, the orthopedic patient, the emotionally disturbed, and other persons who spend long periods of time in hospital. Though it is practiced in some prison settings, conjugal visiting has not yet been recognized as an acceptable practice in cases of chronic hospitalized illness.

The cardiac patient is given advice on diet, exercise and recreation, weight control and the dangers of tobacco, but most often not on his sex life. Usually he is only vaguely told to 'take it easy', which is interpreted as an interdiction to sexual intercourse, or is laden with some equally anxiety-producing meaning.

Handbook of Sexology, edited by J. Money and H. Musaph
© *Elsevier/North-Holland Biomedical Press, 1977*

In a survey of patients who had had myocardial infarcts (Tuttle, 1964), fully two-thirds of the surveyed group reported a marked and lasting reduction in the frequency of intercourse. Tuttle concluded: "Having received little or no advice from their physicians, these patients set their own patterns which represented a considerable deviation from their previous activity. Our interviews suggested that this change in behavior was based on misinformation and fear."

Tuttle's study dealt with men only, because the rate of heart attacks is much greater among men than among women. These factors apply almost equally to women, however, and women are, in addition, often involved in the role of spouse or partner of a cardiac patient. Sexual counseling for the partner of cardiac patients should therefore not be overlooked. As Koller and others (1972) have pointed out, reduced sexual activity may lead to frustration and marital problems, which may in turn impede recovery.

It is imperative, then, that the patient's doctor give specific advice on sexual activity to both patient and partner. Until recently, however, little information on the effects of sexual activity on the heart has been available to him. A number of studies, dating back to 1925, sheds some light on the matter, although some have raised more questions than they answered. Several are fascinating as much for the methods used as for the results obtained.

2. STUDIES IN HEALTHY INDIVIDUALS

In 1930, J.C. Scott studied the reaction of the heart to sexual and other emotional stimuli in 100 male medical students who were shown "the usual love scene of the 'movies' plus a suggestive (nude) dance." Nearly all subjects showed an immediate sharp increase in blood pressure.

In 1932, Boas and Goldschmidt isolated men and women volunteers in private hospital rooms, wired their bodies to recording instruments and measured heart rates as the volunteers went about their "normal" daily routines. Only one couple had sexual intercourse during the experiment. Results showed that the average maximum heart rate was higher during orgasm (148.5 beats per min) than for any other activity, although orgasm was followed by an immediate and dramatic decrease in heart rate. The investigators concluded, on the basis of data for the one couple only, that sexual activity results in a tremendous increase in the rate of the heartbeat and is therefore one of the most strenuous of activities for the heart.

A 1950 study by Klumbies and Kleinsorge concentrated on the effects of auto-arousal on the heart. The study involved just two subjects: a woman who brought herself to orgasm solely through erotic fantasy, and a man who masturbated to orgasm. Though this remarkable woman remained perfectly still while she came to orgasm, her heart rate rose from 60 bpm to a maximum of 103 bpm, and her systolic blood pressure climbed from 110 mm Hg. at rest to 160 mm Hg. at orgasm, after which it fell rapidly to normal. The man showed equally impressive increases in heart rate and blood pressure, although his heart rate returned from 142 bpm at orgasm to 67 bpm in just four seconds.

A 1956 study by Bartlett, which concentrated on respiratory reactions during sexual intercourse, illustrates the laboratory atmosphere of many scientific studies requiring physiological measurements during sexual activity. Four leads made from wire mesh were secured with elastic bandages to the upper thighs and upper arms of each volunteer to measure heart rates; both partners wore valved mouthpieces to measure respiratory rate; the subjects' noses were clamped to reduce error in measuring exhaled air; and they were told to press a button at different stages of intercourse. Remarkably, the males succeeded in having an erection and in having intercourse until orgasm. The results confirmed the findings of earlier studies, showing in addition sharp increases in respiratory rates during intercourse.

Masters and Johnson (1966) found hyperventilation developing just prior to and during orgasm to be a normal occurrence and reported heart rates increasing parallel to rising sexual tensions, peaking during orgasm at 110 to 180 or more beats per min. Considerable elevations in blood pressure were also recorded for both male and female subjects.

The general pattern of these studies is quite clear: rather dramatic increases in heart rate, blood pressure and respiration, which would seem to indicate that sexual activity is a very strenuous form of exercise. But, until recently, there has been no information available on the impact of sexual activity on the damaged heart. A study by Hellerstein and Friedman (1969) provided the first significant findings.

3. STUDIES IN CARDIAC PATIENTS

These investigators did not discount the results of earlier studies which showed 'marked' and 'tremendous' cardiopulmonary changes during intercourse. They merely argued that, having dealt mostly with healthy, recently married young subjects or with older subjects many of whom did not belong to established marital units, these studies were not applicable for the mainly middle-aged males who have had heart attacks, or might be highly infarction-prone. Additionally, the earlier studies had been conducted in laboratory environments, and often involved direct human and photographic observation, as well as instrumental measurements, all of which could influence performance.

The subjects for the Hellerstein and Friedman study were chosen randomly from men participating in a physical fitness evaluation program. They were classified into two groups: those who had suffered an acute myocardial infarct and thus had atherosclerotic heart disease (ASHD), and those who were normal but deemed highly 'coronary-prone' (NCP). There were 48 ASHD subjects, average age 53 years; and 43 NCP subjects, average age 48 years.

Data obtained from each of the subjects included psychological and medical information, as well as heart rate and other data recorded while the subjects were wearing portable electrocardiographic tape-recorders continuously for 24 to 48 h. The subjects were told not to deviate from their usual activities and were not told of the investigators' particular interest in response during sexual activity. Of the 91 subjects, 14 engaged in sexual activity while being monitored, providing some very significant findings.

Analysis of the heart rate recordings showed that the mean maximal heart rate during sexual activity (which occurred at orgasm) was 117.4 bpm, with average heart rates of 87 bpm two minutes prior to orgasm, and 85 bpm two minutes after orgasm. Comparing maximal heart rates during sexual activity and during work activity, Hellerstein and Friedman found that the mean maximal heart rate during work activity was 120.1 bpm, slightly higher than that for sexual activity.

In the case of a 48-year-old attorney with ASHD in this group, the heart rate response during sexual activity "was exceeded by that during a brisk walk to the courthouse, during conferences with the presiding judge and opposing counsel during a trial, while engaging in a telephone dispute with another attorney, and while walking to the washroom." Worthy of note also: during dinner with his family the attorney's heart rate increased to approximately the same levels as during intercourse.

From their case histories alone, Hellerstein and Friedman put together interesting information on the effects of ageing and heart disease on the frequency of sexual activity. As might be expected, sexual activity decreased with age, and even more after a heart attack. The average for all subjects was about 4 orgasms per week during their first year of marriage or at age 25, whichever was first. At age 45, the average was down to 2 orgasms per week; and for those who had had a heart attack, there was a further decrease to 1.6 orgasms per week. Change in sexual desire, wife's decision, feeling of depression, fears, and coronary symptoms were among the reasons given for decreased sexual activity.

Hellerstein and Friedman concluded: "The physical expression of conjugal sexual activity in middle-aged men is not very impressive when compared with other physical activities." There appears to be a large discrepancy here between results of earlier studies and those of Hellerstein and Friedman. These investigators point out that the older age of their own subjects, the longer duration of marriage, the effects of the heart disease itself, the performance of the sex act in the privacy of the home rather than in the laboratory, and the absence of direct human or photographic observation, all contributed to the lower heart-rate response obtained in their study.

This study included only male cardiac patients. Masters and Johnson (1966) have shown that heart function during orgasm is virtually the same in both sexes. Therefore we can assume that, for the middle-aged, long-married woman, sexual activity probably has the same cardiac costs as for the male.

Sexual activity, then, in its effects on the heart, is similar to other forms of exercise and should be treated as such. Far from being harmful, the evidence clearly points to substantial benefits from physical exertion for both diseased and normal hearts. When a body unused to exercise gradually strengthens through conditioning based on cardiovascular principles, a 'training effect' occurs (Cooper, 1968). Of interest here is Masters and Johnson's finding that "the slower the initial heart rate at resting stage, the lower the rate during sexual stimulation" (1966).

Over 40% of the cardiac patient subjects in the Hellerstein and Friedman study had symptoms associated with sexual intercourse. The main symptom was awareness of very rapid heart action; other patients experienced angina pectoris. Awareness of very rapid heart action occurs in people without heart illness, and in this context is never thought of as a symptom. Almost no patients ceased sexual activity because of symptoms. In general, those who experienced symptoms during sexual activity had waited longer (an average of 16.4 weeks) to resume sexual relations than those who had no symptoms (an average of 11.7 weeks). Those who were more sexually active before their heart attacks were more likely to resume sexual activity earlier.

The individual himself, if in condition, is less likely to experience breathlessness, rapid heart pounding, and other symptoms of myocardial insufficiency. For those who do have anginal symptoms during brisk walking, Hellerstein and Friedman recommend the prophylactic use of nitroglycerin before intercourse and/or the initiation of a conditioning program. They feel that sexual intercourse should be denied only those patients with severe congestive failure. Any person with any other type of heart disease who can comfortably climb one or two flights of stairs, or take a brisk ten minute walk, is ready to resume sexual activity.

Nevertheless, wives of cardiac patients share the fear that sexual activity will precipitate another heart attack, with the additional nightmarish fantasy that their partner will die during intercourse, and on top of them.

4. SUDDEN DEATH DURING INTERCOURSE

The only factual information available on the possibility of succumbing to a heart attack during intercourse is from a study by Ueno (1963) of the Tokyo Medical Examiner's office. Ueno was able to ascertain that out of 5559 cases of sudden death, 34 (0.6%) were specifically precipitated by sexual activity. The deaths occurred in a variety of situations, but significantly, 27 (77%) of the 34 cases, occurred during extramarital sexual activity. In addition, 18 (53%) of the deaths reported were in hotels. It is possible, of course, that more of the coitus-precipitated deaths were reported by hotel physicians than by private family physicians, who may have listed some other cause of death out of deference to the family of the deceased. Or the wife may have chosen to state that her husband died in his sleep, an option not available to an extramarital partner in a hotel. A pattern is clearly evident, however: coital death most often occurs during intercourse with other than an 'established' marital or sexual partner, in a secretive encounter in a hotel rather than in the privacy of one's home.

We may reasonably conclude that a sudden myocardial infarction, or even death, is a very remote possibility for middle-aged males who have sex with familiar partners of 20 years or more, in a familiar setting and with proper restrictions on the amount of food and alcohol consumed before intercourse. New, often nonmarital encounters, may be a different story, however, because of the various emotional and physical stresses mentioned above.

5. MASTURBATION

A study just completed at the University of Washington School of Medicine, measured cardiopulmonary effects of masturbation in a sample of ten young men in three separate sessions each. Tentative results indicate that for a masturbation-achieved orgasm, the heart rate rises to not more than 130 bpm, and remains between 110 and 130 bmp for only a very short time. The rates recorded during the third experimental sessions were significantly reduced, supporting the criticisms made by Hellerstein and Friedman of earlier artificial laboratory studies, which had not used repeated measurements. These values are especially favorable when compared with the heart rate increases to 190 bpm reached during coitus by a comparable sample of young men in the Masters and Johnson study.

When he feels that a maximum heart rate of 110—130 beats per min will do the patient no harm, the physician should consider recommending to infarction and infarction-prone patients the use of masturbation as a comfortable and the earliest possible method for the resumption of sexual activity, but only for patients with no moral or religious misgivings about it.

6. THE MALE-SUBORDINATE POSITION SAFER?

In previous writing (Wagner, 1974) we have urged the resumption of intercourse in the male-subordinate or side-by-side positions for males resuming sexual behavior after a myocardial infarction. Though good data on the cardiac costs of different positions were not available, we hypothesized that the male-superior position resembled the isometric position of exercises such as push-ups and therefore would possibly be more stressful.

We now have data on eight males 20—40 years old with a mean age of 29.25. The subjects were monitored in the male-subordinate and male-superior positions with their wives, or partners of at least six months, in the privacy of their bedrooms (Rhodes, 1974). Each subject was requested to collect data during five instances of coitus.

The mean maximal heart rate for the male-superior position at orgasm was

114 as compared to 117 in the male-subordinate position. Mean systolic and diastolic blood pressures were found to be slightly higher in the male-superior position at orgasm 163/81, as compared to 161/77 in the male-subordinate position. The differences in mean heart rate, blood pressure and pressure/rate product were not statistically significant with regard to position at orgasm or at other measured times — resting, intromission, and 30, 60, and 120 sec after orgasm. Clearly, position of intercourse is not an important variable for cardiac patients.

The concurrence of the Rhodes (1974) data and the Hellerstein and Friedman (1969) data is remarkable. The heart rates are almost identical despite the younger age of the Rhodes group. The blood pressures are also remarkably similar, although Hellerstein and Friedman used an indirect method of estimating blood pressure. These two separate investigations by unrelated investigators add strong weight to the view that sexual behavior in natural settings, as compared to laboratory ones, is a much less stressful activity.

7. PRACTICAL GUIDELINES

Here are some guidelines concerning sexual activity for counseling anyone who has suffered a heart attack or is considered by a physician to be infarction-prone:

(a) Although coitus in the case of middle-aged males seems to be only a moderately stressful activity, it is nevertheless a form of physical exercise. As with other physical exercise, the higher the state of physical conditioning, the easier and thus more enjoyable is sexual intercourse. Hellerstein and Friedman found that postinfarction patients reported significant change in both the frequency and quality of sexual activity after participating in a physical fitness enhancement program, with frequency improving in 30.2% and quality improving in 39.5% of the subjects. Additionally, after physical conditioning fewer subjects developed heart symptoms such as angina pectoris or arrhythmias, during intercourse.

(b) Resuming sexual activity after a heart attack should be planned with due consideration of the patient's level of sexual activity before the infarction. A return to this level of activity is a reasonable goal for most patients, but the stress of intercourse should not be imposed on a patient who has been sexually inactive for years.

(c) The partner can be of immeasurable value in any program for rehabilitation of cardiac patients, sexual activity included. If the wife is reassured that the physiological costs of intercourse are modest, she can be confidently warm and responsive to her husband, helping him to regain his masculine identity and sense of worth.

(d) Food and alcohol intake before intercourse must be kept low, as they introduce further stress which, in combination with the stress of intercourse, might produce adverse effects. Precautions such as familiar surroundings and a familiar partner will help insure against difficulties in the early stages of re-habilitation.

(e) Patient and physician must decide together when the patient has re-covered sufficiently to resume sexual intercourse. Before the point is reach-ed, masturbation may serve as a useful sexual outlet, except for the individ-ual whose moral or religious belief makes it unacceptable. Interviews with cardiac patients make it clear that masturbation, even during the hospital re-covery period, is not uncommon, and it can be seen as a positive step in the resumption of the sex life of the individual. In addition to reduced cardio-pulmonary load, the interpersonal emotional stress required in the resump-tion of intercourse is thus also diminished. The worry about potency is so common after myocardial infarction as to be described as normal. Following masturbation, however, the fear of impotence is reduced, and with it the fear of resumption of intercourse.

(f) When the cardiac patient does resume sexual activity with his or her partner, anxiety may also be reduced by using some of the relaxing sexual-stimulation exercises devised by Masters and Johnson. The advantage to the exercises is that they take away the pressure for a certain kind of sexual per-formance. There is no time at which erection, penetration, or even orgasm should occur; indeed these are not seen as goals, or even necessarily attain-able end points at all. The goal is simply pleasurable sexual activity without anxiety. And, as Brenton (1968) points out, there are couples who discover themselves becoming less inhibited sexually as a result of having had the heart patient's special requirements force them to experiment.

In sum, sexual activity may be resumed, after a bout of heart disease, in exactly the same way other types of exercise may be resumed: gradually and carefully. The patient who has had a heart attack can quickly learn to moni-tor his or her own functioning, avoiding angina pectoris as much as possible. Cardiac costs of sexual activity are much lower than previously thought.

BIBLIOGRAPHY

Bartlett, R.G. (1956) Physiologic responses during coitus. *J. Appl. Physiol.* 9, 469—472.

Boas, E.P. and Goldschmidt, E.F. (1932) *The Heart Rate.* (Charles C. Thomas, Spring-field, Ill.)

Brenton, M. (1968) *Sex and Your Heart.* (Coward-McCann, New York.)

Cooper, K. (1968) *Aerobics.* (Bantam Books, New York.)

Hellerstein, H.K. and Friedman, E.H. (1969) Sexual activity and the post coronary pa-tient. *Med. Aspects Hum. Sex.* 3 (3) 70 ff.

Hellerstein, H.K. and Friedman, E.H. (1970) Sexual activity and the post coronary pa-tient. *Arch. Intern. Med.* 125: 987—999.

Klumbies, G. and Kleinsorge, H. (1950) Circulatory dangers and prophylaxis during or-gasm. *Int. J. Sexol.* 4: 61—66.

Koller, R., Kennedy, J.W., Butler, J.C. and Wagner, N.N. (1972) Counseling the coronary patient on sexual activity. *Postgrad. Med.* 51: 133—136.

Massie, E., Rose, E.F., Rupp, J.C. and Whelton, R.W. (1969) Viewpoints: sudden death during coitus — fact or fiction. *Med. Aspects Hum. Sex.* 3 (6) 22 ff.

Masters, W.H. and Johnson, V.E. (1966) *Human Sexual Response*. (Little, Brown and Co., Boston.)

Rhodes, E.D. (1974) *Blood Pressure and Heart Rate Responses During Sexual Activity*. (Unpublished Master of Nursing Thesis. University of Washington, Seattle.)

Scheingold, L. and Wagner, N.N. (1974) *Sound Sex and the Aging Heart*. (Human Sciences Press, New York.)

Scott, J.C. (1930) Systolic blood pressure fluctuation with sex, anger, and fear. *J. Comp. Physiol*. 10: 97—113.

Tuttle, W.B. and Cook, W.L. (1964) Sexual behavior in post myocardial infarction patients. *Am. J. Cardiol*. 13. 140 153.

Ueno, M. (1963) The so-called coition death. *Jap. J. Legal Med*. 17: 333—340.

Wagner, N.N. (1972) Sexualleben nach Herzinfarkt. *Sexualmedizin I* 29—32.

Wagner, N.N. (1974) Sexual adjustment of cardiac patients. *Br. J. Sex. Med. I* 17—22.

CHAPTER 78

Psychomotor epilepsy and sexual function

JOHN MONEY and GLORIA PRUCE

1. INTRODUCTION

Etiologic, prognostic and therapeutic relationships between epilepsy and sexuality have been postulated since antiquity. The epileptic seizure was compared to the sexual act, and both Hippocrates and Democritus were credited with stating that 'coitus is a slight epileptic attack' (Daremberg, see Temkin, 1971). The ancients cogently observed that the age of puberty was decisive in the course of epilepsy, a finding that has remained essentially true to the present day (Livingston, 1963). Consequently, some physicians of antiquity, for example, Aretaeus, attributed the 'cure' of epilepsy at this period of life to the practice of intercourse and even did 'violence to the nature of children by unseasonable coition' as an endeavor to hasten this beneficial event. However, most physicians of that era believed that coitus was harmful for epileptic patients and advised abstinence; according to Daremberg, some even recommended castration as a therapeutic measure.

Many ancient physicians considered sexual activity to be an etiologic factor in the pathogenesis of epilepsy. 'Untimely intercourse' was designated as a cause of this disorder (Galen), and epileptiform seizures in pregnant women were attributed to the uterus (Paulus of Aegina).

The ancient beliefs relative to epilepsy and sex persisted until the Middle Ages and the Renaissance, at which times the prevailing opinion was that sexual excesses aggravated pre-existing epilepsy (Sennert, see Temkin, 1971), while complete abstinence might also precipitate epileptic seizures. From the latter half of the eighteenth century to the turn of the 20th century, masturbation was generally considered to be a prime etiologic factor in the development and pejoration of epilepsy (Gowers, 1881; Bacon, Tissot, van der Kolk cited in Temkin, 1971), and castration (Bacon) and circumcision (Gowers) were performed in appropriate cases.

It is noteworthy that bromide, the first effective antiepileptic medication, was introduced by Locock (1857) as a treatment for epileptic patients whose

Handbook of Sexology, edited by J. Money and H. Musaph
© *Elsevier/North-Holland Biomedical Press, 1977*

disorders were associated with sexual features. His initial use of the drug was based on a report by a German physician (Butzke, see Temkin, 1971) that potassium bromide produced temporary impotence and upon an abstract of an article (Huette, 1850) which stated, in part: 'The bromide possesses also remarkable power in inducing torpidity of the genital organs. A patient tormented by a vivid imagination, and subject to frequent consequent pollutions, found himself quite freed from his infirmity after having taken 15 grains per diem for three days.'

Apparently, the first physician to report a relationship between abnormal sexual function and almost unquestionable psychomotor epilepsy was Griesinger (1868), who observed 'sexual weakness' in the great majority of his male patients. He also reported 'long-lasting decidedly morbid sexual excitement' in rare cases.

An inextricable association between epilepsy and sexuality has existed from ancient times to the present; however, it is obviously virtually impossible to implicate specific seizure patterns in writings prior to the 19th century, particularly psychomotor attacks, which even today, resist specific classification and diagnosis in many instances (Schmidt and Wilder, 1968). Lennox (1960), for example, aptly stated that psychomotor epilepsy 'is indeed a jungle-land for the explorer', and that 'the burden of proof rests on anyone who contends that a given psychic episode, isolated from other evidence of epilepsy, is epileptic.' Nevertheless, the introduction of sophisticated diagnostic techniques, such as electroencephalography, and the delineation of precise clinical criteria have resulted in the recognition of psychomotor seizures as a specific, although multifaceted, epileptic entity.

Employing current classificational methodology, it is reasonable to assume that a large number of sexual 'aberrations' attributed to epilepsy in general were actually manifestations of psychomotor epilepsy. Recent scientific investigations, in addition to the observations of astute physicians of the 19th century, have confirmed the fact that psychomotor epilepsy is the seizure pattern most frequently associated with abnormal sexual activity.

Psychomotor (temporal lobe) epilepsy may be related to sexual assertiveness and/or hyposexuality. Temporal lobectomy may have an effect on the sexual behavior of patients with psychomotor epilepsy as well as on their seizures.

2. ANIMAL STUDIES

Evidence confirming a direct association of the temporal lobes with abnormal sexual behavior was supplied by Klüver and Bucy (1939), whose experiments established that in primates other than man, the removal of major portions of the temporal lobes and rhinencephalon (amygdala, uncus, hippocampus and hippocampal gyrus) leads to striking alterations in behavior. Klüver and Bucy observed that bilateral temporal lobectomy produced the following symptoms in sexually mature rhesus monkeys: (1) Visual agnosia — although the animal exhibits no gross defects in its ability to discriminate visually, it appears to have lost the ability to recognize and detect the meaning of animate and inanimate objects on the basis of visual criteria alone. (2) Oral tendencies — there is a strong tendency to examine all objects by mouth. Such an oral examination generally consists of putting the object into the mouth, licking, biting, chewing and touching with the lips. (3) Hypermetamorphosis — there is a pronounced tendency to take notice of and attend to every visual stimulus. In addition, the animal tends to touch every object in sight, as if it were under the influence of some irresistible impulse. (4) Changes in emotional behavior — there is an absence or diminution of emotional responses in the sense that there are essentially no stimuli capable of eliciting the motor, vocal or other forms of behavior generally associated with anger and fear reactions. The facial expressions of emotion are often entirely lost. (5) Changes in dietary habits — immediately subsequent to the operation, the monkey will accept and eat large quantities of ham, bacon, ground beef, broiled lamp chops, smoked white fish and other kinds of meat. Normal rhesus monkeys are generally frugivorous, and almost never even touch meat when it is offered to them. (6) Changes in sexual behavior — there is a dramatic increase in sexual activities and in the diversity of sexual manifestations. This hypersexuality, which generally appears initially several weeks after the surgical procedure, is exhibited not only when the monkey is caged with other animals, but also when it is left alone. Various forms of heterosexual, homosexual and autosexual behavior rarely or never observed in normal monkeys can be seen frequently, and an intensification of sexual responses may even be found in castrates and pseudohermaphrodites. Females may display a complete lack of maternal behavior.

3. HUMAN STUDIES

The occurrence of hyposexuality in patients with psychomotor epilepsy originally reported by Griesinger in 1868 was rediscovered and documented in 1954 by Gastaut and Collomb. These investigators had encountered hyposexuality in several hundred patients with psychomotor epilepsy and confirmed their observations in 26 of 36 patients who were studied systematically. They stressed that the sexual alteration was not a simple impotence or frigidity, but was in addition, a pronounced disinterest in all of the libidinous aspects of life. Besides a lack of desire for sexual intercourse, there was a marked decrease or absence of sexual curiosity, erotic fantasies and sensual dreams. This global hyposexuality occurred subsequent to the onset of the psychomotor attacks and developed two to four years after the presumed rhinencephalic lesion. Based upon the electroencephalographic changes and the ictal and interseizure clinical manifestations, the authors postulated that the hyposexuality was primarily associated with 'rhinencephalic psychomotor epilepsy.'

Of particular significance is the fact that the loss of sexual interest and activity occurred in patients who were not routinely receiving antiepileptic drugs; however, the administation of anticonvulsant drugs, barbiturates and hydantoinates, 'actually led, upon control of seizures to return of sexual response' in a number of patients.

Gastaut and Collomb stated that the hyposexuality could be observed 'fairly frequently' in patients without overt psychomotor attacks but whose electroencephalograms contained temporal spikes.

In 1967, Blumer and Walker reported the results of a unique investigation designed to determine the sexual changes that occur in the course of psychomotor epilepsy subsequent to unilateral temporal lobectomy. Their study group consisted of 21 patients who underwent physical and neurological examinations, testing for aphasia, an ophthalmologic examination and an electroencephalographic examination. After temporal lobectomy, all patients were personally followed, and changes in memory function, general disposition and sexual behavior were recorded. Comprehensive information was obtained on many aspects of sexual activity, such as the frequency, consummation and satisfaction of intercourse or masturbation, libidinous feelings, erotic fantasies and sexual talk that might result in arousal or erection. A patient was considered hyposexual if he or she were deficient in all of these aspects of sexual activity, or if the individual did not experience at least one sexual arousal or response every two months.

Prior to surgery, 11 of the 21 patients were diagnosed as 'clearly hyposexual.' Their disorder was global and pertained to 'all aspects of the sexual appetite: cognitional libidinous desire and imagery, genitopelvic arousal and response.' The hyposexuality was definitely related to the course of the epilepsy: in six patients who developed psychomotor attacks between 13 and 15 years of age, an essentially total lack of response had always been present; in three patients with the onset of seizures between 17 and 22 years of age, it became established late with exacerbation of the epilepsy; and the two remaining patients became completely impotent within one year following the initial psychomotor attack.

Following unilateral temporal lobectomy, the 11 hyposexual patients could be distinctly divided into the following three groups: 4 exhibited a persistent lack of sexual response; 4 experienced a lasting improvement of the hyposexuality; and 3 displayed a temporary increase of sexual functions. The authors found that 'these changes closely correlated with the postoperative course of the seizure condition.'

This investigation confirmed the findings of Gastaut and Collomb relative to the incidence of hyposexuality in psychomotor epileptic patients, and in addition, supports Gastaut's hypothesis that an excitatory state of the limbic system, caused by epileptic discharges in the anterior temporal lobes, results in global suppression of sexual functions. Blumer and Walker concluded that the presence of excessive neuronal activity in the limbic portions of the temporal lobes produced suppression of sexual behavior, and that lack of neural activity in the same structures favored sexual arousal and responsiveness.

Blumer reported the results of his expanded neurosurgical—psychiatric study of 50 patients with psychomotor epilepsy in 1970. Twenty-nine of the patients in his series manifested a global hyposexuality, with inability to achieve orgasm as the predominant feature. Twenty-four of the 29 patients underwent anterior temporal lobectomy, and postoperatively, eight (33.3%) experienced a permanent improvement in sexuality. The increase in sexual activity was again significantly related to the degree of surgical success in abolishing the seizures.

In contrast to previous publications relative to psychomotor epilepsy and sexuality, Blumer emphasized the occurrence of hypersexuality in his article. Seven (14%) of the 50 psychomotor epileptic patients in his study group exhibited distinct episodes of hypersexuality. In 6 patients, the hypersexual activities followed the abrupt termination of temporal lobe seizure activity, either subsequent to surgical intervention or the seizure, per se. One of these patients also manifested an increase in sexual drive following suppression of seizure activity by anticonvulsant medication, and another patient experienced the feeling of sexual climax with each of his attacks.

Homosexuality, transvestism and fetishism have been observed in a small number of patients with psychomotor epilepsy (Blumer, 1969). A possible relationship between paraphilia and temporal lobe abnormality is suggested by two cases in which the paraphilia was totally eradicated following 'cure' of the psychomotor epilepsy by unilateral temporal lobectomy (Hunter et al., 1963; Mitchell et al., 1954). Two patients studied by Blumer and Walker (1975) experienced a disappearance of homosexual behavior following unilateral temporal lobectomy, despite the fact that the surgical procedure did not completely eliminate the seizures.

Sufficient evidence has been presented in the literature to substantiate the belief that epilepsy and abnormal sexual activity are closely associated. On the other hand, the ancient Roman adage, 'Coitus brevis epilepsia est' suggests a relationship between the 'Sacred Disease' and normal sexual functioning: the mood of sexual desire is analogous to the prodrome of an epileptic seizure, the premonition of orgasm to the aura, the sexual climax to the epileptic paroxysm and the sleep and diminished tension following sexual intercourse to the postconvulsive sleep or drowsiness (Taylor, 1971). The reputation of epileptics in past years as being sexually deviant and/or suffering with excessive sexual arousal is probably based upon the observation of abnormal sexuality in a very few patients at the time of an attack. The dramatic effect of an epileptic seizure with sexual components on the observer undoubtedly eradicated all previous experience with sexually normal epileptic patients. It is no wonder that old textbooks on psychiatry stressed the belief that sexual abnormalities were indigenous to persons with epilepsy. The essentially normal sexual behavior of most epileptics was overlooked or ignored in favor of the aberrations of a few.

Most publications in the relatively recent literature designate psychomotor (temporal lobe) epilepsy as the seizure pattern most clearly associated with abnormal behavior, particularly in the sphere of sex. However, investigation of the authors of such articles reveals that the preponderance consisted of psychiatrists and/or neurosurgeons, members of the disciplines that would routinely encounter the most serious cases of epilepsy. The neurosurgeon, for example, only rarely operates on an epileptic with a seizure pattern other than psychomotor. The following criteria outlined by Walker (1964) are generally employed for selection of patients for surgical consideration: (1) At least one disabling attack occurs per month despite adequate medication. (2) The focus is clearly defined by electroencephalography at the time of a spontaneous or induced attack. (3) The focus is located where its removal would not further impair functions such as speech or motor power. (4) The patient is not so debilitated that even if the seizures were eliminated, he would still be disabled. These indications would almost automatically exclude cases of petit mal and childhood myoclonic epilepsy and would apply to only a tiny percentage of those with major motor (grand mal) seizures, and then only to patients with focal grand mal seizures refractory to all of the available antiepileptic agents.

The psychiatrist is in a similar position, in that only patients with very serious epileptic disorders or epileptic patients with severe emotional disturbances are generally referred for treatment. This specialist only rarely, if ever, treats the 'average' epileptic patient, because such an individual is generally satisfactorily controlled by anticonvulsive medication and presents no serious deficits in behavior. Therefore, the psychiatrist, like the neurosurgeon, is almost invariably exposed to a very biased section of the overall epileptic population. The results of their studies cannot, therefore, be directly applied to the average, ambulatory person with epilepsy. While the universal opinion among psychiatrists is that psychomotor epilepsy is the form most frequently associated with abnormal behavior, and sexual aberrations in particular, this view is not shared by many epileptologists with extensive clinical experience. For example, Small and co-workers (1962) compared a group of patients with psychomotor epilepsy with a series of 'nontemporal' epileptics, and found no statistically significant differences between the two groups with respect to psychopathology, personality characteristics or psychologic test scores. Stevens (1966) also presented evidence that temporal lobe epileptics do not differ from other patients in the incidence or severity of psychiatric disorders. Livingston (1972) reported that the incidence of behavioral and personality aberrations is higher in patients with major motor (grand mal) epilepsy than in those with other types of epileptic seizures.

Despite the convincing evidence presented in the literature relative to the high incidence of global hyposexuality in patients with psychomotor epilepsy, other factors may have been responsible, at least in part, for this deficiency. Behavioral difficulties observed in epileptic patients are frequently related to anxiety and/or depressive states which stem in most instances from fear of being out of contact for a period of time, fear of injury as a result of a seizure, or fear of having their disorder exposed to the public. Therefore, epilepsy as it manifests itself in the personality development of the individual, is a psychosocial and psychophysiologic disturbance rather than a simple physiologic one, because of the insecurity resulting from the anticipation of experiencing a seizure and its accompanying social implications. Because of this, many patients with epilepsy seek seclusion and are thus denied the normal social contacts that form the basis for accepted social behavior. Unmarried epileptics in normal social situations may be more apprehensive about experiencing a seizure than confident in establishing social relationships with members of the opposite sex. The epileptic patient is ever fearful of being suddenly thrust into a state of unconsciousness. This fear of loss of contact with his environment is one of the most disturbing problems with which the epileptic must learn to live. The suddeness and unpredictability of most seizures certainly must tend to make many, if not most, patients tense and apprehensive. Under such conditions, it is not surprising that an epileptic patient may manifest signs of hyposexuality. It is exceedingly distressing for the person with epilepsy to realize that one minute he may be engaged in the performance of some activity, such as sex, and the next minute he may be in the throes of a seizure. In addition, epileptics frequently exhibit continual anxiety related to the recurrence of seizures because of the pronounced effect which attacks exert on the observer.

It is quite obvious that any individual, epileptic or nonepileptic, who is continuously exposed to obstacles created by social and economic rejection and discrimination and who is denied privileges that are considered to be basic human rights is likely to develop emotional difficulties, especially attitudes of inferiority, with respect to sexual activity. A hostile society that has relegated the epileptic to 'second class' citizenry since the dawn of recorded history is undoubtedly responsible for some epileptics' believing that they are also 'second class' in their sexual performances.

Serious consideration should also be devoted to the side-effects of some of the antiepileptic agents ingested by psychomotor patients in the etiology of hyposexuality. Conventional dosages of some standard drugs, such as mephenytoin (Mesantoin), methsuximide (Celontin), phenobarbital and primidone (Mysoline), frequently produce severe and persistent drowsiness and lethargy (Livingston, 1972), which might impair normal sexual desires and performances. Some antiepileptic agents, such as phenacemide (Phenurone), have provoked emotional and psychiatric disturbances and these drug-induced aberrations might interfere with normal sexuality. In addition, cosmetically objectionable side-effects of phenytoin (Dilantin), such as gingival hyperplasia and hypertrichosis, constitute an almost insuperable obstacle in the initiation and maintenance of heterosexual social contacts. Moreover, some patients require maximal dosages of medication to satisfactorily control their seizures that render them constantly drowsy and dull, a condition hardly compatible with a robust sexual program.

4. SUMMARY

A relationship between sexuality and epilepsy, particulaly psychomotor epilepsy, has been noted throughout the ages since ancient times. Although global hyposexuality is associated, in a limited number of patients with psychomotor epilepsy, the incidence of this disturbance has been exaggerated by physicians who see a biased segment of the psychomotor epileptic population. Improvement in hyposexuality subsequent to anterior temporal lobectomy confirms a relationship of sexuality and psychomotor epilepsy; however, the strength of the relationship is compromised by other factors, such as the untoward effects of anticonvulsant drugs and emotional disturbances related to a discriminatory society and a community still imbued with Biblical misconceptions of epilepsy.

ACKNOWLEDGEMENTS

This work was supported by USPHS grant no. HD 00325 and funds from the Grant Foundation, New York.

BIBLIOGRAPHY

Aretaeus, cited in Temkin (1971).

Bacon, cited in Temkin (1971).

Blumer, D. (1969) Transsexualism, sexual dysfunction, and temporal lobe disorder, In: (R. Green and J. Money, Eds.), *Transsexualism and Sex Reassignment.* (Johns Hopkins Press, Baltimore.)

Blumer, D. (1970) Hypersexual episodes in temporal lobe epilepsy. *Am. J. Psychiat.* 126: 1099—1106.

Blumer, D. and Walker, A.E. (1967) Sexual behavior in temporal lobe epilepsy. *Arch. Neurol.* 16: 37—43.

Blumer, D. and Walker, A.E. (1975) The neural basis of sexual behavior. In: (D.F. Benson and D. Blumer, Eds.) *Psychiatric Aspects of Neurologic Disease.* (Grune and Stratton, New York.)

Butzke, F., cited in Temkin (1971).

Daremberg, cited in Temkin (1971).

Galen, cited in Temkin (1971).

Gastaut, H. and Collomb, H. (1954) Etude du comportement sexuel chez les épileptiques psychomoteurs. *Ann. Med. Psychol.* 112: 657—696.

Gowers, W.R. (1881) *Epilepsy and Other Chronic Convulsive Disorders.* (Churchill, London.)

Griesinger, W. (1868) Ueber einige epileptoide Zustaende. *Arch. Psychiat. Nervenkrankh.* 1: 329.

Huette, M. (1850) Recherches sur les propriétés physiologiques et therapeutiques du bromure de potassium. *Br. Foreign Med. Chirurg. Rev.* 6: 556.

Hunter, R., Logue, V. and McMenemy, W.H. (1963) Temporal lobe epilepsy supervening on longstanding transvestism and fetishism. *Epilepsia* 4: 60—65.

Klüver, H. and Bucy, P.C. (1939) Preliminary analysis of functions of the temporal lobes in monkeys. *Arch. Neruol. Psychiat.* 42: 979—1000.

Lennox, W.G. (1960) *Epilepsy and Related Disorders.* (Little, Brown and Co., Boston.)

Livingston, S. (1963) *Living with Epileptic Seizures.* (Charles C. Thomas, Springfield, Illinois.)

Livingston, S. (1972) *Comprehensive Management of Epilepsy in Infancy, Childhood and Adolescence.* (Charles C. Thomas, Springfield, Illinois.)

Locock, C. in discussion, Sieveking, E.H. (1857) Analysis of 52 cases of epilepsy observed by the author. *Lancet* 1: 527.

Mitchell, W., Falconer, M.A. and Hill, D. (1954) Epilepsy fetishism relieved by temporal lobectomy. *Lancet* 2: 626—630.

Paulus of Aegina, cited in Temkin (1971).

Schmidt, R.P. and Wilder, B.J. (1968) *Epilepsy.* (F.A. Davis Co., Philadelphia.)

Sennert, cited in Temkin (1971).

Small, J.G., Milstein, V. and Stevens, J.R. (1962) Are psychomotor epileptics different? *Arch. Neurol.* 7: 187—194.

Stevens, J.R. (1966) Psychiatric implications of psychomotor epilepsy. *Arch. Gen. Psychiat.* 14: 461—477.

Taylor, D. (1971) Appetitive inadequacy in the sex behavior of temporal lobe epileptics. *J. Neuro-Visceral Relations,* suppl. X, 486—490.

Temkin, O. (1971) *The Falling Sickness.* (Johns Hopkins Press, Baltimore.)

Tissot, S.A., cited in Temkin (1971).

van der Kolk, S., cited in Temkin (1971).

Walker, A.E. (1964) Surgical treatment of epilepsy. *Modern Treatment.* (Harper and Row, New York.)

Personal and social implications of diseases of the genital tract

Section coordinator: C.B.S. Schofield

CHAPTER 79

Introduction

C.B.S. SCHOFIELD

In this Section, are described the venereal and sexually transmitted diseases, not so much from the clinical point of view but rather emphasising the social and epidemiological factors. It should be noted that in those countries where the whole spectrum of sexually transmitted diseases is recognised and reported by official agencies, the proportion of those diseases labelled venereal has fallen over the years, while that of the other sexually transmitted diseases, especially those caused by viruses has risen. In addition, the social and psychological backgrounds of the patients who acquire these infections is considered, along with the precautions that can be taken by men and women indulging in any sexual activity, promiscuous or otherwise, with or without protective rubber condoms, which would cut down the rate at which infections are spread, if used correctly.

The main problems in attempts at disease control are emphasised by each author. In the chapters on the diseases themselves, it is pointed out that no infectious or contagious disease has even been treated to extinction, and this is certainly true of those transmitted sexually. Effective cures for the major sexual diseases have been available for over a quarter of a century, during which time the incidence world-wide has nonetheless increased at an alarming rate.

Possibly the greatest problem to be overcome is lack of awareness by the patients of the fact that they have been infected, women not noticing lesions in the vagina, homosexuals unaware of rectal lesions, and all patients not associating lesions on or within the genitals, the ano-rectum or oro-pharynx as being acquired by a sexual activity. Too many doctors and those in the paramedical professions fail to take cognizance of the fact that these diseases are transmitted during sexual activity, and that the sexual contacts need treatment, if for no other reason than that they will infect others and possibly reinfect the patient already treated, and also to protect them from chronic untreated, albeit currently asymptomatic infection. In addition, some forget that sexually transmitted diseases are passed on other than genitally;

Handbook of Sexology, edited by J. Money and H. Musaph
© *Elsevier/North-Holland Biomedical Press, 1977*

and they appear ignorant of the increasing numbers of infections acquired anally and orally.

As far as the general public is concerned, sometimes there is not merely lack of awareness but also an apathy to the problems. This can be engendered by those having so-called moralistic attitudes who often believe that ignorance is better than sex education, and that suppression of information about prophylaxis will cut down the amount of sexual experimentation and, therefore, the amount of disease. It is to be hoped that sufficient evidence is presented in this section to resolve, once and for all, these misguided and repressive opinions which, in certain areas, add immeasurably to the difficulties encountered in attempts at disease control.

Far too many patients with sexually transmitted diseases receive no more than first-aid treatment, but their proper management entails much more than the mere doling out of the required amount of antibiotics to cure the disease discovered. A proportion needs psychological support at the time of diagnosis, especially those who are not indiscriminately promiscuous. This is needed to help them over what is to them a severe and acute crisis. This support should be included with discussions during the whole period of surveillance as to the ways and means of preventing exposure to infections in the future. The confidence of patients must be gained so they will trust those treating them and not fear to disclose their sex contacts, because they may believe that their sexual activity might not have been socially acceptable. At the present time, the best hope of disease control is by effective treatment combined with rapid tracing of sexual contacts.

The consideration shown to patients while being diagnosed and treated will be reflected by their cooperation in giving all the information required in the tracing of their contacts and in their attending for posttreatment examination. Patients default usually because of mismanagement, but it is essential that they continue to attend because often more than one sexually transmitted disease is present at one time, although not all may be diagnosed at the initial visit. Surveillance is required for a sufficient period of time to ensure that all diseases will have been diagnosed and that, when the patients are dismissed as cured, they need worry no more.

The use of antibiotics without any attempt at making a diagnosis in the prophylactic, or more correctly, abortive treatment of the sexual contacts of patients with early syphilis and gonorrhea which is mentioned in the chapter on the prevention of the sexually transmitted diseases, does cause controversy among members of the medical profession. However, it must be stated that in those countries lacking an effective, official service for the diagnosis and treatment of these diseases, this form of treatment is almost essential in an attempt at disease control. Nevertheless, in those countries with an established and developed service, it is of little or no consequence and is a violation of the fundamental principle of good medical practice, namely, diagnosis before treatment. Acceptance of a lowered standard of medical care for those people unlucky enough to have acquired a sexually transmitted disease will only play into the hands of those with moralistic attitudes, and give credence to their oppressive attitudes.

The oldest established form of prophylaxis among the venereal diseases is the installation of various drops into the eyes of the newborn in an attempt to prevent the development of gonococcal infections. This practice carried out as a routine in some countries, has been criticized for several reasons. No type of eye-drop has ever been shown to prevent every case of gonococcal infection of the eyes. In developed countries treatment with diagnosis of eyes which do become inflamed is so successful that no damage occurs and, more over, the mother will be diagnosed and treated. Whenever the prophylactic treatment is successful, then the mother remains with gonorrhea which will not be diagnosed until it becomes symptomatic, possibly as a salpingitis, which complication is not uncommon in the puerperium, or she may later be named as a contact having infected other people. This might well be considered a greater public health hazard than awaiting the development of inflammation in the eyes of the newborn.

CHAPTER 80

Psychological and sociological considerations

C.B.S. SCHOFIELD

1. INTRODUCTION

The acquisition of a venereal or sexually transmitted disease by an individual is accidental. It is a matter of chance whether or not the sexual partner has an infection that can be transmitted sexually. The type of sexual behavior of a person is intentional and when it is promiscuous, the chances of acquiring an infection are highest. Promiscuity may take a number of forms. It may be indiscriminate when risks are taken with unknown and casual partners or discriminate when only with known friends. It may be persistent when risks with a number of partners are taken regularly, or intermittent when they are only taken at intervals, often only very occasionally. The risks may be concurrent with a number of partners during one period of time or sequential with one partner only during any given period (Schofield, 1975).

In general, the types of sexual behavior reflect the various psychological and sociological backgrounds of people, an understanding of which is there fore essential for the proper management of those patients suffering from sexually transmitted diseases (Schofield, 1975). These are social diseases, influenced by many facets of day to day life. Consequently they have attracted the attention of authors throughout the world, and many of their publications are included in an annotated bibliography (Darrow, 1971). Morton (1973a) suggested that the rise in the incidence of venereal diseases should be viewed against the background of an increasing incidence of many adverse phenomena in society which suggested that social ill-health has become much commoner. He further stressed the need to develop social indicators of a predictive nature.

Antibiotics, with the ability to cure venereal infection, have been available for over a quarter of a century, but in no country has medical treatment lead to control of these diseases. In fact, as Willcox (1972) notes, the increase in the incidence of venereal diseases and especially that of gonorrhea, has affected all the continents.

Handbook of Sexology, edited by J. Money and H. Musaph
© *Elsevier/North-Holland Biomedical Press, 1977*

Apart from the psychological and sociological backgrounds to the sexually transmitted diseases, which will be discussed below, climate also appears to be a factor. In the U.S., according to Cornelius (1971), the highest incidence of gonorrhea occurs during the third quarter of each year, the relative incidences by quarters being 94 : 97 : 110 : 100. The corresponding figures for Scotland are similar, namely 85 : 91 : 117 : 107. It would be of interest to know if the same holds good for countries in the Southern hemisphere, or whether the peak incidence there occurs during the first quarter.

2. PSYCHOLOGICAL CONSIDERATIONS

A number of social scientists have studied the psychological background of patients with sexually transmitted diseases. Some have used standardized instruments for which normal controls are available but the significance of any differences noted are, on occasion, questioned by others. Without doubt, these attempts at objective observations confirm the impressions of those concerned with the management of these patients, that there is a proportion whose attitudes towards themselves and society are at variance with what is considered 'normal'. It should also be noted that 'normality' is not a stable entity. It varies from time to time and from place to place.

Psychological background

Vera Stark-Romanus (1973) noted three types of patients. In the largest group, venereal infection was only one of many signs of social maladjustment. The second group comprised the sexually promiscuous who were otherwise not maladjusted. The last group consisted of people from any social class, with stable personalities who occasionally had sex with someone other than their regular partner. A danger in these latter cases was the possibility of a crisis of confidence in the innocent partner.

Wells (1969 and 1970) using the Eysenck Personality Inventory (EPI) and the Psychoticism, Extroversion, Neuroticism (PEN) Inventory found male and female patients attending a VD clinic to be a markedly neurotic group, the males tending to be extroverted while the females were introverted. In males there was a decrease in extroversion and neuroticism with age, and an increase in representatives of the lower social strata, also noted by Hart (1973) who further found a correlation between extroversion in military personnel and alcohol, civil arrests and frequent military charges. Differences were observed according to the source of infection. Males infected by casual consorts rated most highly for extroversion and neuroticism. Marked degrees of psychoticism were found only in the female patients, those infected maritally rating as high as the promiscuous, both having scores comparable with psychiatric in-patients, the differences between them being that the former rated higher for neuroticism and were markedly introverted while the latter were extroverted. Default from observation after treatment was associated in males with high scores for neuroticism and psychoticism, those completing observation having normal scores and in women, with extroversion alone.

The main differences between heterosexual males and females attending the clinics were that the former tended to score highly for extroversion and moderately for neuroticism while the latter, highly for neuroticism and they were also introverted. A different pattern was found among homosexual males. Wells and Schofield (1972) using the EPI Inventory, found that affected homosexuals as a group scored lower for extroversion than did affected heterosexual males, but like them were significantly more neurotic than the general population. The only difference between homosexuals following 'active' and 'passive' risks was a difference in neuroticism, the latter attaining higher scores, comparable with clinical neurotics.

Promiscuous women, especially teenagers, have been investigated by a number of authors. Palmgren (1966) studied teenagers with repeated infections and found no correlation between intelligence or the Minnesota Multiphasic Personality Inventory (MMPI) results and eventual social adjustment. However, those with abnormal personalities were most likely to continue their socially delinquent behavior. Datt (1971) observed similar patterns in Indian teenagers. The association between sexual promiscuity and other antisocial behavior was also noted by Thompson and Rutherford (1972) and by Pemberton and co-workers (1972).

With regard to males, Singh and associates (1966) noted that they were often educational dropouts and Glass (1967) that many could not form adequate interpersonal relationships. He further pointed out that in certain 'subcultures' within the society, promiscuity may be accepted as normal from the immediate group's point of view. The variations of sexual behavior in different cultures were also observed by Garcia (1971).

Immediate psychological effects

Seale (1966), among others, has noted that highly promiscuous and socially irresponsible patients show little concern or emotional disturbance when they acquire a sexually transmitted disease. By contrast, even profound guilt is found among intelligent, socially responsible and law-abiding husbands. There is fear of the physical consequences, of harming a spouse, lover or children, and a belief that acquiring a venereal disease is a sin and a disgrace. This can lead to the breakdown of a previously good personality and, when the reactive anxiety state is unchecked, to chronic anxiety neurosis according to Kite (1971). In this context, Giard (1972) emphasized the need for clinic staffs to develop an immediate rapport with their patients. Novotny (1971) outlined the different psychological approaches to venereophobes and patients lacking discipline. Seale (1966) also noted that wives infected with gonorrhea from their husbands often developed severe symptoms of anxiety and depression when made aware that they had venereal disease.

Those not made aware of the diagnosis rarely developed any depression whatsoever. The need to recognize and deal with the emotional, as well as the clinical aspects of these infections has been stressed by Mbanefo (1968) and Boneff (1971).

The thought of having to attend a Special Clinic for a sexually transmitted disease can be most stressful, especially for men with their very first infection. In a recent study in Glasgow (Schofield et al., 1975), 9.5% of such men had blood ethanol levels in excess of 10 mg/100 ml compared with only 4.1% of repeaters and those on observation after treatment. Only 1% of women attending for the first time and none on observation, had similar blood ethanol levels which were found in 9% of repeaters, most of whom were promiscuous if not outright prostitutes.

Late psychological effects

It appears that once over the initial shock, and with correct management, the majority of patient's anxiety starts to wane in about a week (Bindemann et al., 1974), especially if the clinical progress has been satisfactory. Seale (1966) observed that nonspecific urethritis was associated with a greater number of emotional disturbances than was gonorrhea, and this was probably due to the difficulty in preventing relapses in the former condition. In an investigation into patients who had been treated for venereal disease in the past, Kelus (1973) did not find any difference with regard to neuroticism between the former patients, male or female, and the controls. He pointed out that the emotional upsets were only temporary and had no lasting ill-effects. Geiger (1973) noting the dramatic decline in the reported incidence of venereal diseases in The People's Republic of China, drew attention to the rehabilitation, without stigma, of prostitutes who were formerly a major source of infections. As part of the psychological rehabilitation 'bitterness sessions' were held so that they could understand how they had been exploited and abused in the past. These techniques might not be applicable in every society, but nowhere else has prostitution been so effectively eliminated as is claimed for China.

3. SOCIOLOGICAL CONSIDERATIONS

Among the sociological factors implicated in the world-wide increase in the incidence of the venereal and sexually transmitted diseases over the past twenty years, the most commonly cited is the increase in population mobility. Other factors have a greater or lesser part to play in different parts of the world. They include the increase in populations at risk, permissive societies, hostilities and civil strife, alcohol and drug abuse, certain groups identified as being at special risk, and the lack of awareness of the problem by the medical and allied professions and the public at large. Darrow (1971) prepared an annotated bibliography on the behavioral aspects of venereal disease control. In England and Wales between 1963 and 1970, Morton (1973a) noted the rising incidence of a number of social phenomena, some paralleling the rise of gonorrhea. Among them were the rising incidence of indictable offences, violence against the person, the consumption of alcoholic spirits, illegitimate births and legal abortions, divorces filed and divorces made absolute, and casualities and deaths following road accidents.

The majority of patients seen by Stark-Romanus (1973) came from a poor social background in large cities. Their education had been bad and they were in unskilled jobs. Most of them gave histories of juvenile delinquency, alcohol and drug abuse, and a number had been under psychiatric care. They had received some sex education but had not utilized it, and they had a poor knowledge of venereal diseases.

In any given area, the incidence of sexually transmitted diseases depends to a great extent on the social climate, be it good, bad or indifferent. From the fairly general increase in the incidence of these diseases throughout the world, it would appear that the social climate is rarely good, although the underlying causes may vary from place to place and from time to time.

Increase in populations at risk

Following World War II, there was a sharp increase in the number of births in many countries throughout the world. Over the past few years, those concerned in this 'bulge' in the populations have reached sexual maturity (Morton and Harris, 1975) and at an earlier age than before (Catterall, 1965). Nowadays, in some populations, the majority are aged 25 years or younger. This is in part due to a decline in infant mortality in developing countries, while disease control by such chemicals as DDT, together with improved hygiene and medical services, has cut down morbidity, making for healthier and more virile populations. The years of the greatest sexual activity usually are from 15 to 25 years, so it is understandable that there has been an increase in the population at risk of acquiring and of transmitting sexually transmitted diseases. One special form of disease control is worthy of note. Yaws, the tropical treponematosis which provides some immunity against acquiring syphilis, has been eradicated from a number of areas by the World Health Organization in collaboration with the countries concerned. This has increased further the population at risk of acquiring venereal syphilis, according to Guthe and colleagues (1972) although Idsøe and Guthe (1967) had noted that despite the increase in world population over the past 100 years, there had been a general regression in the incidence of syphilis.

Increase in population mobility

In this section mobility will be discussed mainly as it affects single people, especially the young and sexually active. Migration may be international, usually from a developing to a developed country or, as part of its economic evolution, from rural to urban areas within the same country. Tourism, which has expanded greatly over the past decade, is mainly from developed industrialized countries to those less well developed or from urban to more rural areas. Occupational travel includes not only that of merchant seamen, air crews and armed forces, which is often intercontinental, but also that of people attending conferences or business gatherings at some of which 'entertainment' is provided or made available. In all these circumstances, single people, male and female, are removed from their home environments into others which may be strange, exotic and even frightening, but mainly just lonely. It is not surprising that a number of those concerned change the standard of their sexual behavior, having a relationship which otherwise they would be afraid to have for fear of discovery.

Immigration
The effects of immigration on the venereal diseases rates in Britain have been studied in some detail over the years. The results are of relevance elsewhere. The position was reviewed by Willcox (1965, 1966, 1970a) who had organized the studies. As also noted by Idsøe and Guthe (1967), he observed that, in general, immigrants did not import much venereal disease apart from syphilis, but the single men and women concerned had higher rates of infection than did the home population. In England and Wales, between 1955 and 1958, immigrants were responsible for over 75% of the increase in the ascertained incidence of gonorrhea in male patients. Up to the mid-1960s, the vast majority of immigrants were males, but such is the tendency of 'like' to consort with 'like' that a female immigrant with gonorrhea was seven times more likely to have acquired her infection from a male immigrant than from a male born in the U.K. He further noted that the high gonorrhea rate among male immigrants and among teenage females born in the U.K. overlapped only in some areas.

In considering the social reasons for the high rates of venereal disease among immigrants, Willcox stated that a number of immigrants came from areas where sexual promiscuity was common; that once in the U.K., they were removed from the restraining influence of home, family and religion; and that differences in language, color and culture made it more difficult to find suitable accommodation and to establish a steady relationship with a member of the opposite sex. Many immigrants earned far more money than they had been accustomed to previously. The sex ratio being disproportionate in favor of male immigrants, the men resorted to prostitutes and other casually promiscuous women, who benefited from the money, but had high rates of venereal infections.

Willcox did not see any hope of reduction of venereal disease in male immigrants until they were accepted into the community, and until a more equitable number of female immigrants arrived. The former part of his solution takes time and patience on both sides, but the effect of the arrival of the families of unaccompanied men can cause a dramatic fall in the rates of venereal disease as reported by Oller and Wood (1970). If immigration were confined to families or married couples, then the rates of venereal disease among immigrants would be less than that of the indigenous population.

Economic evolution

In the developed countries, especially in Europe, urbanization has been progressing at varying rates since the time of the industrial revolution. Elsewhere it has occurred later, thus, according to Idsøe and Guthe (1967), whereas only 6% of the population of the U.S. lived in cities in the year 1880, the proportion had risen to about 70% by 1960. Since World War II, industrialization has continued apace in the developed countries invading hitherto rural areas. Epidemics of venereal infections have been reported from several countries in relation to the implantation of large industrial complexes into rural areas (Idsøe and Guthe, 1967). The acceleration of population mobility in association with industrialization has also been noted in the U.K. by Willcox (1970a).

The economic evolution of the developing countries has occurred mainly in the past 30 years, the acceleration in industrialization and urbanization having been very rapid indeed. In Kenya, Verhagen and Gemmett (1972) observed that gonorrheal infections were mainly associated with the migration of single men caused by economic changes in modern Africa, while Faye (1972), reporting from Senegal, observed that while venereal diseases there were found mainly in the lower classes, there had been a sharp rise in the incidence among students aged between 16 and 18 years. He put this down to changes in habits due to the economic and social progress in the country with urbanisation and migration. Dogliotti (1971) commented on the difficulties in venereal disease control in those areas in South Africa which had only limited medical resources. Morton (1970) discussing the situation in Singapore, stated that the richer developing countries could adopt the Western style of venereal disease control successfully.

Tourism

Morton and Harris (1975) commented upon the economic independence of young people consequent upon industrialization and Idsøe and Guthe (1967) observed that economic affluence was linked with peace-time tourism in replacing the epidemiological element previously represented by the movements of armed forces. They noted that the numbers of tourists arriving in 26 countries rose from 55.25 million in 1959 to 127.99 million in 1966, an increase of 132%. Over the past few years the increase has levelled off but still masses of people, many of them young and single, visit other countries each year and contribute to the increase in gonorrhea (Guthe, 1972). Some groups of tourists have just as high infection rates as merchant seamen, who have always been noted to have very high rates (Idsøe et al., 1972).

Occupational travel

Merchant seamen comprise the largest group of occupational travelers and consequently many investigations have been made into their role in the transmission of venereal diseases. They have higher rates of venereal disease than are found among the general population (Idsøe et al., 1972) and in the past they imported a large proportion of gonorrhea found in seaports. Magnusson and Otterland (1964) found that over two-thirds acquired their infections abroad compared with about 10% for other male patients, figures similar to those quoted by Schofield (1965), who further reported that between 1960 and 1962 an average 25.6 seamen attended his clinics for every 1000 ships entering the port (Schofield, 1964a). The problem of the amount of venereal disease in seamen was noted to be increasing for some time, and was possibly related to the increase in world tonnage of shipping, which rose by 2.5 times between 1945 and 1963 according to Idsøe and Guthe (1967). Schofield (1964b) however, saw some hope that seamen would import fewer venereal infections as an increasing number of ships carried antibiotics with which to cure infections while seamen were still at sea. More recently, the various forms of commercial and business travel have been noted as playing a part in importing venereal disease (Willcox, 1972).

Armed forces stationed abroad, whether concerned in hostilities or not, still maintain high rates of venereal disease, higher among Australian volunteer regular servicemen than conscripts according to Hart (1974), who reported incidences of 12.7% and 5.2%, respectively. Greenberg (1972) had noted higher rates in soldiers serving abroad, but did not think they imported many infections into the U.S. The highest rates reported by the U.S. Army for the calender year 1970—1971 were from the Far East, in some areas in excess of 500/1000 population/year. The lowest, between 11 and 17/1000/year were from Europe. Those from the continental U.S. were 36.1/1000 year according to the ASHA (American Social Health Association, 1972, 1973). ASHA (1975) statistics show that these rates rose in 1972 in Vietnam to 61.6/1000/month. The rates in Thailand had risen to 53.4 and 54.9/1000/month, in1972 and 1973, respectively; in the U.S. they were 3.3 and 3.5/1000/month; and in Europe 1.7 and 2.3/1000/month. These different rates are obvious reflections on the disease rates among the indigenous populations.

Permissive societies

In some societies, changes in perspective and in public opinion over the past generation have come to favor and facilitate, among other things, an increase in sexual activity. In these so-called permissive societies, there is less stigma to premarital and extramarital intercourse, to illegitimacy, homosexuality and venereal disease, but the same social climate that has permitted this enlightenment has also been blamed with rises in the rates of suicide, premarital conceptions, and addictions to drugs and alcohol, paralleling the rise in the incidence of sexually transmitted diseases. There is no valid theory of cause and effect.

In his book 'Sexual Freedom and Venereal Disease', Morton (1971) surveyed the whole social background and expressed concern for the future. In a warning against the excesses of freedom or licence, depending on one's views, Wigfield (1971) came out against the controllers of mass media and the cult of the sensuous, salacious and sensational.

The confidential treatment of venereal disease in minors, without the need for parental consent or even knowledge, has now been accepted in many countries and, although it is still a controversial issue, has been welcomed in the U.K. (Br. Med. J., 1971) and in the U.S. (American Social Health Association, 1973). There are, however, some signs of a reaction against some aspects of sexual permissiveness, among which it may be noted that abortion on demand has recently been de-legalized in Romania (Teitelbaum, 1974).

Hostilities and civil strife

Ever since the siege of Naples in 1494, if not well before that time, wars have always been associated with an increase in venereal disease. Idsøe and Guthe (1967) noted that there had been a general recession in the incidence of syphilis over the past 100 years but that recrudescences occurred during war-time. More recently, the highest incidences of venereal diseases in the U.S. Army have been found in South East Asia in relation to the conflict in Vietnam, in which country the incidence in 1970 was 233/1000 troops/year. This was not as high as that in Thailand, one of the main leave or furlough areas, where the rate was 545.5/1000 troops/year, according to the American Social Health Association (1972). Hart (1974) noted that among Australian troops in Vietnam, 27% of those exposed to infection acquired venereal disease, while Morton (1974) found that the current problem of venereal disease in Bangladesh was associated with poverty and the aftermath of war.

Civil strife can also inflate venereal disease rates, firstly by disruption of medical services and secondly, by the inability of those infected to make their way to available medical services, especially if they are on the side opposed to the establishment. Siboulet and co-workers (1974) noted a substantial increase in the numbers of cases of gonorrhea in Paris at the time of the 'Student Revolution'. In an unrelated context, Harris and associates (1973) reported treating 5 cases (3 in men) of gonococcal arthritis between September 1968 and September 1971, during the civil strife in Belfast. This complication of neglected gonococcal infection is rarely seen elsewhere in the UK, and is usually found in women.

Special 'at risk' groups

Apart from population mobility, already noted, certain groups have been identified as being at special risk of acquiring sexually transmitted diseases by their behavior and social background. The greatest amount of publicity has been given recently especially in the medical press, to the teenage problem, closely followed by that of homosexuals. The sexual emancipation of women following the introduction of effective contraception and abortion on demand has brought to light other groups. Last, but by no means least, mention must be made of prostitutes, still the major source of infection in some parts of the world, while elsewhere they appear to be a dying profession.

Young people
Genuine sexual promiscuity in young people is usually associated with other evidence of social maladjustment. Most authors are agreed that the problem is worse in large cities, that many of them come from a poor social milieu and often from broken homes, they leave school early and have frequent changes of jobs, mainly of an unskilled nature. Those with venereal infections have started a full sex life earlier than others and have had many brief liaisons. Although they have had as much or as little sex education as others, they have a poor knowledge of venereal disease, and no fear of infection, together with little concern with contraception, especially among the males (Ekstrøm, 1966, 1970; Juhlin, 1968a,b; Stark-Romanus, 1973).

Among others, Morton (1971) has observed that many single young people have achieved economic independence and have a disproportionate amount of spending money compared with married couples with families. Lourie (1966) noted that there had been marked scientific and technological progress, but insufficient education of the individual to keep pace with it. Commerce and the mass media have not been slow to direct most of their advertising and propoganda towards the young who are good customers for a large range of consumer goods. The association between permissive sex and the desired goods is often underlined.

Morton (1966a) stated that young females were at special risk, and McNeil and Schofield (1973) noted that in Scotland, between 1968 and 1971, the incidence of gonorrhea in those aged 15—19 years rose, in boys from 158 to 224/100,000 but in girls from 138 to 286/100,000. Ekstrøm (1966) stated that many young girls were prostitutes or semiprostitutes, and De Lune (1971) spoke of their sexual vagabondage. A possible explanation for the reason why girls in general are at special risk is proferred by Reiss (1971) who noted that an emotionally close relationship (falling in love) influences teenaged girls and promotes permissiveness so that sexual intimacy would not be wrong. He further observes that the influence of love is not present for males.

In the course of interviews with youthful patients, aged 25 years and under, attending a special clinic, Bindemann and colleagues (1974) found that 78% of females and 16% of males cited the contraceptive pill as one of the reasons for the reported increase in sexual activity, thus confirming from the patient's point of view what many authors have been claiming, among them Juhlin (1968b) and Morton (1971).

Dominian (1972) observed that breakdown of the parents' marriage was a factor in subsequent breakdown of in the marriage of the child, while Eskstrøm (1970) warned that it was essential to prevent the often illegitimate children of teenagers inheriting their parents' poor social beckground.

Arya and Bennet (1967) observed that in Uganda there was not the usual inverse ratio between social class and the incidence of venereal disease. They noted a high incidence among freshmen at university. A similar finding among students in Dakar was reported by Faye (1972), and in Sheffield by Morton (1966c). The common factor in all the reports was that the students affected were mainly living away from home, sometimes in a foreign country.

It is usually the male who introduces a sexually transmitted disease into what has hitherto been a stable partnership, the danger being greater among those who have married as teenagers. The most common time for such an occurrance is in late pregnancy or the puerperium, when the wife does not wish to have coitus as often as previously. This sexually unfaithful behavior in expectant fathers was noted by Hartman and Nicolay (1966).

Homosexuals
Michael Schofield (1964) stated that nearly all homosexuals were fearful of social disapproval and of legal punishment. Loneliness and social isolation was reported by Bird (1965) to be the lot of many homosexuals. Bird also noted that many were very ambitious. It is not surprising that large numbers of homosexuals seek the anonimity and opportunities offered by large and capital cities (Racz, 1970) where, unfortunately, many of their V.D. contacts are untraceable according to Harris and co-workers (1972). The penile and urethral lesions of homosexuals are usually symptomatic or noticeable while those of the anus, rectum and mouth are not. Some homosexuals with penile lesions are afraid to admit the true source of their infection and blame an unknown woman.

In the U.K., it was noted in the study of the British Co-operative Clinical Group (1973) that relatively few homosexuals attended special clinics in the provinces, as compared with those in London where they were concentrated mainly in the clinics in the West End. Fluker (1972) reported that in one of those clinics, patronized by homosexuals, 82% of infectious syphilis treated between 1968 and 1971 was in homosexuals. Schofield (1964) noted that there was room for improvement in the manner in which homosexuals were treated in some clinics. Possibly, they were attracted to those clinics in which they or their friends had been treated best and vice versa, thus accounting for some of the wide variations in attendance rates.

Idsøe and Guthe (1967) commented upon the risk for homosexuals in the transmission of sexually transmitted diseases, especially of syphilis, because of promiscuity. The risk may be increased because a number might still believe that venereal diseases can only be passed between a man and a woman (Schofield, 1964). The spread of infection is even wider among those homosexuals who are bisexual, according to Neser and Parrish (1969).

Pedder (1970) found that the typical male homosexual attending a special clinic was single, aged between 20 and 40 years, and born in the U.K. His motivation for 'help' with his homosexuality was low, few accepting and fewer pursuing the offer of psychiatric help. For this, one might possibly be thankful, because it is now generally recognized that homosexuality is not a disease which is to be cured but a condition of a minority which they, and the heterosexual majority, must learn to accept.

Females
It is only since the recent introduction of effective contraceptive methods, under the direct control of women themselves, that they have achieved the same freedom to express themselves sexually as men have had throughout history. It is therefore not surprising that some will now take more sex partners than they were prepared to do when there was the fear of an unwanted pregnancy, and that more are now acquiring sexually transmitted diseases (Juhlin and Lidén, 1969). Nevertheless, there is no evidence that women in general will become as promiscuous as have been men over the ages. It might appear that some of the criticism leveled against the contraceptive pill is no more than an expression of male chauvinism.

The ready availability of effective contraception and abortion on demand in some countries, has had no effect on those women who are feckless and often casually promiscuous. These women have far higher rates of sexually transmitted diseases than do those who are discriminating in the choice of their sex partners (Thompson and Rutherford, 1972). In addition, they are producing an increasing number of illegitimate children, despite all the campaigns set up to prevent unwanted pregnancies, possibly because, while a number of them don't care one way or another, some do want to become pregnant.

Effective contraception Morton (1971) devoted a chapter to the social consequences of the contraceptive pill, and expressed reservations as to its use by single women. He expressed the view that as a direct result of its use, the accumulation of cases of long-term individual misery and venereal diseases could be calamatous. Criticism has been leveled against these Calvinistic views because only a minority abuse the effectiveness of the contraceptive pill and the intrauterine device. Juhlin and Lidén (1969) noted that the frequency of sexual intercourse and the number of partners increased after starting use of the contraceptive pill but that the incidence of gonorrhea among their female patients was the same whether or not they were taking the pill.

It has been said that the greater increase in the number of women with gonorrhea in the U.K., 106.6% of the post-war peak in 1968 compared with only 88.3% in men (Willcox, 1970b), may be due to use of effective contraception. Certainly, in England and Wales the male to female ratio fell between 1961 and 1970 from 4 : 1 to 2.2 : 1 (Morton, 1973b) and, in Scotland between 1968 and 1971, from 2 : 1 to 1.8 : 1 (McNeil and Schofield, 1973) but during those periods there had been a marked increase in the amount of effective contact-tracing carried out, which brought to treatment an increasing number of women with asymptomatic gonorrhea. Nevertheless, as has been mentioned previously, the vast proportion of female patients with sexually transmitted diseases themselves believed that the contraceptive pill was one of the reasons for the reported increase in sexual activity (Bindemann et al., 1974).

Women with other social problems   Higher rates of sexually transmitted diseases are found among girls and women initially presenting with other social problems. Thus Gallacher (1970) found that, among girls aged 14 to 17 years remanded into custody by the courts, 9% had gonorrhea and 7% were pregnant. Boys in remand homes are rarely found to have sexually transmitted diseases, their crimes usually being associated with larceny, vandalism, or crimes against the person. The girls however, have often run away from home, become casually promiscuous as a result of which pregnancy and sexually transmitted diseases are not infrequent sequelae. As a consequence of either of these, they may be rejected by their men friends and at this time suicide attempts are often made. Some are cries for help, others are deadly serious, but none should be taken lightly. The four entities of leaving home: promiscuity, pregnancy, sexually transmitted diseases and suicide attempts form a fairly regular pattern of behavior (Schofield, 1975).

Another group of women found to have higher rates of gonorrhea than expected are those requesting abortion, according to Geizer and Kopeký (1972) who reported an incidence of 8%.

Schofield (1969) investigating the medicosocial background of mothers whose babies had developed gonococcal opthalmia neonatorum shortly after birth found that many of the women had a number of adverse social factors in their lives which would have been discovered if a social history had been taken as part of their antenatal care. He cited such factors as being unmarried, having other illegitimate children, being known as promiscuous, having a recent history of venereal disease, not attending for antenatal care, teenage marriage in late pregnancy, husbands working mainly away from home, and the family living on National Assistance. In an investigation of 1000 pregnant women attending one unit in a maternity hospital, Cassie and Stevenson (1973) discovered only two cases of gonorrhea. However, gonococcal ophthalmia neonatorum was found in 4 babies whose mothers attended other units in the same hospital during the relevant period.

In the U.S., where mass screening programs have been devised to detect asymptomatic gonorrhea in women, 4.3% were found to be infected in 1971. High rates were noted in patients attending antenatal, obstetric and family planning clinics both public and private, while the highest rate of 11.6% was found among women prisoners (report of the International Travelling

Seminar on Venereal Disease in the U.S. (1973). By fiscal year 1973–1974, the overall rate had dropped to 2.7%, according to the American Social Health Association (1975).

Infertility of the husband may not normally be considered a social problem but women have been known to have been infected with gonorrhea acquired in association with artificial insemination by a donor, A.I.D. (Bakker, 1972; Fiumara, 1972).

Prostitutes Prostitution in the developed countries is mainly a problem found in large cities (Morton and Harris, 1975), and in seaports where the customers are often foreign seamen (Thompson and Rutherford, 1972). Oller and Wood (1970) noted that single immigrant men were usually infected by prostitutes who, in some areas, visited the rooming houses where the men were congregated. The proportion of men with gonorrhea acquired from prostitutes attending one London clinic fell from 31% in 1960 to 14% in 1969 according to Dunlop and co-workers (1971) while in Glasgow the proportion fell from 14.2% in 1967 to 5.3% in 1972 (Schofield, 1975).

In Africa (Verhagen and Gemmett, 1972) and the Far East (Johnson et al., 1969) prostitutes have been reported mainly to pick up men in bars, in some of which they were employed as hostesses. Some still claim that organized prostitution helps to curtail the incidence of venereal disease. Thus Luger (1971) claimed that cases of gonorrhea were 10 to 50 times more frequent among unregistered prostitutes in Vienna, than among those who were registered and controlled. On the other hand, very high rates of gonorrhea in prostitutes have been reported from many parts of the world, between 21 and 35% in Kenya according to Verhagen and Gemmett (1972), in 44% of those arrested in Australia (Wren, 1967) in 44.6% in the Phillipines following several examinations as reported by Johnson and co-workers (1969) and in as many as 80% of prostitutes in Bangladesh (Morton, 1974). The dangers of consorting with prostitutes in any part of the world are apparent. Their persistent and indiscriminate promiscuity with many unknown casual customers, which is necessary to them economically, renders them exceedingly liable to infection, despite what the apologists for prostitution may say.

It is the opinion of some that prostitution is a social evil reflecting discredit on those societies where it is prevalent. Few countries will be able to follow China where stringent controls acceptable in an atmosphere of intense political fervour have eliminated prostitution and, according to Geiger (1973), enabled the social and moral rehabilitation of the women concerned. Elsewhere, and especially in the developed countries, whenever a sufficient proportion of men are able to have sexual intercourse with the increasing numbers of women who are only intermittently promiscuous, having achieved freedom for sexual expression due to effective contraception, then prostitution will become less viable economically (Schofield, 1975).

Abuse of alcohol and drugs

The association between sexually transmitted disease and alcohol has been accepted for centuries, but in recent years attention has been focussed on the nontherapeutic drugs as well. In some cases they have supplemented and in others supplanted alcohol. Similarly, as far as commercial vice is concerned, prostitution is associated with narcotics as well as alcohol abuse. It would appear that many men, and women also, require the lowering of their inhibitions before they can partake of promiscuous sexual intercourse. Moreover, it is chiefly in bars that strangers to a town or city, or even lonely inhabitants, can meet and make friends, at short acquaintance, with others.

Alcohol abuse

As one of the factors in the increase in sexually transmitted diseases, Morton and Harris (1975) have noted the increase in alcohol consumption in many parts of the world, while the close association between alcohol and acquiring gonorrhea from an unknown contact was pointed out by Wells and Schofield (1970). About 90% of the men and women concerned had been to a bar or hotel, even if they had not met there. The proportions actually having met in a bar varied from 10% for teenagers to 75% for those aged 50 years and over.

It is not surprising that, in the armed forces, higher rates of venereal diseases are found among servicemen who drink heavily, alcohol abuse still being a major factor leading to infection in the Royal Navy according to Wheldon (1964). The same was also observed by Brody (1948) during World War II and by Hart (1973) in Vietnam, both noting that those men concerned also had high rates of military charges and civil arrests. Juhlin (1968a) noted that alcohol was a common problem among those patients of his who were not students. It was especially severe among males aged from 20 to 25 years and in women aged 25 years and over.

That alcohol is a positive factor in facilitating casual acquaintances to have sexual intercourse, is seen in the work of Bindemann and colleagues (1974). Of the male patients interviewed, 64% reported that alcohol made their women acquaintances more willing to have sex, while 54% of the female patients stated that alcohol made them more relaxed. Furthermore, 48% of the women claimed that alcohol increased their interest in and enjoyment of sexual intercourse.

Drug abuse

There are wide variations in the reported incidence of drug taking among patients with sexually transmitted diseases. Linken (1968) found that 23% of females and 18.8% of males admitted to drug experiences, mainly with cannabis and amphetamine, while the incidences were 45% and 63%, respectively, in another clinic (Rawlins, 1969). Ponting and Nicol (1970), also reporting from London, found that only 3.1% of their patients who were interviewed admitted to being drug users.

In Glasgow between 1970 and 1972, 15% of patients aged from 16 to 24 years admitted to having taken nontherapeutic drugs within a week of interview. In all, 43% of male patients and 36% of females admitted to having taken drugs at some time, and usually more than one drug. Of male drug takers, 93% had used cannabis, 43% lysergic acid diethylamide (LSD), 34% oral barbiturates and amphetamines, 19% tranquillizers and 12% intravenous heroin. Of the females who had taken drugs, 79% had used cannabis, 34% LSD, 29% oral barbiturates, 22% amphetamine, 14% tranquillizers and 12% intravenous heroin. It is worthy of note that prior to local voluntary control by Glasgow doctors in the prescribing of barbiturates and amphetamines in 1971, the incidence of their misuse by females had been 65% and 50%, respectively, and by males 40% for both types of drugs (Schofield, 1975).

Patients claim that drugs do have an effect on their enjoyment of sexual intercourse. According to Linken (1968), males thought that drugs improved their sexual feelings while females felt that theirs were decreased. Bindemann and co-workers (1974) obtained different opinions from their patients. An improvement in sexual intercourse was generally associated with cannabis by both males and females, and by barbiturates, especially Mandrax, by females alone, but only occasionally by LSD in either sex. Males and females differed in the manner in which they appreciated the improvement. Males rated most highly the increase in sex drive, then the prolongation of coitus and finally the heightened climax. Females, on the other hand, allowing that coitus was prolonged, appreciated more the relaxation which the drugs gave them, as a result of which there was a greater chance of achieving an orgasm which was heightened.

It appears that drug taking and sexual promiscuity are associated. In Glasgow, Bindemann (1974) found that drug takers of both sexes had had, on average, 37% more sex partners than nondrug takers of the same age group. Smith and Rose (1968) found that there was a higher incidence of venereal disease among drug takers than among controls attending the Haight-Ashbury medical clinic of San Francisco. Blair (1946) noted that the incidence of syphilis in women imprisoned for liquor or narcotic offences was higher than that for those convicted on sex charges. Possibly the former had been less discriminating in the choice of their sex partners in their urgent need to get sufficient money for the liquor or narcotics. Certainly, a number of female addicts have turned to prostitution, and vice versa, whereas the male addicts usually obtain the money by theft, especially by mugging.

Education and information

In general it might be said that the subjects of sex and venereal diseases were considered taboo until well into the 20th century. Even today, specialists from throughout the world continue to urge the need for more and better education, in these subjects, of medical and paramedical personnel as well as of the public at large. This need has become apparent because of the world-wide increase in sexually transmitted diseases despite the availability of the drugs with which to cure them.

It is the responsibility of each government to give its citizens every opportunity of leading a healthy life, and so to educate them. An uneducated public cannot be expected to cooperate with those attempting to help it. To inform the public effectively, all health education material must be presented in a manner which is understandable and acceptable. To do this efficiently, sufficient finance has to be allocated to health education and units set up specializing in the dissemination of information, staffed by specialists in the field of advertising, education and medicine. It is the responsibility of local authorities to make the fullest use of all health education material available and of the specialist in sexually transmitted diseases to give advice to those producing health education material as to the contents so that the facts are accurate (Schofield, 1975).

With regard to the dissemination of information mention must be made of the World Health Organization's 'Documents on Venereal Diseases and Treponematoses' which are available free of charge to those interested, as is 'Current Literature on Venereal Diseases' published by the U.S. Department of Health, Education and Welfare. Two internationally established journals concerned with sexually transmitted diseases in the broadest sense are the 'British Journal of Venereal Diseases', edited for the Medical Society for the Study of Venereal Diseases and published by the British Medical Journal and 'Information sur les Malades Vénériennes,' published by the Institut Alfred-Fournier on behalf of la Société Française de Prophylaxie Sanitaire et Morale and la Ligue Nationale Française contre le Péril Vénérien. Publication by the American Venereal Diseases Association of an 'American Journal of Venereal Diseases' was announced in 1974 and one hopes and expects that in a short period of time it will establish itself in the international field. Between them, the publications mentioned cover all the important work on sexually transmitted diseases being carried out throughout the world.

Professional awareness
In general, the medical profession has appeared unaware of and uninterested in the problems associated with sexually transmitted diseases, their correct diagnosis and treatment, and especially of the need to trace and treat the sexual contacts of those infected. This is due, in part, to the fact that those doctors trained in the 1950s when there were few cases, received inadequate instruction, especially as it was considered at that time that the effective treatments then available would cure all cases. Under the auspices of the International Union against the Venereal Diseases and Treponematoses and with the cooperation of the World Health Organization, Webster (1966) circularized a questionnaire asking for information as to the teaching of venereal diseases to 709 medical schools throughout the world. From the 450 which replied, it appeared that interest in the social aspects was not great

while the public health and epidemiological aspects appeared to be receiving only a minimal amount of attention. He expressed the need for an expansion of teaching and for a realignment of interest along the lines of the newer aspects of venereal disease control. That universities and medical schools were slow to take up the challenge can be seen from the report of a subcommittee on sexually transmitted diseases set up in Scotland (Scottish Home and Health Department, 1973) which, among other things, pointed out the need for universities to review their policy for providing teaching about sexual problems and the sexually transmitted diseases and from Webster (1972) who still found in the U.S. that there was inadequate undergraduate teaching and a need to recruit specialists into the subject.

The situation in the U.S. has been under close scrutiny in recent years. In 1971, the government set up a National Commission on Venereal Diseases (1972) while many parts of the country were visited by teams from the Travelling Seminar on Venereal Disease in the U.S. (1973). The reports of both groups recommended expansion of training of medical undergraduates and the development of postgraduate education in sexually transmitted diseases, in order to produce specialists in the subject, albeit associated with some allied specialty. It was also noted (Webster, 1970) that one of the great problems of disease control in the U.S. was that the majority of cases of venereal disease were treated privately, without notification of the authorities, and without contact-tracing action taken, conditions as bad as those in Bangladesh where Morton (1974) found that 5—6 times as many with gonorrhea got treatment privately rather than from public authority clinics.

Wood (1974) noted among medical students and interns in California, as have others elsewhere, that many feel inadequate to help patients with such complaints as impotence, frigidity, masturbation and homosexuality, and that a number had problems of a sexual nature themselves. They felt that medical education had failed to increase their intellectual comprehension of sexuality. The author urged the need for the interdisciplinary teaching of sexuality which should include sociology, psychology and anthropology.

Public awareness
The public should be made aware of the clinical facilities available in each locality. This information should be so widely displayed that the general public, whether strangers or local inhabitants, do not have to make great efforts to seek it out. Until recently this sort of advertising was mainly covert, notices being posted in a few public lavatories. Nowadays, in many areas, the notices can be found in the open. In some localities notices are accepted by the press, and information given over the radio or on television. Telephone directories often list the addresses of the local V.D. Clinics and in addition, a special phone number is reserved for a recorded message giving information as to the times that the clinics are open, their locality and their phone numbers. Wells and Schofield (1970) noted certain 'target' sites for

such information and urged that it should be available in the lavatories and elsewhere in bars and dance halls where many casual contacts are made.

There is little public awareness of the problems of sexually transmitted diseases. Factual knowledge is usually poor and often inaccurate. Even when there is any amount of knowledge the possibility of involvement, either personally or of a friend or relative, is usually discounted. Seale (1966) found that married persons who had never had extramarital intercourse were the least well informed, while Morton (1973b) found that best informed were men aged 25 years and over, and the worst informed were women of the same age group. Under the age of 25 years, both sexes were equally well informed through schooling, films, lectures and discussions as well as from television and magazines. The value of the mass media was discussed by Fluker (1966). The need for the wider dissemination of information and education of the public in the U.S. was made by the National Commission on Venereal Diseases (1972) and by the Travelling Seminar on Venereal Disease (1973); and in the U.K. by Morton (1966b), following his circular of a questionnaire to British venereologists asking their opinions on the education of the public about venereal diseases. Most of them felt that they could best help teach the eventual teachers of the public, but some had reservations as to the effect of health education in controlling the spread of venereal disease, certainly as it was carried out at that time. With regard to teaching school children about venereal disease, Neser and Wiechmann (1967) found that teachers in training supported compulsory instruction. Not only were the vast majority prepared to teach it, but all would have permitted their own children to be taught. They believed that effective teaching would reduce the risks of the pupils catching venereal disease and encourage prompt attendance should an infection be acquired. Lack of concern with obtaining a correct diagnosis and proper treatment together with the problem of antibiotics, freely available to the public in Lebanon, was noted by Atallah (1972), who expressed the need for stricter control.

Many campaigns to educate the public have proven fruitless and a waste of money. Dalzell-Ward (1973) discussed the preliminary research required prior to health education campaigns concerning sexually transmitted diseases. First it is necessary to study the target group in the population, to ascertain the disease incidence in the group, and be fully informed with regard to the demographic characteristics of the area in which the operation is to be carried out. Later assessments must be made of the impact of each communication method on the target group.

Stark-Romanus (1973) reported on an apparently successful sex education campaign carried out in Sweden using posters. Essentially the style was humorous and the text simple. A tolerant attitude was portrayed without any moralizing. That it has been acceptable and effective might be inferred by the reported decrease in the number of cases of gonorrhea in Sweden from 38,885 in 1970 to 26,490 in 1973 (American Social Health Association, 1975).

1004

BIBLIOGRAPHY

American Social Health Association (1972, 1973, 1975) *Today's V.D. Control Problem,* (American Social Health Association, New York) p. 19, 1972; pp. 16, 26, 1973; pp. 20, 50, 62, 1975.

Arya, O.P. and Bennett, F.J. (1967) Venereal disease in an elite group (university students) in East Africa. *Br. J. Vener. Dis.* 43: 275—279.

Atallah, F. (1972) Gonorrhoea in the Middle East. *Postgrad. Med. J.* 48: suppl. 1, 38—43.

Bakker, P. (1972) *Iatrogenic gonorrhoea.* (Paper read at the Jubilee Meeting of the Medical Society for the Study of Venereal Diseases, Glasgow. 8—11 June, 1972.)

Bindemann, S. (1974) *A Study of Drug Taking and Personality in a Special Clinic Population.* (Thesis submitted to University of Strathclyde, U.K.)

Bindemann, S., Martin, F.M. and Schofield, C.B.S. (1974) *Preliminary Report of Research into Personality, Family Dynamics and the Social Background of Patients Attending the Special Clinics in Glasgow,* (submitted to the Scottish Home and Health Department).

Bird, M.S. (1965) Some emotional problems dealt with in a special clinic. *Br. J. Vener. Dis.* 41: 217—220.

Blair, H.I. (1946) The venereal disease problem in a women's federal reformatory. *Am. J. Syph. Gonorrhea Vener. Dis.* 30: 165—172.

Boneff, A.N. (1971) Psychopathology in V.D. practice. *Ind. J. Dermatol.* 16: 51—54.

British Cooperative Clinical Group (1973) Homosexuality and venereal disease in the United Kingdom. *Br. J. Ven. Dis.* 49: 329—334.

British Medical Journal (1971) Leading article on legal aspects of V.D. in teenagers. *Br. Med. J.* 1: 190.

Brody, M.W. (1948) Men who contract venereal disease. *J. Vener. Dis. Inform.* 29: 334—337.

Cassie, R. and Stevenson, A. (1973) Screening for gonorrhoea, trichomoniasis, moniliasis and syphilis in pregnancy. *J. Obstet. Gynaecol. Br. Commonw.* 80: 48—51.

Catterall, R.D. (1965) Venereal disease and teenagers. *Practitioner* 195: 620—627.

Cornelius, C.E. (1971) Seasonality of gonorrhea in the United States. *Health Services and Mental Health Administration Health Reports* 86: 157—160.

Dalzell-Ward, A.J. (1973) The design of action research experimental campaigns. *Br. J. Vener. Dis.* 49: 171—173.

Darrow, W.W. (1971) *Selected References on the Behavioral Aspects of Venereal Disease Control.* (U.S. Department of Health, Education and Welfare, Washington, D.C.)

Datt, I. (1971) Psycho-social aspects of venereal disease in teenagers. *Ind. J. Dermatol.* 16: 27—35.

De Lune, H. (1971) Epidemiological trend of gonorrhoea in recent years. *Br. J. Vener. Dis.* 47: 377.

Dogliotti, M. (1971) The incidence of syphilis in the Bantu. Survey of 587 cases from Baragwanath hospital. *South Afr. Med. J.* 45: 8—10.

Dominian, J. (1972) Marital pathology. A review. *Postgrad. Med. J.* 48: 517—525.

Dunlop, E.M.C., Lamb, A.M. and King, D.M. (1971) Improved tracing of contacts of heterosexual men with gonorrhoea. *Br. J. Vener. Dis.* 47: 192—195.

Ekstrøm, K. (1966) One hundred teenagers in Copenhagen infected with gonorrhoea. A socio-psychiatric study. *Br. J. Vener. Dis.* 42: 162—166.

Ekstrøm, K. (1970) Patterns of sexual behaviour in relation to venereal disease. *Br. J. Ven. Dis.* 46: 93—95.

Faye, I. (1972) Epidemiological aspects of gonococcal infections in Dakar. *Postgrad. Med. J.* 48: Supplement 1, 43—45.

Fiumara, N.J. (1972) Transmission of gonorrhoea by artificial insemination. *Br. J. Vener. Dis.* 48: 308—309.

Fluker, J.L. (1966) Venereal disease and the public. *Br. J. Vener. Dis.* 42: 244—246.

Fluker, J.L. (1972) Syphilis. *Practitioner* 209: 605—613.

Gallacher, E. (1970) Genital infection in young delinquent girls. *Br. J. Vener. Dis.* 46: 129—131.

Garcia, J.C. (1971) Aspectos psicológicos, sociales y culturales de las enfermedades venéreas (Psychological, social and cultural aspects of venereal diseases). *Bol. Ofic. Sanit. Panam.* (Wash.) 70: 79—94.

Geiger, J. (1973) Behind the bamboo curtain. *World Med.* 8 (22) 15—23.

Geizer, E. and Kopeký, K. (1972) *Gonorrhoea in a selected group of women requesting abortion.* (World Health Organization VDT/72.379)

Giard, R. (1972) Male gonococcal urethritis and its psycho-emotional effects. *Postgrad. Med. J.* 48, suppl. 1: 47—53.

Glass, L.H. (1967) An analysis of some characteristics of males with gonorrhoea. *Br. J. Vener. Dis.* 43: 128—132.

Greenberg, J.H. (1972) Venereal disease in the armed forces. *Med. Clin. North Am.* 56: 5, 1087—1100.

Guthe, T. (1972) Present status of gonorrhoea control. *Postgrad. Med. J.* 48: suppl. 1, 7—11.

Guthe, T., Ridet, J., Vorst, F., D'Costa, J. and Grab, B. (1972) Methods for the surveillance of endemic treponematoses and sero-immunological investigations of "disappearing" disease. *Bull. WHO* 46: 1—14.

Harris, J.R.W., Mahony, J.D.H., Holland, J. and McCann, J.S. (1972) Sexually transmitted diseases in homosexual relationships. *J. Irish Med. Assoc.* 65: 62—64.

Harris, J.R.W., McCann, J.S. and Mahony, J.D.H. (1973) Gonococcal arthritis — a common rarity. *Br. J. Vener. Dis* 49: 42—47.

Hart, G. (1973) Social aspects of venereal disease II. Relationship of personality to other sociological determinants of venereal disease. *Br. J. Vener. Dis.* 49: 548 552.

Hart, G. (1974) Factors influencing venereal infection in a war environment. *Br. J. Vener. Dis.* 50: 68—72.

Hartman, A.A. and Nicolay, R.C. (1966) Sexually deviant behavior in expectant fathers. *J. Abnorm. Psychol.* 71: 232 234.

Idsøe, O. and Guthe, T. (1967) The rise and fall of the treponematoses: 1. Ecological aspects and international trends in venereal syphilis. *Br. J. Vener. Dis.* 43: 227 243.

Idsøe, O., Rizzo, N. and Guthe, T. (1972) *Venereal diseases among Italian seafarers.* (World Health Organization VDT/72.378.)

Johnson, D.W., Holmes, K.K., Kvale, P.A., Halverson, C.W. and Hirsch, P.A. (1969) An evaluation of gonorrhea case finding in the chronically infected female. *Am. J. Epidemiol.* 90: 438—448.

Juhlin, L. (1968a) Factors influencing the spread of gonorrhoea. 1. Educational and social behaviour. *Acta Dermato-venereol. (Stockholm)* 48: 75—81.

Juhlin, L. (1968b) Factors influencing the spread of gonorrhoea. ii. Sexual behaviour at different ages. *Acta Dermato-venereol. (Stockholm)* 48: 82—89.

Juhlin, L. and Lidén, S. (1969) Influence of contraceptive gestogen pills on sexual behaviour and the spread of gonorrhoea. *Br. J. Vener. Dis.* 45: 321—324.

Kelus, J. (1973) Social and behavioural aspects of venereal disease. *Br. J. Vener. Dis.* 49: 167—170.

Kite, E. de C. (1971) Good personality breakdown in patients attending venereal diseases clinics. *Br. J. Vener. Dis.* 47: 135—141.

Linken, A. (1968) A study of drug-taking among young patients attending a clinic for venereal diseases. *Br. J. Vener. Dis.* 44: 337—341.

Lourie, R.S. (1966) Mental health aspects of venereal disease in adolescents. *Arch. Environ. Health* 12: 684—685.

Luger, A.F. (1971) Problems concerning gonorrhoea in Austria. *Br. J. Vener. Dis.* 47: 378.

McNeil, N. and Schofield, C.B.S. (1973) Sexually transmitted diseases in Scotland 1968—1971. *Health Bull. (Edin.)* 31: 61—66.

Magnusson, B. and Otterland, A. (1964) An intensified international programme to combat venereal disease in young seafarers. *Acta Dermato-venereol.* (Stockholm) 44: 141—145.

Mbanefo, S.E. (1968) Emotional problems of gonorrhoea. *J. R. Coll. Gen. Pract.* 15: 272—279.

Morton, R.S. (1966a) Social aspects of gonorrhoea in the female. *Med. Gynaecol. Sociol.* 1: 2—6.

Morton, R.S. (1966b) Education of the public about venereal diseases. Some views of venereologists. *Br. J. Vener. Dis.* 42: 238—243.

Morton, R.S. (1966c) Students as special clinic patients. *Br. J. Vener. Dis.* 42: 280—282.

Morton, R.S. (1970) Modern trends in diagnosis, treatment and control of the venereal diseases. *Singapore Med. J.* 11: 214—221.

Morton, R.S. (1971) *Sexual Freedom and Venereal Disease.* (Peter Owen, London) pp. 68—70, 75—91.

Morton, R.S. (1973a) Social indicators and venereal disease. *Br. J. Vener. Dis.* 49: 155—156.

Morton, R.S. (1973b) Public education and V.D. control in Great Britain. *Proc. 3rd Int. Vener. Dis. Symp.* (New Orleans May 31—June 2, 1973.)

Morton, R.S. (1974) Venereal diseases in Bangladesh. *Br. J. Vener. Dis.* 50: 64—67.

Morton, R.S. and Harris, J.R.W. (1975) *Recent Advances in Sexually Transmitted Diseases.* (Churchill Livingstone, London, Edinburgh and New York.)

National Commission on Venereal Disease (1972) *Report to the Assistant Secretary for Health and Scientific Affairs, Department of Health, Education and Welfare.* (DHEW Publication No. (HSM) 72-8125.)

Neser, W.B. and Wiechmann, G.H. (1967) Attitudes of prospective school teachers on teaching venereal disease information. *Public Health Rep.* 82: 917—920.

Neser, W.B. and Parrish, H.M. (1969) Importance of homosexuals and bisexuals in the epidemiology of syphilis. *South. Med. J.* 62: 177—180.

Novotny, F. (1971) Psychologické aspekty ve venerologi (Psychological aspects in venereology). *Cesk. Dermatol.* (Praha) 46: 77—82.

Oller, L.Z. and Wood, T. (1970) Factors influencing the incidence of gonorrhoea and non-gonococcal urethritis in men in an industrial city. *Br. J. Vener. Dis.* 46: 96—102.

Palmgren, L. (1966) Sociopsychiatric investigation of teenage girls with gonorrhoea. *Acta Psychiat. Scand.* 42: 295—314.

Pedder, J.R. (1970) Psychiatric referral of patients in a venereal diseases clinic. *Br. J. Vener. Dis.* 46: 54—57.

Pemberton, J., McCann, J.S., Mahony, J.D.H., MacKenzie, G., Dougan, H. and Hay, I. (1972) Socio-medical characteristics of patients attending a V.D. clinic and the circumstances of infection. *Br. J. Vener. Dis.* 48: 391—396.

Ponting, L.I. and Nicol, C.S. (1970) Drug dependence among patients attending a department of venereology. *Br. J. Vener. Dis.* 46: 111—113.

Racz, I. (1970) Homosexuality among syphilitic patients. *Br. J. Vener. Dis.* 46: 117.

Rawlins, D.C. (1969) Drug-taking by patients with venereal disease. *Br. J. Vener. Dis.* 45: 238—240.

Reiss, I.L. (1971) *The Family System in America.* (Holt, Rinehart and Winston, New York) pp. 151—181.

Report of the International Travelling Seminar on Venereal Disease in the United States of America. (World Health Organization, Scientific Publication No. 280.)

Schofield, C.B.S. (1964a) The epidemiology of venereal disease in visiting mariners. *Acta Dermato-venereol.* (Stockholm) 44: 445—459.

Schofield, C.B.S. (1964b) Treatment of mariners suffering from urethritis before attendance at a V.D. clinic. *Br. J. Vener. Dis.* 40: 181—190.

Schofield, C.B.S. (1965) Venereal disease imported by mariners. *Br. J. Vener. Dis.* 41: 51—59.

Schofield, C.B.S. (1969) Medicosocial background to gonoccal ophthalmia neonatorum. *Lancet* 2: 1182—1185.

Schofield, C.B.S. (1975) *Sexually Transmitted Diseases*, 2nd edn, (Churchill Livingstone, Edingburgh, London and New York.)

Schofield, C.B.S., Wilson, E., Patel, A.R., McGhie, T. and Wilson, G.M. (1975) Blood ethanol concentrations of patients attending special (V.D.) Clinics. *Br. J. Vener. Dis.* 51: 340—344

Schofield, M. (1964) Social aspects of homosexuality. *Br. J. Vener. Dis.* 40: 129 104.

Scottish Home and Health Department (1973) *Sexually Transmitted Diseases*. Report of a joint sub-committee. (H.M.S.O. Edinburgh.)

Seale, J.R. (1966) The sexually transmitted diseases and marriage. *Br. J. Vener. Dis.* 42: 31—36.

Siboulet, A., Neil, G., Egger, L., Majewski, E. and Busquet, P.Y. (1974) *Gonococcal infection of the uro-genital tract. Clinical, therapeutic and epidemiological study*, 1961—1972. (World Health Organisation, VDT/74.392.)

Singh, K., Mohamed, F. and Sukija, C.L. (1966) Psychosocial background of servicemen contracting venereal diseases. *J. Ind. Med. Assoc.* 46: 270 274.

Smith, D.E. and Rose, A.J. (1968) Observations in the Haight-Ashbury medical clinic of San Francisco: health problems in a 'Hippie' subculture. *Clin. Pediat.* 7: 313—316.

Stark-Romanus, V. (1973) Social and behavioural aspects of venereal disease. *Br. J. Vener. Dis.* 19: 163—166.

Teitelbaum, M. (1974) The de-legalisation of abortion in Romania. *Fam. Plann.* 23: 38 41.

Thompson, B. and Rutherford, H.W. (1972) Aberdeen venereal diseases clinic, 1960—1969. Perspective on female attenders. *Br. J. Vener. Dis.* 48: 209—217.

Verhagen, A.R. and Gemmett, W. (1972) Social and epidemiological determinants of gonorrhoea in an East African country. *Br. J. Vener. Dis.* 48: 277—286.

Webster, B. (1966) Teaching of venereal diseases in medical schools throughout the world. *Br. J. Vener. Dis.* 42: 132—133.

Webster, B. (1970) Venereal disease control in the United States of America. *Br. J. Vener. Dis.* 46: 406—411.

Webster, B. (1972) Professional education and the control of the venereal diseases. *Med. Clin. North. Am* 56: 5, 1101—1104.

Wells, B.W.P. (1969) Personality characteristics of V.D. patients. *Br. J. Soc. Clin. Psychol.* 8: 246—252.

Wells, B.W.P. (1970) Personality study of V.D. patients using the psychoticism, extroversion, neuroticism inventory, *Br. J. Vener. Dis.* 46: 498—501.

Wells, B.W.P. and Schofield, C.B.S. (1970) 'Target' sites for anti-V.D. propaganda. *Health Bull. (Edinburgh)* 28 (1) 75—77.

Wells, B.W.P. and Schofield, C.B.S. (1972) Personality characteristics of homosexual men suffering from sexually transmitted diseases. *Br. J. Vener. Dis.* 48: 75—78.

Wheldon, G.R. (1964) A poor man's 'Kinsey'. *J. R. Nav. Med. Serv.* 4: 342—345.

Wigfield, A.S. (1971) Attitudes to venereal disease in a permissive society. *Br. Med. J.* 4: 342—345.

Willcox, R.R. (1965) Venereal disease and immigrants. *Practitioner* 195: 628—638.

Willcox, R.R. (1966) Immigration and venereal disease in Great Britain. *Br. J. Vener. Dis.* 42: 225—237.

Willcox, R.R. (1970a) Immigration and venereal disease in England and Wales. *Br. J. Vener. Dis.* 46: 412—422.

Willcox, R.R. (1970b) Perspectives in venereology — 1969. *Abstr. Hyg.* 45: 993—1026.

Willcox, R.R. (1972) A world-wide view of venereal disease. *Br. J. Vener. Dis.* 48: 163—176.

Wood, S. (1974) The sexual problems of doctors. *Br. J. Sex. Med.* 1 (4) 9—13.

Wren, B.G. (1967) Gonorrhoea among prostitutes. *Med. J. Aust.* 1: 847—848.

CHAPTER 81

Venereal diseases

R.S. MORTON

1. INTRODUCTION

The term 'venereal diseases' is a restricted one and nowadays covers only a proportion of a growing number of diseases which may be transmitted from person to person during sexual activity. In some countries venereal diseases have been, and still are, defined by law. For example, in the U.K., the term applies only to syphilis, gonorrhea and chancroid. With increasing recognition of the wide variety of infections which may be listed as sexually transmissible, the term 'venereal disease' is bound to become outmoded. It is used here only for convenience, and in this instance, will cover syphilis, gonorrhea, lymphogranuloma venereum, chancroid and donovanosis.

2. SYPHILIS

Historical background

There are a number of diseases in the world recognized as treponemal in origin, that is, they are caused by a treponeme, a small corkscrew-like organism formerly called a spirochete. The most notable member of this group is syphilis. It has world-wide distribution and with few exceptions, is acquired by sexually active adolescents and adults during sexual contact. An endemic form of syphilis may be acquired by social rather than by sexual contact. It is now nearly extinct. Other treponemal infections, namely yaws, pinta, bejel and a few others in Africa are diseases acquired usually by children during social contact. Many such social treponemal diseases were formerly predominant in Europe.

Discussion of the origin of syphilis generally surrounds the epidemic of the so-called Morbus gallicus which raged throughout Europe from about 1496 to 1610. There are two schools of thought on the origin of this epi-

Handbook of Sexology, edited by J. Money and H. Musaph
© *Elsevier/North-Holland Biomedical Press, 1977*

demic. The Unitarian theory gives it that the many treponemal diseases are one and the same infection, clinical presentation varying with social conditions, personal habits, climate and, perhaps, absence of herd immunity. Thus, Unitarians talk of treponematosis in contrast to the supporters of the Columbian theory who see the treponemal diseases as separate clinical entities and so talk of treponematoses.

The first theory believes that the European epidemic began as a disease of Africa which, on introduction in Europe, overwhelmed the previously unaffected and vulnerable population. This theory sees the disease as originally one of social contact of near-naked people in a hot and humid climate, changing to a disease of sexual contact between generally clothed people, in a colder climate, whose warm and moist areas met only during sexual activity. Some Unitarians believe that the European treponemes may have existed in that continent and suddenly developed a new and deadly virulence.

The Columbian theorists give it that the infection which was to rage throughout Europe, was introduced by the sailors of Columbus on their return from discovering the New World. According to this theory, no sooner had the disease arrived in Europe, than it spread like wild-fire throughout the continent.

The division between Unitarian and Columbian opinion is understandable, for it is well recognized that the treponemes in each and all the diseases mentioned are morphologically indistinguishable and that they prompt the appearance of the same series of antibodies in the blood of infected persons. These antibodies may be detected by a wide variety of serological tests.

Whatever the truth, the epidemic of the Morbus gallicus subsided in the course of a century and it is not until the early 17th century that clinical descriptions match those of the syphilis we recognize today.

A third theory has recently been put forward. It suggests that two forms of treponemal disease, one from Africa and one from the New World coexisted in Europe throughout the 16th century and together, and undifferentiated, formed the Morbus gallicus. This theory does go some way to explain the bizarre clinical appearances reported in the early years of the outbreak, the various changes of the appearance of the diseases during the 16th century and the later recognition of the co-existence in Europe of both venereally acquired syphilis and other socially acquired forms of treponemal disease.

Epidemiological considerations

Syphilis is recognized as a world-wide endemic infection. This endemic state is seen as punctuated from time to time by epidemic peaks. In the last couple of centuries, these peaks have tended to be less marked. They continue in parts of the world to be associated with war and poverty particularly when these occur together. During and after World War II, the incidence of syphilis was therefore high. It fell within a few years and this occurred not only because of the absence of the war situation and the discovery and use of penicillin, but because of actively pursued control measures. In the second half of the 1950s, however, some countries began reporting increased numbers of fresh syphilitic infections. By 1962, 76 of 105 countries were reporting rises in the disease to the World Health Organization. The upward trend has continued and is slowly spreading to involve one country after another. According to a United Nation's report, referring to 1967 "there are in the world between 20 million and 50 million cases of venereal syphilis".

This recrudescence has occurred during years of relative peace in the world and in times of growing prosperity. Almost everywhere the trend has tended to follow, by two to five years, a similar trend in the prevalence of gonorrhea. There are many reasons for the differing epidemiological picture in the two infections. Syphilis is not as infectious as gonorrhea. More often than in gonorrhea, more than one exposure is required to become infected with syphilis. So the chances are greater that the sex partner or contact of a syphilitic is known, or at least is more easily traceable. Furthermore, a syphilitic is more easily and certainly rendered noninfectious by antibiotics. Prescribing of antibiotics is extremely common. Their frequent use in infections generally, and in gonorrhea in particular, may well have aborted, masked or cured many concomitant syphilitic infections, and so have effected a measure of control.

The cause, course and cure

The causative organism of syphilis is called the treponema pallidum or the pale treponeme. Its length is little greater than that of the diameter of a red blood cell. It spirals on itself, has a slight concertina action and is given much to angling in a brisk but elegant fashion. In the early stages of infection, it doubles its numbers within the body every thirty hours or so. So, if at the time of the infecting exposure, the new victim acquires 1000 treponemes, by the time the first ulcer appears, usually three weeks after infection, the body is harboring at least ten million treponemes.

The primary sore or ulcer, sometimes called a chancre, usually appears on the genitals. In about a quarter of infected women it arises on or in the cervix of the uterus. Infected passive homosexuals may have peri-anal or rectal chancres. Extragenital primary sores are commonest on lips or fingers. Typical chancres are single, and up to 1 cm in diameter. They are regularly edged, regularly based, hard and button-like and have a tendency to ooze serum and develop a crust. Unless secondarily infected they are seldom painful. Less frequently, primary syphilis may present as multiple, small ulcers of fleeting duration. It is therefore wise to treat all genital sores as syphilitic until serum from them has been repeatedly searched, microscopically, for the causative organism. Blood tests for syphilis are of very limited value in the first 5 to 6 weeks — that is, the results are negative. It is only after this space of time that antibody levels rise high enough to make blood-test results positive.

The body mobilizes other defenses. The ulcerated area and the local lymph glands which defend the primary site of infection become packed with defensive white cells. Typically, in the groins, these glands enlarge and can be felt as discrete and rubbery. These defenses are, however, soon breached. Widespread dissemination of treponemes supervenes, and all organs are invaded in some degree. The presence of the all-pervasive treponemes is most obvious in the most widespread and obvious organ of the body, the skin. Typically, the rash is not itchy; it is coppery-red and symmetrically distributed. For example, it may appear on the fronts of both forearms or on the soles of both feet. Sores may also appear in the mouth. The appearance of the skin rash varies according to the type of skin the patient has, the state of personal hygiene, and the duration of the infection. Furthermore the rash tends to come and go and shows a tendency to localization and fading.

Syphilitic rashes frequently imitate other skin diseases and may well deceive both patient and doctor. Antibodies to the circulating treponemes are always present in this second stage of the disease and so blood tests are always positive. Common accompaniments of the second stage are mild fever, aches and pains, anemia, tiredness and falling hair. Certain organs may be seriously involved, for example, the liver, giving rise to hepatitis and jaundice, or the meninges, giving rise to subacute meningitis with cranial nerve involvement. Syphilitic tonsillitis and laryngitis are not uncommon.

The infectious second stage lasts no longer than four years. Thereafter the disease enters the latent or dormant stage when it can be detected only by blood tests. Although latent syphilis is not contagious, it may be transmissible by an infected women to her unborn child.

If undetected, latent syphilis may last from 5 to 50 years. Thus, many live and die without their disease being found and treated. Some are inadvertantly cured, or partially cured, by antibiotics given for some other infection. In about 1 in 4 however, syphilis redeclares itself sooner or later in a chronic, crippling or killing form. This may be as skin lesions or as a single gamma — a syphilitic tumor with a tendency to ulcerate. More usual however, are cardiovascular or neurological complications. The first of these leads to cardiac crippling and is the commonest cause of death from the disease. The second may take the form of a paralysis of the legs, sometimes with blindness, and is known as tabes dorsalis or locomotor ataxia. Parenchymatous involvement of the brain gives rise to general paralysis of the insane (GPI) or syphilitic insanity. About a third of cases of GPI are, inspite of treatment, unable to maintain themselves in society. Their permanent hospitalization may last many years and be very costly. About 2% of all beds allocated to the mental health services in the U.K. are at present occupied by such cases. In the Republic of Singapore in 1970 the corresponding figure was 4%. Hospitalization of syphilitic cardiac cripples and the syphilitic blind add to these costs.

An expectant mother may infect her fetus only after formation of the placenta. The more recent the mother's infection, the more likely she is to transfer her infection and the more likely it is that the fetus will be overwhelmed and killed. All gradations of congenital infection may occur. The mother may abort; miscarry late in pregnancy; have a stillborn child; have a live but obviously infected baby; have an apparently healthy child which, after weeks or a few months, shows evidence of infection; or have a healthy child whose mild, early infection is missed or misdiagnosed. In some, congenital syphilis does not become obvious till adolescence or even later, presenting with inflammation of the eyes or deafness. In some such cases examination reveals old scars in skin or bones or teeth.

The treatment of syphilis is relatively simple. Penicillin is the drug of first choice. Treponemes divide about every 30 hours and are then at their most vulnerable. To ensure death to all treponemes, treponemicidal blood concentrations of penicillin should therefore cover at least 10 days. Treatment, even late in pregnancy, can ensure a healthy baby. Views vary about the treatment of contacts. Some authorities treat all such persons. Others follow the principal of diagnosis before treatment and yet others claim to be selective in those contacts they treat and those they observe.

Social considerations

With the advent of penicillin and control measures, the post-war peak in the incidence of syphilis rapidly plummeted so that by the early 1950s it was being labelled 'a dying disease.' In 1960, however, recrudescences of early infectious syphilis were being reported from the U.S., Belgium, Denmark, Italy and elsewhere. With the exception of only a few countries, syphilis is everywhere growing more prevalent. Especially in the Western World the trend has been associated with relative peace and prosperity. Prosperity with its scientific and technological advances also brings changing attitudes regarding the use of leisure, changed methods of birth control, and demands for greater freedom, including sexual permissiveness. So changing patterns of behavior have developed. This applies to both developed and developing countries and factors facilitating the spread of infection have prevailed over those inhibiting dissemination.

Prevalence of infection varies widely. In Ethiopia, in 1968, 30—50% of the young were believed to be syphilitic. No less than 80% of Ethiopian prostitutes were diseased. In other parts of Africa similar morbidity rates have prevailed. In the U.S. control was lost in 1970. Few countries continue to maintain control of syphilis.

Notable "at risk" groups include immigrants; they seldom import infection, but acquire it from partners in their land of adoption. Returning tourists are said to account for 20—25% of infections in Holland and Sweden. Merchant seamen are now recognized as 15—20 times more at risk for infection than are landlubbers. Prostitutes are a common source. In Brazil, for example, 20% are infected. The corresponding figure for Australia is 2%. In some centers syphilis is widely believed to be commoner in homosexual than in heterosexual applicants for treatment. In the U.K., for example, about 1 in every 3 infected men seeking treatment admits to having acquired his infection homosexually. In London they form about half of the cases. Similar reports are available from other countries, notably Holland, France and Hungary, as homosexuals become more sophisticated regarding early V.D. diagnosis and treatment.

The control of syphilis

One of the characteristics of those countries where syphilis is still reasonably well controlled is that they did not disband their V.D. services in the early 1950s. Amongst them are Russia, Sweden, U.K., and the People's Republic of China.

The control of syphilis depends primarily on early and accurate diagnosis. If facilities are widely available and treatment is prompt, and followed by surveillance for at least a year, the chances of control are favorable. Diagnosis in early and infectious cases is best and most rapidly made by dark field microscopy. Antibiotics, locally or parentally, should be avoided until diagnostic specimens have been obtained. Serological tests can offer confirmation and are useful to assess response to treatment.

Blood tests for syphilis are of two kinds. First, are those which detect the increase in the blood of a substance called reagin. This substance increases markedly in syphilis and may also rise in a wide variety of other conditions. The most popular of many tests for detecting reagin are the V.D.R.L. (V.D. Reference Laboratory Test) and the Wassermann test. All are cheap and easy to perform. They are widely used for screening large numbers as they are very sensitive to the presence of increased blood levels of reagin.

Second are tests to detect a variety of antibodies which appear in the blood of syphilitics and only very seldom in others. The most popular of these tests include the Reiter Protein Complement Fixation Test (R.P.C.F.T.), the Treponemal Hemagglutination Test (T.P.H.A.), the Fluorescent Treponemal Antibody Test (F.T.A.), and the Treponemal Immobilisation Test (T.P.I.). All these tests are highly specific for syphilis but not as sensitive as the reagin-based tests.

The ideal test would be one which, with a delicate balance of sensitivity and specificity, would give positive results in all cases of syphilis. By using one or more tests from each of the groups described, something approaching 100% accuracy can be achieved.

The V.D.R.L. is used in mass surveys. For example, it is applied to the routine testing of expectant mothers, blood donors, members of 'at risk' groups and in pre-employment examinations.

It is essential to good antenatal care that every pregnant woman has a blood test for syphilis in each and every pregnancy. A higher percentage of positive results is everywhere found in the multiparous than in the nuliparous. Similarly, each and every donation of blood from a donor should be tested. In some countries such testing is demanded by law.

Such simple and cheap means of detection has a major part to play in locating individual cases and, by contact tracing, other positive reactors. Individual doctors can do much to prevent personal and family tragedies and family disasters. In the area of one Regional Hospital Authority in England concerned with the care of 4.5 million people, between 100 000 and 120 000 screening tests are carried out annually. In the U.S. something approaching 32 million serological tests for syphilis were carried out in one recent year.

Mass survey techniques have been employed in many countries, particularly in tropical areas. These surveys have been largely aimed at detection of the nonvenereal treponemal disease called yaws. In the last quarter of a century many millions of yaws-infected persons and their relatives have been treated. The disease is now relatively rare. One drawback is feared. Yaws gave some measure of immunity to syphilis — a partial, herd-type immunity rather than individual immunity. Syphilis, for the reasons mentioned, such as industrial development and urbanization, is now spreading in some of the tropical areas, particularly Africa. Thus, for some developing countries, civilization means syphilization.

Another means of control lies in public and professional education. In terms of public education, even where the disease continues to be relatively rare, syphilis should not be neglected. Professional education particularly of medical students and doctors is everywhere necessary. Many doctors currently qualify without having seen a single case of early syphilis. This could prejudice control. The process of education about syphilis should be a continuous and continuing one. Short-lived campaigns of blood testing have only limited value. All too often the campaign disappears rather than the disease. Gaining control costs money. Its maintenance is no less expensive.

The tracing and treating of infected contacts of those found to have syphilis is perhaps the most effective method of control. It is work which calls for skilled interviewing, tact, patience, assertiveness and speed. It should be based on an estimate of the duration of the infection in the original patient. As already mentioned, syphilis is not so infectious as gonorrhea and for some, several exposures seem to be required. In contact-tracing terms, the chances are therefore, that a higher percentage of syphilitic contacts will be known than is the case in gonorrhea. This, and the more serious nature of syphilis, conspires to make the procedures of interviewing and tracing very worthwhile.

3. GONORRHEA

Historical background

Knowledge of gonorrhea dates from Biblical times. In Leviticus, XV, the Bible says that when a man has an 'issue', meaning a urethral discharge, he is 'unclean' or infectious. The need for washing after intercourse is stressed. In Numbers, XXXI, Moses decreed that all Midianite women taken prisoner after a battle were to be isolated for seven days and that those 'that have known man by lying with him' were to be killed. The aim was to prevent 'a plague among the congregation'. By contrast, one learns little about gonorrhea from the classical writings of Greece or Rome.

Probably the first mention of the disease in medieval Europe is contained in a local London Act of 1191. This forbade the brothel keepers of Southwark in London to house 'women suffering from the perilous infirmity of burning'. The term 'burning' or 'brenning' matches the French term 'la chaude pisse'. The word 'clap', for gonorrhea, first appears in the writings of John of Arderne in 1378 and the term 'infirmatas nefanda', or hidden disease, in a London order of 1430. The importance of these writings lies in the fact that although medievalists attributed diseases as having their origins in earthquakes, comets or miasmas, gonorrhea was clearly seen as a disease of sexual contact.

In spite of this, syphilis and gonorrhea were later believed to be one and the same disease, the clinical presentation being said to vary with the site attacked by the 'poison'. It was not till some 50 years after the famous London surgeon John Hunter (1728—1793) had 'proved' this by a self-inoculation experiment that the truth of the separate identity of the two conditions was accepted.

Present epidemiological and social considerations

Gonorrhea gradually came to be seen as a world wide endemic disease with epidemic peaks of incidence associated principally with wars and closely allied to social deprivation and poverty. World War II was no exception. The post-war period showed a steady decline in the incidence of gonorrhea and many believed that, as a result of control measures and the advent of penicillin, it was a 'dying disease'. Great reliance was placed on penicillin and some countries were so misguided as to close clinics. They missed the epidemiological fact that no disease has ever been treated out of existence. The backlash started in the mid-1950s. By 1960 the World Health Organization was reporting that 15 to 22 countries had noted rises. Three years later such rises were notified from 53 (47.7%) of 111 countries (WHO, 1963). This trend has continued so that from an annual incidence of 60 million infections in the world, each year there are now over 200 million.

It is not possible to compare with confidence the reported morbidity rate of one country with that of another because the arrangements for treatment, diagnosis and notification vary widely from place to place. The trends, however, are unmistakable. Two notable features of the rising incidence of gonorrhea are of significance. In many Western countries the trend has been accompanied by parallel trends in other age-old manifestations of what might be called social pathology, for example, premarital conceptions, self-poisoning episodes, drug and alcohol abuse, juvenile delinquency, and crimes of violence. Secondly, and in marked contrast to past history, high infection rates are now clearly associated with relative peace in the world and growing affluence in many countries. This has had a marked influence in varying the complex balance of forces which, on the one hand, contain the incidence of gonorrhea and, on the other, promote its spread.

The cause, course and cure of gonorrhea

The causative organism is the *Neisseria gonorrhea*, one of the family of diplococci staining red or negative by Gram's staining process. The paired organisms, often in groups, may appear in specimens of secretion or discharge smeared and stained on microscope slides. Organisms may be seen free in the discharge or may be seen undergoing phagocytosis within white cells. When infectious discharge dries, the delicate gonococcus dies rapidly. Infection of adults by articles which have been in contact with infected persons and their discharges, such as lavatory seats, towels, and clothing is at best very rare, if indeed it happens at all.

The gonococcus is not easy to grow in the laboratory. It requires considerable expertise from bacteriologists to gain consistently high 'yields' of positive cultures. The growth and identification of gonococci has been greatly facilitated in recent years by the use of selective growth media. Such media contain a variety of antibacterial substances, mostly antibiotics, which inhibit the growth of contaminating organisms and thus allow free growth of the gonococcus, and so its readier recognition. It can be differentiated from other members of the *Neisseria* group by chemical and/or immunofluorescent techniques.

The organism can usually be found 2—5 days after exposure to infection, but in vivo incubation periods of up to three weeks are said to occur.

The sites for early uncomplicated gonorrhea in the female are usually the urethra and/or the cervical canal. The secretion of the vagina is too acid for the delicate organism to establish a vaginitis, and tests limited to vaginal specimens will fail to find one infection in three. Rarer sites of primary infection are the rectum and pharynx. Failure to take specimens from the rectum of females who have been in contact with the disease will result in failure to diagnose one infected woman in twenty. Failure to take specimens for culture from the pharynx will miss at least one in a hundred. Between 70—80% of women with early uncomplicated gonorrhea have no symptoms. Those with symptoms such as dysuria or vaginal discharge are all too frequently misdiagnosed as having simple cystitis or vaginitis.

Undetected or inadequately treated, the disease may spread to cause complications such as enlargement of Bartholin's glands or skenitis. The commonest complication, however, is salpingitis and this occurs in 10% of cases. It may be acute, subacute or chronic. The acute form may require to be differentiated from appendicitis, ruptured ectopic pregnancy, other forms from 'grumbling appendix', chronic pelvic sepsis, oophoritis, and ovulatory or menstrual dysfunction. Salpingitis is always bilateral. The tubes, in combating the infection, may become blocked by scar tissue or become two sealed bags of pus. The sterility consequent upon such deformities is to be measured in many tens of thousands annually in the world. In the U.K. alone, it must now be approaching 500 in any one year. The distress and personal misery accruing is great. It may be said that men are treated for gonorrhea and women suffer from it.

In men the disease is usually obvious with a complaint of urethral discharge and burning on micturition. In recent years, however, as more men than ever before are named as contacts and attend for investigation, it has been learned that there is a substantial number of men who are asymptomatic carriers of gonorrhea. As do so many women, such men require scientifically based investigation, sometimes on several occasions, before the diagnosis can be established. The gonococcal urethritis of the active homosexual is no different from that acquired by the heterosexual. Passive homosexuals present with proctitis, and this is most often symptomless. Some homosexual men may have both urethritis and proctitis. Fellatio is common sexual practice, and the incidence of gonococcal pharyngitis may be higher among homosexuals than heterosexuals. Complications in men include parameatal gland involvement; peri-urethral abscess, leading on healing to urethral stricture; prostatitis; trigonitis; and epididymitis. The latter is probably the commonest. It is usually unilateral. On healing the fine tubing of the epididymis is scarred and the corresponding testicle is thereafter unable to contribute spermatozoa to the ejaculate. Gonococcal pharyngitis in heterosexual males may be acquired by cunnilingus. It is probably less common than in heterosexual females or homosexual males.

In both men and women whose early gonorrhea goes unrecognized, septicaemia may supervene. Gonococcal septicaemia is believed to be commoner in women. It is now the commonest form of septicaemia in Sweden. It usually presents as low-grade intermittent fever, arthritis and tiny skin blisters, the contents of which contain the organism.

If an infected woman gives birth, the baby's eyes may be infected. In some parts of the world this is still common. In the Republic of Singapore, for example, one baby in every 500 develops gonococcal ophthalmia. Girls infected before puberty develop a gonococcal vulvo-vaginitis.

In spite of much research, which continues, no adequate or reliable blood test for the detection of gonorrhea exists. A mass survey approach to detection therefore consists of the relatively cumbersome and time-consuming method of examination associated with microscopic and cultural techniques on several occasions. In countries where control measures are inadequate to meet the needs, between 1 and 7% of women attending family planning and gynecological departments may be found to be infected.

The drug of first choice for the treatment of gonorrhea is penicillin. The aim in uncomplicated cases is to cure with one injection. In patients sensitive to penicillin a wide variety of other antibiotics is available. More prolonged treatment is indicated in complicated cases and these may require hospital care. Follow-up examinations are essential. Any schedule of treatment giving less than a 95% cure rate in a series of cases is a cause for concern and review.

The reason for this has become clearer with the years in several parts of the world. Inadequate treatment, rather than killing the gonococcus, is presumed to enable the organism to develop resistance. Although exposed to only one antibiotic, such resistant strains may develop resistance to several antibacterials. Propagation of such strains locally and world-wide, by travellers, makes for epidemiological problems and contributes to the failure of control measures.

Patients react in widely different ways to being told the diagnosis. Some react with common sense, some with stoic resignation. Concern, anxiety, remorse or guilt are manifest by others. Yet others express aggression towards the source of their trouble and threaten violence. Some are concerned for their family and friends. Occasionally the venereologist is blamed!

The control of gonorrhea

The basis of control lies in an appreciation and understanding that gonorrhea is a by-product of the structure and function of any society. Epidemiological data and identification of 'at risk' groups, and how they contribute to the local or nationwide problem, is no less vital.

All the measures available may be grouped under one of three approaches: (a) provision of an adequate network of clinics offering scientific diagnosis and treatment; (b) the tracing and treating of the sex partners of all infected persons; and (c) education of the public and health professions about gonorrhea.

Countries in northern Europe were amongst the first to recognise that venereal diseases constituted a social as well as a medical problem. They saw the venereal diseases as too prevalent, distressing, devastating and costly to be left to the care of quacks, pharmacists or even private physicians. It becomes clearer year by year that such countries have had all too few imitators. There is no doubt that medical administrators, sociologists and politicians could show a greater awareness and be more helpful. Existing evidence shows that an adequate network of clinics, manned by well-trained staff offering scientific and compassionate care with dignity in well appointed premises, does contribute to prevention, early cure without complications, and the avoidance of costly, permanent disability.

Widespread and well-manned clinical services form the only effective foundation for the second control measure — the tracing and treating of the sex partners of those infected with gonorrhea. Contact tracing is a two-part endeavor. The first part consists of interviewing the infected person about his or her contacts, both primary (or source) contact and secondary contacts, that is, any persons with whom the patient has had sexual contact subsequent to the infecting exposure. This is time-consuming and painstaking work. The second part consists of action taken on the contact data. In this part the patient's help may be sought. Telephone calls, letters and telegrams may be indicated, but the surest means is a visit to the named contact by a suitably trained and experienced social health worker. The essence of effective contact tracing is speed.

The third means of control consists of education of the public and the health professions about gonorrhea. In terms of the young, this should be based on sex education, at school, in youth groups, from religious leaders, and from parents. Such education should concern itself not only with hazard avoidance, but also with the advantages of a positive approach in terms of emotional, social and physical health. Late teenagers and adults have, by and large, formed their sexual attitudes and behavior patterns. These are unlikely to be effectively changed by education. Healthy attitudes can, however, be reinforced. For others, discussion of risk, factual information regarding signs and symptoms, the need for seeking early treatment and the wisdom of a medical consultation should doubt arise, are all essential. When and where treatment can be obtained, and also the privacy of treatment, are no less important. There are many approaches to meeting the needs of young people for health information. In recent years many large cities have established a telephone, crisis-answering service.

In the present social and epidemiological situation, improved professional education about gonorrhea has been widely canvassed. It is seen as imperative that medical students, doctors, nurses, midwives and all employed in social services concerned with young people should be thoroughly acquainted with the problem of gonorrhea. The indications for testing for gonorrhea are not only medical. They may well be implicit in the life style of those under the care of social workers.

In any area it is for the doctor dealing with the sexually transmitted diseases to acquaint all concerned, even remotely, with the size and nature of the local problem, and to initiate, maintain and expand, persistently and relentlessly, all available control measures along multidisciplinary lines.

4. LYMPHOGRANULOMA VENEREUM

This disease is caused by a relatively large virus-like organism, a chlamydia. It is one of a group, other members of which cause parrot disease or psitticosis, a form of pneumonia in humans. Trachoma, the world's commonest cause of blindness, is caused by another member of this group.

Lymphogranuloma venereum is usually sexually transmitted. The initial lesion is a short-lived, small lesion of the genitals usually appearing one to four weeks after exposure. Rarely the condition presents as nongonococcal urethritis. Enlargement of the glands in one or both groins follows. In women the initial sore may be internal and the glands in the pelvis then enlarge. Healing in such cases may lead to severe stricture of the rectum.

The condition has world wide distribution being endemic in South American ports, the West Indies, Madagascar, and the West African coast, and elsewhere. It appears from world-wide reports to be presently on the wane. In England and Wales in 1971 there were only 47 cases. In the U.S., 615 cases were diagnosed in 1971 compared with 2858 in 1944. The great majority of cases are diagnosed in males and may be associated with other forms of sexually transmitted disease.

Culture of organism, a skin test, biopsy material and a blood test can all contribute to the diagnosis. The drugs most widely used in treatment are the tetracyclines and the sulphonamides. Repeated courses are generally recommended. Late complicated cases may require surgery. Follow-up examinations are essential.

5. CHANCROID

Chancroid, or soft sore, is a form of acute destructive ulceration of the genitals. The incubation period is generally 2—5 days. The condition is painful and this, with the spread of ulceration, prompts early treatment. Enlarged and painful groin glands are a common accompaniment. The condition has to be differentiated from syphilis.

Chancroid was formerly found world-wide but is nowadays common only in tropical and some subtropical countries. It was prevalent amongst armed forces during the Korean and Vietnam wars. In England and Wales in 1971 only 55 cases were noted; 50 of them were in men. In the U.S. in the same year, 1507 cases were diagnosed, and in France 93 cases of whom 83 were in males. It would appear, therefore, that females may be more generally undiagnosed. In men the infection is associated with lack of hygiene.

Identification of the causative organism by smear and culture is not easy, and skin testing is of limited value. Diagnosis is, therefore, generally based on clinical criteria. Sulfonamides, tetracyclines and streptomycin have been successfully used for treatment.

6. DONOVANOSIS (GRANULOMA INGUINALE)

Donovanosis is caused by an unusual form of bacterial life. The disease is only mildly contagious but tends to be chronic. It presents to the physician in a wide variety of forms of ulceration of the genitals, most commonly associated with beefy, velvety granulations.

The disease is endemic in the southern areas of India, particularly ports on the east coast. Outbreaks were formerly relatively common in South America and New Guinea. The most recent outbreak has been in Samoa. Only 5 cases were seen in England and Wales in 1971, and 103 in the U.S. in the same year.

The great majority of these infections were in men. Poor hygiene is a generally associated factor. The low infectivity of the disease means that only about half the sex partners are found to be infected, and this has led to doubts as to whether the disease is spread exclusively by coitus. Cancer may develop at the site of the lesions. This complication appears to be a real probability in some 10% of cases.

Examination of smears or biopsy material are the methods of diagnosis. Many antibiotics have been used in donovanosis, but the tetracyclines and streptomycins are the most favored.

7. SUMMARY

Today's increasing prevalence of both syphilis and gonorrhea is associated more with peace and prosperity than with war and poverty. Social factors facilitating spread are currently outweighing those favoring containment of the diseases within readily manageable proportions, even though diagnosis can be accurate and treatment simple, cheap and effective. In contrast to other common infectious diseases, syphilis and gonorrhea have defied public health attempts to control them. Their continuing threat to the public health is one of the outstanding anachronisms of modern medicine.

BIBLIOGRAPHY

Dunlop, E.M.C., Lamb, A.M. and King, D.M. (1971) Improved tracing of contacts of heterosexual men with gonorrhea. *Br. J. Vener. Dis.* 47: 192—195.

Ekstrøn, K. (1970) Patterns of sexual behaviour in relation to veneral disease. *Br. J. Vener. Dis.* 46: 93—95.

King, A.J. and Nicol, C.S. (1969) *Venereal Diseases*. 2nd edn (Balliere, Tindall and Cassell, London).

Morton, R.S. (1971) *Sexual Freedom and Venereal Disease*. (Peter Owen, London.)

Morton, R.S. (1973) *Venereal Diseases* 2nd edn (Penguin Books Ltd., Harmondsworth, Middlesex, U.K.) Translations of 1st edn available in French, German and Spanish.

Morton, R.S. and Harris, J.R.W. (1976) *Recent Advances in Sexually Transmitted Diseases*. (Churchill Livingstone, London and Edinburgh.) In press.

Schofield, C.B.S. (1976) *Sexually Transmitted Diseases*, 2nd edn (Churchill Livingstone, London and Edinburgh) In press.

Schofield, M. (1965) *The Sexual Behavior of Young People*. (Longmans, London.)

Willcox, R.R. (1964) *A textbook of Venereal Diseases and Treponematoses*, 2nd edn (Heinemann, London).

Wisdom, A. (1973) *A Colour Atlas of Venereology*. (Wolfe Medical Brooks, London.)

World Health Organization (1963) *Technical Report No. 262 Expert Committee on Gonococcal Infections*. First Report. (WHO, Geneva.)

CHAPTER 82

Other sexually transmitted diseases

J.R.W. HARRIS

1. INTRODUCTION

Diseases which are transmitted on close contact can be passed on during sexual intercourse. The category sexually transmitted diseases, therefore includes both venereal diseases, and a much larger group of conditions which have a high infectivity rate during a short contact time. The immunological processes which can result from such infections and certain maternal/neonatal situations where the infant is infected by the mother must be considered.

As the venereal diseases have already been discussed in the preceding chapter, this chapter will be concerned with nongonococcal urethritis, nongonococcal proctitis, herpes genitalis, hepatitis B, condyloma accuminata, *Trichomonas vaginalis*, nonspecific genital infection in females, candidiases, Reiter's syndrome, scabies, pediculosis pubis and *Corynebacterium vaginale.*

During the next few years the lay public and the medical profession will have to come to terms with these infections. One might hope that the intolerance and guilt attitudes which have been associated in the past with syphilis and gonorrhea will not be applied here. Perhaps man will learn from his experience.

2. NONGONOCOCCAL URETHRITIS

Historical background

The differentiation of this condition from gonococcal urethritis was facilitated by the discovery of methods for culturing the gonococcus at the end of the last century. Yet medical awareness of the condition took many years to develop. It was only in the 1940s, with the advent of a satisfactory method of treatment of gonorrhea that attention was turned to nongonococcal urethritis. The associations with Reiter's syndrome had been established in 1916; in the mid-1970s knowledge of this condition is, at best, imperfect.

Handbook of Sexology, edited by J. Money and H. Musaph
© *Elsevier/North-Holland Biomedical Press, 1977*

Present epidemiological and social considerations

There is general agreement that nonspecific genital infection is acquired by sexual intercourse. This view is largely based on epidemiological evidence from the U.K. The prevalence of gonorrhea and nongonococcal urethritis have increased pari-passu for more than 20 years, and both conditions exhibit the same seasonal variation.

A total of 62,498 cases of nonspecific urethritis were notified in England and Wales in 1972; it is the commonest sexually transmitted infection in this country today. Seale (1966) noted that the marital situation was more likely to be disturbed by nonspecific urethritis than by gonorrhea in the husband. He also observed that the wife was less likely to have severe symptoms than the wife with gonorrhea. Other workers have stated that a significant proportion of married men with nongonococcal urethritis deny extramarital intercourse. Certainly no one has been able to explain why nongonococcal urethritis is more common among Caucasian patients. Many have the clinical impression that the more introspective patient is a likely candidate for recurrent nongonoccocal urethritis. Perhaps these individuals have a low symptom threshold.

The variable response to treatment, allied to the lack of a definable cause and the similarity of the symptoms to gonorrhea make this a more diffcult condition to manage than uncomplicated gonorrhea. Anxiety levels and distrust engendered in the previously stable sexual relationship can be marked. The problem of recurrent episodes of nongonococcal urethritis is a frequent and perplexing one.

The cause, course and cure of nongonococcal urethritis

Chlamydia, mycoplasma and *C. vaginale* are all believed to cause nongonococcal urethritis. The disease has a longer incubation time than gonorrhea, and the first symptoms are those of early morning urethral discharge accompanied by a hot or itchy feeling inside the penis. Dysuria occurs later and the intensity of the symptoms vary from individual to individual. Prostatitis can be an associated feature and 1—2% of those affected will develop Reiter's syndrome. Subsequently, 10—30% of patients develop relapses.

Therapy is given over a 21-day period, and many believe that the sexual partners should also be treated. Various tetracycline preparations are utilized.

Control

No country has claimed success in controlling nongonococcal urethritis. In those countries where gonorrhea rates are being held in check or are falling, such as the U.K. and Sweden, the incidence of nongonococcal urethritis has continued to rise.

Positive identification of the etiological agent, allied to contact-tracing may eventually control the syndrome complex.

3. NONGONOCOCCAL PROCTITIS

Historical background

The medical profession has only in recent years become aware of the clinical spectrum of disease associated with homosexual sexual practice. Hence, a consideration of historical background is irrelevant in this case.

Present epidemiological and social considerations

The condition occurs as a result of rectal intercourse. This occurs, for obvious reasons, frequently among male homosexuals. The prevalence of the condition in any area will be related to the number of sexually active homosexuals, and to the diagnostic quality of the medical care available. Thus one expects to find a much higher incidence of the condition in a metropolis, such as London, than in a rural area.

Accurate statistics are at present unavailable, as recording of data in the U.K. does not differentiate between the various forms of nonspecific genital infection.

The cause, course and cure of nongonococcal proctitis

The etiology of nongonococcal proctitis is unknown. Certain workers believe that Chlamydia should be indicated. Others (Dunlop, personal communications) do not recognize the condition, and feel that many of the cases are due to Neisserian infections which are not diagnosed. The most common symptoms are a feeling of wetness in the perianal area and the passage of flecks of mucus—pus on the feces. The degree of involvement of the rectal wall is variable, and ranges from the occasional granular proctitis to apparently normal, with minimal evidence of mucus—pus.

Unfortunately, the course of the condition may be very prolonged with relapses alternating with remissions. The symptoms subside with broad-spectrum antibiotic therapy, but tend to flare up again even through further sexual exposure does not occur.

Control

Control of a condition which is ill-defined and of which the etiology is poorly understood is difficult. The proctitis tends to settle if sexual intercourse does not occur. This is, however, unlikely to be a permanent solution for many patients.

4. HERPES GENITALIS

Historical background

The herpes virus was first isolated in 1938 by Dodd and co-workers (1939). Since then the existence of herpes virus hominis type I and herpes virus hominis type II has been established. Type I is more common in oral and type II in genital infections.

Present epdidemiological and social considerations

Herpes genitalis has a world-wide distribution. Almost certainly a number of the patients who were previously diagnosed as having chancroid were suffering from herpes genitalis (Minkin and Lynch, 1968). Little is known about the morbidity rate of infection on an international scale. In England and Wales in 1972, 4380 cases were treated in units specializing in sexually transmitted diseases, according to the Extract from the Annual Report of the Chief Medical Officer of the Department of Health and Social Security for year 1971 (Sexually Transmitted Diseases, 1971). Indeed herpetic lesions are now the most common form of genital ulceration in the U.K.

Nahmias and his colleagues (1969) had little doubt that sexual transmission of the virus frequently occurs. Fellatio and cunnilingus play a part, since 15% of the viruses recovered from the genital lesions are of the type I variety. Willcox (1968) has already noted how much more frequently the condition is recognized in the male than in the female. This is not surprising, as it is now realized that the inoculation site in the female is frequently the cervix uteri.

Yen and his co-workers (1965) noted that the most important factor about the epidemiology of genital herpes was that as many as 90% of primary infections are subclinical. Recurrences are common and troublesome, and may interfere with a regular sex life (Morton, 1975). Distinct socioeconomic differences in infection rates have been found between Caucasians of upper socioeconomic groups and Negroes of lower socioeconomic groups. A significantly higher incidence of antibody to herpes virus hominis type II was found among the lower socioeconomic groups (Rawls and Laurel, 1971). The disease occurs more frequently among the more promiscuous members of society. The consequences of neonatal, or intrauterine infection by the virus from the infected mother have been fully discussed by Nahmias and his colleagues (1969).

The social trauma of severe recurrent herpes genitalis cannot be too greatly emphasized. To the lay public the appearances of these lesions are inseparable from venereal disease. The relatively unsatisfactory therapeutic measures at present available, and the recurrent nature of the lesions, tend to undermine the patient's confidence, and ultimately, the doctor/patient relationship. The opinion of Rawls and his associates (1971) that herpes virus type II is a likely candidate as a cervical carcinogen has been widely publicized, and is a source of concern to some patients.

The cause, course and cure of herpes genitalis

It has been stated already that 85% of lesions are due to herpes virus hominis type II and 15% to herpes hominis type I. Following inoculation with the virus only 10% of patients will have symptoms, although considerably more may have lesions. However, as the inoculation site may be rectal, pharyngeal or cervical the asymptomatic nature of such infection is not suprising. Certain patients who were initially asymptomatic may have symptomatic recurrences, and the great majority of those who are initially symptomatic will have recurrences. The primary infection may be severe with marked regional adenitis and systemic symptoms. The itchy blisters which characterize the first stage of herpes genitalis usually break down within 24 hours, and present as a cluster of small, round, regularly edged, areolated and painful shallow ulcers. These ulcers take some days to heal and during this time fresh lesions appear. In fetal and neonatal infections there is a wide clinical spectrum ranging from the asymptomatic carrier state to disseminated herpetic disease and death.

There is no cure for genital herpetic infections. Simple hygiene and the avoidance of corticosteroids are of value. Many use 5-iodo-2-deoxyuridine as a topical application, while excellent results for photodynamic inactivation of the herpes virus have been claimed by Wallis and co-workers (1969) and Friedrich (1973).

5. HEPATITIS B

Historical background

For many years serum hepatitis was believed to be transferred solely by parenteral means. The discovery of Australia antigen (HBAg) by Blumberg, Alter and Vismith in 1965 and its association with viral hepatitis type B has meant that the occurrence of cases of the disease with no history of parenteral exposure has been observed. Blumberg and associates (1968) felt that homosexual practice might well be responsible for the predominance of males among those affected by type B hepatitis. Harris (1975) observed that multiple sexual partnerships was a significant factor among those patients with type B hepatitis who had no history of parenteral therapy.

Present epidemiological and social considerations

The incidence of Australia antigen is much higher in developing countries than in the western world. In Europe itself there is considerable variation in prevalence between Mediterranean countries and those in the northern areas of the continent. Recent surveys in the U.K. have been concerned with both those patients who are hospitalized with type B hepatitis, and those who are attending units for the diagnosis and treatment of sexually transmitted diseases. Heathcoate and Sherlock (1973), in a study of 67 patients with acute type B hepatitis concluded that sexual or close contact was the definite or most likely source of infection in 27 patients (40%). Vahrman (1973) noted that 65% of 110 patients with type B hepatitis were male, and that there was a highly significant correlation between homosexuality and the recognition of viral hepatitis. Jeffries and his colleagues (1973) observed that the incidence of HBAg among 1650 patients attending a unit for sexually transmitted diseases was more than 10 times the rate noted in blood-donor populations. They speculated that transmission might well take place through the skin and muscus membrane lesions which commonly occur in sexual practice. They also felt that serious consideration must be given to the possibility of oral spread of HBAg by blood and serous exudates (Krugman and Giles, 1970). Fulford and his co-workers (1973), in discussing the possible mechanisms of transmission, found no evidence to indite parasitic transferrance by lice or scabies mites.

Recent work from Germany involving a large survey of prostitutes has indicated that the probable explanation of the high incidence of HBAg among homosexuals in this country is not related to homosexual practice, but is rather a measure of promiscuity.

There is little doubt that when the lay public become more aware of this method of transmission, the social implications of acute hepatitis B will alter. Conversely, when the medical profession becomes aware of the sexual transmission, then they will begin to search for other sexually transmitted diseases in these patients.

The cause, course and cure of hepatitis B

The great majority of infections with this virus are asymptomatic. In the remainder the clinical manifestations follow a characteristic pattern, although in a few patients the clinical course terminates fatally. The preicteric phase is of abrupt onset with fever, marked fatigue and anorexia. Generalized lymphadenopathy is frequent. The urine darkens due to the presence of bilirubin and the patient develops jaundice. The jaundice increases rapidly, reaches a maximum within 14 days and then recedes over the next six weeks. The posticteric phase, during which the patient feels quite well but has not completely recovered is of variable length.

There is no cure for hepatitis B, and the differential diagnosis and management of the individual case is a matter for the specialist physician.

Control of hepatitis B

The sexually transmitted cases might decrease in numbers if there is a greater medical and lay awareness of the potential risk of promiscuity.

6. CONDYLOMATA ACCUMINATA

Historical background

Man has been aware of the sexually transmitted nature of genital warts since the middle ages. At the beginning of this century, medical textbooks described these lesions as 'venereal warts'. For some time they were assumed to be associated with gonococcal infection, and many believed that the lesions only developed in those patients with gonorrhea. Differentiation from the condylomata lata of syphilis was facilitated by the development of serological tests for the latter condition. Eventually a clear distinction was made between condylomata accuminata and both syphilis and gonorrhea.

In the late 1960s, Teokarov (1966) of Omsk demonstrated that 69.5% of the sexual contacts of 428 patients with condylomata accuminata had similar lesions in the genital area. The longest incubation period was eight months. In 1969, after much work, he concluded that genital condylomata were probably independent of ordinary skin warts, and certainly sexually transmissible. Oriel (1971) had similar findings.

Present epidemiological and social considerations

In many countries of the world there has been a growing recognition of the condition during the past fifteen years. This may be due either to improved diagnosis or to a real increase in the number of cases, since many of the patients were primarily seen in gynecological, dermatological, urological, or rectal clinics.

Oriel (1971), and Harris and co-workers (1972) have reported on the incidence of perianal lesions among homosexual patients.

Warmth and moisture appear to encourage the growth of genital warts. The recent fashion in both sexes of wearing tight, supporting, stretch nylon underwear tends to facilitate such conditions. Rapid growth is also associated with trichomoniasis, thrush, pregnancy and a long prepuce.

Patients can see these lesions and assess their rapid growth. Cancerphobia can, on occasions, be an important feature. Association with venereal disease is frequently in the patient's mind. Unfortunately the condition tends to be relatively resistant to therapy, and recurrences lower the individual's morale.

Though condylomata accuminata are frequently sexually transmitted, in 30% of infections the sexual contact will not have any lesion. Hence, the physician must take care not to precipitate unnecessary social trauma. Skill and tact will be required to encourage the other sexual partners to attend for examination and treatment if necessary.

The cause, course and cure of condylomata accuminata

Condylomata accuminata are caused by a pappiloma virus. There is no morphological difference between the virus of ordinary skin warts and that causing genital warts, although there may be antigenic differences.

Following inoculation the virus proliferates and after a time varying from weeks to some months, the mass becomes visible to the naked eye. The lesions continue to grow and the surface may become infected, indented by local pressure, or traumatized, resulting in hemorrhage. In the great proportion of cases the lesions reach an optimum size, and can disappear spontaneously. In a few individuals condylomata accuminata extend to the genito-ano-rectal region, and treatment can be long and tedious.

A wide variety of treatment is available. Local applications of CO_2 snow, trichloracetic acid, or podophyllin 25% in spirit are amongst those preferred. Curettage may be used under local or general anesthetic. Cryosurgery has been of value in some instances.

Control of condylomata accuminata

The infection rate, and delay in attending for treatment will be reduced when the medical profession and the public understand the problem.

7. TRICHOMONAS VAGINALIS

Two major conferences, one in Rheims in 1957 and the other in Montreal in 1959, did much to accelerate agreement that this is one of the commonest of sexually transmitted diseases. Dunlop and Wisdom (1965) reviewed the situation in the U.K. and emphasized the need, not only for the investigation of the male, but also for the concurrent treatment as a means of preventing reinfection.

The most recent detailed review of trichomoniasis is by Catterall (1972). He deals with the wide variety, and variable intensity of signs. He draws attention to cases of acute onset, and notes the frequency with which young women develop trichomoniasis a week or more after their first sexual experience. There is a comprehensive list of complications of the infection. Diagnosis is made by wet film examination, cytology examination and culture. A proportion of male patients with nonspecific urethritis harbor the parasite, and treatment of the trichomoniasis cures the urethritis.

The disparity of symptoms and infestation rates in males and females causes some confusion for the majority of patients. As the infection is common, patients usually do not associate extramarital exposure with the diagnosis, and the social situation is easily handled. It is debatable whether one should make the patient fully aware of the social implications of infection. At the same time, a full clinical serological and microscopic examination to exclude other sexually transmitted diseases is mandatory.

8. NONSPECIFIC GENITAL INFECTION IN FEMALES

Although nonspecific genital infection in men is the most perplexing clinical problem in modern venereology, there is no directly comparable condition in women. Yet many thousands of women who are the sexual contacts of men with nonspecific urethritis, will be examined each year. Obviously, these women will require some explanation and reassurance. The great majority of them are asymptomatic and they are likely to be very concerned, as their sexual partner has urethral symptoms.

As has already been mentioned in the section on nonspecific urethritis, the indicted agents at present include mycoplasmas, chlamydiae and corynebacterium species. Many believe that abacterial pyuria, cervicitis, Bartholinitis, the urethral syndrome and postcoital cytisis are the manifestations in the female of infection with these agents. Complications such as acute follicular conjunctivitis, Reiter's syndrome and anterior uveitis rarely occur. However, the mere demonstration of infectious agents in the asymptomatic female does not necessarily mean that they are the cause of the symptoms in the male. Frequently one presumes that this is so and treats accordingly.

On occasions nonspecific ophthalmia neonatorum infections are acquired during delivery from the mother's birth canal. Many of these infections were originally sexually transmitted (Schofield, 1972).

Symptoms in the male partner may recur, and if the female has symptoms she may relapse. These two situations engender concern and may traumatize the doctor/patient relationship. It is always difficult to reassure a patient when the doctor is on occasions uncertain as to the exact nature of the disease process.

9. CANDIDIASIS

Historical background

In 1920 Sigman reported that organisms belonging to the genus Candida can be sexually transmitted. This was corroborated by Odland and Hoffstaedt (1929). By the 1950s it was generally accepted that candidal infection of the male sexual partner was frequently undiagnosed (Waisman, 1954). In 1971 Catterall observed that *Candida albicans* was the commonest infectious agent isolated from female patients attending units for the diagnosis of sexually transmitted diseases.

Present epidemiological and social considerations

Demonstration of candida in the genital tract does not necessarily mean that the patient has clinical disease. This factor has obviously made epidemiological studies difficult. Infection by candida species is almost world-wide. The probable association with diets high in fruit and carbohydrate indicate some differences in the frequency of its presence in the intestinal tract of man. Differing climatic zones and varied social or economic circumstances (Emmonds et al., 1970) will obviously affect recovery rates.

There are certain well-known predisposing host factors which were summarized by Catterall (1971). During pregnancy physiological factors produce a favorable genital environment. Climatic factors, obesity and maceration can on occasions provide ideal growth conditions. This has been observed with diabetes mellitus, hypoparathyroidism, hypothyroidism, Addison's disease and pancreatitis.

Candidiasis is common among those on oral contraceptives and frequently accompanies malnutrition and debilitation. Fungi are common secondary invaders, especially following therapy with broad spectrum antibiotics.

Diddle and his co-workers (1969) postulated that the pattern of transference was a sexual one in at least 10% of patients with candidiasis. Spitzbart (1968) noted that in 18.5% of female patients with candidiasis, clinical cure was obtained only when the male contact was also treated. Rohatiner (1966) conjectured that rectal infection was a potentially important factor in the epidemiology of genital candidiasis, and Gardner and Kaufman (1969) conjectured that the oral cavity could be an important source of infection among those who practised oral sex.

The cause, course and cure of candidiasis

Fungi of the genus *Candida* are the primary etiological factor in the clinical spectrum of candidiasis. However, the individual's response to the infection determines much of the clinical picture. Kudelko (1971) considered that in certain cases there is evidence of an allergic diathesis.

In the male the glans penis, prepuce and urethra can be infected with *Candida albicans*. Genitourethral candidiasis also occurs, and several workers have noted hypersensitivity or toxic reactions of the glans penis following intercourse with patients who have vulvovaginal candidiasis. Perianal candidal infection is usually secondary to broad spectrum antibiotic therapy but can occur in other susceptible persons.

Pruritus vulvae is the cardinal symptom of *Candida albicans* in the female. It varies in degree but on occasions is intolerable (Dewhurst, 1972). Gardner and Kaufman (1969) have noted that burning is a common complaint, as is dyspareunia. Some patients notice burning and itching immediately after intercourse, and certain workers believe that this is an allergic reaction to the candidial organism in the ejaculate.

The course of the disease complex is variable. The patient factor is extremely important since a similar degree of infection will produce an intolerable clinical situation in one patient, and a barely perceptible pruritus in another.

Treatment involves eradication of the fungus from the genital, oral and rectal areas, and at the same time identifying the predisposing factor, or treating also the infected sexual contact. Fewer than 20% of cases of genital candidiases are said to be of sexually transmitted etiology.

10. REITER'S SYNDROME

In patients attending venereology units in the U.K. the onset of Reiter's syndrome is related to sexual intercourse. This syndrome appears to have a sexually transmitted origin in the U.K., the U.S. (Nicol, 1966), Russia (Klinyshkova, 1972), and Papua and New Guinea (Maddocks, 1967). Outbreaks are also associated with certain forms of dysentery and this has been documented in Europe, Asia and North Africa. The sexually transmitted and dysenteric types can co-exist in the same community as shown by Davies and co-workers (1969).

The clinical syndrome has been documented (Harris, 1975). The presentation to various specialities of this multisystem disease process is well known. Many patients relapse and a high percentage of those with the syndrome may have a genetic predisposition which renders them susceptible (Harris et al., 1975).

Affected patients find difficulty in relating locomotor and ophthalmic disease to sexually transmitted infection. Sexual contacts are usually seen and treated epidemiologically with broad spectrum antibiotics. Relapses occur without further sexual exposure. Female patients rarely develop the syndrome, but those who do may eventually have sacro-ileitis and peripheral large joint involvement with recurrent iritis.

11. SCABIES

This is a disease of close social or bodily contact. The most intimate form of social contact occurs during sexual intercourse.

During the 1960s there were numerous reports of the rising incidence of scabies (Danby et al., 1967). The most notable increase was in those aged 10—29 years. Changing sexual mores, a possible decrease in resistance, and poor diagnostic ability among doctors were all indicted. In Ontario in 1970 Pace and Pures (1970) reported a 10-fold increase in scabies during a 6-month period. Orkin in 1971 published a world wide survey of the condition and observed that, while scabies had been uncommonly reported in the 1950s, it started to increase around 1963, and concluded that the international resurgence of scabies was due to poverty and poor hygiene, sexual promiscuity, misdiagnosis, migration, increased travel and loss of hard immunity.

Frequently, male patients with genital lesions resulting from scabies infestation believe that they have syphilis, and adequate reassurance must be given following clinical and serological exclusion of syphilitic infection. Benzyl benzoate application is the most effective treatment for scabies and both the sexual and social contacts should be treated.

12. PEDICULOSIS PUBIS (CRABS)

Infestation with *Phthirius pubis* is believed to have increased in the U.K. during the last fifteen years. The louse is frequently transferred during sexual intercourse, and is classically found in the pubis region. Fisher and Morton (1970) noted that the age, sex and marital status of patients infested with *Phthirius pubis* and those infected with gonorrhea were similar. Altchek (1970) suggested that, following the diagnosis of *Phthirius pubis* infestation, a clinical and bacteriological examination should be made to exclude concomitant gonorrhea.

The initial symptom is pruritus. The itching may be almost unbearable, or scarcely noticeable. A patient's reaction to self-diagnosis may be panicky or pragmatic. The louse can be easily killed with dicophane (D.D.T.) emulsion or talc, or with benzene-hexachloride. The eggs or nits are attached to the base of hairs, and must be killed as they hatch. Thus the medication needs to be applied at least once a day for at least three days.

13. CORYNEBACTERIUM VAGINALE

Since 1953 when Leopold described this organism there has been controversy about its pathogenicity. Doll (1958), Heltai and Taleghany (1959), and Lapage (1961) were unable to demonstrate a pathogenic role. Gardner and Dukes (1955) found significant differences in the incidence of *Candida albicans* in cultures from patients with vaginitis and symptomatic vaginal discharge compared with control groups. Dunkelberg and Woolvin (1963), noted that *C. vaginale* was the predominant bacterial organism in the urethral discharge of nongonococcal urethritis, and Gardner and Kaufman (1969) felt that the *C. vaginale* infection was less common than gonorrhea or infestation with *Trichomonas* species.

While *C. vaginale* is the most benign of the common infections qualifying as a sexually transmitted disorder, its significance is related to its benign quality. Because many medical units do not provide facilities for its diagnosis, a number of patients are likely to have recurrent symptoms and infection. Since the most distressing symptom in the female is malodor, one can understand the problems for the unfortunate patient who has a malodorous vaginal discharge for which she can find no diagnosis or treatment. One can only hope that a greater awareness of the condition will lead more physicians to accept a physical basis for the symptoms in affected individuals.

BIBLIOGRAPHY

Altchek, A. (1970) Epidemic pediculosis and gonorrhoea. *Obstet. Gynaecol.* 35: 638–641.

Blumberg, B.S., Alter, H.J. and Visnich, S. (1965) A 'new' antigen in leukaemia sera. *J. Am. Med. Assoc.* 191: 541—546.

Blumberg, B.S., Sutnick, A.I. and London, W.T. (1968) Hepatitis and leukaemia: their relation to Australia antigen. *Bull. N. Acad. Med.* 44: 1566—86.

Catterall, R.D. (1971) Influence of gestogenic contraceptive pills on vaginal candidiasis. *Br. J. Vener. Dis.* 47: 45—47.

Catterall, R.D. (1972) Trichomoniasis. Venereal disease. *Med. Clin. North Am.* 26: 1203—1212.

Danby, P.R., Church, R.E. and Sneddon, I.B. (1967) Eradicating Scabies. *Br. Med. J.* I: 496—497.

Davies, N.E., Haverty, J.R. and Boatwright, M. (1969) Reiter's syndrome in Shigella dysentery. *South. Med. J.* 62: 1011—1014.

Dewhurst, C.J. (1972) *Integrated Obstetrics and Gynaecology, for Postgraduates* (Blackwell, Oxford and London) 580 p.

Diddle, A.W., Gardner, W.H., Williamson, P.J. and O'Conner, B. (1969) Oral contraceptive medications and vulvovaginal candidiasis. *Obstet. Gynaecol.* 34: 373—377.

Dodd, K., Buddingh, J. and Johnston, L. (1939) Herpetic stomatitis, *J. Paediatr.* 12: 95—102.

Dunkelberg, W.E. and Woolvin, S.C. (1963) Haemophilus vaginalis relative to gonorrhoea and male urethritis. *Milit. Med.* 128: 1098—1100.

Dunlop, E.M.C. and Wisdom, A.R. (1965) Diagnosis and management of trichomoniasis in men and women. *Br. J. Vener. Dis.* 41: 85—89.

Dunlop, E.M.C., Hare, M.J., Darougar, S., Jones, B.R. and Rice, N.S.C. (1969) Detection of chlamydia in certain infections of man II. Clinical study of genital tract, eye, rectum and other sites of discovery of chlamydia. *J. Infec. Dis.* 120: 463.

Emmonds, C.W., Binford, C.H. and Utz, J.P. (1970). *Medical Mycology* 2nd edn (Lea and Feibiger, Philadelphia) 177 p.

Fisher, I. and Morton, R.S. (1970) Phthirius pubis infestation *Br. J. Vener. Dis.* 46: 326—329.

Friedrich, E.G. (1973) Relief for herpes vulvulitis. *Obstet. Gynaecol.* 41: 74—77.

Fulford, K.W.M., Dane, D.S., Catterall, R.D., Woof, R. and Denning, J.V. (1973) Australia antigen and antibody among patients attending a clinic for sexually transmitted diseases *Lancet* I: 1470—1473.

Gardner, H.L. and Dukes, C.D. (1955) Haemophilus vaginalis vaginitis. A newly defined specific infection previously classified "non-specific" vaginitis. *Am. J. Obstet. Gynecol.* 09: 909 970.

Gardner, H.L. and Kaufman, R.H. (1969) *Benign Diseases of the Vulva and Vagina* 1st edn (C.V. Mosby, St. Louis) p. 191.

Harris, J.R.W., Mahony, J.D.H., Holland, J. and McCann, J.S. (1972) Sexually transmitted diseases in homosexual relationships. *J. Irish Med. Assoc.* 65: 62—64.

Harris, J.R.W. (1975) In: (R.S.M. Morton and J.R.W. Harris, Eds.) *Recent Advances in Sexually Transmitted Diseases,* (Churchill Libingstone, Edinburgh and London) p. 302.

Harris, J.R.W., Gelsthrope, K., Doughty, R.W., Lee, D. and Morton, R.S. (1975) HLA27 and W10 in Reiter's syndrome and non-specific urethritis. *Acta Dermatovenerol. (Stockholm)* 55: 127—132.

Heathcote, J. and Sherlock, S. (1973) Spread of acute type B hepatitis in London. *Lancet* I: 148—1470.

Jeffries, D.J., James, W.H., Jefferiss, F.J.G., Macleod, K.G. and Willcox, R.R. (1973) Australia (hepatitis associated) antigen in patients attending a venereal disease clinic. *Br. Med. J.* 2: 455—456.

Klinyshkova, K.M. (1972) Chlamydia in Reiter's syndrome. *Vestnik Dermatol. Venerol.* II: 31—36.

Krugman, S. and Giles, J.P. (1970) Viral hepatitis — new light on an old disease. *J. Am. Med. Assoc.* 212: 1019—1029.

Kudelko, N.M. (1971) Allergy in chronic monilial vaginitis. *Ann. Allerg.* 29: 266—267.

Lapage, S.P. (1961) H. vaginalis and its role in vaginitis. *Acta Pathol. Microbiol. Scand.* 52: 34—54.

Leopold, S. (1953) Heretofore indescribed organisms isolated from genitourinary system. *U. St. Forces Med. J.* 4: 263—266.

Maddocks, I. (1967) Reiters disease in Port Moresby, Papua. *B. J. Vener. Dis.* 43: 280—283.

Minkin, W. and Lynch, P.J. (1968) Herpes progenitalis. *J. Am. Med. Assoc.* 203: 526.

Morton, R.S. (1976) In: (R.S. Morton and J.R.W. Harris, Eds.) *Recent Advances in Sexually Transmitted Diseases*, (Churchill Livingstone, Edinburgh and London) p. 333.

Nahmias, A.J., Dowdle, W.R., Baib, Z.M., Josey, W.E., McLone, D. and Domescik, G. (1969) Genital infection with type 2 herpes virus hominis. *Br. J. Vener. Dis.* 45: 294—298.

Nicol, C.S. (1966) Reiter's Disease. In: *Symposium on Advanced Medicine.* (Pitman, London) p. 187.

Oriel, J.D. (1971) Natural history of genital warts. *Br. J. Vener. Dis.* 47: 1—13.

Orkin, M. (1971) Resurgence of scabies. *J. Am. Med. Assoc.* 217: 593—597.

Pace, W.B. and Purres, J. (1970) Resurgence of scabies. *Can. Med. Assoc. J.* 104: 719.

Rawls, W.E., Gardner, H.L., Flanders, R.W., Lowry, S.P., Kaufman, R.H. and Melnick, J.L. (1971) Genital herpes in two social groups. *Am. J. Obstet. Gynecol.* 110: 682.

Rohatiner, J.J. (1966) Relationship of *Candida albicans* in the genital and anorectal tract. *Br. J. Vener. Dis.* 42: 197—200.

Schofield, C.B.S. (1972) *Sexually Transmitted Diseases*, (Churchill Livingstone, London and Edinburgh) p. 176.

Seale, J.R. (1966) The sexually transmitted diseases and marriage. *Br. J. Vener. Dis.* 42: 31—36.

Sexually Transmitted Diseases (1971) Extract from the Annual Report of the Chief Medical Officer of the Department of Health and Social Security for the year 1971. *Br. J. Vener. Dis.* 49: 89—95.

Spitzbart, H.F. (1968) Die Beweiskraft des Bakterioskopischen Bildes bei der Vaginalmykose. *Mykosen* II: 457—458.

Teokharov, B.A. (1966) Accuminata Condylomata, *Akusherstvi I Ginekol. (Moskova)* 42: 41—46.

Teokharov, B.A. (1969) Nongonococcal infections of the female genitalia. *Br. J. Vener. Dis.* 45: 334—340.

Vahrman, J. (1973) Hepatitis B. *Lancet* ii: 157.

Waisman, M. (1954) Genital moniliasis as conjugal infection. *Am. Med. Assoc. Arch. Dermatol. Syphilis* 70: 718—722.

Wallin, J. (1974) Sexually transmitted diseases. Clinical and microbiological studies. *Acta Univ. Upsaliensis I* 6. (Abstr. Uppsala Disserations Med.).

Wallis, C., Trulock, S. and Melinick, J.L. (1969) Inherent photosensitivity of herpes virus and other enveloped viruses. *J. Gen. Virol.* 5: 53—61.

Willcox, R.R. (1968) Necrotic cervicitis due to primary infection with the virus of herpes simplex. *Br. Med. J.* I: 610—612.

Yen, S.S.C., Kegan, J.W. and Rosenthal, M.S. (1965) Herpes simplex infection in female genital tract. *Obstet. Gynaecol.* 25: 479—492.

CHAPTER 83

Prevention of the sexually transmitted diseases

EDWARD M. BRECHER

1. INTRODUCTION

Control of venereal diseases in some countries depends solely on the treatment of symptomatic cases. Other countries also engage in the tracing and testing of the sexual contacts of those cases, and a few also screen various population groups for inapparent infections. The difficulty is that, even when all three methods of control are used, each 100 cases on the average give rise to slightly more than 100 fresh infections before diagnosis and treatment.

One way to interrupt this series of infections, and to curb the sexually transmitted diseases, is through prophylaxis — here defined as measures taken before, during, or shortly after exposure to reduce the likelihood of disease transmission or to abort an incipient infection. Unlike the other forms of control, VD prophylaxis is effective before there is any opportunity for further transmission, and thus has a greater effect on curbing future incidence. Reviewed here are eleven methods of prophylaxis, all designed to reduce the likelihood that an infection will be passed along when a man has sexual relations with an infected woman or when a woman has sexual relations with an infected man. Several of these methods are also usable for homosexual encounters, and for oro-genital and ano-genital as well as genito-genital contacts. Many of the methods are effective against monilial, trichomonal, and other infections as well as against syphilis and gonorrhea.

Like other medical procedures, none of these is 100% effective. Prophylaxis should therefore be considered along with, not in place of, the case-finding and treatment procedures described elsewhere. Each method of prophylaxis, however, can contribute to individual protection and thus to a downturn in the incidence and prevalence of VD.

Handbook of Sexology, edited by J. Money and H. Musaph
© *Elsevier/North-Holland Biomedical Press, 1977*

2. PRECOITAL INSPECTION OF THE MALE GENITALIA

A skilled physician is able to spot infection during a 'short-arm inspection' of the male genitalia, including a 'milking' of the urethra for gonococcal exudate, in a high proportion of cases. Many prostitutes are at least equally skilled in making a short-arm inspection (Brecher, 1973; Stein, 1974); this no doubt explains the relatively low rate of infection in well-trained prostitutes as compared with untrained promiscuous amateurs, reported from various cities in various decades *.

The technique of the short-arm inspection can be easily taught to a woman, prostitute or not, if moralistic qualms do not intervene. If signs of infection are noted, a woman then has her choice of refusing sexual relations or of agreeing to them but using one of the other modes of protection listed below. (The inspection of the female genitalia by the male can also be taught; but a much smaller proportion of infected women can be thus identified.)

3. DISINFECTION OF THE PENIS PRIOR TO COITUS

Soap-and-water disinfection is simplest (Buchan, 1793; Reasoner, 1917; Walker, 1926; Luys, 1917). Whether use of a medicated soap increases effectiveness is not known, but seems likely (A.M.A. 1944). The douching of the female genitalia before coitus may also be an effective form of prophylaxis for the male (Luys, 1917), but effectiveness is likely to be limited.

4. THE CONDOM

The effectiveness of the condom for preventing VD transmission is well-established (Cautley et al., 1938; Special Joint Committee, 1940; Medical Letter, 1971). Use of the condom is actively promoted by public health authorities in Sweden and a few other countries. In many cities and countries, however, its value for VD prophylaxis is still insufficiently known to the public. Indeed, some public health authorities still seek to discredit the condom on the specious ground that it is less than 100% effective; and there are still legal restrictions on its availability in several countries (including some states in the U.S.). The chief drawback of the condom is its interference with male,

---

* "Fournier's statistics (1906) show that this disease is far more common among kept women, actresses (138 out of 387), and working girls (126 out of 387), than amongst the regular prostitutes (12 out of 287). This discrepancy is no doubt due to the exquisite knowledge of venereal diseases which many prostitutes can boast of. 'They understand how to examine the man who is about to obtain their favors', (Verchère, 1894); they douche properly after each coitus, and resort to a series of other precautions which safeguard them". (Luys, 1917).

and to a lesser extent female, sensory input. Greatly improved condoms, less than one-third as thick as conventional models, and made of a plastic with good heat-transmission characteristics, have been developed in Japan and the U.S., but have not as yet been generally marketed. If, as is likely, they prove more acceptable to male users and their partners than traditional condoms, they may contribute notably to a downturn in the VD incidence curve.

5. VAGINAL PROPHYLAXIS DURING COITUS

Neisser (1919), the discoverer of the gonococcus, reported that the introduction of petrolatum jelly into the vagina before coitus would provide a physical barrier to the transmission of disease agents in either direction; to increase the effectiveness of the barrier, Neisser proposed that suitable antiseptics be added to the petrolatum jelly. Several such products were subsequently marketed, based on petrolatum jelly or other viscous agents, but were used primarily by prostitutes. The effectiveness of at least one such product, Progonasyl®, has been demonstrated under experimental conditions (Porter et al., 1949). A recent field trial of Progonasyl® in the U.S. (Edwards and Fox, 1974) provided additional evidence of effectiveness.

Curiously enough, millions of women the world over have no doubt been unwittingly protected from VD by such products when used for contraception rather than prophylaxis. The effectiveness of the common contraceptive creams and jellies against the treponeme and gonococcus as well as against spermatozoa was understood by physicians in Britain, the U.S., and no doubt other countries at least as early as the 1920s, but the information was not well disseminated among the public. Studies in the 1970s have confirmed what was known half a century earlier, namely, that several of the agents used in vaginal contraceptive products to kill spermatozoa are also highly effective not only against syphilis and gonorrhea but also against several other sexually transmitted diseases. Field trials under way in Pittsburgh, U.S.A., in 1974 indicate a considerable degree of effectiveness for at least one brand of contraceptive cream in common use; for a list of other brands shown to be effective during in vitro tests. (see Singh et al., 1972a,b; Bolch and Warren, 1973). It is hoped to popularize vaginal creams, jellies and foams as 'pro-cons' — that is, preparations useful for both VD prophylaxis and contraception.

The recent switching of many millions of women in the Western countries from vaginal contraceptive agents (which are also prophylactic against VD) to the contraceptive pill and the IUD (which are not) * was no doubt one

---

* The possibility of an IUD which is prophylactic against VD as well as contraceptive is, however, under study. The gonococcus and the treponeme are both exquisitely sensitive to very low concentrations of copper — concentrations of the order of magnitude found in the internal genitalia of women wearing IUDs containing copper. Observations are currently under way to determine whether women now wearing copper IUDs are in fact enjoying a lower VD rate than those wearing IUDs made of other substances.

factor in the recent rise in VD in those countries. The switch from the condom to the newer forms of contraception may also have contributed, though some studies indicate that relatively few users of the contraceptive pill and IUD are drawn from former condom users.

6. POSTCOITAL URINATION

Urination by the male immediately after coitus has long been recommended by some authorities, including the U.S. Army, Navy, and Air Force (USDA 1965; Special Joint Committee, 1940; Medical Letter, 1971). The acidity of the urine provides an environment hostile to gonococci; and both they and other pathogens may be flushed out.

7. POSTCOITAL DISINFECTION FOR THE FEMALE

A medicated douche preparation for use after coitus, developed in the Venereal Disease Research Laboratory of the U.S. Public Health Service, proved quite effective during field trials in Guatemala (Funes and Luz Aguilar, 1952); other douche preparations have been shown in vitro to be effective against the treponeme, the gonococcus, and other vaginal infective agents (Singh et al., 1972a, b). Some prostitutes use the postcoital douche for VD prophylaxis as well as for common cleanliness (Brecher, 1973; Stein, 1974). In some European countries the bidet takes the place of the douche (Fournier, 1906); some authorities attribute the remarkably low gonorrhea rate in France to prompt postcoital use of the bidet in most strata of French society. Males also can (and should) use the bidet before and after exposure.

Lacking bidets, some American prostitutes (and some other women as well) wash their outer and inner genitalia thoroughly while sitting over the washbowl after coitus (Brecher, 1973; Stein, 1974). Promptness is probably as important as thoroughness in these procedures. This technique can be readily taught to women, whether or not they are prostitutes. Indeed, a public health official in Detroit, Michigan, U.S.A., is reported to have taught postcoital soap-and-water disinfection to 4000 women during the 1920s, with good results in terms of VD control (Dickinson, 1938).

8. SIMPLE POSTCOITAL DISINFECTION OF THE MALE

Fallopius in the 16th century urged the thorough washing of the male genitals both before and after exposure. Thorough washing of the penis and surrounding area with water and soap (medicated or not) as soon as possible after exposure has long been recommended by those public health authorities not opposed to prophylaxis on moralistic grounds (Buchan, 1793; Special Joint Committee, 1940; USDA, 1965; Medical Letter, 1971).

9. TOPICAL PREPARATIONS FOR POSTCOITAL USE BY THE MALE

During the late 19th century, at least a dozen European studies conclusively demonstrated that a simple ointment containing mercury is highly effective in preventing the transmission of syphilis if applied to the penis promptly after exposure (Maisonneuve, 1908; Kolmer, 1926). This 'secret' was known at least as early as 1733 by Agate and Desault (Kolmer, 1926; Schamberg and Wright, 1932). Metchnikoff and Roux (1903-1907) at the Institut Pasteur in Paris, placed postcoital topical mercury on a scientific basis with a series of primate and human experiments demonstrating that a simple salve composed one-third of calomel is almost 100% effective in preventing genital syphilis in the male if it is thoroughly rubbed into the penis and surrounding areas within one hour after exposure; some protection is afforded even if the salve is used after several hours' delay (Maisonneuve, 1908). Adopted by the armed forces of many countries as early as 1908, the 'Metchnikoff ointment' proved its worth during countless military studies over a period of 50 years (Vedder, 1918; Reid, 1920; Walker, 1922; Sternberg et al., 1960), and remained in routine military use until the end of World War II; but moralistic considerations in most countries prevented its popularization for civilian use (Moore, 1926; Sternberg et al., 1960).

Various silver compounds and other antiseptics were similarly used in military medicine for decades for the prophylaxis of gonorrhea in the male; the antiseptic in fluid or gel form was injected up the male urethra as soon as possible after exposure (Reid, 1920). During World War II, U.S. government studies established the fact that drugs of the sulfonamide group, introduced into the urethra shortly after coitus, were even more effective against gonorrhea and more acceptable to the exposed men; and 'Pro-Kits' containing both calomel and a sulfa drug (Sternberg and Larrimore, 1945; Sternberg et al., 1960) were manufactured and distributed for use by American armed forces throughout the world — except those stationed in the U.S., where moralistic hostility to prophylaxis prevailed. The chief drawback of all male postcoital methods of VD prophylaxis, however, is that they protect only the male. From the public health point of view as well as from the female point of view, protection of the female is even more important, since early diagnosis is so much more difficult and less likely in the female.

10. SYSTEMIC PREPARATIONS BEFORE PENICILLIN

Mercury was the treatment of choice for syphilis from the 16th through the 19th century. Some physicians and laymen knew at least as early as the 18th century that very small doses of mercury, administered systemically only once or a few times, could prevent a syphilitic infection which would require massive doses over a period of months or years if treatment was delayed until symptoms appeared. As various new agents for treating syphilis took the place of mercury, it was again and again discovered that very small systemic doses at the time of exposure can prevent hard-to-cure infections. Ehrlich's salvarsan (606), neosalvarsan, other arsenicals, bismuth, and other agents were each in turn found to be effective for syphilis prophylaxis (Michel and Goodman, 1920; Moore, 1936; Kolmer, 1926; Kolmer and Rule, 1931; Eagle et al., 1944) but once again, their introduction was blocked except among some populations of prostitutes. Studies in these prostitutes showed a high degree of effectiveness (Sonnenberg, 1935; Levaditi, 1936).

11. PILLS TO PREVENT VD

Shortly after it was discovered that small doses of penicillin will cure both syphilis and gonorrhea, it was similarly discovered that even smaller doses, taken orally at or shortly after the time of exposure, will prevent gonorrhea and probably syphilis (Eagle et al., 1948). The common view that small doses merely mask the symptoms of early syphilis was proved false (Babione et al., 1952; Willcox, 1954; Woodcock, 1971). Oral penicillin prophylaxis was widely used in the U.S. armed forces after World War II, and proved close to 100% effective in numerous studies, even with doses as low as 100,000 or 200,000 units (Eagle et al., 1949; Babione et al., 1952, and studies therein cited). Oral penicillin dosage needed to prevent gonorrhea today, with resistant strains prevalent, is unknown but no doubt remains lower than the dosage needed for cure. However, Smartt and co-workers (1974) reported that a single 200 mg dose of doxycycline, taken orally shortly before or after exposure, provides effective prophylaxis. A research group drawn from the U.S. Navy Division of Preventive Medicine, the U.S. Center for Disease Control, and the U.S. Public Health Service — University of Washington Hospitals, in a double-blind field trial with placebo controls, found that the incidence of gonorrhea was significantly reduced following administration of 200-mg doses of minocycline reasonably soon after exposure, even in a locality where highly resistant strains were prevalent (Holmes, 1974). The doses of doxycycline and minocycline used in these two field trials were modest fractions of the doses prescribed for treatment after symptoms appear. The frequency risk of individual sensitivity to these drugs, in the dosage given, remains to be ascertained.

12. LOCAL ANTIBIOTIC PROPHYLAXIS

The Japanese have developed a proprietary preparation, Penigin®, composed of penicillin or some other antibiotic contained in an effervescing tablet, for introduction into the vagina before coitus. Field trials have shown a substantial degree of effectiveness (Ohno et al., 1958)

The prophylactic use of antibiotics and other potent chemotherapeutic agents to prevent rheumatic fever, malaria, and tuberculosis is almost universally accepted (Willcox, 1974); but the similar prophylactic use of such agents to prevent sexually transmitted infections still arouses great hostility in the medical and public health professions. One reason commonly given for this hostility to prophylaxis is that antibiotics produce adverse side effects. This objection will be considered below.

In addition to the readily available or potentially available methods of VD prophylaxis described above, several other methods have been proposed, such as vaccines for syphilis and gonorrhea. The relatively trivial scientific efforts to develop such vaccines — standing in stark contrast to the vast efforts invested in producing vaccines for infections which are not sexually transmitted — afford further evidence of tight moralistic curbs on the medical and scientific approach to the sexually transmitted infections. Recent work on vaccines for syphilis, gonorrhea, and genital herpes suggests the slow erosion of these curbs, though work on a genital herpes vaccine is motivated more by a concern for cancer of the cervix than by a desire to curb acute genital herpes (Hilleman, 1974).

The public health importance of popularizing these or other forms of VD prophylaxis depends upon a fact of nature which is generally overlooked. Under stable conditions, each 100 venereal infections on the average give rise to 100 fresh cases before they are diagnosed and cured. If each 100 infections give rise to 101 fresh cases, the result is a disatrous epidemic in a remarkably short time. With gonorrhea, for example, the difference between 100 fresh cases and 101 fresh cases arising from each 100 preexisting cases can mean the difference between a stable incidence rate and a rate which rises by 15% or more per year — the kind of rise currently reported in several countries. Conversely, a rapidly falling incidence rate results if each 100 infections give rise to only 98 or 99 fresh cases. Thus even a relatively ineffective form of prophylaxis, used by relatively few members of the population at risk, can mean the difference between a rising and a falling VD rate. Lee and associates have calculated that a method of gonorrhea prophylaxis which is only 50% effective can, even if used by only 20% of a population at risk, reduce the incidence of gonorrhea in that population by 90% in less than two years (Lee et al., 1972).

A clinician who diagnoses and cures a symptomatic gonorrhea infection accomplishes very little toward curbing the disease; for, on the average, each patient has already infected one additional person prior to diagnosis and cure. The prevention of one infection, in contrast, also prevents all of the subsequent cases which would otherwise stem from that case through the years ahead. It is not unrealistic to estimate that the prevention of one gonorrhea infection today will also on the average prevent several hundred additional gonorrhea infections during the next two decades.

The current incidence of fresh gonorrhea cases in the U.S. is estimated at 2.5 million per year — 50 million infections over the next twenty years, even if the rate does not continue to rise. Thus only a few hundred thousand cases need be prevented in the U.S. in order to prevent the subsequent 50 million; for all 50 million future cases will stem from the few hundred thousand infectious cases present in the population on any given day.

In this perspective, the hazard of side effects from antibiotic prophylaxis can be evaluated. In the absence of prophylaxis, one can expect in the U.S. that massive doses of penicillin or other antibiotics will be needed to cure some 50,000,000 gonorrheal infections over the next 20 years, and that gonorrhea will remain at least as prevalent at the end of that period as today. This is clearly a policy likely to perpetuate the need for antibiotics and the hazard of antibiotic side effects. Prophylaxis (including antibiotic prophylaxis) offers hope of curbing the disease and thus curbing the hazard of antibiotic side effects through the decades ahead.

13. CONCLUSION

The more effective the modes of VD prophylaxis made available to the public, and the more wholehearted the effort to popularize their use, the more rapidly the incidence curve is likely to fall. No other available method of control of the sexually transmitted diseases, especially gonorrhea, gives promise of accomplishing the same result.

ACKNOWLEDGEMENT

This work was supported by a grant from the Long Island Jewish—Hillside Medical Center, New York.

BIBLIOGRAPHY

American Medical Association Council (1944) Pharmacy and Chemistry. "Germicidal" soaps. *J. Am. Med. Assoc.* 124: 1195—1201.
Babione, R.W., Hedgecock, L.F. and Ray, J.P. (1952) Navy experience with the oral use of penicillin as a prophylaxis. *U.S. Armed Forces Med. J.* 3: 974—990.
Bolch, O.H. and Warren, J.C. (1973) In vitro effects of Emko on Neisseria gonorrhoeae and Trichomonas vaginalis. *Am. J. Obstet. Gynecol.* 115: 1145—1148.
Brecher, E.M. (1973) Women: victims of the VD rip-off. *Viva* 1: (October and November).
Buchan, W. (1793) *Domestic Medicine:* A Treatise on the Prevention and Cure of Diseases. (Printed by Joseph Bumstead for James White and Ebenezer Larkin, Boston) pp. 349—350.
Cautley, R., Beebe, G.W. and Dickinson, R.W. (1938) Rubber sheaths as venereal disease prophylactics. *Am. J. Med. Sci.* 195: 155—163.
Cleugh, J. (1954) *Secret Enemy: The Story of a Disease,* (Thomas Yoseloff, New York) p. 150.
Comfort, A. (1967) *The Anxiety Makers.* (Nelson, London — Dell, New York) pp. 136—183.

Dickinson, R.L. (1938) *Control of Conception*, 2nd edn, (Williams and Wilkins, Baltimore) pp. 170—171.

Eagle, H., Gude, A.V., Beckmann, G.E., Mast, G. and Sapero, J.J. (1949) Prevention of gonorrhea with penicillin tablets. *J. Am. Med. Assoc.* 140: 940—943.

Eagle, H., Gude, A.V., Beckmann, G.E., Mast, G., Sapero, J.J. and Shindledecker, J.B. (1948) Prevention of gonorrhea with penicillin tablets. *Public Health Rep.* 63: 1411—1415.

Eagle, H., Hogan, R.B. and Fleischman, R. (1944) The local chemical prophylaxis of experimental syphilis with phenyl arsenoxides. *Am. J. Syph. Gonorrhea Vener. Dis.* 28: 661—681

Edwards, W.M. and Fox, R.S. (1974) Progonasyl[®] as an anti-VD prophylactic. (Paper presented at Ist. Natl. Conf. Meth. Vener. Dis. Prevent., Chicago, November 1974).

Forsyth, W. (1785) *A Review of Venereal Disease.* (London) p. 82.

Fournier, A. (1906) *Treatment and Prophylaxis of Syphilis.* Translated by C.F. Marshall (Rebman, London and New York).

Funes, J.M. and Luz Aguilar, C. (1952) Mapharsen-Orvus solution in the prophylaxis of gonorrhea in women. *Bol. Olic. Sanit. Panam.* 33: 121—125.

Gutie, T. (1958) Prevention of venereal infections. *Bull. W. H. O.* 405—426.

Hilleman, M.R. (1974) Human cancer virus vaccines. *Ca — A Cancer Journal for Clinicians* 24: 212—217.

Holmes, K.K. (1974) Advantages and hazards of antibiotic prophylaxis. Paper presented at Estret. Natl. Conf. Meth. Vener. Dis. Prevent. Chicago, November 1974.

Kolmer, J.A. (1926) *Chemotherapy, with Special Reference to Treatment of Syphilis.* (Saunders, Philadelphia, London) pp. 933—944.

Kolmer, J.A., and Rule, A.M. (1932). Stovarsol in the prophylaxis and treatment of trypanosomiasis and syphilis. *Am. J. Syph.* 16: 53—67.

Lee, T.Y., Utidjian, H.M.D., Singh, B. and Cutler, J.C. (1972) Potential impact of chemical prophylaxis on the incidence of gonorrhea. *Br. J. Vener. Dis.* 48: 376—380.

Levaditi, C. (1936) *Prophylaxie de la Syphilis.* (Librarie Maloine, Paris).

Luys, G. (1917) *A text-Book on Gonorrhea and Its Complications*, 2nd revised edn (William Wood, New York) pp. 4, 5, 270.

Maisonneuve, P. (1908) *The Experimental Prophylaxis of Syphilis.* (John Wright and Co., Bristol — Shenheil, Paris).

Medical Letter (1971) Treatment and prevention of syphilis and gonorrhea. *Med. Lett. (Drugs and Therapeutics)* 13: 87

Metchnikoff, E. and Roux, E. (1903-1907) Experimental studies in syphilis. *Ann. Inst. Pasteur* 17: 809 (1903); 18: 1—6, 657—671 (1904); 19: 673—698 (1905), 20: 785 800 (1906); 21: 753—759 (1907).

Michel, L.L., and Goodman, H. (1920) Prophylaxis of syphilis with arsphenamin. *J. Am. Med. Assoc.* 75. 1708 1770.

Moore, J.E. (1926) Prophylaxis and treatment in the control of syphilis. *South. Med. J.* 30: 149—153.

Moore, J.E. (1936) Editorial, The prophylaxis of syphilis. *Am. J. Syph. Gonorrhea Vener. Dis.* 20: 683—685.

Neisser, A. (1919) Is it really impossible to make prostitution harmless as far as infection is concerned? In: (W.J. Robinson, Ed.). *Sexual Truths versus Sexual Lies, Misconceptions and Exaggerations.* (Eugenics Publishing Co., New York) pp. 261—274.

Ohno, T., Kiyoshi, K., Nagata, M., Hattori, N. and Kanakawa, H. (1958) Prophylactic control of the spread of venereal disease through prostitutes in Japan. *Bull W. H. O.* 19: 575—579.

Porter, H.H., Witcher, R.B. and Knoblock, C. (1939) Social diseases at the crossroads. *J. Oklahoma State Med. Assoc.* 32: 54—61.

Reasoner, M.A. (1917) The effect of soap on treponema pallidum. *J. Am. Med. Assoc.* 68: 973.

Reid, G.A. (1920) *The Prevention of Venereal Disease.* (Heinemann, London.)

Schamberg, J.F. and Wright, C.S. (1932) *Treatment of Syphilis,* Prophylaxis of syphilis, (Appleton, New York and London) pp. 382—396.

Singh, B., Cutler, J.C. and Utidjian, H.M.D. (1972a) Studies on the development of a vaginal preparation providing both prophylaxis against venereal disease and other genital infections and contraception. II-Effect in vitro of vaginal contraceptive and non-contraceptive preparations on *Treponema pallidum* and *Neisseria gonorrhoeae. Br. J. Vener. Dis.* 48: 57—64.

Singh, B., Cutler, J.C. and Utidjian, H.M.D. (1972b) III. In vitro effect of vaginal contraceptive and selected vaginal preparations in *Candida albicans* and *Trichomonas vaginalis. Contraception* 5: 401—411.

Smartt, W.H., Bograd, G. and Dorn, R. (1974) Prophylaxis of venereal disease with doxycycline. (Paper presented at 1st Nat. Conf. Meth. Vener. Dis. Prevent. Chicago, November, 1974.)

Sonnenberg, E. (1935) Abstracted in *Vener. Dis. Inform. XX:* 19—20.

Special Joint Committee (1940) Appointed by Am. Soc. Hyg. Assoc. and U.S. Public Health Service. The chemical and mechanical prevention of syphilis and gonorrhea. *Vener. Dis. Inform.* 21: 311—313.

Stein, M.L. (1974) *Friends, Lovers, Slaves.* (Putman, New York.)

Sternberg, T.H. Howard, E.B., Dewey, L.A., and Padget, P. (1960) Venereal disease. In U.S. Army Med. Dep. *Preventive Medicine in World War II,* Vol. 5, *Communicable Diseases Transmitted Through Contact.* (Office of the Surgeon General, Department of the Army, Washington, D.C.) pp. 139—331.

Sternberg, T.H. and Larrimore, G.W. (1945) Army contributions to postwar venereal disease control planning. *J. Am. Med. Assoc.* 127: 211.

USDA (1965) United States Department of the Army. Treatment and management of venereal disease. *Tech. Bull. Med.* 230.

Vedder, E.B. (1918) *Syphilis and Public Health.* (Lee and Febiger, Philadelphia, New York.)

Verchère (1894) La Blennorrhagie chez la Femme. (Rueff, Paris.)

Walker, G. (1922) *Venereal Disease in the American Expeditionary Forces.* (Medical Standard Book Co., Baltimore.)

Walker, J.E. (1926) The germicidal properties of soap. *J. Infect. Dis.* 38: 127—130.

Willcox, R.R. (1954) Treatment before diagnosis in venereology. *Br. J. Vener. Dis.* 30: 7—18.

Willcox, R.R. (1974) Prophylaxis of non-venereal conditions. (Paper presented at 1st Nat. Conf. Meth. Vener. Dis. Prevent., Chicago, November 1974.)

Woodcock, J.R. (1971) Re-appraising the effect on incubating syphilis of treatment for gonorrhea. *Br. J. Vener. Dis.* 47: 95—101.

SECTION XIV

Special issues: social

Section coordinator: A.J.W. Taylor

CHAPTER 84

Introduction

A.J.W. TAYLOR

It is a salutary feature of the times that sex and sexuality can at last be raised as topics for serious consideration by scholars and practitioners from various disciplines in various countries. They, none of them, need now fear that they might jeopardize their professional standing, as was once the case, by presenting their empirical data and considered opinions to their colleagues and to society at large. In retrospect, the calumny that was directed to the earlier sex researchers was but a reflection of the anxiety, embarrassment and inadequacy that the topic evoked. People preferred to engage in sexual activity, sometimes according to religious and legal prescriptions, rather than to consider their biological, psychological, sociological and cultural motives for doing so. Now more honesty and courage, and a broader view prevails, as the series of most informative sections in this book indicate. The present section on Social Issues, in particular, shows how primitive attitudes and primitive knowledge of sex were built early into different customs, practices and social behavior. New knowledge now necessitates a change of attitude towards the toleration of deviants, and the development of skills that will help rather than oppress those who previously were derided or punished. In the ultimate, true justice might prevail in which every individual and every minority group might gain acceptance rather than rejection.

The various chapters in the ensuing section are by eminent practitioners and researchers. Richard Green and Judd Marmor review the research that bears upon homosexuality, and suggest there is little scientific evidence on which society can base its prejudice. They refer to the professionals' role in helping troubled individuals either to accept or to reorient themselves sexually. They have opened the question of what part the professionals might play in helping society to restructure itself so as to become more accepting of, and less oppressive towards, homosexuals.

Paul Gebhard clarifies the definition of sex offenders and, after reviewing their salient characteristics, comments upon the growing acceptance by many people of sexual behavior that is shared by consenting adults in pri-

Handbook of Sexology, edited by J. Money and H. Musaph
© *Elsevier/North-Holland Biomedical Press, 1977*

vate as distinct from in public. Martha Stein draws from her own experience and research to deduce five psychosexual functions of prostitution and to point out the valuable sexual health service which they provide at an informal level. Murray Jarvik and Edward Brecher review the literature about the sexually inhibiting and enhancing effect of drugs, and end with a plea for researchers to conduct much better clinical trials than they have done so far. They state quite clearly that no important human activity has been subjected to so little sound research as sexual activity.

Sherwin Woods draws attention to the teaching of sexual education in the curriculum for medical students, and refers to different teaching aids that have proved effective in removing prejudice, guilt, fear and shame from everone who is involved in the teaching process. Finally, Robert Sherwin takes a critical look at different laws pertaining to sexuality, and concludes that they were framed in a prescientific era. He suggests some changes that could now be made to reduce the gap between the current law and knowledge of sexual behavior.

CHAPTER 85

Homosexual behavior

JUDD MARMOR and RICHARD GREEN

1. INTRODUCTION

The common phenomenon

Genital sexual interaction between same-sexed individuals is present in most, if not all, human societies and has occurred for at least thousands of years. While same-sexed genital behavior is also observable in nonhuman species, this chapter deals exclusively with human behavior.

Societal attitudes

Homosexual behavior has aroused considerable controversy among many professional groups that are involved with the control of other people. Religious leaders have attempted to eliminate such behavior by viewing it as sinful, and punishable by the Church; legislators by making it illegal and punishable by the State; and psychiatrists by labeling it a mental illness, and trying to cure it. None of these strategies has eliminated homosexuality, and it is questionable whether any has reduced its incidence. What they have accomplished, however, is frequently to induce in the 'same-sexed-oriented' person, a sense of guilt, alienation, and stigmatization.

The varied groups which exert social control have modified their attitudes in recent years. Some small religious bodies are even comprised entirely of homosexual congregations with homosexual ministers, and major religious sects occasionally appoint homosexual ministers to lead their congregations. Some States have repealed laws regulating sexual behavior between consenting adults in private, and some communities in which such laws are still on the statute books, rarely or never enforce them. In 1974 the Board of Trustees of the American Psychiatric Association decreed that homosexuality per se was no longer to be considered a mental disorder, although a diagnosis of 'sexual orientation disturbance' could be made if a homosexual

Handbook of Sexology, edited by J. Money and H. Musaph
© *Elsevier/North-Holland Biomedical Press, 1977*

were to consult a psychiatrist either to seek heterosexual reorientation or to relieve stress caused by homosexual orientation. The decree was challenged by a small group of psychiatrists who initiated a full membership referendum on the issue, but the decision of the Board of Trustees was upheld by a wide margin.

Public attitudes have also modified, at least of the younger generations, with such persons more likely to view the homosexual as a member of a repressed minority group that should be allowed to 'do its own thing' so long as there is no intrusion into the lives of heterosexuals. Nevertheless, at the civil level, many problems remain. For example, New York City recently rejected a law which would have eliminated same-sexed genital orientation as an impediment for employment and house occupancy.

Definitions

'Homosexuality' has been defined in multiple ways, and various interpretations have been offered of its behavioral significance. As a working definition, homosexuality can best be described as a strong preferential attraction to members of the same sex.

Obligatory homosexuality refers to an erotic orientation exclusively directed toward same-sexed partners. Facultative (or situational) homosexuality refers to same-sexed relationships which exist under circumstances of heterosexual deprivation (such as prison). 'Pseudohomosexuality' refers to fears of homosexuality based on feelings of masculine inadequacy (Ovesey, 1969). A male may experience homosexual fears less out of a primary desire for genital sexuality and love with another male than out of concern over not fulfilling his personal definition of masculinity.

Perhaps the most confused term has been 'latent' homosexuality. On a theoretical psychoanalytic basis, all persons, in consequence of their basic 'bisexuality' (Freud, 1905), can be construed as possessing a latent homosexual component (as well as a 'latent' heterosexual one). Their overt sexual behavior may be exclusively heterosexual, but their fantasies contain, occasionally or frequently, homosexual content. The latter may cause them anxiety over whether to engage in overt same-sexed behavior, or may result in a sexual dysfunction with an other-sexed partner.

Kinsey (1948) devised a useful seven point scale of sexual orientation which took into account both an individual's overt behavior and his fantasy. Zero represents exclusively heterosexual overt behavior and fantasy, and six exclusively homosexual overt behavior and fantasy. The sexuality of individuals may thus be plotted more precisely than by merely designating them as either 'heterosexual' or 'homosexual'. The scale also enables individuals to be plotted, whose sexual experiences are 'bisexual', that is, typically directed toward members of one sex but who, on occasion, may engage in experiences with persons of the other sex. In its strictest sense, the term bisexual should be confined to those whose orientation falls between two and four on the Kinsey scale.

Incidence

Except for the U.S., the incidence of homosexual behavior by males and females in recent years, has not been accurately determined for most nations. In the U.S., the research of Kinsey and co-workers (1948, 1953) still stands as a benchmark. Kinsey's survey of 11,000 adults, (5000 males, 6000 females) conducted over two decades ago, revealed that for males about 50% had had a same-sexed genital experience before puberty, 33% had had a post-pubertal same-sexed experience leading to orgasm, 10% were predominantly homosexual for a 3-year period after puberty, and 4% were exclusively homosexual throughout adolescence and adulthood. The survey data showed that homosexual behavior for females was roughly 50% that for males.

Earlier studies of the incidence of exclusive homosexuality in other cultures obtained figures a bit lower than the Kinsey 4%, but nevertheless they reflected substantive numbers of individuals. Nearly 70 years ago a study in Holland found exclusive homosexuality in about 2% of 600 university students (Römer, 1906), and some fifty years ago Hirschfield (1920) surveyed 3500 German males and calculated 2.3% to be exclusively homosexual.

It is alleged that in some societies homosexuality does not exist, or is at least reported to be absent (Bieber, 1965; Gebhard, 1974) while elsewhere it is described as a typical part of nearly all psychosexual history (Ford and Beach, 1951). Doubts have been raised about the reported nonexistence of homosexual behavior in some societies. For example, Bettelheim (1969) stated that homosexuality was nonexistent among males raised on Israeli Kibbutzim, but that statement has been challenged (M. Rosenbaum, 1974, personal communication).

2. THEORIES OF DEVELOPMENT: BIOLOGICAL

Genetics

Kallmann (1952) startled the behavioral science community when he claimed 100% concordance for homosexuality in a study involving pairs of monozygotic male twins. Although others have since questioned his methodology, and some have reported discordant pairs of monozygotic twins (Kolb, 1963), his finding remains provocative and suggests the possibility that some genetic loading may contribute to a homosexual life style. However, before the nature/nurture elements can be dissected, it is necessary for researchers to obtain a series of monozygotic twins, reared apart from birth, at least one of whom is homosexual (such a sample has not been studied and would be difficult to obtain).

Hormones

A hormonal basis for the genesis of homosexuality has recently enjoyed a resurgence of interest. Whereas earlier findings based on crude measures failed to demonstrate a hormonal distinction between heterosexual and homosexual subjects, some more sophisticated studies that used more sensitive assays have allegedly yielded such differences. Margolese (1970), for example, uncovered a different ratio of the stereoisomeric urinary breakdown products of testosterone (androsterone and etiocholanolone) in 20 heterosexual and 20 homosexual males. However, that biochemical finding may not be specific for genital orientation because a handful of diabetic or depressed heterosexuals were found to have had excretion ratios similar to the homosexuals. Nevertheless, the results have been repeated by Margolese and Janiger (1973), and doubtfully by Evans (1972), although not by others, including Tourney and Hatfield (1973).

Another biochemical study of homosexual males to achieve wide notice was that of Kolodny and co-workers (1974). In that study the researchers found a reduction in plasma testosterone and reduced spermatogenesis in about 25% of a volunteer group of 30 homosexual males, as compared with 30 heterosexual males. Subsequent studies did not confirm the finding (Barlow et al., 1974; Pillard et al., 1974) and one project reported homosexual males as having higher, rather than lower testosterone levels (Brodie et al., 1974). Another, as yet unreplicated study by Doerr and his colleagues (1973), while finding no differences in plasma testosterone, found homosexual males to have an elevated estradiol level. Finally, Dörner and associates (1975), in an intriguing study designed to assess plasma luteinizing hormone (LH) levels after an intravenous injection of estrogen (a pattern which shows differences between typical males and females), found male homosexuals to have a response pattern, more characteristic of females than males, of a decrease in LH, followed by a positive rebound above baseline. In contrast, the heterosexual male pattern showed a similar decrease but no rebound. Endocrine studies of female homosexuals have been practically nonexistent, with the exception of Lorraine and co-workers (1971), who found differences in a very small sample (n = 4), that might not be replicated with a larger group.

There is some evidence to suggest sex steroid levels might affect postnatal sexual behavior. The levels of androgen to which both the human and nonhuman fetus is exposed in utero may affect not only anatomical differentiation in a male or female direction, but also their postnatal behavior, including rough-and-tumble, aggressive, and parental play during childhood, and, especially in monkeys, the degree of interest shown to babies of the same species. Thus, a young female rhesus monkey, exposed as a fetus to exogenously introduced testosterone, is born with a penis and subsequently behaves somewhat more like a male than a normal female monkey in chasing young female monkeys, and rough-housing with other male monkeys, that is, she becomes a 'tomboy' monkey (Young et al., 1964).

Consider, too, the human female born hermaphroditic because exposed in utero to excessive adrenal androgen (in consequence of her having the adrenogenital syndrome and thus overproducing virilizing adrenal cortical hormones). She also is likely to behave more like males of her age group than most typical females do. When these androgen-exposed girls are compared with their hormone-normal sisters, or with girls from other families, they are found to be more interested in rough-and-tumble athletic pursuits, less interested in doll play, and less interested in mothering human babies (Ehrhardt and Baker, 1974).

While provocative, these studies are far from definitive. So many factors appear to influence sex steroid levels and their behavioral significance, that it is hazardous to assign causality to them. General stress, recency of sexual behavior, cigarette smoking, day-to-day hormonal fluctuations in a given individual, wide variation in the 'normal' range of hormone levels, and perhaps interindividual tissue differences in response to the same plasma hormone level, need to be controlled in such studies. However, it is refreshing that scientists are now taking a broader look at the various potential contributing factors to a homosexual or heterosexual life style, but caution needs to be exercised against overinterpretation of endocrine correlates.

3. THEORIES OF DEVELOPMENT: FAMILY BEHAVIORAL PATTERNS

Male—female balance

Up to the turn of the present century, European researchers postulated predominantly an organic basis for homosexuality based on the central nervous system. Krafft Ebing (1889), viewed sexual orientation as a product deriving from the dominance of either a postulated male or female brain sex center. Freud subsequently drew an analogy between the concept of embryologic bisexuality and that of psychosexual bisexuality, and hypothesized that bisexuality was the initial state of all persons, with homosexuality a failure to develop psychologically to the heterosexual phase. Some contemporary psychoanalysts reject the concept of universal bisexuality and assert that heterosexuality is the innate 'natural' state and that homosexuality is not an arrest of development but rather a pathological direction of development (see Bieber et al., 1962).

Anamnesic recall

Most developmental research into the psychosexual development of homosexuals sought information about their parents and early life experiences. Information has been generated during the course of prolonged psychotherapeutic intervention (Bieber et al., 1962; Socarides, 1968; Hatterer, 1970) from structured interviews (Saghir and Robins, 1973; Bell, 1975a), or from psychometric testing (Siegelman, 1972). Depending on the sample, the strategy, and the researcher, a number of patterns emerged, some of which were conflicting and some consensual.

Bieber and his several psychoanalytic colleagues filled out questionnaires concerning the background of some 100 homosexual and 100 heterosexual males whom they had seen in therapy. It belabors the obvious to question the scientific validity of conclusions drawn from a patient sample which might not necessarily be representative of the population from which it was drawn. Further, these conclusions are based on the patient's recall of parental attributes from decades past, as related to a therapist with a theoretic bias regarding the development of the behavioral state being studied, who himself subsequently had to recall, interpret and code these recollections in statistical calculations. Discounting for a moment the considerable overlap of family dynamics between the homosexual and heterosexual patient samples (which in itself challenges the specificity of the statistically significant intergroup differences), and even accepting the validity of the reported differences in mother—son closeness and father—son distance recalled by the homosexual males, the gnawing question remains as to whether this early-life triadic relationship is the product of a parental 'conspiracy' to abort heterosexual development, or is the product of an unique child who conditions each parent differentially to the 'etiologic' pattern observed.

To be more specific, the Bieber study reported that the homosexual male had a history of having been less rough-and-tumble and athletic and of having related poorly to other boys. He was called 'sissy', and had a "close-binding, intimate relationship" with mother and a distant, alienated, or absentee relationship with father (at least more often than did the heterosexual group). However, Siegelman (1974) found less evidence of such a triadic relationship in families in which the homosexual son was low on measures of neuroticism, which suggests that the parenting configuration may be more related to the development of neuroticism than to the development of a homosexual orientation.

Feminine boys

Green (1974) studied a group of feminine preadolescent boys who may be prehomosexual or pretransexual because their behavior is similar to that recalled by adult male homosexuals and transexuals. They prefer the dress, toys, and activities of girls, role-play as females, and may state their wish to be girls. They dislike the rough-and-tumble, outdoor, or athletic interests of their fathers, brothers and peers, and prefer the more sedentary, esthetic, indoor activities of their mothers, sisters and other girls. He found that these boys, unlike the masculine-behaving boys in his comparison group, had closer relationships with their mothers than their fathers. However, some of the fathers had made considerable efforts to engage their sons in mutually enjoyable activities but, receiving no positive reinforcement for the effort, they retreated from the relationships. They gave the label 'mamma's boy" to their sons, and left them to develop a close relationship with the one parent whose interests the son did share.

Cross-cultural aspects

Many cultures, particularly the Western, ascribe gender-dimorphic terms to certain behavior such as rough-and-tumble play and doll play. Thus a male child who dislikes rough-and-tumble play and enjoys doll play may have a significantly different early peer-group experience and a notably different style of relationship with each parent than his athletically oriented counterpart.

Parent—child relationships

As noted above, there is overlap between the parental constellations postulated to exist in the developing homosexual male's household and those that are reported to exist in other households. It may be that, having unhappy parents, an alienated relationship with one or both parents, and being apart from one's peer group nonspecifically are predispositions for a socially deviant life style. However, data are missing to determine whether a deviant life style will take the specific form of alcoholism, criminality, depression, schizophrenia, homosexuality, or some other atypical pattern of behavior.

Peer-group relationships

There appears to be some link between the kind of poor group relationships during grade school years and later sexual orientation. Boys whose best friends at age 8 are female, appear more likely to have male lover(s) at 28, and the converse appears to hold for young girls. A homosocial peer group during pre-adolescence appears to be correlated with a heterosexual life style during adulthood, and an early heterosocial peer group with a homosexual life style.

4. HOMOSEXUAL BEHAVIOR AND RELATIONS

Homosexual activity between males

Many heterosexuals are ignorant about the sexual behavior of same-sexed partners. Two males may kiss, tongue-play, caress nipples by hand or mouth, mutually masturbate, perform sequential or concurrent fellatio, or engage in anal intercourse. Any or all of the behavior may exist during a given sexual experience or may vary according to the mood, special preferences, and preferences of the partners. Generally, no pattern is practiced exclusively by a given homosexual male, despite the popular mythology of the 'active' and 'passive' or 'male' and 'female' homosexual. While some may have preferences, their actual sexual behavior will be dependent to a considerable degree on the individual relationship (Hooker, 1965).

Cultural differences

Differences may exist, however, in preferred sexual practices of male—male partnerships in different societies. In the U.S. mutual masturbation is common between males, but in a study conducted in Mexico, anal intercourse was found to be more common. Furthermore, with reference to childhood behavior, those Mexican males who preferred the insertee role were found to have been often 'feminine' as boys, whereas those adult males who preferred the insertor role were found to more often have been 'masculine' boys (Carrier, 1971).

Homosexual activities between females

In female—female relationships, despite men's assumptions, prosthetic penises (dildoes) are not commonly utilized in sexual relations. Generally, the women kiss, tongue-play, stimulate breasts and each others' genitals, and perform sequential or simultaneous cunnilingus. Again, the actual behavior varies according to the specifics of the situation and preferences of the partner.

Promiscuity and permanence

Homosexual behavior, particularly that of males, is frequently regarded as promiscuous because of the fleeting sexual encounters that take place in gay bars, and public toilets. However, that blatant portion of the male homosexual subculture clearly does not represent the entire culture and indeed may be either a minor component, or represent one phase some individuals experience during the ontogeny of their homosexual life style. By contrast, there are male homosexual dyads which have remained intact and private for decades.

Transience and stability

Male—male relationships appear to be more transient than those of male—female, but the research on the topic is scanty. The transience does not necessarily signify an intrinsic defect in the male homosexual's capacity to engage in enduring, committed relationships because the culture in which the homosexual lives stigmatizes his behavior and drives him 'underground'. Inevitably their relationship becomes more visible as they proceed without children into the years when their age cohort is married. The absence of children in the typical male—male relationship eliminates another bond that holds together some male—female couples who would otherwise seek alternate partners (Hoffman, 1968). Additionally, their culture does not provide them with comparable social support systems as it does to heterosexual couples. They have no legal marriage nor tax advantage, for example.

Female—female relationships appear to be more enduring than those of male—male. If indeed female—female relationships are more long-lasting, and transient encounters fewer, it may again be explained in sociological terms that do not necessarily reflect issues of psychological adjustement/maladjustment. Cultural socialization patterns, beginning during childhood, place greater emphasis on the emotional relationship to be developed by the female prior to sexual intimacy, in contrast to that 'taught' the male (Gagnon and Simon, 1973). Both heterosexual and homosexual females generally have fewer sexual partners than do males (Kinsey, 1953). Further, the majority culture does not stigmatize the homosexual female to the same extent it does the male: it may 'look the other way' when two women live together for many years, perhaps dismissing them 'merely' as heterosexual spinsters. Finally, some female—female couples have a child within the household (for example, from one person's former marriage) which often provides them with an element to bind them into a more enduring family relationship.

Occasional homosexuality in males

A closing note about participants in 'impersonal' male—male sexual relationships: Humphreys (1970) conducted a study of males who frequented 'homosexual' public restrooms for casual sexual encounters. He found that, contrary to popular mythology, not all of them were exclusive homosexuals. Indeed, 54% of these males were married and living with their wives and children in middle-class households.

5. HOMOSEXUALITY AND MENTAL ILLNESS

Normal or pathological

The equation that homosexuality is synonymous with mental illness has come under increased clinical scrutiny during recent years and has become the eye of a political storm. Historically, Freud vacillated in his view of the 'pathological' significance of a same-sexed partner preference. He generally considered it less than an ideal outcome of psychosexual development, but perceived it as an 'arrest' in normal development towards heterosexuality. However, he refused to label homosexuality a mental 'illness', and pointed out that many homosexual persons (typically males) clearly demonstrated cultural and interpersonal competence. Freud's letter, late in his life, to the mother of an American homosexual has often been quoted:

"Homosexuality is assuredly no advantage, but nothing to be ashamed of, no vice, no degradation; it cannot be classified as an illness: we consider it to be a variation of the sexual functions produced by a certain arrest of sexual development" (1935).

On the other hand, some of Freud's followers took a much more dogmatic line regarding homosexuality as an illness. Bergler (1951) labelled homosexuality 'counterfeit sex' and leaned heavily on a masochistic genesis. Fenichel (1945) invoked the concept of castration fear, as he did for most 'perversions', and Socarides (1970) said that homosexuality signalled impending ego disintegration and is a disease of 'epidemiologic' (sic) proportions.

Empirical studies

Only in recent years have empirical studies of the state of psychologic functioning of homosexuals been conducted. In a classic study, Hooker (1957) matched heterosexual and homosexual males on gross life adjustment variables, and then administered the Rorschach, Thematic Apperception, and Make-a-Picture-Story tests. She discerned no group differences in neurotic signs, nor in Rorschach records, but, as might be expected, the TAT discriminated between the groups based on sexual story themes.

Statistically, one may not use the general psychiatric literature on homosexual samples as a basis for understanding the entire homosexual population. Until the 1970s the psychiatric literature consisted mainly of patient case reports and clinical impressions of the 'homosexual state' based on troubled persons who sought psychotherapy. While heterosexual patients consulted psychiatrists for a wide variety of unresolved neurotic conflicts, the profession did not generalize from these nonrepresentative samples to the heterosexual population to consider the symptoms of depression, anxiety, and difficulties in maintaining stable interpersonal relationships as a direct derivative of the 'heterosexual state'. The invalidity of basing the psychiatric illness model of homosexuality on patient samples has been emphasized during the past decade by a number of psychiatrists (Marmor, 1965, Hoffman, 1968; Green, 1972). Still lacking, however, were controlled studies of homosexual and heterosexual persons which looked critically at specific components of their psychological and sociological functioning.

Contemporary research strategies have included administering batteries of psychometric instruments and structured clinical interviews to noncaptive and nonclinical populations. Siegelman (1972) distributed paper and pencil tests to nearly 450 male homosexual subjects who were recruited from homophile organizations with the cooperation of proprietors of homosexually oriented bookstores. He recruited a heterosexual comparison group mainly from graduate and undergraduate university students. He found differences between the groups on dimensions of tendermindedness, goal directedness, submissiveness, self-acceptance, nurturance, and anxiety, and a total neuroticism score with homosexuals scoring higher. Heterosexuals scored higher on depression. No differences were found on dimensions of alienation, trust, and dependency. A study of female homosexuals and heterosexuals conducted by Hopkins (1969) showed the homosexual subjects to be more independent, resilient, reserved, dominant, bohemian, self-sufficient, and composed.

Such studies represent a partial antidote to the previously uncontrolled, small-number patient reports. Their deficiency, however, lies in the degree to which these samples, too, are representative of the homosexual and heterosexual populations and the degree to which such paper and pencil tests, without clinical interviews, validly reflect psychopathology. However, Saghir and Robins (1973) interviewed over 300 male and female heterosexual and homosexual subjects. They recruited homosexuals from homophile organizations and heterosexuals, unmarried to control for marital state, from a large apartment complex. They found a comparable number of subjects in each group with some history of psychiatric or psychologic treatment, typically for depression resulting from the breakdown of an important interpersonal relationship, and a greater frequency of alcohol abuse among the female homosexuals compared to the female heterosexuals. They stated their conclusions as follows:

"Finally, it is apparent from our findings that homosexual men are strikingly similar to single heterosexual men in most areas of psychopathology ... [and] ... while female homosexuals have a higher prevalence of psychiatric disorders than heterosexual women, especially in the area of alcohol abuse, their degree of functional disability as a result of these disorders or of their homosexuality is not greater."

Again, the question of sample representativeness might be questioned, and while the inclusion of unmarried heterosexual groups indeed controls for life-style variables associated with childbearing and various social support systems, other research indicates a greater frequency of psychiatric symptoms in unmarried adults. An alternative, ambitious design might include eight groups, rather than four, to encompass heterosexuals and homosexuals living in continuing dyadic relationships. What emerges from these studies, however, is a new picture of the general life adjustment of the homosexual adult, a picture which, with the exception of the anatomy of sexual partners, varies little from that of heterosexuals.

Present position

Do such studies settle the 'homosexuality equals mental illness' equation? The evolutionary argument can be cited for heterosexuality being the 'natural' state, and thus define homosexuality, sui generis, as a disorder. Psychoanalytic theories which demand the heterosexual developmental outcome as a sine qua non of oedipal conflict resolution, and of the universal rite of passage to mental health, may also be used to define homosexuality as a disorder. Green (1972) and Marmor (1973, 1975) have presented arguments against both those positions, and space requirements preclude their review here. Suffice it to say that the Nomenclature Committee of the American Psychiatric Association has recently attempted to view behavioral states in uniform terms of order/disorder with respect to general areas of psychological functioning (Spitzer, 1973). The Committee suggested that when a behavioral state is such that its full-blown form causes great inner distress, and/or significantly interferes with social functioning (for example, schizophrenia, suicidal depression, chronic brain syndrome), mental disorder is considered present. Clearly, homosexuality per se does not necessarily meet these criteria.

6. PREVENTION AND TREATMENT

The right to intervene

Psychotherapeutic intervention into the lives of children who appear to be headed toward a homosexual adulthood, and into the lives of adults who are homosexual, is a controversial question that raises complex ethical, research, professional, and civil rights issues. Some of those issues will be considered here.

Three follow-up studies in small samples of feminine boys (Zuger, 1966; Lebovitz, 1972; Green and Money, 1974) indicate the majority to be currently transexual, transvestic, or homosexual. Retrospective reports given by nearly all transexuals (Benjamin, 1966; Green and Money, 1969) and approximately one-half of transvestites in one large series of 500 (Prince and Bentler, 1972), indicate that cross-dressing and other aspects of feminine behavior during pre-adolescent years is correlated with the adult pattern of atypical sexuality. Finally, a recent report (Saghir and Robins, 1973) of 90 adult male homosexuals, indicate that about two-thirds showed a considerable degree of 'girl-type' behavior during pre-adolescent years.

Questions then arise as to whether the intervention should be attempted with children who show dramatically atypical manifestations of gender role. Grade-school-aged boys in America who show very feminine behavior by their gestures, preference for dressing as girls, strong preference for doll play, and aversion to associating with males, and who make statements of wishing to be a girl, encounter severe social ostracism from their same-sex peers. They experience considerable social conflict because of their atypical behavior. Their parents typically request help for them in the hope that they will fit more comfortably into their peer group. Except in extreme instances, grade school girls in America who show masculine behavior do not experience comparable social conflict because of the disparate manner in which their culture views the overlap of stereotypic masculine and feminine gender roles for males as compared with females at all age levels. An argument can be made for intervention that will reduce the immediate considerable conflict of the child, as well as his potential conflict in subsequent years. Although societal attitudes toward transexuality and homosexuality are moving in the direction of greater liberalization, the atypical adult, particularly the male, continues to experience a considerable degree of societal stigmatization.

The conflicts and stigmatization are seen in the most extreme form in transvestism and transexualism, both of which represent final extreme sequence of earlier sex-role problems. Transvestites, in view of their compulsion to wear women's clothing, experience significant conflict within their family, and also from laws proscribing cross-dressing. Transexuals, whose desire to make their anatomy conform to their psychology is so great as to make them undergo extensive hormonal and surgical therapy, present the most extreme group for whom intervention has to be considered.

The purpose of intervention, with the help of parents, is to broaden the child's interests and social skills so as to facilitate better social, peer-group relations. The intervention need not shape the child to fit a cultural sex-role stereotype (Green et al., 1972; Bates et al., 1975). If the intervention were to abort the development of transexualism, it will have delivered a considerable service to that individual. In the event that transvestism is also aborted, the individual should also experience less personal and social conflict in later life. The positive service regarding the possible development of homosexuality is much less clear. However, intervention that enables the dramatically atypical and ostracized boy to experience a wider range of social integration during childhood, and integration into a peer group which includes males, may promote the capacity for bisexual or heterosexual response during later years. Thus, through therapeutic intervention, an individual previously directed toward exclusive homosexuality may be capable of a bisexual or heterosexual life style, should this be his election. While the counterargument could be made that children who appear to be directed toward an exclusively heterosexual orientation should also be treated to permit the capacity for homosexual response, it is a fact of life in Western culture that the majority life style is predominantly reproductively heterosexual rather than bisexual, and that it is, therefore, socially advantageous to fit into the society's heterosexual lifestyle, so that the masculine-conforming boy does not experience gender-related societal conflict, and that today's parents do not bring children to treatment with that goal.

It can also be argued that the physician ought to try to change the societal values that discriminate against an atypical gender-role in a boy, girl, or adult, as well as to treat the child. Professionals do have a responsibility to help reduce such societal discrimination, but they also have a responsibility to their patients' immediate welfare, concurrent with such efforts at social change. It is, however, an unavoidable dilemma that behavioral intervention with the child may be seen as reinforcing the very societal bias which the therapist would like to change (Green, 1974, 1975).

Intervention with adults

The treatment of adults with sexual orientation disturbance is a topical controversy. Davison, (1975), argues that treatment of any adult homosexual with the object of heterosexual reorientation, even though that individual wants such reorientation, reinforces the societal stigmatization of homosexuality including bisexuality. The opposing argument, however, is that there are adult males who are unable to respond sexually to females, who nevertheless desire marriage, parenthood and family life, and the social support systems and emotional satisfactions that accompany such a life style. Is it justifiable to withhold attempts at reorientation from such individuals?

The decision for a heterosexual, homosexual or bisexual way of living clearly should rest with the patient and not with the clinician alone. Prior to any intervention there should be comprehensive exploration as to its feasibility. It is not justifiable to attempt sexual reorientation solely because of guilt harbored by the individual based on family or societal discrimination, religious conviction, fear of public discovery, or self-diagnosis as psychologically 'sick' exclusively because of his or her sexual orientation. However, when an individual has a strong ambivalence in favor of a heterosexual life style, and has thoroughly considered the various options available, he or she should be free to make a choice to engage a therapist who will try to help achieve the desired reorientation.

Effects of treatment

What of the effects of treatment intervention? Several reports indicate that a variety of interventions with very feminine boys may result in more masculine-appearing behavior (Greenson, 1966; Green et al., 1972; Reekers and Lovaas, 1974; Bates et al., 1975; Green, 1975). The enduring significance of the changes on sexual orientation, however, is not clear because follow-ups with such boys during adult years have not been conducted.

With regard to treatment of adult homosexuals, it appears that a variety of techniques, including psychoanalytic intervention of several hundred hours duration (Bieber, 1962), group treatment (Hadden, 1972), or short-term intervention (Hatterer, 1970), in appropriately selected cases, results in behavioral change in about one-third of the cases. Behavioral modification technique utilizing noxious stimuli paired with visual stimuli of a homosexual content (MacCulloch and Feldman, 1967), is also associated with sexual reorientation, at least temporarily, in about one-third of appropriately selected cases. Followup reports for these adult former homosexuals appear to indicate that the heterosexual reorientation persists for the majority of those reoriented (Bancroft, 1974). The majority of homosexual adults, however, neither seek nor desire therapy, and the majority of those who do seek therapy continue to remain homosexually oriented. In general, those homosexuals who are younger, below 35 years of age, who are less 'feminine', have had their first overt homosexual experience after the age of sixteen, and who give a history of some potential for heterosexual arousal, have a better prospect for achieving some sexual reorientation so as to include some degree of heterosexuality. The same type of change may occur developmentally, without treatment.

7. SOCIAL CHANGE

Social activism

Perhaps the most revolutionary aspect of human homosexuality during recent years has been the role of homosexuals in the forefront of social activism. While a few homophile organizations had previously existed, and published newsletters or other periodicals (in the U.S. the Mattachine Society; One, Inc.; Daughters of Bilitis) their visibility to the majority heterosexual population was low, their involvement in civil rights litigation minimal, and their support by prominent citizens virtually absent. While Hollywood gossip columns and magazines would report on the homosexual orientation of major personalities (with the same gossipy taste displayed toward their heterosexual subjects), socially or professionally prominent people did not step forward to declare their homosexuality. Governmental agencies were not challenged in courts of law for denying homosexual persons the same constitutional protections granted heterosexuals, and there was no regular publication of wide-circulation newspapers that were dedicated to a homosexually oriented readership. Public movie theaters did not display explicitly sexual films with same-sexed partners, homosexuals did not hold public parades or demonstrations, homosexual students did not hold dances and public meetings on college campuses, and acknowledged homosexuals were not elected to office in the state legislature. Now the times have changed, and homosexuals are coming to the fore in much the same way as heterosexuals.

Green, while serving as a member of a National Institute of Mental Health Study Section, recently visited a research group that proposed a study of some aspects of homosexuality in which the principal investigators, university professors with graduate degrees, openly acknowledged their homosexual orientation in their research grant application. A few weeks later, his psychology undergraduate course on atypical sexual life styles was addressed on the subject of female homosexuality by two lesbian members of the class. Also, in recent months the same author was involved in court cases in which homosexual parents were in child-custody contests. In one case the court permitted two female homosexual parents to live together in a common household with their five children, despite the strenuous objections of their former husbands, both of whom had remarried.

Indeed, the candor with which human sexuality in general has been publicly examined in recent years may be surpassed only by the candor of representatives of homosexual life styles. "Out of the closets and into the streets" has captured the imagination and conduct of the contemporary homosexual (Teal, 1971). With some foot-dragging, state legislatures have begun to eliminate laws regulating sexual conduct between consenting adults in private, as was recommended many years ago by the American Law Institute in its Model Penal Code. Thus the 'infamous crime against nature', the act not to be mentioned among Christians, the love that dared not speak its name, and a form of human behavior uniquely condemned by medicine, the law and theology as an illness, a crime, and a sin, is being recast against a new backdrop in the 1970s.

8. CONCLUSION

Homosexuality, shorn of prejudice hiding under the cloak of biological, psychological and social truths, is emerging as a variant of human sexual behavior.

The future should witness greater knowledge and understanding of people with homosexual life styles and thus moderate the repressive forces that have for so long been wielded against them.

BIBLIOGRAPHY

Bancroft, J. (1974) *Deviant Sexual Behaviour.* (Oxford University Press, Oxford, London.)

Barlow, D., Abel, G., Blanchard, E. and Mavissakalian, M. (1974) Plasma testosterone levels and male homosexuality: a failure to replicate. *Arch. Sex. Behav.* 3: 571—76.

Bates, J., Skilbeck, W., Smith, K. and Bentler, P. (1975) Intervention with families of gender-disturbed boys. *Am. J. Ortho-Psychiat.* 45: 50—57.

Bell, A. (1975a) The homosexual as patient. In: (R. Green, Ed.) *Human Sexuality: A Health Practitioner's Text.* (Williams and Wilkins, Baltimore.)

Bell, A. (1975b) Research in homosexuality: back to the drawing board. In: (E. Rubinstein, R. Green and E. Brecher, Eds.) *Sex Research: Future Directions.* (Plenum, New York.)

Benjamin, H. (1966) *The Transsexual Phenomenon.* (Julian Press, New York.)

Bergler, E. (1951) *Neurotic Counterfeit Sex.* (Grune and Stratton, New York.)

Berler, E. (1951) *Neurotic Counterfeit Sex.* (Grune and Stratton, New York.)

Bettelheim, B. (1969) *Children of the Dream.* (McMilland, New York.)

Bieber, I. and associates, (1962) *Homosexuality: A Psychoanalytic Study.* (Basic Books, New York.)

Bieber, I. (1965) In: (J. Marmor, Ed.) *Sexual Inversion.* (Basic Books, New York.)

Brodie, H.K., Gartrell, N., Doering, C. and Rhue, T. (1974) Plasma testosterone levels in heterosexual and homosexual men. *Am. J. Psychiat.* 131: 82—83.

Carrier, J. (1971) Participants in urban Mexican male homosexual encounters. *Arch. Sex. Behav.,* 1: 279—91.

Doerr, P., Kockett, G., Vogt, H., Pirke, K. and Dittmar, F. (1973) Plasma testosterone, estradiol. and semen analysis in male homosexuals. *Arch. Gen. Psychiat.* 29: 829—33.

Dorner, G., Rohde, W., Stahl, R., Knell, L. and Masius, W. (1975) A neuroendocrine predisposition for homosexuality in men. *Arch. Sex. Behav.*, 4: 1—8.

Davison, G. (1975) Presidential Paper, American Association for the Advancement of Behavior Therapy.

Ehrhardt, A. and Baker, S. (1974) Fetal androgens, human central nervous system and behavior sex differences. In: (R. Friedman, R. Richart and R. Vande Wiele, Eds.) *Sex Differences in Behavior.* (Wiley, New York.)

Evans, R. (1972) Physical and biochemical characteristics of homosexual men. *J. Consult. Clin. Psychol.* 39: 140—147.

Fenichel, O. (1945) *The Psychoanalytic Theory of Neurosis.* (W.W. Norton, New York.)

Ford, C. and Beach, F. (1951) *Patterns of Sexual Behavior.* (Harper, New York.)

Freud, S. (1905) *Three Essays on the Theory of Sexuality.* Standard edn, (Hogarth, London) 1953, 7: 125—245.

Freud, S. (1951) Letter to an American mother. *Am. J. Psychiat.*, 107: 786—87.

Gagnon, J. and Simon, W. (1973) *Sexual Conduct.* (Aldine, Chicago.)

Green, R. (1972) Homosexuality as a mental illnes. *Int. J. Psychiat.*, 10: 77—98.

Green, R. (1974) *Sexual Identity Conflict in Children and Adults.* (Basic Books, New York—Gerald Duckworth, London.)

Green, R. (1975) Human sexuality: research and treatment frontiers. In: (D. Hamburg and H.K. Brodie, Eds.) *American Handbook of Psychiatry*, 2nd edn. (Basic Books, New York.)

Green, R. and Money, J. (eds.) (1969) *Transsexualism and Sex Reassignment* (Johns Hopkins Press, Baltimore.)

Green, R. and Money, J. (1974) In: (Green, R., Ed.) *Sexual Identity Conflict in Children and Adults.* (Basic Books, New York.)

Green, R., Newman, L. and Stoller, R. (1972) Treatment of boyhood "transsexualism". *Arch. Gen. Psychiat.* 26: 213—17.

Greenson, R. (1966) A transvestite boy and a hypothesis. *Int. J. Psychoanal.* 47: 396—403.

Hadden, S. (1972) Group psychotherapy with homosexual men. In: (H. Resnik and M. Wolfgang, Eds.) *Sexual Behaviors.* (Little, Brown and Co., Boston.)

Hatterer, L. (1970) *Changing Homosexuality in the Male.* (McGraw-Hill, New York.)

Heston, L. and Shields, J. (1968) Homosexuality in Twins, *Arch. Gen. Psychiat.*, 18: 149—60.

Hirschfeld, M. (1920) *Die Homosexualitat des Mannes und des Weibes.* (L. Marcus, Berlin.)

Hoffman, M. (1968) *The Gay World: Male Homosexuality and the Social Creation of Evil.* (Basic Books, New York.)

Hooker, E. (1957) The adjustment of the male overt homosexual. *J. Project. Tech.*, 22: 33—54.

Hooker, E. (1965) Male homosexuals and their worlds. In: (J. Marmor, Ed.) *Sexual Inversion.* (Basic Books, New York.)

Hopkins, J. (1969) The lesbian personality. *Br. J. Psychiat.*, 115: 1433—36.

Humphreys, R.A.L. (1970) *Tearoom Trade.* (Aldine, Chicago.)

Kallmann, F. (1952) Comparative twin study on the genetic aspects of male homosexuality. *J. Nerv. Ment. Dis.*, 115: 283—98.

Kinsey, A., Pomeroy, W. and Martin, C. (1948) *Sexual Behavior in the Human Male.* Saunders, Philadelphia.)

Kinsey, A., Pomeroy, W., Martin, C. and Gebhard, P. (1953) *Sexual Behavior in the Human Female.* (Sanders, Philadelphia.)

Kolb, L. (1963) Therapy of homosexuality. In: (Masserman, J., Ed.) *Current Psychiatric Therapies* Vol. 3 (Grune & Stratton, New York) pp. 131—137.

Kolodny, R., Masters, W., Hendryx, J. and Toro, G. (1971) Plasma testosterone and semen analysis in male homosexuals. *New Engl. J. Med.*, 285: 1170—74.

Kolodny, R., Masters, W., Kolodner, R. and Toro, G. (1974) Depression of plasma testosterone levels after chronic intensive marihuana use. *New Engl. J. Med.*, 290: 872—74.

Krafft-Ebing, R. (1931) *Psychopathia Sexualis.* 1st edn 1886 (Physicians and Surgeons Book Co., Brooklyn).

Kreuz, L., Rose, R. and Jennings, J. (1972) Suppression of plasma testosterone levels and psychological stress. *Arch. Gen. Psychiat.*, 26: 479—82.

Lorraine, J., Adamopoulos, D., Hirkham, K., Ismail, A. and Dove, G. (1971) Patterns of hormone excretion in male and female homosexuals. *Nature*, 234: 552—55.

MacCulloch, H. and Feldman, M. (1967) Aversion therapy in the management of 43 homosexuals. *Br. Med. J.*, 1: 594—97.

Margolese, S. (1970) Homosexuality: a new endocrine correlate. *Horm. Behav.*, 1: 151—55.

Margolese, S. and Janiger, O. (1973) Andosterone-etiocholanolone ratios in male homosexuals. *Br. Med. J.*, 2: 207—10.

Marmor, J. (Ed.) (1965) *Sexual Inversion: The Multiple Roots of Homosexuality.* (Basic Books, New York.)

Marmor, J. (1973) In: (R. Stoller, J. Marmor, I. Bieber, R. Gold, C. Socarides, R. Green and R. Spitzer) A Symposium: Should Homosexuality be in the APA Nomenclature. *Am. J. Psychiat.*, 130: 1207—16.

Marmor, J. (1975) Homosexuality and sexual orientation disturbances. In: (A.M. Freedman, H.I. Kaplan and B.J. Sadock, Eds.) *Comprehensive Textbook of Psychiatry.* Vol. II (Williams and Wilkins Co., Baltimore) pp. 1510—1520.

Ovesey, L. (1969) *Homosexuality and Pseudohomosexuality.* (Science House, New. York.) York.)

Pillard, R., Rose, R. and Sherwood, M. (1974) Plasma testosterone levels in homosexual men. *Arch. Sex. Behav.*, 3: 453—58.

Pirke, K., Kockett, G. and Dittmar, F. (1974) Psychosexual stimulation and plasma testosterone in man. *Arch. Sex. Behav.*, 3: 577—84.

Prince, C. and Bentler, P. (1972) Survey of 504 cases of transvestism. *Psychol. Rep.* 31: 903—17.

Reekers, G. and Lovaas, I. (1974) Behavioral treatment of deviant sex-role behaviors in a male child. *J. Appl. Behav. Anal.* 7: 173—190.

Romer, L. von (1906) Die uranische familie. *Beitr. Erkentniss Uranismus*, Vol. 1.

Saghir, M. and Robins, E. (1973) *Male and Female Homosexuality* (Williams and Wilkins, Baltimore.)

Siegelman, M. (1972) Adjustment of male homosexuals and heterosexuals. *Arch. Sex. Behav.*, 2: 9—25.

Siegelman, M. (1974) Parental background of male homosexuals and heterosexuals. *Arch. Sex. Behav.*, 3: 3—18.

Socarides, C. (1968) *The Overt Homosexual.* (Grune and Stratton, New York.)

Socarides, C. (1970) Homosexuality and medicine. *J. Am. Med. Assoc.*, 212: 1199—1202.

Spitzer, R. (1973) In: (R. Stoller, J. Marmor, I. Bieber, R. Gold, C. Socarides, R. Green and R. Spitzer) A Symposium: Should Homosexuality be in the APA Nomenclature. *Am. J. Psychiat.*, 130: 1207—16.

Stoller, R. (1968) *Sex and Gender: The Development of Masculinity and Femininity.* (Science House, New York.)

Teal, D. (1971) *The Gay Militants.* (Stein and Day, New York.)

Tourney, G. and Hatfield, L. (1973) Androgen metabolism in schizophrenics, homosexuals and controls. *Biol. Psychiat.*, 6: 23—26.

Yalom, I., Green, R. and Fisk, N. (1973) Prenatal exposure to female hormones - effect on psychosexual development in boys. *Arch. Gen. Psychiat.*, 28: 554—61.

Young, W., Goy, R. and Phoenix, C. (1964) Hormones and sexual behavior. *Science*, 143: 212—18.

Zuger, B. (1966) Effeminate behavior present in boys from early childhood. *J. Pediat.* 69: 1098—1107.

CHAPTER 86

Prostitution

MARTHA L. STEIN

1. REVIEW OF THE LITERATURE

Prostitution, often referred to as 'the world's oldest profession', is an enduring social institution that cuts across all levels of societies from the lowest to the highest. Its practitioners sell sexual services, which must be paid for each time in money or equivalent goods. The most common prostitute—customer relations are female—male or male—male.

History

Long a subject of fascination, it has been looked at from many viewpoints by laymen and by a variety of academic disciplines. For comprehensive historical over-views, the reader is referred to Vern Bullough's 'History of Prostitution' (1964) and Fernando Henriques' 3 volume survey, 'Prostitution and Society', from classical times to the modern day (1962, 1963, 1968). Henriques amply illustrated his central thesis that prostitution's organization and status were directly related to the familial and marital institutions of its society, be it classical Greece, mid-Victorian England or 20th century America. These extensive bibliographies also acquaint one with the historical body of unscientific, heated literature concerned with prostitution's immorality and decadence. More contemporary, reasoned discourses on prostitution, its morality and its criminality, were made by Benjamin and Masters (1964) and Burnstin and James (1971). Sociologists examined prostitution's relationship to society as a deviant subculture, and as an occupation with an ideology of its own (Davis, 1961; Bryan, 1965, 1966; Gagnon, 1968; Winick, 1971). Psychologists, in turn, focused on prostitutes in terms of their psychological personalities (Greenwald, 1970), and their own sexuality (Pomeroy, 1965). Anthropologists applied an ethnographic semantic approach to the study of streetwalkers as an urban subculture (James, 1969, 1970, 1972), and examined the counterpart to the street-walker subculture, name-

Handbook of Sexology, edited by J. Money and H. Musaph
© *Elsevier/North-Holland Biomedical Press, 1977*

ly the world of the black pimp (Milner and Milner, 1973). Journalist Gail Sheehy (1973) has written about the panorama of 'hustling', including streetwalkers, call girls, courtesans and mistresses. Not to be neglected either is an extensive subgenre of participants' own stories, some of the more sensational in recent times being those by Iceberg Slim (1969), Xavier Hollander (1972), and Monique Von Cleef (1973).

The customer

Yet in this outpouring of writings, not enough serious attention was paid to the customer, without whom the entire industry would not exist. Only a chapter on this topic can be found in the writings of Kinsey and associates (1948), Henriques (1968), Benjamin and Masters (1964). Winick (1962) was one of the first to ask what functions a visit to a prostitute served in the personality economy of the man and how he perceived himself and the prostitute. The answers, obtained through interviews of 732 men, suggested that the prostitute served many different symbolic and fantasy functions for her clients and that these did not differ appreciably among clients from different socioeconomic groups. Those conclusions were confirmed by Stein (1974) in a study of prostitution in New York City, with the cooperation of 64 call-girl prostitutes, in which she was able to observe and document some of their transactions with their clients — 1242 upper middle class, caucasian males.

The call girls

Call-girl prostitutes formed only one sector in the complex world of prostitution. They were considered 'high class' prostitutes both by other kinds of prostitutes and by the men who employed them. As their name suggests, they were contacted via telephone from people who had learned of them from female associates or previous clients. Their high status was also the result of their fees — in 1972, in New York City, they were charging a minimum of $50 for an average 40-minute session that involved one orgasm.

Field work data
During the course of her field work, Stein eventually became acquainted with male and female prostitutes from other levels of society. In addition to call girls, she contacted prostitutes who worked in the locale of streets, bars, houses of prostitution, massage parlors and those who were contacted through limousine or cab drivers, hotel employees, restauranteurs. Homosexual prostitution had similar divisions. There were call boys, street boys, bar boys, and so on. From her documented observations of the call-girl level of prostitution, extended informal discussions with other prostitutes and a survey of the literature, she concluded that sexual services were inextricably intertwined with customers' psychological needs. Like Winick (op. cit.), she

asked what psychological and sexual functions prostitution performed or what psychosexual needs were met through prostitution. To answer these questions, the prostitute—customer relationship was defined as a psycho-sexual transaction, that is, their transaction involved the exchange of an agreed sum of money for the provision of both physical and psychological satisfactions, within a specified time. Both parties adopted roles appropriate to the sexual and emotional satisfactions being sought, the amount of money involved, and the time for which the service was agreed.

Both prostitutes and clients referred to their encounters as 'scenes', and they recognized the element of conscious creation involved in them. The word 'scene' was an appropriate noun because the basic structure of sessions paralleled that of a drama; each transaction was a self-enclosed and highly structured event which began when the client contacted the prostitute, reached a climax with orgasm, and ended when the client left. The clients knew the kind of atmosphere and activities they wanted and what services they expected. They gave appropriate cues, and the two participants impro-vised a sexual drama accordingly.

Based upon the role play, a typology of nine distinct behavior patterns emerged, namely, opportunist/hooker, adventurer/playmate, lover/romatic partner, friend/confidante, slave/dominatrix, guardian/daughter-figure, juve nile/mother-figure, fraternizer/party girl, promoter/business woman (Table I). The different patterns reflected the clients' reasons for coming to the pros titute and the kind of psychological and physical satisfactions they sought. Together the nine types of transactions resulting from the nine behavior pat-terns pointed to five psychosexual functions of prostitution.

Table I
Psychosexual functions of prostitution

Psychosexual function	Role-play	
	Client	Prostitute
1. Sexual release	Opportunist	'Hooker'
2. Sexual expansion	Adventurer	Playmate
3. Relationship Object:		
Romance	Lover	Romantic partner
Companionship	Friend	Confidante
Domination	Slave	Dominatrix
Filial affection	Guardian	Daughter-figure
Maternal comfort	Juvenile	Mother-figure
4. Sociosexual entertainment	Fraternizer	Party girl
5. Status enhancement	Promoter	Business woman

2. FIVE PSYCHOSEXUAL FUNCTIONS OF PROSTITUTION

Men interested in quick and convenient sexual release saw prostitution primarily as a sexual service. Clients seeking sexual expansion called on prostitutes' guidance and expertise as they moved into areas where mental stimulation became increasingly important. Clients concerned with establishing particular types of relationships made highly complex demands on prostitutes, putting them in the position of satisfying emotional needs concomitantly with sexual ones. Those interested in social entertainment or status enhancement responded to prostitution as an institution which could influence social and economic relationships by providing shared sexual experiences. The nature of the different role designations will become obvious during the following discussion of the five functions — release, expansion, relationship, entertainment, status.

(a) Sexual release

Sexual release underlay all other functions, but for many men it was the primary object of the encounter, whereas for others, it was complicated by an overlay of psychological factors that needed to be met in order for sexual satisfaction to take place. These clients were referred to as Opportunists, because they sought convenience, instant availability, variety, and lack of commitment. Any time of night or day, men were able to locate a prostitute with specified physical characteristics. Their usual requests were for someone attractive, friendly, nice body and, most importantly, a good 'mechanic'. Some were even more specific as to height, hair color, bust measurements, body shape, age, ethnic origins. And for those men who were limited by time, there were prostitutes, particularly in New York's garment district, who worked a 6 a.m. to 9 a.m. shift in order to see their office worker clients before they had to be at work. Other prostitutes handled an afternoon trade that was geared towards the married commuter, and still others worked late into the night. The prostitutes considered the passing clients the 'bread and butter' of the trade and referred to them as 'quickies', 'gypsies', 'butterflies'. The men, in turn, used the argot word 'hookers' to describe the prostitutes from whom they obtained convenient unemotional and straightforward sexual service.

Convenience

Examples of convenience were legion: a salesman who had forty minutes between appointments and would only see someone within a four-block radius of his next appointment; another would double-park outside his call girl's luxury apartment for a brief twenty-minute session; the homeward bound automobile driver would pick up a streetwalker, drive around the block long enough for fellatio and then continue his journey over bridge or tunnel; lonesome Chinese immigrants, living in the crowded boarding house hotels of

Chinatown, would seek a prostitute who might swiftly service ten to twenty men an hour.

Absence of emotional obligations
Coupled with the convenience of availability was the convenience of no emotional obligations. Having paid their fee, the men felt they had discharged their commitment. According to Kinsey (1948, p. 589) "There seems to be no question but that the human male would be promiscuous in his choice of sexual partners throughout the whole of his life if there were no social restrictions. This is the history of his anthropoid ancestors and this is the history of unrestrained males everywhere". Many men resolve the conflict between the social ideal of marital fidelity and their natural urge for a variety of sexual experience by their extensive contacts with prostitutes.

Variety of sexual service
The sexual services that Opportunists requested were very straightforward. They were representative of the universe of prostitute customers in that about half chose to abandon established sex roles and preferred to have the prostitute be the active, initiating sex partner. Unlike other clients, however, they devoted minimal time to conversation, seduction, foreplay. Their sexual activity generally consisted of fellatio (among call-girl clients, an incidence of 83%) or basic 'half and half' — fellatio followed by coitus. Their most common choice was the female superior position. However, if the customer did not climax quickly in that position, the prostitute switched to the male superior position — a position known in the trade for leading to a quick orgasm. The women who specialized in volume business were known as 'flatbacks'.

It was common for men to request fellatio because of the prostitutes' expertise, the diffidence of their wives and girlfriends for oral sex, and their own desire to avoid venereal disease. Incidentally, although the concern of prostitution as a venereal disease carrier has been expressed repeatedly in the literature, it is more a myth than a reality. Most 'houses' use physicans where girls must be checked out weekly and return with a doctor's certification note, and call girls employ their own private physicians. Cleanliness is stressed in all encounters — men and women wash before and after sexual intercourse with the simple, but effective routine of soap and water.

(b) Sexual expansion

Many men wanting more than sexual release turned to prostitution for sexual expansion. The kind of sexual expansion they sought varied: some wanted education in basic sexual techniques; some wanted to explore ways of making sex more exciting; some used experimentation to make themselves feel liberated, attractive and adventuresome; some needed an opportunity to act out a particular set of socially taboo desires; some sought the psychic release that sometimes follows an intense sexual experience (see James, 1970).

Adventurers all, they required a prostitute who would appear enthusiastic, eager to explore, a playmate who would show them the way.

Sex education

For many the way meant basic sex education. No different from the rest of their society, they brought their inhibitions, guilts, and curiosity to the sexual arena. It mattered not whether the client be a 17-year-old, brought by an older male relative to be initiated; a middle-aged man beginning to 'stray'; or a seasoned 'john' (an argot word for a prostitute's customer). His education generally consisted of fellatio, cunnilingus, coital variations, hygiene and a generous heaping of reassurance.

For those Adventurers who sought more advanced exploration, the importance and meaning of experimentation can be seen from the statistics on selected practices of the total sample of clients of call girls versus these Adventurers (Table II).

Imaginative factors

Besides being instructors, prostitutes had to be imaginative sex partners and facilitators. They had to create quickly an erotic, nonjudgmental atmosphere in which relaxation and fantasy played a crucial role in exciting their men. Prostitutes and clients both used all available stimulants to the imagination: pornographic literature and movies, drugs (marijuana, cocaine, amylnitrate) dildoes, vibrators, massagers, costumes (the favorites being the proverbial garter belt, silk stockings and high heels), mouthwash concentrates, flavoring creams, liqueurs, hot water, foods, bubble baths and showers. Most of all, they used stories and discussions about homosexuality, masochism, voyeur-

Table II
Comparison of selected sexual practices of adventurers versus total sample of call-girl clients

Selected sexual practices	Total (%) (n = 1230)	Adventurers (%) (n = 216)
1. Fantasy/relaxation	39	56
2. Sex aids	20	34
3. Drug use	9	21
4. Erotic costumes	12 *	7
5. Troilism	11	67
6. Homosexuality (lesbianism)	10	15
7. Male anal stimulation	30	42
8. Masochism	17 **	13
9. Voyeurism/Exhibitionism	37	62

* This figure includes Slaves, 71% of whom requested that the prostitute wear an erotic costume.
** This figure includes Slaves, 100% of whom were scored under masochism.

ism and exhibitionism. In particular, female homosexuality fascinated a large portion of the men, and they would avidly question prostitutes about their often-fabricated lesbian activities.

Troilism
In many cases, 'sex talk' led to 'sex action'. So that, in the spirit of adventure and liberation, troilism, a three-way sex scene, usually between the client and two female prostitutes, was very popular. Troilism included a 'lesbian' show that served the functions of arousal, visual education leading to correction of myths and fears about female homosexuality, harem or 'pasha' fantasies, and pleasurable identification with one of the women. A smaller percentage of men took the opportunity to explore vicarious homosexual impulses.

Homosexuality
Included in this category were clients who fantasized out loud about sexual play with another male; clients who asked the prostitute to arrange a session with another male; clients who liked the prostitute to strap on a dildo and penetrate them anally, requesting deep, regular thrusting; clients who performed fellatio on a dildo; clients who engaged in troilism with a girl and another man in a manner suggesting that their primary interest was in the other male; clients who asked a girl to allow them to perform cunnilingus on her before she washed from a previous encounter, specifically stating that they wanted to taste the former client's semen. The latter were regarded as expressing heterosexual rather than homosexual desires.

Repetition and variety
Some Adventurers were flexible and sought a different expansive experience each time, but others insisted that the identical erotic procedures be repeated each time. All in all, the Adventurers' psychosexual needs — to have a variety of sexual experiences, to feel they were erotically sophisticated, to act out unusual desires, to have an intense experience that would allow them temporarily to forget their problems — were an impressive demonstration of the complexity of sexuality as dealt with in the prostitution setting.

(c) Relationship

For other men, sexuality demanded its expression in the context of a relationship meaningful to them. The object varied — romance, companionship, domination, filial affection, maternal comfort. The pleasure they derived from the sexual and social elements of the encounter depended on the prostitute's success in playing the part they assigned to her. Selected psychosexual variables from the call-girl/client relationship patterns illustrate the multifaceted nature of these relationships (Table III).

Table III
Selected psychosexual variables from call-girl/client relationship

Selected variables from call-girl/client relationships	Psychosexual behavior patterns (%)					
	Total (n = 1242)	Lovers (n = 171)	Friends (n = 149)	Slaves (n = 156)	Guardian (n = 76)	Juvenile (n = 43)
Pattern of use						
Identification given	43	37	49	46	61	35
Lengthy session	35	35	27	40	26	19
Extended relationship	51	43	80	52	72	49
Social behavior						
Extrovert	72	81	77	57	92	74
Introvert	28	19	23	43	8	26
Prostitute as confidante						
Imposition of therapeutic role on prostitute	52	74	75	100	86	77
Sexual dysfunctions						
Premature ejaculation	6	4	8	11	4	5
Erective and/or ejaculatory impotence	19	25	18	17	26	14
Problematic behavior *						
Emotionally demanding	26	28	26	49	37	40
Self-abasing	18	9	8	100	1	23
Negative mental states	18	19	10	51	12	28

* The three categories, emotionally demanding, self-abasing, and negative mental states, overlap. The incidence of the three kinds of problems is recorded, not the number of men who had a problem.

Identification

Almost half (43%) gave the prostitute their real name and home or business telephone number. Giving identification was considered to be an indication of trust and of a desire to maintain contact. For 35% of the men time was essential for developing the right kind of atmosphere, and many required appointments that lasted for two or more hours. Over half (51%) saw the prostitutes at least five times in a one year period. Thus the prostitutes were able to become familiar with the personality, personal problems, interest and sexual preferences of some of their clients. In fact, some of the women were so resourceful as to file these observations on index cards in order to play their role more successfully.

Emotional roles conferred

Almost three-quarters of the men (72%) spoke easily with their prostitutes, without prompting, socialized actively and articulated their desires. Half (52%) of the men actually imposed a therapeutic role on the prostitute, and they included men who went partly for help in dealing with the kind of problems that people customarily take to professional therapists. They used the prostitute for: (1) ego support and reassurance in the face of business, marital and personal problems; (2) crisis intervention in situations such as divorce, death, loss of a job, severe financial difficulties; (3) help in expressing suppressed sexual material that usually involved such socially disapproved impulses as masochism, homosexuality, and transvestism, (4) sex counseling, including information, instruction in basic techniques, exploration of variations, elaborations of basic techniques, and help with sexual dysfunctions (25%). Of the latter, 6% were premature ejaculators, and they and others with performance problems would ask for assistance before the sex play began.

Stimulation control

Prostitutes would help the premature ejaculators to delay orgasm by carefully controlling their level of stimulation. Initially they would avoid their genital areas and instead concentrate on other erogenous zones. During fellatio they would stimulate less sensitive areas of the penis (the underside of the testicles, the testicles, the lower part of the shaft) and use only very light pressure. During intercourse they would move very slowly, stopping to rest whenever the client's level of excitation appeared to be building too rapidly.

Problem solving

Nineteen percent had trouble achieving or maintaining an erection, or, in a few cases, ejaculating. Most tended to aggravate their difficulty by worry and redoubled effort. To counteract this, prostitutes would encourage their partners to relax with conversation, gentle caresses, massage, nongenital forms of stimulation, and fantasy exploration. They preferred oral sex as the technique in dealing with impotence because it gave more control over the intensity of stimulation. When the man was partially erect, the prostitute might have him enter her and then bring him to a fuller erection by contracting her vaginal muscles. Often she would simulate an orgasm herself to excite the client sympathetically. She might stimulate the client's testicles, perineum, anus, nipples and offer verbal encouragements ('talk him into coming'). She was especially careful to explain to the older men that it wasn't necessary to have an orgasm every time they made love but that it was only important for both partners to enjoy themselves.

Client personality defenses
The therapeutic nature of the relationship can be further understood by looking at the data on problematic behavior (Table III above).

The clients who made insistent demands with regard to money, sexual practices, or emotional assurances were classified as emotionally demanding. Others were considered self-abasing when they denigrated themselves to the prostitute, either directly by self-criticism, by reporting criticism of themselves by others, or by making frequent and uncalled for apologies. A motley group of men who were hyperactive, incessant braggers, whose responses were unpredictable and inappropriate, withdrawn, depressed, extremely nervous, tense, guilty or anxious, were included in the umbrella term 'negative mental states'.

These figures give some indication of the overall nature of the complex relationships, but for a clearer understanding of their specific object, a brief sketch of the Lovers, Friends, Slaves, Guardians, and Juveniles is necessary.

Lovers Lovers behaved toward prostitutes in a highly active and romantic fashion, professing love, affection or infatuation, and requiring reciprocity from them. It was not uncommon for new clients, upon seeing the prostitute for the first time, to give deep, passionate embraces and kisses. They wooed prostitutes by flattering them and advertising themselves. They enjoyed prolonged foreplay, showing great concern about their own skill as lovers and demanding frequent expressions of praise and affection. Their need to have their romantic self-image consistently affirmed made them demanding clients.

In the call-girl study, 46% of the Lovers were in their forties. In many cases, their need for ego support was related to an ongoing midlife crisis. Their conversations were studded with feelings about lost youth, awareness of middle age, of stagnation, questioning of life's values, and escape fantasies. Their most typical fantasy was that of taking a vacation with the prostitute, and they often referred to the session itself as a brief fantasy vacation. For the moment, she became the mistress in a special love affair that was desired but unrealized.

Friends Friends came for companionship and relaxation as much as for sex. Like Lovers, Friends wanted to please the prostitutes and were eager to elicit support and affection from them. The Friends differed from the Lovers in that they were more interested in ventilating their real problems than in projecting a flattering image of themselves. Being liked and listened to was more important to them than being adored. Several Friends referred to the prostitute as 'my second wife'. As one girl remarked, "They're all looking for Doris Day".

They were called 'steadies' by the women. Some of these relationships lasted years. Most of them visited regularly, whether weekly, bi-weekly, or monthly, and they valued the friendship to overcome their loneliness. Insufficient attention has been paid to loneliness as a motivating factor in these clients. As Henriques (1968, p. 266) wrote "Loneliness is a component which has become very significant as urban life has increased with its inevitable emphasis on the anonymous and the impersonal. The therapeutic aspect of the prostitute's role in Western society has been overshadowed by the more sexually obvious characteristics of that role . . .".

Slaves   Slaves came to prostitutes to act out sexual fantasies of submission to a sensual and strict Dominatrix. It was clearly the loss of control and submission to someone who was mentally stronger, that excited these men, not pain of itself.

The Slaves' submission and humiliation were only symbolic. The masochists always retained the ultimate control. Some surrendered totally and at once to the Dominatrix, others enjoyed struggling before they gave in, but all the men submitted themselves only within the framework of a carefully circumscribed and mutually agreed upon sexual game. Bondage and discipline were used to heighten their feelings of helplessness and submission. Restraint and mild pain also served as their direct sexual stimulants. As a number of the men explained, "the purpose of the physical 'punishment' was stimulation, not destruction".

The slave scenes functioned therapeutically by allowing clients to enjoy various sexual practices without guilt, to relieve anxieties by a symbolic retreat into childhood, to compensate for sadistic or domineering behavior in other areas of their lives, to act out self-destructive impulses toward a pleasurable end. The sessions certainly enabled the men to relieve sexual tensions by acting out fairly strong desires they would otherwise suppress.

In addition, the prostitutes eased the guilt of their clients by reassuring and educating them about masochism, by telling them about other men who had the same desires, and by providing a nonjudgmental environment where each client could feel free to talk about his fantasies.

Guardians   Guardians specifically requested very young and inexperienced prostitutes, treating them as an uncle would treat his niece, a father his daughter, or a guardian his ward — whereas ordinary clients basically wanted a pretty young woman and if they found one they liked wouldn't much care if she were 18 or 23. For the Guardians, however, the girl's numerical age was terribly important and 18 was definitely preferable to 23. Many of them liked prostitutes who giggled, acted impulsively, got confused, and needed their help. A sophisticated 18-year-old prostitute would not do for their purposes. Unlike most other clients, they advertised their age to the prostitute and played the role of the wiser, older man. Some of the clients sought a young woman partly because they enjoyed creating a semipaternal relationship. Others devoted less attention to establishing themselves as paternal figures and instead used the transactions to act out sexual fantasies about very young girls. Some sought the augmentation of status that comes with being the protector and lover of a beautiful young girl.

Juveniles Juveniles requested older, large, full-figured women to whom they could look for comfort and counsel as well as sexual pleasure. Many of them seemed to have a confused sense of masculinity and they expressed the fear that they might be homosexual. Their lack of sexual maturity could be seen in their anxious interest in genital mechanics, and their concern about the size of their penis and quality of their ejaculate. Many explained that they had little sexual experience and had difficulty relating to women.

When Juveniles found prostitutes who responded to their needs, they derived multiple benefits from their session with them. The prostitutes satisfied their need for physical and emotional closeness with a woman; their maternal and tolerant attitude allowed them to express sexual desires which they could not express with 'straight' women; they could turn to them for information and advice about women; their responsiveness, their build, and the sex act itself made the Juveniles feel more masculine. Throughout the sex play and after, prostitutes had to reassure the Juveniles by correcting their misconceptions about sex and by complimenting them on their body or sexual skill. They also had to be prepared to offer minicourses in anatomy and technique.

In these five role situations, role-playing served several functions. Clients and prostitutes were able to establish easily a familiar atmosphere of intimacy by modeling their behavior after one of the ways men and women commonly relate to each other in our society. Some men enjoyed the role-playing for its own sake, much the way people may enjoy imitating favorite movie scenes. Others found it sexually arousing. The role they chose for the prostitute, whether that of Romantic Partner, Confidante, Dominatrix, Daughter-figure or Mother-figure, reflected their sexual fantasies as well as their personality and self-image. Perhaps most importantly, role-playing enabled clients to express emotional needs and to elicit the appropriate emotional response without experiencing any of the ambiguity or anxiety that can come with committed involvement. Thus the Lover was guaranteed praise and tenderness, the Friend attention and sympathy, the Slave a complete sense of belonging and submission, the Guardian filial affection and the Juvenile maternal comfort.

(d) Sociosexual entertainment

Many men used prostitution services only for purposes of recreation or social entertainment. Some shared their encounters in pairs, others in groups that ranged from three to thirty. In this context, sex served a variety of functions. In some instances, it was used as an additional component to a successful social evening, along with good food, drink, social conversation, card playing, bowling, attending a sport or theatrical event, and such like. It provided men with a means to relieve emotional tensions attendant upon a strenuous business session. It was one of the unlisted attractions at conventions, and a necessity at stag and bachelor parties.

For some it served as a continuation of postadolescent days — sex as practiced in a fraternity or in the army, a reaffirmation of boyhood ties and its camaraderie. The bawdy, uninhibited atmosphere of the parties encouraged some Fraternizers to try new eroticisms. They were able to act out voyeuristic and, in the case of men who participated in 'lesbian' shows, very explicit, exhibitionistic impulses. They found the high incidence of exhibitionism, of public and semipublic sexual performances and partial nudity in itself was exciting and disinhibiting.

The sessions also allowed Fraternizers some experience of both female and male homosexuality. Many men exhibited a complex, erotic fascination with lesbianism. Troilistic sessions and 'orgies' provided others with a way of acting out homosexual tendencies, while protecting them from any need to confront these tendencies. The pleasure the men derived from creating the kind of male-to-male ties usually associated with youth suggested that the Fraternizers had a need for intimacy with members of their own sex that was not provided for within the respectable framework of their lives. Perhaps they fell back on adolescent models of behavior because society provided too few models for friendship between mature men. In any case it seemed that Fraternizers had a strong desire, not sexual in the limited sense, to feel emotionally and physically close to other men and they enjoyed group sessions with the prostitutes partly because the girls generated such feelings of closeness.

(e) Status enhancement

Many men formed extended associations with prostitutes in order to enhance their economic or social status. Their employers customarily provided buyers or associates from out of town with food, drink, and sexual pleasures. They contracted prostitution services to further their economic interests by setting up sessions in order to win a client's good will and sometimes to learn of his sexual tastes; by arranging for the prostitute to assess a client's thinking about a given project or to influence him to the Promoter's advantage; and by contracting her to adopt the role of a nonprofessional date, and in that role to persuade a client to finalize a contract. The prostitute functioned, in these instances. as a business partner. Many such associations lasted years and prostitutes were even put on company payrolls.

Promoters increased their social status and popularity within the group and gained a prestigious reputation for sexual sophistication by establishing themselves as a sexual liaison for their social circle. Their role of providing sexual contact made them feel important, and they derived a sense of personal power from their knowledge of their friend's sexual activities. Some men also derived feelings of self-esteem from seeing themselves as important and sexually powerful men, depended on and admired by both prostitutes and male associates.

3. PROSTITUTION: AN UNDERGROUND SEXUAL HEALTH SERVICE

Though prostitution is not a socially approved institution, it is patronized by respectable members of society, and plays an ongoing role in their lives. For example, in the call-girl-clients' study, the majority were middle aged (73% in their 40s and 50s; 58% married), businessmen and professionals. Men sought a wide variety of satisfactions from their encounters: sexual release; sexual expansion; sex with a woman who would provide romance, sympathy, domination, filial affection or maternal support; social entertainment; and status enhancement.

Economics

Unfortunately, reliable figures about the size and economics of prostitution are difficult to obtain. Winick and Kinsie (1971, p. 14) estimate that "of 95,500 prostitutes (based upon 1968 U.S. arrest figures) who earn $894 million (based on 18 clients per week at $10 per contract) is extremely low when compared with other figures that have been suggested". Sheehy (1973, p. 59) made a higher estimate of 200,000 to 250,000 prostitutes in the U.S., at the lower limit of which at $20 per time their "millions of clients . . . . contribute . . . . the incredible sum of between $7 and $9 billion annually".

Frequently full-time call girls see twenty to thirty clients a week (approximately 100 men per month) and receive at least $50 from each client. Working steadily at that rate, a call-girl will earn between $50,000 and $100,000 a year. Making an extremely modest assumption that there are 1000 full-time call girls in New York City, each earning only $30,000 a year, then a minimum of 30 million dollars is spent each year in New York alone. This figure does not include other levels of prostitution. Obviously, a staggering amount of psychosexual demand is being met through financial transactions.

Therapeutic considerations

Couple this fact with its therapeutic implications, and the study of prostitution as a meaningful social institution becomes even more complex and compelling. Since prostitutes enable men to achieve sexual satisfaction they often cannot get elsewhere, and since in relieving sexual tensions they relieve psychological tensions as well, the process can be considered restorative and therapeutic. The word therapy is generally used to refer to healing or curative treatment. However, it is also used to characterize any treatment or activity intended to alleviate a disorder or undesirable condition. Drug therapy, for example, contributes to a person's health by controlling symptoms rather than by eliminating their causes. Hence, the prostitute's services may be considered therapeutic in that they help a client maintain a healthy state by giving him the opportunity to act out desires and impulses.

Bolstering the social fabric

When the full range of functions is considered, it appears that prostitution has been operating unrecognized as an underground sexual health service, and a lucrative one at that. Some of the clients had no apparent sexual outlet other than prostitution: they were single or widowed and uninvolved; or, more often, their wives were sick or did not want sexual relations as they did. Many of the married men explained that they were committed to their marriages, although they were not sexually satisfying: they took their sexual needs to prostitutes because adultery might threaten their marriages, but the use of prostitution services would not. For these men the opportunity for sexual release was in itself therapeutic.

Professional intimacy

Other men had satisfying sexual relationships with wives or girlfriends but did not feel they could explore their sexuality fully within these relationships. Prostitution provided them with an opportunity to have a variety of partners, to talk openly about sex, asking questions and verbalizing fantasies, to abandon established sex roles, and to engage in various sexual activities that appealed to them. The visits also provided men with a chance to talk and be listened to. Sexual relations between clients and prostitutes created feelings of intimacy and trust which facilitated verbal confidence. At the same time the prostitute remained removed from their lives, so that the clients could say anything to her without fear. Further, the prostitute remained nonjudgmental and would rarely talk back or confront the men with problems of her own. Many men used the sessions to temporarily escape from stressful feelings, often arranging a session spontaneously in the midst of a particularly trying day.

Inducing self-esteem

In addition to enabling men to talk freely and unwind physically, the visits helped them deal with anxiety by heightening their sense of self-esteem.

Most of the roles the men chose for themselves served to enhance their self-image and to invite praise or reassurance. Successful completion of the sex act in itself appeared to reinforce feelings of self-esteem for the men who expressed doubts specifically with regard to their sexual abilities or their desirability. Sometimes clients expressed their sexual worries directly. In other cases a need for reassurance or information was evident in a client's desire for verbal feedback during sex, interest in the sexual practices of other men, personal vanity, or his statements and questions about sexuality and aging.

Changing sexual image

Some of the men appeared to be struggling to develop a sexual self-image appropriate for the middle years. These men seemed to see the visits as a way of proving to themselves that they could still function well sexually, or as an opportunity to experiment with practices popularized by the sexual liberation movements of a younger generation.

By providing men with a convenient source of sexual relief, with a place to freely explore their sexuality, with an opportunity to temporarily escape their problems, unwind and talk freely, and by meeting individual needs for ventilation of problems, crisis intervention, the expression of suppressed desires and sexual counseling, the institution has been serving as an unrecognized therapeutic facility.

4. SUMMARY

The question posed is: what are the psychological and sexual functions prostitution performs or, alternately, what psychosexual needs of customers are met through prostitution? Based upon documented observations of high-level, call-girl prostitutes, informal discussions with prostitutes from other levels, and in the literature, a typology of nine psychosexual transactions has been developed. There are five major functions of prostitution. As a sexual service, it provides convenient sexual release, sexual expansion, a variety of emotional relationships, social entertainment or recreation, and status enhancement through involvement in business associations. In many cases, the relationship is restorative and therapeutic. Taking into account its full range of functions, prostitution can be considered an underground sexual health service.

BIBLIOGRAPHY

Benjamin, H. and Masters, R.E.L. (1964) *Prostitution and Morality.* (Julian Press, New York.)

Bryan, J.H. (1965) Apprenticeships in prostitution. *Soc. Problems* 12: 3: 287—297.

Bryan, J.H. (1966) Occupational ideologies and individual attitudes of call girls. *Soc. Problems* 13 (4) 441—450.

Bullough, V.L. (1964) *The History of Prostitution.* (University Books, New York.)

Burnstein, E.J. Jr and James, J. (1971) Prostitution in Seattle. *Washington State Bar News*, Aug.-Sept., 5—8, 28—30.

Davis, K. (1961) Prostitution. In: (R.K. Merton and R.A. Nisbet, Eds.) *Contemporary Social Problems*, pp: 262—288. (Harcourt Brace and World, Inc. New York.)

Gagnon, J.H. (1968) Prostitution. In: (D.L. Sills, Ed.), *International Encyclopedia of the Social Sciences*, Vol. 12, (Crowell Collier, New York) pp: 592—597.

Greenwald, H. (1970) *The Elegant Prostitute.* (Ballantine Books, New York.)

Henriques, F. (1962) *Primitive, Classical and Oriental, Vol. I of Prostitution and Society.* (MacGibbon and Kee, London.)

Henriques, F. (1963) *Prostitution in Europe and the New World, Vol. II of Prostitution and Society.* (MacGibbon and Kee, London.)

Henriques, F. (1968) *Modern Sexuality, Vol. III of Prostitution and Society.* (MacGibbon and Kee, London.)

Hollander, X. (1972) *The Happy Hooker.* (Dell Publishing Co., New York.)

James, J. (1969) Sweet cream ladies: an introduction to prostitute taxonomy. (Unpublished paper, New Orleans, Am. Anthropol. Assoc. Meet.)

James, J. (1970) *Ethnographic Semantic Approaches to the Study of an Urban Subculture: Streetwalkers.* (Unpublished doctoral dissertation, University of Washington.)

James, J. (1972) On the block, urban research perspectives. *Urban Anthropol.* 1: 2: 125—140.

Kinsey, A.C., Pomeroy, W.W., Martin, C.E. and Gebhard, P.H. (1948) *Sexual Behavior in the Human Male.* (W.B. Saunders, Philadelphia.)

Milner, C. and Milner, R. (1973) *Black Players, The Secret World of Black Pimps.* (Bantam Books, New York.)

Pomeroy, W.B. (1965) Some aspects of prostitution. *J. Sex Res.* 1: 3: 177—187.

Sheehy, G. (1973) *Hustling.* (Delacorte Press, New York.)

Slim, I. (1969) *Pimp, the Story of My Life.* (Holloway House Publishing Co., Los Angeles.)

Stein, M.I. (1974) *Lovers, Friends, Slaves . . .* (Berkeley Publishing Co., New York)

Von Cleef, M. (1973) *The House of Pain.* (Olympia Press, Paris.)

Winick, C. (1962) Prostitutes' clients' perceptions of prostitutes and of themselves. *Int. J. Soc. Psychiat.*, 8: 4: 289—297.

Winick, C. and Kinsie, P. (1971) *The Lively Commerce.* (Quadrangle Press, New York.)

CHAPTER 87

Sex offenders

PAUL H. GEBHARD

1. DEFINITIONS

Sex offense

The criteria by which behavior is judged to be a sex offense vary in different societies, so that what may be an offense in one culture may in another be acceptable or even normative behavior. Also within a society the meaning attached to a given behavior depends upon a number of variables so that an act which is acceptable in one social context is an offense in another.

In order for a behavior to be a sex offense two conditions are requisite: (1) the behavior must be primarily motivated by a desire for sexual gratification as a direct consequence of the behavior, and (2) the behavior must be contrary to the prevailing mores of the society in which it occurs. The behavior itself must be expected to be sexually gratifying; less direct derivative sexual motivation cannot be accepted since many crimes may be sexually motivated (for example, embezzling to support a mistress, or murdering a spouse or rival).

Sex offender

In order for a person to be labeled a sex offender a third requisite exists: the person must be socially identified as having performed the behavior contrary to the sexual mores. In brief, one requires direct sexual motivation, behavior defined as deviant by the society, and identification. Consequently, a functional definition of a sex offender would be: a sex offender is a person who has been publically identified as having committed an overt act, for his or her own immediate sexual gratification, which is contrary to the prevailing sexual mores of the society.

In our western societies the criteria used in determining sex offenses are: (1) the presence or absence of consent, (2) age of the individual or individ-

Handbook of Sexology, edited by J. Money and H. Musaph
© *Elsevier/North-Holland Biomedical Press, 1977*

uals, (3) the degree of privacy, and (4) the degree of conflict with sexual morality. This last criterion is notable since nearly all other laws are concerned solely with protection of person or property, but many of the sex laws are concerned only with enforcing Judeo—Christian sexual morality.

This chapter will first deal with the major categories of sex offenses in western societies and later focus on the individuals who commit these offenses to ascertain what, if any, social or personality characteristics distinguish them from the general population.

2. MAJOR CATEGORIES OF SEX OFFENSES

Sex offenses based on the element of consent

Sexual acts without the consent of the other person or persons involved are always liable to be defined as sex offenses. If the act does not involve serious force or duress, does not include genital contact, and occurs between persons known to each other, it is less likely to be treated as an offense. Forcing an embrace and kiss upon a female friend is usually treated as an indiscretion rather than a sex offense, even though consent was lacking. If the female were a stranger or if genital contact were made, the behavior could very easily result in a charge of assault or attempted rape.

Consent cannot legally be given by individuals who are mentally defective, psychotic, seriously intoxicated, or under a stipulated age. Consent given by a normal adult is discounted, if it was obtained by deception (as through a false marriage ceremony) or threat of violence. Duress not involving physical force or valid danger, as in the threat of job loss, does not invalidate consent.

In addition to statutory rape, attempted rape, and rape, there are a number of sex offenses not involving physical contact which are based on lack of consent: peeping, exhibitionism, and obscene communications.

Sex offenses based on the element of age

Sex offenses based upon the element of age are those involving sexual contact between adults and nonadults (for example, child molestation, contributing to the delinquency of a minor, and statutory rape) or between nonadults (who may be labeled juvenile delinquents). Some societies have provided certain exceptions to the general opposition to sexual contact between juveniles and adults, or simply between juveniles, by allowing marriage near puberty. Recently some legal reforms have taken cognizance of the relative ages of the participants rather than relying on an arbitrary adult—juvenile dichotomy. As long as adulthood has been achieved by the participants, age discrepancy no longer is of legal concern, although society frowns on great age discrepancies — especially if the young person is very young, or if the female is many years older.

Sex offenses based on the element of privacy

The element of privacy in sexual activity is important to western societies which view public sexual behavior as disruptive and offensive. Consequently there are laws and ordinances designed to prevent sexual activity in public places, and to prevent overly blatant sexual solicitation. The restrictions go beyond these two justifiable aims and attempt to encompass anything of a sexual or presumably sexual nature which might affront the public, for example, nudity of certain body parts, pretending to be of the gender one is not, and exhibiting words or pictures of an 'obscene' nature.

Sex offenses based on religion

The majority of sex offenses in western societies are based primarily on an effort to maintain Judeo—Christian sexual morality rather than on matters of consent, age, and privacy. In many localities nonmarital coitus between consenting adults in private is still punishable as fornication or adultery. Homosexual activity is also commonly punishable, and the penalties are sometimes extremely severe. Sexual contacts between humans and animals are almost universally prohibited, as are sexual contacts between a living and dead human. Prostitution, essentially a contract for services between consenting adults, is often forbidden or controlled, and hence merits consideration as a sex offense. Lastly, certain techniques, specifically mouth—genital contact and anal coitus, are punishable in various countries. In the U.S. they are legally labeled "sodomy" in the majority of states.

3. MAJOR CATEGORIES OF SEX OFFENDERS

General discussion

With such a wide gamut of sex offenses, it is no surprise to find a great diversity of people being labeled as sex offenders. Indeed, if the various statutes and ordinances were strictly enforced, it is clear that in some countries the majority of the population would at some time be liable to prosecution as sex offenders. Since only a very tiny percentage of the population is ever charged with a sex offense, it is equally obvious that some selective processes are operative, and that there must be certain characteristics which render persons more liable to the commission of, and conviction for sex offenses.

One such characteristic is being male. Except for prostitution, females are rarely charged with sex offenses. There are several reasons for this. Western societies have trained females not be aggressive sexually, either physically or verbally. The incidence of homosexuality and paraphilias seems markedly less in females than in males. Society allows females certain behavior which in a male would be suspect or punishable. Thus a female pedophile could indulge in considerable contact with children and be thought of as simply someone who loved children; females can wear male apparel; females can indulge in socially tolerated exhibitionism in mode of dress and in 'accidental' exposure; and females can live together and enjoy public physical contact without being immediately labeled homosexual. Lastly, prosecutors are loathe to charge females with sex offenses, and juries are reluctant to convict them.

Focusing then only on male sex offenders, one can differentiate five major categories:

Offenders with defects of intellect or thought processes

This group includes the mentally retarded; those who were once normal, but later suffered deterioration or brain damage; the psychotic, and the seriously intoxicated (alcohol or drugs). They show no strong predisposition to any major offense category, but appear in many as minority constituents. This is because the intoxicated are liable to commit offenses fortuitously. If one considers only the retarded, brain damaged, and psychotic, these persons constitute 10—15% of the offenders against female and male children (including rape), peepers, and exhibitionists. In other categories they seem rare to absent, but an occasional rapist of adult females is clearly psychotic.

Offenders with defects of socialization or learning

Offenders with defects of socialization or learning consist mainly of two sorts. First is the sociosexually underdeveloped individual who has often grown up in a sexually repressive milieu, and is far behind his peers in knowledge and experience. His timidity and ineptitude may lead him to seek children rather than adults, or approach adults in highly inappropriate ways. However, he is most apt to be a harmless peeper. Rarely, a sociosexually underdeveloped person with powerful antisexual attitudes and guilt feelings may explode in some violent and dangerous outburst which might classify him as a psychotic. Second is what one might call the subculture offender; a person reared in a subculture which has sexual mores not in keeping with those of the larger society of which it is a part. Such subculture offenders are most apt to be found convicted for statutory rape or incest.

Offenders with defective personality development

This is a category hard to define since the defect is not one of intelligence, knowledge, or acculturation. Instead the defect is one of conscience and ethics. These offenders are basically amoral and have little regard for others. They have long been recognized and given labels such as 'psychopathic personality', 'sociopath', and 'amoral delinquent' (my term). Such individuals often view all females regardless of age as sexual objects whose role is to provide sexual pleasure, and while their consent is to be sought, their refusal can be ignored. These men often have other criminal records for they are inclined to take what they want, whether money, material, or women, and they generally have poor impulse control. Hence they are particularly liable to rape adult or minor females. The only other sex offense category in which they constitute as much as 10% is incest with children.

Offenders with neuroses and deviations

Offenders with neuroses and deviations consist of persons who have developed some sort of neurosis, fixation, or paraphilia which brings them into conflict with society although in all other respects they appear to be normal. There are various subtypes in the category. Sadomasochists are, with a few notable exceptions, no threat to society since they confine their ritualized and basically careful activity to themselves. Occasionally, a masochist may stage-manage his own murder. The man with an unconscious strong sadistic component may be dangerous, and is usually the man perpetrating the assaultive rape which involves unnecessary violence and cruelty. This assaultive type seems the commonest variety of rapist. Exhibitionism is the most compulsive and repetitive sex offense. Most exhibitionists are harmless victims of their compulsion; only those who seek lone females and approach them closely might be dangerous. Some peepers may be classified as neurotic deviants. So may also a minority of homosexuals. The majority of fetishists and pedophiles (those who prefer children) probably may be so categorized; little is known of the etiology. Lastly, the inept, dependent type of man who constitutes most of the incest offenders with children, should probably be classed here.

'Normal' offenders

'Normal' offenders may be defined as individuals whose behavior and general life-style is like that of a substantial part (or even the majority) of the population; they are sex offenders only because their commonplace behavior is against the law and for some reason, often fortuitous, has come to the attention of law-enforcement agencies. Such 'normal' offenders include the great majority of those convicted of fornication (premarital coitus), adultery (extramarital coitus), mouth—genital contact, anal coitus, and of statutory rape and of contributing to the delinquency of a minor cases, when the age discrepancy is not great. In addition, most persons convicted of homosexual behavior belong in this category, and so do some peepers. The convicted 'normal' offenders differ from the general population not only in being unlucky, but in being less intelligent, less educated, and less affluent.

4. CRIMINALITY OF SEX OFFENDERS

Nonsex offenses

The majority of sex offenders also have records of convictions for offenses not of a sexual nature, but these offenses are less numerous than their sex offenses. Many of the 'nonsex offenses' are not of major importance: petty theft, vagrancy, disorderly conduct, and such like. The exception to this generalization consists of sex offenders who use physical force or threat: these aggressors include a large number of men who are highly criminal and have more 'nonsex offenses' than sex offenses.

Specificity of sex offenses

Sex offenders who have been convicted of more than one sex offense show a strong tendency to repeat either the same sort of offense or one similar to it. Such specificity is particularly true of incest offenders, homosexuals, and those whose offense was with willing adult females. The offenders who use force or threat, the peepers, and the exhibitionists are most apt to commit a wider diversity of sex offenses.

Recidivism

The same is true for recidivism: the incest offenders and offenders with consenting adult females are least apt to be convicted of more than one sex offense, whereas those who use force or threat, the peepers, and the exhibitionists, are most likely of all groups to repeat their sex offense.

Escalation in seriousness of offense

In general there does not appear to be an escalation in the seriousness of sex offenses. The peeper, for example, seldom metamorphoses into a rapist, and the homosexual offender against adults only rarely turns to children later on. Instead, as noted above, sex offenders tend to stay within one category of offense.

5. SEXUAL PSYCHOPATHY

Roughly half of the states in the U.S.A. have sexual psychopath (or a synonymous term) laws based on the concept that there exists an identifiable clinical entity consisting of persons likely to commit repeated sex offenses. The criteria in judging a sexual psychopath are chiefly: compulsiveness, repetitiveness, and/or some bizarre quality of the sexual behavior. Those judged to be sexual psychopaths are supposed to be sent to a mental, rather than penal, institution, or to receive some other special treatment. Most psychiatrists, psychologists, and penologists believe that sexual psychopathy is a legal rather than a medical entity. There are a small number of sex offenders whose crimes were particularly heinous or bizarre and earned them the label of sexual psychopath, though most sexual psychopaths' crimes are quite similar to the crimes of those not judged to be psychopaths. Sexual psychopaths when compared to other sex offenders, appear to be more amenable to treatment in being younger, more intelligent, better educated, and more like the sort of patient a clinician would deal with outside of prison.

In brief, the sexual psychopathy statutes function more or less as devices enabling us to segregate for special treatment (1) the most salvageable and (2) the most pathological, though not systematically so.

6. SOCIAL CONTROL OF SEXUALITY

Society always controls to some degree the sexual behavior of its constituent members. The majority of individuals and organizations (for example, the American Law Institute, and the Group for the Advancement of Psychiatry) who have studied this matter agree that social control should be invoked only in (1) cases involving threat, force, or duress, (2) cases involving sexual activity between children and adults, and (3) cases of sexual activity or solicitation so open as to constitute a public affront or nuisance. It is clear that Western civilization is gradually moving toward the belief that what consenting adults do sexually in private should not be governed by law, and this concept is being recognized increasingly in recent revisions of sex laws and in court decisions.

7. SUMMARY

Sex offenses are defined differently by various societies. European—American culture defines them on the basis of consent, age, privacy, and Judeo—Christian mores. Since males are viewed as the initiators of sexual activity, far more males than females are charged with sex offenses other than prostitution. The males most likely to be convicted of sex offenses are those with one or more of the following conditions: (1) permanent or temporary mental impairment, (2) inadequate socialization and learning, (3) inadequately developed conscience, and (4) emotional problems such as neuroses and fixations. Probably because of the same defects most sex offenders also have records of convictions for nonsexual offenses. A number of seemingly normal males are convicted for forms of sexual behavior which represent frequent (for example, homosexual acts) or normative (for example, coitus before marriage) behavior. Recidivism varies greatly according to the type of offense, and those who repeat sex offenses tend to commit the same or similar offense; there is no trend for offenses to become more serious. In recent decades an increasing number of states in the U.S. have been revising their sex laws.

CHAPTER 88

Drugs and sex: inhibition and enhancement effects

MURRAY E. JARVIK and EDWARD M. BRECHER

1. INTRODUCTION

Through the ages men have searched for sexual stimulants (aphrodisiacs) to enhance their normal sexual functioning, to compensate for a perceived decline in their sexual functioning, to enhance the arousability and responsiveness of their sexual partners, and to serve as an adjunct in their seduction of females or other males. More recently, a few therapists have begun relatively casual trials of various drugs in the therapy of sexual dysfunction.

At least since the Victorian era, sexual depressants (anaphrodisiacs) have also been sought to curb libido in rapists, pederasts and homosexuals, and to deter masturbation in females and males.

To what extent are particular drugs, in fact, capable of enhancing or depressing (a) human sexuality in general, or (b) specific features of human sexual response such as libido (sexual desire), erection in the male, lubrication in the female, and orgasm in either sex? Can they either lengthen or shorten the time between the onset of sexual arousal and orgasm in either the female or the male? Can they lengthen or shorten the refractory period in the male — the period between orgasm and rearousal? Can they either intensify or curtail the pleasure of a sexual encounter? What other parameters of human sexuality can they affect?

Research trials

Numerous imposing obstacles stand in the way of establishing reliable answers to the previous questions. One is suggestibility or the placebo effect; a person who believes that a drug will have a particular effect, sexual or otherwise is very likely to experience the expected effect. To eliminate this common source of error, drug trials must be well-controlled and double-blind. Neither subjects nor controls nor investigators should know, until after the results have been recorded, which individuals have received the active drug and which have received an inert placebo.

Handbook of Sexology, edited by J. Money and H. Musaph
© *Elsevier/North-Holland Biomedical Press, 1977*

The inherent sexual puritanism of Western culture and of scientific and medical institutions within that culture, however, stands in the way of such well-controlled, double-blind trials. As a result of this antisexual bias, neither staffing nor funding has, with rare exceptions, been available for the scientific study of potentially stimulating sexual effects. Studies of depressant effects are less subject to cultural taboos; no doubt for this reason, well-controlled anaphrodisiac studies are a bit less scarce. For both sexual stimulants and sexual depressants, however, the vast bulk of necessary research still lies ahead.

Even if adequate staffing and funding were available, the task of exploring the sexual effects of drugs would remain formidable. Psychoactive drugs, especially mood-altering drugs, rarely produce uniform effects; and it is unlikely that sexual effects will prove uniform. Drugs that facilitate sexual arousal in one individual, or in some individuals under some circumstances, may impair sexual arousal in other individuals, under other circumstances, or at other dosage levels. We may also expect to find that tolerance develops, slowly or rapidly, to the sexual effects of some drugs. Finally, drugs which have no specifically sexual effects may be found to affect sexual response by stimulating or depressing physiological or psychological function in general. A substantial research effort will no doubt be required to explore these and other intricacies — especially dose-related and mood-related variations in effects.

Another area which has been almost wholly neglected is the relation of general health to sexual response. It seems probable that any drug which contributes to sound health will facilitate sexual functioning and that any drug which impairs health will impair sexual functioning. Thus, in the presence of pain, an analgesic which ordinarily depresses sexual function may instead be found to improve it. When anxiety impedes sexual function, a tranquilizer might be expected to help. A CNS stimulant might be expected to improve sexual function in a fatigued female or male, and an antidepressant drug might be expected to restore potency in a patient whose impotence is secondary to depression. A soporific drug prescribed for insomnia may improve sexual response following a restful sleep. A nauseant drug other than apomorphine no doubt impairs sexual function while the nausea lasts. We regret to report that only the barest beginnings have been made in the scientific exploration of these and other promising hypotheses (Nowlis, 1974).

In the absence of well-controlled trials, one must rely primarily, in the drug-by-drug survey that follows, on the subjective, retrospective reports of drug users themselves, on opinion survey data, on anecdotal evidence, on a modest array of uncontrolled human studies, and on an equally modest group of uncontrolled studies in infrahuman species. Even less is known about the sexual effects of drugs in human females than in males. While we have sought to rely on the best available evidence, we make no claim that it is sound evidence.

2. FOLK APHRODISIACS

Inert substances

In various cultures at various times, several substances have been touted for their favorable sexual effects — including potatoes, onions, oysters, asparagus, mint, garlic, radishes, pepper, lampreys, fish, caviar, chocolate, eggs, powdered rhinoceros horns, and many more (Ellis, 1936; Ellis and Abarbanel, 1967). Ginseng root is widely relied on among the Chinese, and has a continuing market also in the U.S. and Europe. Faith in such substances may produce a placebo effect and thus, perhaps, aid sexual response, at least temporarily, in some cases.

Pharmacologically active substances

Yohimbine and cantharides (Sollman, 1936) are best-known. The former, an alkaloid obtained from the West African yohimbine tree, has vasodilating and other effects which may or may not enhance the male erection. Cantharides (Spanish fly) is a rubefacient, vesicant, and urethral irritant which may produce priapism; its use is hazardous and deaths have been reported (Goodman and Gilman, 1970). The aphrodisiac use of psychedelic mushrooms and other psychedelic substances in folk medicine has been reported (see below). Henbane, belladonna, *Nox vomica* (strychnine), nutmeg, *Datura stramonium*, and betel nut are other pharmacologically active substances valued in some cultures as aphrodisiacs. When wide-ranging scientific studies of the sexual effects of drugs are eventually launched, at least some attention should be paid to the more promising folk aphrodisiacs.

3. SOPORIFIC DRUGS

The opiates and opioids (including heroin and methadone)

These drugs bridge the gap between folk medicine and scientific medicine. Opium was traditionally used by males in India to prolong erection by delaying orgasm (Ellis, 1936); and there are anecdotal accounts of 19th century American prostitutes who placed their lovers on opium and morphine to produce this effect (Terry and Pellens, 1928). It has been quite generally noted, however, that the opiates and opioids lower serum testosterone levels and lead to drug-dependent (reversible) impotence in a substantial proportion of cases (Azizi et al., 1973; De Leon and Wexler, 1973; Mendelson et al., 1974a; Mann, 1968).

Doubts nevertheless remain. Cushman (1973), for example, reported a marked rise — from very low initial levels — in the proportion of males maintained on methadone for one year who reported normal libido, normal potency, and normal ejaculation time as the months rolled by, suggesting a gradually developing tolerance for sexually depressant drug effects. Becoming a heroin addict or a methadone patient, moreover, has effects on nutrition, life style, sleep patterns, and other parameters which may contribute as much or more to the reported effects as the pharmacology of the drug (Wieland and Yunger, 1971).

The depressants

Alcohol
Like the opiates, alcohol bridges the gap between folk medicine and contemporary scientific inquiry. In primitive societies, it was widely observed that alcohol releases inhibitions and thus frees men and women alike for sexual enjoyment (Gallant, 1968). Contemporary observations of alcohol use in moderate amounts in civilized societies tend to confirm this view (Gay and Sheppard, 1973). The tranquilizing effect of modest amounts of alcohol can perhaps improve sexual response in some anxious persons.

In large quantities, of course, alcohol impairs all reflexes including sexual reflexes (Merari et al., 1973; Hart, 1968; Beach, 1967). Shakespeare said it best; alcohol "provokes the desire, but it takes away the performance". Further, numerous studies have reported impaired sexual response in the chronic alcoholic (Lemere and Smith, 1963; Stein, 1974). Masters and Johnson (1970) have reported alcohol as an important factor in some cases of secondary male impotence. A man is shocked to find himself impotent on one occasion as a result of fatigue, too much alcohol, or other factors; he therefore turns to alcohol again for relief of anxiety prior to his next sexual encounter — and fails again. Now fear of failure is added to the depressant effects of alcohol and anxiety; the cycle is repeated with more anxiety and more alcohol — until chronic impotence appears. Sex therapy in such cases, Masters and Johnson add, is often successful. Much remains to be learned about the sexual effects of alcohol, both stimulant and depressant.

The barbiturates and minor tranquilizers
The sexual effects of these drugs have not been scientifically explored; but it is reasonable to expect that they parallel the action of alcohol in this as in other respects. Confirmatory studies are needed.

One minor tranquilizer, methaqualone, is widely reputed among drug users to have sexually arousing effects or to increase sexual enjoyment, but no controlled studies either confirming or refuting these anecdotal reports have been published.

4. THE CNS STIMULANTS

Cocaine
Some users report a notable enhancement of libido and sexual responsiveness

immediately following cocaine use; others report either no effect or an impeding effect. The sexual effects, like other cocaine effects, are said to be short-lived (Gay and Sheppard, 1973). The subjective reports are consistent with the view that in fatigued or depressed individuals, a CNS stimulant at a suitable dosage level may facilitate sexual response, but that hyperstimulation reverses the effect. Anecdotal evidence suggests that cocaine also increases self-confidence and improves the self-image; this may facilitate sexual function in those who suffer from impaired self-confidence. Prolonged use at high dosage levels is generally reported to impair sexual response.

The amphetamines and nonamphetamine CNS stimulants

These drugs, like cocaine, appear to have varying effects at varying dosage levels and on varying individuals (Bell and Trethowan, 1961; Mann, 1968; Greaves, 1972; Gay and Sheppard, 1973), but the effects may be longer-lived than cocaine effects. The remarks above on cocaine also appear to be true of the amphetamines (Leavitt, 1969), and the amphetamine-like CNS stimulants such as phenmetrazine — including impaired sexual response following prolonged use at high dosage levels.

5. LSD AND LSD LIKE DRUGS

Widely used among primitive societies, the LSD-like drugs (peyote, fly agaric, other psychedelic mushrooms, ololiuqui or morning glory seeds) were valued in some cultures though not in others as aphrodisiacs. Contemporary subjective reports among LSD users suggest that LSD alters sexual as well as other responses, but is neither aphrodisiac nor anaphrodisiac (Gay and Sheppard, 1973). Some users report greatly increased enjoyment of sex on some occasions; others report that the LSD experience is incompatible with sexual response. The distorting effect of LSD on the time sense, and the enhanced focus on sensory input, may or may not explain the reported sexual effects. The need for more definitive research is clearly indicated (Wolls, 1974). One psychedelic drug, MDA (α-methyl-3,4-methylene-dioxyphenethylamine) is reported to increase libido (Gay and Sheppard, 1973).

6. TOBACCO

To the extent that smoking impairs general health, it almost certainly impairs sexual response. Nicotine's vasoconstrictive effects may or may not have a specific inhibiting or facilitating effect on male erection and female lubrication. Some smokers report a marked increase in sexual response when they stop smoking. But there may be another side to the story. Nicotine acts as both a CNS stimulant and tranquilizer, and might therefore be suspected of having mildly favorable sexual effects in some people under some circumstances and at some dosage levels. Chronic smokers develop at least partial tolerance to some nicotine effects, including perhaps sexual effects. A smoker in the throes of nicotine withdrawal is hardly likely to find that condition conducive to sexual enjoyment. More and better data on these and other possible effects of smoking on sexuality are clearly needed (Kole, 1974).

7. CANNABIS (MARIJUANA AND HASHISH)

Of all the drugs in common use today, marijuana has by far the widest reputation for enhancing sexual enjoyment (Gay and Sheppard, 1973; Klein, 1972). In numerous opinion surveys, nearly half of all users report that marijuana increases desire, and more than half report that it increases sexual enjoyment (Robbins and Tanck, 1973; Koff, 1974; Goode, 1969, 1972). Women respondents are more likely to report an increase in desire, men are more likely to report an increase in enjoyment — but both phenomena are commonly reported by both sexes (Koff, 1974). Some women report that they were unable to have orgasm until they began using marijuana; both men and women report that orgasm is more intense and enjoyable under marijuana (Lewis, 1970). The dosages used are almost always low (one 'joint' or less); there is a report that marijuana is less sexually enhancing if two or more 'joints' are smoked (Koff, 1974).

Numerous explanations have been offered for these reports. Perhaps marijuana, like alcohol, loosens inhibitions. Perhaps it enhances 'sensate focus', that is, a person's attention to sensuous input in contrast with the nonsensuous content with which the mind is commonly burdened. Users similarly report heightened enjoyment of food (the 'munchies'), music, and other experiences under marijuana. Reports of enhanced sexual enjoyment may result from this nonspecific enhancement of a sense of enjoyment. The tendency of time to seem to pass more slowly, and thus the tendency of events to seem to endure for a longer time span, may partially explain reports of more enjoyable orgasm. The circumstances in which marijuana is often smoked — relaxed, with one's lover, the day's work done or cast aside, anticipating a pleasant occasion — are surely contributing factors. Finally, marijuana's reputation for sexual enhancement almost certainly helps produce a placebo effect which accounts at least in part for the reports of sexual enhancement.

Kolodny and associates have reported a lowering of male serum testosterone levels in a group of frequent marijuana smokers, and a rise in levels when marijuana use is discontinued (Kolodny et al., 1974). Mendelson (1974b) administering known doses in a controlled investigative design, failed to find any effect on serum testosterone. More research is needed, both on serum testosterone levels in relation to sexual performance and enjoyment, and on other sexual parameters of marijuana use.

8. DRUGS AFFECTING ONE PHASE OF THE SEXUAL RESPONSE CYCLE

One reason for confusion with respect to the sexual effects of drugs may be the crudity of the concept of 'aphrodisiac' in common use. It is not unlikely that some drugs may enhance libido, others may facilitate erection or lubrication, others may facilitate or delay orgasm in the female or male or both, others may shorten the refractory phase between orgasm and subsequent orgasm and so on. Thus a highly potent drug effect may be missed if the wrong measure is selected to gauge its effects. Two classes of drug in particular are reputed to have an effect on only one phase of the response cycle.

Topical anesthetics

A number of topical anesthetics sold over the counter in the U.S. and other countries, are alleged to prolong erection and delay male orgasm when applied to the surface of the penis before coitus. No double-blind studies have been reported either confirming or refuting this claim (Merck Manual, 1972).

Amyl nitrite

This drug has vasodilating and other cardiovascular effects. In the U.S., and perhaps other countries, it is sometimes inhaled at the moment of orgasm to enhance the intensity of orgasmic feeling. Some female and male users who have trouble in reaching orgasm report that amyl nitrite triggers the sexual climax if inhaled at a moment of intense sexual arousal (the plateau phase). No controlled studies have been published (Everett, 1972; Gay and Sheppard, 1973; Stein, 1974).

9. SEXUAL SIDE EFFECTS OF PRESCRIPTION DRUGS

Under the regulations of the U.S. Food and Drug Administration, prescription drugs (with some exceptions) must be accompanied by full statements of side effects reported for the drug. Story (1974) has gleaned from these statements and other sources a list of 58 prescription drugs, marketed under 117 brand names, which have been reported to have sexual side effects. He has classified most of these drugs under six rubrics — antihypertensives, antihypertensive—diuretic combinations, antianxiety agents, antidepressants, antipsychotic agents, and anorexics (among which are listed the amphetamines and other CNS stimulants). Kaplan (1974) has also reviewed the sexual side effects of some prescription drugs.

Among the sexual or quasisexual side effects reported for various drugs in the Story survey are gynecomastia in the male; breast enlargement, lactation, and galactorrhea in the female; male impotence, inhibition of ejaculation, delayed ejaculation, and aspermia; changes in libido (increase or decrease) in both sexes; testicular swelling; amenorrhea and other menstrual disorders; and a few others. With two exceptions, increased libido is reported only for drugs which are also reported to cause decreased libido; the exceptions are fluphenazine hydrochloride and butaperizine maleate, both of which are alleged to produce increased libido in females (but impotence in males).

The Story review is important as a reminder to physicians to check sexual side effects when prescribing a drug, and to check drug use when patients complain of sexual dysfunction. However, reported side effects are not reliable guides to the actual effects of the drugs. A side effect may be listed even though only a small proportion of users report it; only rarely have well-controlled studies been run to check the reported associations of a drug with its sexual side effects (Money and Yankowitz, 1967).

10. TESTOSTERONE AND OTHER ANDROGENS

It is well established that male sexual function is dependent upon an adequate supply of testosterone, mostly of gonadal origin (Goodman and Gilman, 1970). Thus, if the endogenous supply of testosterone is low, suitable doses of testosterone or some other androgen may improve sexual response and function. There is no evidence that adding testosterone when the endogenous level is already adequate will enhance male libido or function, except maybe for a few hours.

Testosterone increases libido in the female, and is on occasion administered for this purpose (Kennedy, 1973). The problem is to find a dosage level and schedule of administration which will achieve the desired effect without giving rise to somatic masculinizing side effects, such as beard growth.

11. ANAPHRODISIACS

Saltpeter (potassium nitrate) is a diuretic which was once reputed to be an anaphrodisiac and was therefore sometimes added to the diets of schoolboys, prisoners, and other institutional inmates for the purpose of decreasing libido. There is no reason to believe it has the alleged effect. In folk medicine, camphor and syrian rue (the latter said to contain harmine and harmaline) have been used (Ellis, 1936).

Some 'major tranquilizers' used in the treatment of psychoses sometimes produce decreased libido as a side effect, and several have been tested as anaphrodisiacs — thioridizine for 'the control of homosexual practices', fluphenazine enanthate 'to control deviant sexual behavior', and benperidol 'for the treatment of excessive and disinhibited sexual behavior' (Tennent et al., 1974). Their clinical effectiveness remains in doubt.

The estrogens are highly potent anaphrodisiacs in men, depressing all testosterone-dependent functions. Nausea, vomiting, and feminization are among the distressing side-effects. Medroxy-progesterone acetate, a synthetic progestin, has also been tried as an anaphrodisiac (Money, 1972, Money et al., 1975).

Like the estrogens, the antiandrogen drug cyproterone acetate depresses all testosterone-dependent functions including libido, and produces demasculinizing effects. It has been experimentally used to lower libido in sex offenders and for 'therapy in deviant hypersexuality' (Cooper et al., 1972).

12. USE OF DRUGS IN THE THERAPY OF SEXUAL DYSFUNCTION

Until recently, the therapy of sexual dysfunction was primarily in the hands of psychiatrists and psychologists whose main mode of therapeutic intervention was psychotherapy. Since the publication of *Human Sexual Inadequacy* by Masters and Johnson (1970), numerous centers have sprung up in the U.S. to treat male impotence, premature ejaculation, and orgasmic incompetence, as well as female vaginismus, dispareunia, and anorgasmia through a more direct behavioral approach. Neither approach has been accompanied by more than feeble and sporadic efforts to explore the potential usefulness of drugs as an adjunct of therapy for sexual dysfunction.

Kaplan (1974) has summed up the current situation. Concerning alcohol, for example, she reports that "it is important to ascertain the drinking habits of every sexually dysfunctional patient on initial evaluation. Often, the man who complains of erectile difficulties is found to drink three martinis at lunch, a scotch before he gets on the train and three more drinks at dinner. Such an alcohol intake may significantly depress his sexual response; before commencing sexual therapy, he must first reduce his drinking substantially". Concerning testosterone replacement therapy for the aging male, she notes: ". . . Some men do seem to show a decrease in depression and an increase in energy and optimism, while sexual functioning improves. Others report that they feel no particular benefit from replacement therapy". Concerning testosterone in the sexually dysfunctional male generally, she adds: "An important immediate goal is to enable the patient to function adequately on a single occasion; this initial successful experience then serves as the foundation for treatment. The use of testosterone can facilitate the implementation of this initial crucial objective by strengthening the patient's libidinal drive and enhancing his sexual response. Although similar results can usually be obtained by purely psychological means, we believe that testosterone should be administered when it appears likely that its use may facilitate this process. Occasionally, we also prescribe testosterone in cases where the patient's sex drive seems to be particularly weak. However, this medication is always prescribed within the matrix of the therapeutic format". The effect, if any, is that of a placebo. (See also Kennedy, 1973.)

13. PHEROMONES

It is now well known that pheromones (odor signals) are important sexual stimulants in some infrahuman species, including primates. It is possible that sexual odors play a more significant role in human sexual response than is as yet appreciated.

14. RESEARCH IN PROGRESS

Within the past few years, experimental neuropharmacological studies of the major CNS neurotransmitters — including serotonin (5-hydroxytryptamine, 5HT), dopamine, norepinephrine, and acetylcholine — seem to be approaching new and potentially very fruitful insights into the sexual effects of drugs. These recent studies in various animal species suggest (though they do not yet establish) that serotonin is the basic inhibitor of sexual function and dopamine the basic facilitator (Gessa and Tagliamonte, 1974; Malmnas, 1974; Meyerson et al., 1974). If so, the effects of a number of other substances (L-DOPA, PCPA, apomorphine, and pargyline, as alleged sexual facilitators, pimozide and pilocarpine, as alleged inhibitors) can be explained through their effects on the serotonin and dopamine systems. The sexual role of the prostaglandins and of oxytocin are also being explored in current research.

15. SUMMARY

This review of the sexual effects of drugs leads us to four major conclusions:

The drugs currently known appear to modulate rather than determine sexual response; and this is quite likely to prove true as well of drugs hereafter discovered. Human sexual response is too complex a phenomenon, with too many antecedents, any one of which may impair sexual response, to warrant much hope that a universal aphrodisiac will be found. True anaphrodisiacs and inhibitors of sexual function, in contrast, are likely to be found in ever-increasing numbers.

No significant human activity has been subjected to so little sound scientific research as sexual activity, including female and male sexual responses to drugs. More and better research is urgently needed.

In the present state of knowledge, one fruitful approach may be to explore the hypothesis that whatever contributes to healthy human functioning generally contributes specifically to enhancing libido and sexual response, and that whatever impairs healthy human functioning impairs libido and sexual response.

Intensive study of this and other hypotheses is warranted in part by a simple humanitarian desire to minimize the damage done by human sexual dysfunction, in part by a concern with the effects of sexual dysfunction on self-esteem and other important parameters of human life, in part by a concern with the debilitating effects of aging, and also by a concern for the enrichment of the human condition generally.

BIBLIOGRAPHY

Azizi, F., Vagenakis, A.G., Longcope, C., Ingbar, S. and Diaverman, L. (1973) Decreased serum testosterone concentration in male heroin and methadone addicts. *Steroids* 22: 467—472.

Beach. A.F. (1967) Cerebral and hormonal control of reflective mechanisms involved in copulatory behavior. *Physiol. Rev.* 47: 289—316.

Bell, D.S. and Trethowan, W.H. (1961) Amphetamine addiction and disturbed sexuality. *Arch. Gen. Psychiat.* 4: 74—78.

Cooper, A.J., Ismail, A.A.A., Phanjoo, A.L. and Love, D.L. (1972) Antiandrogen (cyproterone acetate) therapy in deviant hypersexuality. *Br. J. Psychiat.* 120: 59—63.

Cushman, P. Jr. (1973) Plasma testosterone in narcotic addiction. *Am. J. Med.* 55: 452—458.

De Leon, G. and Wexler, H. (1973) Heroin addiction: its relation to sexual behavior and sexual experience. *J. Abnorm. Psychol.* 81: 36—38.

Ellis, A. and Abarbanel, A. (Eds) (1967) *The Encylopedia of Sexual Behavior.* 2nd edn (Hawthorn Books Inc., New York).

Ellis, H. (1936) *Studies in the Psychology of Sex,* Vol. 2. (Random House, New York) pp. 172—177.

Everett, G.M. (1972) Effects of amyl nitrite ("poppers") on sexual experience. *Med. Aspects Hum. Sex.* 6 (12) 146—151.

Gallant, D.M. (1968) The effect of alcohol and drug abuse on sexual behavior. *Med. Aspects Hum. Sex.* 2 (1) 30—36.

Gay, G.R. and Sheppard, C. (1973) "Sex-crazed dope fiends" — myth or reality? *Drug Forum,* 2 (2) 125—140.

Gessa, G.L. and Tagliamonte, A. (1974) Possible role of brain serotonin and dopamine in controlling male sexual behavior. In: (E. Costa, G.L. Gessa and M. Sandler, Eds.), *Advances in Biochemical Psychopharmacology,* Vol. 11. (Raven Press, New York) pp. 217—228.

Goode, E. (1969) Marijuana and sex. *Evergreen Rev.* 13 (66) 19—21, 72—73.

Goode, E. (1972) Drug use and sexual activity on a college campus. *Am. J. Psychiat.* 128 (10) 1272—1276.

Goode, E. (1972) Sex and marijuana. *Sex. Behav.* May, pp. 45—51.

Goodman, L.S. and Gilman, A. (Eds) (1970) *The Pharmacological Basis of Therapeutics,* 4th edn (The Macmillan Co., London and Toronto).

Greaves, G. (1972) Sexual disturbances among chronic amphetamine users. *J. Nerv. Ment. Dis.* 155 (5) 363—365.

Hart, B. (1968) Effects of alcohol on sexual reflexes and mating behavior in the male dog. *Quart. J. Stud. Alcohol,* 29 (4) part A, pp. 839—844.

Kaplan, H.S. (1974) *The New Sex Therapy.* (Brunner/Mazel, New York.)

Kennedy, B.J. (1973) Effect of massive doses of sex hormones on libido. *Med. Aspects Hum. Sex.* 7 (3) 67ff.

Klein, D. (1972) *Everything you Always Wanted to Know about Marijuana.* (Tower Publications, New York) pp. 147—162.

Koff, W.C. (1974) Marijuana and sexual activity. *J. Sex. Res.* 10 (3) 194—204.

Kole, J. (1974) Cigarettes can kill — your sex life! *Penthouse/Forum,* August, pp. 6—11.

Kolodny, R., Masters, W., Kolodner, R. and Toro, G. (1974) Depression of plasma testosterone levels after chronic intensive marihuana use. *New Engl. J. Med.* 290 (16) 872—874.

Leavitt, F.I. (1969) Drug-induced modifications in sexual behavior and open field locomotion of male rats. *Physiol. Behav.* 4 (5) 677—683.

Lemere, F. and Smith, J. (1973) Alcohol-induced sexual impotence. *Am. J. Psychiat.* 130 (2) 212—213.

Lewis, B. (1970) *The Sexual Power of Marijuana.* (Peter H. Wyden, Inc., New York.)

Malmnas, C.O. (1974) Opposite effects of serotonin and dopamine on copulatory activation in castrated male rats. In: (E. Costa, G.L. Gessa and M. Sandler, Eds.), *Advances in Biochemical Psychopharmacology*, Vol. 11 (Raven Press, New York) pp. 243—248.

Mann, T. (1968) Effects of pharmacological agents on male sexual functions. *J. Reprod. Fertil.* suppl. 4, pp. 101—114.

Masters, W.H. and Johnson, V.E. (1970) *Human Sexual Inadequacy.* (Little, Brown, Boston.)

Mendelson, J. Mendelson, J.H. and Patch, V. (1974a) Effects of heroin and methadone on plasma testosterone in narcotic addicts. *Fed. Proc.* Abstr. 166, 33 (3) part 1, p. 232.

Mendelson, J.H., Kuehnle, J., Ellingboe, J. and Babor, T.F. (1974b) Plasma testosterone levels before, during, and after chronic marijuana smoking. *New Engl. J. Med.* 291: 1051—1055.

Merari, A., Ginton, A., Heifez, T. and Lev-Ran, T. (1973) Effects of alcohol on mating behavior of the female rat. *Quart. J. Stud. Alcohol.* 34 (4) part A, pp. 1095—1098.

Merck Manual (1972) Holvey, D.N. and Talbott, J.H. (Eds), *The Merck Manual of Diagnosis and Therapy.* (Merck Sharp & Dohme, Rahway, New Jersey).

Meyerson, B.J., Carrer, H. and Eliasson, M. (1974) 5-Hydroxytryptamine and sexual behavior in the female rat. In: (E. Costa, G.L. Gessa and M. Sandler, Eds.), *Advances in Biochemical Psychopharmacology*, Vol. II (Raven Press, New York) 229—242.

Mikuriya, T.H. (Ed) (1972) *Marijuana: Medical Papers 1839—1972.* (Medi-Comp Press, Oakland, California.)

Money, J. (1972) The therapeutic use of androgen-depleting hormone. In: (H.L. Resnik and M.E. Wolfgang, Eds.), *Sexual Behaviors: Social, Clinical and Legal Aspects.* (Little, Brown & Co., Boston) XIII, p. 448.

Money, J. and Yankowitz, R. (1967) The sympathetic-inhibiting effects of the drug ismelin on human male eroticism, with a note on mellaril. *J. Sex Res.* 3 (1) 69—82.

Nowlis, V. (1975) Categories of interest in the scientific search for relationships (interactions, associations, comparisons) in the domain of human sexual behavior and drug use. In: (M. Sandler and G.L. Gessa, Eds.) *Sexual Behavior: Pharmacology and Biochemistry.* (Raven Press, New York) pp. 93—96.

Robbins, P.R. and Tanck, R.H. (1973) Psychological correlates of marijuana use: an exploratory study. *Psychol. Rep.* 33 (3) 703—706.

Sollmann, T. (1936) *A Manual of Pharmacology and its Application to Therapeutics and Toxicology.* (W.B. Saunders Co., Philadelphia.)

Stein, M.L. (1974) *Lovers, Friends, Slaves . . .* (Berkeley Publishing Corp., New York) pp. 91—94.

Story, N. (1974) Sexual dysfunction resulting from drug side effects. *J. Sex Res.* 10 (2) 132—149.

Tennent, G., Bancroft, J. and Cass, J. (1974) The control of deviant sexual behavior by drugs: a double-blind controlled study of benperidol, chlorpromazine and placebo. *Arch. Sex. Behav.* 3 (3) 261—271.

Terry, C.E. and Pellens, M. (1928) *The Opium Problem.* (Committee on Drug Addictions and the Bureau of Social Hygiene, Inc., New York.)

Wells, B. (1974) *Psychedelic Drugs.* (Penguin Books, Baltimore) pp. 132—149.

Wieland, W. and Yunger, M. (1971) Sexual effects and side effects of heroin and methadone. *Proc. 3rd Nat. Conf. Methadone Treatment (1970)* pp. 50—53.

CHAPTER 89

Sex education in medical schools

SHERWYN M. WOODS

1. INTRODUCTION

Rationale and goals

The physician plays a pivotal role in both the sexual ills and the sexual health of the population. It is to the physician that many people turn for sexual advice, information, counseling, and the treatment of sexual problems. There is no reason to expect a doctor to be either competent or effective without considerable education in basic science and clinical medicine. Accordingly it is a wonder that only in recent years has sex education begun to become firmly established within American medical schools. There is no reason to believe that medical sex education is more advanced elsewhere in the world.

Knowledge of sexual anatomy, physiology and individual sexual psychology is necessary but not sufficient for the practice of sexual medicine. Also necessary is a broad, sensitive awareness of the family as it functions as a dynamic social unit within the context of the community, and a sensitivity for those social forces which determine values, morality, attitudes, and the behavior of both individuals and families. Such sensitive awareness is not bestowed upon medical students simply by having grown up within the society, nor can the physician rely upon generalizations from his own background of experience. Indeed, personal or ethnocentric generalizations, indiscriminantly applied, can serve to distort perceptions rather than to enlighten.

The path to professional identity is a tortuous one, and the practice of medicine is art as well as science. The most important therapeutic instrument is often the self — the kind of person one is, one's capacity to establish relationships and rapport, and the ability to elicit cooperation. The task of medical education is not merely to teach a science of techniques, but to help the student reach his full potential as a therapeutic person.

Handbook of Sexology, edited by J. Money and H. Musaph
© *Elsevier/North-Holland Biomedical Press, 1977*

Special educational problems

As in other aspects of medical training, there are special educational problems because of the high degree of emotionality, and often anxiety, associated with sex. The student arrives at the subject with many pre-existing prejudices and personal anxieties (Lief, 1964, 1969; Woods and Natterson, 1967), as well as socioculturally determined attitudes (Woods, 1969), all of which may act to affect the learning process. Effective education must take into account where the student has come from, and where the student is going with regard to attitudes, knowledge and beliefs. The success of educational efforts is often related to the instructor's ability to identify in advance those situations which will prove stressful, thus allowing him to orient his instruction so as to foster learning rather than to augment stress.

2. HISTORICAL

Early history and pioneers

In 1960 there were only three medical schools in the U.S. which offered formal courses in sexuality. By 1968, there were thirty schools which had initiated such programs, and by 1973 almost all were involved in the teaching of human sexuality in the medical curriculum (Lief and Ebert, 1976). Courses were not always established with ease (Tyler, 1970), and indeed the early pioneers encountered great resistance, mostly from faculty and administration, in accomplishing their goals. Resistance was related to anxieties and uncertainties about sexuality becoming a part of the curriculum, competition for curriculum time, faculty anxiety, and the taboo on sex. In many schools it was student pressure which helped to establish courses.

The development of sex education in American medical schools was largely facilitated through the pioneering efforts of Harold Lief and the Center for the Study of Sex Education in Medicine, established in 1968 at the University of Pennsylvania (Lief, 1970). Also important were the activities of the Sex Education Information Council of the United States (SEICUS), under the leadership of Mary Calderone (Lief, 1970). It was rapidly established that medical students were anxious about sexuality, had a great many sexual problems of their own, and felt incapable of dealing with the sexual problems of their patients (Lief, 1964; Woods and Natterson, 1967).

Other influences on medical education

The greater public respectability of sex has made it easier for both patients and students to ask questions, and thus consumer pressures on medical curriculum have been heightened. In 1965 a committee of the American Medical Association developed a teaching guide for problems of human sexuality

(AMA, 1965), and an increasing body of research data into human sexual response and sexual development appeared in the literature. The work of Masters and Johnson (1966), and the wide public dissemination of their findings, served in particular to accentuate both student and patient interest. In addition, some schools were beginning to develop specific educational methodology. A comprehensive presentation of human sexuality in medical education was developed in a book by Vincent (1968). This methodology largely addressed itself to dealing with the anxieties and attitudes of students which could in turn affect the learning process and its clinical application. It was particularly aided by the increased availability of high quality explicit sexual films, and an expanding bibliography of resource papers in sex education (Seruya et al., 1972).

Future prospects

While virtually all American medical schools now have some sex education within their curriculum, it should not be presumed that it is of adequate scope or comprehensiveness. There has been enormous variation in the degree to which sexuality has been included (Lief and Ebert, 1976), and too few schools have been able to provide comprehensive clinical opportunities for students to actualize, under supervision, their didactic education. In 1974 the Center for the Study of Sex Education in Medicine convened a small national working conference of experienced sexual educators. This group surveyed all of the important issues related to the development of sex education in medicine, including a model curriculum, and their findings are to be detailed in a book by Lief and Karlen (Lief and Ebert, 1976).

3. GENERAL TEACHING METHODOLOGY

Survey of current education methods

By far the most comprehensive survey of sex education in U.S. medical schools has been accomplished by Lief and Ebert (1976) who contacted 110 of the 114 medical schools in the U.S., and received responses from 105 of the 106 which had programs in sexuality. Seventy-two percent had a specific sex education course, while 60% reported teaching human sexuality as a part of the core curriculum. Many of the schools teach human sexuality in an interdisciplinary fashion, but in rank order psychiatry is the most frequently involved department, followed by obstetrics—gynecology. Classes in the first and second years are typically large, with more than 100 students, while in the third and fourth years the classes are smaller (usually fewer than 25), and the primary teaching method shifts to small-group instruction. The typical medical school offers 42 h of teaching, and at least half encourage the attendance of the student's spouse. Eighty-seven percent of the schools use small group discussions, and skills are more often taught by case demonstration than by actual clinical work under supervision. Although 'affective learning' is thought to be the most important need of the medical students, only a small minority use sensitivity training techniques, while almost all use erotic films followed by discussions. Lack of experienced and knowledgeable teachers is the most frequently cited reason for difficulties in establishing courses, while a low faculty priority is the single most important reason for difficulties in continuing them.

Educational strategies

Experienced sex educators are almost unanimous that effective education must address itself to all three areas: sexual attitudes, sexual knowledge, and relevant clinical skills. It is generally agreed that multidisciplinary teaching is more effective than is teaching by a single speciality (Lief, 1969), and that it is essential to deal with the student's preexisting attitudes and anxieties (Lief, 1964; Woods, 1967). Romano (1968) has argued in addition for the teaching of sex as a part of many interdisciplinary courses in medicine, rather than as a specifically demarcated course in sex. Most would agree that the following format is a minimum: pretest for attitudes and knowledge, desensitization and resensitization, basic data, skills, integration into medical practice, and posttest with evaluation.

4. ANXIETIES AND ATTITUDES: IDENTIFICATION AND MODIFICATION

Importance for educational planning

It is unlikely that there will be much learning of either data or skills in the presence of great anxiety. Such anxiety may arise from the student's personal conflicts, or it may be a part of a more generalized sense of discomfort, shame or guilt about discussing sexuality with others. Such difficulties interfere not only with the acquisition of knowledge, but with the development of clinical skills and the application of these skills in practice. Additionally, since sexual values and attitudes are highly determined by sociocultural influences, it is unlikely that the student will be able to make appropriate application of his knowledge unless he is aware of his cultural bias and ethnocentric thinking (Woods, 1969; Reiss, 1971).

Instruments of assessment

Two commonly used means to assess these potential interferences with the learning process involve either personal interviews or small group discussions. Specific tests are also available, and by far the most commonly used is the

Sex Knowledge and Attitude Test (SKAT) which was developed at the Center for the Study of Sex Education in Medicine and which is now used by 47% of the medical schools in the U.S. (Lief and Ebert, 1976). The SKAT allows the student to compare himself with peers, to identify data about himself which may be useful to his sex education. It also profiles the class and thus assist the instructor in educational planning.

Attitudes and anxieties of medical students

There is a significant body of research data which indicates that a large percentage of medical students have significant sexual anxieties and problems (Lief, 1964; Woods et al., 1966; Woods and Natterson, 1967; Mudd and Siegel, 1969). The studies by Woods and his co-workers indicated that well over half of a large sample of medical students considered themselves to have significant enough emotional problems to wish for counseling or psychotherapy, and up to three quarters of these described sexual conflicts or problems as a major motivation. Fifty-five percent of these students had problems of impotence or frigidity, 40% were concerned about masturbation, and 40% had anxieties about homosexuality though actual homosexuality was reported rarely. Mudd and Siegel (1969) reported that one in four unmarried preclinical students is virginal. It was also widely reported by students that they had great difficulty in discussing sex with patients, partly due to social taboos.

Especially important is the fact that a significant number of medical students subscribe to popular myths and misconceptions regarding sexuality, or tend toward sexual stereotypes and value judgments which are determined by their past experiences. It is possible for one of today's physicians to have been told, during the course of his professional lifetime, that masturbation causes insanity, or that oral stimulation between marital partners represents perversion. Less dramatic, but equally important, are the subtle effects of conflictual attitudes and values.

Goals of attitude modification

Most courses have the goal of increasing the student's awareness that he will encounter a wide variety of sexual problems in medical practice, that he will need knowledge and skills which go far beyond personal experience and private opinion in order to assist these patients, and that his professional practice could be severely handicapped by his own personal taboos, prejudices, and anxiety-based reactions to sexual information and stimuli. A second set of goals is to make the student more aware and tolerant of the wide spectrum of 'normal' human sexual behavior, to be open-minded about various points of view in controversial sexual issues, and to 'desensitize' him against anxiety or prejudice-driven reactions to sexual stimuli encountered in practice. The third goal is to 'resensitize' the student such that in the practice of medicine he becomes comfortably, compassionately, and professionally involved in understanding human sexuality and the management of sexual problems or issues of sexual health. These principles are not too dissimilar from those outlined by Pellegrino (1974) in his plea for medical schools to educate humanist physicians.

Methods of attitude modification

In order for students to become coparticipants in the issue of attitude modification, they must first consciously identify the nature and substance of their reactions to issues of human sexuality as well as sexual stimuli. This occurs as a natural consequence to learning new data, as a result of the SKAT examinations, and during discussions with peers. Small group discussions serve not only to facilitate communication and decrease associated anxiety, but also rapidly establish normalcy as a relative rather than absolute concept. Students as a group usually represent a very wide range of both developmental and current attitudes and behavior. The group is therefore a miniature community, facilitating student awareness of both differences and similarities as related to family style, social class, ethnic and religious background, and other factors (Woods, 1969).

By far the most popular means of helping students confront their own anxieties, attitudes and values is through the use of explicit erotic films. Direct confrontation with explicit eroticism, also known as pornography, can be a valuable technique in sexual education (Money, 1971). As typically used, such films, sometimes several projected simultaneously on multiple screens, are presented to the students in a 'massive dose' followed by small group discussion. They typically include very explicit presentations of sexual intercourse, methods of sexual stimulation, masturbation, homosexuality and sexual deviations. Students have a wide variety of reactions including interest and curiosity, anxiety and guilt, shame and disgust, as well as sexual stimulation. Few students come away without an awareness of their various reactions to such stimuli, and discussion of these reactions often brings into sharp focus any sexual mythology, stereotypes, or nontherapeutic attitudes which might interfere with clinical functioning. This experience also sets the stage for a greater openness to learning about the subject material, including greater freedom to discuss sex among themselves and with patients.

The use of such presentations to desensitize and resensitize has been highly developed by the National Sex Forum, by Chilgren and co-workers in the program in human sexuality at the University of Minnesota, and by Vandervoort and his associates at the University of California at San Francisco (Vandervoort, 1974). The process has been labeled Sexual Attitude Restructuring (SAR), and is described as an educational process and art form depending heavily upon the use of media to convey substantive information and to assist individuals to accept and to relate to their own and other's sexuality, as well as to accept sexuality as a natural and positive element of life.

5. BASIC INFORMATION ON HUMAN SEXUALITY

A cognitive basis for clinical practice

Attitudes about sexuality already described are necessary, but not sufficient, for appropriate clinical practice. Additionally required are those skills, interactions and interventions which have been built upon a scientific base of knowledge. This base must include the social as well as the biological sciences. In recent years there have been a number of textbooks and antholo gies which have addressed themselves to developing a comprehensive general scientific base for sex education for medical practice (Taylor, 1970; Vincent, 1968; AMA, 1972; Katchadourian and Lunde, 1972; McCary, 1973).

Biological basis

There has been an increasing fund of basic biological research knowledge, and this has been important in the development of clinical techniques for dealing with sexual problems. As a minimum, the student should be familiar with the anatomy of the sex organs and the physiology of sexual function; the genetics, embryology and physiology of sexual development and gender determination (Money and Ehrhardt, 1972); the physiology of human sexual response (Masters and Johnson, 1966); and the biological issues associated with reproduction. With such knowledge the student will be better able to understand sexual disorders and sexual dysfunction, and to develop skills in examination, diagnosis and treatment. Particularly important is the development of skills in making appropriate diagnostic distinctions between biological and psychological etiology, or combinations thereof.

Sociological basis

A student cannot understand a patient's sexuality without an understanding of the historical, social and cultural influences which helped to shape that sexuality. Such issues include moral, religious and legal influences; the role of social learning as it relates to erotic sexual and overall gender role; and the complicated interactions of family style and family life as they relate to sexual development and sexual relationships. An important resource, in this regard, is the monograph by Reiss (1971). Equally important is an understanding of alternative life styles, including sexual life styles, as well as an appreciation of the various counter-cultures within society at large. Without this understanding, the student is predisposed to superimpose his own attitudes and values indiscriminately upon patients, or to attempt to understand their sexuality in terms of his own life experience.

Psychological basis

The third essential area for an understanding of human sexuality is an understanding of the psychological basis of human sexuality. Biology and sociology are insufficient without knowledge of the influences of conditioning, learning and psychodynamics in the shaping of sexual development and the emotional experience of sexuality. This blending of internal and external factors is particularly well illustrated in the book by Stoller (1968) entitled 'Sex and Gender.' It is necessary for the student to understand the integration of sexuality into the personality and emotional life at all stages of the life cycle from infancy to old age, and to understand the psychological aspects of pairing and mate selection. It is unlikely that the patient's sexual problems can be meaningfully understood without an appreciation of the psychological forces of historical and current importance. Equally important are those psychological factors which relate to the patient's emotional and sexual health, for all therapeutic interventions will be built upon that foundation.

The student must also understand the various interpersonal uses of sex for love, for pleasuring, and for procreation. The patient's sexual life can only be adequately understood within the broad context of his general emotional life and particularly the nature and quality of interpersonal relationships. There should be a sensitive, empathic and psychodynamic understanding of auto-eroticism, heterosexual behavior, homosexual behavior, and aberrant sexual expression.

Methodology

Data about sex are usually presented, for efficiency's sake, in the form of lectures and other group presentations. Erotic films, video tape interviews, demonstration interviews, and panel discussions of controversial issues all may play a role in helping to acquaint the student with all aspects of the human sexual experience. As in all education, the goal is not merely the acquisition of knowledge, but the creation of a general openness to new learning which hopefully will persist throughout professional life. It is likely that the management of the student's anxiety will play a significant role in determining whether or not such openness occurs, for otherwise there is little choice but to retreat behind protective psychological defenses.

6. BASIC CLINICAL SKILLS

Interviewing and sexual history taking

While in many ways obtaining a sexual history does not differ from obtaining the general medical history, in other respects it differs significantly. Students are unaccustomed and sometimes anxious about having access to personal and intimate information, and must become comfortable about making appropriate inquiries. Students may experience sexual arousal, with considerable guilt and shame, while taking a sexual history or conducting a physical examination. It is important that this be understood and the anxiety resolved. Since patients also are often uncomfortable about discussing sexuality, the student must learn how to put a patient at ease and elicit cooperation. Labby (1971) discussed some of the special problems in the teaching and learning of skills in history taking. Supervised experience with patients is essential, if the student is to learn how to make those fine judgments which are necessary to elicit appropriate information: what to ask, when to ask, and how much to ask.

The educational process should include assisting student doctors to integrate sexual interview skills into general medical interviewing and evaluation. Even greater skill may be necessary in making an appropriate exploration of the effects of the patient's medical or surgical illness on sexual life.

Examination of the patient

The student must learn to examine the genitals, and understand those aspects of the general body examination which relate to sexuality. This should include an ability to evaluate findings early in childhood, particularly as related, for example, to the early diagnosis of intersex problems. The student must be able to recognize and deal with the anxiety or discomfort sometimes associated with such examinations. This is true not merely with respect to the patient's anxiety, but also to discomfort experienced by the physician which might influence his judgment in deciding whether or not to include sex related aspects of the examination. It is likely that a great many 'deferred' genital and rectal examinations, for example, are in deference to the physician's lack of ease rather than to good clinical judgment.

Diagnostic evaluation

As a minimum, there must be an ability to make at least gross differentiation between normal variation and pathology as it applies to both the findings of the physical examination and the patient's sexual beliefs and behavior. There must be the capacity to evaluate whether organic factors are a significant etiological issue, and to make judgments about the role of the patient's psychologically determined attitudes and experiences.

Consultation and referral

Dependent upon the ultimate nature of the student's medical practice, it is likely that he will often be faced with a task of arranging a consultation or making a referral. The manner in which he approaches and accomplishes it, may well determine the success of the consultation or referral. In addition to the sorting of data in order to make an appropriate decision, there is the matter of presentation to the patient, the form of which will often determine the degree of cooperation. Sexual dysfunction clinics, with a multidisciplinary staff, are a particularly rewarding educational experience for the student in learning what each specialty has to offer, as they should provide a model for interdisciplinary collaboration.

7. INTEGRATION INTO MEDICAL PRACTICE

Sexual issues in illness and disease

Attitudes, knowledge and basic skills must be blended into the general practice of medicine and incorporated into the every day work of the physician. Sexual problems are encountered in virtually all specialties of medicine; Burnap and Golden (1967) confirmed this and estimated that 15% of patients in general practice have sexual problems. Lief (1971) describes some of the ways that sexual problems may present themselves in clinical practice.

Perhaps the most sensitive skills and judgments are necessary when the physician interacts with patients whose medical or surgical illness disrupts or threatens to change sexual desire, sexual function, or usual sexual behavioral patterns. Some disorders which commonly have such effects are: neurological disorders, gynecologic disorders, diabetes, prostatitis, hormonal or surgical castration, rectal surgery, heart disease, and virtually any chronic or debilitating disorder.

The management of a patient following myocardial infarction provides another excellent example. Issues of sexual tension and frustration, or stress and anxiety regarding effects of the illness on sexual functioning, can only be understood in a context of understanding the patient's pre-illness sexuality and developmental history. Masturbation during the recovery phase may involve less cardiac work and physiological stress than intercourse, but to give such advice without exploring the patient's attitudes and concerns may augment rather than reduce stress. For example, the patient's problem may be less a sexual frustration than it is a fear of the associated disruption in interpersonal relationships, or the patient may have personal anxiety or moral and religious objections which would accentuate rather than reduce stress.

Additional groups of patients to be concerned with are those whose sexuality is an etiological or complicating factor such as those with venereal disease or problems of fertility and pregnancy, those whose emotional or physical illness is stress-related or significantly influenced by emotional factors related to their sexual lives, and those with chronic illness or disability, such as paraplegics, who are profoundly influenced by the way in which the physician does or does not deal with this sexuality.

Sexual dysfunction and sexual disorder

While many sexual disorders and problems of sexual dysfunction are within the realm of the specialist and, therefore, of speciality training, it is nevertheless true that many problems respond to simple reassurance, re-education, counseling or minor medical procedures. Such skills should certainly be within the armamentarium of the general physician, particularly as it relates to the capacity to reassure and re-educate. This is particularly true of problems such as impotence and frigidity, where good results are often achieved with only elementary interaction with the physican. It is particularly important that the physician have an awareness and understanding of the wide range of sexual behavior encountered in his patients, as well as the associated special physical and emotional problems. For example, it is not likely that one will appropriately manage the medical and health care of homosexual patients unless there is an understanding of their life circumstance; and it is similarly unlikely that the physician will be able to accomplish appropriate premarital or marital counseling, much less assist the sexual health care of the recent paraplegic, without similar understanding of the patient's past and present sexual attitudes and behavior.

Sexual counseling

Since doctors are frequently the source of sex information for concerned parents, they should be skilled in integrating such counseling into medical practice. This should include the ability to provide appropriate information and to maintain an appropriate dialogue with both parents and children. The ability to do simple premarital and marital counseling, when indicated or requested, is likewise essential (Vincent, 1973). Equally important is the ability to counsel with regard to reproductive problems that do not require referral to a specialist.

Sexual health care

It is important that the student not view his involvement with human sexuality as simply an involvement with 'disease,' but that he view himself as having an important role in sexual health care. One can easily turn to the definition of general health care by the World Health Organization and find appropriate similarities in sexual health care including: awareness, information, enrichment, counseling, therapy, clinical services and community support. Bearman (1968) has pointed out how medical students and physicians can provide sex education in the community, and both Israel (1967) and Lief (1971) have noted the physician's role in 'family-life education' and in preventive as well as therapeutic medicine.

Methodology

It is likely that the integration of knowledge, attitudes and skills into medical practice will require some sort of opportunity to utilize the educational input in actual clinical practice. One of the most effective means of accomplishing this is the preceptorship experience. It may occur in general medicine or in any of the specialities which encounter problems of human sexuality. As noted earlier, an especially valuable experience is to be found in multidisciplinary sex clinics. In the best of all possible worlds, the student would have many such experiences within the various specialty clinics, as well as within clinics devoted exclusively to sexual problems. Such education and skills should of course be expanded upon during postgraduate specialty training.

8. SEX EDUCATION OF OTHER HEALTH PROFESSIONALS

Important roles in the community

The physician is not the only important health professional involved with human sexuality within the community. Nurses, teachers, public health personnel, counselors and others are all involved to a greater or lesser degree. All such health professionals should have training which in general approximates that described for medical students. Some aspects of training might be emphasized and others de-emphasized, but of necessity all health care professionals should be aware of issues of human sexuality as it affects their clinical work. The well-trained physician can play an important role in the educational process for such health professionals, as well as serving as a resource person within the community (Branch, 1968).

General principles

The general principles involved in sex education for health professionals are the same as those for medical students. Human sexuality is a part of the human experience and problems of human sexuality are part of the problems of living. All those individuals who are involved in health care or health maintenance fields must be as aware of sexuality as they are of the other aspects of human life which are also essential to the healthy human condition. Their role, like the role of the physician, should be one which focuses not only on dysfunction or disorder, but which emphasizes also issues of sexual health.

9. SUMMARY

The physician plays a pivotal role in both the sexual ills and the sexual health of the population. Sex education in medical schools must address itself, frequently with special educational techniques, to three areas: sexual attitudes, sexual knowledge, and relevant clinical skills. Of particular importance are techniques to modify anxieties and attitudes which interfere with learning and distort clinical effectiveness. A cognitive basis for clinical practice includes the biological, sociological, and psychological data necessary for clinical practice. Basic clinical skills include interviewing, sexual history taking, examination of the patient, diagnostic skills, and skills in consulation and referral. Adequate sexual education of medical students should result in an integration of knowledge and skills into all areas of medical practice, including that of sexual health care, not merely the treatment of disease or disability.

BIBLIOGRAPHY

American Medical Association (1965) 1970. A teaching guide for the problems of human sexuality in medical education. In: (C.E. Vincent, Ed.), *Human Sexuality in Medical Education and Practice*. (Charles C. Thomas, Springfield, Illinois) pp. 92—98.

American Medical Association (1972) *Human Sexuality*. (American Medical Association, Chicago.)

Bearman, D. (1968) The medical student in a community sex education program. *J. Med. Educ.* 43: 855—858.

Branch, C.H. (1968) The role of the physician as sex educator and advisor. *Rocky Mount. Med. J.* 65: 39—42.

Burnap, D.W. and Golden, J.S. (1967) Sexual problems in medical practice. *J. Med. Educ.* 42: 673—680.

Israel, S.L. (1967) The role of the physician in family life education. *Mich. Med.* 66: 567—571.

Katchadourian, H.A. and Lunde, D.T. (1972) *Fundamentals of Human Sexuality*. (Holt, Rinehart and Winston, Inc., New York.)

Labby, D.H. (1971) Techniques in teaching medical students to take a sexual history. In: (V.W. Lippard, Ed.), *Macy Conference on Family Planning, Demography, and Human Sexuality in Medical Education*. (Josiah Macy, Jr. Foundation, New York) pp. 88—97.

Lief, H.I. (1964) Sexual attitudes and behaviors of medical students: implications for medical practice. In: (E.M. Nash, L. Jessner and D.W. Alse, Eds.), *Marriage Counseling in Medical Practice*. (University of North Caroline Press, Chapel Hill) pp. 301—318.

Lief, H.I. (1969) Sex education of the physician. In: (P.J. Fink and V.O. Hammett, Eds.), *Sexual Function and Dysfunction*. (F.A. Davis Co., Philadelphia) pp. 87—100.

Lief, H.I. (1970) New developments in the sex education of the physician. *J. Am. Med. Assoc.* 212: 1864—1867.

Lief, H.I. (1971) Medical aspects of sexuality. In: (P.B. Beeson and McD. Walsh, Eds.), *Cecil-Loeb Textbook of Medicine*, 13th edn (W.B. Saunders Co., Philadelphia) pp. 128—131.

Lief, H.I. and Ebert, R.K. (1976) Survey of sex education in United States medical schools. In: (H.I. Lief and A. Karlen, Eds.), *Sex Education in Medicine*. (Spectrum, New York.)

Masters, W.H. and Johnson, V.E. (1966) *Human Sexual Response*. (Little, Brown and Co., Boston.)

McCary, J.L. (1973) *Human Sexuality*. 2nd edn (Van Nostrand-Reinhold Co., Princeton, N.J.)

Money, J. (1971) Pornography and medical education. In: (V.W. Lippard, Ed.), *Macy Conference on Family Planning, Demography, and Human Sexuality*. (Josiah Macy Foundation, New York) pp. 98—109.

Money, J. and Ehrhardt, A.A. (1972) *Man and Woman, Boy and Girl*. (Johns Hopkins University Press, Baltimore and London.)

1120

Mudd, J.W. and Siegel, R.J. (1969) Sexuality: the experience and anxieties of medical students. *New Engl. J. Med.* 281: 1397—1403.

Pellegrino, E.D. (1974) Educating the humanist physician: an ancient ideal reconsidered. *J. Am. Med. Assoc.* 227: 1288—1294.

Reiss, I.L. (1971) *The Family System in America.* (Holt, Rinehart and Winston, Inc., New York.)

Romano, J. (1968) Teaching of medical students about population, sexual practices, and family planning. *J. Med. Educ.* 43: 898—906.

Seruya, F.C., Losher, S. and Ellis, A. (1972) *Sex and Sex Education: A Bibliography.* (R.R. Bowker, Co., New York and London.)

Stoller, R.J. (1968) *Sex and Gender.* (Science House, New York.)

Taylor, D.L. (1970) *Human Sexual Development.* (F.A. Davis Co., Philadelphia.)

Tyler, E.A. (1970) Introducing a sex education course into the medical curriculum. *J. Med. Educ.* 45: 1025—1031.

Vandervoort, H.E. (1974) Specific courses taught by human sexuality program. Presented to World Health Organization Meeting on education and treatment in human sexuality, Geneva 1974.

Vincent, C.E. (Ed.) (1968) *Human Sexuality in Medical Education and Practice.* (Charles C. Thomas, Springfield.)

Vincent, C.E. (1973) *Sexual and Marital Health: The Physician as a Consultant.* (McGraw-Hill, New York.)

Woods, S.M., Natterson, J. and Silverman, J. (1966) Medical students' disease: hypochondriasis in medical education. *J. Med. Educ.* 41: 785—790.

Woods, S.M. and Natterson, J. (1967) Sexual attitudes of medical students: some implications for medical education. *Am. J. Psychiat.* 124: 232—332.

Woods, S.M. (1969) A course for medical students in the psychology of sex: training in socio-cultural sensitivity. *Am. J. Psychiat.* 125: 1508—1519.

CHAPTER 90

Law and sex

ROBERT VEIT SHERWIN

1. ORIGINS OF LEGAL AND ILLEGAL SEXUAL BEHAVIOR

Social responsibility

The science of the administration of law has always been approximately forty to sixty years behind other sciences such as psychiatry and medicine, which explains in part the reason for the archaic nature of laws concerning sexual behavior. The underlying purpose of law is the coercion of social responsibility between persons to persons, persons to government, and government to persons. Laws, for example, concerning family obligations, are designed to make each person responsible for offspring and spouse.

Population needs

Until more recent times the population problem was exactly the reverse of that which we find today. For centuries life expectancy hovered around the age 35—45, plagues wiped out whole peoples, and infant mortality rates were high. Population replenishment and increase was the issue, and laws concerning sex were formed in general to prohibit any form of sex expression which allowed orgasm to be achieved without the possibility of procreation.

Inheritance problems

In addition to the need for population increase, laws concerning sex in many instances reflected the protection of personal property. For example, in medieval England the husband could have sexual intercourse outside of his marriage without fearing arrest and conviction, whereas the wife was sentenced in many cases to long terms of imprisonment, if she were caught having relations with a man other than her husband. Oddly enough, in this instance the reason was not an example of the 'double standard', about which more

Handbook of Sexology, edited by J. Money and H. Musaph
© *Elsevier/North-Holland Biomedical Press, 1977*

will be said further on in this chapter. The reason actually was because women could not own real estate or hold title. Title could only be passed on by the male owner to his offspring born of the marriage. Therefore, if the wife had intercourse outside her marriage there was the 'danger' that her offspring, if illegitimate, might derive a defective title from the husband, thus causing untold ramifications at a later date, in some cases making the husband's estate worthless from the standpoint of conveying it to generations that lay ahead.

Position of church law

In medieval times in Europe, and prior to the concept of separation of church and state, sex behavior was largely controlled by the church. What can be regarded as a sex code can be found in the Bible, the Talmud and the Koran. As State or National governments developed they incorporated acts concerning sexual behavior into their criminal codes. An interesting effect of this gradual 'take-over' of sexual behavior can be seen in the State of Louisiana Criminal Code of the U.S. The State of Louisiana, in the days before it became a state of the U.S., was known as The Louisiana Territory. Its population, largely of French origin, brought the Napoleonic Criminal Code from France. As a result, the State of Louisiana even to this day does not include in its criminal code the acts of fornication and adultery, since those acts were included in the church law of France which stayed in France.

2. NATURE OF SEXUAL BEHAVIOR APPLICABLE TO LAW

Dual problem

In order to understand how the law of sexual behavior differs from laws concerning all other forms of human behavior, it is necessary to differentiate between desire and behavior resulting from the desire.

Desire and behavior

The basic desire for money is universally acceptable as legal, but there are limitations on the methods used to obtain it. Certain methods of obtaining money are defined as illegal behavior. Thus, crimes concerning embezzlement, robbery, burglary, fraud, forgery, are all defined as illegal.

The real distinction between legal and illegal aspects of sexual desire and behavior is often minimal and in many instances nonexistant, yet the consequences can be severe. For example, the act of a 'Peeping Tom' should be normal in terms of behavior in that it is considered normal for a male to wish to view a female either undressing or undressed. The illegal behavior of the 'Peeping Tom', therefore, should not be his desire to see, but rather his invasion of the privacy of the female by peeping without her explicit permission. Therefore, the crime is clearly one of trespass, not one concerning a sexual desire. To illustrate further, the underlying criminal aspect of rape should not be the desire to have intercourse with a member of the opposite sex, but rather in the use of violence in the behavior selected to satisfy the desire.

When one studies the laws concerning sexual behavior it becomes abundantly clear that what is being punished is the desire to have sex, and not the method or behavior chosen to satisfy that desire: this can be deduced from the extreme variance in the punishment for the illegal behavior. For example, in the U.S. the penalty for adultery can range from a maximum penalty of ten days in prison to five years, depending on the state in which the act is committed. On the other hand, the penalties for illegal methods of obtaining money are not only quite similar in all of the fifty states, but compare quite favorably in terms of penalty gradation as it affects the size of the crime (for instance, general larceny carries more penalty than petty larceny, and those penalties also increase for a third and subsequent offense). The concept that different attitudes obtain towards sexual and monetary crimes are reflected in the definition and punishment of those crimes as will become clear as the major sexual acts deemed to be criminal are reviewed.

Crimes against persons

At the risk of over-simplifying, it would seem expedient to differentiate between illegal behavior which victimizes as a direct result of the criminal act, and those acts of illegality which are often called 'victimless'. Where the laws have been redefined, such laws concentrate on acts against persons.

Rape
Rape is usually defined as sexual intercourse that is achieved by force or by threat of force. Originally the law required that there be penetration into the vagina and a resulting orgasm on the part of the male. Now in most jurisdictions the basic requirement for the commission of the crime has been reduced to penetration alone. Statutory rape which, ironically, should not come under the title of rape at all, is defined as intercourse with a female under a specified age, regardless of her consent. The age of the female can range anywhere from thirteen to twenty-one years of age, depending on the jurisdiction of the courts in which the offense was alleged to have been committed. Hence, the sole criterion for conviction for statutory rape is whether or not the female was under the legal age, regardless of the age of the male participant. Many boys of fourteen years of age have been convicted in certain jurisdictions, even though their partners were older. Nevertheless, the boys were convicted of statutory rape. The case might be even more unfair in which the girl is a known prostitute and has been paid for the services, but if in fact she is under the legal age of consent the male customer can be convicted of statutory rape.

Forced sodomy
More will be said below about the broad legal definition of sodomy, but it suffices to say here that the same definition for rape applies to sodomy in that penetration is the necessary component of the offense.

Sexual acts against children
The act of seducing a child in most jurisdictions is usually entitled, 'Impairing the Morals of a Minor'. Indecent exposure in a public place with a child present would certainly come under this heading, to say nothing of all other sex acts such as masturbation and fellatio, in which the child may be used.

Sex acts done in public
These acts would include indecent exposure, petting in public, and all other forms of sex acts done in parks, theater balconies, public vehicles and in automobiles, that can easily be seen. The basic crime involved would seem to be the performance of an act which might be extremely offensive to people who were not involved in the particular act themselves.

Peeping
The act of peeping on other people, usually in the confines of their bedroom, is an invasion of privacy. Though certainly at the other end of the spectrum in terms of harm to the victim when compared with the act of rape, the act of peeping nevertheless might possibly do serious harm to some of the persons peeped upon.

Victimless crimes

Masturbation
Although masturbation was considered a serious offense in the holy books, it would appear to be the one act of a sexual nature which does not follow the pattern described in Biblical times. However, in almost all jurisdictions where masturbation is legal, it becomes illegal if not done in privacy or by oneself to oneself. This observation may seem self-evident until the problems of certain therapists are described as noted below.

Mutual masturbation
In many jurisdictions one can be arrested and convicted for mutual masturbation even when done in private, under statutes which may be specifically entitled 'Mutual Masturbation' or statutes entitled 'Crimes Against Nature', the sodomy statutes, or even under such vague criminal acts entitled, 'For Any Act Tending to Outrage Public Decency'. It is important to note in connection with this last crime that the act itself need not necessarily be committed in public, but it is sufficient that it would tend to outrage public decency (whatever that might mean).

Sodomy

Medically speaking, sodomy is usually defined as a connection between the male organ and any anus of a human being or animal. Legally speaking, the title sodomy is often included as part of the act entitled 'Crime Against Nature'. In certain jurisdictions almost any form of sexual expression other than the actual connection of the penis and the vagina is deemed as illegal. Such illegality would, of course, include mutual masturbation, oral contacts with the genitalia (male or female), connection of the penis with the anus, connection of the penis in merely the labia of the female and, finally sexual contact of the clitoris with the clitoris. In many places the crimes just described can be regarded as felonies that incur a maximum penalty of about twenty-five years imprisonment, but in some jurisdictions the penalty could be so severe as to run from sixty years to life imprisonment. In one state known to the author, a minimum penalty for such crimes is life imprisonment at hard labor. In many of these same jurisdictions it matters not whether the male and female performing the illegal sexual acts with each other are married to each other.

Adultery

Adultery is usually defined as illicit sexual intercourse between a male and a female who are not married to each other. However, several jurisdictions assume that heterosexuality is involved because they define adultery as illicit sexual intercourse 'between two persons', neither of whom are married to each other. As mentioned before, the penalty can range from ten days to five years but in earlier times being stoned to death was not unusual.

Fornication

Fornication is usually defined as illicit sexual intercourse performed by two people who are neither married to each other nor to anyone else. In some jurisdictions, therefore, if one of the persons indulging in sexual intercourse is married and the other is not, the married person would be convicted of adultery and the single person convicted of fornication. The penalty for fornication is usually far less than the penalty for adultery.

Lewd and lascivious living

This offense arises when a married person receives or visits another in the confines of a private place. It constitutes a lesser crime than adultery and fornication and does away with the necessity of proving sexual activity in obtaining a conviction. The only evidence needed would seem to be several visits of a male to a female, not his wife, in her home, or of a female to a male, not her husband, at his home.

3. THE CURRENT SCENE AS IT AFFECTS THE LAW

The fact that laws concerning sexual behavior are archaic is abundantly clear when they are seen in the light of development in the science of sexual behavior. The laws have not kept apace with the enlightened and now classical data provided by Kinsey, and Masters and Johnson. Nor have the laws been modified to allow for changing attitudes to sexuality and changing relationships between men and women.

The sexual emancipation of women

Sexual rights
The demands of the woman concerning sexual fulfillment can be regarded as generally accepted — that is to say, the demands and not the fulfillment. The double standard, although in some areas appearing in different forms, is nevertheless very much a part of many cultures.

The female orgasm
The achievement of female orgasm, as has been more amply described elsewhere, is accepted in most areas as the legal right of the woman, yet orgasm is still surrounded in all but a few jurisdictions by laws which make illegal the methods used by males or other females to help women achieve it. The laws proscribe mutual masturbation, masturbating another person and the various oral—genital contacts, but those techniques are all prescribed in the very best of scientific treatises.

The homosexual involvement

The same legal and biological conflict occurs when two homosexuals (whether they are male and male or female and female) relate to one another sexually. In order to achieve sexual satisfaction they, too, would have to indulge in mutual masturbation, cunnilingus, fellatio, and/or a connection of either the penis with the partner's rectum or the clitoris upon clitoris.

The therapists

In most jurisdictions, anyone who advises the commission of an act which is defined as being a crime is guilty of the same crime. Therefore, therapists who are aiding their patients to achieve better sexual relationships with their partners, lovers or spouses by committing any of the aforementioned acts are liable themselves to be prosecuted. Some such prosecutions have occurred, but it is very seldom that prosecutions have occurred for simply advising a patient.

Sex surrogates

Sex surrogates have been introduced into sex therapy only in recent years as an aid in sexual relationships, and there is little that can be said about the law concerning them at this time. Technically speaking, the sex surrogate is a person who, under the direction of a psychiatrist or a psychologist, makes actual sexual contact with the patient or patients to illustrate the various methods which might improve the patient's sexual relationships.

Needless to say, at the moment in most jurisdictions, the act of sex surrogate is completely illegal. A surrogate's activities would be regarded like the crime of prostitution in which money is accepted for having sexual contact with another person.

Teachers

Since there are materials in other chapters of the present book concerning sex education, it is sufficient to refer to the vulnerability of a teacher who lectures to his or her class on sexual relationships. Such lectures can be defined as illegal under statutes entitled 'Contributing to the Delinquency of a Minor'; 'Lewd and Lascivious Behavior or Inciting to Lascivious Behavior'; 'Behavior Unbecoming a Licensed Teacher' or under some catch-all statute described below.

Pornography

Since a special chapter covers pornography in general, mention here is restricted to the use of pornography in modern-day therapy to aid in the sexual arousal of patients suffering from frigidity, the inability to have an orgasm, or the inability to avoid one. The showing of pornographic materials by the therapist to the patient can involve the therapist in the crimes of lewd and lascivious behavior, an attempt to seduce the patient, behavior unbecoming to the professional, and many forms of malpractice actions.

Abortion

In those jurisdictions where abortion has been legalized there is, nevertheless, the indirect blocking of abortions in any number of ways. For example, in those American States which have legalized abortion, some courts in cities and towns have closed medically proper abortion clinics on the ground that although the state law removed the statute making abortion illegal, it did not replace it with a statute making it legal. Therefore each township or city in the State can assert its legal right to decide whether or not an abortion clinic should exist in its domain. The matter is often confused by the fact that other courts of another county in the same state may have forbidden their towns and city courts to close such clinics.

Insurance companies, also under the pressure of one group or another, will deprive patients of medical coverage for an abortion, thus making it impossible for a patient who is not rich to take advantage of what is otherwise a legal right. And, as a final illustration, private hospitals have committees designed specifically to deny a physician the use of hospital facilities if he were to perform an abortion in their hospital even though such an operation were legal in the state jurisdiction.

4. THE BEHAVIOR OF THE POLICE, DISTRICT ATTORNEYS AND JUDGES

Direct and indirect impact

The malfunctioning of the judicial procedure can be recognized in the examination of police, district attorneys and judges in administering laws concerning sex. Ordinary rules of procedural methods and precedence, upon which the administration of law depends, are often completely disregarded. For example, quite recently the crime of 'loitering' for purposes of prostitution was declared unconstitutional in a jurisdiction of the U.S. The act of loitering was standing in a doorway waiting for a customer to approach for the purpose of making a 'deal'. Loitering was declared unconstitutional on the grounds that one cannot be convicted for having done nothing. Ordinarily, the new decision would have meant that all police in the jurisdiction would be forbidden to arrest a person for an act that had been declared unconstitutional — except, it would seem, where sex is concerned. The Police Department in this specific jurisdiction continues to arrest, in droves, those who loiter. When newspaper reporters asked the Police Department to justify the time wasted in continuing to concern itself with an unconstitutional act, the answer given by the head of the department went as follows:

'In the first place, many of the girls arrested are unaware of this recent decision and we therefore convict and sentence them accordingly. Those who do know about the decision we release, but the next morning, making them spend the night in prison (admittedly a horrible experience), and we feel that by doing this night after night it might very well scare a good many prostitutes away from our town'

The point being made is not intended either to support or to refute the case concerning prostitution, but the incident is recorded only to illustrate the incredible variance of legal administration when one is dealing with sex as compared to law enforcement that pertains to other subjects.

Catch-all statutes

It would appear that in no area other than sex are there so many vague and really unenforceable statutes. Such statutes as 'Disturbing the Peace', 'Disorderly Conduct', 'Behavior Unbecoming to . . .', are used again and again to prosecute sexual behavior especially where a court may have declared a sex act to be legal which had been previously specifically prohibited. For example, a bookstore owner may find himself arrested for selling a book that has been declared not obscene. In his case the obscenity laws would not apply, but other statutes such as 'Disturbing the Peace' or 'Behavior Unbecoming A

Community Bookstore Owner' would. Few judges these days have the courage to risk the wrath of a vocal minority in the community in which they live by rejecting such legal manipulation, and as a result the bookstore owner may find himself without a legal defense. However, an entire chapter could be written about the vaguest statute of all: 'For Any Act Tending to Outrage Public Decency And For Which There Is No Other Statute' — particularly to the use by judges, police and district attorneys of that seemingly perfectly simple and innocuous statute.

Inappropriate versus the archaic

The problem is not the elimination of all laws concerning sex but rather the substitution of appropriate laws for those that are archaic.

Homosexuals

The legal problem of homosexuality is in transition at the moment and great strides are being made concerning it, socially, psychologically, psychiatrically, and even theologically. To be a homosexual in and of itself is not illegal. It is the fact that all forms of sexual expression available to the homosexual with another homosexual are illegal in most jurisdictions. Mutual masturbation, sodomy, cunnilingus, and fellatio have already been alluded to with heterosexuality, but the same observations about them apply to homosexuality. It is only in those jurisdictions which make any sexual act performed by consenting adults in privacy legal that the homosexual may express himself freely.

Transvestites and transsexuals

As defined in other chapters, the transvestite is a person who usually has relationships with a member of opposite sex while dressed in the clothing of the opposite sex. In other words, as a rule the act performed is not homosexual but cross-dressing is involved. One of the major distinctions between the homosexual and the transvestite is the fact that the homosexual prefers his or her own sex as a partner whereas the transvestite, although wearing clothes of the opposite sex, commonly is a person who prefers intercourse with the opposite sex. The cross-dressing and not the sexual behavior is declared illegal in many jurisdictions, usually under the heading of masquerading and causing a public disturbance. In some cases the so-called public disturbance has consisted of a lone male transvestite dressed in female clothing walking a public street at two o'clock in the morning, without another soul in sight.

The transsexual, on the other hand, is a person who does not merely dress as a member of the opposite sex but goes further in that, with the aid of hormonal treatments, electrolysis and surgical operations, he or she actually tries to become a member of the opposite sex. Legally speaking, the main problems revolve around attempting to amend the birth certification (in terms of sex), changing one's name legally, obtaining an automobile license, social security number, insurance policies, passport, and charge accounts in the new name, and, of course, getting married in the 'new sex', and perhaps later getting a divorce.

The problems are vast, but suffice it to say for the purposes of this chapter that birth certificates cannot generally be rewritten under the new sex, but they can be amended. One unfortunate consequence is that every time a person needs to use a birth certificate the change in sex is revealed. However, some progress is being made to change the law relating to birth certificates. At the moment it is best to avoid the court wherever possible until medical science can provide the necessary knowledge and understanding of transexual problems. Perhaps then the appropriate laws will be written, passed and enforced on proper grounds.

5. MARRIAGE AND DIVORCE

Common law marriage

Common law marriage or marriage without benefit of clergy or civil authority has been declared illegal in more and more jurisdictions in recent years but despite that the living together of man and woman without legal sanction does seem to be increasing. Such marriages include the begetting of children and the behaving in every way by a couple as if married, but without bothering to sanctify the relationship in accordance with the law or the church. However, although the parties may be 'allowed to live' without legal restraint, society expresses its disapproval by depriving the parties of what otherwise would have been a legal right to inherit property when the other partner dies. Society also retains the right to remove children from the custody of either parent should any custody dispute arise, finding it 'morally' better to incarcerate children in a foster home or in some children's institution than to leave them with either of the natural parents.

Therapists, sex clinics and encounter groups

As stated earlier in this chapter, many new forms of marriage counseling have arisen and, as is the case with new procedures, old laws are often applied to the outcome of new methods with devastating results. Very faint noises here and there indicate that new laws may be in the offing, but to the knowledge of the author no fresh laws have as yet been passed. Needless to say, divorce has occurred where the wife or the husband has named as a correspondent either the therapist, sex surrogate or other clinician involved when suing for divorce on grounds of adultery.

Divorce grounds

Homosexual
There is a growing tendency (as in New York State for example) to expand

the ground of adultery to include homosexual behavior on the part of the erring spouse. At the same time, there is an absence of law that might protect the defendant in such a divorce from being arrested and convicted for sodomy or other criminal behavior already described. Considering the antipathy involved in many divorce situations, the possibility of such a criminal conviction is sometimes used with extortionary and blackmailing effect.

Adultery (criminal)
The ground of adultery is being used less and less for purposes of divorce as grounds for divorce increase in the no-fault area. In some jurisdictions it is sufficient for the parties to indicate mutual incompatability rather than to proceed to the point of committing a marital offense. However, the ground still does exist in most jurisdictions, and the criminal act of adultery continues to remain an ever-present threat, especially when one considers the economic needs of a divorcing parent.

Custody problems
Despite the current emancipation and liberation of women, the double standard still remains to plague divorcing parents where child custody is involved. For example, if a wife lives alone, her husband having left, justly or unjustly, her male neighbor whose advances she may have rejected, can seek his revenge by furnishing so-called evidence of the woman's misdeeds. Judges frequently accept the flimsiest of evidence of her sexual behavior and rule against her having custody of her children, and so put further pressure on her in an already exacerbated situation.

Artificial insemination

Artificial insemination of a spouse has become more increasingly used as children for adoption become less available for childless couples. Here again, old laws continue to be applied to a comparatively new scientific method of meeting human needs, but the existing law doesn't protect the husband, the wife, the donor and the resulting child. On the contrary, divorces in both England and the U.S. have been granted on the ground of adultery when the adulterous act consisted of the insertion of the syringe by the physician into the wife's vagina. The incredibility of such decisions can only be attested to by persons who have been subjected to such acrimony.

Sexual impotence and frigidity as grounds for divorce or annulment

Although psychiatric and/or psychological impotency and frigidity have long been recognized, there are few jurisdictions that recognize the problems as providing legitimate grounds for divorce or annulment of marriage. Those states that did recognize frigidity or impotence acknowledged them under two circumstances only. The first was in cases where either a physical obstruction of the vagina or a defective male organ (perhaps lost in war or born defective) were present. The second was in cases where the husband or the wife deceived the other and such fraud or deception could be proved as evidence of his or her sexual deficiency.

The problem, however, will soon be greatly diminished in light of new divorce laws that will make divorce possible without either party having to prove fraud or fault.

6. CONCLUSION

The principal problem in the legal administration of sexual behavior lies in the fact that the interdisciplinary sciences of psychiatry, medicine, psychology and human relationships in general would seem to be thirty to sixty years ahead of the present body of laws which concerns itself with the regulating of sexual activity between humans. The results of the lapse can be devastating to those persons who may be involved, innocently or otherwise, with an infraction of the archaic laws.

It is true that seldom is a concerted effort made to arrest and convict everyone who deviates from current laws, but the mere presence of the laws remains a threat not only to the personal behavior of each individual who might be arrested, but also it acts as a deterrent to those who may wish to seek help in their problems. The archaic law also confuses judges who may either refuse to enforce laws which are truly ridiculous and inappropriate, or allow a seriously dangerous person to cause untold damage in the community where he or she lives. Either the failure to enforce or the enforcement of inappropriate laws in effect creates a state of lawlessness.

In those jurisdictions which have attempted to deal with the problems discussed in this chapter, the following laws should be enforced while all others are omitted:

— Laws concerning any act involving violence, such as forcible rape, forced sodomy, or a sex act involving a person who is retarded or incompetent and thus unable to protect his or her self from this sexual trespass.

— All laws concerning the imposing of sexual acts on children by an adult, including certain forms of statutory rape.

— All laws prohibiting any sex act done in a public place.

BIBLIOGRAPHY

Benjamin, H.B. (1966) *The Transsexual Phenomenon.* (Julian Press, New York.)

Donnelly, R.C., Goldstein, J. and Schwartz, R.D. (1962) *Criminal Law, New York.* (Free Press, Glencoe.)

Drzazga, J. (1960) *Sex Crimes* (Charles C. Thomas, Springfield, Ill.)

Gagnon, J.H. and Simon, W. (Eds.) (1970) *The Sexual Scene.* (Aldine, Chicago.)

Gebhard, P.H., Gagnon, J.H., Pomeroy, W.B. and Christenson, C.V. (1965) *Sex Offenders*. (Harper and Row, New York.)

Goode, E. and Troiden, R. (Eds.) (1974) *Sexual Deviance and Sexual Deviants*. (Morrow, New York.)

Katchadourian, H.A. and Lunde, D.T. (1972) *Fundamentals of Human Sexuality*. (Holt, Rinehart and Winston, New York.)

Magee, B. (1966) *One In Twenty*. (Stein and Day, New York.)

Ploscowe, M. (1951) *Sex and the Law*. (Prentice-Hall, New York.)

Schulz, G.D. (1965) *How Many More Victims*. (Lippincott, Philadelphia.)

Sherwin, R.V. (1949) *Sex and the Statutory Law*. (Oceana Publishers, New York.)

Sherwin, R.V. (1950) *Some Legal Aspects of Homosexuality. Int. J. Sexol.* 4: 22—26.

Sherwin, R.V. (1951a) Sex expression and the law. I. The law of rape. *Int. J. Sexol.* 4: 206—210.

Sherwin, R.V. (1951b) Sex expression and the law. II. Sodomy: a medico-legal enigma. *Int. J. Sexol.* 5: 3—13.

Sherwin, R.V. (1952) Prostitution: a study of law and disorder. *Int. J. Sexol.* 5: 201—205.

Sherwin, R.V. (1965) *Sodomy in Sexual Behavior and the Law*. (Charles C. Thomas, Springfield, Ill.)

Sherwin, R.V. (1969) *Compatible Divorce*. (Crown Publishers, New York.)

Williams, G. (1957) *The Sanctity of Life and the Criminal Law*. (Knopf, New York.)

SECTION XV

Special issues: personal

Section coordinator: Herman Musaph

CHAPTER 91

Introduction

HERMAN MUSAPH

In this section are collected three issues with some qualities in common. They are all issues of personal relevance, which, as a matter of course, do not fit easily into any other section. Their meaning, from the practical point of view, is of such importance that they could not be left out of the Handbook.

Little is known about experimental investigation on masturbatory behavior in children and adults. Knowledge of masturbation is mostly based on retrospective research in the psychoanalytic situation. This individual approach gives information concerning sexual fantasies, defense mechanisms and symptom formation. But this information is confined to a certain individual in a certain development, within a certain culture pattern, and is not easy to generalize. Elisabeth Frijling-Schreuder gives an overall view and succeeds very well in putting masturbation problems in the framework of emotional development of normal human beings, without neglecting the most common derailments.

Every experienced sex therapist knows that many problems he is asked to solve are not originally sexual at all. Many tensions, for example, in the relationship with parents or superiors, find their outlet in sexual disorders. Treating the disturbed relationship with an emotionally important person in one's life is much more appropriate than confining the therapy to sex behavior alone. Roeland Pierloot, a clinical psychiatrist, gives a survey of masked adjustment problems. He also treats problems in sexual adjustment presenting themselves as nonsexual. He is especially interested in relational interaction, which is extremely important from the therapeutic point of view.

The role of the skin in erotic and sexual contact has become of increasing interest in the last decade, due especially to the development of modern psychodermatology. Touching is integral to the thinking model of the child psychologist with special interest in the mother—child relationship. In modern group psychotherapy, touching techniques play an important part.

Handbook of Sexology, edited by J. Money and H. Musaph
© *Elsevier/North-Holland Biomedical Press, 1977*

The psychology of massage until now has been neglected. So there is a chapter on this issue in this section.

The behavioral biologist, specializing in primatology, has much that is new to say about unusual sexual behavior in both captive and free-ranging primates. Maple's survey can help us to put the immense human diversity of sexual behavior in a wider perspective for the better understanding of sexology.

CHAPTER 92

On masturbation

ELISABETH FRIJLING-SCHREUDER

1. MASTURBATION IN INDIVIDUAL DEVELOPMENT

Masturbation was for a long time a very forbidden subject. In so far as the phenomenon was not denied completely, it was seen as the cause of the most diverse disturbances. How can it be that a way of sexual pleasure which is so universal was judged so severely?

The role of masturbation in individual development gives us the clue to this problem. One cannot gain insight into the influence of the vicissitudes of masturbation on character development and symptom formation by considering only the motor activity. For the purpose of this paper I understand masturbation as the whole complex of the act and the accompanying emotional attitudes, affects and fantasies. The place of masturbation in adulthood is determined partly by external circumstances and partly by its developmental vicissitudes

In young children masturbation serves three functions; it strengthens pleasure in and knowledge of the functioning of the body. If it is severely forbidden or repressed altogether general clumsiness may be the outcome. The second function lies in its being a way of mastering of all kinds of disappointments and frustrations, a kind of general comfort. Especially in children who do not get enough love and support in the development of their personality from outside, excessive auto-erotism may indicate that something is wrong. The third function of masturbation in early childhood is the canalization of excitement arising from the oedipal phase.

Not only the sexual feelings towards the parents, the sexual curiosity, the stimulation stemming from oedipal love, but also the feelings of frustration of hate and anger at the impossibility of fulfillment find their outlet in masturbation. The death-wishes towards the parents that inevitably arise and the incest barrier make masturbation the forbidden activity it has been and partly still is in many cultures, especially among members of those religions in which masturbation is tabooed.

Handbook of Sexology, edited by J. Money and H. Musaph
© *Elsevier/North-Holland Biomedical Press, 1977*

Castration-anxiety in its male and female forms is as universal in the oedipal situation as is masturbation itself. Normally it only leads to a temporary lowering of the pain barrier, a short time of whining and weeping behavior which stands in contrast to the stoic indifference to bumps and hurts of the toddler and of the latency boy. This period may be short and light, but if castration anxiety is heightened by threats from the parents, by surgical interventions or other anxiety-provoking life situations, masturbation may be completely repressed. Sometimes it may be replaced by other autoerotic behavior, such as enuresis, thumb-sucking, nail-biting, obsessive scratching and hair-pulling (Musaph, 1964). Not infrequently, such behavior is already symptom formation: it expresses an unconscious conflict in a compromise which means gratification as well as punishment.

In normal development, masturbation of the oedipal phase is accompanied by typical oedipal fantasies: fantasies of grandeur in which the child is a much greater hero than his father, a mysterious king or warrior, a television hero, the garbageman driving his enormous car with much noise through the street. He fights and kills and is himself inviolable, but he may well be prone to anxiety about burglars or tigers in the night, and so be driven to the parent's bed from which he feels excluded. In the life of a normal young child these anxieties evaporate easily. Only when they become rigid over a longer period is there reason to suppose that something has gone wrong.

In the latency period masturbation may be temporarily given up. Mostly it continues less frequently, but so far as I can see modern cultural trends tend to shorten latency. This is already true physically, puberty starting earlier, but it is far more true in the psychological sense. I am not clear about the causes and not even quite sure that it is true as extensive research is not available.

Masturbation fantasies are in latency very difficult to get at. We know their contents from child-analysis, but then we are already dealing with disturbed children. The contents of these fantasies in normal development may be guessed partially from the hobbies of the child and from the kind of play he prefers. In the first half of latency we see the contents of the fantasies in the endless pursuit play of children in the street. Cops and robbers, sheriff and murderer, and war and taking prisoners may form the cherished play of children who in other ways are not overly aggressive. They themselves give rules to their play which prevent accidents. Only if the excitement gets too high, or if a disturbed child in the group has to vent too much aggression, does the play become dangerous. In normal cases it helps to conquer residual castration-anxiety and to develop motor-skills. In the second half of latency this play gives way to the more organized forms of sport and skill.

Actual masturbation, in so far as it takes place may be felt as a hurt to the child's self-esteem, assuming that the child has incorporated the parent's prohibitions against it. A child may well feel the inhibition of masturbation in latency as an achievement, and may feel disappointed if he falls short of his ideal. Nonetheless, I am convinced that in boys as well as in girls, masturbation may go on in latency without guilt feelings, but as a general comfort, a simple bodily pleasure as in early infancy. This will be the case only if the parents have a lenient attitude towards sexual pleasure, without overstimulating the child, and if the oedipal complex has been sufficiently resolved.

2. CULTURAL DIFFERENCES

In Western culture, overstimulation possibly becomes more and more a threat to mental health in children, especially those with so-called progressive parents. Leniency towards the impulsive behavior of children is quite different from confrontation with adult sexual and aggressive behavior which is too difficult for the children to master, when the society, in its other rooms, prohibits such behavior. Chronic overstimulation may hinder the solution of the oedipal conflict and may make it permanent. Violent jealousy, continuous sexual excitement with difficulties in behavior control and concentration, or in the other extreme, severe inhibitions, may result. One can never make too sure predictions of the outcome of harmful parental behavior, because there are so many factors involved which are not predictable. Authorities are not unanimous regarding objective knowledge on this subject. Questionnaires can only reveal how the child or his parents see the question, and what they are able to tell about their behavior, not how their behavior is in reality and what it means. If taken at face value, statistics on the incidence of masturbation show great differences from one country to another and variations even within short periods. Especially for females the incidence figures vary enormously from nearly ubiquitous in some studies to only 12% at age 21 in Japan (Asayama, 1975).

3. POST-OEDIPAL FANTASIES

Masturbation fantasies after the oedipal period may be of great influence in general character-formation (Lampl-de Groot, 1965). Fantasies of grandeur, of being a hero, that helped the young boy to master the narcissistic hurt of being unable to take father's place with mother may be continued when the oedipal context is already repressed and when masturbation is given up, temporarily or permanently. These fantasies may be integrated in the formation of the ego-ideal and in this way may have permanent influence on behavior, as in denial of pain and danger, in a fighting attitude, and in striving for high achievement.

Beating fantasies which were part of the mastering of the castration anxiety by shifting punishment from the penis to the buttocks may become part of a masochistic perversion or of a severe character deformation in a period of life where the recollection of the infantile masturbatory activities is lost completely. In so far as masturbation leads to severe guilt feelings, the continuous loss of the battle against it may lead to a general feeling of unworthiness. In prepuberty, masturbation may be rediscovered. Infantile masturbation is often intensely repressed and the young pre-adolescent or adolescent may well feel that he finds this genital pleasure for the first time.

It is very difficult to uncover the fantasies which often form the deepest secret of the early adolescent child. There may be a split between daydreams and masturbation fantasies. Daydreams may contain the fantasies of grandeur, the high ideals, the fantasies of romantic love, whereas during masturbation there are fantasies of crude sexual or sadistic acts. This split indicates guilt feelings about masturbation. The masturbatory act perceived as dirty and bad, cannot be combined with beautiful fantasies. The accompanying fantasies have to be 'low' and 'dirty'. On the other hand this partial regression to anal sadism makes the masturbation still more forbidden and indulgence may alternate with periods of severe asceticism.

In the development to normal adulthood such episodes may be changed completely into dating and falling in love. Disappointments and severe narcissistic hurts in this period may drive the adolescent back to masturbation, and may heighten the aggressive component of the fantasies. The resulting guilt feelings may inhibit the progressive developmental process and reactivate the infantile oedipal conflicts to adult neurosis. Sometimes in young adulthood or in late adolescence simple enlightenment and reassurance may be enough to free the developmental process.

There are, however, many adult neurotics who started pubertal masturbation at the normal time and who use this masturbation often without concomitant fantasies and without conscious guilt feelings to ward off the affects, fantasies and guilt-feelings of early masturbation. In the diagnostic process they may well tell sincerely that their sex life is without difficulties. The attentive consultant may sometimes hear in the indifferent tone that this declaration only means that sexuality must be excluded from discussion. Often he has to leave the question open for further exploration.

4. ADULT VICISSITUDES OF MASTURBATION

The enormous influence of the vicissitudes of masturbation on adult sex life is not always recognized. Fleeting and short-lived sexual relations may well indicate an unconscious problem about masturbation. The flight into an unhappy marriage may occur as a defense against masturbation.

I once saw an outbreak of mutual masturbation, intensive sex-play and general unruliness in a home for neglected boys, where one boy in the group was very anxious about masturbation. A little help to this boy effectively cleared up the whole situation. During the identity-crisis of puberty masturbation may be followed by feelings of depletion and depersonalization, (le Coultre, 1972). In normal youth, however, the strong feelings of gratification may help to strengthen the feeling of self. The strangeness of the own body with all its changes may be heightened as well as mastered by these feelings. The masturbatory fantasies in later adolescence may be trial activity, for the finding of a partner and for the sexual act.

In adulthood masturbation continues mostly less frequently. During marriage mutual masturbation may be one of the variations of sexual pleasure, giving the opportunity for relief of infantile strivings. Lonely masturbation during marriage mostly means — as far as my experience goes — an outlet of infantile fantasies which are so forbidden that they must be hidden from the partner and/or the release of an amount of aggression against the partner which is too strong to be admixed to love in normal coitus.

Lonely people use masturbation normally as an outlet. If their loneliness is incidental — when they have lost a partner and not yet found another — the fantasies may be about normal coitus. However, I saw a reactivation of infantile fantasies after the loss of a partner in the period of mourning. Fantasying about the lost partner was too painful, fantasies about a new real partner were not yet acceptable. This accentuates that it is always false to diagnose from one aspect only: if the diagnostician only takes into account the manifest contents of the masturbation-fantasies in such a period he would diagnose a more severe disturbance to the neglect of the normal grief.

With today's greater sexual freedom a new taboo against masturbation seems to come to the fore. Its importance for mental health as well as for neurosis is neglected. Masturbation equivalents are described as childhood neurotic phenomena or as behavior difficulties. They may be punished and persecuted as masturbation was formerly, but they often are not recognized in their relation to masturbation. In the diagnostic process the vicissitudes of masturbation in its emotional context and with the concomitant fantasies ought to play an important role, but very often it is ignored completely.

I do not say that it is always possible to establish a rapport which enables the consultant to ask about the intimate details of sexual life without harm to the patient. But from many case histories it is clear that it was not this consideration which deterred the consultant from asking the relevant questions, but that he, for personal reasons, had to ignore masturbation.

5. SUMMARY

The vicissitudes of masturbation during childhood development form a pivot for development towards either mental health or neurosis. A permissive and lenient attitude of the parents towards the bodily and sexual pleasures of their child, without overstimulation, helps the child toward normal development. Even so, masturbation during the oedipal phase is linked with guilt feelings. In adverse circumstances, because of strong taboos in society, or because of parents who lack a healthy sexual life, guilt feelings may persist and may become a hindrance to normal development. During latency and puberty, both the freedom to masturbate and the freedom to conquer masturbation are normal. Obsessive masturbation may be an expression of a neurotic conflict as may also the complete inhibition of masturbation. Conflicts about masturbation may also lead to different forms of acting out. In the diagnosis of psychic disturbance, the vicissitudes of masturbation including masturbation fantasies should be kept in mind. If obtainable, data on masturbation should become a part of the total assessment.

BIBLIOGRAPHY

Asayama, S. (1975) Adolescent sex development and adult sex behavior in Japan *J. Sex. Res.* 11: 91—112.

Lampl-de Groot (1965) On masturbation and its influence on general development. In: *The Development of the Mind.* (I.P.N., New York.)

Laufer, M (1968) The body image, the function of masturbation and adolescence: problems of the ownership of the body. *Psychoanal. Stud. Child* 23: 114—137.

Le Coultre, R. (1972) *Psychoanalytische Themas en Variaties.* (Van Loghum Slaterus, Deventer.)

Musaph, H. (1964) *Itching and Scratching. Psychodynamics in Dermatology.* (Karger, Basle.)

CHAPTER 93

Masked sexual adjustment problems: presentation of the wrong symptom and/ or wrong patient

R.A. PIERLOOT

1. THEORETICAL BACKGROUND

The assumption that symptoms and complaints, offered to a doctor by his patients, are manifestations of underlying psychological problems, addresses itself implicitly to the psychodynamic viewpoint. The reference towards conflicts in the sexual sphere forms the essence of classic psychodynamic methodology.

Breuer and Freud (1895) recognized sexuality as the source of psychic dream content and as the motive for the denial and repression of concepts from consciousness, a phenomenon to which they ascribed a leading role in the pathogenesis of hysteria. In the same year, Freud (1895a) described the mechanism of anxiety neurosis as the abnormal resolution of somatic sexual excitement, which then finds its expression through an inappropriate psychic discharge. In the compulsion neurosis the symptoms would revolve around transformed and substituted self-guilt and blame, with regard to early childhood sexual pleasure (Freud, 1895b).

In the further expansion of psychoanalytic conceptuology, the role of sexuality in the genesis of the most diverse psychopathological and psychosomatic syndromes seemed clearly demonstrated.

In 'The Psychoanalytic Theory of Neuroses' by Fenichel (1945), it appears rather difficult to find any condition in which sexual conflicts, in one form or the other, are not present.

In this very broad sense one can, indeed, stamp the most diverse and disparate clinical phenomena as expressions of sexual maladjustment. When reducing this conceptualization to a more limited and workable scope, the question arises as to which criteria may best be employed in arriving at a usable description and categorization of these entities.

Information concerning the actual sexual behavior of the patient is only of limited value in determining the real pathogenetic significance of the sexual problems. As soon as an individual, for one reason or the other, be-

Handbook of Sexology, edited by J. Money and H. Musaph
© *Elsevier/North-Holland Biomedical Press, 1977*

comes disturbed in his psychic or somatic functioning, it is to be expected that his adjustment in the sexual sphere will be adversely affected. The question remains as to what degree sexual dysfunction may be viewed as a secondary epi-phenomenon of illness, or can be implicated as a primary disturbance of function, which plays a definite contributory role in the genesis of the sick or morbid state.

It is clear that only through a thorough and in-depth analysis of the sexual evolution in the personal biography of the patient a judgment may be reached over the eventual patterns of sexual maladjustment, their relation to the current symptomatology and their importance as contributory factors. This evaluation of sexuality by no means excludes the role of other pathogenetic factors, the more since most illnesses are multiconditionally determined.

On what grounds then is it justifiable to speak of maladjustment in the sexual sphere as a potential pathogenetic factor? It is unavoidable that the place of sexual maladjustment in the pathogenesis is somewhat arbitrary and poorly delineated borders must be drawn. In this context the concept of sexual maladjustment may be at once too narrowly and too broadly envisioned.

It would seem rather one-sided and insular to consider only the classic sexual deviations and so-called perversions. Moreover, certain so-called perversions, such as homosexuality, are no longer currently viewed, per se, as maladjustments. Focusing on copulative and orgasmic dysfunctions, grouped by Masters and Johnson (1970) as 'Human Sexual Inadequacy', also only represents a unilateral consideration of the problem. This consideration does not exclude that the presence of some forms of so-called perversion and/or sexual inadequacy can signify important indications of maladjustment in the elaboration of sexual life.

A singular emphasis on instrumental sexual functioning appears much too narrow to serve as a point of departure. On the other hand it is difficult to justify by the finding of some conflicting sexual problems — formulated in a broad psychoanalytic perspective of personality development — an explanation in terms of sexual maladjustment for the symptoms and complaints which the patient offers. This would irrevocably lead to so extreme a broadening of the concept of sexual maladjustment that, at least in our context, it would no longer be relevant.

The dilemma of a too-narrow versus a too-broad conceptualization can be avoided if we consider sexuality as a specific form of relational interaction. The evaluation of sexual behavior in the biography of the patient is centered round the criterion of the degree to which the patient is successful in bringing sexual activity to a personally meaningful and affective form of interaction between partners. In this concept, emphasis is placed upon the level of a mutually satisfying and shared experience among equals. This can be more or less optimally realized, but serious failure in this domain will necessarily lead to tensions which will become exteriorized in many diverse forms of disturbances.

It is difficult to estimate the full range of symptoms that can be ascribed to sexual maladjustment. The nature of the complaints with which one is confronted depends to a large degree on the medical speciality which the patient consults. For instance, to a gynecologist, the patient will present with low abdominal or back pain, while the internist is often confronted with an anorexia nervosa or gastrointestinal disorders. The 'battered child' in pediatrics may be a victim of parental sexual maladjustment, while the 'battered wife' may wind up in the department of surgery. In neither case is the true history disclosed. The psychiatrist is more often consulted for an anxiety or depressive syndrome. It is important not to lose sight of the fact that all too often release will be sought in alcohol and drug abuse, which all too easily leads to toxicomania.

The age of the patient and reactions of the partner, as well as constitutional and exogenous factors, play a role in the choice of a syndrome. A tolerant partner will usually promote psychosomatic disturbances, while anxiety or depressive reactions and behavioral disorders are more often associated with overt reactions of the partner. At middle age, a predilection towards depressions dominates, whereas conversion symptoms usually emerge at a younger age.

Any attempt at a complete survey of symptoms pointing towards masked sexual maladjustment is a patently impossible task. I shall attempt to indicate some principal categories, based on clinical observations, through which an understandable connection can be drawn between sexual failure and manifest illness. Before turning to these categories, it is useful to describe some of the most important areas in which these sexual failures occur; such as become manifest in a clinical context.

Overt conflicts with the partner provoking a basic disharmony, or temporary or permanent separation are the most easily recognized forms. However, one must often deal with more subtle disturbances in sexual relations which are revealed only through a deeper and more thorough analysis of the significance and experiences of the patient's sexual activity. Both the choice of partner and the mutual relationship of the pair are testimony to sexual maladjustment; these two aspects are usually finely interwoven.

The significance of incestuous desire in partner choice is extensively covered by Musaph (1970). An affective fixation with a parental figure in the oedipal phase of development may prove an obstacle to partner choice or may prove directive in the choice; for instance the choice of an older person or one who shares many of the character traits of the parental figure. In this last case a furtherance of incestuous anxiety may prove a severe handicap to sexual activity (Duyckaerts, 1964).

In other cases, sexuality is made difficult by reason of insecurity relative to identity problems of the individual. In the most extreme cases the own sex is viewed as repellent, combined with the desire to belong to the opposite sex (Green, 1974). The problem may be much more limited and center itself around doubt concerning one's own sexual potency. In addition, the fear of losing one's 'self' in sexual relationships may exist. Sexual activity is experienced as threatening to the individual's narcissistic anchorage.

A strong mixture of aggressive and sexual drives invests sexual activity with an anxiety-producing character; one is afraid of harming either the partner or being harmed oneself. Some sadomasochistic partner relations, wherein reciprocal hurt is the dominating element, function temporarily quite well but almost invariably lead eventually to the arousal of serious tensions.

The diverse mechanisms just touched upon, often occur in mixed forms. All of these mechanisms rest upon disturbances in the development of a mature adult sexuality, in which a partner relationship based on mutual equality and affective exchange without guilt or anxiety feelings is not realized.

Such disturbances, labeled as sexual maladjustment, can lead to a wide variety of somatic, psychic and social dysfunctions. On the other hand, some sexual difficulties rather may reflect deficiencies in self-esteem or aggression-regulation, on which the development of a satisfying sexual adjustment is largely dependent. Therefore, apart from the description of certain syndromes referring to sexual maladjustment, we shall also mention the connection between territoriality and sexuality in the genesis of some difficulties in sexual interaction.

2. ADDICTION

Addiction is discussed first, because it usually represents the consequence of an initial attempt to lower the growing tensions, created by sexual conflicts, in a troubled individual. The patient attempts to deny these conflicts through the use of 'mood elevators', It starts with the ingestion of an apparently innocent medication or the search for solace in alcohol to decrease disillusion over sexual failure.

A rather small number of these persons become genuine addicts. In most cases the abuse limits itself to a rather excessive use of alcohol or drugs. In this category numerous women must be included who consume large amounts of analgesic, sedative and hypnotic drugs. Insomnia, headache and other general complaints form too easily a socially acceptable explanation of their drug abuse. Men are more inclined toward the excessive use of alcohol. It is self-evident that these stop-gap procedures are only successful in camouflaging, for a time, the real problem. This precarious equilibrium is easily shattered and additional complications lead to crisis situations and psychic decompensations.

Abuse and addiction are merely quantitative extensions of each other. Indeed it seems compatible, according to the view of Van Dyk (1969), that addiction is a transcending of this quantitative boundary. In this regard two characteristics are essential: the uncontrollable drive towards the addictive drug, and the inability to give up using the product. Addiction is an autonomous, self-perpetuating syndrome.

It is generally accepted that fundamental personality characteristics, such as an oral fixation are important predisposing factors to addiction. Since these personality traits also contribute to disordered sexual patterns, we are dealing with an intertwining of predisposing and precipitating factors that lead to addiction.

A multitude of studies has been devoted to partner choice among alcoholics. Unfortunately, whether the alcoholism preceded the choice of partner was not discerned in most of these studies. The question remains unanswered as to whether the inadequate partner preceded or provoked the drinking. Still, it is noteworthy that Malzberg (1949) found, in a study of 516 hospitalized alcoholics, that 36.4% of these patients were never married. Amark (1951) described that a considerable number of male alcoholics were married to cool, affectionless and hysteroid wives.

Excessive drug or alcohol use is undeniably a cause of increasing sexual failure. Conversely, sexual anxiety or inadequacy is an equally valid cause of the individual's turning to the search for an artificial euphoria through the use of toxic products. This bilaterality of causation and effect must be taken into account when one discusses drug abuse.

Matussek (1959) studied a group of 91 subjects suffering from addiction to diverse products. In 38 of these patients marital disharmony could be cited as a provoking factor. Moreover, the question arises as to what degree other precipitating factors such as boredom, feelings of insecurity and inhibition rest upon a basic sexual maladjustment.

The morbid jealousy displayed by many alcoholics is often too easily explained away as a consequence of sexual problems arising from the alcoholism itself. However, there are strong indications that this behavior arises from more basic personality traits. Fantasies over unfaithfulness of the partner and the inability to attain a deeply meaningful sexual relationship often precede the alcoholism.

Conversely, it is generally valid to assume that the personality disintegration as a consequence of addiction reveals and accentuates the deeper underlying personality problems. In this view one has to be careful not to interpret disturbances of sexual adaptation one-sidedly as a consequence of toxicomania but also to consider the converse perspective.

3. DEPRESSIONS

Psychodynamically the pathogenesis of the depressive syndrome is considered in the light of a series of connecting psychic processes. The point of departure is conceptualized as a threatening of the individual's feelings of self-esteem due to the loss of an esteemed worth-giving object. The aggression hereby aroused is insufficiently, or not at all, externalized or even felt as such, but internalized and directed towards the individual himself.

In this scheme the relation between depression and sexual failure is clear.

Sexual adaptation disturbances give rise to conflicts that readily lead to abandonment experiences and situations. Sadomasochistic elements as well as inhibition in sexual contacts may contribute to the production of this abandonment. This does not exclude the possibility that, because of the individual's sexual immaturity, the lost partner is deeply experienced as an indispensable narcissistic object. The loss of this object precipitates the depression.

Such depression is usually not very deep, and only rarely becomes psychotic in severity. The general mood of the patient is one of dejection. The verbalizations, revolving around feelings of discouragement, apathy, hopelessness and self-depreciation, seem quite appealing. But the sympathy and support extended by others who involve themselves with the patient offer only a partial and ephemeral relief to his feeling of being abandoned.

The mood of the patient is labile. In the company of others a feeling of well-being is engendered, but this is illusory and quickly changes to feelings of depression and self-depreciation. It is difficult to predict when these depressive states will end; they readily evolve to a state of remission with short periods of relapse.

The occurrence of depressions of this type is related to the person's age when sexual maladjustment leads directly to abandonment, or when the loss of compensating esteemed objects occurs. In this last regard one or both parents may be retained in an infantile bond with the patient and function as a principal compensating object. It is also true that an individual's children may be invested with the full sum of energy which couldn't be discharged satisfatorily in sexual relations. Generally speaking, women are more vulnerable in this respect than are men.

The period of initial partner choice and the search for a lasting partner relation can bring with it considerable disappointment which doesn't necessarily lead to depression. To the extent that partner choice is predicated on the basis of infantile fixation, the chance that failure will lead to depressive states is increased. The amount of narcissistic investment in the partner determines to what degree a failure or break in the relation will be experienced as a depreciation of self-esteem. The following case nicely illustrates this problem:

Case 1

This 21-year-old girl was admitted to the department of psychiatry because of an agitated depression. She was excited and desperate, and made spectacular threats of suicide because 'life is devoid of meaning'. She appealed strongly for help, and was afraid of being left alone. It was difficult to converse with her but, finally, she admitted that everything was the consequence of her breaking up with her fiancé a few days earlier. Within a few days she appeared much calmer, although still evasive, whimsical and unpredictable.

She was an intelligent girl who finished high school with ease, but later failed in diverse fields of higher education. She was the second in a family of 4 children. Her father was a college graduate and worked as an administrator. She described him as a warm, pliant and passive man. Her mother was authoritarian and domineering. As a child she was withdrawn and subservient to her mother, but as she grew older she had more open conflicts with her mother.

From the age of 16 on she adopted a hippy life style, frequented rather extravagant bars and experimented with drugs. She had casual sexual relations, that brought little satisfaction, with quite a few men. A year ago, she established a more lasting relationship with an older student who pictured himself as a 'savior'. He directed her to a psychiatrist who, however, didn't meet her demanding and capricious expectations. Sexual relations with her fiancé were markedly sadomasochistic. Her attitude toward him was one of continually challenging behavior to put him to the test. On the one hand she refused to use any contraception, on the other hand she threatened to kill herself if she became pregnant. Demonstrations of an absolute need for support were alternated with aggressive proddings toward a break-up of the relation. When the relationship finally did end, she went into the aforementioned depression.

Partner relations that enjoy official sanction, particularly marriage, can be both sexually and affectively very unsatisfactory. This may lead to a severance of the relation accompanied by a possible depression. In most cases, however, it is the sexual relation that is depreciated and compensatory forms of satisfactions are sought. The husband often finds these outlets in his work; the wife more often finds this compensatory fulfillment in her children. One can also find succour in a return to a parent—child form of relationship. One of the partners then assumes a parental role towards the other; or there may be a re-establishment and revaluation of the relationship with the individual's still living parent. The loss of a parent in these situations often precipitates depression.

A great number of depressions are seen to occur first at middle age when a child marries or leaves home. These events represent the loss of an object which functioned as a narcissistic compensation for a failed marital relation.

The origin of depressions is, undoubtedly, a very complex process in which neurochemical and diverse psychological factors interweave. In the preceding exposition an attempt has been made to underline the important link between disturbances of sexual adaptation and the origin of these syndromes.

4. CONVERSION AND PSYCHOSOMATIC DISORDERS

Clinical experience confronts one regularly with patients presenting diverse somatic complaints which one may assume rest on disturbances in the sexual life of the patient. The formulation of the connection between these sexual disturbances and their somatic expression remains a subject of much controversy. The original conversion theory assumed that energy, originally coupled to libidinous sexual fantasies, was displaced from consciousness and reinvested into somatic functions, in this way producing somatic symptoms. These symptoms may contain a certain symbolic, expressive form which gives reference to the original sexual fantasy.

It is incontestable that this explanatory hypothesis is clearly illustrated in a number of clinical cases. As an explanatory framework for all somatic disturbances of psychic origin, however, this conceptual base is too restricted in scope. The restriction is apparent in two directions. On the one hand, conversion mechanisms are not restricted to sexual symbolic contents (Chodoff, 1974). On the other hand, other types of relation between psychic content and somatic disturbance must be considered, in addition to the concept of somatization of displaced energy bonded to sexual fantasy.

Conversive significance is most clearly apparent in acute or subacute disorders involving adaptation difficulties in the initiation of sexual life and are particularly situated in the genital region. In this category one finds a considerable number of patients with 'honeymoon cystitis' or other 'female complaints' occurring in connection with initial sexual relations which are, due to infantile fixations, experienced as being especially traumatizing. Vomiting or hyperventilation may often be coupled to infantile aversive fantasies about fellatio and oral insemination.

Case 2

A 19-year-old girl was admitted for observation in the department of gynecology. Her complaints were low back and abdominal pain, paired with vulvar pruritus. The possibility of an infection was explored but proved negative. After learning of the negative clinical findings the patient was capricious and defiant in manner. She demanded new tests and emphasized the severity of her symptoms. Back at home, she threatened to leave home and was alternatively aggressive and depressive. She was then referred to a psychiatrist.

Soon it became clear that her complaints could be traced to her first and only sexual experience. This had taken place several months previously, abroad, where she had travelled to learn the local language. She met a boy and after an acquaintance of three weeks they went to bed. She experienced sex as painful, anxiety provoking and unpleasant. Immediately after this happening she returned home and related in a dramatic way her sexual adventure to her puritanical, sixty-year-old mother. Her mother reacted spectacularly with alternating commentaries of disgust and pity.

The patient is the only daughter in a well-placed family. Her parents married rather late (father 41 years and mother 32 years old) and a son was born two years later, who died shortly after birth. After an interval of six years the patient was born. Her mother assumed a domineering and overprotective posture towards her daughter. The father remained in the background and allowed his wife — a nervous, unstable, puritanical woman — full rein in the upbringing of their daughter.

This patient is an intellectually gifted girl who completed high school with a minimum of effort. She was athletic and somewhat of a tom-boy. At the age of fourteen she had a relationship with a boy, six years her senior; they frequently went riding in his sports car. When he approached the patient sexually, she ended the relationship. She enjoyed dating a boy as long as no sexual demands were involved. When she began her university studies she had difficulty in contact with her peers. She complained of 'low morality' and a 'bohemian milieu', and terminated her studies to go abroad and learn a foreign language. After a week away she met the boy with whom she had the aforementioned traumatic sexual experience.

In other nonhysterical syndromes the relation between sexual conflict and somatic symptoms is much more complex. A typical example is anorexia nervosa in which a regressive tendency, provoked by fear of adult feminine maturity, plays an important role. In many chronic gynecologic complaints (Roemer, 1953), tensions arising from chronic sexual inadequacy must be considered. The manner in which sexual frustration leads to chronic tensions in these conditions or to acute exacerbation of them, must be viewed in connection with a number of other psychic mechanisms; pronounced suppression of aggression and a conventionality of attitude, play significant roles. In each case it must be individually determined to which of those factors a dominant role must be ascribed.

5. REPERCUSSION ON THE PARTNER AND CHILDREN

Sexuality is an interaction-process between two people. An insufficiency in sexual adjustment must be considered a disturbance of both partners. The patient who consults his doctor is not, by reason of initial consultation, the most disturbed. The partner who first consults might prove to be the least stoic, defensive and denying; he or she might be in a socially subordinate position or may show the most marked symptoms. This may make one of the partners 'the patient' while one may question whether the disturbance rests chiefly with the noncomplaining or consulting partner.

In this regard one may see partner discordance, including physical violence and a battered wife syndrome, while the greater pathology is to be found in the husband. When similar rage is discharged upon a child, as in the battered-child syndrome, it is the sexual pathology of the partners that manifests itself in injury to the child who, in turn, serves as patient.

In addition to sexual immaturity in both partners, morbid jealousy and a sadistic predilection in the man is considered by Scott (1974) to be an important factor in the battered-wife syndrome. Addictions probably more often co-exist with battering than cause it.

Disequilibrium in the sexual relation of the partners can reflect itself in disturbances in the child. The most extreme case is the battered child as a form of child abuse. In this case, according to Jack (1973), the marriage is the patient. Sexual approaches towards one's own children, leading to incestuous relations, are self-evidently a witness to disturbed sexual relations between parents.

A symbiotic marital relationship mirrors, compounds and fuses earlier pathology to produce the lethal dynamics of child abuse. It is predominantly the frustration of a partnership based on 'rescue-attitudes' which in this form of pathology attains a marked degree of significance.

Certainly, not all disturbances based on an unsatisfactory sexual relationship are so fulminantly manifested. One must also think of the coronary patient married to a frigid hysterical woman or the delicate colitis ulcerosa patient whose rather primitive husband offers so little in the way of tenderness and affection. The disorder described in Case 2 also reflects in a typical way the sexual maladjustment of the parents.

6. SEXUALITY AND TERRITORIALITY

In order to establish an adequate sexual interaction it is necessary that a partner can allow another to share his own and unique privacy, This signifies that the individual must be ready and capable of effectively regulating the aggressive reactions, triggered by the violation of his 'territory'.

In the clinical practice of marital difficulties, one may often erroneously ignore or minimize the regulation of aggression necessary to overcome this invasion of privacy. Sexual failure in the nature of disturbances of potency and frigidity are often significant with respect to securing one's own territory, paired with a suppression of the aggression called forth by the invasion of the 'other' in his territory.

Exercising a limited and regulated exchange of aggression between partners, as the basis of a relaxed sexual interaction, is an essential element of a method such as the 'pairing' of Bach and Deutsch (1971). In this form of therapy, the idea that every sexual contact contains an aggressive element is stressed and it is emphasized that only through an adequate resolution of this aggression is a fulfilling and affective exchange possible.

7. SUMMARY

Sexual maladjustment is considered as a failure in bringing sexual activity to a meaningful and affective form of relational interaction, a mutually satisfying and shared experience among equals.

This failure may express itself in different disturbances, offered as symptoms to the doctor: addiction, depressions, conversion and psychosomatic disorders, and repercussion syndromes in partner or children. On the other hand, complaints about sexual functioning may reflect deficiencies in self-esteem or aggression regulation.

BIBLIOGRAPHY

Amark, C. (1951) *A Study in Alcoholism.* (Munksgaard, Copenhagen.)
Bach, G.R. and Deutsch, R.M. (1971) *Pairing.* (Avon Books, New York.)
Breuer, J. and Freud, S. (1895) *Studiën über Hysterie.* (Deuticke, Leipzig and Wien.)
Chodoff, P. (1974) The diagnosis of hysteria: an overview. *Am. J. Psychiat.* 131: 1073—1078.
Duyckaerts, F. (1964) *La Formation du Lien Sexuel.* (Dessart, Brussels.)
Fenichel, O. (1945) *The Psychoanalytic Theory of Neuroses.* (Norton, New York.)
Freud, S. (1895a) *Uber die Berechtigung von der Neurasthenie einen Bestimmten Symp-*

tomenkomplex als *"Angstneurose' abzutrennen.* Gesammelte Werke I, 313 (Imago, London).

Freud, S. (1895b) *Obsessions et phobies.* Gesammelte Werke I, 343 (Imago, London).

Green, R. (1974) *Sexual Identity Conflict in Children and Adults.* (Basic Books, New York.)

Jack, M.A. (1973) *Marriage, the Murderer in Parents who Kill.* Audio Digest. 2, no. 1 (Los Angeles).

Malzberg, B. (1949) First admission with alcoholic psychoses in New York State. *Quart. J. Stud. Alcohol.* 10: 461—478.

Masters, W.H. and Johnson, V.E. (1970) *Human Sexual Inadequacy.* (Churchill, London.)

Matussek, P. (1959) Süchtige Fehlhaltungen. In: (V. Frankl, V.E. von Gebsattel and J.H. Schultz, Eds) *Handbuch der Neurosenlehre und Psychotherapie,* Vol. II (Urban und Schwarzenberg, München and Berlin) pp. 188—212.

Musaph, H. (1970) *Seksualiteit en Partnerkeuze.* (Erven Bohn, Haarlem.)

Roemer, H. (1953) *Gynäkologische Organneurosen.* (Thieme, Stuttgart.)

Scott, P.D. (1974) Battered wives. *Br. J. Psychiat.* 125: 433—441.

Van Dyk, W.K. (1969) Psychopathologische gezichtspunten in zake excessief gebruik en verslaving. *Feiten* 5 (3) 70—75.

CHAPTER 94

Skin, touch and sex

HERMAN MUSAPH

1. CULTURAL CUSTOMS

It is clear that, in man, the skin plays a predominant role in erotic and sexual contact. This could explain the remarkable fact that there is, in our culture pattern, a strict taboo on certain skin contacts, not only in but also outside the sexual sphere. In the affective sphere one can distinguish between covered and uncovered skin. If skin which is normally covered is revealed, feelings of shame are usually aroused in the person concerned, while a spectator experiences erotic feelings. The sight and displaying of skin which is normally covered awakens feelings in the sexual sphere. In any culture pattern, the rules for ths skin contact we may have with our fellow human beings are firmly laid down. In our culture pattern the handshake is usually the only permissible skin contact between complete strangers. The manner of kissing in public between friends is equally governed by certain rules, depending on the culture pattern and the relationship between the persons concerned.

Furthermore, the way in which people do not have skin contact often expresses a relationship. Thus, the rules determine at what distance from the skin of another a person should remain. This is of great importance for smell contact, since the skin gives off a certain smell which can have strong emotional attraction or repulsion. To a large extent, fashion determines which parts of the skin may be visible. Intuitive judgment of a person is often determined by the way in which he or she is dressed, that is to say the way in which the shape of the body is displayed and accentuated, especially by the relation between covered and uncovered skin.

It is possible to assess the mother—child relationship by the skin contact which the mother has with her child. The same can be said, mutatis mutandis, of the father—child relationship.

From the above it appears that it would be useful to investigate whether, for reasons of mental hygiene, skin contact in our culture pattern should not be better programmed in order to achieve better communication between human beings.

Handbook of Sexology, edited by J. Money and H. Musaph
© *Elsevier/North-Holland Biomedical Press, 1977*

2. BEAUTIFUL AND UGLY SKIN

When seeing someone for the first time one gets an impression which can be rated on a scale ranging from very unfavorable via indifferent to very favorable.

The condition of the skin plays an important part in the forming of this impression. One speaks of a beautiful or an ugly skin and is inclined to let this weigh heavily in the irrational judgment. A beautiful skin is erotic, attractive and awakens in the observer the desire to touch and caress it. The benevolent visual perception is then reinforced by the anticipated pleasant tactile and olfactory perception. Social rules determine whether or not one will actually go on to skin contact of this kind. In our culture pattern contact generally will occur only with children. The same impulse is often felt when one gets the impression of a beautiful head of hair.

An ugly skin awakens in the observer all sorts of negative feeling. The judgment of the personality depends to a large extent on such feeling. We call this phenomenon in human communications the halo phenomenon. The classic example of this is the judgment of another person who is suffering from acne vulgaris. This is a skin disorder in which pimples appear on the face, mainly during or after puberty. In the face, chest, top part of the back, and upper arms there are sebaceous follicles which begin to develop in puberty, stimulated by androgenic hormones. This development is coupled with an increase in the production of sebum. Free fatty acids are responsible for the perifollicular symptoms of inflammation in acne vulgaris. The entire mechanism is not yet known; specifically there is as yet no satisfactory explanation of the fact that the acne usually disappears after adolescence. The belief is still fairly widely held among laymen that acne vulgaris in adolescents is the proof of the existence of masturbation conflicts. Extensive research has shown that there is absolutely no causal connection between the occurrence of acne vulgaris and the appearance of surface total lipids on the one hand and the existence of an emotional conflict situation on the other (Kraus, 1970).

Since every skin disease gives the observer the impression that the skin, and by extension the person under this skin, is 'ugly', feelings of shame, inferiority and aversion are projected on to the skin disease by the skin patient as well as the observer. Also, since shame and inferiority are closely associated in our culture pattern with sexual feelings, it is obvious that patient and observer associate an ugly skin with 'dirty', and sexual inferiority. A beautiful skin is on the other hand associated with sexual superiority, great attractiveness and charm. The halo phenomenon also plays a part in fetishistic and antifetishistic responses in human contacts. Fetishistic features are sexually stimulating and provoking and have a symbolic significance. For instance, though fetishism is not imperative to their sexual arousal, there are people who become extremely excited sexually by seeing underwear. If one leaves aside the possible psychopathology of human sexual behavior, one can say that a beautiful skin or beautiful hair, form a fetishistic feature for the observer. That is to say, he or she can be strongly stimulated erotically by the beautiful skin or hair. One can also speak of an antifetishistic feature when the observer is repulsed erotically precisely because of these attributes of hair and skin.

It will be clear that these fetishistic features do not occur exclusively in the visual sphere. The smell of someone's skin, the look in the eye, the walk, can also have a certain influence. Here immense personal differences occur, which are of great interpsychic significance in human interaction. At the same time these factors clearly fluctuate in intensity in the life of one individual. A well-known example of this fluctuation is that a 3-year-old girl can become sexually excited by seeing a penis, while the same organ can have an antifetishistic effect on the same girl seven years later. In general, one can say that in our culture pattern, since most people are dressed, near nudity usually produces stronger sexual stimulation in the observer than total nudity does. By contrast, the sexual stimulation in a nudist camp is decidedly less than on the beach, where people wear a minimum of clothing. Nonetheless it is probably the partial revealing of the breasts and pubic hair and the surrounding area of a woman which cause the strongest and most titillating sexual stimulation in heterosexual males. In homosexual males it is the bulge of the genitals and the buttocks of men which are sexually exciting. In females, we think the whole figure of the sex object is more important.

In many people, the experiencing of sexual feelings goes hand in hand with certain fears. If these fears are not too strong they can be experienced as positive and pleasurable. One thinks here of the enjoyment of horror films and the experiencing of sexual adventures which are not entirely free from danger. The experiencing of erotic and sexual feelings depends to a large extent on the possibility of allowing fantasy a free rein, so that there is an element of wish fulfillment for the individual concerned. It is for this reason that people can be erotically stimulated by tight-fitting clothes, which reveal the shape of the body, without actually being able to see the skin. Movements of the body can then at the time awaken associations with sexual foreplay and intercourse. It is because of this that watching people dancing, particularly dancing couples, can be so pleasant.

3. TOUCH

It is difficult to overestimate the emotional value of touch in interhuman contact. It begins with the skin contact between the newborn baby and his mother and finds expression many times a day in the handshake. In human interaction, skin contact can be the expression of deeper feelings, which cannot be verbalized. People in love walk hand in hand as an expression of the unity each experiences with the other. The handshake of a more senior person expresses power. Between these extremes there lies a scale of possibilities for human expression.

Years ago the Queen took her then 8-year-old daughter on a visit to the zoo. The little girl saw an animal which caught her interest and left her mother for a moment to look in the cage. Another visitor to the zoo who recognized the princess and wanted to be friendly, stroked her hair. The Queen was furious, went over to the friendly man and said: "On ne touche pas une princesse d'Orange!" (You shouldn't touch a princess of Orange). The touch of a common citizen could rob the princess of her dignity — could degrade her magically. An example of the other side of the coin is the expression of feelings of contempt by refusing to take someone's outstretched hand. The experiencing of skin contact with another person is at the same time the experiencing of his sympathy, his love. The beating of the skin is, in many cultures, an expression of rage, and is undergone as a punishment.

The taboo on touching, as expressed in certain culture systems of human interaction, underlines the inability to achieve genuine emotional contact and creates a gap which cannot be bridged. One could put forward the idea that the isolation of the individual in our achievement-orientated society can be measured by the impoverishment of skin contacts. Older people, who are gradually becoming increasingly isolated, are having less and less skin contact with their fellow human beings.

4. SKIN CONTACT IN MOTHER—CHILD RELATIONSHIP

The differences in the mother—child relationship and the father—child relationship can best be judged by the way in which the child is held, particularly while it is still very small. In a good mother—child relationship there will be a maximum contact between the hands of the mother and the skin of the child on her lap. The mother's hands are completely open, with the fingers slightly curved in the relaxed position. If the relationship between the mother and child is not so good, then she will hold her child with clenched fingers. In particular, the left hand of a right-handed person, and vice versa, will betray the fear of contact. In extreme cases we may find the mother expressing her unconscious aversion and negative feelings towards the child on her lap by hitting it, pinching it and boxing it with her left hand — and all this while she is completely unaware of what she is doing. At the other end of the scale is the behavior of the mother who uses her left hand to stroke, fondle and caress the child in the same way she strokes, fondles and caresses her sexual partner. One can make similar observations in the father—child relationship.

The skin contact between mother and child was systematically researched by René Spitz (1965) on children suffering from infantile eczema. He found with these patients that the mother of an eczemateous child has difficulty in touching it, because she often has repressed aggressive feelings and feelings of guilt towards her child. Only too often the mother feels that it is her fault that the child has a skin disease. She can give these guilt feelings, which are almost always neurotic in nature, all sorts of content, depending on her life history. These mothers are often relieved if other women pay a lot of attention to their child and handle the diseased skin. Thus there exists a certain taboo on touching in precisely that phase of life when the child needs extra skin contact. It is then made extra difficult for the child to identify with the mother, which can impede normal emotional development.

There are indications that one of the most important factors in this emotional development is skin contact. Harlow and Harlow's researches (1962) on rhesus monkeys showed clearly that if these animals are separated from the mother, shortly after birth, they will cling to a dummy covered with a towel fabric, but not to a dummy made of wire in which two nipples with bottles of monkey's milk are fastened. In the human child, too, skin contact in the first years of life is of immense importance in the formation of attachment behavior between the child and its mother.

Spitz carried out his investigations in children with infantile eczema. One could raise the objection that the strong need of skin contact is mainly present in children with a dermatosis. Although this is certainly correct, children with a healthy skin have also a fundamental need for skin contact. On the other hand, children with a dermatosis who are neglected by their mother in their stronger demand for skin contact, need help to prevent a disturbance in their emotional development. I can give the following practical example: children who are suffering from infantile eczema can be rubbed with a medicated cream or lotion. If the child is neglected by the mother in tactile contact I prescribe a cream which has to be used 5 or 6 times instead of once a day. The advantage of this prescription is clear: the caressing of the skin will take place much more frequently, which is of great importance for the dermatosis and the child. There are many mothers, who are still childlike themselves, who have to be taught how to caress and touch their baby. The skin contact behavior pattern is part of the mother's social learning process. She will demonstrate, without realizing it, how she has been treated by her own mother. To change her pattern of behavior one must combat an archaic, rigid pattern (Klaus et al., 1970).

It seems justifiable to conclude that people in our society must develop another strategy in order to achieve better skin contact in our culture pattern between mother and child in the first years of life. This seems to be essential for a more healthy emotional development of the child. We shall have to try and lift the taboo on the touching of large areas of our skin. It is unfortunately true that in playing with children in our culture, only that part of the skin is stroked which remains uncovered in adults. In tropical and subtropical regions, children are more pampered in their skin contact with others. Thus, the nearly naked child may be carried on the bare back of one of the parents or a sister. The child is then regularly comforted by the warm touch of the skin of the adult. This must awaken and maintain a feeling of trust, belonging and acceptance.

If one takes as one's starting point the idea that an extension of the skin contact between mother and child is very desirable in our culture pattern, one should advise all young mothers to offer a bare breast at every feed, even bottle-feeds, as a surface of contact with the nearly naked or naked baby. I would even maintain that the great advantage of breast-feeding over bottle-feeding is the better skin contact given by the mother's bare breast (Musaph, 1969; Newton, 1971). This can then be a positive factor in the formation of the child's attachment behavior (Bowlby, 1969), which in itself is a positive factor in normal emotional development.

5. MASSAGE

A clear example of a taboo which in our pattern of culture lies on large regions of our skin is massage. Until recently, people were massaged only if suffering from muscular pains or rheumatism or if competing in sports. In other peoples, for example the Japanese, this is totally different. Even an erotic massage is considered as normal for everyone. In our culture pattern this is only done in massage parlors, which are considered as hidden or public brothels. Independent of the physiotherapeutic value, massage has undoubtedly a psychological effect by the sensory intimacy of skin contact between two people. For this reason, massage therapy can provoke anxiety relating to sexuality and nudity. If this anxiety is strong, the person who is massaged will constrain himself. If the anxiety can be overcome, the massaged person will be able to enjoy sensual pleasure without sexual involvement. Then an empathy between the masseur and the massaged comes into being, which can be part of a psychotherapeutic process.

Actually during massage, many people take courage to confess spontaneously just as during narcoanalysis. Skin contact including mild pleasure and intense communication feeling is then the ambiance in which abreaction or catharsis is possible. The person who is weak in personal contact can often be helped by intensive skin contact in order to learn to communicate. One can speak literally of a psychophysical treatment. There are indications that, especially in depressive persons, massage of the neck and the lumbar area facilitates the working of the classical antidepressive drugs (Maurer-Groeli, 1973). I think this phenomenon might be explained from regressive attitudes which can appear during therapy. As a result infantile primary reactions can be reactivated.

According to Bowlby (1969), attachment behavior has been defined as seeking and maintaining proximity to another individual. Massage is a method to advance this proximity.

6. TOUCHING IN PSYCHOTHERAPY

Recently various techniques of group therapy have been developed, in which skin contact is used as a method to improve emotional contact and socialization, and to decrease anxiety. It is assumed that via skin contact with members of the group, better self-acceptance can be reached. Improvement of a disturbed body-image may ensue. It is quite understandable that, in group therapy, a member of the group who dares to express his real feelings is loudly praised by the other members of the group with touching and caressing (Bindrim, P. 1968; Rogers, 1973).

The technique of skin contact varies from touching the normally uncovered skin, via touching the covered skin, to touching the naked body. One can differ in opinion about the therapeutic value of these various techniques. The success of treatment is not dependent solely on the quantity of the skin surface which is touched during the therapeutic sessions. In my opinion time has not yet come to give a final evaluation of these touching techniques. Nonetheless, it is clear that skin contact in psychotherapy can be used in the growth of a normal and disturbed emotional development. The normal resistances which belong to the introduction of these not yet sufficiently tested techniques are reinforced by our social taboos on touching. One could ask oneself why it is generally accepted that a gynecologist can touch a woman and why a psychotherapist should not employ touching techniques (Forer, 1969; Mintz, 1969).

7. TOUCHING IN DYING PATIENTS

There is another group of patients for which skin contact is essential, namely the dying patients. When dealing with a dying patient, I make a plea for a maximum skin contact. I point out to the nurse or the relatives who might be present, the possibility of taking the hands of the dying patient and to caress them. For the patient it must be beneficial to undergo this vital contact, whether he has a decreased consciousness or not. It is not difficult to succeed in calming down a disturbed and disquieted dying patient by caressing the hands and head. People are used to doing these things only in an intimate situation, which implies that, by doing so, one transfers a feeling of sympathy, of being at home. One may consider it a welcome addition to the 'bedside manner' if one could overcome resistance to applying this touching to unfamiliar people as well.

8. AGEING AND TOUCH

In our culture pattern adult sexual behavior is mainly seen as genital contact. Aged people have full right in a sexual life in which genital contact is not the main contact. Here the skin contact will play an important role, and sexuality becomes more and more identical with sensitivity.

9. SUMMARY

The skin is the organ with which human beings can express and experience their erotic and sexual feelings. In our culture pattern there is still a taboo on the touching of certain parts of the skin, even without sexual implication. Within any given culture pattern there are hard and fast rules governing the skin contact one may have with one's fellow man. The way in which we judge other people depends to a great extent on the way in which we experience their skin — the halo phenomenon. For example, acne vulgaris is often wrongly associated with masturbation.

The emotional value of touching in human contact is difficult to overestimate. The isolation of the individual in our achievement-orientated society can be measured by the impoverishment of skin contact. The mother—child relationship can be judged by the skin contact which the mother has with her child. A good relationship is expressed in optimum skin contact, a bad relationship in minimum contact. In particular, the left hand of a right-handed caretaker can betray the emotional relationship as either negative or positive. It is to be recommended in our culture pattern that the young mother be taught to improve skin contact with her baby in order to advance the baby's emotional development. It is advised that mothers who bottle-feed their baby's should offer the bottle while the child is held against the mother's bare breast, as if the child were being breast-fed.

Recently touching has been introduced in various techniques of psychotherapy, especially in groups. The psychotherapeutic influence of massage has not yet been finally evaluated. Touching in aged people plays an important role in their sexual life. One can help dying people, calming them by caressing their hands and head.

BIBLIOGRAPHY

Bindrim, P. (1968) A report on a nude marathon. *Psychother.: Theory, Res. Pract.*, 5: 3180—3188.

Bowlby, J. (1969) *Attachment and Loss. Vol. 1: Attachment.* (Hogarth Press, London.)

Forer, B.R. (1969) The taboo against touching in psychotherapy. *Psychother. Theory, Res. Pract.*, 6: 229—231.

Harlow, H.F. and Harlow, M.K. (1962) Social deprivation in monkeys. *Sci. Am.* 473: 1—11.

Klaus, M.H., Kennell, J.H., Plumb, N. and Zuehlke, S. (1970) Human maternal behavior at the first contact with her young. *Pediatrics*, 46: 187—192.

Kraus, S.J. (1970) Stress, acne and skin surface free fatty acids. *Psychosom. Med.* 32: 503—308.

Maurer-Groeli, Y.A. (1973) *Zur Begründung und Indikationsstellung der Massage in der Therapie depressiver Patienten.* (Ciba-Geigy A.G. Med. Diss. 186., Basle.)

Mintz, E.E. (1969) On the rationale of touch in psychotherapy. *Psychother.: Theory, Res. Parct.*, 6: 232—234.

Musaph, H. (1969) Aggression and symptom formation in dermatology. *J. Psychosom. Res.* 13: 257—264.

Musaph, H. (1974) The role of aggression in somatic symptom formation. *Int. J. Psychiat. Med.* 5: 449—460.

Newton, N. (1971) Psychological differences between breast and bottle feeding. *Am. J. Clin. Nutr.*, 24: 993—1004.

Rogers, C.R. (1973) *Encounter Groups.* (Pelican Books, Harmondsworth.)

Spitz, R. (1965) *The First Year of Life.* (Int. Univ. Press, New York.)

CHAPTER 95

Unusual sexual behavior of nonhuman primates

TERRY MAPLE

1. INTRODUCTION

Primates in general

The sexual behavior of primates is currently receiving much attention from life scientists. The result has been the accumulation of useful data regarding characteristic sexual habits throughout the primate order, from prosimians to *Homo sapiens*. With the establishment of norms there followed a description and explanation of unusual modes of sexual conduct. This chapter is an attempt to provide such a description with respect to both captive and free-ranging nonhuman primates, leaving clinicians and behavioral scientists to draw comparisons that might apply to humans.

Primate species

It should be recognized that an unusual pattern for primates in general may be a pattern fairly common for a particular species. Similarly, a given behavior pattern may be idiosyncratic to a particular group within a species or to a particular member of a group. Captivity may also strengthen some behavior which occurs with less frequency in nature. In some species, reproductive maturity, for example, appears to be advanced in captivity as compared to the wild (see Maple et al., 1973). In this chapter, therefore, unusual is used as a catch-all term for behavior which is not generally well described, well known or well understood. With respect to sexual behavior, unusual behavior patterns are explainable and seem to be, in many cases, functional in the given context of expression.

Handbook of Sexology, edited by J. Money and H. Musaph
© *Elsevier/North-Holland Biomedical Press, 1977*

2. EARLY EXPERIENCE

Sexual encounters

Sexual behavior does not miraculously appear when a monkey or ape reaches sexual maturity. Prior experience with other animals is necessary for the proper sequence of behavior to develop. Erwin and Mitchell (1975) studied the first heterosexual encounters of twelve 3-year-old rhesus monkeys, and observed the occurrence of both aggressive and affiliative responses. While the initial responses of most of the subjects were awkward and uncoordinated, appropriate behavior leading to sexual intercourse was eventually acquired through repeated efforts. The fact that adequate sexual posturing was acquired so quickly in these heterosexually naive subjects was thought to be the result of prior experience with a 'like-sexed' animal.

3. DEPRIVATION EFFECTS

Lack of early social experience

Sexual development is greatly affected by a lack of early social experience. Harlow (1962) demonstrated that rhesus monkeys reared on surrogate mothers without early peer experience were incapable of reproduction. Even after group therapy on a 'zoo island' little change was noted in their sexual proclivities. Similar results have been obtained with captive chimpanzees (Rogers and Davenport, 1969).

Adult sexual behavior

In a major study of adult sexual behavior, Senko (1966) studied both male and female rhesus monkeys reared under three conditions: (1) in a feral environment and brought to the lab prior to puberty; (2) in wire cages without peer contact for 18—24 or 48 months; and (3) on cloth surrogates without peer contact for 18—24 or 48 months.

Laboratory rearing

In heterosexual tests with sophisticated partners, all laboratory rearing conditions produced inadequate female sexual behavior. For example, laboratory females exhibited more self-clasping and self-directed aggression, and directed more hostility toward their male partners than did feral monkeys. Laboratory-reared females also received lower scores for grooming their partners, adequate sexual posturing, willingness to support the male during copulation, and insemination success.

In laboratory males, self-clasping, self-biting and partner-directed hostility were more frequent. In these animals there were fewer sexual initiations, more episodes of sexual unresponsiveness, little thrusting during copulation, and little success at insemination as compared with feral subjects. In frequency of penile erection and autoeroticism, however, laboratory males proved to be as aroused sexually as feral males. Apparently, laboratory rearing did not destroy sexual motivation, but produced abnormalities in performance of precopulatory and copulatory behavior (Sackett, 1968). Peer deprivation appeared to be more devastating in its effects on males as compared to females.

Deprivation acts
The abnormalities discussed by Sackett have been classified as deprivation acts (Berkson, 1967); the most bizarre of which is self-biting. However, Erwin and co-workers (1973) found that self-biting occurred in captive animals which had not experienced severe deprivation. In addition, they described the case of an adult male which, despite severe self-biting during copulation bouts, succeeded in carrying out the characteristic mounting sequence to ejaculation (Maple et al., 1973).

Reproductive problems of captive apes

A lack of early social experience is especially troublesome in zoo-raised anthropoid apes. Judging from field observations (Schaller, 1963; MacKinnon, 1974; McGinnis, pers. commun.) and films of sexually active captive groups (Hess, 1972), young apes are especially interested in the mating activity of adults. * In many cases, copulations take place with the young clinging to the mother's back. Sham copulations between young animals often take place at an early age, suggesting the need for peer contact as well as the observation of adult interactions (see Fig. 2). Apes reared by humans typically exhibit little sexual interest in their own kind (Land, 1972). It is difficult but not impossible to obtain a recovery of sexual interest in other apes. In this regard, Lang's words are instructive: "... a female chimpanzee, which had grown up in our collection in the company of juvenile orangs and gorillas, was presented with a mate. The mate, a strong, healthy animal, had been raised with other juvenile chimpanzees; he had not experienced any sexual behavior. After an initial period of apparent indifference, the two made friends but that was all. The female regularly came into heat but neither animal reacted. Some time later an experienced 14-year-old female, acquired from the London Zoo, was introduced to the pair. During her very first heat in Basel she taught the male to copulate."

---

* De Benedictis (1973) has suggested that young monkeys may also obtain much of their sexual knowledge by observation of others' sexual activity (see Fig. 1).

Fig. 1. Oral—genital contact between a male (top) and female gorilla. Note the interest of the younger male to the right (photo by W. Angst and J.P. Hess).

Fig. 2. Sham copulatory movements directed by immature male gorilla to adult male. Interactions of this kind are thought to be an important component in the sexual development of this species (photo by W. Angst and J.P. Hess).

Self-sucking

An especially difficult problem with young animals raised without their mothers is the development of self-sucking. Both digit sucking and penis sucking are acts which apparently develop in response to the lack of nipple contact (Berkson, 1968). Because self-sucking becomes so habitual, available peers are generally ignored and social maturation of behavior is arrested (Maple and Laub, 1975). A lack of nipple contact is also blamed for the development of other-directed penis-sucking in an infant female raised with an adult male rhesus monkey (Gomber and Mitchell, 1974).

While young animals may penis-suck as a nipple substitute, older animals apparently do so for purposes of sexual stimulation. Other forms of auto-eroticism such as scrotum sucking, scrotum clasping, rectum manipulation ('reaching behind'), stereotyped masturbation, ejaculate eating, and 'agonistic' masturbation have been observed in idiosyncracies of isolate-reared adult male rhesus monkeys (Fittinghoff et al., 1974).

4. MASTURBATION

In males

Many examples of self-stimulation in nonhuman primates have been reported. For example, males appear to masturbate more often than females — a statistic which agrees with our knowledge of humans (Ford and Beach, 1951). Although Hamilton (1914) considered nonhuman primate masturbation to be abnormal, it occurs in free-ranging as well as captive animals. Carpenter (1942b) observed male masturbation to ejaculation by wild rhesus monkeys on three occasions: "By a priori reasoning it was expected that masturbation would be observed in isolated males or immature males . . . [however] during this study three observed instances of self-stimulation to the point of ejaculation occurred in adult, mature males during association with females!"

In a recent study of free-ranging rhesus monkeys, Lindburg (1967) saw males masturbating while being groomed by females. Masturbation by males also occurred during those times when female interest was low (Neville, 1966; Agar and Mitchell, 1975). Among new world primates, Spider monkeys (*Ateles geoffroyi*) also masturbate, using their prehensile tail to stimulate themselves. Observing animals in a two-acre enclosure, Hanby and colleagues (1971) recorded 27 episodes of masturbation in Japanese macaques (*Macaca fuscata*) during the breeding season. In this group, 13 of the 19 males known to ejaculate with females also masturbated to ejaculation, despite the presence of 22 receptive females. The copulation rate remained high during this period, but apparently did not inhibit masturbation.

In females

While sexual pleasure can be realized by females through the active mounting of other conspecifics, masturbation by females has been rarely observed in most species. However, Chevalier-Skolnikoff (1974) observed considerable masturbation in her captive stumptailed females. An interesting example of cooperative masturbation occurs with some regularity in a captive adult male orangutan (*Pongo pygamaeus*) which resides at the Sacramento Zoo in California. On many occasions he has been observed masturbating in proximity to his female cagemate. During these episodes he often clasped the female's hand, drew it towards his genitalia and holding it there, completed the masturbation sequence to ejaculation.

Motivation for masturbation

The motivation for masturbation is subject to some disagreement. Citing Yerkes, Ford and Beach (1951) have written that masturbation in adulthood is exclusively a substitute for sexual intercourse, with a likelihood of disappearance when a mature heterosexual partner is accessible. Phoenix and Jensen (1973) found evidence of a high incidence of ejaculation, in the absence of a female partner, which was unrelated to concurrent tests of sexual behavior with females. In addition, ejaculation in the home cage within 22 h, or less, of sex tests did not affect the frequency of ejaculation with female partners. Regarding the outcome of this study, the authors' concluding remarks are especially informative: "An extreme example of the range of variables that influence ejaculation was seen in one of our sperm donors. Male rhesus need to be restrained when electrodes are attached to the penis. After repeated trials, the animals put up little resistance to the procedure. The male in question, however, presented a problem as a sperm donor because he ejaculated the moment he was restrained and before the experimenter could properly position the sterile tube in which semen was usually connected. This behavior resembles an extreme case of human ejaculatio praecox and suggests that a learning process is involved in controlling the response. The behavior of this animal is only a few conditioned responses removed from that of our male which was prompted to masturbate when other males were being taken to the test room for their daily test of sexual behavior."

5. HOMOSEXUAL BEHAVIOR

Mounting

While homosexual mounting in primates is often displayed in a nonsexual context such as dominance or greeting rituals, sexually motivated inter actions have been reported under both field and laboratory conditions. In the rhesus monkey (*Macaca mulatta*), homosexual behavior appears to be more common in males than in females (Carpenter, 1942a; Kaufmann, 1967). However, Loy (1970) observed a 3-year-old female mount a fully adult female in a series of fifteen mounts and partial mounts. Carpenter (1942b) observed eight different females engaged in homosexual activity, reaching the following conclusions about female homosexual behavior:

(i) The female who plays the masculine role in a pair attacks the subordinate or receptive female in a manner similar to the way in which males normally attack females prior to mating, and subsequently these active females carry out irregular successions of mounting with the receptive females.

(ii) The observations show that the female who is mounted is usually more strongly motivated for sexual behavior than is the mounter.

(iii) Homosexual behavior may occur along with, preceding, or following normal heterosexual behavior.

(iv) In two cases sexual receptivity (quasi-estrus) to an animal of the same sex occurred after an interval of time within the range of a normal menstrual cycle. This may have been a fertile cycle, and homosexual behavior may have occurred during a period of early pregnancy.

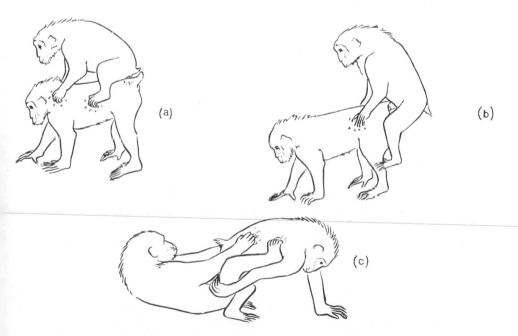

Fig. 3. (a) Female—female homosexual mounting posture of *M. arctoides* (b) the common heterosexual coital position and (c) a supine position observed during both heterosexual coitus and female—female homosexual interactions (drawings by S. Chevalier-Skolnikoff, 1974).

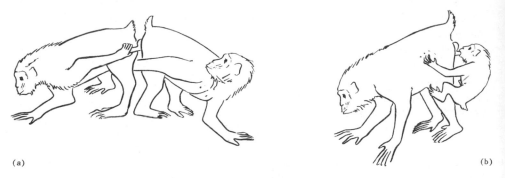

Fig. 4. (a) Mutual presentations with manual genital stimulation between two male *M. arctoides* and (b) mounting with unilateral oral genital stimulation between two males (drawings by S. Chevalier-Skolnikoff, 1974).

Male and female

More recently, Chevalier-Skolnikoff (1974) reported both female and male homosexual behavior in captive stumptailed monkeys (*Macaca arctoides* Figs. 3 and 4). In females, oral—genital stimulation in a variety of postures was observed, as well as mounting behavior for the purposes of genital stimulation. This latter behavior has been observed in many other species including baboons (Zuckerman, 1933; Bolwig, 1959; Anthoney, 1968; Kummer, 1968), tree shrews (Michael et al., 1974), vervet monkeys (Gartlan, 1969), talapoin monkeys (Wolfheim and Rowell, 1972), pigtail monkeys (Tokuda et al., 1968), chimpanzees (Goodall, 1965) and gorillas (Hess, 1973). Many of these female mounting episodes were directed toward males, suggesting that genital stimulation is not specifically homosexual in character. While similar behavior occurs in the wild and is, therefore, unlikely to be an artifact of captivity, its frequency may be changed under captive conditions (Michael et al., 1974).

Oral—genital manifestations

Male homosexuality in Chevalier-Skolnikoff's (1974) stumptailed group was also characterized by oral—genital manipulation. Some of the postures assumed for reciprocal and simultaneous stimulation are especially bizarre in comparison to the known repertoire of other species. In this same colony, confirmed episodes of anal penetration during male—male interactions have been reported. Erwin and Maple (1976) have also described anal penetration between two male rhesus monkeys. In this pair, the animals were united for a period of 19 months after 8 months of life with their mothers. Both animals exhibited normal heterosexual mating behavior when paired with females. On several occasions, however, when the subjects were reunited with each other, reciprocal mounting with anal penetration was observed. In a study of partner preference, the two males were introduced into a cage containing a receptive female. Both males exhibited aggression toward the female, but directed sexual and grooming behavior toward each other.

6. OBJECT-DIRECTED SEXUAL BEHAVIOR

Cloth-covered models

In a recent study by Deutsch and Larsson (1974), rhesus monkeys reared on cloth-covered surrogate mothers were exposed to a stationary cloth-covered model. All four of these subjects (two males, two females) displayed sexual behavior toward the model. The males repeatedly mounted the model, with one of the males ejaculating while both females presented themselves to the model. The surrogate-reared males proved to be sexually inadequate when allowed access to normally reared females. Apparently, these animals had a specific behavioral attachment to the inanimate model that did not prepare them adequately for the complexities of social interactions with animate peers.

Objects or surfaces

Objects or surfaces have occasionally been used for the purposes of genital stimulation. For example, Ford and Beach (1951) describe a full-grown chimpanzee which placed a mango upon her external genitalia. Unable to achieve the proper amount of stimulation, she then placed the mango on the floor, sat down upon it, and twisted and rubbed against it continually. In the same publication the authors include a quote by Bingham (1928): "On another occasion, Malapalga inserted the stem of a leaf . . . (in her vagina), then turned posteriorly to the bars of the cage and swayed back and forth. The leaf was thus pushed from bar to bar. As it slipped from one bar to the next there was set up considerable vibration in the stem, to which the inner walls of the vagina were evidently sensitive. In these scattered observations on masturbatory practices there is evidence of experimental procedure . . . The variety of methods employed by the female chimpanzee is especially significant."

7. BIRTH PROCESS AS SEXUAL STIMULUS

Observation of birth process

An interesting observation by Mitchell and Brandt (1975) concerned the stimulating effects of the birth process on an observing male rhesus monkey. In this case, a $3\frac{1}{2}$-year-old rhesus monkey was present at the birth of an infant of which he was the biological father: "The young pair of parents had been housed together for the full term of the pregnancy, from conception through birth. Prior to delivery the young male, who was socially reared in the laboratory, had an erection and attempted to mount the female. The female did not present and the male thrusted against her back three or four times. Throughout the labor, the male frequently yawned, carefully approached the female, and looked intently at the female's vagina. He frequently pushed the female's body into a different position so that he could inspect her posterior ... He attempted to touch the infant but the female again withdrew and grimaced, after which the frustrated male shook the cage and settled down for a while to a brief bout of self-grooming and some self-directed sexual behavior."

Sensory stimuli

Gouzoules (1974) has also reported sexual arousal at delivery by an alpha male stumptailed macaque and several high-ranking juveniles, suggesting a 'confusion of olfactory and/or other signals that are present during delivery with some that are present in the estrous female'.

8. GENERALIZATION OF AFFECTION

Alien species in freedom

A most unusual event in free-living nonhuman primates is the expression of affection or sexual interest toward a member of an alien species (Fig. 5).

Fig. 5. A young orangutan (left) investigates a young gorilla. Reared with a member of an alien species, as is often the case in zoos, an animal may develop a preference for the alien species over its own species (San Diego Zoo photo).

Episodes of this kind have been observed, but the variables which affect interspecies social behavior are not well studied (Maple, 1974c).

In captivity

Primates are especially gregarious animals under all conditions, wild or captive. The following examples indicate the potential for interacting with other species when social contact is possible.

Laboratory experiments with monkeys

Hamilton (1914) conducted a series of laboratory experiments which were designed to examine the natural sexual tendencies of monkeys. His subjects were 18 macaques and 2 baboons. Hamilton observed mutual lip-smacking and frequent copulations between his macaques and his baboons. When the female baboon and her macaque consort were separated, both of the subjects reacted aggressively if another mate was introduced to the other within view.

Primates and nonprimates

In addition to the relationships established between baboons and macaques, Hamilton experimented with the reactions of his animals to nonprimate species. At the introduction of a snake, kitten, puppy, and fox, each of the male animals exhibited curiosity and eventually manifest sexual responses toward the stranger. On several occasions, one of the female macaques accepted intromission from a mature dog. *

Recent laboratory experiments have clearly demonstrated the social flexbility of primates (Maple, 1975a). Mason and Kenney (1974) raised infant rhesus monkeys with dog surrogates. Observations of the monkeys' behavior during the cohabitation period revealed that the monkeys displayed the 'basic features of attachment described by Bowlby, Cairns and others''. Through the use of choice tests, Mason and Kenney clearly demonstrated that a prior social bond with a conspecific does not preclude the formation of a new attachment to a member of an alien species.

Maple (1974a) studied interactions between a baboon (P. anubis) and a rhesus monkey in both the laboratory and outdoor cage, and followed the development of sexual responsiveness for nearly two years in a long-term study of an adult heterosexual relationship (Maple et al., 1975). The baboon female was aggressive and the male rhesus avoided social contact with her for the first six months. Eventually, however, they exhibited mutual grooming and tolerance of proximity, and after one year of cohabitation, ngaged in sexual intercourse (Fig. 6). Subsequently, sexual behavior became

---

Hediger (1950) observed that if animals are reared from infancy with an alien species, exual responses may be directed towards these alien species and, where reproductive proesses are compatible, as between Alpaca and Vicuna, hybridization may occur.

Fig. 6. An adult male rhesus monkey copulates with an adult female baboon. Animals which exhibit similar expressions and postures are likely to find it easier to communicate and develop strong social attachments (photo by T. Maple).

exceedingly frequent and enthusiastic, and it coincided with a change in the male's aggressiveness. Where he was previously subordinate to the baboon, he has recently become at least co-equal.

Baboon—rhesus pairs

Maple (1974b) also studied groups of younger homosexual and heterosexual baboon—rhesus pairs, and observed episodes of sexual intercourse which occurred in both groups. The results of these experiments were contrary to a statement by Abernethy (1974) that "female dominance inhibits male copulation".

In the wild

Rowell (1966) described a baboon troop in southern Africa in which a single vervet monkey travelled and actively groomed other members of the troop. She also observed copulation between the vervet and baboons, despite the fact that baboons sometimes preyed on vervet monkeys (Rowell, pers. commun.)

Possibly this particular animal was stolen as an infant by a baboon female, and grew up in the troop as an acceptable conspecific.

Kummer (1968) conducted a field experiment in which four *Papio hamadryas* females were transferred into a group of *P. anubis*. None of the mature anubis males copulated with the hamadryas females, although, when in estrus, the females were consorted by juvenile anubis males.

Nagel (1973), working with Kummer, recently described interspecific interactions between hamadryas and anubis baboons in which hybrids were produced. In agreement with the views of Kummer on 'abduction', Nagel describes the behavior of a female anubis baboon: "On October 31, 1968, an adult anubis female, which I had not encountered in the five previous days of close group observation, appeared in the hamadryas group on the west side of the hybrid zone (group C5). The next day, I saw her in close association with a young adult hamadryas male which had no other females. Since I was not able to recognize all the male group members individually, it was not clear whether this male was a newcomer or a group member; the group, however, did not treat him like a stranger. On November 6, there was a fight between the 'owner' and two other hamadryas males over the anubis female, which the 'owner' won. Until the end of the field study the pair remained in group C5, with the anubis female following her leader like a hamadryas female. It seems likely that the pure anubis females which were seen in other hamadryas and hybrid groups had been 'imported' by young group males in the same way".

Nagel failed to discover any evidence that anubis × hamadryas crosses occurred in anubis groups. Although hamadryas males were found within anubis groups, no estrous mating was observed. It is also apparent that anubis males do not consort with hamadryas females, even though individuals were occasionally observed to be in contact with hamadryas groups. One of the mechanisms which seems to prevent male anubis from capturing hamadryas females appears to be the strong attachment of the hamadryas female to her conspecific harem leaders.

Interactions between baboons (*P. anubis*) and chimpanzees have been reported by Goodall (1965). An especially remarkable event has been described in which an adult male chimpanzee directed species-typical courtship gestures toward an adult female baboon. The baboon responded by assuming her species-typical sexual presenting posture which, in turn, stimulated the chimp to push her into a position approximating that of a chimpanzee present posture (Goodall, pers. commun.). Similarly, Bauer (pers. commun.) has observed sexual behavior between adolescent chimps and adolescent baboons at Goodall's Gombe Research Center in Tanzania.

Richard (1970) recently reported attempted interspecies copulation between a young male cebus (*Cebus capucinus*) and a female spider monkey (*Ateles geoffroyi*). It is surprising, given the close proximity of overlapping new world species, that so few reports of naturally occurring interactions exist (but see Maple and Westlund, 1975).

Hybridization

Maples and McKern (1967) discovered several baboon groups in Kenya which included yellow (*P. cynocephalus*) × olive (*P. anubis*) hybrids. This report, like that of Fooden (1964) on crab-eating (*M. irus*) × rhesus (*M. mulatta*) hybrids, offers few behavioral data. In fact, few reports of primate hybrids of any variety contain behavioral data, for example, Gijzen (1973) gives 12 comparative categories and lists, none of which is behavioral.

While naturally occurring hybrids are rare, many combinations have been produced under captive conditions, most of which were mistakes. Gray (1972) lists many nonhuman primate hybrids, of which the following macaque—baboon hybrids are a sample: *M. mulatta* × *hamadryas* (Montagu, 1950), *M. nemestrina* × *P. anubis* (Zuckerman, 1933), *M. nemestrina* × *P. hamadryas* (Chiarelli, 1963), *M. nemistrina* × *P. ursinus* (Blythe, 1863). In all, Gray lists nine presumed cases.

MacDonald (1965) reported that L.G. Voronin of Moscow University had found hamadryas to be especially good breeders with all baboon species as well as macaques. Intergeneric mating, however, was judged to be less productive of offspring.

Nesturkh (1959) adds: "A noteworthy case of an intergeneric hybrid occurred at the Sukhumi Medico-Biological station at the beginning of 1949; a female hamadryas baboon bore a female offspring, Prima, by a male macaque that was itself a hybrid produced by crossing a pig-tailed macaque with a macaque rhesus. Prima bears obvious characteristics of both her parents. The same parents soon produced another hybrid offspring, also a female, named Marquise."

While several researchers in the field have provided data on interspecies interactions, it is characteristically incomplete because interspecies social behavior has been rarely the focus of field work. In zoos and laboratories hybrids have usually been produced by accident rather than design. Hybrids when they occur, are usually described as to their morphological characters alone. The behavior of adults that produce hybrids is rarely studied and the behavior of hybrids themselves is virtually unknown. When laboratory hybrids occur, as at Sukhumi, it is usually for purposes other than the study of behavior, for example, the introduction of hybrid vigor (Terry, personal communication).

In addition to the reproductively successful baboon hybrids reported by Nagel, a confirmation of hybrid fertility in a blue (*Cercopithecus miti stulhmanni*) × redtail (*C. ascanius schmidti*) monkey has been recorded by Aldrich-Blake (1968). The hybrid was a female which bore an infant while residing in the blue monkey troop. Neither the hybrid nor its offspring behaved differently than the blues. The hybrid female was observed in frequent grooming sessions with the other troop members, and she was seen mating on one occasion. Her infant regularly played with blue infants with no apparent difficulty. While the blue troop was often seen in association with redtail parties, the hybrid moved off with the blues whenever they departed. Since the hybrid was obviously attached to the blue monkey troop, it is reasonable to assume that her mother was a blue monkey. A factor which no doubt facilitated the cross-specific consort is that the postures and expressions of the two species are very similar (Andrew, 1963). The following comments by Aldrich-Blake merit consideration: "It is interesting that an animal that appears, to the human eye at least, to look quite different to a typical blue monkey, should nevertheless be accepted as a member of the group, particularly since interspecific isolating mechanisms appear to be largely dependent on differences in colouration. This could be taken as an indication of the importance of socialization processes in integrating a monkey with the rest of the group. Assuming that the hybrid was born in the group, it would have had ample opportunity to learn the 'correct' responses to blue monkey behavior patterns."

Bernstein (1968) discovered the unusual case of two pig-tailed macaque (*M. nemestrina*) X crab-eating macaque (*M. irus*) hybrids which were observed living in a wild troop of crab-eaters in Malaysia. Bernstein found that the two hybrids (a male and a female) maintained stable positions in the group status hierarchy. The male was the alpha animal in the troop, while the female enjoyed an unchallenged intermediate rank. The hybrid male appeared to be the oldest member of the troop, and he was effective in controlling intratroop disturbances. The hybrid male also exhibited defense behavior when the group was chased by dogs or people.

Bernstein adds that the social behavior and communication of the two hybrids created no apparent problems in the troop and appeared similar if not identical to that shown by other troop members. An area in which the hybrid male appeared to be deficient was that of reproductive behavior. During the course of the study, no sexual behavior by the hybrid male was observed. Moreover, no births occurred during this time, despite the observations of births in an adjacent pure crab eating troop. Whether the hybrids were fertile is not known. Bernstein believes that the shooting of *nemestrina*, especially males, contributed to their eradication in the study area. Thus, with only a few females left, it is likely that they attached themselves to the irus troop and produced the hybrids observed by Bernstein.

Zoomorphisms

Hediger (1950) has spoken of the animalizing tendency by which animals in captivity come to regard people as members of their own species: "In practice, an unpleasant result of the animal's tendency to assimilation is that the favoured man is not only accepted by them as one of their own species, but is considered and treated as a fellow member of a particular sex; thus during the breeding season they either try to fight over him or to mate with him."

Such behavior is especially likely where animals have been raised by human caretakers. An especially interesting tendency can be observed in small animals which tend to direct sexual responses to only a part of a person. Hediger describes an otter, raised alone, which regarded its keeper's leg as a mate: "Clearly the otter bites the back of the female's neck during mating, because this particular male invariably grasped hold of his keeper's trouser leg during his attempt at copulation and seized a fold of the cloth between his teeth."

Early experience with humans
Lang (1972) regards the problem of reproduction in captive apes to be due in part to their frequent early experience with humans instead of conspecifics. In this regard, Reynold's (1967) description of the experiences of a female gorilla (Toto), which grew up from infancy in the home of a Mrs. A.M. Hoyt is especially interesting: "Toto now had estrous cycles, and for a few days each month, became surly, and more uncontrollable than usual. She fell in love each time, with one or other of the male staff, and followed him around, trying to touch the frightened individual."

9. IMPLICATIONS FOR *HOMO SAPIENS*

Psychopathology

Much if not all, of the behavior reported here for nonhuman primates has been considered at one time or other as being psychopathological when it occurs among humans. It is clear, however, that these responses are situationally adaptive, and occur under a variety of conditions. The scientific study of this behavior cannot fail to shed important light on the incidence of similar patterns in *Homo sapiens*. This follows from the view that the proper study of mankind is not only man, but all of nature (Jensen, 1973). Our closest living relatives, the nonhuman primates, offer an opportunity to construct models for human behavior.

Evolutionary selection

Regarding the issue of sexual behavior between alien species, for example, it is possible that evolutionary selection pressure has favored behavioral tendencies for generalization in primates. Certainly the expanded cerebral cortex of monkeys, apes, and people facilitates generalization of affection to other animals. Human beings are especially prone to regard all animals as objects of affection. This tendency has manifested itself in anthropomorphic writing about animal habits, animalistic religions, and sexual relations with animal substitutes. This latter category has been well-documented by Kinsey and co-workers (1948). Perhaps the basis of such habits can be understood by reference to the individual's history of man—animal relations. Peripubertal contact with animals may be particularly persistent if sexual arousal is classically conditioned to a particular member of that species. Thus, the animal may become a kind of fetish.

Value of nonhuman primate studies

Nonhuman primates are a most appropriate model for comparison in the realm of human social behavior. Although, from taxon to taxon, nonhuman primates exhibit great variability in particular behavioral traits, they are universally complicated, sensitive, and adaptable. In both their usual and unusual attributes they resemble man. Their responses to stress, danger and social deprivation are especially relevant to our research into the nature of human behavioral disorders.

There can be no doubt that a firm understanding of nonhuman primate sexuality in all its aspects will prove to be of great value as we strive to understand the biobehavioral basis of human sexuality.

10. SUMMARY

Unusual sexual behavior in animals occurs infrequently, is not well described, well known or well understood. The incidence of behavior such as homosexuality, lack of sexual interest, self-sucking, masturbation, object-directed sexuality, birth-induced sexual responses, and the generalization of sexual behavior to alien species varies according to the individual, region, and species. Most of these types of behavior have been observed in both captive and free-ranging animals, and can be said to be functional in certain respects. Since all primates are socially flexible, the universality of these behaviors may be generalized to *Homo sapiens*. The study of unusual sexual patterns in nonhuman primates may provide relevant models for the better understanding of human sexual behavior. Much has been learned from studies of nonhuman primates, but more research is required if we are to completely understand the relationship between our primate heritage and our human nature.

BIBLIOGRAPHY

Abernethy, V. (1974) Dominance and sexual behavior. *Am. J. Psychiat.* 131: 813—817.

Agar, M. and Mitchell, G. (1975) Behavior of free-ranging and wild rhesus adults: a review. In: (G. Bourne, Ed.) *The Rhesus Monkey.* Vol. I (Academic Press, New York) pp. 324—343.

Aldrich-Blake, F.P.G. (1968) A fertile hybrid between two Cercopithecus species in the Budongo Forest, Uganda. *Fol. Primatol.* 9, 15—21.

Andrew, R.J. (1963) The origin and evolution of the calls and facial expressions of the primates. *Behaviour,* 20, 1—109.

1184

Anthoney, T.R. (1968) The ontogeny of greeting, grooming, and sexual motor patterns in captive baboons (supersp. *Papio cynocephalus*). *Behaviour*, 31, 358—372.

Berkson, G. (1967) Abnormal stereotyped motor acts. In: (J. Zubin and H. Hunt, Eds.), *Comparative Psychopathology*. (Grune and Stratton, New York) pp. 76—94.

Berkson, G. (1968) Development of abnormal stereotyped behaviors. *Dev. Psychobiol.* 1 (2) 118—132.

Bernstein, K.S. (1968) Social status of two hybrids in a wild troop of *Macaca irus*. *Fol. Primatol.* 8, 121—131.

Bingham, H.C. (1928) Sex development in apes. *Comp. Psychol. Monogr.* 5, 1—161.

Blythe, E. (1863) Report of the Curator, Zoological Department. *Proc. Soc. Bengal; Asiatic Soc. Bengal*, 32, 455—456.

Bolwig, N. (1959) A study of the behavior of the chacma baboon, *Papio ursinus*. *Behaviour*, 14, 136—163.

Carpenter, C.R. (1942a) Sexual behavior of free-ranging rhesus monkeys (*Macaca mulatta*), I. Specimens, procedures, and behavioral characteristics of estrus. *J. Comp. Psychol.* 33, 113—142.

Carpenter, C.R. (1942b) Sexual behavior of free-ranging rhesus monkeys (*Macaca mulatta*), II. Periodicity of estrus, homosexuality and non-conformist behavior. *J. Comp. Psychol.* 33, 143—162.

Chevalier-Skolnikoff, S. (1974) Male-female, female-female, and male-male sexual behavior in the stumptail monkey, with special attention to the female orgasm. *Arch. Sex. Behav.* 3, 95—116.

Chiarelli, B. (1963) Observations on hybridization in primates. *Symp. Zool. Soc. Lond.* 10, 277—279.

De Benedictis, T. (1973) The behavior of young primates during adult copulation: observations of a *Macaca irus* colony. *Am. Anthropol.* 75, 1469—1484.

Deutsch, J. and Larsson, K. (1974) Model-oriented sexual behavior in surrogate-reared rhesus monkeys. *Brain, Behav. Evol.* 9, 157—164.

Erwin, J. and Maple, T. (1976) Ambisexual behavior with male—male anal penetration in male rhesus monkeys. *Arch. Sex. Behav.* 5 (1) 9—14.

Erwin, J. and Mitchell, G. (1975) Adolescent initial heterosexual behavior of rhesus monkeys (*Macaca mulatta*). *Arch. Sex. Behav.* 4 (1) 97—104.

Erwin, J., Mitchell, G. and Maple, T. (1973) Abnormal behavior in non-isolate-reared rhesus monkeys. *Psychol. Rep.* 33, 515—523.

Fittinghoff, N.A., Lindburg, D.G., Gomber, J. and Mitchell, G. (1974) Consistency and variability in the behavior of mature, isolation-reared, male rhesus macaques. *Primates*, 15 (2-3) 111—139.

Fooden, J. (1964) Rhesus and crab-eating macaques: Intergradation in Thailand. *Science* 143, 363—365.

Ford, C.S. and Beach, F.A. (1951) *Patterns of Sexual Behavior*. (Harper and Row, New York.)

Gartlan, J.S. (1969) Sexual and maternal behavior of the vervet monkey. *J. Reprod. Fertil.* suppl. 6, 137—150.

Gijzen, A. (1973) Two accidentally bred monkey-hybrids grew up. *J. Hum. Evol.* 2, 27—29.

Gomber, J. and Mitchell, G. (1974) Preliminary report on adult male isolation-reared rhesus monkeys caged with infants. *Dev. Psychol.* 9, 419.

Goodall, J. (1965) Chimpanzees of the Gombe Stream Reserve. In: (I. DeVore, Ed.) *Primate Behavior*. (Holt, Rinehart and Winston, New York) pp. 452—473.

Gouzoules, H.T. (1974) Group responses to parturition in *Macaca arctoides*. *Primates*, 15 (2—3) 287—292.

Gray, A.P. (1972) *Mammalian Hybrids*. (Commonwealth Agricultural Bureau, Farnham Royal, U.K.).

Hamilton, G.V. (1914) A study of the sexual tendencies in monkeys and baboons. *J. Anim. Behav.* 4, 295—318.

Hanby, J.P., Robertson, L.T. and Phoenix, C.H. (1971) The sexual behavior of a confined troop of Japanese Macaques. *Fol. Primatol.* 16, 123—143.

Harlow, H.F. (1962) The development of affectional patterns in infant monkeys. In: (B.M. Foss, Ed.) *Determinants of Infant Behavior.* (Wiley, New York) pp. 75—97.

Hediger, H. (1950) *Wild Animals in Captivity.* (Butterworths, London.)

Hess, J.P. (1972) On the sexual behavior of captive lowland gorillas. (16-mm film). (Basel.)

Hess, J.P. (1973) Some observations on the sexual behavior of captive lowland gorillas. In: (R.P. Michael and J.H. Crook, Eds.) *Comparative Ecology and Behavior of Primates.* (Academic Press, New York) pp. 507—520.

Jensen, G.D. (1973) Human sexual behavior in primate perspective. In: (J. Zubin and J. Money, Eds.) *Contemporary Sexual Behavior: Critical Issues in the 1970s.* (Johns Hopkins University Press, Baltimore) pp. 17—31.

Kaufmann, J.H. (1967) Social relations in adult males in a free-ranging band of rhesus monkeys. In: (S.A. Altmann, Ed.) *Social Communication Among Primates.* (University of Chicago Press, Chicago) pp. 73—98.

Kinsey, A.C., Pomeroy, W.B. and Martin, C.E. (1948) *Sexual Behavior in the Human Male.* (Saunders, Philadelphia.)

Kummer, H. (1968) *Social Organization of Hamadryas Baboons.* (University of Chicago Press, Chicago.)

Lang, E.M. (1972) Experience with breeding apes in Basel Zoo. In: *Breeding Primates.* (Karger, Basel) pp. 34—37.

Lindburg, D.G. (1967) A field study of the reproductive behavior of the rhesus monkey (*Macaca mulatta*). Doctoral dissertation, University of California, Berkeley.

Loy, J.D. (1970) Behavioral responses of free-ranging rhesus monkeys to food shortage. *Am. J. Phys. Anthropol.* 33, 263—271.

MacDonald, J. (1965) *Almost Human.* (Chilton Books, Philadelphia.)

MacKinnon, J. (1974) *In Search of the Red Ape.* (Holt, Rinehart and Winston, New York.)

Maple, T. (1974a) Basic studies of interspecies attachment behavior. Doctoral dissertation, University of California, Davis.

Maple, T. (1974b) Dominance tests and individual differences. *Percept. Mot. Skills,* 39, 29 00.

Maple, T. (1974c) On the need for studies of interspecies social behavior within the order of primates. *J. Behav. Sci.* 2, 63—66.

Maple, T. (1975) Fundamentals of animal social behavior. In: (E.S.E. Hafez, Ed.) *Behaviour of Domestic Animals.* 3rd edn, (Balliere-Tindall, London) pp. 171—181.

Maple, T. (1976) Interspecific social contact in the primate order: laboratory experiments and field observations. In preparation.

Maple, T., Erwin, J. and Mitchell, G. (1973) Age of sexual maturity in laboratory-born pairs of rhesus monkeys (*Macaca mulatta*). *Primates,* 14 (4) 427—428.

Maple, T., Erwin, J. and Mitchell, G. (1974) Sexually aroused self-aggression in a socialized adult male monkey. *Arch. Sex. Behav.* 3 (5) 471—475.

Maple, T. and Laub, R. (1975) Interspecies adoption. Unpublished manuscript.

Maple, T., Scott, S. and Redican, W.K. (1975) Intergeneric sexual behavior between an adult baboon and an adult macaque. (Unpublished manuscript.)

Maple, T. and Westlund, B. (1975) Social interactions between capuchin and spider monkeys in captivity. *Appl. Anim. Ethol.* 1, 305—308.

Maples, W.R. and McKern, T.W. (1967) A preliminary report on classification of the Kenya baboons. In: (H. Vagtborg, Ed.) *The Baboon in Medical Research.* (University of Texas Press, Austin) pp. 13—22.

Mason, W.A. and Kenney, M.D. (1974) Re-direction of filial attachments of rhesus monkeys: dogs as surrogate mothers. *Science,* 183, 1209—1211.

Michael, R.P., Wilson, M.K. and Zumpe, D. (1974) The bisexual behavior of female rhesus monkeys. In: (R.C. Friedman, R.M. Richart and R.L. Vande Wiele, Eds.) *Sex Differences in Behavior*. (Wiley, New York) pp. 399—412.

Mitchell, G. (1970) Abnormal behavior in primates. In: (L. Rosenblum, Ed.) *Primate Behavior*. Vol. 1, (Academic Press, New York.) pp. 195—249.

Mitchell, G. (1973) Comparative development of social and emotional behavior. In: (G. Bermant, Ed.) *Perspectives on Animal Behavior*. (Scott-Foresman, Glenview, Illinois) pp. 102—128.

Mitchell, G. and Brandt, E.M. (1975) Behavior of the female rhesus monkey during birth. In: (G. Bourne, Ed.) *The Rhesus Monkey*. Vol. II (Academic Press, New York) pp. 232—245.

Montagu, A. (1950) A hybrid gibbon. *J. Mammal.* 31, 150—153.

Nagel, U. (1973) A comparison of anubis baboons, hamadryas baboons and their hybrids at a species border in Ethiopia. *Fol. Primatol.* 19, 104—165.

Nesturkh, M. (1959) *The Origin of Man*. (Foreign Language Publishing House, Moscow.)

Neville, M.K. (1966) A study of the free-ranging behavior of rhesus monkeys. (Doctoral dissertation, Harvard University, Cambridge, Mass.)

Phoenix, C.H. and Jensen, J.N. (1973) Ejaculation by male rhesus in the absence of female partners. *Horm. Behav.* 4 (3) 231—238.

Reynolds, V. (1967) *The Apes*. (E.P. Dutton, New York.)

Richard, A. (1970) A comparative study of the activity patterns and behavior of *Alouatta villosa* and *Ateles geoffroyi*. *Fol. Primatol.* 12, 241—263.

Rogers, C.M. and Davenport, R.K. (1969) Effect of restricted rearing on sexual behavior of chimpanzees. *Dev. Psychol.* 1, 200—204.

Rowell, T.E. (1966) Forest living baboons in Uganda. *J. Zool.* 147, 344—364.

Sackett, G.P. (1968) Abnormal behavior in laboratory-reared rhesus monkeys. In: (M.W. Fox, Ed.) *Abnormal Behavior in Animals*. (W.B. Saunders Co., Philadelphia) pp. 293—331.

Schaller, G.B. (1963) *The Mountain Gorilla*. (University of Chicago Press, Chicago.)

Senko, M.G. (1966) The effects of early, intermediate and late experiences upon adult macaque sexual behavior. (Unpublished M.S. thesis, University of Wisconsin.)

Tokuda, K., Simons, R.C. and Jensen, G.D. (1968) Sexual behavior in a captive group of pigtailed monkeys (*Macaca nemestrina*). *Primates*, 9, 283—294.

Wolfheim, J.H. and Rowell, T.E. (1972) Communication among captive talapoin monkeys (*Miopithecus talapoin*). *Fol. Primatol.* 18, 224—255.

Zuckerman, S. (1933) *Functional Affinities of Man, Monkeys and Apes*. (Harcourt, New York.)

SECTION XVI

Treatment and counseling for sexual problems

Section coordinator: John Bancroft

CHAPTER 96

Introduction

JOHN BANCROFT

In the Western World awareness of sexuality and sexual problems has increased as a combined effect of the various media and the relaxation of inhibitions towards the discussion of sex. This has had two effects so far as treatment and counseling are concerned — first it has altered the sexual expectations of many people, generating new problems for some and lessening old ones for others. Secondly, it has facilitated the request for help resulting in an increased demand for treatment. It is impossible at the present time to know whether this also reflects a genuine increase in the incidence of such problems, but that the demand for help has grown seems to be beyond dispute. In company with these changes there has been some lifting of obstacles to research in the area of sexuality. Following the work of first Kinsey and his associates and later Masters and Johnson, the wide variety of patterns of sexual behavior and the psychophysiological basis of sexual response has become much more clearly recognized. This has been associated with a retreat from the traditional medical dichotomy of etiology into the organic and the psychological and a reduction in the number who assume that sexual dysfunction and sexual deviance are manifestations of fairly profound personality or neurotic difficulties which are either resistant to ordinary treatment or require long-term psychotherapy. The results of modern treatment methods indicate that there are many cases where relatively brief intervention can produce important changes. This has led to an undoubted upsurge in therapeutic optimism most marked in relation to sexual dysfunction. We are in the midst of a therapeutic vogue.

This recent development has not yet found a realistic balance. Very few controlled outcome studies have been completed and we are a long way from knowing how generally useful these new approaches are. This is important in transferring new methods from one culture to another particularly when sexual attitudes which are so sensitive to cultural factors are involved.

When considering etiology we should not reject the idea that sexual dysfunction or deviance may be manifestations of severe personality disorder or

Handbook of Sexology, edited by J. Money and H. Musaph
© Elsevier/North-Holland Biomedical Press, 1977

illness. Clearly this is often the case and it would indeed be surprising if sexuality, which is so central to dyadic relationships, did not reflect much of the morbidity to which humans are prone. On the other hand when one considers the subtle interaction of psychological and physiological mechanisms involved in sexual functioning, it would also be surprising if this function was not often disturbed by situational factors.

Attitudes to sexual deviance have also changed. Though there is still a widespread tendency to assume that deviant sexuality is a manifestation of illness which should be treated, there is a growing acceptance that sexual relationships other than 'normal' heterosexual, can be both adaptive and optimal for many individuals. Increasingly, the emphasis is on establishing mutually rewarding sexuality with all the positive binding effects it has on dyadic relationships, whether heterosexual, homosexual, or otherwise. In the past the medical and other helping professions have divided sexual problems very definitely into sexual deviance (often pejoratively labeled perversion) and sexual inadequacy or dysfunction. For the first, the role of the therapist was to eliminate the deviant pattern; for the second, it was a restoration of 'normal' function. Now in line with the changes in attitude already mentioned, there is a much more general aim of establishing rewarding relationships of varying kinds. The increase in the self-control of undesirable behavior is still sometimes necessary, especially behavior that is highly antisocial or heavily proscribed.

Nevertheless the treatment or counseling of sexual problems still raises difficult ethical questions which should be briefly considered.

The enormous growth of sex therapy since Masters and Johnson's pioneering work has been largely based on an American middle-class value system. The nature of the sexual relationship which is pursued in such therapy usually involves a very much two-way giving and loving process. Whilst this may seem to many to be a natural and appropriate goal, in some cultural and subcultural settings such a value system would seem strange and quite threatening to the individuals concerned. Often the male's sense of masculinity is largely based on a particular form of sexual dominance; the limits of the females' enjoyment may be strictly set by religious beliefs.

Middle-class professionals are often accused of imposing their values on to other groups. In this particular case I would defend what seems to me to be the intrinsic value of a mutually rewarding 'middle-class' sexual relationship. One can speculate on the benefits that might accrue if such value spread into other cultures. Nevertheless, as therapists we should be aware that by disturbing a long-established value system and attempting to replace it by one which would be in conflict with the patient's culture, we may be adding to that individual's or couple's problems. We should therefore think carefully before challenging culturally determined values and also remember that however good we may be as therapists, there are social processes at work in many cultures that are more powerful than we can ever hope to be. With time we should recognize the limitations of these new methods; in the meantime we should proceed cautiously.

There is a further ethical issue which is even more vexed and emotive. This concernes the acceptability of treatment or counseling that aims to help an individual alter his or her sexual preferences; in particular, helping the homosexual to establish rewarding heterosexual relationships (for fuller discussion of these issues see Bancroft, 1974, 1975). Over the years attitudes towards such help have become entangled with attitudes to homosexuality or deviant sexuality per se. Early attempts to reduce stigma associated with homosexuallty involved the notion of responsibility and culpability. The homosexual could not be blamed or held responsible for his sexual preferences because they were the products of some congenital or innate process. Hence the behavior should be tolerated and the stigma reduced. Any evidence that homosexual preferences were modifiable by treatment was a threat to this point of view. If they were modifiable they were presumably acquired rather than congenital and hence no different from any other 'sin'. Furthermore such evidence would lay responsibility on the homosexual individual to seek such modification to 'put himself right'. Attempts to treat 'homosexuality' were therefore strongly attacked. The situation now is different in certain respects though the basic entanglement continues. Those who strive to protect the interests of homosexual and other sexual minorities no longer rely on these earlier apologetic arguments of reduced culpability of the individual but rather shift the emphasis to the culpability of 'normal' society for stigmatizing the deviant individual. If there are problems in being a homosexual, it is argued, they stem from society's rejection of the homosexual. The important need is for a change in social attitudes, a lessening of stigma. Attempts to 'treat' the homosexual are attacked therefore because it is assumed that they reinforce these negative social values. In any case they can be seen as imposing conformity, which to many is a most undesirable activity. Thus from such a point of view the only acceptable help for the homosexual is help in continuing as a homosexual.

For many people this is a nonissue as the acceptability of help aimed at sexual reorientation will depend on the recipient choosing and actually wanting to receive it, but some would say that such 'choice' is spurious and evidence that the individual is succumbing to social pressures to conform. Thus even if the individual asks for such help the therapist would be wrong to give it. This is a form of argument which evades logical counter. However, at the present time the individual uncertain or unhappy with his sexual identity is subjected to two types of pressure — that from 'straight' heterosexual society to conform, and that from sexual minorities such as Gay groups who often insist that any evidence of homosexual feelings is sure proof of the individual's homosexual nature which he should henceforth accept. For understandable if unjustifiable reasons, any evidence of mobility between sexual roles is rejected by such groups and the recent emergence of bisexuality as a lifestyle is regarded as a threat by many Gay people.

If in fact we had evidence that either a homo- or a heterosexual identity was an immutable and fundamental aspect of an individual's nature, then any attempt to modify such an identity would be inappropriate and unjustifiable. But there is no such evidence and we know that many individuals pass through a phase of homosexuality or bisexuality into a stable heterosexual role, and many more in the opposite direction. Such individuals usually need time to work out the role which suits them best. They may seek help during that period of their lives. Whatever attitudes to treatment may have prevailed in the past I would suggest that now there is a need to help such individuals by protecting them from the various social pressures and facilitating their exploration of new roles whether they be heterosexual, homosexual or transexual. The basic choice should be with the patient — it is another and rather ironic form of oppression that tells the individual he only has one choice and that any other is spurious and compliant.

A final factor is of special relevance to this Section. The therapeutic approach to sexual problems, as well as to other types of interpersonal difficulty has been a battleground of polemic dogma for a long time. In particular the psychoanalytic schools and directive or behavioral schools have been at each other's throats in this area as much as any. Hopefully, the need for such heated and usually unproductive controversy is passing and perhaps it will be in the field of therapy for sexual problems that it will be first laid to rest. The psychosomatic nature of sexual response, the undoubted role of early experiences and of conditioning in sexual development, the basic if obscure contribution of hormones, the importance of sexual technique and counseling and the very central part that sexuality plays in the personality structure and dyadic relationships of all of us ensures that any rational approach to treatment will be eclectic and multidisciplinary.

One of the principal areas of ignorance at the present time is the choice of treatment approach. How do we sensibly choose between brief behavioral and directive methods, more long-term psychotherapeutic approaches, or the use of drugs or hormones? To what extent can they be usefully combined? They all appear to have a place in the modern treatment. It is in this spirit that this Section has been collected. It contains contributions from people with not only different styles of writing but also very different therapeutic approaches which in the past would have been considered irreconcilable. At the moment how they relate to one another must remain unclear. Perhaps in the future it will be possible to gather them together in some internally consistent whole.

As we are in the midst of important changes, what now is the range of objectives for treatment? The recent shift of emphasis from the elimination of undesirable behavior to the re-establishment of mutually rewarding sexual relationships has made us aware of the ill-defined difference between education and therapy. When does education become counseling? When does counseling become therapy? If unequivocal illness is involved this distinction presents no problem and the majority of people seeking help with sexual problems would not be deemed ill, but rather suffering from the consequences of a variable period of faulty or maladaptive learning. This issue is not merely a semantic quibble as it raises questions of who is qualified to give what type of help? Counseling implies a form of education in which special attention is paid to the needs or shortcoming of the individual recipient. With therapy there is the connotation of 'sickness' which, as has already been suggested, can be usefully avoided in the majority of cases seeking help for sexual problems. 'Treatment' is a less specific term and may be preferred. Nevertheless we should remember that the historical development of the helping role has relied both on the contribution of the educator and of the therapist. Probably the contribution of the therapist which has the most general relevance is his skill in exploiting and managing the client—therapist relationship. Obviously his more traditional functions are still relevant in those cases where 'illness' is a useful concept or where the use of drugs or specifically medical techniques is to be considered.

Debate on who should receive counseling and who therapy, and who should deliver such help is complicated at the present time by the current widespread enthusiasm for sex therapy and the consequent exploitation by people whose qualifications to help are disputable. Unfortunately reaction to such factors is often as much influenced by the vested interests of professional groups as by the real needs of the public. There can be little doubt that the resources of the medical profession and allied professional groups would in any case be hard pressed to meet the apparent demand. Needless to say this issue will not be resolved in this introduction but has been raised to explain the criteria for inclusion in this Section. We are confined to those objectives which can currently be met by seeking help from trained therapists or professional sex counselors. We are not including the fundamentally important role of counseling and education that should be provided by a wide range of health personnel in the course of more general functions. This is not to say that the principles of treatment discussed in this Section will not be relevant to these nonspecialists but rather that their proper use may require experience of handling the 'therapeutic' relationship.

With these qualifications let us consider the range of therapeutic objectives.

(1) Establishment of rewarding sexual relationships
We are concerned here with the individual who, because of a lack of sexual responsiveness, ignorance of how to proceed, or anxiety is unable to initiate and maintain a rewarding relationship. Obviously such a relationship could be either heterosexual or homosexual.

(2) Improvement of sexual function
This covers the range of sexual dysfunction that affects a sexual relationship once started. It includes problems of erectile and ejaculatory dysfunction in the male, impaired arousal, orgasmic dysfunction and vaginismus in the female.

(3) Self-control of unwanted sexual behavior
Though now regarded as of secondary importance compared to objectives (1) and (2), there remain some indications for facilitating self-control, particularly where the unwanted sexual behavior is dangerous or incurs heavy penalities, for example, pedophilia.

(4) Adaption to a deviant role
In many cases when the individual has no choice but to adopt a deviant sexual role, help may be needed in coping with pressures imposed by society or in learning to adapt successfully in a nondeviant culture. There are two particular types of person that come into this category; the first is the homosexual living in a predominantly heterosexual society, and secondly the transexual attempting to 'pass' as normal.

Let us now turn to the contributions in this Section and place them within this framework. Most of the methods making up the new vogue in sex therapy have a behavioral basis even though many are eclectic. In the first chapter, a behavioral model for approaching the first three of the above objectives, is provided and the historical development of some of these methods is considered.

Most of the current optimism concerns the treatment of sexual dysfunction in the couple (objective 2 above). For this reason special emphasis is given to this new style of couple therapy in the chapter by Joseph LoPiccolo.

Ismond Rosen in his chapter describes the basic principles that the psychoanalytic therapist uses in approaching the first three objectives, revealing some of the main differences from the behavioral approach.

The fourth objective, adaptation to a deviant sexual role, is dealt with in three separate chapters. Bradford Wilson discusses counseling the male homosexual. This chapter clearly indicates how much of the help required by the homosexual in coping with his relationships is basically the same as that required of a heterosexual relationship. Pamela Oline and Tina Mandel describe their counseling approach to the female homosexual. In both chapters the reader will recognize a predominantly psychoanalytic orientation. John Money and Paul Walker describe their approach to helping the transexual, covering in addition to their counseling the hormonal and surgical procedures that will be involved.

In the final chapter John Money and Jean Daléry review the use of drugs and hormones in striving for all four of the treatment objectives. It will be clear from this chapter how uncertain we are of the proper place for drugs in our therapeutic armamentarium.

Many types of treatment and counseling have not been described in this Section. In particular the use of group processes is of increasing importance though as yet substantial experience in applying group methods to sexual problems is still lacking.

BIBLIOGRAPHY

Bancroft, J.H.J. (1974) *Deviant Sexual Behaviour.* (Clarendon Press, Oxford.)
Bancroft, J.H.J. (1975) Homosexuality and the medical profession: a behaviourist's view. *Br. J. Med. Ethics* 1: 176—180.

CHAPTER 97

The behavioral approach to treatment

JOHN BANCROFT

1. INTRODUCTION

Behavioral methods of treatment come in different disguises, reflecting their differing historical origins and theoretical bases. Terms such as behavior therapy, behavior modification, applied behavioral analysis, and directive psychotherapy, all convey different biases or emphases in approach. They have in common their principle objective which is the modification or change of specific behavior. Something else that they share is the hostility they frequently arouse in nonbehaviorists.

In this chapter we will briefly consider the ethical and methodological issues that underlie this hostility and trace the main historical milestones in the development of these methods. The efficacy of the various methods in the treatment of sexual problems will then be reviewed before concluding with a description of the clinical approach that I currently use. This, though somewhat idiosyncratic, is representative of much of modern sex therapy and is certainly derived in large part from several other workers in the field.

Techniques such as aversion therapy have not surprisingly been likened to methods of 'thought control' or brainwashing. But even more gentle or more positive approaches evoke criticism. Either they are seen as methods of inducing conformity in the hapless victim who by nature needs to conform to different standards or they are seen as changing the manifestations of the problem without tackling the cause. The first attack comes from those who fear the potentially evil controlling forces of applied psychology; the second from those who for one reason or another feel happier with the psychoanalytic approach to treatment.

Hopefully it will become clear by the end of the chapter that the first fears are in fact quite unfounded. Not only are the vast majority of behavior modifiers caring and compassionate professionals wanting to help, but their influence is in any case confined within limits set by the patient himself. Whatever efficacy 'brainwashing' may have it is in a different class both qual-

Handbook of Sexology, edited by J. Money and H. Musaph
© *Elsevier/North-Holland Biomedical Press, 1977*

itatively and quantitatively from that which concerns us here. Unfortunately much of the blame for this misunderstanding must rest with us behaviorists, not because of any unethical aims or methods but because we have formulated what we do, and communicate it to each other, and inevitably to everybody else also, in terms which systematically dehumanize the therapeutic process. Whatever heuristic value this conceptual dehumanization may have had in scientific terms, its effect on public relations has probably been devastating at a time when behavior modifiers, for good reasons, have wanted to extend their influence. Hopefully this chapter will go some way towards correcting this misunderstanding.

To the psychoanalytic attack, the reply must be that the evidence does not support it. The value of a treatment method must be judged by its effects. If causal mechanisms that underly the problem still operate, then no doubt the behavior will be that much more difficult to modify. 'Symptom substitution' has not emerged as a serious problem mainly because as a concept it was ill-conceived. On the other hand, what has become clear is that often, before the behavioral goals of treatment can be achieved, other changes in attitudes or behavior may have to be induced first.

2. HISTORICAL DEVELOPMENT OF BEHAVIORAL METHODS

Two principal factors have influenced the development of behavioral methods in this area. The first is the change in social and medical attitudes to sexuality in general and to sexual problems in particular. The second is the theoretical basis of such treatments, in particular the influence of modern learning theory.

Behavioral methods were in use long before modern learning theory was developed. The most striking example, as far as sexual disorders were concerned, was the hypnotherapy used widely at the end of the 19th century. The best description of this approach is by Schrenk-Notzing (1895) who made it quite clear that he regarded his treatment as educational, based on the principle that abnormal sexuality is a result of faulty learning and therefore modifiable by re-learning. He considered that the aim of education was to create a series of habits by means of direct persuasion, acts, immitation and admiration using hypnotic suggestion when necessary.

He and other hypnotherapists applied these principles to a variety of sexual problems, though mainly to homosexual behavior. He accepted the current view of the harmful effects of masturbation which he therefore strongly discouraged. He did encourage the patient to use heterosexual fantasies and to attempt 'regulated sexual intercourse' with selected prostitutes often using hypnotic suggestions of success. His aim was the establishment of heterosexual relationships rather than the elimination of homosexual interest. He reported a success rate comparable to that of most present-day therapists. Although his writing reflected many 19th century attitudes, his therapeutic approach was curiously similar to much of modern behavior therapy.

He and his fellow hypnotherapists were attacked vigorously by those such as Havelock Ellis who were concerned about the position of the homosexual in society, presumably because his approach implied that homosexual behavior was learnt and not constitutional or innate. This would make the homosexual vulnerable to the accusation that his behavior was a crime or sin rather than an innate condition for which he could not be held responsible. This relationship of etiology to responsibility has bedeviled the question of treatment of homosexuality ever since (Bancroft, 1974).

Hypnotherapy, for various reasons, faded in popularity in the early 20th century as psychoanalysis began to establish itself. The behavioral approach to sexual problems reappeared in another form resulting from the application by experimental psychologists of their laboratory principles of learning to the treatment of abnormal behavior. One of the most obvious models of learning for such application was conditioned aversion whereby an unpleasant response was conditioned to be associated with a previously pleasant or neutral stimulus. Aversion therapy was born, later to become one of the main theoretical spearheads of modern behavior therapy. Because of its nature, aversion therapy was only soon to be useful for getting rid of unwanted behavior. Abnormal sexuality, such as homosexuality, and alcoholism were the most obvious targets, fitting readily into the 'medical model' of illnesses prevalent at the time. As it happened aversion therapy was first used in a few cases of deviant sexuality, but in the 1940s and 1950s it was used extensively to treat alcoholism (Voegtlin and Lemere, 1942). Although early reports claimed startling success rates (Lemere and Voegtlin, 1950) by the mid-1950s its relative superiority over less unpleasant treatment was in doubt and since then it has not been widely used for alcoholism.

In the late 1950s and early 1960s, however, the use of aversion therapy for deviant sexual behavior reappeared. It was at this stage that modern behavior therapy was establishing itself and aversion therapy together with systematic desensitization for phobias, were the two principle techniques. In spite of the fact that learning was at the basis of both the early hypnotherapy and this modern treatment, the emphasis was quite different. The first had aimed at the re-education of 'normal' behavior; the second the conditioned elimination or suppression of abnormal behavior. This theoretical concern with conditioned aversion may explain why, until very recently, the main target of behavior therapists in the sexual field was deviant behavior rather than the far more common problems of sexual dysfunction. There may be other important factors accounting for this split which seems to have prevailed for some time in medical circles. Sexual dysfunction has been curiously ignored; medical teaching on the subject, if it has occurred at all, has concentrated on the more bizarre aberrations of human sexual behavior very much in the Krafft-Ebing tradition and sex in the curriculum has often been confined to the forensic medicine section where it can be safely separated from one's ordinary everyday experiences. As indicated in the introduction to this Section, attitudes to sex and to deviant sexuality are changing and this is having major repercussions in the field of sex therapy and medical sex education.

The late 1960s was a period of proliferation of techniques — initially variants of aversion therapy, competing with one another for technical ingenuity or striving to make the technique less unpleasant while retaining its efficacy. Later these techniques gave way to a variety of more positive methods such as systematic desensitization of heterosexual anxiety, the 'shaping' of fantasies or the 'positive conditioning' of erections, all of which were aimed at the establishment of 'normal' sexual responses. We were returning in some respects to the Schrenk-Notzing era, to the emphasis on the re-education of 'normality'.

By the end of the 1960s the behavior therapists' attention to sexual dysfunction had been confined to a few rather desultory attempts to use general techniques such as systematic desensitization or assertive training. No new technique had been evolved specifically for these problems. Then in 1970 came the major contribution of Masters and Johnson with their book 'Human Sexual Inadequacy', describing a comprehensive treatment approach to sexual dysfunction and claiming impressive results in large numbers of patients. They were not avowed behaviorists but were eclectic and had incorporated various techniques described by earlier workers (for example, Seman's (1956) technique for premature ejaculation). Nevertheless they had brought it all together in a way which made sense to many people, particularly those with a behavioral orientation, and provided a clinical approach which was far more comprehensive than any of the behavioral techniques described hitherto.

Their impact on sex therapy has been enormous. No doubt important changes in attitudes were already underway. Homosexuality was beginning to lose some of its stigma and regarding it as an illness to be cured was becoming old-fashioned and reactionary in medical and psychological circles. In any case those who attempted to help homosexuals achieve rewarding heterosexual relationships were realizing that the main emphasis should be on the heterosexual rather than the homosexual behavior. Aversive and other negative techniques were not only seen to be increasingly inappropriate for the majority of patients but their efficacy was being increasingly questioned.

A further major influence in behavioral psychology contributed to this period of reappraisal and re-orientation. This was the operant school of behavior modification pioneered by the work of B.F. Skinner. Whilst the influence of this school is far ranging, one aspect is particularly relevant here. The operant approach to modifying behavior involves a very careful analysis of the behavior in question and the use of positive and negative reinforcers appropriate for the particular individual. In other words, although certain basic principles are applied, the modification is tailor-made to fit the individual subject — something quite different from the traditional medical approach of using a particular technique such as aversion therapy, to treat a particular condition, such as pedophilia. These various influences have come together to produce the current approach to the treatment of sexual problems which first emphasizes the establishment of rewarding and acceptable sexual behavior and, secondly, encourages this by means of a program which is designed to suit the particular individual or couple concerned; an approach which is much more educational than medical.

Many of the various techniques that have been developed earlier are still potentially useful, being incorporated into the individual program when appropriate. Before considering the basic principles of the current approach in more detail, let us therefore review briefly the main techniques that have been used and consider the attempts made to evaluate their efficacy.

3. TECHNIQUES APPLIED TO DEVIANT SEXUAL BEHAVIOR

The first type of aversion therapy to be widely used was chemical aversion. An emetic drug was given to the patient timed in such a way that the onset of nausea and vomiting would follow the presentation of the deviant stimulus, the procedure being repeated many times. The theoretical objective was to condition nausea to the previously pleasurable deviant stimulus. Not only is chemical aversion exceedingly unpleasant, but also the emetic effects are difficult to control, making precise temporal association of stimulus and response difficult. Occasionally the effects of emetic drugs can be dangerous.

For these various reasons attention was turned to electric shock as the noxious stimulus for aversion. Not only could its timing be precisely controlled, but the severity of the shock could be reduced to a minimum necessary for treatment. More precise conditioning paradigms were possible of which three were principally used. The 'classical conditioning' model is the simplest; this involves a repeated pairing of the conditioned (deviant) stimulus with the shock (unconditioned stimulus). Typically a slide or picture of the deviant stimulus is used. This procedure was described by Feldman and MacCulloch (1971).

Punishment, * in experimental learning terms, means the application of a noxious stimulus following a response in order to reduce the likelihood of that response recurring. A punishment procedure in aversion therapy has been used in various ways, involving different types of 'response-to-be-punished'. With punishment of fantasy (Marks and Gelder, 1967) the patient is asked to produce a fantasy or mental image of the deviant act. He then

---

* 'Punishment' is an example of a term which has moral connotations that are not intended when it is used in this precise technical sense by behaviorists. 'Punishment' is being applied to the behavior and not to the person who may in fact be applying the 'punishment' himself.

signals the presence of the image and immediately receives a shock. Punishment of overt behavior has been used in the treatment of transvestism and fetishism (Marks and Gelder, 1967) where the actual behavior, cross-dressing or holding a fetish object, is carried out in the treatment session and associated with shock in this way. Obviously there are relatively few such behaviors that could be modified in this manner. Penile erection, a specifically sexual response in the male, has also been used as a response-to-be-punished, a shock being administered (to the arm or leg) whenever an erection of a certain magnitude occurs in response to a deviant fantasy or stimulus (Bancroft, 1969).

The other principle method of aversive learning is avoidance learning; a response is learned which enables the subject to avoid noxious stimuli. This type of procedure has been used most extensively by MacCulloch and Feldman (1967) in their 'anticipatory avoidance' procedure. The subjects, whilst looking at a slide of a deviant stimulus, received a signal indicating that a shock will follow within a certain period of time (8 sec). Unless the subject switched off the slide he received a shock. This procedure was repeated many times, but as used by MacCulloch and Feldman was made more complex by the incorporation of a proportion of learning trials in which the patient was shocked whether he switched off the slide or not, and others in which there was a delay between his 'switching off' and the disappearance of the slide.

A variant of aversion therapy was reported by Thorpe and co-workers (1964) and called 'aversion relief'. In this a series of deviant words was presented to the patient. He was required to read out each word, whereupon he was immediately shocked. At the end of this series of words a nondeviant (heterosexual) word was presented and acted as a signal that the aversive series was over. The rationale for this procedure was that the relief engendered by the end of the aversive series was associated with the nondeviant (heterosexual) word. A similar principle was also incorporated into MacCulloch and Feldman's 'anticipatory avoidance' procedure. In a proportion of their trials the patient would be 'rewarded' for switching off the deviant slide by the presentation of a nondeviant slide.

Aversion therapy, whatever its efficacy, is an unpleasant treatment to receive and to administer. Not surprisingly, attempts were made to achieve its effects with less unpleasantness. Covert sensitization was introduced by Cautela (1966). This is, in effect, imaginary aversion therapy where both the deviant fantasy and the noxious stimulus are imagined by the patient, the latter usually being a frightening or unpleasant fantasy that is relevant to the deviant behavior. Thus the patient may be asked to follow his fantasy of a deviant act with a fantasy of being caught by the police, or of feeling nauseated. Individuals vary considerably in the intensity with which they can image unpleasant scenes and for those with vivid imagery, this procedure can be quite powerful.

A variety of more positive techniques has also been reported. Some in volve the gradual modification of fantasies. By starting with deviant fantasies that are normally sexually arousing, the patient is asked very gradually to change the fantasy in the direction of 'normal' sexuality. Each change may need to be small if the erotic response is to be maintained (Bancroft, 1971). An analogous approach has made use not of fantasies but of slides of deviant erotic stimuli. These were projected onto the same screen as a normal erotic stimulus but initially the deviant stimulus had maximum light intensity, the normal stimulus very low intensity. Gradually the ratio of the light intensities of the two slides was altered so that progressively the normal slide became more noticeable. In a small number of cases this was reported to produce transfer of erotic response from deviant to normal stimulus (Barlow and Agras, 1971).

Where anxiety about sexual behavior is marked, and particularly where it has a phobic quality, systematic desensitization can be used (Bancroft, 1974). Thus, as with the treatment of other types of phobia, the patient is taught to relax and then asked to imagine the situations of graded threat which, in the form of a hierarchy, are chosen after careful discussion between patient and therapist. Starting with the least threatening item on the hierarchy, each one is imagined in a relaxed state until it produces no subjective anxiety, whereupon the next item in the hierarchy is presented. This hierarchy of imaginary situations also provides a list of real behavior patterns for the patient to attempt between treatment sessions.

Penile erection is probably an unusually conditionable response which may contribute to the extraordinary range of sexual responsiveness in human males. Attempts have also been made to condition erectile responses to new 'normal' sexual stimuli. Both 'classical' and 'instrumental' conditioning procedures have been used. In the first, the new 'normal' stimulus, the conditioned stimulus (CS), is followed by the deviant unconditioned stimulus (UCS) which usually produces an erectile response. After repeated pairings of this kind the erectile response starts to occur to the conditioned stimulus alone (CR; Rachman and Hodgson, 1968; McConaghy, 1969; Quinn et al., 1973; Herman et al., 1974). In the 'instrumental' procedure the erectile response to the appropriate stimuli is rewarded in some way, such as by giving fluid to the subject who is experiencing an induced thirst. By rewarding changes which are initially very small, the erectile response is encouraged or 'shaped' into existence (Quinn et al., 1970).

Efficacy of techniques

As in many areas of treatment, much more energy has been expended in innovating new treatment procedures than in properly evaluating old ones. This of course reflects the fact that the first task is very much easier than the second.

The use of behavioral techniques for modifying deviant sexual behavior has suffered the same neglect. Most attention has been paid to the modification of homosexual behavior. The results from a number of series have been reported, mostly using aversion therapy of one sort or another. The duration of follow-up and method of reporting and measuring change, have been so variable and often so ill described that it is almost meaningless to compare the results of one study with another.

The best results have been reported by MacCulloch and Feldman (1967) whose 'anticipatory avoidance' technique was associated with a successful outcome in 57% of a series of 47 cases. They reported a similar outcome in a later series (Feldman and MacCulloch, 1971). The success rate in most series, however, has varied between 25 and 35%, suggesting that it is very much a minority of homosexuals who seek treatment who are substantially helped in this way.

Very few reports of the treatment of pedophiliacs have appeared. Mellor (1972) using the anticipatory avoidance procedure reported successful outcome in 8 out of 12 pedophiliacs.

Good results in the treatment of transvestites and fetishists have been reported by Morgenstern and co-workers (1965); 12 out of 13 transvestites had stopped or largely reduced their cross-dressing behavior, though the follow-up period was short. Marks and associates (1970) reported a successful outcome in two-thirds of transvestites at two years follow-up. In a further group of transvestites with transexual tendencies, however, none did well. The presence of transexual urges in transvestites is probably an important negative prognostic factor in any attempt to reduce cross-dressing behavior.

In the treatment of exhibitionism, Evans (1970) reported a 50% success rate after 6 months. Rooth and Marks (1974) at 12 months follow-up found that only 5 out of 12 patients had succeeded in avoiding further exhibitionist behavior.

So far very few prognostic factors have been established for any of these groups. Apart from the presence of transexual feelings in transvestites, referred to above, the absence of any previous heterosexual interest in homosexuals seeking re-orientation is also considered to make substantial change very unlikely (Feldman and MacCulloch, 1971).

Comparative studies

Few studies have been reported in which one method of treatment has been compared with another. McConaghy (1969, 1970) compared two types of aversive procedure, chemical aversion and aversion relief using electric shock, to treat 2 groups, each of 20 homosexual patients. The measures of change used, whilst not entirely satisfactory, indicated very little difference in outcome between the two groups. There was a tendency for those receiving chemical aversion to show greater reduction in homosexual behavior and those receiving aversion relief, more increase in heterosexuality. These differences were in the expected direction but the results were inconclusive. McConaghy and Barr (1973) went on to carry out further studies, comparing one type of aversive treatment with another, but again failed to demonstrate and differences.

Feldman and MacCulloch (1971) after the success of their earlier series (MacCulloch and Feldman, 1967) attempted to assess the relative importance of their specific aversive technique, 'anticipatory avoidance' learning. They compared it with a simple classical aversive procedure, as described earlier, and included in the study a third group who received brief psychotherapy; 10 patients were treated in each group. Unfortunately there were various methodological flaws in the study which reduced its usefulness. One can conclude, however, that there was no appreciable difference between the two aversive procedures whereas the comparison with the psychotherapy is not conclusive.

Birk and co-workers (1971) compared a computerized modification of the MacCulloch and Feldman avoidance method with a 'placebo' method which was identical except that instead of receiving or avoiding a shock, a light was involved; 8 homosexual patients were treated by each method. Their results suggested that the real aversive procedure was more effective than the placebo in producing changes in the short term. By a year or more of follow-up, however, there was virtually no difference between the two groups. This study was confounded by the fact that both groups were receiving group psychotherapy throughout the study.

Bancroft (1970) compared electric aversion therapy with systematic desensitization; 15 homosexual patients were treated by each method. The aversive procedure was in two parts; for the first half of the course of treatment a 'punishment-of-erection' procedure was used, using pictures as stimuli. For the second half, a 'punishment-of-fantasy' procedure was adopted. In the systematic desensitization method the homosexual patient was treated on the assumption that he had a phobia of heterosexuality, with basically the same approach as is used in the desensitization of other phobias (Wolpe, 1958). Various measures of change were used, including ratings of homosexual and heterosexual behavior, sexual attitudes and erectile responses to homo- and heterosexual stimuli. After a short follow-up there were no significant differences in outcome between the two groups. What was noticeable, however, was that those who showed changes in their sexual behavior ratings (both homosexual and heterosexual) also showed changes on the other measures which were significantly greater in the heterosexual than in the homosexual range. This suggested that treatment, when effective, whether it be aversive or nonaversive, produced its effects principally on the heterosexuality rather than on the homosexuality. This was further support for the change of emphasis in treatment from reducing deviant behavior, to increasing 'normal' behavior.

In none of these studies so far, was any attempt made to include clinically relevant patient characteristics as variables in a balanced design. A further study by James and co-workers (1974) went on to do this in a simple way. They hypothesized that homosexuals who were manifestly anxious about heterosexuality would do better with systematic desensitization than with aversion; those who were not heterosexually anxious would do better with aversion. They used a simple factorial design in which they allocated the homosexual patients to heterosexually phobic and nonphobic groups and then randomly allocated half of each group to either aversion (a modification of MacCulloch and Feldman's anticipatory avoidance procedure) or systematic desensitization. Desensitization produced more improvement than aversion in both phobic and nonphobic groups, but the effect was particularly marked in the phobic patients.

The results of these two last studies throw serious doubt on the efficacy of aversion therapy and its preference to nonaversive methods, at least as far as homosexual behavior is concerned.

Rooth and Marks (1974) using a cross-over design, compared aversion, self-regulation (similar to covert sensitization) and simple relaxation in a group of 12 exhibitionists. The results were again inconclusive though they suggested a slight superiority of aversion over the other two methods.

Callahan and Leitenberg (1973), using a series of individual case studies, compared covert sensitization with a 'punishment-of-erection' procedure. The two methods were alternated repeatedly and the results suggested slightly more change with covert sensitization.

With one or two exceptions, these various studies are consistent in failing to find substantial differences in outcome between different methods. This may simply be indicating that these specific techniques are only one part of the treatment and therefore cannot be adequately evaluated in isolation from the less specific aspects of the treatment program. If so, this poses formidable problems for outcome research although it is true to say that the possibility of evaluating more flexible and comprehensive treatment programs has not yet been adequately explored (see Bancroft, 1974, for further discussion).

Three further conclusions can be drawn. Firstly, aversion therapy does not appear to be justified on the grounds of efficacy except possibly in a small proportion of cases. Indications for this more limited use have yet to be properly defined, though in my opinion they are likely to be confined to those cases where self-control of sexual behavior is the principal problem (see below), or where response to certain erotic stimuli (for example, fetishism) can be usefully reduced without having to establish major changes of stimulus class. There seems little place for aversion in changing a homosexual orientation to heterosexual. Secondly, a close look at the effects of aversive procedures (Bancroft, 1974) does not permit the conclusion that changes produced by them are dependent on the laboratory models of aversive learning which provided their theoretical basis; when aversion therapy works, we do not understand why. Finally there are various pointers to the general principle that treatment should be aimed at establishing 'normal', rewarding, sexual behavior rather than eliminating the 'abnormal'.

4. TECHNIQUES APPLIED TO SEXUAL DYSFUNCTION

Until recently, behavior therapists have paid scant attention to the treatment of sexual dysfunction. Where anxiety has been an obvious factor, systematic desensitization has been used. Lazarus (1963) reported encouraging results in women with 'frigidity' and Friedman (1968) achieved success in a small series of males with erectile impotence using desenisitization combined with methohexital relaxation. O'Gorman (1974) has used group desensitization techniques for 'frigid' women with some success.

The use of graded dilators for vaginismus has been used for many years by many therapists and combined in various ways with other treatment strategies. Ellison (1968) combined the use of dilators with insight therapy and reported an 87% success rate in 100 cases of nonconsummation. The Family Planning Association has adopted a comparable approach, though the use of digital exploration has been preferred to dilators. This has been best described by Friedman (1962) and Tunnadine (1970).

Semans (1956), a urologist, introduced a special technique for treating premature ejaculation in which the male stimulated himself repeatedly to a point just short of ejaculatory inevitability. Hastings (1963) advocated masturbation techniques for some anorgasmic women and for some time Schultz (1951) has been reducing anxiety in sexually dysfunctional couples by banning intercourse in the initial stages of treatment.

Most of these therapeutic endeavors, although behavioral and practical in form, have not been pioneered by behavior therapists. Apart from systematic desensitization, which is of course used for a wide variety of behavioral problems, the only therapeutic innovation in this area to come from behavior therapists has been 'positive conditioning' of erections for erectile impotence (Quinn et al., 1970). As mentioned earlier, erections do seem to be peculiarly conditionable, but much therapeutic efforts are very preliminary and it is too early to know whether this is a technique for general application.

Masters and Johnson (1970) modified several of these earlier techniques and incorporated them into their comprehensive package. Other workers have further modified their approach, making it more flexible and adaptable and incorporating further treatment innovations (Lobitz and LoPiccolo, 1972; Kaplan, 1974; Bancroft, 1975). LoPiccolo will expand on his approach more fully in a separate chapter. The basic principles, however, are of general relevance and will be discussed in more detail in the final part of this chapter.

Masters and Johnson (1970) claimed results which were not only generally superior to other workers, but involved large numbers. Both their series and those mentioned previously are uncontrolled, however. Important selection factors might have operated in producing such good results and careful controlled evaluation is required.

Comparative studies

Comparative studies for treatment of sexual dysfunction have only just started. Obler (1973), reporting the first, compared a combination of desensitisation and role-rehearsal with both traditional group therapy and 'no treatment'. There were 22 subjects in each group. He claimed superior results with the first method, 18 out of the 22 being sexually functional at follow-up. Both the other methods were significantly less effective. The subjects in the study were university staff and students, both male and female, and no details were given of the nature of their sexual problems. The conclusions that can be drawn from this study are therefore limited. It is notable that in this study systematic desensitization was combined with another technique, that is, role-rehearsal.

Kockott and co-workers (1975) using systematic desensitization alone, compared it with 'routine' therapy (usual outpatient support) and 'no treatment'. The patients were all men with erectile impotence and there were 8 in each group. The results failed to show any superiority of systematic desensitization over the other methods except that the desensitized patients reported less anxiety in sexual situations after treatment. These workers went on to give these patients and their partners 'couple therapy' along the lines of Masters and Johnson and reported much better results. However, this comparison was not in any sense properly controlled, and the difference is not therefore conclusive.

In a recent study (Mathews, 1975), three methods of treatment were compared. The first was a Masters and Johnson procedure modified to be used in a National Health Service setting (Bancroft, 1975). The second was a 'postal' version of Masters and Johnson. The couple were seen initially as in the first method. In addition they were interviewed half way through treatment and at the end. Between these sessions, however, all contact between patient and therapist was by post. The therapists would send instructions and a set of questions and comments on the couple's previous reply. The couple would reply with answers to the questions and a progress report. The third method combined systematic desensitization with counseling aimed at modifying relevant attitudes revealed during treatment. The purpose of this comparison was to separate the specific Masters and Johnson behavioral directions (included in the postal method) from the nonbehavioral counseling part of the Masters and Johnson approach included and combined with systematic desensitization in the third group; 12 couples with various types of sexual dysfunction were treated in each group. There was a trend in favor of the full Masters and Johnson method, though in most measures this was not significant and only reached the 10% level of significance in ratings of female sexual enjoyment and frequency of intercourse. Also included in the study was a comparison of the use of one and two therapists. When only one therapist was involved he or she would be the same sex as the presenting partner in the couple. There were no significant differences in outcome between the use of one or two therapists although there was a weak interaction effect (significant at the 10% level) suggesting that the use of two therapists may have an advantage in the full Masters and Johnson procedure. This find ing, however, was not sufficiently strong to support the general use of two therapists when economic factors have to be taken into consideration. It may eventually be possible to identify those couples who would justify the use of co-therapists.

In these few comparative studies it has become abundantly clear that we lack satisfactory outcome measures. Although sexual behavior is more tangible than most behavior types representing to the therapist, a sexual relationship is a complex matter and until some appropriate multivariate methodology, using properly established measures, is developed these controlled studies will lack relevance and comparability. This represents one of the main areas of priority for research in this field.

5. THE CURRENT CLINICAL APPROACH

The preceding section has shown that so far very few clinically relevant questions have been answered by research. The methodological problems involved in treatment outcome research are considerable. Hopefully recent improvements in research method will continue and in time more answers will be forthcoming. In the meantime clinical problems continue and the demand for help with sexual problems is increasing dramatically.

This section will aim to provide a balanced clinical approach based on behavioral principles and incorporating such research evidence as is available and relevant. It contains many assumptions which, in time, should be tested and modified. In no sense does it aim to provide a definitive treatment method but rather an approach which can be used as a starting point for the individual therapist to employ or modify as he finds suits him.

Basic principles

Inherent in this approach are some basic principles which deserve emphasis at this point.

The relationship between patient and therapist of 'adult—adult' type
Behavior modification as a discipline has paid scant attention to the patient—therapist relationship. Whilst the therapist has been recognized as a crucial source of both positive and negative reinforcement for patient behavior, such reinforcement can occur within a variety of types of relationship, the natures of which are difficult to define in behavioral terms. To describe that which is basic to this clinical approach it is proposed to borrow from the transactional analyst the concept of an 'adult—adult' relationship. This implies that responsibility for the choice of treatment objectives and the onus for achieving them lies with the patient who exploits the expertise and therapeutic concern of the therapist. This is to be distinguished from two types of relationship both of which impart principal responsibility for

change and treatment to the therapist. The first can be called the 'parent—child' type of relationship where the patient relates in a child's role. The second is the 'doctor—sick patient' relationship, where responsibility is transferred to the therapist because of 'illness' in the patient. Neither of these is compatible with the treatment approach advocated here, though it may be true that during the course of treatment the relationship temporarily becomes of either kind. The ultimate success of treatment will then depend on establishing or regaining the basic 'adult—adult' form.

In this way, not only is the patient made aware of the active part that he must take but it is also easier to avoid the therapist uncritically imposing his own personal and cultural values and the patient passively accepting them.

The objectives of treatment are agreed and made explicit at the start
The main types of objective, as mentioned in the introduction to this section, are as follows:

(i) The establishment of a rewarding sexual relationship (which may be either hetero- or homosexual).

(ii) The improvement of sexual function within the sexual relationship.

(iii) The self-control of unwanted sexual behavior.

The fourth category, nonsexual and social adjustment to a deviant sexual role, whilst perfectly compatible with a behavioral approach, will not be considered further in this chapter. For the homosexual this objective is considered in the Chapters 100 and 101, and for the transexual in Chapter 102.

Although it is clearly the therapist's responsibility to ensure that the objectives of treatment are those wanted by the patient, it does not follow that the therapist should necessarily accept the patient's objectives. He may reject them on the grounds that they are in his opinion impracticable or doomed to failure, incompatible with the needs and personality of the patient, or unacceptable on ethical grounds. In each case he should make his reasons clear to the patient, who is then in a position to seek help elsewhere.

A recurring problem to the sex therapist is whether to accept objectives of a nonsexual kind. This is particularly important in the counseling of couples where frequently, at the outset, it is not clear whether the sexual problem is secondary to other interpersonal problems or vice versa. If in doubt on this point, it is my policy to focus on the sexual relationship, providing that the couple accepts the goals of treatment as relevant and sufficiently important. In such a case it can be pointed out that nonsexual aspects of the relationship will be dealt with when they are clearly relevant to the sexual relationship (for example, when resentment about role conflicts leads to avoidance of sexual contact), and that improvement in the sexual relationship, particularly as it affects communication will frequently spread to other aspects of the relationship. If it becomes clear during the course of treatment that the principal focus should be changed, then the objectives of treatment are re-negotiated.

In establishing the treatment contract with the patient or couple, it is advisable to agree on the approximate duration and extent of therapy. If the therapist is uncertain of the appropriateness of this approach it is useful to agree on a much more limited contract — of say 3 or 4 sessions with the proviso that at the end of that time further treatment will be considered and will depend on initial progress. It is fortunate that those who ultimately do well with this behavioral approach usually show encouraging changes in the first few sessions and it is becoming increasingly evident that some of the best predictors of outcome lie in these early responses to treatment (Mathews et al., 1974).

This is primarily an educational approach
The emphasis is on the establishment of rewarding sexual behavior rather than the elimination of psychopathology or the treatment of illness. Clearly there are important medical aspects of human sexual problems. In a small proportion of individuals the primary problem will be medical and require attempted medical treatment (for example, vaginal infections causing painful intercourse or diabetes mellitus causing erectile impotence). In others there may be consequences of sexual behavior that necessitate special medical advice, such as the effects of sexual arousal on the damaged myocardium. The relationship between sexual problems and psychiatric illness is more complex. Depression is a common accompaniment to sexual difficulties. Often this is an understandable reaction to the interpersonal and sexual problems. Not uncommonly, one partner of a marriage may have been regarded as suffering from depressive illness and treated as such, when it was the marital relationship that required attention. Nevertheless there are obviously instances when it is appropriate to treat the patient as ill. If so, as indicated earlier, this should be dealt with before embarking on this approach to the sexual problems. Similarly, it is assumed that any organic medical problem has been excluded or dealt with before embarking on this approach.

The approach is flexible and eclectic
The approach is designed to meet the needs of the individual case. We have moved quite definitely from the stage when treatment was a matter of applying specific techniques, such as aversion therapy, to a specific condition, such as fetishism typical of the traditional medical approach to disease. Masters and Johnson (1970) made the first important step by introducing a program which was sufficiently comprehensive to meet the various needs of their patients. Whilst there have been some who have applied their principles rather inflexibly, the impetus for exploring new treatment approaches has been such that the Masters and Johnson procedure has not been allowed to become frozen by dogma, in the manner that has characterized so many schools of psychotherapy.

The approach is based on certain principles of behavioral psychotherapy
The theoretical or learning paradigm that may be applied will not only vary

from therapist to therapist according to their inclinations but also within any one program of treatment in an eclectic manner. Nevertheless there are certain underlying behavioral principles of general relevance that will prevail in any case. These are as follows:

(i) At each treatment session, the target behavior forms are defined and the patient or couple asked to carry them out before the next session. These usually represent small steps towards the final treatment goal.

(ii) At the next session the patient is asked in detail about his efforts to carry out those behavior forms and any problems or negative feelings that resulted.

(iii) In this way key attitudes or resistances to change are identified.

(iv) These attitudes are then modified if possible.

(v) A new set of target behavior forms is defined before the end of the session.

(vi) In the next session the process is repeated.

(vii) If no behavioral progress is made, then either the objectives are re-negotiated or treatment is stopped.

The patient is always given something to do between sessions and not only does this represent behavioral progress during treatment but it is a remarkably powerful method for revealing the underlying problems and the attitudes that block change.

It is in the modification of such attitudes that the behavioral approach is less clearly defined and it is here that the main source of variance between therapists, and overlap with other psychotherapeutic approaches occurs.

Kaplan (1974) applies psychoanalytic principles at this point. I prefer to formulate my strategies in terms of an attitude-change model which does not depend on any psychodynamic interpretation of the origins or content of such attitudes but rather on mechanisms for modifying them. The source of this model is the social psychology of attitude change and persuasion; the mediating mechanism is assumed to be the reduction of inconsistency between one attitude and another, between attitudes and incontrovertible facts or between attitudes and behavior. The therapist's task is to provoke those inconsistencies and the strategies he uses can be categorized into three main groups:

(i) *Cognitive* in which the individual is confronted with reality and its incongruence with his attitudes and expectations. Some patients respond particularly well to such an approach; others are apparently immune to it. The criteria for predicting who will respond remain to be clarified.

(ii) *Behavioral* where one relies on the inconsistency between behavior and beliefs or feelings. An attitude can be changed by gradually and insidiously encroaching on it with incongruent behavior. Here the hierarchical approach is important. It may not be possible to persuade a woman to initiate genital contact because of its incompatibility with her role as the 'good woman', but it may be possible to persuade her to initiate a very much more limited act. Then, gradually, she is persuaded to initiate more and more so that eventually she changes her idea of the 'good woman's' role. In sex therapy in particular, the patient can be confronted with any pleasurable sensation that he or she experienced which may be inconsistent with previous attitudes. Various techniques can be used to elicit incompatible behavior during the treatment session, which thereby facilitate behavior change outside the treatment session. Procedures such as desensitization in imagination or aversion therapy, can be seen to work in this way, although they are traditionally regarded as methods of teaching new behavior.

(iii) Noncognitive   which, for want of a better term, is used to cover a miscellany of strategies which rely either on the expression of affect or on the quality of the patient—therapist relationship. The following are examples from this category. Attitudes may be changed by facilitating the expression of affect such as anger or guilt. This facilitation may depend on the sense of security instilled by the therapist as well as direct encouragement. The therapist may himself hold and express attitudes which are incompatible with those not only of the patient but of other important authority figures in the patient's life (such as parents). This is particularly likely where sexual behavior is concerned. If the patient regards the therapist positively then this discrepancy may influence the patient's attitude. This latter process is obviously comparable to the 'cognitive' mechanisms described above but the emphasis here is on the discrepancy between 'values' rather than 'meaning'. Once the patient is aware of discrepancies between his attitudes and reality or of a need to explain his behavior, an explanation by the therapist, if chosen carefully, may facilitate attitude change. The value of such 'interpretations' is probably determined as much by their timing as by their content! If given before the patient has need of explanation they may be less effective.

The principle objectives of treatment can now be considered in more detail.

Specific methods

The establishment of a rewarding sexual relationship
The problems to be overcome may include the following:
   — A general lack of sexual interest or responsiveness.
   — Lack of sexual responsiveness to particular types of person.
   — Anxiety or uncertainty about sexual relationships which is sufficient to inhibit the initiation or seeking out of such relationships. This anxiety may be associated with either the social or sexual part of the relating process.
   — Problems in maintaining a relationship with a sexual partner other than those involving specifically sexual dysfunction (for example, inappropriate

'dating' behavior, general communication, coping with anger, role conflicts, and so on).

General lack of sexual responsiveness   Clearly there is considerable individual variation in the degree of sexual responsiveness and some individuals will be at the very low end of the distribution. The factors determining such variance or indeed determining sexual responsiveness at any level, are far from clear. From the therapist's point of view the most helpful and constructive hypothesis to explain a low level of responsiveness is that the individual's normal level is inhibited by psychological mechanisms — either direct inhibition or the interfering effects of manifest anxiety. Treatment is thus aimed at reducing such inhibition or anxiety whilst at the same time encouraging a learning approach to one's own bodily responses.

The first objective therefore is to help the individual to accept and experience his or her own sexual feelings. The patient is encouraged to explore his body, along the lines of Masters and Johnson's 'senate focus' approach, though here used on an individual basis. Initially, genital areas are avoided whilst all other parts of the body are explored. The aim is to achieve a combination of a relaxed state and pleasurable sensations. Once nongenital pleasuring is successful, the process is extended to the genital areas and eventually more direct genital stimulation is encouraged with lubricant cream, and if necessary stimulating aids like vibrators. In addition to setting these precise behavioral goals, the therapist aims to reduce guilt or anxiety reinforcing the idea that such behavior is good and an important step towards enjoying a sexual relationship. In the course of pursuing such goals, key attitudes may be revealed.

Case example   A 23-year-old single male graduate presented with the absence of any genital sensations. Sexual intercourse had been achieved but was a pleasureless, neutral experience for him. After individual 'sensate focus' and the use of lubricating cream, he discovered that the corona of his penis was exquisitely and pleasurably sensitive in a way that he had never experienced before. His level of sexual arousal increased until he experienced a feeling of apprehension, lost his erection and stopped stimulating himself. On close questioning about his apprehensive response, he revealed that he was frightened of losing control of himself, something that he never did in any situation. Also, although intellectually he could reject the idea, he felt emotionally that sensual pleasure was in some way sinful. After revealing these attitudes, and being reassured about the likely consequences of continued arousal, he was able to repeat the experience without anxiety.

Although such inhibition most commonly reflects the avoidance of sexuality in general, in some cases it may be a fear of a particular type of sexual response that leads to inhibition.

Case example   A 21-year-old girl asked for help to overcome her homosexual interest, and to regain a heterosexual interest that she had previously experienced. She had never experienced a homosexual relationship and rejected the idea of doing so. When first seen she described very little sexual responsiveness of any kind and no masturbation.
   Initially individual 'sensate focus' achieved very little. Once a vibrator was introduced

she started to experience strong arousal and orgasm. At this stage she was able to accept her homosexual feelings and has enjoyed a lesbian relationship since. Her earlier rejection of her homosexuality had led to a general inhibition of her sexual responsiveness and once that was overcome it was earlier with reassurance from the therapist for her to re-accept her homosexual feelings.

A not uncommon account from a young male is the awareness of some sadistic tendency and the avoidance of sexual arousal for fear that the sadistic impulse will get out of control.

Ignorance often needs to be tackled and information given about appropriate methods of stimulation and sensitive body areas.

If anxiety about body contact or sexual response is marked and consistent, showing a phobic quality, systematic desensitization may be useful (Bancroft, 1974). The more formal method of desensitization in which the presentation of hierarchy items is combined with muscular relaxation, although sometimes useful, is not necessarily the most appropriate method. It may be preferable for the therapist to present items in a more educational, informative way but following a graded hierarchical approach. Thus, pictures of genitalia or sexual activity can be presented and discussed in the session. In addition the hierarchy of imaginary situations which may be used can also provide a sequence of behavior to be carried out between treatment sessions.

Erotic stimuli   films, literature, tape-recordings, may be useful adjuncts to increase arousability, or desensitize anxiety.

Lack of responsiveness to particular types of person   The commonest examples of this problem are those where there is adequate responsiveness to homosexual partners, or fetishistic stimuli but inadequate response to heterosexual partners. (The ability to respond to heterosexual stimuli but not homosexual is obviously very much more common but is seldom, if ever, presented as a problem.)

Early approaches using aversion concentrated simply on suppressing the initial responsiveness in the hope that the alternative and desired responsiveness would somehow emerge. It is now generally agreed that the emphasis should be on encouraging a new, rewarding responsiveness.

The most direct and most feasible approach is the 'shaping' of fantasies. Assuming that a sexual response occurs to the patient's usual fantasies, he is advised to modify these fantasies during masturbation. Such change in the fantasy may have to be very gradual to avoid losing the sexual response. He should be encouraged to experiment with fantasies, in order to find the most successful way of changing them. In the course of doing this much may be learned about the nature of his particular sexual anxieties and key attitudes that may require modification.

Case example   A 30-year-old male with homosexual interest and several previous homosexual relationships sought help to establish a heterosexual relationship. He was asked to experiment with his masturbation fantasies. He reported that the only fantasy of a heterosexual kind that was compatible with sexual arousal involved a woman taking all the initiative sexually and producing in him a full erection. On discussing the contrast between this fantasy and others in which he took a more active role it became clear that he was considerably threatened by the degree of activity and initiative that might be expected of him in a heterosexual relationship and the fear of failure that would result. This reflected an important aspect of his personality which had not prevented him from participating in a passive way in homosexual relationships.

Case example   A 20-year-old lesbian girl who wanted to relate heterosexually was asked to fantasize about a man whom she liked and found attractive. She was able to produce an image of his face but could not extend this to include his whole body. When asked to do so she was able to imagine him standing behind a bar but could not imagine him walking from behind the bar so that the lower part of his body became visible. It soon became clear to her that she had a phobia of male genitalia that she had not previously recognized. This was then tackled by means of imaginal desensitization.

When fantasies are predictably associated with sexual arousal which can be measured in the treatment session by penile or vaginal plethysmography, then modification or shaping of fantasies can be carried out in the session. By monitoring the physiological responses, fantasies can be modified sufficiently gradually and in the appropriate direction. In this way the therapist can be more involved in the modification process and can obtain much additional information. An example of this approach used with a masochist is reported elsewhere (Bancroft, 1971).

Other specific and ingenious techniques for generalizing sexual responsiveness from one set of stimuli to another have already been described. They are time-consuming, require equipment and as yet their usefulness has not been adequately assessed. Further details of these various reports are provided by Bancroft (1974).

It is often the case that erotic responses established early in sexual development have an intensity which is greater than that of those acquired later. Although novelty often enhances sexual responsiveness, it seems that such novelty is confined within a particular class of stimulus and docs not necessarily extend to new classes. The determinants and limits of such classes of stimulus and individual variations in the effects of novelty are, needless to say, ill understood and provide an important area for research. The patient should be told that change in response from one class of stimulus to another will be gradual, that the quality of a newly acquired sexual response is likely to be different, and that the value of the sexual response is determined less by its intensity than by the rewards and satisfactions associated with it in a sexual relationship. Also, satisfaction and pleasure may be enhanced by the passage of time and the development of intimacy and good communication within a stable relationship. It is sometimes necessary to counter in this way, the patient's belief that failure to achieve at an early stage the same intensity of sexual response to new stimuli, means that treatment has failed.

Anxiety or uncertainty about sexual relationships   There are relatively few individuals who pass through their adolescence without some apprehension in approaching or establishing sexual relationships. The behavioral repertoire of the adolescent probably depends to a great extent on learning from the peer group. In some, lack of awareness of the effects of their behavior may create for the would-be partner the impression of insensitivity to the feelings of others. In some, undue anxiety about the effects of their behavior may seriously impair effective sociosexual behavior. In either case a vicious spiral of anxiety or lack of self-confidence and social incompetence may become established, and may be sufficient to keep the individual away from potential sexual relationships altogether, or encourage him to enter into relationships of a kind which make no demand on him. This perhaps is especially likely in those who had insufficient contact with a mixed-sex peer group in late childhood and adolescence and who tended to be isolated or involved more in same-sex pairings than in groups.

After a time the anxiety becomes self-perpetuating because the individual reaches an age where social and sexual competence is expected of him. Sometimes his anxiety and lack of self-confidence is a manifestation of a neurotically low self-esteem and not understandable as a result of failure in interpersonal contacts.

Whatever the cause of such anxiety it may have various negative effects. It may inhibit or prevent the initiation of appropriate behavior; in some cases it may inhibit sexual responsiveness and interest, whilst in others it may lead to an anxious preoccupation with sex.

The therapeutic approach to such anxiety is to agree on limited behavioral goals of a sociosexual kind. The male patient is asked to initiate very limited contact with an attractive girl. He then reports back in detail to the therapist how he carried out the encounter. Inappropriate behavior may be revealed and alternatives suggested. Also sources of anxiety and other obstructive attitudes may be revealed and require modification. Often such a person needs help in setting limits to such encounters so that he can minimize the fear that once initiated they will become out of control and lead to a repetition of earlier failure.

Case example   A 25-year-old male had discovered himself impotent in an earlier relationship with a girl. This led to a break up of the relationship. He had completely lost confidence in his ability to relate to girls and feared further sexual failure. He was advised to initiate a further relationship by dating a girl but was prepared with the account that he was still feeling the loss of his earlier girlfriend. This he could use, if necessary, to explain his reluctance to go too far sexually in the new relationship.

Much anxiety of this kind stems from ignorance of what to expect and what is expected of one. Much can be done by informing the patient of the norms of behavior though great care must be taken to choose the norms from the appropriate subculture. A male therapist is in a particular position to advise male patients on appropriate male behavior whilst a female therapist can indicate what male behavior is acceptable or unacceptable to females, and vice versa. Obviously the use of male and female co-therapists has advantages but is expensive in therapist time. In choosing the sex of the therapist consideration should be given to the main source of sexual anxiety and whether a female therapist would be more or less effective than a male in reducing it.

The use of videotape feedback of the patient's behavior in groups or using role-playing techniques, can be valuable in modifying and improving social approach behavior. Social skills training of this kind (Argyle et al., 1974) is expensive and requires special equipment and as yet is not generally available. Also its relative efficacy in modifying sociosexual behavior is not yet established.

Case example   A 19-year-old boy presented complaining of lack of sexual interest. Questioning revealed that his earlier sexual fantasies were of a homosexual and mildly sadistic kind. He was adamant that he would not accept a homosexual role and had consequently suppressed his sexual interest in general. He was shy and had had little contact with girls. He had no idea how to start a relationship and was given social skills training in a mixed-sex group. After 8 sessions he felt sufficiently confident to start dating a girl; 6 months later he is seeing her regularly and enjoying limited sexual contact with her.

Problems in maintaining a sexual relationship   Apart from specific sexual dysfunction, which will be considered in the next section, problems in interpersonal behavior may make not only the initiation but also the maintenance of the sexual relationship difficult or impossible. If the relationship starts during the course of therapy or is of very recent origin it is less likely that the therapist will have access to the partner. Frequently, however, much counsel can be given about what is expected in the early stages of a sexual relationship; the sequence of sexual behavior that is commonly involved, the significance of what the partner is doing or saying. Here again the same-sex therapist may have special value as a model whilst the opposite sex therapist will be able to interpret the likely reactions of the partner to the patient's behavior.

Case example   A 20-year-old male was excessively shy of girls and before treatment had started had never had a steady girlfriend. Once he started such a relationship, careful analysis of his 'dating' behavior revealed that he had made minimal sexual approaches on the first date which had been rather uncertainly rejected. It was explained to him that from his background the girl would feel it necessary to reject initial sexual advances to avoid being regarded as 'too keen' but would be hoping that the boy would persist so that she could concede after a 'decent' interval.

There are in addition certain basic principles of dyadic behavior (behavior between two people in a special or 'pair-bond' relationship) which can be suggested to the individual but which are most useful if explained to both members of the pair jointly.

(a) Maintain good communication. Work hard at ensuring that the other knows how you feel and in this way keep close emotional contact.

(b) Resolve anger when it arises. Probably more dyadic problems stem from unresolved hostility than any other single cause. Many couples fail to develop a pattern of expressing and communicating anger that is suitable for them. Often this is because one or both partners have grown up believing it wrong to express anger and consequently 'bottle it up.' In others their individual methods of dealing with anger interact unfavorably. Frequently it is not realized that this basic aspect of dyadic behavior requires special attention and development if the dyad is to become stable.

(c) Emphasize positive rather than negative reinforcement. Many dyads are controlled by a mutually coercive pattern (Patterson and Hops, 1972) where each controls the other by aversive methods (punishing the partner for unwanted behavior) or negative reinforcement (maintaining some punitive behavior such as nagging or sulking until the desired response is forthcoming). Each member of the pair is advised to encourage or reinforce desired behavior in the partner by rewarding them in some way when they occur. It is frequently necessary to get individuals or couples to define precisely what it is about the partner's behavior that is desirable or undesirable. This very process of behavioral analysis is often effective in facilitating their communication. In addition it provides detail for some negotiated agreement between them; that is, which desirable behavior will be carried out by each member. This type of marital 'contracting' may involve trading off one comparable behavior for another (Patterson and Hops, 1972) or even the use of tokens whereby each partner can 'buy' a desired response by paying a token (Stewart, 1969). As the number of tokens in such a 'marital economy' is fixed, positive behavior must be reciprocated if the system is to keep moving. Usually such precise or tangible methods of contracting are not necessary or only needed for a short period. Hopefully the inherent advantages of these basic principles are quickly recognized by both partners so that the system becomes self-maintaining.

Improving sexual function within a relationship
The majority of people seeking help for sexual dysfunction are involved in a relationship at the time. The recent upsurge in therapeutic optimism and apparent efficacy has depended very much on the treatment of the couple rather than the individual. LoPiccolo will be talking about couple therapy in more detail in the next chapter. Only a brief description will be presented here. Following this, the treatment of sexual dysfunction in the individual without a partner will be considered.

The approach described by Masters and Johnson (1970) provides the basis for most current treatment of sexual dysfunction. This approach has two components, (1) 'sensate focus', and (2) specific techniques.

'Sensate focus' is a term used by Masters and Johnson to describe the basis of their program. The couple is instructed to explore each other's body in order to find out which parts are pleasurable to the touch and how best to touch them. This process of 'pleasuring' relies on appropriate feedback from the partner and hence brings into focus any communication problems that exist. Initially there is not only a ban on intercourse but also on any genital contact. This authoritative setting of limits by the therapist plays a crucial part in reducing performance anxiety. As progress is made with sensate focus, genital contact is involved and a gradual series of steps towards vaginal intercourse agreed on. In this way there is no dramatic switch from foreplay to intercourse and at each stage it is explicitly agreed that the next step will only be undertaken if both partners are ready to do so.

During this process much in the way of attitudes or resistances that block behavioral change are revealed and dealt with during therapy along the lines already discussed.

This gradual extension of sensate focus may be all that is required, but the use of one or other of the specific techniques may become necessary. These include either the 'stop—start' or 'squeeze' technique for premature ejaculation, the use of graded dilators for vaginismus and 'superstimulation' of the penis for ejaculatory failure. These are described in detail by LoPiccolo.

The individual without a partner who seeks treatment is in most instances less easy to help. This does depend, however, on the nature of the problem. The main difficulty concerns generalization of any change in solitary behavior to behavior with a partner. The male whose relationship has ended because of erectile impotence might be quite difficult to help until he has started another relationship. The young male who has never ejaculated presents a rather easier problem; usually the ejaculatory failure is part of a generally inhibited sexual pattern. He may have avoided a sexual relationship both because of his fear that there was something abnormal about him and because of his generally inhibited attitudes to sex. Reassurance and reduction of guilt, and advice about masturbation techniques may lead to successful orgasm quite quickly, though initially the intensity of orgasm may be relatively low. Following this there may be important changes in the individual's sexual identity and subsequent attempts at forming a relationship. This approach is an extension of the individual sensate focus described earlier for increasing general sexual responsiveness.

A comparable problem is the anorgasmic woman who with a similar approach, sometimes involving a vibrator, may be able to achieve orgasm quite quickly. It does not, of course, follow that in either case the individual's problems are over and further help may be required once a sexual relationship is started. But often the change is sufficiently reassurring and disinhibiting to make the next step feasible.

Whenever there is a clearly phobic response to sexual stimuli, systematic desensitization or some method of anxiety control on an individual basis may help and successes have certainly been reported when such an approach is combined with appropriate counseling. O'Gorman and her colleagues (personal communication) have found the use of group desensitization techniques for unresponsive women to be of some value, even though their partners were not involved.

At the present time most sex therapists would see little point in treating the individual when the partner is available and prepared to cooperate. We would also consider it of bad prognostic significance if a partner exists and yet will not participate in treatment. Our evidence for this conclusion, however, is not very substantial and we should certainly keep an open mind on this point. The Family Planning Association (F.P.A.) in the United Kingdom has been providing psychosexual counseling for many years, long before Masters and Johnson established themselves. Because of the nature of these clinics, the tradition of treating only the female partner became established. It is noteworthy that they have had many successes, particularly with non-consummated marriages and vaginismus, often only requiring one, two or three treatment sessions (Tunnadine, 1970). Their approach inspired by the ideas of Michael Balint, relies a great deal on the vaginal examination by a female doctor and the recognition and interpretation of emotional reactions and attitudes elicited by that examination. In that sense it is similar to the general approach advocated here in that the setting of specific behavioral goals reveals the relevant attitudes to be modified. In this case, however, the behavioral goals are principally within the treatment session (the vaginal examination), whereas in the Masters and Johnson approach they are principally outside the treatment session. F.P.A. doctors have attempted to develop a comparable approach with male presenters but have found nothing that is comparable to the vaginal examination in facilitating behavioral change in the male (Tunnadine, personal communication). Hartman and Fithian (1972) on the other hand, have made use of physical exploration of both partners, though in their case the examination is more explicitly sexual.

It is quite possible that the nature of F.P.A. clinics in some way attracts women who are not only easy to help but can be helped without involving their spouses. This is an issue which deserves careful enquiry.

Self-control of unwanted sexual behavior

By now it should be clear to the reader that this writer's preference is to concentrate on facilitating positive rather than negative changes; on building up rewarding behavior rather than reducing unrewarding behavior. Nevertheless there remain some patients who either because of the negligible potential for positive change or because of the risk that their current behavior entails, leave the therapist with little to offer except help in controlling their unwanted sexuality. Self-control is something that is necessary and desirable in any social situation and when sexual offences are concerned, it is as often the lack of control as it is the nature of the behavior that needs modification. Fantasy life may be boundless and by its variety contribute in some way to the richness of one's experience. When, however, we fail to control the transition from fantasy to reality, we find ourselves in a very vulnerable and sometimes dangerous situation.

Types of behavior that most commonly present themselves in this respect are exhibitionism, pedophilia and rape. In these cases there is something unusual about the content of the behavior as well as its control. Nevertheless even though modifying the pattern of their sexual relationship requires the positive development of preferable alternatives, the enhancement of self-control is still the most direct and immediate means of keeping out of trouble.

In seeking improvement of self-control, the first step is a careful analysis of the sequence of events leading up to the unwanted acts. In some individuals this sequence is relatively predictable; in others it is not, the behavior seemingly arising out of the blue, or precipitated by a variety of nonspecific stressful events. In the second case, the therapist's task is much more difficult. Where predictability or consistency of behavior is involved there is much more scope for therapeutic intervention. A predictable sequence may offer a number of stages when alternative or incompatible behavior can be introduced. They are then clearly defined and rehearsed repeatedly either in fantasy or reality. In this way the patient knows full well that when the crucial point in the sequence is reached, he has a well-rehearsed alternative behavior pattern to carry out.

Case example A 22-year-old laborer sought help after being convicted of indecent exposure. He exposed himself quite frequently and in addition often showed 'peeping Tom' behavior for which he had not hitherto been convicted. Analysis of the usual sequence showed that these incidents usually occurred when he was returning home after drinking. It was agreed first that he would reduce his alcohol intake and secondly, arrange his drinking so that he always had a friend with whom to return home. He also had a tendency to walk along the riverbank when he would quite often expose himself to girls passing by in boats. It was agreed that he would not go for walks along the river unless accompanied by a friend.

The ability to comply with such self-regulatory rules obviously requires a strong wish to succeed in increasing self-control. It is also necessary to accept that such compliance may be made more difficult by the strength of the urge to carry out the deviant act. Frequently therefore it is helpful to combine this type of self-regulating rule-setting with some procedure which reduces the strength of the behavioral drive. It is here that either aversive techniques or covert sensitization may be useful.

It has already been mentioned that the original theoretical rationale for such procedures is not adequately supported by the available evidence. Precisely how such techniques do help remains uncertain but a plausible and therapeutically useful explanation is that they facilitate self-control by providing a well-rehearsed aversive fantasy situation which can be used to avert or weaken the urge to act. Thus in addition to the deployment of alternative behavior the patient can counter the urge to proceed by rehearsing in fantasy the aversive procedure previously experienced (or fantasized, if covert sensitization was used.) Whether the aversive procedures actually reduce the basic attractiveness of the behavior remains problematic, but it is probably therapeutically sensible to emphasize that the onus for self-control still rests with the individual and should not be attributed to some mysterious 'curative' action of the original treatment. This once again is making explicit where the responsibility lies.

Covert sensitization is more likely to be effective if the patient is capable of vivid and anxiety provoking imagery. Also where there is any degree of general anxiety, covert sensitization is probably preferable to the use of overt aversive techniques which have been shown to be less useful in anxious individuals.

If an aversive technique is to be used there seems very little reason to choose one technique rather than another except on the grounds of practical convenience. It is theoretically possible, however, that if the noxious stimulus is in some way relevant to the behavior, such as an emetic in the case of alcoholism, its effect will be increased. This remains to be demonstrated. If visual stimuli such as pictures, play an important part in the usual behavior pattern, then it is sensible to include them in the aversive procedure. On common-sense grounds it seems probable that the more the patient plays an active part in the procedure, as in the punishment-of-fantasy method when he has to signal the presence of the fantasy, or in anticipatory avoidance learning when he has to switch off to avoid the shock, the more likely is he to be influenced by the procedure. It is also possible that the use of computerized aversive procedures may, because of the impressive 'hardware' involved, be more powerful in influencing the suggestible patient.

The use of some self-punitive device such as a pocket shock-box or even the painful twang of an elastic band may be a further aid to self-control when used in the tempting situation.

The therapist's role, in addition to negotiating these behavioral rules with the patient, or administering aversion therapy or covert sensitization, is to maintain contact with the patient with gradually decreasing frequency. This is in order to remind the patient and hence reinforce his commitment to these goals and behavioral constraints. The worst enemy of the potential sex offender is his tendency to resort to mechanisms of denial with excusatory comments like: "I don't know what came over me", or "I have no idea how I came to be there". The therapist acts constantly to confront him with reality.

6. CONCLUSION

The position of the section on self-control at the end of this chapter and its relative brevity are indications of its lesser importance when compared with earlier sections. Nevertheless it is important not to end on such a negative note and to reinforce the idea that by far and away the most important function of the sex therapist is to encourage and facilitate the good, positive aspects of sex, that can do so much to bind relationships and promote well-being. This message is of special importance for the medical profession, which, following a long tradition, is much better equipped to deal with pain than with pleasure.

BIBLIOGRAPHY

Argyle, M., Trower, P. and Bryant, B. (1974) Explorations in the treatment of personality disorder and neurosis by social skills training. *Br. J. Med. Psychol.* 47: 63—72.

Bancroft, J.H.J. (1969) Aversion therapy of homosexuality. *Br. J. Psychiat.* 115: 1417—1431.

Bancroft, J.H.J. (1970) A comparative study of aversion and desensitisation in the treatment of homosexuality. In: (L.E. Burns and J.L.Worsley, Eds.) *Behaviour Therapy in the 1970's.* (Wright, Bristol) pp. 12—33.

Bancroft, J.H.J. (1971) The application of psychophysiological measures to the assessment and modification of sexual behaviour. *Behav. Res. Ther.* 9: 119—130.

Bancroft, J.H.J. (1974) *Deviant Sexual Behaviour: Modification and Assessment.* (Clarendon Press, Oxford.)

Bancroft, J.H.J. (1975) The Masters and Johnson approach in a National Health Service setting. *Br. J. Sex. Med.* 1: 6—10.

Barlow, D.H. and Agras, W.S. (1971) An experimental analysis of 'fading' to increase heterosexual responsiveness in homosexuality. Paper presented at South Eastern Psychological Association meeting, Miami Beach, Florida, April 1971.

Birk, L., Huddleston, W., Miller, E. and Cohler, B. (1971) Avoidance conditioning for homosexuality. *Arch. Gen. Psychiat.* 25: 314—323.

Callahan, E.J. and Leitenberg, H. (1973) Aversion therapy for sexual deviation: contingent shock and covert sensitization. *J. Abnorm. Psychol.* 81: 60—73.

Cautela, J.R. (1966) Treatment of compulsive behaviour by covert sensitization. *Psychol. Rec.* 16: 33—41.

Ellison, C. (1968) Psychosomatic factors in the unconsummated marriage. *J. Psychosom. Res.* 12: 61—66.

Evans, D.R. (1970) Subjective variables and treatment effects in aversion therapy. *Behav. Res. Ther.* 8: 147—152.

Feldman, M.P. and MacCullogh, M.J. (1971) *Homosexual Behaviour: Therapy and Assessment.* (Pergamon Press, Oxford.)

Friedman, L.J. (1962) *Virgin Wives. A Study of Unconsummated Marriages.* (Tavistock, London.)

Friedman, D. (1968) The treatment of impotence by Brietal relaxation therapy. *Behav. Res. Ther.* 6: 257—261.

Hartman, W.E. and Fithian, M.A. (1972) *Treatment of Sexual Dysfunction.* (Center for Marital and Sexual Studies, California.)

Hastings, D.W. (1963) *Impotence and Frigidity.* (Churchill, London.)

Herman, S.H., Barlow, D.H. and Agras, W.S. (1974) An experimental analysis of classical conditioning as a method of increasing heterosexual arousal in homosexuals. *Behav. Ther.* 5: 33—47.

James, S., Orwin, A. and Turner, R.K. (1974) Treatment of homosexuality. Paper read at IVth Annual Conference, European Association for Behaviour Therapy, London, July 1974.

Kaplan, H.S. (1974) *The New Sex Therapy.* (Brunner Mazel, New York.)

Kockott, G., Dittmar, F. and Nusselt, L. (1975) Systematic desensitisation of erectile impotence in a controlled study. *Arch. Sex. Behav.* 4: 493—500.

Lazarus, A.A. (1963) The treatment of chronic frigidity by systematic desensitisation. *J. Nerv. Ment. Dis.*, 136: 272—278.

Lemere, F. and Voegtlin, W.L. (1950) An evaluation of the aversion treatment of alcoholism. *Quart. J. Stud. Alcohol.*, 2: 199—204.

Lobitz, W.C. and LoPiccolo, J. (1972) New methods in the behavioural treatment of sexual dysfunction. *J. Behav. Ther. Exp. Psychiat.* 3: 265—271.

McConaghy, N. (1969) Subjective and penile plethysmograph responses following aversion-relief and apomorphine aversion therapy for homosexual impulses. *Br. J. Psychiat.* 115: 723—730.

McConaghy, N. (1970) Subjective and penile plethysmograph responses to aversion therapy for homosexuality: a followup study. *Br. J. Psychiat.* 117: 555—560.

McConaghy, N. and Barr, R.F. (1973) Classical, avoidance and backward conditioning treatments of homosexuality. *Br. J. Psychiat.* 122: 151—162.

MacCulloch, M.J. and Feldman, M.P. (1967) Aversion therapy in the management of 43 homosexuals. *Br. Med. J.*, 2: 594—597.

Marks, I.M. and Gelder, M.G. (1967) Transvestism and fetishism: clinical and psychological changes during faradic aversion. *Br. J. Psychiat.* 113: 711—730.

Marks, I.M., Gelder, M.G. and Bancroft, J.H.J. (1970) Sexual deviants two years after electric aversion therapy. *Br. J. Psychiat.* 117: 173—183.

Masters, W.H. and Johnson, V.E. (1970) *Human Sexual Inadequacy.* (Churchill, London.)

Mathews, A.M. (1975) Behavioural treatment of sexual inadequacy. Paper read at the Annual Conference of the British Association for Behavioural Psychotherapy. July 1975. York University, York.

Mathews, A.M., Johnston, D.W., Shaw, P.M. and Gelder, M.G. (1974) Process variables and the prediction of outcome in behaviour therapy. *Br. J. Psychiat.* 125: 256—264.

Mellor, V.P. (1972) The treatment of sexual offenders using an automated conditioning apparatus. Paper read at the Northwest Behaviour Modification Study Group, September 1972.

Morgenstern, F.S., Pearce, J.P. and Linford Rees, W. (1965) Predicting the outcome of behaviour therapy by psychological tests. *Behav. Res. Ther.*, 3: 253—258.

Obler, M. (1973) Systematic desensitisation in sexual disorders. *J. Behav. Ther. Exp. Psychiat.* 4: 93—101.

O'Gorman, E. (1974) Sexual inadequacy: Treatment, new therapeutic ways. Paper read at the IVth Annual Conference, European Association for Behaviour Therapy, London, July 1974.

Patterson, G.R. and Hops, H. (1972) Coercion, a game for two: Intervention techniques for marital conflict. In: (R.E. Ulrich and P.J. Mountjoy, Eds.) *Experimental Analysis of Social Behaviour.* (Appleton-Century-Croft, New York) pp. 424—440.

Quinn, J.T., Harbison, J.J.M. and McAllister, H. (1970) An attempt to shape human penile responses. *Behav. Res. Ther.* 8: 213—216.

Quinn, J.T., McAllister, H., Graham, P.J. and Harbison, J.J.M. (1973) An approach to the treatment of homosexuality. In: (J.C. Brengelmann and W. Turner, Eds.) *Behaviour Therapy — Verhaltens-therapie: praktische und theoretische aspekte.* (Urban and Schwarzenberg, München.)

Rachman, S. and Hodgson, R. (1968) Experimentally induced "sexual fetishism": replication and development. *Psychol. Rec.* 18: 25—27.

Rooth, G. and Marks, I.M. (1974) Aversion, self-regulation and relaxation in the treatment of exhibitionism. *Arch. Sex. Behav.* 4: 227—248.

Schrenck-Notzing, A. von (1895) *The use of hypnosis in psychopathia sexualis with special reference to contrary sexual instinct.* Translated by C.G. Chaddock, 1956. (The Institute of Research in Hypnosis Publication Society and the Julian Press, New York.)

Schultz, J.H. (1951) *Autogenic training.* (Grune and Stratton, New York.)

Semans, J.H. (1956) Premature ejaculation: a new approach. *South. Med. J.*, 49: 353—357.

Stewart, R.B. (1969) Token reinforcement in marital therapy. In: (R.D. Rubin and C.M. Franks, Eds.) *Advances in Behavior Therapy, 1968.* (Academic Press, New York) pp. 221—230.

Thorpe, J.G., Schmidt, E., Brown, P. and Castell, D. (1964) Aversion-relief therapy: a new method for general application. *Behav. Res. Ther.* 2: 71—82.

Tunnadine, L.P.D. (1970) *Contraception and Sexual Life: A Therapeutic Approach.* (Tavistock, London.)

Voegtlin, W.L. and Lemere, F. (1942) Treatment of alcohol addiction. *Quat. J. Stud. Alcohol.* 2: 717—803.

Wolpe, J. (1958) *Psychotherapy by Reciprocal Inhibition.* (Stanford University Press, Stanford.)

CHAPTER 98

Direct treatment of sexual dysfunction in the couple

JOSEPH LoPICCOLO

The prevailing view of the best therapeutic approach to sexual dysfunction has undergone a remarkable revolution over the past ten years. Until recently, sexual dysfunctions were widely accepted as symptoms of a deep-seated personality conflict, reflecting the influence of instinctual drives, maturational changes in focus of sexual responsiveness from the oral to the anal to the genital zone, and crucial early childhood experiences (Freud, 1905; Fenichel, 1945). Within this view, sexual dysfunctions could be treated only through individual, insight-oriented psychotherapy requiring "an appointment several times a week for a minimum of eight months" (Bergler, 1947). This requirement, of course, is not a realistic possibility for a large segment of the population. Given this viewpoint, it logically followed that most people suffering from sexual dysfunction could not be helped, or as it has been phrased "as a mass problem, the question of frigidity is unfortunately not to be solved" (Bergler, 1951).

The general public first became aware of the effectiveness of an alternative approach to treatment of sexual dysfunction with the landmark publication of Masters and Johnson's 'Human Sexual Inadequacy' (1970). This approach involves brief, time-limited directive counseling of the couple aimed at symptom removal rather than attainment of insight, uncovering of repressions, or resolution of unconscious conflict. While the direct, symptomatic treatment of sexual dysfunction has received tremendous publicity in the last five years, the roots of this 'new' therapy actually go back over two hundred years. Writing in the mid-18th century, a British physician, Sir John Hunter (cited in Comfort, 1965), described a treatment approach for erectile failure (impotence) which is virtually identical with that described by Masters and Johnson (1970). More recently, effective direct approaches to sexual dysfunction were described by Semans (1956), Hastings (1963), Brown

---

* Preparation of this chapter was supported in part by a grant from the National Institute of Mental Health, U.S. Public Health Service.

Handbook of Sexology, edited by J. Money and H. Musaph
© *Elsevier/North-Holland Biomedical Press, 1977*

(1966) and by a number of behavior therapists (Wolpe, 1958; Lazarus, 1963; Brady, 1966; Kraft and Al-Issa, 1968). It was, however, the publication of Masters and Johnson's (1970) unquestionable data on the effectiveness of the direct approach that led to its general acceptance.

This chapter will describe the basic principles of direct treatment of sexual dysfunction in the couple and review recent work on each of the major types of sexual dysfunction.

1. BASIC PRINCIPLES OF DIRECT TREATMENT

Researchers writing on the treatment of sexual dysfunction tend to use different theoretical labels for rather similar therapy procedures. The virtually standarized treatment procedures now used for erectile failure may alternatively be described as a means of reducing performance demands and the spectator role (Masters and Johnson, 1970); as in vivo systematic desensitization of anxiety through reciprocal inhibition by sexual arousal (Wolpe, 1958); as a way of stopping the couple's attempt to voluntarily control an involuntary behavior (erection) through the use of quasi-hypnotic specific instructions (Haley, 1973); as a way of disrupting a self-maintaining 'vicious cycle' of fear of erectile failure producing erectile failure by preventing sexual arousal (LoPiccolo and Lobitz, 1973); or as anxiety reduction through specific suggestions based on paradoxical intention or successive approximation (Annon, 1974). Rather than attempt to resolve such differences, it seems more reasonable to conceive of direct therapy procedures as complex and multifaceted packages of many different components. Lacking factorial research testing the relative effectiveness of these different components, it is premature to begin theoretical discussion of the underlying mechanisms which account for the effectiveness of the total package (Lobitz and LoPiccolo, 1972). At this point, the 'active ingredients' and 'inert fillers' in the direct therapy package cannot be distinguished, and the explanations offered for the effectiveness of the approach are simply speculations rather than data-based interpretations. With this in mind, it is possible to describe the common elements in various sex-therapy programs, avoiding theoretical interpretation and simply focusing on the actual procedures used.

In varying degrees, the following principles are used by most clinicians who follow the direct treatment approach. Relative emphasis placed on each procedure depends partly on the clinician's theoretical viewpoint, and partly on the needs, history and specific dysfunction of the particular patient couple.

Mutual responsibility

It must be stressed that all sexual dysfunctions are shared disorders; that is, the husband of an inorgasmic woman is partially responsible for creating or maintaining her dysfunction, and he is also a patient in need of help. Regardless of the cause of the dysfunction, both partners are responsible for future change and the solution of their problems. Some patients will resist the notion of mutual responsibility quite vigorously, in a defensive attempt to protect their self-image as sexually adept, or to maintain a position of power and control in their marital relationship. Reassurance, distinction of 'responsibility' from 'blame', and prognosis of successful outcome will usually deal with the self-image issue. Use of sexual dysfunction in a power struggle may be an indication for more general marital therapy instead of sex therapy. If reassurance does not eliminate resistance, raising the defensive spouse's anxiety about his sexual ability may motivate him to enter therapy on an equal basis with his spouse. Therapeutic anxiety can be engendered by such statements as, "I agree that your spouse has severe and long-standing sexual problems, but I know from clinical experience that had you responded differently, she could have overcome these difficulties, and sex therapy would never have been needed". (Further details of this procedure can be found in Lobitz et al., 1974.) Involving both spouses is also made easier by the use of a male—female, co-therapy team, which given each patient someone to identify with. Such co-therapy is common in most sex-therapy programs, but does not seem to be essential (Kaplan, 1974).

Information and education

Most patients suffering from sexual dysfunction are woefully ignorant of both basic biology and effective sexual techniques. Sometimes this ignorance can directly lead to the development of anxiety which in turn produces sexual dysfunction. For example, a recent patient dated the onset of her aversion to sex as beginning when she first noted that her clitoris 'disappeared' during manipulation. She interpreted this normal retraction of the clitoral shaft during the plateau phase of arousal (Masters and Johnson, 1966) as a pathological sign that she was not becoming aroused. This anxiety led to a complete loss of her arousal and enjoyment of sexuality. Similarly, many cases of vaginismus seem to begin as a result of the husband's forceful attempts to accomplish intromission in spite of his uncertainty about the exact location of the vagina. The wife's anticipation of painful battering about her vaginal introitus directly leads to the involuntary spastic contraction of the vaginal musculature called vaginismus. In direct therapy, therefore, the therapist ensures that the patients have accurate knowledge of the sexual response cycle through verbal discussion, providing the patient with appropriate reading materials, and the use of educational films. In addition, specific information is provided (again, by lecture, books and films) on the general principles of effective sexual techniques of kissing, manual and oral foreplay, positions of intercourse, and so forth. While this specific information alone is probably not sufficient to produce symptom remission, it appears to be necessary for treatment to succeed, and its absence may be partially responsible for the generally low success rate of nondirective or dynamic treatment approaches (Lorand, 1939; Moore, 1961).

Attitude change

Negative societal and parental attitudes toward sexual expression, past traumatic experiences and the current acute distress combine to make the dysfunctional patients approach each sexual encounter with anxiety, or in extreme cases, with revulsion and disgust. Because of the double standard type of morality Western nations adhere to (Christensen and Gregg, 1970), these negative attitudes seem to be considerably more common in women than in men. It may be that such negative attitudes towards sex are not really more common, but are only more visible in women than in men. Discussions with the urologists and gynecologists who refer patients to the author's clinical treatment program indicate that males are much more reluctant to accept a referral for sex therapy than are females. Sex therapy may be more threatening to a male's self-image than to a female's, or women may put less pressure on their dysfunctional spouses to enter therapy than do men. The women's liberation movement has rejected 'Kinder, Küche, Kirche' (children, kitchen, church) as the role model for the ideal woman, and now stresses that a 'decent' woman can also be sexually interested, aroused, assertive and orgasmic (Bardwick, 1971; Lydon, 1971). This revolution, however, has occurred too recently, and has been accepted by too small a minority of urban, liberal and educated women to have much impact on the overall incidence of negative attitudes towards female sexuality. Thus, the therapist must directly induce attitude change in such patients. Procedures used may involve having the patient read positive material on sexuality, arranging consultations with sympathetic clergy in the case of religiously based negative attitudes, instructing the husband to make it clear to his wife that he will value and respect her more, not less, if she becomes more sexual (which usually involves resolving the husband's lingering ambivalence about female sexuality and his fears about her becoming unfaithful or too demanding sexually), having the patient attend lectures or workshops on sexuality and sexual values which may be offered by local colleges, churches, or social-interest groups, and use of the therapeutic relationship itself. The psychoterapist in our culture is a respected authority figure. It is also to be hoped that the patients will personally like and respect their therapists. The therapists can use this role and relationship to produce attitude change in the patients through self-disclosure (Jourard, 1964) about their own enjoyment of sexuality (Lobits and LoPiccolo, 1972). Given that the patient has a negative attitude towards sex, and a positive one toward the therapist, the self-disclosure that the therapist enjoys sex creates cognitive dissonance (Festinger, 1957) for the patient: "Someone that I like and respect enjoys something I think is reprehensible, immoral and disgusting". The resolution of this dissonance can lead to acceptance of sex as decent, moral and enjoyable. Alternatively, if such self-disclosure is too extreme, or used too early in therapy, the patients may resolve the dissonance by losing respect for the therapist, or by deciding that the therapist is simply a different type of person. For this reason, self-disclosure probably produces the most attitude change when used by the female co-therapist with the female patient, and by the male co-therapist with the male patient.

Eliminating performance anxiety

In the culture of the 1970s, with its heavy emphasis on youth, beauty, and sexual attractiveness, demands for sexual competence and expertise seem to be assuming a larger role in the development of sexual dysfunction. Accordingly, for therapy to succeed, the dysfunctional patients must be freed from anxiety about their sexual performance. Patients, regardless of the presenting complaints, are told to stop 'keeping score', to stop being so goal centered on erection, orgasm, or ejaculation, and instead to focus on enjoying the process rather than trying for a particular end result. For example, the therapeutic procedure of forbidding intercourse in the treatment of erectile failure makes it possible for the patients to enjoy mutual kissing, hugging, body massage, and manual and oral stimulation of the genitals without anxiety about whether erection sufficient for intercourse will occur. Other techniques include reassuring a woman that she need not feel that she must reach orgasm in order to enjoy intercourse or to confirm her husband's belief that he is a good lover for her, and instructing patients that they can each provide sexual satisfaction for each other through manual and oral stimulation, even when they are not capable or desirous of having intercourse. Giving one partner 'permission' to masturbate as a legitimate route to sexual satisfaction will also reduce demands for performance in some cases.

Increasing communication and effectiveness of sexual technique

Dysfunctional couples tend to be unable to communicate clearly their sexual likes and dislikes to each other, due to inhibitions about discussing sex openly, excessive sensitivity to what is perceived as hostile criticism by the spouse, inhibitions about trying new sexual techniques, and the incorrect assumption that a person's sexual responsiveness is unchanging — that an activity that is pleasurable on one occasion will always be pleasurable. Accordingly, direct therapy encourages sexual experimentation and open, effective communication about technique and response. Procedures that are used include having the patient couple share their sexual fantasies with each other, read explicit erotic literature and see explicit sexual movies which model new techniques, and training the couple to communicate during their sexual interaction. Patients are advised to train each other to be effective sexual partners through demonstrating their own effective masturbation techniques to each other (LoPiccolo and Lobitz, 1972), by guiding their partners hands during genital caressing (Masters and Johnson, 1970) and by giving each other effective feedback during sex. Patients are taught the difference between ineffective, threatening communication ("Stop, I don't like that.") and effective information-rich feedback ("It feels better if you rub a little more lightly and over here instead of there."). It is stressed that patients are simply to ask and tell each other what they would like to do during each particular sexual encounter.

Changing destructive life styles and sex roles

Direct therapy for sexual dysfunction often involves the therapist stepping outside the usual therapeutic posture of responding to the patient, and instead taking an active, directive and initiating role with the patient in regard to general life style and sex-role issues. For example, many dysfunctional patients make sex the lowest priority item in their life. Sex occurs only when all career, housework, childbearing, home management, friendship and family responsibilities have been met. This usually insures that sex occurs infrequently, hurriedly, late at night, and when both partners are physically and mentally fatigued. In such a case, patients may be instructed to make 'dates' with each other for relaxing days or evenings (Annon, 1974). These dates may involve dinner and the theater, a day in the sun at a park or beach, or simply sending the children to the babysitter and staying home with the telephone disconnected and a 'Do Not Disturb' sign on the door. This simple change in itself tends to make sex a more positive experience. Similarly, patients may be advised to disengage from parents or others who are a destructive influence on their sexuality (Snyder et al., 1975), to enter bankruptcy to solve hopeless financial troubles which consume all their emotional energy, or, in a recent case, to quit a job which required the husband to commute four hours daily to and from work.

Rigid and unsatisfying sex-role separation is also a major negative influence on many couples' sexual relationship. If a husband and wife spend virtually no time together, and have no mutual, shared responsibility for the tasks of day-to-day living, it is unlikely that they will find sex to be a rewarding, close, sharing experience. The most common problem of this type involves the 'housewife's lament' syndrome. In this syndrome, an educated, intelligent woman has given up her career or education to become a homemaker, maid, cook, and mother. When her husband comes home from work, he is tired and overstimulated. He wants peace, quiet, the newspaper and a chance to do nothing. In a sense, his day is over. The woman, on the other hand, is also tired from a long day of household and childrearing responsibilities, but still has dinner to prepare, the dishes to do, the children to bathe and put to bed, etc. At the same time, she would like conversation and interaction from her husband after a day of children and housework. If he is unwilling to help reduce her evening work load and increase her life satisfaction, a poor unrewarding sex life is perhaps the best he can hope for in the continuing progress of their relationship. While many men would usually resist taking on more household responsibilities, in the context of sex therapy a change can be produced if the therapists take a strong, directive position on this issue. An effective therapist statement to open discussion is, "You say your wife never wants sex anymore and doesn't enjoy it. It's clear to us that her work load in the evening prevents her getting in touch with her sex drive and her sexual responsiveness. Are you willing to make some changes which will lead to a good sex life for both of you, but will require some effort on your part"?

Prescribing changes in behavior

If there is any one procedure which is the hallmark of direct treatment of sexual dysfunction, it is the prescription by the therapist of a series of gradual steps of specific sexual behavior to be performed by the patients in their own home. This is often described as 'sensate focus' or 'pleasuring' exercises. Typically, intercourse and indeed, breast and genital touching are initially prohibited, and the patients only examine, discuss, and sensually massage each other's bodies. Forbidding more intense sexual expression allows the patients to enjoy kissing, hugging, body massage and other sensual pleasures without the disruption that would occur if the patient anticipated these activities would be followed by intercourse or other sexual behavior that had not been pleasurable in the past. The couple's sexual relationship is then rebuilt in a graduated series of successive approximations to full sexual intercourse. At each step, anxiety reduction, skill training, elimination of performance demands, and the other components described above are used to keep the couple's interactions pleasurable and therapeutic experiences. Exactly what specific behavior is prescribed, and how the other six components discussed above are integrated into the prescription, will be described in the following section on specific types of sexual dysfunction.

Obviously, in prescribing some activities for the patients to perform and forbidding others, the question arises of how the therapist insures patient compliance with these prescriptions and prohibitions. While some clinicians videotape or actually observe their patients' sexual behavior (Hartman and Fithian, 1972), this approach seems unlikely to be acceptable to the majority of sexually inhibited couples. Alternatively, patients may be required to keep separate written records of their 'homework' activities, and to pay the therapists a deposit in advance of treatment. This deposit is refunded in full if the patients comply with mutually agreed upon therapeutic instructions. However, they forfeit (to charity, not to the therapist) increasingly larger portions of this deposit for each successive violation of therapeutic prescriptions. This 'penalty deposit' system seems to work well in maintaining patient compliance with therapist instructions (Lobitz and LoPiccolo, 1972).

2. TYPES OF SEXUAL DYSFUNCTION

Premature ejaculation

There are no objective criteria for what constitutes premature ejaculation. The problem of an objective definition is complicated by the fact that over 25% of women will experience orgasm on 90 to 100% of coital opportunities even when the duration of coitus is less than one minute. At the other extreme, about 10% of women will never or rarely experience coital orgasm even with coitus lasting longer than 16 minutes (Gebhard, 1966). However, data do indicate that increasing ejaculatory latency beyond seven minutes is not strongly associated with increased incidence of coital orgasm for women, and that the median duration of intercourse for men is somewhere between four and seven minutes (Gebhard, 1966). Thus, one might suggest that a latency to ejaculation of less than four minutes may be a tentative indicator for treatment. Such a definition must be tempered by several other factors: how much manual and oral stimulation of his genitals can the male tolerate without ejaculation; is the male unrestrained in intercourse or can he only delay ejaculation by slowing thrusting, thinking unpleasant, anti-erotic thoughts, biting his tongue, or wearing a condom; what is the frequency of intercourse; the age of the patient; how much use is there of alcohol, drugs, and even topical anesthetic creams to dull sexual responsivity and delay ejaculation. It is therefore easier to describe what is not premature ejaculation: both husband and wife agree that the quality of their sexual encounters is not influenced by efforts to delay ejaculation.

Since ejaculation is a response which is enervated by the sympathetic nervous system (Kaplan, 1974), one approach to premature ejaculation involves systematic desensitization (Wolpe, 1958). In systematic desensitization, muscle relaxation is used to elicit parasympathetic arousal, which then reduces sympathetic arousal through reciprocal inhibition. Procedurally, the patient practices deep muscle relaxation while visualizing items from a hierarchy of sexually arousing situations. This procedure is moderately successful in treating premature ejaculation (Cooper, 1968; Kraft and Al-Issa, 1968).

Far more effective is the procedure originally developed by James Semans (1956). Basically, the problem in premature ejaculation is the male's low threshold for amount of stimulation required to elicit the ejaculation response. In the Semans' procedure, the penis is stimulated until ejaculation is imminent. At this point, stimulation is stopped. The male pauses until the sensation of high arousal subsides, then begins stimulation of the penis again. This procedure is repeated over and over again, until the male has experienced a massive amount of stimulation, but without the occurrence of ejaculation. The number of pauses required to sustain stimulation and delay ejaculation rapidly decreases over successive occasions with this procedure, and the male soon gains the capacity for penile stimulation of great duration without any pauses at all. The underlying mechanism in the Semans' procedure may be Guthrie's 'crowding the threshold' process for extinguishing stimulus—response connections; in this case, the connection between minimal stimulation and ejaculation. According to Guthrie, such extinction is produced by gradually exposing the subject to progressively more intense and more prolonged stimulation, but always keeping the intensity and duration of the stimulus just below the threshold for elicitation of the response (Guthrie, 1952).

Masters and Johnson (1970) have modified this procedure by having the wife stimulate the husband's penis and squeeze firmly on the frenulum when a pause in stimulation is needed. This 'squeeze technique' is said to immediately eliminate the urge to ejaculate, and may also cause a partial loss of erection. While there has not been a controlled experimental study of the relative effectiveness of the pause procedure versus the squeeze procedure, at a clinical level, both procedures seem to be quite effective. If the squeeze procedure is used, the patient should be cautioned to release the squeeze immediately if he ejaculates as a result of not stopping stimulation early enough. Ejaculation while physically holding the urethra closed can, in rare instances, produce retrograde ejaculation with concomitant risk of physiological problems.

There is one additional procedure which may enhance the effectiveness of the pause procedure. Contraction of the scrotum and elevation of the testicles occurs during high arousal and orgasm (Masters and Johnson, 1966). Indeed, for some men, cupping the scrotum and pressing it against the perineum will trigger orgasm during high arousal. Conversely, pulling down on the scrotum and testes seems to work like the squeeze procedure to reduce arousal and the urge to ejaculate in many men.

In prescribing homework assignments for the premature ejaculation patient, the first step involves masturbation with the pause procedure, to learn when to pause and to identify the signals of approaching ejaculation. The advantages of beginning with masturbation are 3-fold: (1) the male gains confidence and reduces his anxiety by learning some ejaculatory control before resuming sexual activity with his wife; (2) the male can focus exclusively on learning when and how to pause or squeeze, free of any pressure to also communicate this information to his wife; and (3) the spouse's eagerness to learn and cooperate is enhanced by the husband's report of the success of the procedure. Contrary to what has been reported elsewhere (Masters and Johnson, 1970, p. 113), data from patients treated in the author's clinical research program indicate good transfer of increased latency from masturbation to manipulation by the wife.

Next, the patient may be instructed to try the squeeze procedure, to see if this is more or less effective for him than the simple pause. In the next sessions, the male patient will teach this procedure to his wife. When good tolerance for manual and oral stimulation by the wife is achieved, the couple uses the pause (or squeeze) procedure during stationary vaginal containment of the penis, during slow pelvic thrusting, and finally during full, unrestrained intercourse.

If the patient couple progresses through this procedure on a daily basis, the need to use the pause or squeeze will quickly diminish. Part of this gain is artifactual, however, as latency to ejaculation is greatly increased by frequent ejaculation. Such patients need to be placed on a 'maintenance program' which includes occasional training sessions with the pause—squeeze procedures, to insure that relapse does not occur following the intensive therapy period (Lobitz et al., 1974).

Erectile failure

If the definition of premature ejaculation is complex, the definition of erectile failure is simple: inability of the male to attain or maintain an erection sufficient for intercourse.

The treatment program for erectile failure consists of two basic components: (1) Ensuring that the patient is receiving a high level of physical and psychological sexual stimulation from his wife; and (2) eliminating anxiety and performance demands which interfere with erection despite such adequate stimulation. Illustrating the mutual responsibility of both spouses for a sexual dysfunction, some cases of erectile failure are at least partially the result of the wife's poor sexual technique and her placing strong demands on the male to have erections. For example, in one recent case (Lobitz et al., 1974), the patients were a couple in their fifties, both married for the second time. The wife's first husband had always had an erection before beginning lovemaking, and did not want her to touch his genitals at all. The male patient had been previously married to a woman who manually and orally stimulated his genitals a great deal before intercourse. When the patient couple began their sexual relationship, their very different expectations about the role of foreplay in producing an erection led to conflict. Because of communication difficulties, these conflicts were never resolved. Instead, the wife became quite bitter, frustrated and hostile about 'his' sexual dysfunction.

In such cases of insufficient stimulation and excessive demands for performance by either the wife or the husband's own expectations, a number of therapeutic tactics are indicated. The therapist should instruct the couple that erection is not subject to voluntary control and is neither spontaneous nor instantaneous (especially in older males), but will automatically occur given sufficient stimulation in an anxiety-free setting. Performance demands on the husband and the wife's frustration can be reduced through instructing the couple to assure orgasm for the female by means of manual, oral or electric vibrator stimulation of her genitals, none of which require the male to have an erect penis. Explicit films and books can be used to train the wife in effective stimulation techniques. If the wife makes demanding or derogatory statements about her husband's sexual abilities, the therapist should emphasize that such demands or criticism are counter-productive and increase the anxiety which causes the male's erectile failure. In extreme cases, when all else has failed to change the wife's attitude, an effective statement is, "Most men would find it very difficult to have erections in a sexual relationship with you at this time. We know you can change, and learn to be a more skilled lover and less demanding. Are you willing to accept responsibility and make these changes, with our help?"

An equally powerful source of anxiety, independent of the spouse's reaction, stems from the male's own attitude towards sex, once erectile failure has begun to occur. That is, a male with erectile failure tends to enter his sexual encounters as an anxious observer rather than as an aroused participant. That is, he watches closely for signs of erection, is upset by any lag in gaining erection or any signs of partial loss of erection. Since this anxiety about erection obviously prevents erection from occurring, one therapeutic approach is to use systematic desensitization to eliminate anxiety (Cooper, 1963; Kushner, 1965; Lazarus, 1965; Friedman, 1968).

Alternatively, anxiety reduction can be accomplished by prescribing a course of homework activities for the couple which preclude performance anxiety and insure adequate stimulation for the male. Paradoxical instructions (Annon, 1974) can be utilized in prescribing these activities to further eliminate anxiety. For example, the first set of activities might require the couple only to examine and massage each other's nude bodies, not including any stimulation of the male's genitals. The male is paradoxically instructed that, "The purpose of this exercise is for you to learn to enjoy sensual pleasures, without focusing on sexual goals. Therefore, you should try to not get an erection. Erection would mean you are being sexual rather than sensual". Obviously, a nude massage is a sexually stimulating experience. The paradoxical demand to not get an erection in this setting effectively frees the man from anxiety about getting an erection.

Over successive occasions, the couple's repertoire of sexual activities can now be rebuilt. The next assignment might be for the wife to stimulate the male's penis manually or orally, but to stop such stimulation immediately should an erection occur. Only when the penis is flaccid should stimulation be resumed. This procedure, which has been called the 'teasing technique' (Masters and Johnson, 1970), convinces the couple that if erection is lost, it can be regained. Next, penile insertion into the vagina is allowed, but only with the female physically pushing the male's flaccid penis into her vagina while she sits astride his supine body. Again, the couple is told, "This procedure works best with a flaccid penis. If you can't avoid an erection, it's all right, although not as good, to go ahead and insert anyway. But please try not to have an erection". Once the male has been unable to avoid an erection during vaginal containment, slow pelvic thrusting, vigorous intercourse, and finally, coital ejaculation can be prescribed. The timing of these activities is such that they are only prescribed after the patient have seen that they naturally and automatically occur if the male is stimulated and not anxious.

For example, ejaculation is 'allowed' only after the male has been unable to restrain himself from ejaculating intravaginally (LoPiccolo and Lobitz, 1973).

While this procedure works well with most cases, it has not been found successful in cases where the male has a homosexual orientation (Masters and Johnson, 1970, p. 273). In such cases, lack of psychological stimulation (rather than the male's anxiety and the wife's poor technique) may be a factor. If a male is more aroused by men than by women, removing his performance anxiety may still leave him unaroused in response to his wife's lovemaking, regardless of how nondemanding and skilled she may be. For such cases, addition of a classical conditioning procedure to increase heterosexual arousal seems to increase effectiveness of the basic treatment strategy (LoPiccolo et al., 1972). In this procedure, the male masturbates with his currently arousing homosexual fantasies and explicit stimuli, such as pictures of nude males. Just prior to orgasm, the male is instructed to switch his focus to fantasies of heterosexual activities with his spouse, and to look at erotic photographs of her. Such photos can be discreetly obtained by supplying the couple with a Polaroid self-developing camera. This procedure insures that the pleasure of orgasm occurs in a heterosexual context. On subsequent occasions, this switch can be made earlier in masturbation until fantasies and photos of the wife become effective sexual stimuli in their own right. This stimulus switching procedure can also be used by the couple in their series of prescribed sexual activities.

While all patients seeking sex therapy should receive a complete physical examination before entering treatment, such an examination is especially important in erectile failure cases. Unlike premature ejaculation and female orgasmic dysfunction, there are many organic causes (such as diabetes and vascular disease) for erectile failure (Belt, 1973; Dengrove, 1971).

Ejaculatory incompetence

Ejaculatory incompetence involves the inability of the male to reach orgasm through stimulation by his wife. While failure to reach orgasm is common in women, it is quite rare in men. For example, while Kinsey and co-workers (1948) found that up to 15% of women remain anorgasmic even after many years of marriage, the incidence of orgasmic failure in males is too low to permit statistical study. There may be an evolutionary basis for this difference, in that there is selective pressure on males but not on females to have orgasm. For a male's genes to continue in the gene pool, he must ejaculate (have orgasm) while mating. On the other hand, ovulation and fertilization of the ovum are not related to occurrence of female orgasm.

Treatment of the ejaculatory incompetent couple follows a paradigm which combines elements from the premature ejaculation and the erectile failure programs. As in cases of premature ejaculation, the couple is instructed in the technique of providing massive amounts of stimulation of the male's penis, but without use of the pause or squeeze procedures. Similar to treatment of erectile failure, the wife is trained to be an effective sexual partner for her husband, and, perhaps most importantly, all performance demands upon him for ejaculation are eliminated through the same procedures used to reduce performance anxiety in erectile failure. To increase stimulation, an electric vibrator may be used by the wife or her husband. The previously discussed procedure of cupping the testicles to elicit orgasm may be used, as well as the body posture and muscular procedures used to trigger female orgasm, as described in the following section.

In treating ejaculatory incompetence, it should be ascertained that the patient is not receiving any tranquilizing drugs, especially phenothiazines. Ejaculatory incompetence can be a side-effect of these sympathetic blocking agents.

Orgasmic dysfunction

There are several types of orgasmic dysfunction in women. Primary orgasmic dysfunction refers to the woman who has never experienced an orgasm through any means of sexual stimulation. Secondary orgasmic dysfunction describes a woman who usually cannot experience orgasm during coitus, but who is able to have orgasm through masturbation or through her husband's manual or oral stimulation of her genitals. In discussing a lack of coital orgasm, it must be emphasized that 'coital' orgasm is not synonomous with 'vaginal' orgasm. Psychoanalytic theory makes a specious and now discredited distinction between 'clitoral' and 'vaginal' orgasm (Kinsey et al., 1948, Sherfey, 1966; Lydon, 1971; Weisstein, 1971). In this view, a woman who achieves orgasm through her husband's manipulation of her genitals is considered neurotic, immature, and 'frigid' (Fenichel, 1945). Recent research has now made it clear that all orgasms are physiologically identical (Masters and Johnson, 1966). If a woman has orgasm during coitus, this orgasm is produced in large part by indirect stimulation of the clitoris from the husband's pubis, and by penile thrusting causing the labia to pull on the clitoral hood. Obviously, such stimulation can also be directly produced if the husband (or the woman herself) manually manipulates the clitoris during intercourse. To argue that orgasm produced by direct clitoral stimulation during coitus is somehow more immature and less psychologically healthy than orgasm produced by indirect clitoral stimulation is to draw almost mystical distinctions between the male pubis and the male hand. It should be stressed therefore, that a woman who can have coital orgasm if she receives concurrent manual stimulation of her clitoris does not have secondary orgasmic dysfunction; she is normal. Similarly, a woman who regularly has orgasm during manual or oral stimulation by her husband, and who enjoys intercourse even though orgasm does not occur during coitus, is a candidate for reassurance about her normality rather than for sex therapy. The therapist must take care, however, that reassurance does not have the effect of making a patient couple feel that they cannot or should not want to change sexual patterns which are unsatisfying to them.

In addition to the primary—secondary distinction, a distinction can be drawn between those inorgasmic women who are inhibited and those who suffer from performance anxiety. The inhibited woman approaches the stereotype of the 'frigid' woman. Such a woman has a history of negative parental or religious indoctrination about sex, finds sex repulsive, does not become aroused, and enters therapy reluctantly, perhaps primarily to keep her husband from leaving her. These women need heavy exposure to the information and education, and attitude change procedures previously described. The woman with performance anxiety, on the other hand, often has an unremarkable parental and religious history, enjoys sex, becomes aroused and enters therapy eager for the experience of orgasm for her own gratification. These cases have often been exposed to mass media demands to be multi-orgasmic and supersexual if they are 'real' women. Alternatively, the husbands of such women often have profound doubts about their own masculinity and abilities as lovers, and put their wives under extreme pressure to have orgasm to reassure themselves on this issue. Such cases need more emphasis on the principles of eliminating performance anxiety, and increasing communication and effectiveness of sexual techniques described above.

The role of the husband as an effective and nondemanding sexual partner for his wife is obviously crucial in orgasmic dysfunction, especially secondary orgasmic dysfunction. In one sense, it can be argued that if a woman can produce orgasm for herself through masturbation, but cannot have orgasm with her husband, he is the dysfunctional one. This relates to the old maxim that "There are no frigid women, only clumsy men". In many cases, this is true: the women's sexual responsiveness is entirely normal, but her husband is quite inept as a lover. The principle of mutual responsibility, however, points out that such a woman has failed to train her husband to be an effective lover for her. This suggests a revision of the old maxim: "There are both frigid women and clumsy men, and they are usually married to each other".

The treatment program for orgasmic dysfunction involves four different components. First, for the woman who has never experienced an orgasm, a program of directed masturbation is indicated (LoPiccolo and Lobitz, 1972). The rationale for the use of masturbation includes the fact that it is the sexual technique most likely to produce an orgasm. According to Kinsey et al., (1948) for the average woman, the probabilities of orgasm are 0.95 for masturbation and 0.74 for coitus. In prescribing masturbation, LoPiccolo and Lobitz (1972) describe a 9-step program. In step one, the woman visually examines her genitals with the aid of a hand mirror and diagrams. At this time, she is also placed on a program of Kegel's (1952) exercises to enhance her orgasmic potential through increasing strength and vascularity of the pelvic musculature. In step 2 and 3, the woman tactually explores her genitals, to locate pleasure-sensitive areas. In steps 4 and 5, the woman learns to stimulate intensely these areas while using erotic fantasies or explicit literature and photos to enhance arousal. She is also taught to label her physiologic responses to such intense stimulation as sexual arousal and pleasure, rather than, as often occurs, other states such as anxiety, discomfort or tension. If orgasm has not yet occurred, in step 6 the woman masturbates using the electric vibrator.

Steps 7 through 9 of this program involve the second major component of treatment for orgasmic dysfunction — skill training for the husband. In step 7, he observes his wife's masturbation, to learn what is effective for her. In step 8, he learns to manipulate her to orgasm, and in step 9 this manipulation is paired with coitus. While this program has produced good results, it should be emphasized that it is not used in isolation. Typically, the male is also placed on the same masturbation program, to ensure his cooperation and support of the female. Also throughout this program the couple has a series of prescribed mutual activities to engage in, starting with simple nondemanding body massage and progressing through kissing and hugging, breast stimulation, genital stimulation, penile insertion, slow thrusting, and ending in full intercourse.

A third major component of treatment of orgasmic dysfunction involves disinhibition of arousal. Many anorgasmic women are inhibited from reaching orgasm by fear of loss of control or embarrassment about displaying intense sexual arousal and pleasure in front of their husbands. Such a woman may be able to reach high levels of arousal (but not orgasm) in masturbation, or to masturbate to orgasm when alone but not in the presence of her husband. In such cases, the patient is instructed to repeatedly role-play a grossly exaggerated orgasm with violent convulsions, screaming and other extreme behavior. Knowing that she is merely acting, the couple can engage in this activity quite readily. With repeated role play of exaggerated orgasm during the couple's prescribed homework activities, the initial fear and embarrassment turns into amusement and eventually boredom (Lobitz and LoPiccolo, 1972).

Obviously, all procedures for disinhibiting a woman about displaying her sexuality depend ultimately upon the husband's ability to respond in an unambivalent, positive manner to his wife's increased sexual responsiveness. Many male patients, however, in a seeming paradox, become unenthusiastic, derogatory, negativistic, or even hostile as their previously unresponsive wives show treatment gains. Inquiry typically reveals that these men fear that their wives will become too sexually demanding or promiscuous. Therapist reassurance that these fears are normal, common at this point in therapy, and unfounded will usually allay the husband's anxieties. Failure to deal with these issues will often lead to the husband's counteracting the effects of treatment.

The fourth component of therapy for orgasmic dysfunction involves teaching the woman certain behavior which, if performed during high sexual arousal, will often trigger the orgasm response. This behavior tends to occur spontaneously or involuntarily during intense orgasm (Singer and Singer,

1972), and when performed voluntarily, may initiate orgasm. These 'orgasm triggers' include pelvic thrusting, pointing the toes, tensing the thigh muscles, holding the breath, pushing down with the diaphragm, contracting the vaginal musculature, and throwing the head back to displace the glottis.

All four of the components described above seem to be most effective in cases of primary orgasmic dysfunction. It has been suggested that secondary orgasmic dysfunction is associated with a distressed marital relationship, and may be a symptom and result of this distress rather than a sexual problem in its own right (McGovern et al., 1975). Such cases may respond better to a combination of sex therapy and marital counseling than to pure sex therapy (Snyder et al., 1975).

Vaginismus

Vaginismus refers to involuntary spastic contraction of the vaginal musculature such that intromission cannot be accomplished, or can only take place with great difficulty and pain. If physical examination reveals no organic basis, vaginismus is usually an anxiety response. The woman may fear penetration because of prior painful attempts at coitus due to lack of lubrication, rape, extreme fear or guilt during the first attempt at coitus, or in rare instances, an extremely naive couple who mistake the anus or the urethral opening for the vagina. In treating vaginismus, one addition is made to the usual program for orgasmic dysfunction. A graduated series of dilators is used to enable the woman to learn to tolerate vaginal intromission. This dilation program may be carried out by the gynecologist in the office, or by the woman or her husband at home. Such dilation can also be accomplished with the woman's (or her husband's) fingers (Haslam, 1965; Wolpe, 1969; Masters and Johnson, 1970; Farmer, 1970; Fuchs et al., 1973). In addition, the Kegel (1952) exercises may be utilized, not to strengthen the vaginal musculature, but as a means of enabling the woman to attain voluntary control of these muscles.

3. THE FUTURE: CURRENT TRENDS IN DIRECT THERAPY FOR SEXUAL DYSFUNCTION

While the recent rapid acceptance of direct action modes of therapy for sexual dysfunction has brought effective treatment to many distressed couples, the results of this rapid growth are not unmixed. If the publicity sex therapy has received in recent years has made many couples aware that there is hope for them, it has also attracted many unqualified people into the field and led to outrageous fees being charged for sex therapy.

On the positive side, many investigators are now working on group therapy, instructional books and films, and self-help programs for dysfunctional couples. These procedures should provide wider availability of effective help for many couples who cannot afford the current fees. Similarly, there is a small, but growing trend for medical schools and graduate programs in clinical psychology to include sexual therapy in their curricula, which should lead to an increase in the number of qualified therapists and a decrease in the fees currently charged.

It is to be hoped that the need for sex therapy will eventually disappear entirely. Perhaps in the future our society will come to value sexuality as an expression of one of the least destructive and most loving components of the human personality, and will communicate this clearly to our children. Children raised in such a culture would presumably find the idea of 'sexual dysfunction' to be emotionally incomprehensible. It is the responsibility of the current generation of researchers and clinicians to work in the area of human sexuality to foster this change in our society.

BIBLIOGRAPHY

Annon, J.S. (1974) *The Behavioral Treatment of Sexual Problems.* (Kapiolani Health Services, Honolulu, Hawaii.)

Bardwick, J. (1971) *Psychology of Women.* (Harper and Row, New York.)

Belt, B.G. (1973) Some organic causes of impotence. *Med. Aspects Hum. Sex.* 7, 152—161.

Bergler, E. (1947) Frigidity in the female: misconceptions and facts. *Marr. Hyg.* 1, 16—21.

Bergler, E. (1951) *Neurotic Counterfeit-Sex.* (Grune and Stratton, New York.)

Brady, J.P. (1966) Brietal relaxation treatment of frigidity *Behav. Res. Ther.* 4, 71—77.

Brown, D.G. (1966) Female orgasm and sexual inadequacy In: (R.E. Brecher, Ed.), *An Analysis of Human Sexual Response,* (New American Library, New York.)

Christensen, H.T. and Gregg, C.F. (1970) Changing sex norms in America and Scandinavia. *J. Marr. Fam.* 32, 616—627.

Comfort, A. (1965) *The Anxiety Makers.* (Nelson and Sons, Camden, New Jersey.)

Cooper, A.J. (1900) A case of fetishism and impotence treated by behavior therapy. *Br. J. Psychiat.* 109, 649—652.

Cooper, A.J. (1968) A factual study of male potency disorders, *Br. J. Psychiat.* 114, 719—731.

Dengrove, E. (1971) The urologic aspects of impotence. *J. Sex Res.* 7, 163—168.

Fenichel, O. (1945) *The Psychoanalytic Theory of Neurosis.* (Norton, New York.)

Festinger, L. (1957) *A Theory of Cognitive Dissonance.* (Stanford University Press, Stanford.)

Freud, S. (1905) *Three Essays on the Theory of Sexuality.* Standard edn 7, 1962 (London) p. 125.

Friedman, D. (1968) The treatment of impotence by Brietal relaxation therapy. *Behav. Res. Ther.* 6, 257—261.

Gebhard, P. (1966) Factors in marital orgasm. *J. Soc. Iss.* 22 (2) 88—96.

Guthrie, E.R. (1952) *The Psychology of Learning.* (Harper, New York.)

Haley, J. (1973) *Uncommon Therapy.* (Ballantine Books, New York.)

Hartman, W.E. and Fithian, M.A. (1972) *Treatment of Sexual Dysfunction.* (California Center for Marital and Sexual Studies, Long Beach.)

Haslam, M.T. (1965) The treatment of psychogenic dyspareunia by reciprocal inhibition. *Br. J. Psychiat.* 111, 280—282.

Hastings, D.W. (1963) *Impotence and Frigidity.* (Little, Brown and Co., Boston.)

Jourard, S.M. (1964) *The Transparent Self.* (Van Nostrand, Princeton, New Jersey.)

Kaplan, H.S. (1974) *The New Sex Therapy.* (Brunner/Mazel, New York.)

Kegel, A.H. (1952) Sexual functions of the pubococcygeus muscle. *West. J. Obstet. Gynecol.* 60, 521—524.

Kinsey, A.C., Pomeroy, W.B., Martin, C.E. and Gebhard, P.H. (1953) *Sexual Behavior in the Human Female.* (W.B. Saunders, Philadelphia.)

Kraft, T. and Al-Issa, I. (1967) Behavior therapy and the treatment of frigidity. *Am. J. Psychother.* 21, 116—120.

Kraft, T. and Al-Issa, I. (1968) The use of methahexitone sodium in the systematic desensitization of premature ejaculation. *Br. J. Psychiat.* 114, 351—352.

Kushner, M. (1965) The reduction of long standing fetish by means of aversive conditioning. In: (L.P. Ullmann and L. Krasner, Eds.), *Case Studies in Behavior Modification.* (Holt, Rinehart and Winston, New York) pp. 239—242.

Lazarus, A.A. (1963) The treatment of chronic frigidity by systematic desensitization. *J. Nerv. Ment. Dis.* 136, 272—278.

Lazarus, A.A. (1965) The treatment of a sexually inadequate man. In: (L.P. Ullmann and L. Krasner, Eds.), *Case Studies in Behavior Modification.* (Holt, Rinehart and Winston, New York) pp. 243—245.

Lobitz, W.C. and LoPiccolo, J. (1972) New methods in the behavioral treatment of sexual dysfunction. *J. Behav. Ther. Exp. Psychiat.* 3 (4) 265—271.

Lobitz, W.C., LoPiccolo, J., Lobitz, G. and Brockway, J. (1974) A closer look at 'simplistic' behavior therapy for sexual dysfunction: two case studies. In: (H.J. Eysenck, Ed.) *Case Studies in Behavior Therapy.* (Routledge and Kegan Paul Ltd., London.)

LoPiccolo, J. and Lobitz, W.C. (1972) The role of masturbation in the treatment of orgasmic dysfunction. *Arch. Sex. Behav.* 2, 153—164.

LoPiccolo, J. and Lobitz, W.C. (1973) Behavior therapy of sexual dysfunction. In: (L.A. Hammerlynck, L.C. Handy and E.J. Mash, Eds.) *Behavior Change: Methodology, Concepts, and Practice.* (Research Press, Champaign, Ill..)

LoPiccolo, J., Stewart, R. and Watkins, B. (1972) Case study: treatment of erectile failure and ejaculatory incompetence in a case with homosexual etiology. *J. Behav. Ther. Exp. Psychiat.* 3, 233—236.

Lorand, S. (1939) Contribution to the problem of vaginal orgasm. *Int. J. Psychoanal.* 20, 432—438.

Lydon, S. (1971) The politics of orgasm. In: (Garskof, Ed.) *Roles Women Play.* (Brooks/Cole, Monterey, Calif..)

Masters, W.H. and Johnson, V.E. (1966) *Human Sexual Response.* (Little, Brown and Co., Boston.)

Masters, W.H. and Johnson, V.E. (1970) *Human Sexual Inadequacy.* (Little, Brown and Co., Boston.)

McGovern, L., Stewart, R. and LoPiccolo, J. (1975) Secondary orgasmic dysfunction I: analysis and strategies for treatment. *Arch. Sex. Behav.* 4 (3) 265—275.

Moore, B.E. (1961) Frigidity in women. *Am. Psychoanal. Assoc. J.* 9, 571—584.

Semans, J.H. (1956) Premature ejaculation: a new approach. *South. Med. J.* 49, 353—357.

Sherfey, J.J. (1966) The evolution and nature of female sexuality in relation to psychoanalytic theory. *J. Am. Psychoanal. Assoc.* 14, 28—128.

Singer, I. and Singer, J. (1972) Types of female orgasm. *J. Sex Res.* 8, 255—267.

Snyder, A., LoPiccolo, L. and LoPiccolo, J. (1975) Secondary orgasmic dysfunction II: case study. *Arch. Sex. Behav.* 4 (3) 277—283.

Weisstein, N. (1971) Psychology constructs the female, or the fantasy life of the male psychologist. In: (Garskof, Ed.). *Roles Women Play.* (Brooks/Cole).

Wolpe, J. (1958) *Psychotherapy by Reciprocal Inhibition.* (Stanford University Press, Stanford) pp. 130—135.

Wolpe, J. (1969) *The Practice of Behavior Therapy.* (Pergamon Press, New York.)

CHAPTER 99

The psychoanalytic approach to individual therapy

ISMOND ROSEN

1. INTRODUCTION

This chapter views sexuality, its disorders and their treatment as part of the theory of general personality development, extending from earliest life into adult maturity and old age. Only by furthering knowledge of the psychology and physiology of sexual development and its function at all ages, will one be able to formulate an adequate psychopathology, linked with an understanding of somatic sexual processes, upon which techniques for treating sexual disorders may be based. Adult sexual functions are influenced by early experiences, and reciprocally concerned with relationships between individuals. This viewpoint stems from Freud's earliest observations. Psychoanalysis has continued to grow into a general psychology dealing with the whole of personality development.

In a spirit of cooperation rather than contention with other disciplines, modern psychoanalysis attempts to formulate its general theory to embrace all of sexuality. This does not mean it claims an exclusive therapeutic right, but that psychoanalysis and its applications in psychotherapy remain concerned with all aspects of sexual disorder. A working knowledge of its theory will profit workers in other disciplines, and vice versa. Such an all-embracing approach makes it difficult to set therapeutic aims and appropriate techniques, even within psychoanalytical confines. In practice, sexual disorders range from disturbances in normal development to pathological sexual symptom formation.

Sexual immaturity

Immaturity is fostered by ignorance, social and religious prohibitions. These are the cases which are most easily helped and where counseling, education and the provision of tolerant and encouraging external authority provides an atmosphere for sexual maturation that was lacking. The still controversial

Handbook of Sexology, edited by J. Money and H. Musaph
© *Elsevier/North-Holland Biomedical Press, 1977*

subject of sexual education for the young belongs in this area (Winnicott, 1964; Taylor, 1970). We now know that normal learning is connected with the satisfaction of curiosity in childhood, and that curiosity has origins in infantile sexual explorations, looking, touching and the wish to know about sexual differences and where babies come from (Freud, 1907). Apparent sexual ignorance or shame is often based on childhood sexual overstimulation which has led to inhibition or denial of knowledge. The need for sex education is vital to produce healthy human beings, the provision of sexual techniques and contraceptive advice is also necessary, but is no panacea against promiscuity or unwanted pregnancies which may have their roots in the repetition or displacement of disturbed parent—child relationships. Such cases of promiscuity or pregnancy presenting as ignorance or immaturity, may require intensive psychotherapy for, although the sexuality is apparently not disordered, sexual function is being made to serve a defensive often repetitive role to help an inadequate personality. See also Powers and Baskin (1969), Rosen (1969).

Sexual inhibitions

The so-called disorders of normal sexual functioning, impotence in the male, frigidity or impaired orgastic ability in the female, may both be regarded as the result of an inhibition of psychosexual mechanisms at various levels and sequences in the normal sexual processes. These may be primary and relate to developmental interferences prior to the attainment of sexual maturity, or secondary and stem from specific stresses acting on mature functions which reveal faults in development that had been either overcome or remained latent (Freud, 1926; Fenichel, 1945).

Sexual deviations

This class of sexual deviations deals with disturbances of personality structure. The specific sexual deviations may fall into recognized categories such as homosexuality, exhibitionism, scopophilia, fetishism, transvestism, sadomasochism, cruelty and sexual violence, or contain mixtures of any or all of the above or shade into the sexual inhibitions and immaturities. These types of symptoms are now regarded as major defensive reactions by the personality to protect the self of the individual. Transexualism is a disorder of sexual identity not amenable to cure by psychotherapy where fully developed in the adult, but where techniques are being developed by Stoller and his colleagues to psychotherapeutically alter the pathological influences on the still growing transexual child.

Aims of psychotherapy

The aims of psychotherapy are two-fold: to assist in the maturation of sexual function so that a higher level of satisfaction and object relationship can be achieved, and to remove the barriers erected defensively against such developments, including the giving up of preferred methods of sexual gratification which may in turn threaten the individual's sense of identity. The psychoanalytical theory of sexual maturation is now briefly examined.

2. PSYCHOANALYTICAL THEORY OF SEXUAL DEVELOPMENT

Freud's early theories

Psychoanalytical sexual theory embraces the whole body of psychoanalytical knowledge, and is best understood by studying its development historically.

Infantile sexuality

The basic concepts were enunciated by Freud (1905) in 'The Three Essays on Sexuality'. Briefly, Freud regarded human functions as being based on instinctive drives, conflictual in character, the sexual drive or libido being opposed to other self-preservative or ego instincts. Sexual life did not commence at puberty as was formerly believed, but in infancy.

According to the libido theory, Freud regarded infantile sexuality as a series of maturational stages or phases. These phase sequences have since been confirmed by child observation, and are based on the existence of an erotogenic anatomical zone, the functions of which become invested with pleasure, i.e. cathected with libido. Thus, the names oral, anal and phallic phases are derived from the zones and their functions. Freud postulated that the instinctual drives were associated with particular aims and objects during the phases in a characteristic way; sucking and incorporation of the breast in the oral phase, expulsion and retention of urine and feces in the anal phase, exploration, showing and looking, together with erections in the phallic phase.

These early phases lasting in infancy up to the age of five or six were followed by further phases right into maturity. In particular, a latency phase, where sexual interests were more quiescent, followed the phallic phase, until the onset of puberty and adolescence brought about mature sexual functioning, which differed from the early sexual phases both in quality and intensity. Certain basic drive manifestations seemed to be paired: activity—passivity, showing—looking/touching, masculinity—feminity, sadism—masochism. The pleasure principle of reduction in instinctual tension was the underlying factor in behavior patterns, all of which had definite determinants. Instinctual gratification was accompanied by bodily pleasure. Frustration or over-stimulation led to displeasure, pain or tension and anxiety. All the infantile sexual experiences were merely components which finally became integrated during adolescence when adult genital primacy with its orgastic ability became possible and paramount. Certain infantile sexual components could and do contribute acceptable aspects to sexual fore-pleasure such as looking, showing, touching, kissing, sucking and genital manipulations. Other aspects associated with excretory, sadistic or aggressive aims, or concerning objects that had become taboo, had to be exluded. Freud found that the maturational abilities in childhood, such as the ability to control excretion, had psychological counterparts where gratifications of an earlier phase had to be given up in some degree for the proper cathexis, of libidinal investment, of the next phase activities. For example, pleasurable messing giving way to gratifying control. A hierarchy of instinctual aims and gratifications was set up according to the maturational time-table. However, vicissitudes of instinctual and emotional development occur due to the complexities of individual human and social nature, and disturbances result in a continuum between normal and pathological sexual behavior. Pathogenic influences in infancy could lead to fixations where certain phases or instinctual derivatives remained highly cathected and provided qualities of character and later sexual orientation. Although development proceeded, regression or a return to earlier satisfactions could occur, if life proved too frustrating or unrewarding compared with the earlier pleasures. Conversely, if a highly cathected pleasurable activity later became unwanted due to maturing social attitudes, conflicts would be set up and inhibitions or symptoms ensue. Freud discovered that psychoneurotics suffered from conflicts based on infantile sexual needs that were unacceptable and repressed into the unconscious. Disturbances of infantile sexual pleasure inevitably influenced adult sexual gratifications (Lieberman, 1971).

Object relationships

The child's infantile sexual development of aim- and object-related drives, was set in the family environment of parents, siblings, other persons and material objects. The bodily satisfaction or frustration of inner sexual drives was therefore experienced in relation to persons or objects in the child's ambiance. The quality of the relationships established with these persons or objects depended on and varied with the phase of development.

The term object relationship refers mainly to relationships with people, but the young child can equate animate and inanimate objects in pleasure terms. Remnants of this are found in the normal pleasure derived from objects, or in the sexual displacements onto objects found in fetishism (Freud, 1966; Mahler, 1969).

Part-object relationships

In the early oral phase, the child's interest and attachment was to the feeding breast or caring environment, rather than to any awareness of a whole mother. The child's earliest object relationships could therefore be classified as part-object, where the infantile aim was the fulfillment of its personal needs without regard for the needs of the satisfying object. Persons fixated at this level of sexual functions are selfish, demanding of immediate gratification, find difficulty controlling their emotions and actions, and usually behave with little regard for the needs of their partners. Inconsiderate or criminal sexual acts, especially where violence is a feature, have qualities originating from these earliest phases. The role of aggression in sexuality will be examined later.

The transitional object

Transitional objects and phenomena were described by Winnicott (1953) based on his observations of the earliest experience of the child in relationship to the first possession. Reference to this important literature should be made because of its fundamental importance for the persistence of the significance of certain objects which dating from infantile experience, take on the quality of a fetish. Other writers have explored this linkage (Gillespie, 1964). Winnicott regards the link as a delusion of a maternal phallus. Greenacre (1971) regards the fetish as a concrete, inanimate, special object, the presence of which is necessary for satisfactory completion of intercourse. Its use is largely limited to men. Greenacre discusses certain phenomenological differences between the transitional object and the adult fetish object. "The transitional object represents the infant's persistent but less demanding relationship to the mother during the process of separation. . . . In contrast the fetish, destined to become part of a perversion, arises in response to a focussed need, because of concern about the genitals. The demand for the concrete fetish characteristically emerges as a symptom later than is true of the transitional object, and is not always preceded by a transitional object." In contrast to Winnicott, Greenacre emphasizes the influence of traumas and maternal deprivations for the infant in the first eighteen months after birth in laying the ground for fetish development.

Whole-object relationships

The capacity to relate to a whole person develops in the latter half of the first year of life, and the child's pattern of experience of loving another person or object outside of itself is laid down from these early beginnings.

Where a whole-object relationship has been established with mother, and then for whatever reason mother becomes absent for a significant period of time, the child is subjected to separation anxieties or feelings of loss amounting to depression. Such breaks in relationships may prejudice subsequent sexual attachment behavior. The need never to rely on a single object for fear of the repetition of loss, accounts for much promiscuity, infidelity, or the need to consort with prostitutes. Such men must satisfy their sexual needs without risk to their sensitive self-esteem by rejection or disappointment.

In my experience, many sexual deviants have experienced infantile sexual overstimulation by their mothers very early in life, followed by rejections from mother for which they were unprepared. This cumulative traumatic sequence tends to be experienced repetitively in a compulsive manner thereafter, and the person's sexual interests contain ingredients of the early gratifications together with strong defenses against the possibilities of experiencing the shock and depression they never managed to resolve in childhood (Pollock, 1961; Khan, 1963, 1964; Balint, 1968, 1969).

The oedipus complex

Initially it is the mother or her substitute who is all-important for the child. The capacity to relate to other members of the household is achieved by a process of maturation, and more complex relationships are established. Most notable of the early attachment experiences is the oedipus complex which reaches its height of intensity of feeling during the phallic phase. In the boy, there are love and sexual wishes towards the mother and hostile competitive strivings against the father. This is further complicated by the factor of ambivalence in these early phases, where both love and hate are felt simultaneously but in varying degrees towards both parents. These mixed affects enhance the oedipal conflicts in the child's mind; because conflicts are hard to tolerate, their resolution motivates much of the defensive mechanisms of the ego. Where the conflicts are very intense and the opposing wishes equally strong, repression of the conflict out of awareness and its emergence disguised as symptoms occur. The oedipal phallic phase is characterized by conflicts due to the complicated drives and object relations, and the bodily experiences are centered on the genitals themselves.

Castration anxiety

The boy's wishes to remove the fantasied omnipotent father include fantasies of rivalry of a genital nature. The boy's wish to damage the father's genitals is countered by his fears of father's retaliation which is experienced as a threat to the boy's masculinity and especially to his genitals themselves. This conflict of destructive and retaliation wish fantasies constitutes the concept of castration anxiety. Castration anxiety partakes of all the accumulated anxieties of previous phases, which is the reason it features as a central expository factor in the psychoanalytical theory of sexual disorder.

Identification

Depending on the relative tolerance and balance of instinctual forces within the child and the parents' ability to provide the necessary freedom for their expression and appropriate boundaries to their enactment, the boy resolves his oedipal conflicts by identification with his father, and internalizes the aggressive wishes which go to form the conscience or super-ego.

Disorders of sexual object choice, ranging from repeated marital incompatibilities to homosexuality, always have a history of oedipal difficulties where the identification with same-sex parents and attachments to opposite-sex parents are disturbed. Dual identifications with both sexes of parent are enhanced by primal scene experiences in childhood, such as being present during parental intercourse, and may lead to disturbances of activity and passivity in character and sexual relations, as well as to exaggerated notions of intercourse based on infantile sexual theories.

In the girl, a similar and more complicated process occurs, where father is desired and mother experienced as a hated rival. The development of female sexuality and its disorders will be discussed together later in a separate section.

The oedipus complex is the prism through which all infantile experience passes and it colors uniquely every individual's capacity for sexual enjoyment, loving attachment, and choice of loved ones, rivals and friendships. Patients presenting with sexual disorders invariably have disturbances of their loving relationships with their sexual partners which mirror, in some relative manner, the early oedipal experiences.

Early psychoanalytic therapeutic models

The therapeutic model Freud used early on was certainly a novel one, but relatively simple compared with the modifications that he made later. It still holds good in the way that Newtonian notions relate to Einsteinian notions of physics.

Briefly described, Freud's theory was of the repression of instinctual drives into the unconscious where they remained active, although out of awareness, and strove for expression. As a result, inhibitions were set up to keep them at bay, or the wishes associated with the drives gained expression through the production of symptoms which were compromise formations between the drives and the repressing forces. Therapy consisted of the removal of the resistances to direct expression of the forbidden wishes, a return of the repressed material and the abreaction or release of the highly charged emotions associated with the need for repression.

This theory was put together by Freud from his experiences of the abreactive techniques he had discovered while working with Breuer on the treatment of hysterics. Freud showed that neurotics suffered from reminiscences, that is, from forgotten childhood sexual experiences that had either occurred in reality or been the subject of intense fantasy and feeling in the child, and which led to conflicts when they were repressed. These conflicts were made conscious during the treatment by the techniques of free association and interpretation of unconscious meanings, in which the understanding of dreams could play a vital part.

Freud showed further that, as part of normal sexual development, there was in most people an infantile amnesia, that is, the early infantile sexual experiences, drives, wishes and object relations became forgotten. It became axiomatic therefore that the sexual disturbances associated with severe psychoneurosis or personality disorders could only be dealt with by recourse to analytical techniques which exposed repressed unconscious infantile sexual experiences to the light of conscious awareness. An intellectual understanding of what had taken place was insufficient, and constituted only the first step in therapy. The actual feelings required to be expressed, the so-called abreaction, for insight on an emotional level to be attained that was truly therapeutic. All therapies where patients are encouraged to talk about their feelings and past experiences partake of this abreactive process; the reliving of previously repressed or discarded feelings and painful memories. The use of drugs to facilitate such reliving experiences, including the L.S.D. 'trip', was based primarily on this notion, but such short-cuts are not as efficacious as skilled psychotherapy, where the patient's resistances to actual recall require to be analyzed, rather than breaking through these resistances to the underlying material, which the patient is still unprepared to integrate. Drug abreactions may repeat the trauma and should be avoided. There is still therefore a place for a simple abreactive approach. This would be where unpleasant sexual experiences had occurred in reality, and which had not been sufficiently early or intense to cause structural changes in the personality, but led to inhibition or simple repression. The factor of being able to share sexual feelings and experiences with an unjudging sympathetic understanding person, where previously it was impossible to speak about such matters, is itself highly therapeutic. In these cases, the therapist may play an active encouraging and supportive role, helping the patient to understand why it is so difficult to talk about sexual functions. The patient's lowered self-esteem is restored, and simple inhibitions are lifted so that the patient can attempt intercourse or the pursuit of a sexual partner, especially with continuing support. Some of the simpler cases of secondary impotence, and sexual inhibitions in both sexes are very responsive to such approaches.

All psychotherapies, including behavior therapy, have two main aims. The overcoming of resistances against sexual action based on previous experiences, and the promotion of positive actions towards sexual gratification. In the popular mind, psychoanalysis has been associated more with the former aspect, while the behavior therapies and Masters and Johnson's approach have been associated with the latter. From a psychoanalytical point of view, freeing the drives for full expression may theoretically seem to be all that is necessary for sexual fulfillment to take place. This is certainly sufficient in uncomplicated cases, but in practice, especially where there are also problems of object relationship, patients require to undertake actual sexual and loving approaches in order to analyze the resistances that impede their fulfillment. There is a timing factor based on relative ego strength in the ability to face the demands of a sexual and loving situation internally and in reality.

I have treated patients who were referred by behavior therapists because they became shocked and paranoid by behavioral techniques. One such patient with homosexual fantasies and no sexual experience of any kind finally married successfully after many years of full analysis.

An understanding of the differences and basic similarities in the various psychotherapies requires an examination of the latest developments in psychoanalytical thinking on the nature of the therapeutic relationship, and the function and structure of the human psyche.

Later development in psychoanalytical theory

In 1923 Freud formulated a new structural theory of the psyche out of elements that had been present previously but never quite integrated as such.

Ego psychology
This development, subsequently known as ego psychology focussed on the growth and dynamic relationship between the various psychic 'structures' within the mind. Simply formulated, the new model of mental function had four major components. Within the psyche, there was the id, the unconscious mental representations of the basic drives or energy sources; the ego, which constituted the executive capacities or the personality, conscious and unconscious, and which mediated between the inner drives and the external world and its demands. The latter were enshrined within the psyche in an internalized way in another separately conceptualized structure called the super-ego. This served the functions of conscious and ideals formation. The psyche matures slowly, and the id, ego and super-ego develop from each other in turn. Although considerable controversy still exists as to the initial timing of the function and origins of these hypothetical structures, there is firm agreement that the capacities of the ego and super-ego or their precursors are subject qualitatively to the age and phase of development of the individual. (Hartman, 1939, 1964; Schafer, 1970).

Ego defense mechanisms
The functions of the ego include certain defense mechanisms which regulate the intensity and quality of demands made upon the personality which arise internally from the id and super-ego, and externally from the real world. Refer to Anna Freud (1936) in 'The Ego and the Mechanisms of Defence' for a systematic account.

Because ego mechanisms entail every action taken by the ego to modify sexual and aggressive drives and to maintain inner psychic equilibrium, as well as the task of gaining sexual satisfaction in reality, their variety is considerable. They function hierarchically, linked with phase development, constantly or intermittently in consortium, depending upon requirements. The defensive function, once put to use, remains forever available should the need arise. Hence the need for therapeutic insight into the actual mechanisms that are pathological plus a growth of ego maturity and strength to avoid recourse to old habits when under subsequent stress.

In general, normal defenses are those of projection, introjection, identification, reaction formation, repression and sublimation. Defenses together with regression, splitting of the ego, turning against the self, denial and drive inhibition, have pathological effects where they become exaggerated or intense. Somatic defense manifestations are important in sexual disorders and include hypercathexis or sexualization of areas of the body, the displacement of such hyperlibidinized interests on to objects, and the opposite effect of withdrawal of cathexis or capacity for sexual pleasure from sexual activities or body parts. Still on a physical level, the conversion of conflict derivatives into sexual psychosomatic symptoms is the basis of types of pain or the inhibitions of normal function in impotence and lack of orgastic satisfaction (Arlow and Brenner, 1964).

Ego defenses and sexual symptomatology

Freud's earliest notion of ego defense lay in the explanation of psychoneurotic symptoms as a compromise between infantile sexual wishes which were repressed at the behest of the censoring agency. In contrast to this, he viewed sexual perversions as psychic formations where one component of infantile sexuality such as looking, touching or sadomasochism had become exaggerated and demanded gratification. He coined the phrase 'neurosis was the negative of perversion' in a photographic sense. This formulation was oversimplified and it fell to Hans Sachs to point out that the sexual perversions were also defensive in nature, and that the ego had effected a different kind of compromise by allowing the gratification of some wishes which characterized the behavior, in order to defend against deeper, more dangerous, desires.

In order for such highly complicated sexually deviant maneuvers to take place, as Freud himself pointed out in his paper on Fetishism in 1932, splitting of the ego had to occur. Such ego splits are different from keeping certain unwanted material out of awareness. They presuppose the simultaneous presence of contradictory attitudes which though conscious, are irreconcilable, e.g. certain patients are forced to become voyeurs or indulge in symbolic acts to prove women possess a penis even where they know this to be untrue. This points to one of the basic principles in the perversions. What has become preferred behavior is always an aspect of infantile sexuality, in this example the attitude is drawn from the childhood sexual theory that all beings possess a penis, and it serves to ward off castration anxieties that the penis may actually be damaged or removed. The aims of therapy are to heal such splits in the ego by facing in the adult, the anxieties of childhood sexuality so that an integration of the ego takes place resulting in a strengthening of the ego and sense of self. For an account of stress to the adolescent ego, see Laufer (1975).

The super-ego

In sexually deviant behavior, the super-ego, or conscience, far from being in abeyance, acts in a complicated way. During development it is as if certain 'lacunae' of attitude occurred, so that sexual behavior normally regarded as prohibited became permissible (homosexuality, exhibitionism, transvestism); whereas intense prohibitions were mounted unconsciously within the

self against sexual activity which might be socially correct such as heterosexual intercourse. Because heterosexual intercourse carried the possible significance to the individual of incest, murderous oedipal intent, castration
anxiety and guilt, plus fear of loss of objects and the self, the sexual act was
either prohibited (homosexuality) or required special conditions for its ful-
filment for example, fetishism, transvestism, etc.).

Modification or cure of highly developed sexual deviations therefore requires alterations in structure and function of the ego and super-ego, as well
as changes in drive intensity and preferment. The super-ego which is formed
from the internalization of critical attitudes shown towards the child by the
parents, also uses certain other defense mechanisms in its formation. One of
these is identification with the aggressor, another is turning aggression
against the self. If a critical attitude is repeatedly or traumatically shown towards the child's expression of its normal infantile sexuality, these attitudes
become internalized and persist unconsciously as part of the later developing
super-ego which then exerts an inhibiting or prohibitive effect on adult sexual feelings and behavior (Schafer, 1968).

Aggression and sexuality

Freud's maintenance of the dual instinct theory was finally formulated into
the two basic drives of sex and aggression. Some general remarks are necessary here on the relation between aggression and sexual function, and the
aims of therapy.

The drives of libido and aggression never exist separately, but are fused
and function together except where excessive frustration or deprivation leads
to their instinctual defusion and separation, so that aggressive aims are manifested in their own right. Aggression as a drive does not follow the phase
developments as does libido which is more plastic. The pre-oedipal infantile
phases manifest much aggression which is revealed as sadism, or pleasure in
the suffering of the object. The treatment of aggressive behavior is best
managed by the promotion of satisfactions which are productive of libido,
which then binds the aggression and makes the energy available for constructive purposes. This same principle of libidinization of aggressive drives functions in many sexual and personality disorders. Overt sexual behavior defends
against dangerous aggression in the perversions, defends against depression,
the threat of loss of personality disintegration. The removal of sexual symptoms must therefore be regarded with caution in certain highly disturbed
individuals as they serve a successful defense against destructive or disin-
tegrative behavior. The sexually violent offender is usually someone in whom
the sexually normal or deviant behavior has failed in its defensive function.

Most men suffering from impotence have some degree of anger against
women which requires to be ventilated verbally. Patients with primary impotence which is highly resistant to therapy usually harbor very violent
wishes and fantasies which have been reinforced by the actual witnessing or

experience of violence in childhood. Such cases respond poorly to psycho-therapy or behavioral techniques but may be helped by lengthy full psycho-analysis, or intensive psychotherapy. For modern psychoanalytical theory of aggression see Freud (1972) Rangell (1972) Heimann and Valenstein (1972) and Musaph (1974).

Masturbation

Libidinization of aggression due to deprivation in childhood usually means recourse to masturbation. In normal development masturbation is defined as the gaining of satisfaction by bodily stimulation. Although the genitals are usually the preferred area, the anus or other areas may be libidinized. Genital erection and masturbation occurs at three well-defined ages. In earliest in-fancy as part of body exploration; during the phallic phase; during puberty and adolescence prior to the establishment of sexual intercourse. Masturbation is accompanied by fantasies appropriate to the phases in the latter two stages described (Marcus and Francis, 1975). Greenacre (1952) has shown pre-mature masturbatory activity may be fostered to counter feelings of actual deprivation. Workers dealing with sexual problems usually encounter guilt associated with masturbation. This has to be related to the underlying fanta-sies which are usually forbidden and repressed, as well as to the aggression libidinized by the masturbation itself.

In girls, recourse to clitoral masturbation due to emotional deprivation may continue throughout the latency phase and subsequently undergo massive inhibition leading to lack of orgastic pleasure. In general, it is more difficult to reduce or undo sexual behavior that is highly cathected for many reasons, than to remove inhibitions that are less intensely motivated (Lampl-De Groot, 1950).

Female sexuality

There have been considerable psychoanalytical advances in our understand-ing of female sexual development and the reader is advised to consult recent reviews of this subject. Of particular interest here are the following points. Several of Freud's views of female sexuality are no longer held. The first is that the girl's development psychically is similar to the boy's in the pre-oedipal period. We now accept that children have an innate bisexuality and introject and identify with both parents. The parents, however, respond to the innate femininity in the girl, and masculinity in the boy, and reinforce their sexual gender identities. The child's learning experience in the family is more important than biology. Rejected too, is Freud's clitoral—vaginal transfer theory that the orgastic capacity of the clitoris had to be given up and trans-ferred to the vagina. We now know that the clitoris retains its orgastic capac-ity, but that the vagina can be similarly cathected and the experience of clitoral and vaginal orgasm integrated together. This question of female orgastic capacity and quality is the most vexing theoretical and practical problem in all of sexual psychology. The adult female capacity for orgasm and its anatomic situation depends on her whole developmental sexual history and especially on whether she has been able to form an adequate psychic inner schematization of the organ concerned. It is obviously easier for a boy to visualize his penis and so assist in its cathexis from the dual aspect of the sensations arising in the penis and the picture of the penis in his mind. The girl has a more difficult cathectic task. There is evidence of vaginal awareness of sensation in small girls, but these are difficult to distinguish from anal experiences, and primary repression of vaginal awareness also seems to occur. The mental representation of the genitals is that of a receptacle and the schematization is less clear in girls than in boys. Although clitoral cathexis occurs, actual masturbation may be denied and masturbation fantasy enhanced, which is displaced on to play objects like dolls, and later expressed as the need for lengthy sexual fore-play compared with the male. It is usually only after puberty that girls make a more adequate psychic schematization of the vagina. Those women who retain a strong penis-envy and denial of sexual differences have difficulty in forming such vaginal schematizations. They remain narcissistically sensitive yet vulnerable in their feminine role. Hypercathexis of the clitoris due to masturbatory experiences in childhood may make them unable to deal with deprivations, causing narcissistic self-devaluations, so that they remain fixated to clitoral masturbatory needs, though eschewing masturbation itself. Many women attending family planning clinics have been able to obtain their first schematizations of the vagina whilst being fitted with a contraceptive cap. The doctor in these situations tells the patient how the doctor's hand is in relation within the vagina and the patient can simultaneously visualize and verbalize the experience. While such techniques are now the province of the so-called 'new sex therapy', they are avoided in the purely psychotherapeutic situation because of the seduction fantasies and dangers aroused. It is, however, possible during pure psycho therapy to assist the woman in her ability to cathect clitoral and vaginal areas so that orgasm is possible where previously inadequately experienced. This is achieved by encouraging the patient to verbalize bodily awareness of all kinds, and to analyze and remove the physical sensations of resistance which in somaticized patients impede emotional and physical pleasure experiences. See Chasseguet-Smirgel (1976) and Moore (1976) for reviews of Freud and female sexuality.

3. TREATMENT

Assessment of patients for psychotherapy

Patients presenting with sexual complaints require to be assessed physically to rule out the possibility of organic illness. Conversely, the diagnosis of psychosexual disorders is made on positive grounds rather than on the absence of physical disease. Local genital physical disabilities should be appropriately treated.

Diagnosis
A diagnostic evaluation should be made incorporating several criteria.

A. Clinical phenomenology   Symptoms may be classified as follows:
— Sexual immaturity, ignorance and social inhibitions.
— Disorders of normal function:
　　Male impotence, primary and secondary; disorders of ejaculation: premature, retarded or absent.
　　Female orgastic dysfunction; vaginismus; unconsummated intercourse, marital or premarital.
— Sexual deviations:
　　Disorders of object choice: homosexuality.
　　Disorders of drive: exhibitionism; voyeurism; sadism; masochism; compulsive masturbation or intercourse.
　　Disorders of identification: transvestism; transexualism.
— Character and psychoneurotic disorders:
　　Disturbances in object relationship.
　　Disorders of drive manifestation: passivity; diminished libido; sexual cruelty.
— Psychosomatic disorders:
　　Sexual pain (this is variable in both sexes); dyspareunia; sexual dysfunctions associated with other major psychosomatic illnesses.

B. Individual psychopathology   The diagnostic interviews and history taking should provide sufficient evidence for the presence of psychopathological features in keeping with the dynamic necessity for the sexual disorder.

Discover the duration of symptoms, the precipitating factors, alterations in symptoms consonant with changes in the patient's real life, external stresses and ameliorations (Musaph, 1974).

Gain an account of actual sexual behavior from childhood into maturity with special reference to masturbation, traumas, seductions, sexual preferences and dislikes or phobias.

Particular regard should be taken of the developmental history with regard to object relations with parents, siblings, friends and sexual partners. Be alert to the presence of any patterns of relationship or their endings which are repetitive, and make special enquiries in a subtle way about the oedipal complex and any identifications resulting from this and other periods of life.

C. Current sexual relationship or marital situation   Assessment should be made of the sexual maturity or adequacy of the spouse or partner. The presenting patient or sexual complaint may be in response to sexual difficulties inherent mainly in the partner. If necessary, and this is becoming more the rule than the exception in marital sexual compatibility problems, both partners must be seen and each assessed both separately and together. Analytical psychotherapy is now at a stage where in the treatment a great elasticity and variety of approach is possible in the treatment of marital disorders. The therapy can be suited to the needs of the couple, depending on the degree of individual sexual disorder linked with personality disturbances, to relatively simple compatibility problems. Patients can be seen separately or together or both by the same or separate therapists.

D. Patient's attitude to treatment   Of major importance is the patient's willingness to seek help, the ability to respond to insight and to perform the analytic work (working-alliance).

Final evaluation criteria for treatment choice

While it is neither possible nor desirable to obtain all the details listed above in their true significance during a diagnostic interview, an adequate evaluation of a reliable kind is usually attainable by the skilled analytic diagnostician. The more serious the accompanying personality disorder, the more difficult it is to alleviate the sexual symptoms. Conjointly, the greater the interaction of sexual and object relation difficulties with early development, the more need there is for the psychotherapy to intensify up to full analysis.

Fixed modes of sexual expression, plus patterns of repetition-compulsion in sexual behavior and object relations require proportional degrees of working through of the material indicating lengthy intensive psychotherapy. The criteria are further summarized below.

Techniques of psychotherapy in sexual disorders

Classification
 (1) Counseling
 (2) Supportive psychotherapy; short course adjustment therapy
 (3) Intensive analytical insight psychotherapy
 (4) Full psychoanalysis
This classification is given for purposes of theoretical convenience. In practice, the techniques shade into each other because of the material presented by the patient and the actual therapeutic relationship established. The establishment of proper therapeutic boundaries is important particularly in the treatment of sexual disorders because of the link with the whole personality. Conversely, it may be very important to be able to say to a patient, "your sexual problems are an aspect of deeper underlying personality functioning. You can continue to derive help for the latter even when the sexual presenting symptom has disappeared". This deals with the guilt some patients feel, that they may only receive skilled medical or psychotherapeutic

help if they are actually sick, and assist in focusing the patient's attention during intensive psychotherapy on his basic problems, so that the sexual disorder may soon be given up, as only one expression of the main conflicts.

Indications for specific therapies

Counseling   This method is for immature, youthful or uncomplicated simple sexual inhibitions. The approach would be mainly educative. Facts about sexual physiology, techniques and emotional relationships would be dealt with. In addition there would be the opportunity to correct notions in one or both partners stemming from infantile sexual theories which remain active in the mind, as well as to reduce guilty attitudes associated with masturbation, and to discuss other sexual value judgments imposed previously by family, social or religious groups.

Supportive psychotherapy   Patients who present with sexual inhibitions or simple regressions such as uncomplicated secondary impotence or loss of libido, are best treated with short courses of individual or group therapy. Such analytically based psychotherapy would be employed without the use of transference interpretations, but some interpretation of underlying motivations and resistances would be given. The therapist should explore some of the fantasies associated with masturbation, as well as the affects arising from troubling emotional and sexual experiences and attitudes. These may spring from any of the phases of development previously described. In my experience it is very important for the patient to express overtly the affects or feelings associated with underlying conflicts. These deal in the main with conflicts of love and hate. The extent to which these emotions can gain expression depends in turn on the way in which the affects are defended against by the ego defense mechanisms, and the accompanying degree of structural psychic distortion. * An assessment of these factors helps to determine whether patients will need or respond to analytical psychotherapy employing transference or nontransference techniques. This is where there is an area, hard to define, of choice of technique of psychotherapy.

Intensive analytical insight therapy   The main characteristic of this therapy is that it is based closely on classical psychoanalytical techniques, from which it differs quantitatively, by the patient being seen once to three times weekly, for months or years. Full analysis is usually four or five times weekly and extends for many years because of the time necessary to effect structural changes in the personality concerning events in earliest childhood which are totally unconscious.

---

* The functions of the ego include certain defense mechanisms which regulate the intensity and quality of demands made upon the personality which arise internally from the id and superego, and externally from the real world (see Anna Freud, 1936).

The patient—therapist relationship may vary from face-to-face interviews, to the use of the couch. The latter technique is more valuable in the establishment of a transference relationship, but the transference may be employed in a direct-view relationship. It is more difficult for the patient, because the reality of the therapist may obtrude or be used as a resistance, which must be analyzed in any case.

Transference   Transference is a psychoanalytical process whereby the patient, following the basic rule of free association, relives within the therapeutic situation, past psychic events in their fullest recall. The therapist must understand that during such reliving or spontaneous recall of the past in the present, that the patient is relating to the therapist in the manner the total psyche responded to the events being relived. This means that the therapist is regarded as being the other person or persons in that past relationship or experience. Because of the old ego defense mechanisms, the patient may actually experience within the transference a quality and intensity of experience which was blocked and not fully in awareness at the time it originally occurred. This why analytical procedures are so painful and anxiety producing. The process of verbalizing such reliving, which partakes of abreaction in its emotional expression, in relation to the real internal object in the present as represented by the analyst in the therapeutic situation, is known as working through. Working through is akin to the behavioral desensitization techniques. Behavior therapists now recognize the operation of transference during their treatments but do not deal with it as such (Kraft, 1971). Transference analysis is more specific in nature than any other behavioral technique. This is because the patient's actual emotional awareness and inner psychic reality stemming from past and present are explored in the therapeutic here and now. The specific defenses and resistances by which the ego dealt with the original stresses and traumas are analyzed and given up as ego strength is acquired. Removal of the defenses allows the return of repressed material to gain conscious expression, so that resolution of conflicts and revision of drive aims and intensities can be achieved. Because one is dealing in the sexual disorders with pleasurable aspects which the patient does not wish to give up, and painful guilts, anxieties and losses the patient does not wish to encounter, progress is slow and proceeds against constant resistance. The more problematic sexual symptoms express a typical pattern of repetitive past events, established during the phases of infantile sexuality. As these early experiences are usually unconscious, the patient has to undergo certain regressions to reach them which is in itself a burden. Patients with impotence regularly try to escape from the psychic nature of their malady by repeated reference to its possible physical causation. Such side-tracking has to be firmly resisted by the therapist, and the patient's difficulty in facing his inner conflicts analyzed.

The therapeutic nature of the analysis of the transference relationship with the therapist is based on (a) the working through of past experiences which engage every aspect of the psyche — the drives, the ego, super-ego, and in particular, the object relationships and the patient's self-esteem and sense of self; (b) the experience of gain in maturity of all these psychic structures and functions by having overcome their childhood fixations; and (c) the simultaneous creation of a new relationship of trust and pleasurable relationship with the therapist, where the patient's self-esteem and sense of self are not merely restored but raised to new levels. This is based on the new experience and capacity for object relationships which become part of the patient's internal world and its representations of the self. Such inner representations make for the feeling of self-confidence which allow the patient to function well as regards emotional and sexual relationships with others.

Anything which tends to devalue the patient's sense of self is antitherapeutic, and it is for this reason that the therapist treating sexual problems should avoid anything the patient may contrue as demeaning. Physical actions by the therapist must be avoided because of their experience by the patient as seduction, however pleaded for by the latter. The role of sex therapist and learning techniques in sex therapy must be evaluated finally in proportion to the patient's capacity to form good object relationships as part of their inner psychic representation of themselves. Psychotherapists do not provide sexual partners for their patients, because they regard sex as part of object-relatedness. The patient's problems in being able to find a suitable partner for his or herself is an essential part of the treatment. In this connection one may comment on the 'new sex therapy' of Masters and Johnson. Such patients are usually seen for short-term treatment and must have partners who are also willing to undertake therapy. Psychotherapy often has to deal with the basic faults between partners or the individual patient's inability to find or properly relate to a sexual partner.

Full psychoanalysis Full psychoanalysis is indicated where the aim is to secure significant structural changes in the personality, or where the resistances which maintain the sexual disorder are so intense or elaborate so as to require extensive working through. The frequency of working allows for an intensity and continuity of transference manifestations which are necessary to reach the unconscious infantile fantasy material which require to be reconstructed from the material produced in the analytic situation. The faulty identifications which are basic to personality disorders are related to defenses against loss of significant objects which lead also to a severe sense of inferiority or disturbance of self-esteem. During a full analysis or very intensive analytical psychotherapy it is possible to work through the severe moods of depression which accompany the reliving of early experiences of object loss. The history of many acute sexual disorders shows that the factors precipitating the sexual behavior in question, is in response to an actual or threatened loss. Such losses may be of sexual partner, e.g. depressions or panics; of anything which lowers self-esteem such as loss of job or status or evidence of inadequacy; or symbolic loss which acts as a threat to masculinity or femininity and revives unconscious castration fears or other anxieties. The relating of the precipitating real events to their psychic inner meanings and thence to the prior infantile sexual phase patterning, is the task of insight therapy. The intellectual understanding which is first acquired deepens until an emotional level of insight is reached, by which time the symptom complex or defensive pattern of behavior is dealt with.

Determinants of choice of psychotherapies

The determinants of choice are:

(1) Availability of treatment, both in terms of trained therapists and patient's ability or willingness to work in such treatment or for reality reasons of motivation, time, and resources. It is deleterious to recommend a treatment which will not be available on any of these grounds, unless there is some collusive attitude between therapist and patient that for reality reasons the patient should continue with the symptoms and is now justified in doing so, as a further defense against conflicts too difficult or impossible to resolve. It is better for the patient to face impossible odds directly, in my opinion.

(2) The degree to which the sexual symptom is part of a repetitive-compulsive pattern of behavior, with a developed psychic defensive structure, relating to infantile sexual origins.

(3) The degree to which there are disturbances of object relationships. To what extent is the sexual problem one of sexual compatibility and mutual sensitivities? Both partners and their interaction are the problem. One or both partners require additional individual or marital group therapy. This chapter was written mainly from the individual psychotherapy point of view. Many new techniques of group treatment for sexual problems are currently being developed.

Capacity for bodily cathexis in the female

In selecting appropriate psychotherapy for women patients, one must question whether a disorder of orgastic satisfaction reflects a lack of experience and immaturity that will respond to supportive psychotherapy and the presence of a potent and patient lover. Or to what degree there are sexual inhibitory factors of varying intensity, requiring a proportionate amount of analysis of the resistances which interfere with the woman's capacity for cathecting her genital anatomy and function and thus limiting pleasure. The female psyche seems less tolerant of ego splitting than the male. Some women become orgastically potent in intercourse, as opposed to a masturbatory response, after they have gained an inner psychic representation of themselves as a satisfactory feminine whole person. In such women the wounds to the sense of narcissism have been healed which were acquired during development. Some very narcissistic women have to deny any aspects of personal inadequacy, which are nevertheless real, and which link unconsciously with the girl's notions about her disturbed sense of self. The deep sense of inferiority found in many women is only partly based on the experience or fantasies associated with penis envy, but is more often rather derived from experiences of emotional deprivation from mother and father in turn. The therapist's attitude encourages the patient to test in reality her sexual capacities with an appropriate partner, so that there is a concurrent real life experience accompanying the gains made during analysis which reinforces and cements the sexual and emotional maturation. This is of course equally descriptive of male patients or marital partners.

The treatment approach to homosexuality

Psychoanalysis maintains the viewpoint that homosexuality is the result of developmental psychological factors which include the innate biological tendency towards bisexuality (Freud, 1905). Such a view is consistent with the aim of understanding the mechanisms and psychic structures that produce heterosexuality or indeed any variation of normal or abnormal behavior.

Anna Freud (1966) has pointed out that there is a precarious balance during development of the factors which make for heterosexual or homosexual object choice. In her concept of developmental lines she has systematically outlined the stages and degrees to which specific childhood maturational phases and their accompanying object relationships may influence the final sexual object choice which is made after puberty. External accidental factors also play a part.

Successive psychoanalytic writers have emphasized different oedipal and pre-oedipal factors as being of major contributory importance to the production of homosexuality. Most recent authors emphasize that in both male (Socarides) and female (McDougall) homosexuals there may be basic disturbances of the ability to exist as a separate individual as well as problems of sexual identity. The oedipal level conflicts of negative oedipal feelings and identifications certainly contribute to certain types or manifestations of homosexuality. Newly stressed in the etiology of homosexuality are the pre-oedipal conflicts stemming from separation—individuation fixations, narcissistic disturbances, archaic ego mechanisms of introjection of loved and hated objects. Unconscious identifications with these primitive parental figures who are actually disturbed, are used to deal with the terror of loneliness and fears of loss of the self.

There is a large measure of agreement between psychoanalytic and psychiatric observers of the personalities of the parents of male homosexuals. As a parental couple they are both disturbed, the mother frequently exercising a double-bind effect of excessive closeness coupled with attitudes of rejection of the child's sexual identity role. The fathers are either distant, overtly rejecting or violent and disgusting.

From accounts in the literature and one's own clinical experience, there is no doubt that homosexuality arises from complicated early developmental factors in object relationships, which in severe cases are fixated at the early separation—individuation phase.

Because homosexuality may be either egosyntonic or egodystonic, that is, acceptable or unacceptable to the individual concerned, questions of normality versus pathology as well as treatability are raised.

Treatment for homosexuals depends on the individual's desire to be treated together with the therapist's skill in treatment. Recently, the humane desire for greater tolerance for all human deviation has brought a political aspect into this area. Tolerance of civil liberties in the mature adult should not preclude our understanding of the psychopathology of homosexuality. Neither should any homosexual be put off from securing appropriate help by notions that he is either not in need of assistance, or beyond it by virtue of constitution or so-called normality.

Homosexuality has been treated successfully psychoanalytically in series reported in the literature, summarized by Wiedeman (1974), while many individual analysts can claim successes in unpublished fewer numbers of patients. There are case reports of homosexuals coming into treatment for other reasons who have become heterosexual as part of the resolution of their problems.

In confirmed homosexuals, also known as obligatory homosexuals, it is essential for the psychotherapist to be able to deal with the patient's problems of depression and panic about survival when homosexual relationships are terminated. Because the homosexual solution is the answer to so many inner psychic disequilibria, the rapid substitution of partner, or the intense need for homosexual activity as a relief and defense against depression and anxiety, may render such people liable to acts of importuning and hence to arrest. Psychotherapeutic methods to help improve the quality of relationships are therefore called for.

There are no authoritative, statistically acceptable figures regarding the success rate of individual and psychoanalytic methods of therapy with respect to either homosexuality or any manifestations of sexuality requiring change. The same is true for any other form of therapy.

BIBLIOGRAPHY

Early psychoanalytical models

Refer to Complete Psychological Works of Sigmund Freud. Standard Edn *(S.E.)* (London).
Freud, S. (1905) Three essays on the theory of sexuality. *S.E.* 7: 125—245.
Freud, S. (1907) The sexual enlightenment of children. *S.E.* 9: 129—139.
Freud, S. (1915—7) Introductory lectures on psychoanalysis. *S.E.* Vols. 15, 16.
Freud, S. (1923) The ego and the id. *S.E.* 19: 3—63.
Freud, S. (1926) Inhibitions, symptoms and anxiety. *S.E.* 20: 77—174.
Freud, S. (1932) New introductory lectures on psychoanalysis. *S.E.* 22: 3—182.
Freud, S. (1940) Splitting of the ego in the process of defence. *S.E.* 23.
Lieberman, B. (Ed.) (1971) 111.1 The sexual life of man. S. Freud; 111.2 The develop-

ment of the libido. S. Freud; 111.3 The libido theory of Sigmund Freud. E. Jones. In: *Human Sexual Behavior*. A Book of Readings. (New York.)

Ego-psychology

Arlow, J.A. and Brenner, C. (1964) *Psychoanalytic Concepts and Structural Theory*. (New York.)

Eissler, K.R. (1953) The effect of the structure of the ego on psychoanalytic technique. *J. Am. Psychoanal. Assoc.* 1: 104—143.

Fenichel, O. (1945) *The Psycho-analytic Theory of Neurosis*. (Norton, New York.)

Freud, A. (1936) *The Ego and the Mechanisms of Defence*. (London.)

Freud, A. (1966) The concept of developmental lines. In: *Normality and Pathology in Childhood*. (London.)

Hartmann, H. (1939) *Ego Psychology and the Problem of Adaptation*. 1958 (Int. Univ. Press, New York.)

Hartmann, H. (1964) *Essays on Ego Psychology*. (Int. Univ. Press, New York.)

Schafer, R. (1970) Heinz Hartmann's contributions for psychoanalysis. *Int. J. Psycho-Anal.* 51: 425—446.

Sandler, J., Dare, C. and Holder, A. (1973) Transference, resistance and working through, In: *The Patient and the Analyst*. (London.)

Segal, H. (1973) *Introduction to the Work of Melanie Klein*. (Hogarth, London.)

Object relations theory

Balint, M. (1968) *The Basic Fault*. (Tavistock, London.)

Balint, M. (1969) Trauma and object relationship. *Int. J. Psycho-Anal.* 50: 429.

Greenacre, P. (1970) The transitional object and the fetish with special reference to the role of illusion. *Int. J. Psycho-Anal.* 51: 447—456.

Greenacre, P. (1971) *Emotional Growth*, Vols. 1 and 2 (Int. Univ. Press, New York.)

Heimann, P. (1952) Certain functions of introjection and projection in early infancy. In: (Klein, M., Ed.) *Medical Developments in Psycho-Analysis*. Hogarth, London.)

Joffe, W.G. (1969) A critical review of the status of the envy concept. *Int. J. Psycho-Anal.* 50: 533.

Klein, M. (1957) *Envy and Gratitude*. (London.)

Khan, M.M.R. (1963) The concept of cumulative trauma. *Psychoanal. Stud. Child* 18.

Khan, M.M.R. (1964) Ego-distortion, cumulative trauma and the role of reconstruction in the analytic situation. *Int. J. Psycho-Anal.* 45. (Both in *The Privacy of the Self* (1974) Hogarth, London.)

Mahler, M.S. (1969) *On Human Symbiosis and the Vicissitudes of Individuation*. (London.)

Pollock, G.H. (1961) Mourning and adaptation. *Int. J. Psycho-Anal.* 42: 341—361.

Winnicott, D.W. (1953) Transitional objects and transitional phenomena. *Int. J. Psycho-Anal.* 34. (Also in *Collected Papers: Through Paediatrics to Psycho-analysis* (1958) London.)

Female sexuality including psychosexual disorders and treatment

Bonaparte, M. (1953) *Female Sexuality*. (New York—London.)

Deutsch, H. (1944) *The Psychology of Women*. (New York)

Chasseguet-Smirgel, J. (1976) Contribution to Dialogue on Freud and female sexuality. 29th Congr. Int. Psycho-Anal. Assoc., London. *Int. J. Psycho-Anal.* in press.

Moore, B.E. (1976) Contribution to dialogue on Freud and female sexuality. 29th Congr. Int. Psycho-Anal. Assoc., London. *Int. J. Psycho-Anal.* in press.

Panel discussion (1968) Female sexuality, *J. Am. Psychoanal. Assoc.* 14.

Sherfey, M.J. (1972) *The Nature and Evolution of Female Sexuality*. (Random House, New York.)

Aggression

Freud, A. (1972) Comments on aggression. *Int. J. Psycho-Anal.* 53: 163.
Rangell, L. (1972) Aggression, Oedipus and historical perspective. *Int. J. Psycho-Anal.* 53: 3.
Heimann, P. and Valenstein, A.F. (1972) The psychoanalytical concept of aggression: an integrated summary. *Int. J. Psycho-Anal.* 53: 31.

Masturbation

Lampl-De Groot, J. (1950) On masturbation and its influence on general development. *Psychoanal. Stud. Child* 5: 153—174.
Greenacre, P. (1952) Pre-genital patterning. *Int. J. Psycho-Anal.* 33: 410.
Marcus, I.M. and Francis, J.J. (1975) *Masturbation: From Infancy to Senescence.* (Int. Univ. Press, New York.)

Body-ego

Hoffer, W. (1950) Development of the body-ego. *Psychoanal. Stud. Child* 5: 18—23.
Hoffer, W. (1952) The habitual influence in the development of Ego and Id. *Psychoanal. Stud. Child* 7: 31—41.
Fleiss, R. (1961) Chapter 3. In: *Ego and Body Ego.* (New York.)
Fisher, S. (1973a) Masculine and feminine body feelings. In: *Body Consciousness.* (London and New Jersey.)
Fisher, S. (1973b) *The Female Orgasm: Psychology, Physiology, Fantasy.* (New York.)

Sex education

Taylor, D.L. (Ed.) (1970) *Human Sexual Development. Perspectives in Sex Education.*
Powers, G.P. and Baskin, W. (1969) *Sex Education.* (London.)
Winnicott, D.W. (1949) Sex education in school. In: *The Child and the Outside World,* 1957 (London) or *The Child, the Family and the Outside World,* 1964 (Penguin Books, London.)
Rosen, I. (1969) Fact, fantasy and the under-10s. Leader on Sex Education in *The Observer,* London, 7th November.

Fetishism

Greenacre, P. (1977) Fetishism. In: (Rosen, I., Ed.) *Pathology and Treatment of Sexual Deviation.* 2nd edn (London) in press.

Gender disorders

Stoller, R.J. (1968) *Sex and Gender.* (Hogarth, London.)
Stoller, R.J. (1975) *The Transsexual Experiment.* (Hogarth, London.)

Homosexuality

Wiedeman, G.H. (1974) Homosexuality, a survey. *J. Am. Psycho-Anal. Assoc.* 22: 651—696.
Socarides, C.W. (1977) The psychoanalysis of overt male homosexuality: theoretical, clinical and therapeutic considerations. In: (Rosen, I., Ed.) *Pathology and Treatment of Sexual Deviation.* 2nd edn (London) in press.
McDougall, J. (1977) The homosexual dilemma (female homosexuality). In: (Rosen, I.,

Ed.) *Pathology and Treatment of Sexual Deviation.* 2nd edn (London) in press.

Gagnon, J.H. and Simon, W. (1974) *Sexual Conduct. The Social Sources of Human Sexuality.* (Hutchinson, London.)

Kraft, T. (1971) A case of homosexuality treated by combined behavior therapy and psychotherapy. *Psychother. Psychosom.* 19: 342—358.

Musaph, H. (1960) On Homosexuality. *Psychiat. Neurol. Neurochir.*, 63, 203—211.

Male potency disorders

Cooper, A.J. (1969) Factors in male sexual inadequately: a review. Including *'Outpatient treatment of impotence'. J. Nerv. Ment. Dis.* 149: 337—371.

Cooper, A.J. (1971) Treatment of male potency disorders: the present psychosomatics 12: 235—244.

Johnson, J. (1965) Prognosis of disorders of sexual potency in the male. *J. Psychosom. Res.* 9: 195—200.

Mandell, A.J. (1963) The management of sexual impotence. *Gen. Pract.* 28: 108—112.

Noy, P., Wollstein, S. and Kaplan-De-Noura, R. (1966) Clinical observations on the psychogenesis of impotence. *Br. J. Med. Psychol.* 39: 43—53

O'Connor, J.F. and Stern, L.D. (1972) Results of treatment in functional sexual disorders. *N.Y. State J. Med.* 72: 1927—1934.

Ovesey, L. and Meyers, H. (1968) Retarded ejaculation. Psychodynamics and psychotherapy. *Am. J. Psychother.* 22: 185—201.

Rosen, I. (1965) Looking and showing. In: (Slovenko, R., Ed.) *Sexual Behavior and the Law* (Charles C. Thomas, Springfield, Ill.).

Rosen, I. (1972) The male response to frigidity. In: (Morris, N., Ed.) *Psychosomatic Medicine in Obstetrics and Gynaecology.* (Karger, Basel.)

Sexual perversions or deviation

Lorand, S. (Ed.), (1956) *Perversions. Psychodynamics and Therapy.* (Random House, New York.)

Rosen, I. (1964) *The Pathology and Treatment of Sexual Deviation.* 1st edn (Oxford Univ. Press, London). 2nd edn, revised with new contributors, in press.

Counseling

Lewis, L.S. and Brissett, D. (1970) Sex as work: a study of avocational counseling. In: (A. Shiloh, Ed.) *Studies in Human Sexual Behavior.* (Springfield, Illinois.)

Sex therapy

Kaplan, H.S. (1974) *The New Sex Therapy.* (New York.)

Masters, W.H. and Johnson, V.E. (1970) *Human Sexual Inadequacy.* (London.)

The treatment situation

Green, A. (1975) The analyst, symbolization and absence in the analytic setting. *Int. J. Psychoanal.*, 56: 1.

Laufer, M. (1975) *Adolescent Disturbance and Breakdown.* (London.)

Musaph, H. (1974) The role of aggression in somatic symptom formation. *Int. J. Psychiat. Med.*, 5 (4) 449—460.

Psychotherapy

Alexander, F. (1965) Psychoanalytic contributions to short-term psychotherapy. In: (L.R. Wolberg, Ed.) *Short-Term Psychotherapy.* (New York.)

Bibring, E. (1954) Psychoanalysis and the dynamic psychotherapies. *J. Am. Psychoanal. Assoc.* 2: 745—770.

Ekstein, R. and Wallerstein, R.S. (1972) *The Teaching and Learning of Psychotherapy.* 2nd edn, (New York).

Rangell, L. (1954) Panel report: psychoanalysis and dynamic psychotherapy — similarities and differences. *J. Am. Psychoanal. Assoc.* 2: 152—166.

Panel, N. (1954a) The traditional psychoanalytic technique and its variations. *J. Amer. Psychoanal. Assoc.* 2: 621—710.

Panel, N. (1954b) Psychoanalysis and dynamic psychotherapies: similarities and differences. *J. Amer. Psychoanal. Assoc.* 2: 711—797.

Rosen, I. (1968) The basis of psychotherapeutic treatment of sexual deviation. *Proc. R. Soc. Med.* 61: 793—796.

Group therapy

Daniel, H. and Kreeger, L. (1975) Marital group therapy. *Group Anal.* 8/3.

Rosenberg and Chilgren (1973) Sex education discussion groups in a medical setting. *Int. J. Group Psychother.* 23.

Skynner, R. (1976) *One Flesh, Separate Persons; Principles of Family and Marital Psychotherapy.* English edn (Constable, London). *Systems of Family and Marital Psychotherapy.* (Brunner/Mazel, New York.)

CHAPTER 100

Counseling the male homosexual

BRADFORD WILSON

1. PATIENT AND THERAPIST

Many clients come to therapy waving the banner of their presenting problem while at the same time being vaguely aware that they doubtless have several core problems waiting in the wings which will have to be worked through eventually. When dealing with a male homosexual, however, it is best to bear in mind that he usually comes to therapy more fully convinced than most clients that his presenting problem is the problem for immediate considera-tion. It is in this connection that the therapist may make his first major clinical misjudgement, that is in assuming that the client's core problem is the fact of his being homosexual. Unless the therapist is willing to accept homosexuality as a valid and authentic variant of human sexual expression, he or she had best avoid therapeutic contact with such individuals. The same holds true even when the client himself attributes his difficulties to his homosexuality and asks to be 'cured' of it, were a heterosexual client to make an analogous assertion, is there a psychotherapist in the world who would blandly and confidently undertake to 'cure' him of his heterosexual-ity? To answer, "Well, but heterosexuality is a normal instinct . . ." is to make the dubious assumption that instincts are automatically linked to specific objects. Psychologically the only male sexual 'instinct' consists of an appetite which yearns to stimulate the penis towards ultimate ejaculation. As for the argument that to achieve a homosexual life-style requires consider-able neurotic impetus to thus run counter to the mainstream of societal con-ditioning, it should be borne in mind that most if not all deviant life-styles (artist, composer, tightrope walker) first sprouted in the subsoil of childhood agony and maladjustment. To assume that because this is so the adult life-style must now still partake of that maladjustment is to ignore the role of autonomy and self-fulfillment whereby the psyche, like the resourceful oyster, can make pearls out of its catastrophes.

This is not to suggest, however, that the male homosexual client does not

Handbook of Sexology, edited by J. Money and H. Musaph
© Elsevier/North-Holland Biomedical Press, 1977

have core problems which need to be dealt with. By and large, his underpinnings are more often than not hysterical in nature, and fraught with all the problems revolving around romantic and sexual love which characterize that nosological entity; here again, his difficulty is not with homosexuality but with sexuality per se. Underneath the somewhat hectic (and often promiscuous) sexual acrobatics with which he regales his therapist there often lies a great deal of anxiety about intimacy, sustained warmth, and his basic right to be a sexually loving person. Incest guilt lurks around every corner so that whenever intimacy loses its first romantic blush and the lover begins to take on a 'family' coloration the male homosexual may begin to unconsciously regard the relationship as incestuous. It is at this point that he begins to 'fall out of love' — an involuntary withdrawal of loving and sexual feelings. At this point he may utter any of the following pronouncements: "I guess this lover is not really my cup of tea" or "I don't know where it went, I just turned off" or he may even assert that "I guess maybe homosexuality is not for me" (the latter is best translated to read "I should not allow myself to be sexual.") It is during this withdrawal phase that the anxious male homosexual may unconsciously pick all manner of quarrels with his lover. In this way he creates a smoke-screen of incompatibility under cover of which he can rationalize or justify what is really a headlong flight from sexual and romantic intimacy. Such smoke-screens can be so convincing in their build-up that it is extremely difficult for an observer not to conclude that the couple is indeed highly incompatible.

2. VARIANT MANIFESTATIONS

Since the smoke-screen is such an integral component of hysterically based acting-out, it would seem most useful to list a number of its variants. Following are those which come most readily to mind, couched in the language of their overt manifestations:

— "I have been very close and warm with my lover, but for some reason it's beginning to pall on me. Maybe I need to find someone else."

— "My lover is no longer attractive to me; I'd never hurt his feelings by saying it, but I find him physically disgusting these days."

— "I never realized how many obnoxious qualities he has; everything he does seems to irritate me lately."

— "He is paying a lot of attention to other men recently and I don't have to stand for that kind of treatment!"

— "I don't seem to feel sexually stimulated of late, may be I'm just getting old . . ."

— "He makes such a fuss over me that it's downright embarrassing. It's obvious that he loves me more than I love him, and I don't think it's fair to disillusion him about it any longer.'

— "All we do is fight lately. We've even started to attack each other physically. I think we'd better terminate the relationship before one of us really injures the other."

— "He's getting too serious; all I wanted was a casual relationship. Just because I want to see or talk to him every day doesn't mean I'm in love with him, for God's sake!"

— "I've started to become impotent lately. Could that be because we aren't suited to each other sexually?"

3. IMPOTENCE

Under the impotence rubric I offer the following translations of what the individual's unconscious is most often pantomiming:

— "Deep down I think sex is dirty, and if I love my sex partner, how can I be such a cad as to foist dirty activities upon him? If I withdraw from the situation, then I won't be guilty of inflicting my dirtiness on my beloved partner. Incidentally, I will be disappointed in him if he descends to such dirtiness himself, and so by withdrawing I keep both our loves pure and unsullied."

— "It gives me a sense of power to turn my partner on and then leave him at my mercy — as he makes a fool of himself in the throes of sexual abandon while I keep cool and thus remain in control of the situation."

— "I'm afraid of the helpless abandon I experience with orgasm, somewhere I learned that one can go psychotic from sex, so if I turn off, I can postpone the dreaded moment indefinitely."

— "Deep down, I distrust my partner and simply dare not let go with him, especially when I'm stark naked and vulnerable. Better protect myself by turning off."

— "I'm afraid that I'm not very experienced, and he will have contempt for my performance. If I turn off, I thereby postpone the inevitable driver's test. If I don't give it my all, then I don't have to feel that I flunked."

— "My partner is a typically devouring and demanding bastard, just like all men; just like my mother/father/brother/sister, etc., etc. Well this time I won't let myself be gobbled up and used and manipulated; this time I'm in the driver's seat, and I'll get even for all past grievance by holding out on him, he can eat his heart out!"

— "I'm here to be serviced and taken care of; how dare my partner ask that I give myself over, even temporarily to his needs?! Outrageous! I'll not have any part of it! I'll turn off, that's what I'll do . . ."

— "My responses are so trained to my own hands that any other touch feels alien and unsexual. Sex has always been a private and self-contained activity for me, and I experience his participation as alien and intrusive and hopelessly complicated."

— "I want to be my partner's darling child, and sit on his lap and be cuddled, I'm really not old enough yet to know about such things as sex and orgasms. I want my Mommy/Daddy!"

— "I secretly envy and despise (other) men and by not responding to their sexual blandishments, I can really get even in a big way; try as they might, they will never get any important response out of me! I will make them feel as though their sexuality is of no importance so far as I'm concerned."

— "I will never forgive or forget the numerous wrongs he has done me. The only place I have him at my mercy is in bed, and now it's my turn to inflict a dose of frustration on him." Or "People have always let me down (or failed to respond to me) when I needed them most; and now it's my turn to let them down in their hour of need. I would be untrue to all the neglects I have suffered at their hands if I did not seize this opportunity to avenge myself by turning off on my partner."

— "I am afraid of total involvement and/or total emotional commitment, and this is my way of holding out on it, like a prostitute who steadfastly clings to her independence by making sure never to kiss a client, no matter what other intimate acts they may perform together. For me, sexual turned-on-ness is the ultimate kiss, and I'm afraid to bring myself to that point."

— "I am testing him out to see if it's really me he loves, or only my services as a sex object; once I'm reassured, I'll be OK. Only trouble is that neither he nor anyone else on earth can sufficiently reassure me."

— "He is really too good for me; our happiness together is more than I deserve to have in life, considering what monstrous reservoirs of unconscious hostility I am secretly harboring. Since I'm in fear of eventually being punished for such feelings, if I can make him go away, the loss of him will be my own punishment and my score will thus be evened." (The formulation here is the notion that "if I ever achieve fulfillment somebody — mother/father/sibling/ghost of same — will find me out and destroy me for such impertinence.")

4. PRESENTING PROBLEMS

With the foregoing in mind, we may then turn our attention to some typical presenting problems. Many of these are of such patent validity that the first stages of therapeutic intervention may well require the utilization of ancillary resources. Several examples will suffice by way of illustration:

Coming out

"I have just begun to face up to my homosexuality and I'm a fish out of water. I don't know how or where to go about meeting men who will fulfill my emotional and sexual needs."

The services of a Homosexual Counseling Center would best meet this man's immediate requirements. Such centers provide 'Coming-Out Groups' which meet one evening per week for 6 or 8 weeks during which one or two experienced group leaders (who are themselves homosexual) help newcomers to share their thoughts and feelings relative to their entrance into this new life-style.

Lacking such facilities, the therapist can use behavior modification techniques along the lines of 'assertiveness training' to help the client overcome his diffidence with regard to entering various places where homosexual men congregate, introducing himself, striking up conversations and acquaintanceships. Or, if the therapist is not himself trained in these modalities, he can make the appropriate referral.

Depression

"I'm a newcomer to this locale and I don't know anybody yet and don't know where to go. I'm so lonely and depressed I think I may just kill myself."

While the underlying sense of helplessness here expressed will need eventual therapeutic attention, some good sound advice is what is urgently needed at the outset, viz: "Find the place in this community which is the local equivalent to Piccadilly Circus or Times Square. Go there about 10:30 pm and hang around until you spot someone whom you feel quite sure is homosexual — the more flamboyant the better. Follow him discretely, and chances are nine-out-of-ten that he will lead you to a local homosexual gathering-place. From there you will learn about other gathering-places; go to them all. In this way, you will meet some fellows you can make friends with. If this instance leads perchance to a dead-end, then go back to Piccadilly and find someone else to follow. It's bound to work out sooner or later."

When the client feels better he may disappear and never come back. Although he has not yet dealt with his underlying helplessness, there is the distinct possibility that he may never again feel that helpless, nor that depressed.

Deteriorated partnership

"My lover and I have been together for eighteen years and love each other dearly. But for the past year he has been into heroin/alcohol/etc., and I've reached the end of my tether. I don't want to abandon him in the middle of such torment but I can't seem to be of much help either."

Specialized addiction counseling for the couple is here called for. Unfortunately in these times, the counselors almost invariably address themselves to 'curing' the homosexuality when these individuals show up at addiction counseling centers. It is therefore preferable to locate such facilities under the aegis of an 'umbrella organization' which specializes in homosexual counseling. In any event, addictions usually require the ancillary services of counselors who are specifically trained to treat people with such problems. Considering the long-term implications of such a referral (and provided that suitable resources are available in one of the larger metropolitan communities) it is best to recommend that the client and his lover geographically re-

1276

locate in order to avail themselves of such resources. Despite monumental difficulties relative to vocational rearrangements, such moves are usually possible in the long run, albeit with considerable effort.

Adultery

"My lover and I have been deeply in love with each other for about a year. Now he wants to play around with casual dating of other people while I feel we should be content with each other as we have been up until recently. I'm baffled and hurt and angry about this new direction he's taking, and I don't know what to do about it."

Here the client may require some deep work on his own dependency needs, but his lover is probably acting out a version of the aforementioned insect-guilt smoke screen (for some reason which still puzzles me, this crisis is apt to appear immediately following the ninth month of a relationship; Rankians take note!) and the lover, thus caught up in his own acting-out, is usually not motivated toward any counseling on his own behalf. At best he will consent to come in as an aid to the process of getting the incumbent lover 'off his back'. Clearly this is a matter for what is known in the American centers as Gay Couples Counseling. While this type of problem is by no means unknown to those of us who counsel heterosexual couples, it is almost endemic to homosexual couples. I have found it most useful to simply enunciate my insect-guilt formulations as set forth in this essay. No matter that it will be greeted with skepticism, incredibility, derision or whatever; as is so often the case with offering introspective material, we herein address ourselves to the individual's unconscious and can rest assured that it is not missing a single word. Again, while ancillary counseling services are the treatment of choice here, much can be accomplished for the client by guiding him toward an exploration of the extent to which his lover may be acting out a set of dynamics which he himself might have got caught up in at a later date or in another relationship.

Legal problem

"I was a very competent school teacher until I made the fatal error of succumbing to the blandishments of a youngster who was bent upon seducing me. We were finally caught out and I, of course, was accused of seducing a minor and summarily dismissed. Now my career is wrecked, my marriage is in ruins, and I don't know where to go with my life."

When a man's life is suddenly devastated, the most healing thing for him is to be able to do something about his situation. Legal counsel is the first step in this direction — whether he proves to have a legal 'case' or not. Attorneys are action people, and for the client to be in contact with such a resource provides him with an all-important sense that he is not taking the situation passively. Most homophile organizations provide expert legal counseling services, and a journey of several hundred miles in order to obtain such counsel would have a very stabilizing effect on this client. Other immediate therapeutic measures might involve exploring the guilt-about-being-homosexual which this incident has triggered (just as having venereal disease is apt to trigger any latent sexual guilts which an individual may harbor) as well as helping the client to mobilize and re-package his vocational resources. The services of a vocational advisor would not be amiss at this juncture.

5. SAMENESS PROBLEMS

In addition to the foregoing, there are special problems which seem to occur more frequently in the male homosexual than in his heterosexual counterpart. Most notable among these is a kind of 'twinning' in love relationships — a tendency to over-emphasize shared traits and proclivities while overlooking the differences between each other. This would seem to be a function of the narcissistic component of the hysterical personality; that is, the wish to seek out and affirm the Me in others while treating the Not-Me as an unpalatable threat to be denied or repressed. In couples counseling, it is useful to have each member of the pair describe what he thinks the other's childhood was like. The resultant increase in mutual understanding is edifying and often very moving. It should be added that whereas a heterosexual couple can cushion their awareness of important differences by attributing them to a difference between the sexes, this explanation is not available to homosexual couples except insofar as they may indulge in a kind of husband/wife roleplaying — a posture generally considered outmoded and 'sexist' among present-day homosexual males. Such role-playing is more apt to be found among older couples.

Given that the phenomenon commonly known as 'marriage of opposites' is as frequent among homosexual males as it is in the general population, the special need to expunge differences can place a heavy burden upon the relationship. Inasmuch as each partner is living out certain unexpressed aspects of the other's personality, a fair amount of conflict is apt to develop. Thus an introverted man may find his partner's extroversion very difficult to put up with, and vice versa. If to this is added a tacit assumption that their harmony depends upon 'being alike', each may begin to exert unfair pressure upon the other to conform to his particular biases. These pressures can be worked through if the couple is helped to accept and take pleasure in each other's distinctive differences.

At the opposite end of this spectrum is a fear (usually unconscious) of that fusion which is so eagerly sought; one or both men may experience a frequent loss of boundaries as his life-space and personality seem to be gobbled up by the partner. As in the case of other reaction-formations, insight needs to be brought to bear on the submerged wish for fusion lest one or both partners get caught up in acting out their fears at the expense of the ongoing relationship.

It goes without saying that the lack of societal sanctions and traditions as well as the absence of legal and religous supports deprives the homosexual couple of any social model which might provide guidelines in making necessary adjustments in an ongoing relationship. With virtually no support from the environment (which says that such relationships don't deserve to work out satisfactorily) it is all too easy to give up and dissolve relationships. Non-romantic friendships, however, tend to be every bit as enduring as in the heterosexual populations, if not more so.

To the extent that male homosexuals are, more often than not, estranged (or at least distanced) from their families, it becomes a strong temptation to over-invest family feelings in the partner so that the partnership becomes over-loaded with transferential actings-out. Positive transferential feelings may suffer when a partner's behavior fails to be congruent with that of a beloved family member. At the same time negative transferences may get triggered by trivial stimuli. These transferences become more difficult when we stop to realize that male-to-male transferences may partake of female figures in each partner's background. Thus one man may be drawn to another by transferential qualities which remind him of his mother or a beloved sister and at the same time become enraged because other characteristics are present which trigger hostile feelings toward a younger brother. That these problems often transcend differences in age and physiognomy is a well-known aspect of transferential phenomena. Here insight therapy is the technique of choice in helping both partners to understand and work through the complexity of their reciprocal expectations.

The particular skill required for the counseling of male homosexuals resides in a capacity for comfortably wearing two hats — that of a resource person who is able to draw upon a host of ancillary services when these are available and that of being able at the same time to keep in mind the deeper psychodynamics which hover nearby in the wings, be they hysterical in nature, or obsessive-compulsive, or character disorderly, or phobic, or schizoid, or schizophrenic, or whatever.

In sum, it is not the life-style which engenders trouble for the individual's personality, but rather the underlying personality problems which erode and confound the life-style of the homosexual client.

CHAPTER 101

Counseling the lesbian *

TINA MANDEL and PAMELA OLINE

1. INTRODUCTION

Psychotherapy takes place between two people, client and therapist, who are living in the world. Our aim in contributing to this volume is to suggest a network of contexts whereby, both in its intrapsychic and interpersonal dimensions, the world of the woman who is a lesbian ** might disclose itself in the therapeutic encounter.

While there is an enormous quantity of clinical writing on the subject of homosexuality, its usefulness for counseling the lesbian is limited. First, a large portion is about male homosexuals. More important, the literature tends to focus on the etiology of a pathology, thus robbing the experience of homosexuality of its human meanings. Such a focus tells us nothing about what it is like to be a lesbian in this society today. We propose to use illustrations from case materials to illuminate certain themes which manifest themselves in all human experience but have special meanings for lesbians. In so doing, we hope to suggest to the psychotherapist † (whatever his/her therapeutic orientation) new ways of understanding the implications of the lesbian experience.

---

* This chapter discusses therapeutic issues and is not centrally concerned with explanatory theories. We nevertheless imply that lesbian behavior is a choice. We believe that sexual preference and orientation are chosen to the extent that all human behavior, above the level of autonomous body functions, can be said to be chosen.
** We prefer to use the term lesbian rather than female homosexual because it emphasizes that there is a difference of experience between men and women. In addition it is the term most widely used and preferred by homosexual women themselves.
† In the interest of economy, the generic term psychotherapist will be used throughout to denote persons who may in fact be psychiatrists, psychologists, social workers, psychoanalysts, marriage and family counselors, school counselors, pastoral counselors. A distinction will be made only when particularly germane. In addition, where appropriate, we make a loose distinction between the processes of counseling and psychotherapy. Although in reality the boundary is often blurred, we shall always use psychotherapy to indicate a process where deep personality structures and dynamics are dealt with. Otherwise the terms will be used interchangeably.

Handbook of Sexology, edited by J. Money and H. Musaph
© *Elsevier/North-Holland Biomedical Press, 1977*

2. FIRST THERAPY

The situation of a young woman still in school or living with her parents is a familiar one. If she is adolescent or even technically adult, discovery of her apparent lesbianism might cause her to be judged 'delinquent' by a parent, civil authority, or school official. By virtue of her relative powerlessness or fear of the consequences she is coerced into visiting a psychiatrist chosen by the parents, or perhaps she is sent to the secondary school or college guidance counselor, or a university clinical psychologist.

If the young woman is sent to a private psychotherapist, the psychotherapist will first have to deal with the reality that the client is there unwillingly. At this stage of her life she is undoubtedly struggling with self-definition, although she may well have not conceived it in precisely those terms. One option might be to negotiate an explicit therapeutic contract whereby the exploration of dimensions of self-definition, including the question of sexual preference, become the focus of the therapy. In articulating the concept of a therapeutic contract to which the client is a consenting party, her self-respect and her striving for autonomy are immediately mobilized. The psychotherapy at the outset begins to counter her feelings of rejection and of helplessness. If she is anxious about her homosexual feelings, she can be assured that those feelings are not monstrous. If she is worried that her feelings or behavior mean that she is somehow 'not a proper woman' she can be further reassured. She may be in process of making choices which violate generally unexamined notions of what necessarily constitutes womanhood. In that case she is in the same position as any woman who refuses marriage and/or motherhood, or the woman who, regardless of sexual orientation, decides to become a nuclear physicist or an explorer. She can learn that conventional concepts of gender-role are being re-examined in the university, the church, the legal profession, largely in response to the questioning of women everywhere. Thus a situation which may have begun for the client as disastrous could produce a climate where she could develop a capacity for directing her own life.

We have rather generally described a paradigmatic therapeutic encounter which in its individual manifestations will naturally reflect the unique personalities of both client and psychotherapist. A young woman may claim, for example, that she is already defined by placing herself against the values of her parents and the society she experiences around her. The psychotherapist could then suggest that a definition against a set of values is not in itself a self-definition, but rather only another way of being imprisoned by those same values. Self-definition is a multidimensional continuing process; questions of sexual orientation and gender identity are only two of those dimensions. The young client, on a deeper level, is engaged in an important stage of the classic conflict between dependency on her parents and autonomy.

3. COUNSELING PARENTS

While the therapy might be dealing with the psychodynamics of autonomy, a young lesbian's parents at the same time are interacting in the real world both with her and with the psychotherapist. The young woman might express well-grounded fears about possible rejection by her parents. Furthermore, the psychotherapist might have to respond to the accusation that their specific agenda for their daughter's therapy, that is, to guide her toward heterosexuality, has not been met. If the situation permits, counseling might be suggested for the parents. Such counseling could meet several needs simultaneously. It could enable them to ventilate their fears; it could provide them with accurate information about lesbianism and encourage them to be loving and accepting toward their daughter. We recommend a session at which all concerned persons might be present.

Another possibility is for the parents to participate in a group for parents of homosexuals. Such a group could well be a peer-group facilitated by an experienced and informed parent. If such groups exist in a particular locality, the nearest lesbian or gay liberation organization could provide access to them. * In this connection we note that the advisory board of a counseling service for homosexuals in New York includes the mother of a homosexual.

4. ADMINISTRATIVE PROVISIONS

Much of what has been said could be equally relevant were a school or university psychologist or guidance counselor similarly involved. The crucial difference enters with the implications of the student's and the psychotherapist's respective relationships with the institution. An ethical dilemma might be precipitated out of the conflict between protecting the confidentiality and/or anonymity of the client and considering the 'best interests' of the employer institution. Such dilemmas are never easily resolved but are particularly complex where an issue as controversial as youthful sexuality is concerned, let alone homosexuality.

On the other hand, this same institutional connection could give a school counselor the possibility of performing an important function, particularly if she were a woman. She might be in a position to organize a project designed to prevent the social isolation of those young students who are in touch with their strong emotional and/or erotic feelings for members of their own sex (peers or older women). Such feelings appear to be widespread during preadolescence and adolescence. The intention would be to provide accurate and matter-of-fact information in a format that would encourage expression of feelings. An informal discussion group, for example, would

---

* If such an organization is difficult to find, the National Gay Task Force in New York is a clearing house for all such information, both inside and outside the U.S.

provide a setting for these young girls to talk freely with their peers without fear that confidentiality would be violated or that there would be any risk of exposure. The counselor who carries out this project can only do so successfully if she is accepting of and comfortable with her own sexual feelings.

Whoever instigates such a program cannot ignore certain social realities, particularly in a secondary school where the students are still legally minors. We recommend that these implications be confronted squarely. An undertaking of this seriousness must be officially supported by a key member of the school administration who would be prepared to talk to angry parents who might accuse the school of 'encouraging deviance.' * The fact is that this kind of program might help everyone concerned to realize that experiencing homo-erotic feelings is indeed common and does not automatically imply that one is irrevocably lesbian. It could lead some of the students involved to decide that lesbian behavior is only one of a wide variety of hitherto unconsidered options. For those students who continue to feel convinced that they are lesbians such an opportunity to talk freely could perform the enormously valuable function of discouraging them from isolating themselves.

5. ISOLATION: CASE EXAMPLE

Possibly the single most frequently occurring problem which might induce a lesbian to seek help is her feeling of isolation. Isolation has many dimensions, both interpersonal and intrapsychic.

For example, a 29-year-old physician who is attracted to women but whose religious beliefs tell her that such feelings are sinful has had a sexual relationship with another woman since both were medical students. Both women continually denied the possibility of any feeling other than friendship toward each other and expected that they would each eventually marry. Both dated men, sometimes together, and found themselves baffled by the tensions which would arise between them on such occasions. When one of them had the opportunity to move to another city to take up a research fellowship, both women agreed that separation would be constructive and would leave them more free to relate to men and to marry.

A year later our client finds that her friend is indeed about to marry and wonders why she, herself, persists in the feelings she alternately characterizes as adolescent and sinful. Having sought information on lesbianism from the only book she could find on the subject written by a psychiatrist †, she

---

* Sex educators and student groups in secondary schools often invite speakers from Gay Liberation organizations to visit classes. In some New York City secondary schools, discussion groups focusing on issues of sexuality already exist led by students and/or counselors.

† Until 1971, 'Female Homosexuality' by Frank S. Caprio, published in 1954, was the

believes that lesbians in general are immature, irresponsible, promiscuous and unfeminine. She knows that none of these words, except perhaps the first, apply to her. Nonetheless, she finds herself feeling abandoned by her friend and, increasingly depressed, wonders whether perhaps she is indeed a lesbian. It is at this point that she consults a psychotherapist. Almost immediately apparent is the extent to which this woman has eliminated any possibility of validation or support for her feelings. Her stereotyped notions of lesbianism prevent her from recognizing and exploring commonalities with other women who feel as she does. Indeed her agenda is to be 'cured' of these feelings. An easy, open acceptance of homosexuality on the part of the therapist would be viewed with suspicion by this woman. Her particular religious background has taught her to consider psychotherapy as a variant of the confessional and to expect to do penance for her sins and then to be absolved of them. The concept that psychotherapy is nonjudgemental is one that she expects her therapist to pay lip service to but not to believe in deeply or to act upon.

It might be fruitful first to deal concretely with her notions of sin and sinfulness and to explore against whom, indeed, she sinned in her relationship with her friend, and by the persistence of those deep feelings. Then, in terms of dealing with the client's personality, the therapist's orientation will determine the specific way in which this woman's harsh self judgment might be made less tyrannical without necessarily attacking or undermining her religious beliefs. Only when this woman begins to experience a greater degree of self-acceptance will she be open to suggestions of exploring such resources as the Gay Physicians' Alliance recently formed in the U.S. and Dignity, an organization of Roman Catholics who are homosexual.

The woman cited above isolated herself from both homosexual and heterosexual society, finding herself an outcast and agreeing that such should be her status. Her unquestioning acceptance of traditional stereotyped views of lesbians led her to deny the reality of her experience and of her feelings.

6. EFFECTS OF ISOLATION

Internalization of stereotypical images of lesbians may lead many a woman to believe she is doubly aberrant. Not only does she fail to conform to her concept of a proper woman, but also, because she differs from the stereotype, believes she is not even a proper lesbian. Such thinking leads her to despair of ever finding companionship within the lesbian subculture. The obvious recourse of testing her expectation against the reality brings the isolated les-

---

only available book by a psychiatrist on the subject of lesbianism. Klaich (1974, pp. 98—101) points out that the source of some of his case histories is 'Life Romances'. Perjorative words such as obsessive, parasite, compulsive, insecure, prostitute, mannish, cannibalistic, regression, and narcissism are found on almost every page.

bian into confrontation with other dimensions of her isolation; the paranoid fantasy for example. If she were to go to a lesbian meeting place, ranged outside and possibly inside would be members or representatives of her family, her employer, her church, the law. By setting foot in such a place she might run the risk of losing her family, friends, job and even of going to jail. On the face of it this fantasy seems exaggerated even to the fantasizer, but its power in nonetheless great enough to immobilize her.

The final dimension is the expectation that she is the only isolated lesbian. This fantasy takes the shape of assuming that were she to go to a meeting place, be it bar or lesbian organization, she would be an outsider. Every woman she would encounter would know every other woman and no one would have the same need to make contact as she. The existence of this fantasy was confirmed in an informal survey conducted by one of the authors of this paper. Three-fourths of the respondents felt that most of the other woman present would have more women to call in the event of loneliness than they. One of every six respondents knew not one person in the meeting place whom they would feel free to call.

When we remember that the women surveyed above had actually brought themselves to at least one meeting of a lesbian group we begin to see how real is the isolation of which we speak.

An almost universal dimension of lesbian isolation is self-rejection. This raises a thorny issue which can be expected to emerge in the context of the psychotherapeutic relationship. During the course of the initial consultation or soon after the client will ask the following question, whether explicitly or indirectly: "Do you, psychotherapist, whom I assume to be a heterosexual, consider my lesbianism to be the problem, and will you try to 'cure' me?". This theme may be translated into transferential terms as "Will you, like the rest of the society I see around me, like my parents and the friends I grew up with, believe that my life-style precludes the kind of happiness and security I seek?". Assuming that the above does not represent the psychotherapist's attitude, we may nonetheless expect it to emerge and re-emerge at every point of resistance during the course of the therapeutic relationship. When handled sensitively, the question finally to be reached is, of course, that of the client's lack of self-acceptance; her own self-rejection which all too easily focuses on her lesbianism rather than on far more primitive material. If, however, the psychotherapist introduces this interpretation too early in the course of treatment, the entire relationship is apt to be endangered by the client's resultant defensive attitude.

The relationship between self-rejecting and self-condemnatory feelings and guilt about being a lesbian needs some clarification. We regard self-rejection as a universal primitive phenomenon originating in early infancy. * Much

---

* In his object-relations theory, Ronald Fairbairn posits the creation and maintenance of an intrapsychic self-persecutory system. The explanatory theory underlying this hypothesis is an elaboration and modification of Freudian theories of repression, introjection, and splitting-off of parts of the self.

later in life, when the lesbian begins to experience rejecting social responses to her lesbian orientation, this real persecution in the external world is internalized and becomes absorbed into the long-established primitive intrapsychic self-rejecting system. A major task for the psychotherapist is to enable the lesbian to distinguish between what she actually experiences in the external world and her internal self-criticism.

7. PARTNER RELATIONSHIP

Living in a society in which women are encouraged to derive a great part of their sense of self-worth and, indeed, their identity from relationships, (while men are expected to derive theirs from accomplishment in the outside world) lesbians often seek to solve the knotty problems of self-rejection by finding a lover who will accept them. While in heterosexual couples generally only one partner places this demand for validation on the relationship, with a lesbian couple the likelihood and intensity of this pressure is increased considerably. Often, therefore, among the issues at stake when a couple present themselves for counseling is the possibility that either or both of them find their entire infrastructure of identity and competence endangered. In such a situation, regardless of the degree of satisfaction or lack thereof to be found within the relationship, partners tend to cling ever more tightly and exclusively to each other.

The counseling task then becomes one of bringing to light the burden placed upon the relationship by these needs, helping each partner deal with them explicitly, and eventually shifting the weight of expectation from the relationship to the self. One way of achieving this end has been by means of a couples' group. While both the authors have counseled lesbian couples individually, in terms of this specific issue we regard a couples' group to be the preferred therapeutic modality. The group provides a stage upon which each of the members sees enacted the conflicts and consequent resentments which arise when responsibility for self-definition is vested in another person or upon a relationship. Watching other woman struggle with this dilemma is both enlightening and supportive for group members. The therapeutic goal in such a group would be for the woman to redefine relationships as a commitment between more autonomous partners.

Another expectation which lesbians are likely to place upon a relationship is that, since both are women, they are necessarily alike. This fantasy raises profound issues deriving from the 'Garden of Eden' experience in infancy of closeness with the mother and with it the conflicting struggles for fusion and for individuation. Dealing with this issue in depth clearly involves an intense long-term commitment on the part of both therapist and client and may not at all relate to the expectations of a couple who consult a counselor because, "we fight all the time." In such situations women have experienced enlightenment and greater capacity to deal with each other as they come to realize that the real differences between them such as social class, ethnic background, and personal style influence the way in which they perceive the world and in which they communicate these perceptions. When sexual problems arise, although they are not necessarily different from those of heterosexual women, the expectation of likeness and reciprocity may add a dimension of almost primal disappointment which the therapist must recognise and communicate to the couple.

8. LESBIAN MOTHERS

Somewhat more complex situations arise when one of the partners has children. A case in point might be that of a couple in which one of the women has two children and who seek help in deciding whether to live together. Neither woman is clear about how involved the lover should be in parenting the children nor what effect their choice to live together might have on the children. A therapeutic contract could be negotiated in which both members of the couple might feel free to discuss their positive feelings and their reservations about living together as a family.

Both women recognize that the children, while fond of the mother's lover, have grown used to living alone with their mother and feel that they must now compete for attention with an interloper. On the other hand, the lover, who has never before been involved in a relationship in which children are present also finds herself, to her chagrin, competing with the children for her lover's attention. Other complicating factors include the mother's fear that discovery of her lesbianism might lead to her children being ostracized in the suburban community in which they live.

Neither of the women has ever felt free to discuss these fears and reservations with each other before. Having accepted the Hollywood model that a couple fall in love and live happily ever after, it seemed to them that any expression of negativity might denote lack of faith in the lover and in their relationship. As they find themselves able to express their reservations they begin to feel renewed faith in the possibility of working them through. Through a homophile organization in the nearby large city, the women are referred to a lesbian mothers' therapy group which is also open to the mother's lover. In this group they discover that their situation is not unique and find the necessary support and insight to sustain a growing relationship.

9. CHANGING VIEWS

In presenting fragments from the lives of lesbians as they might unfold in the counseling situation, we realize that we have only begun to suggest the flavor and quality of those lives. The sample is limited, furthermore, to women who live in the U.S., and to women who need and seek psychotherapy. For a more complete picture of the lesbian experience as it is embedded in the particular cultural climate of the U.S. we recommend three recent books which we review briefly in the bibliography: Abbott and Love (1972), Lyon and Martin (1972), and Klaich (1974). Wolff's (1971) book which includes verbatim interviews and autobiographies, delineates the world of the lesbian in England today.

After being almost literally invisible for most of the recorded history of humankind, the lesbian almost overnight now finds herself a member of an articulate minority. If she is fortunate, she may also be a member of a community which may or may not have ties with a larger feminist community. She also now sees herself in the context of a rapidly changing scientific and intellectual climate characterized by a proliferation of research on sexuality. The first Kinsey studies mark the beginning of a new era in the scientific study of sexuality where values have painfully begun to extricate themselves from facts.

As the world of the lesbian is in a rapid process of flux, so is the world of the psychotherapist. The 'immutable' facts behind theories of gender identity and gender role turn out to be both time-bound and culture-bound. The medical model in psychotherapy has been eroded. Concepts of 'mental health' and corresponding 'pathology' exist side by side with humanistic ideas of 'growth,' 'self-realization,' or existential perceptions of 'being' and 'meaning'. To the extent that these worlds are internalized they are brought into the consulting room by both participants in the therapeutic dialogue. The goal of this dialogue is to enable the client to develop her capacity for self-definition and self-direction. For this process she needs peer support out in the world as well as the internal supports which psychotherapy can provide.

ANNOTATED BIBLIOGRAPHY

Abott, S. and Love, B. (1972) *Sappho was a Right-On Woman*. (Stein and Day, New York.) An account of the lesbian experience written by lesbians. It is addressed to lesbians as well as the general public.

Baum, G. (1974) Catholic homosexuals. *Commonweal* 99: 479—482. Sensitive theological reflections on the self-affirmation of gay Catholics and the creation of the organization Dignity.

Blair, R. (1974) Gay couple counseling: proceedings of a conference. *Homosex. Couns. J.* 1: 88—139. The proceedings include a panel of female couples. The *Homosexual Counseling Journal* is a quarterly published by the Homosexual Community Counseling Center in New York.

Fairbairn, W.R.D. (1952) *Psychoanalytic Studies of the Personality*. (Tavistock Publications, London.)

Klaich, D. (1974) *Woman Plus Woman*. (Simon and Schuster, New York.) A critical survey of religious, scientific, social and literary attitudes toward lesbianism.

Lyon, P. and Martin, D. (1972) *Lesbian/Woman*. (Glide Publications, San Francisco.) A practical informative book written by the founders of the Daughters of Bilitis, the oldest lesbian organization in the U.S.

1288

Reiss, B.F., Safer, J. and Yotive, W. (1974) Psychological test data on female homosexuality: a review of the literature. *J. Homosex.* 1: 71—85. This journal is edited by Charles Silverstein, director of the Institute of Human Identity in New York. It contains an annotated bibliography of recent (beginning January 1974) periodical literature on homosexuality, transexualism, and gender identity from a number of fields. It will cumulate annually with a subject/author index.

Reiss, B.F. (1974) New viewpoints on the female homosexual. In: (V. Franks and V. Burtle, Eds.) *Woman in Therapy*, (Brunner/Mazel, New York.) pp: 191—214. Discussion of changing attitudes and recent research. The volume has a valuable first chapter: Changing views of women and therapeutic approaches: some historical considerations.

Weinberg, G. (1972) *Society and the Healthy Homosexual.* (St. Martin's Press, New York.) A critique of current societal attitudes. It includes a valuable chapter on communication with parents.

Wolff, C. (1971) *Love Between Women.* (St. Martin's Press, New York.) A study of considerable psychological, sociological and philosophical depth and breadth by a British psychologist. While the author has a strong critical sense, traditional psychiatric attitudes to lesbianism appear on isolated pages and seem 'out of key' with the rest of the book.

CHAPTER 102

Counseling the transexual *

JOHN MONEY and PAUL A. WALKER

1. INTRODUCTION

The unique biography and complaint brought to the counselor by each patient needs to be handled in an individualized manner. Nonetheless, a particular syndrome carries with it a set of psychological needs and problems not
necessarily expressed by the patient. The counselor needs therefore, to understand the psychologic concomitants of a syndrome before attempting
individualized therapy. This is especially true regarding sex reassignment, as
requested by a transexual.

2. DEFINITION OF TRANSEXUALISM

Professional definition

Transexualism is a form of gender dissatisfaction or dysphoria. In the idealized case of transexualism, the inner conviction of gender identity, and its
public manifestation as gender role are persistently, and consistently discordant with the anatomic sex of the genitals. Gender identity/role is both the
inner, personal awareness and conviction of the sex a person believes he or
she is, as well as the public expression of that internal conviction. The iden-
tity/role may be male, female or ambiguous. There are many varieties or gradations of all three, forming a spectrum or continuum in which typologies
cannot be clearly discerned.

   Transexualism is not homosexuality or transvestism, even though it has
components of both. The homosexual typically enjoys the sensations and
feelings of his or her genitalia and would regret their loss. An extremely ef-

* Supported by USPHS Grant No. HD-00325 and funds from the Grant Foundation, New
York, and the Erickson Educational Foundation, Baton Rouge, La.

Handbook of Sexology, edited by J. Money and H. Musaph
© *Elsevier/North-Holland Biomedical Press, 1977*

feminate male homosexual or virilistic lesbian may, on occasion, request surgical sex reassignment in order to escape social stigma, or at a time of personal distress over failed love affairs. To avoid subsequent regret, there should be no impulsive decisions for sex reassignment.

Like a homosexual, a transvestite may impulsively decide that sex reassignment will resolve the anguish of an on-again/off-again history of cross dressing and cross-gender living, with two names, two wardrobes and two personalities (Money, 1974). Such a decision is usually not reached until the fourth decade of life. Even though impulsive, sex reassignment may prove successful, but haste is not to be recommended.

Definition by the patient

A transexual typically defines his/her condition as a conviction, dating from childhood, of rightfully belonging to the other sex. Through the public media, today's patient soon learns to name his or her gender dissatisfaction as transexualism, if that is what it is. Before the publicity given to the famous case of Christine Jorgensen in 1952 (Jorgensen, 1967) the term, transexual, was not in current use. Patients then identified themselves, therefore, as transvestites or, when the compulsion for sex reassignment was particularly demanding, as probable hermaphrodites whose sex had been wrongly assigned.

Once the patient has settled on the self-definition of transexual, available medical facilities are sought and utilized. The presenting complaint and accompanying biography (subject possibly to either intentional distortion or selective recall, or both) are expressed in terms most likely to ensure that the professionals in charge of authorizing surgery will confirm the patient's self-diagnosis. In some cases, the maneuvers to bring about a favorable response are very manipulative, even to the point of impostering. When professionals are not trained to be aware of patient manipulation, the unwary may find themselves being played off against one another. In some cases family collusion may be involved.

To prevent the dangers of manipulativeness, every transexual needs a primary professional person through whom all decisions are made and announced. He holds and accepts the ultimate responsibility for the patient.

3. REHABILITATIVE GOAL OF THERAPY

Sex reassignment for transexualism is therapeutically a form of rehabilitation, not of cure. It is not possible to set cure as the goal, for none of today's psychiatric, neurosurgical, or psychoendocrine techniques can be guaranteed to bring about a cure of the bona fide transexual. In fact, they have so far proved singularly ineffectual. Experimental psychiatric attempts to bring about a cure are so expensive and time consuming, that they can be applied only on a clinical research basis (Barlow, 1973). They raise the thorny question of the patient's ethical right of informed consent to treatment, for the bona fide transexual vehemently resists treatment other than sex reassignment. A compromise can be reached perhaps in the case of a young teenager for whom the youngest age of surgical sex reassignment, according to today's custom, is eighteen. Even at the onset of adolescence, however, a transexual may insistently resist any therapy aimed at other than ultimate sex reassignment. The alternative would be suicide.

4. DIAGNOSIS

Laboratory testing

Standard laboratory tests are for the most part noncontributory to the diagnosis of transexualism. They are necessary, however, to rule out possible contraindications or risks of surgery. Chromosomal determination will indicate when transexualism coexists with Klinefelter's (47,XXY) syndrome. Plasma hormonal measurements will reveal sex-hormone anomalies if present — possibly as a result of hormones self-administered in secret. Neither finding contraindicates sex reassignment. The electroencephalogram (EEG), if abnormal, may indicate a temporal lobe epileptic lesion for which neurosurgery might be indicated. Theoretically, if brain surgery is effective, epilepsy and transexualism may both remit, though no known cases at present have been recorded.

Psychologic testing

There is no psychologic test, or combination of tests for the diagnosis of transexualism. Psychologic tests are given in order to help rule out secondary diagnoses, especially depression, thought disorder, intellectual impairment, or psychopathic character disorder. Such conditions do not necessarily rule out sex reassignment, but they may necessitate delay while themselves being treated.

Diagnostic interview

The major source of diagnostic information comes from the diagnostic interview. This interview, which may require several sessions, is conducted according to a planned Schedule of Inquiry (Money and Primrose, 1969), so as to ensure that no pertinent topics are omitted. It is tape recorded and transcribed. The information given by the patient is checked against that given by at least one family member. If necessary, it is also checked against the history as recorded in school, hospital, social agency, or police files.

Real-life test

The diagnosis of transexualism is best confirmed by the two-year, real-life test. This test allows the rehabilitative effect of sex reassignment to be observed and recorded as it occurs. It requires that the person become rehabilitated hormonally, socially, vocationally, financially and interpersonally in the sex of reassignment prior to the irrevocable step of surgery. The one surgical exception is that female-to-male transexuals may require mastectomy in order to function vocationally as males. The majority of male-to-female transexuals require electrolysis of the beard during the test period. Some male-to-female patients request and get, possibly on their own initiative at another hospital, various plastic surgical procedures to feminize the appearance of the face, hips and breasts.

The real-life test allows a transexual to experience what it means to be treated, day in, day out, as a member of the other sex. This experience is imperative to complement the solipsistic, inner conviction and imagery of being a member of that sex.

A few patients extend the real-life test beyond two years. A few give up and establish themselves as homosexuals whose dress and appearance is more unisex than a full impersonation of the other sex. They may resume the real-life test again, later in life.

Some patients have lived the real-life test long before they seek surgery. Others can be monitored during the course of the two years. The monitoring of male-to-female transexuals includes their reaction to hormonal, estrogenic demasculinization, which is, in fact, a functional castration, highly prized in the majority of cases. The voice is not hormonally demasculinized, but a change of pitch upward, with never a deviation, becomes second nature with practice.

The dosage of the hormones given, orally or by injection, parallels that given in standard physiological replacement therapy. In this way, there is no risk of hormone-related malignancy (for example, breast cancer) over and beyond that found in normal individuals.

The most up-to-date schedule of medication for the male-to-female transexual recommended by Claude Migeon, is diethylstilbestrol (numerous manufacturers), administered 0.25—0.50 mg daily with medroxyprogesterone acetate (Provera, Upjohn) 2.5—5.0 mg daily. Ethinyl estradiol (Estinyl, Schering) 0.02—0.05 mg daily, or a preparation of conjugated equine estrogens (Premarin, Ayerst), 1.25—2.50 mg daily, might be substituted for diethylstilbestrol. Before gonadectomy, the treatment would take place every day for a minimum of 4—8 months. Following surgery, treatment could be clinical: daily for the first three weeks of each month, then not at all during the fourth week.

An alternative to the foregoing combination of estrogen plus progestin taken separately would be a commercial product combining the two, for example, norethindrone, 1 mg, and mestranol, 0.05 mg (Ortho-Novum 1 mg,

Ortho) norethindrone acetate, 1 mg, and ethinyl estradiol, 0.05 mg (Norlestrin 1 mg, Parke-Davis); or Provera, 10 mg, and ethinyl estradiol, 0.05 mg (Provest, Upjohn). The dosage of these preparations is one tablet daily for the first three weeks of each month.

If the patient prefers not to accommodate to a daily oral therapy but to an intramuscular one instead, then the following could be prescribed: estradiol valerate (Delestrogen, Squibb), 5—20 mg, plus hydroxyprogesterone caproate (Delalutin, Squibb), 62.5—125 mg, every two weeks. Another intramuscular combined treatment could be Depo-Estradiol Cypionate (Upjohn), 1—5 mg, plus medroxyprogesterone acetate (Depo-Provera, Upjohn), 25—100 mg, every two weeks. After 4—8 months of biweekly therapy, the same dosages could be given once every 3 or 4 weeks.

If, in the preoperative state, these stipulated dosages prove insufficiently effective after 4—6 weeks, then they could be doubled. Otherwise, the rule is to use the dosage that is thought presently to be replacement therapy for normal women.

In the female-to-male transsexual, hormonal, androgenic defeminization brings about anovulation and inhibition of the menses. The clitoris enlarges. The orgasm becomes stronger, but the female capacity for multiple orgasm does not change. Beard and body hair grow, and the voice permanently deepens.

For the female-to-male transsexual, Migeon recommends testosterone enanthate (Delatestryl, Squibb) or testosterone cypionate (Depotestosterone Cypionate, Upjohn), 200—400 mg every 3—4 weeks. If a 400 mg dosage is prescribed the injections should be divided half in each buttock or arm. The injectable testosterones produce the best results and are more expeditious. However, if necessary, buccal tablets (Oreton Methyl, Schering), 20—30 mg per day or oral tablets (Halotestin, Upjohn), 5—10 mg per day could be prescribed. For further details concerning the hormonal treatment of male and female transsexuals, (see Money, 1972; Green and Money, 1969.

5. COUNSELING DURING THE REAL-LIFE TEST

The real-life test is difficult and demanding, in keeping with the gravity and irreversibility of sex reassignment itself.

Legal counseling

Dependent on facilities available, legal counseling may be given by a lawyer, or by his/her surrogate. Sex difference is so completely taken for granted in society that there is no legal definition of sex. Therefore, there is no agreed-upon body of knowledge defining the status of the transsexual (Holloway, 1972; Clayton D., in Laub and Gandy, 1974) or of any other form of indeterminate sex.

In the U.S., it is legal to change one's name by personal decision, provided there is no intent of fraud. Thus there is no legal requirement for a transexual change of name. Change of name as well as sex on the birth certificate does require legal intervention. In most jurisdictions in the U.S., a court-endorsed order of change of name and sex, on the basis of medical certification, is sufficient to ensure a reissued, short-form birth certificate showing only the current name and sex. This reissued certificate is sufficient to ensure legal change of all other documents.

In jurisdictions, like New York City, which do not legally recognize a transexual's change of sexual status, it is most expeditious to counsel the transexual whose birth certificate is therein registered, to be overt, not secretive regarding the medical and social change of status. For documentary purposes, as in obtaining a driver's licence, the new sexual status is so self-evident that, except for unusual legal niceties, it is impossible to refute it. Jurisdictions that fail to recognize the legal sexual status of sex-reassigned transexuals are totally unable to deal also with the legal status of people born with the wrong genetic or chromosomal sex: women with 46,XY, (typically found in males) or men with 46,XX, (typically found in females).

During the two years of the real-life test, it is helpful and reassuring for a transexual to carry a medical statement of the diagnosis, treatment, and prognosis. Such a document can prevent unnecessary harassment in the event of say, a traffic violation.

Counseling for medical examinations

Some transexuals, during the period of the real-life test, are very resourceful in negotiating a routine medical examination, as for employment. Some male-to-female transexuals fake embarrassment over a menstrual period. Others, along with female-to-male transexuals, know enough about hermaphroditism that they explain their condition as hermaphroditism. Still others declare themselves as transexuals and find that their diagnosis is not a hindrance to their employment. Although individuals invariably make their own decisions, the soundest counseling is that they not get themselves involved in a lie that eventually proliferates into a chain of lies that cannot be covered.

Employment counseling

It is so atypical for a clinical service in a hospital to be directly connected with a genuine job-finding agency that transexuals, in almost all instances, are obliged to rely on their own resources regarding employment. The majority are exceedingly resourceful, especially if they can rely on their hospital-based counselor for a medical report to the employer, as requested, by phone or mail. Some transexuals, after they begin the real-life test, are retained in the same job and the same place of employment. Others begin afresh in a new job, with a new employer who may or may not know their diagnosis.

Counseling for cosmetics and appearance

Many prospective sex-reassignment patients are so adept in the role or the real-life test that they could be instructors at a charm school of modeling academy. The minority exaggerate — female-to-male transexuals with too much macho swaggor, and male to females with too much of the appearance of a midnight whore in broad daylight. Both minorities need counseling and tutoring in dress style, cosmetic appearance, and the body language of sexually dimorphic gait, posture, and manner.

Counseling regarding sexual activity and romance

Some transexuals, as they embark on the real-life test, are in the course of breaking up a failed heterosexual marriage, sometimes amiably, sometimes with attendant litigious vindictiveness. With or without a history of marriage, many male-to-female transexuals have a phobic avoidance of their own genitals, and are erotically apathetic or inert. Some settle into a life of celibacy. Some are very prudish about the possibility of an overt sexual relationship with a man, and moralistic about crossing that bridge when they get to it postsurgically. A few have a partner with whom they play the role of premarital chastity in order not to reveal their anatomy. Others have already established a relationship which society would regard as homosexual, but which is not so regarded by the transexual or the partner. A few have had many partners, or have impersonated a female prostitute. Sexual practices with the partner are manual, oral or anal. The male-to-female transexual commonly prohibits attention to her own genitals. Her pleasure lies in gratifying the partner.

Female-to-male transexuals embarking on the real-life test commonly have, or have had a steady partner in what society would call a lesbian relationship, but which they perceive as simulating a heterosexual one. Unlike their male-to-female counterparts, they are rarely phobic of their own genitalia, but may be of their breasts.

There is no fixed rule in counseling as to what kind of erotic experience a transexual should or should not have during the real-life test. However, the implications of each transexual's erotic partnership, or lack of partnership, certainly require investigation. Fact needs also to be sifted from fiction and moralism, as some patients, alert to society's sexual taboo, say what they think will be most favorably received.

Counseling for sexual surgery

Surgical technique for the sex-reassignment operation is not standardized, for surgeons continue to adopt new modifications and improvements (Laub and Gandy, 1974; Granato, 1974). Thus, there is no standard formula for counseling regarding what to expect surgically. Some generalizations are possible, however.

The male-to-female transexual can expect either one or two surgical admissions. In two-stage surgery, usually the first operation is a vaginoplasty, and the second a cosmetic completion of the external labia. The two-stage design allows time for relocated tissues to heal, establish a good blood supply, and thus not be in danger of necrosing or sloughing off. The choice between a one- or two-stage design is the surgeon's. It depends on how he utilizes the skin of the penis and scrotum for feminization, and whether he utilizes an additional skin graft from the buttock. In the absence of infection or other complications, the hospital admission may be as brief as two weeks, or shorter for the stage-two procedure. Postsurgically it is imperative to wear a stent or form in the vaginal cavity in order to prevent shrinkage and contracture. Eventually, sexual intercourse alone may be sufficient to keep the vagina open and functional. Urethral stricture is a possible postsurgical complication and may itself require surgery if not responsive to dilatation.

The amount of erotic sensation or feeling experienced in the genitalia after surgical feminization depends on the degree to which the nerves of sexual sensitivity have remained intact, which in turn depends partly on the surgical method employed for reutilizing the skin of the penis and scrotum. Postoperatively, male-to-female transexuals vary in their reports of erotic feeling and orgasm. All report the presence of erotic feeling. Some report an orgasm as climactic as formerly. Others report a more diffuse orgasmic glow. Complaints about loss or diminution of erotic gratification are conspicuous by their absence.

Surgical masculinization of the female-to-male transexual is arduous and requires multiple hospital admissions. One operation is required for mastectomy, to flatten the chest, and another for hysterectomy, including removal of the ovaries. Some female-to-male transexuals are wisely able to desist from further surgery, whereas others insist on being unable to live without some attempt at phalloplasty. Regardless of type, phalloplasty always requires multiple admissions, even as many as a dozen or more, and the result is never coitally satisfactory in the complete sense.

One type of transexual phalloplasty is designed on the model of the repair of severe congenital hypospadias of the penis in the male (Tank et al., 1976). That is to say, the vagina is excised, the labia majora are fused, and the urethra is made to traverse the clitoris which slightly enlarges under the influence of androgen therapy. The resulting clitorine penis is too small for sexual intercourse, and is also too small to manipulate for urination in the standing position. The risk of urinary infection is increased. Erotic feeling and orgasm are not impaired.

Another type of transexual phalloplasty is designed to make a copulatory but not a urinary organ. The urinary orifice is left intact. An apron of skin is peeled downward from the abdominal wall, from below the navel, left attached, and used in such a way as to make a hollow tube. For sexual intercourse, a prosthetic device is inserted into the hollow tube, which is then firm enough to enter the vagina. Erotic feeling and orgasm are intact, for the clitoris is imbedded into the base of the tube.

A third type of transexual phalloplasty (Hoopes, 1969) is designed to construct a would-be penis, complete with urinary tube. It is flabby and unable to be used in sexual intercourse, unless supported inside of a hollow, prosthetic penis. In a complex series of operations, it is fashioned from abdominal skin and is hung in the position of a penis, with the clitoris imbedded into its base. The grafted-skin part of the organ is numb, but the clitoris retains its feeling and capacity to produce orgasm. The risk of urinary infection is increased. It is often difficult to get complete healing of the urinary tube, without which urine leaks out in the wrong place, requiring still further surgery.

The expense of transexual surgery is a difficult hurdle for the majority of patients. Some medical/surgical insurance policies will cover it, but most will not. It is not wise for a patient to embark on the first stage of surgery, as some have done, without a financial guarantee of being able to complete the next stage or stages. Most hospital administrations require prepayment at the time of each admission for sex reassignment. The exact cost cannot be specified, as the number of admissions and the number of days per admission cannot be precisely predicted.

6. POSTSURGICAL COUNSELING

Postsurgical follow-up is partly for the benefit of the patient, and partly for the purpose of accumulating information on outcome that will benefit future patients (Money, 1971; see also reports in Laub and Gandy, 1974).

The topics of postsurgical follow-up counseling are: surgical outcome with respect to cosmetic appearance and erotic function; endocrine medication, dosage regulation and effects; plans, if any, for additional cosmetic surgery; effectiveness of overall rehabilitation; presence or absence of psychiatric problems and of need for psychotherapy; and need to counsel family members, friends, lover, employer, or others.

7. COUNSELING RELATIVES

Parents

Ideally, both parents should be seen for counseling, as well as to give information, at the time the transexual patient prepares to embark on the real-life test. The ideal cannot always be met, especially in the case of the older patient.

The average person does not know that it is possible for a genetic female with ovaries to be born with a penis, nor for a genetic male with testes to be born with a vulva. This information, together with clinical pictures (Money, 1968; Money and Ehrhardt, 1972), helps parents explain their predicament to relatives and friends. They are helped also by diagrams of embryonic sex differentiation, showing the homologous nature of the male and female organs; and by a simple explanation of the effect of prenatal sex hormones on brain differentiation.

By and large, parents benefit by having the syndrome of transexualism defined and conceptualized medically, instead of legally as a crime against nature, or moralistically as a sin. In the medical context, their transexual son or daughter becomes a person whom they can help rather than repudiate. Today, through reading, some parents have already arrived at this point of view before their first counseling session.

Families differ in the extent of the compromise they can work out with a son or daughter who goes through with sex reassignment. In some cases the sex-reassigned member is reintegrated into the kinship as a member of the new sex. In others there is only a formal, infrequent visiting relationship. In a few, there is a break, and virtually no contact. It usually works out to the benefit of the transexual to be able to maintain family ties and psychologic support.

Siblings

Siblings as well as parents benefit from counseling and a medical orientation toward transexualism. Young children can be given a simple explanation in terms of a person's being born with the wrong sex organs. For them an explanation is a necessary prophylaxis, without which they could infer that sex reassignment is arbitrary, and a possibility for them too. Other young children of the household or kinship need the same prophylaxis. When there are too many juveniles to be seen in person by one counselor, one or two adults in the family can be tutored to do the job.

Spouse

By the time a married transexual has reached the stage of embarking on sex reassignment, the marriage has failed. The quality of the ensuing relationship between the two is as varied as in other separations and divorces. It is colored by the psychodynamic collusion or reciprocity that is often found in a couple one of whom is transexual. Some married male-to-female transexuals have a fantasy of staying married, but redefining the relationship as sisterly. Legally, it is preferable to obtain a divorce. As a safeguard against possible malpractice charges, divorce is imperative.

For the spouse of a transexual undergoing sex reassignment, at least a few sessios of counseling or psychotherapy are imperative, preventively, if not for the actual treatment of symptoms.

Children of transexuals

The long-term effect a transexual parent's sex reassignment has on his or her children is not known. In some families the children are not directly informed, but are given a cover-up story when they and the one parent leave the transexual parent for good. In other families, the children and the sex-reassigned parent maintain contact. For these children, as for the spouse of a transexual, preventive psychologic counseling should be a routine

Ideally a transexual parent would postpone sex reassignment until the children were, at youngest, adolescent. This ideal is not always met. If one clinic refuses surgery, the patient may go elsewhere.

8. COUNSELING PARTNERS

Presurgery

The presurgical transexual's lover, if the relationship is romantic and not overtly genital, may be unaware of the transexual's genital status. The counseling of such a person about the diagnosis may not arise. Rather than to allow the lover to find out the true status, the male-to-female transexual may decide to simply break up the relationship.

Usually the lover of an unoperated transexual knows the true story. The couple stay together because they form a complementary pair, sometimes in a psychopathologic sense, sometimes not. The partner seldom needs counseling. Usually, he or she is quite amiable about being interviewed, if requested.

Postsurgery

Some postsurgical transexuals do not withhold information about themselves from a lover or prospective spouse. Others are ingenious at passing themselves off as quasi-hermaphrodites with a mild birth defect. A few male-to-female transexuals say nothing, and are asked nothing.

There is no standard formula the counselor can fall back on, except, perhaps, that direct lying eventually leads to more and more lying, which finally can't be covered up.

Transexuals who have told their partners less than the whole truth must shield their partners from possible leakages from their past life. Therefore, they vigorously exclude the partner from all hospital and counseling contacts.

Partners who know the transexual's story are available for counseling. Usually they do not need it, except insofar as anyone may sometimes require counseling. An exception might arise should there be a threat of exposure of the transexual's status to family or friends who had hitherto been unsuspecting.

Partner's children

Some transexuals marry a partner who is already a parent. Young children accept the new stepmother or stepfather as they might anyone else with the same role. Adolescent and adult offspring who might learn of the transexual's status usually have little difficulty accepting the new step-parent at face value. Counseling is not specially indicated.

9. COUNSELING THE COMMUNITY

It is inherent in the psychodynamics of the transexual syndrome to be a celebrity, as if to announce to the world one's triumph, "See, I made it, even though you said I couldn't." Paradoxically, it is also inherent in the psychodynamics of transexualism to pass so convincingly as a member of the reassigned sex that one's partner, or potential partner, or at least his/her family never guesses the earlier history.

A transexual may live trapped in this paradox, allowing the sex reassignment to be known to some, while hiding it from others. The alternative is to become either a celebrity, self-declared as a transexual, and known to all; or to melt away into the populace at large, forever vigilant to obliterate all traces or voices of the past.

Rumor thrives on lack of information. A transexual who becomes the victim of rumor may well be counseled, therefore, to respond with an enlightening public announcement. A candid, informative letter to the editor of the small-town newspaper was the medium utilized by one gossip victim, a male-to-female whose small business was being boycotted by the townspeople (Money et al., 1975). The letter was effective in bringing people back into her store.

As the syndrome of transexualism becomes more well known and less stigmatized, it will be increasingly feasible for transexuals not to have to hide their change of status. In the meantime, professionals who undertake the education of either the professional or the lay public are restricted to presenting only those transexuals who enjoy celebrity status, or whose life situation permits them to sacrifice their privacy, or part of it.

10. SUMMARY

Transexualism is that form of gender dysphoria in which the gender identity/role is permanently discordant with the anatomic sex of the genitals. It resists treatment other than sex reassignment. Reassignment is rehabilitative rather than curative. There is no single diagnostic test or battery of tests. A systematic diagnostic interview is indispensable, supplemented with corrobative information from outside sources. Two years of living in the new sex — the real-life test — is the most satisfactory test for confirming the diagnosis. During this time hormonal reassignment is begun. Female-to-male transexuals may receive a mastectomy. Surgical reassignment counseling precedes surgery of the genitalia, the final step. Counseling during the two year period is designed to help effect a complete rehabilitation socially, vocationally, financially and interpersonally. The counseling of parents and other kin facilitates rehabilitation and also protects relatives, especially juveniles, from unnecessary psychologic trauma. Postsurgically, the counseling of partners and the children of partners, if present, depends on how much of the transexual's history has been revealed. Likewise with community counseling. In general, candidness is preferable to secrecy.

BIBLIOGRAPHY

Barlow, D.H., Reynolds, E.J. and Agras, W.S. (1973) Gender identity change in a transexual. *Arch. Gen. Psychiat.* 28: 569—576.

Granato, R. (1974) Surgical approach to male transexuals, *Urology*, 3: 792—796.

Green, R. and Money, J. (Eds.) (1969) *Transexualism and Sex Reassignment.* (Johns Hopkins Press, Baltimore.)

Holloway, J. (1972) Transexuals — some further legal considerations, *Comp. Int. Law J. South. Africa*, V: 71—88.

Hoopes, J. (1969) Operative treatment of the female transexual. In: (R. Green and J. Money, Eds.) *Transexualism and Sex Reassignment.* (Johns Hopkins Press, Baltimore.)

Jorgensen, C. (1967) *Cristine Jorgensen: A Personal Autobiography.* (Paul S. Eriksson, New York.)

Laub, D. and P. Gandy, (Eds.) (1974) *Proc. 2nd Interdisciplinary Symp. Gender Dysphoria Syndrome.* (Stanford University Medical Center, Stanford.)

Money, J. (1968) *Sex Errors of the Body: Dilemmas, Education and Counseling.* (Johns Hopkins Press, Baltimore.)

Money, J. (1971) Prefatory remarks on outcome of sex reassignment in 24 cases of transexualism. *Arch. Sex. Behav.* 1: 163—165.

Money, J. (1972) Sex reassignment therapy in gender identity disorders. In: (H. Resnik and M. Wolfgang, Eds.) *Treatment of the Sex Offender* (Little, Brown and Co., Boston.)

Money, J. (1974) Two names, two wardrobes, two personalities. *J. Homosex.* 1: 65—70.

Money, J., Clarke, F. and Mazur, T. (1975) Families of seven male-to-female transexuals after 5 to 7 years: Sociological sexology. *Arch. Sex. Behav.* 4: 187—197.

Money, J. and Ehrhardt, A. (1972) *Man and Woman Boy and Girl: The Differentiation and Dimorphism of Gender Identity.* (Johns Hopkins University Press, Baltimore.)

Money, J. and Primrose, C. (1969) Sexual dimorphism and dissociation in the psychology of male transexuals. In: (R. Green and J. Money, Eds.). *Transexualism and Sex Reassignment* (Johns Hopkins Press, Baltimore.)

Tank, E., Pauly, I., McCraw, L., Petty, W., Rowland, W. and Durfee, R. (1976) Paper presented at the 1975 Harry Benjamin Fourth International Conference on Gender Identity, Stanford University. (In press.)

CHAPTER 103

Sexual disorders: hormonal and drug therapy

JOHN MONEY and JEAN DALÉRY

1. INTRODUCTION

Sexual disorders are defined for present purposes not as disorders of fertility or procreation but as disorders of eroticism and sexual participation with a partner. The etiology may be hormonal, neurogenic, or psychodynamic. Disorders of hormonal origin may in some cases be successfully treated with hormones, and disorders of psychodynamic origin may in some cases be successfully treated with some form of psychotherapy or counseling. Other forms of therapy, notably pharmacologic therapy, are based on trial and error, rather than systematic theoretical principles. For many disorders, including those of neurogenic origin, the definitive form of therapy has not yet been discovered.

2. HYPOSEXUAL BEHAVIOR AND REPLACEMENT OR ACTIVATION THERAPY

Hyposexual behavior related to endocrine disorders

Hyposexual behavior can be the consequence of hypogonadism, with or without hyposecretion of the gonadotropic hormones (hypogonadotropinism).

In males
Gonadal failure of puberty leads to failure of the secondary sexual characteristics. The body proportion is eunuchoid. Sexual function is variably affected: erections may occur, as may romantic dreams, and even orgasm without emission, though there are many exceptions. For complete pubertal

---

* Supported by USPHS Grant No. HD-00325 and funds from the Grant Foundation, New York, and from La Fondation de l'Industrie Pharmaceutique pour la Recherche, Paris.

Handbook of Sexology, edited by J. Money and H. Musaph
© *Elsevier/North-Holland Biomedical Press, 1977*

development, androgen replacement therapy is necessary. In timing the onset of therapy, it is necessary to balance the onset of height age and social age.

Gonadal failure of postpubertal onset is rare, except in advanced old age. The secondary sexual characteristics partially regress. Sexual function is gradually affected with a diminution of the frequency of erections and ejaculations, and possible difficulty in the maintenance of both. Erotic imagery also diminishes in frequency.

Androgen replacement therapy produces good somatic as well as behavioral erotic results in hyposexuality related to hypogonadism without hypogonadotropinism (Money and Alexander, 1967). It permits the development of a normally virilized male with more frequent and longer lasting erections. Ejaculation is restored or experienced for the first time. Treated patients report another type of orgasm with an extra pleasure added by ejaculation. The threshold of response to erotic stimuli is lowered. The frequency of erotic dreams is greater, though their content is not modified. If treatment is discontinued, sexual function becomes less active.

Androgen replacement therapy produces less satisfactory somatic results in hyposexuality related to hypogonadism with hypogonadotropinism. All too often virilization is inadequate, and patients continue to appear too young in physique age. In consequence, partners fail to respond to them on the basis of their chronological age. Patients may manifest an erotic inertia in arousal from erotic imagery, in the initiation of erotic partnerships, and in the low frequency of achieving an orgasm (Money and Clopper, 1975).

Different androgen preparations are available *. The most active forms of androgen are still being tested. Their schedule of administration varies. For the average-sized adult, an injection every three weeks of a long acting testosterone (testosterone enanthate, 200 mg per injection) seems to obtain the best results.

In females
Except for Turner's syndrome, hypogonadism with or without hypogonadotropinism is more rare in females than in males. Partly for this reason, but also for the universal tendency to neglect female sexual eroticism, it is not yet possible to make strong and definitive behavioral statements. It is by no means clear what role estrogens and progestogens play in erotic behavior of human females, except for the estrogenic effect of vaginal lubrication.

A growing body of evidence shows that androgens are the libido hormones for both sexes. In females, the necessary amount of androgens for sexual response may well be of adrenocortical origin. Alternatively, they may be synthesized from estrogens in the target receptor cells.

Estrogen replacement therapy in female hypogonadism is necessary to

---

* For complete therapeutic details, the reader can consult endocrine textbooks such as Gardner (1975), Williams (1974) or Wilkins (1965). For further reference to behavioral details and case management see Money (1968) and Money and Ehrhardt (1972).

trigger the onset of puberty. In timing the onset of puberty in girls, the same principles apply as in boys (see above). Romantic interest increased in response to induced puberty, according to a study of Turner's syndrome (Money and Mittenthal, 1970).

In order to obtain good pubertal development and a well-developed proliferative endometrium, estrogen therapy is prescribed daily during the first three to six months (Premarin®, 2 to 4 mg daily). Then, cyclic therapy is instituted with three weeks on daily estrogen, and one week off. Menstrual flow usually starts within two to five days from the last dose of estrogen. Whether there is an advantage in administering progesterone associated with estrogen, as long-term therapy, has not been satisfactorily ascertained.

Gonadal failure of postpubertal onset is rare, except for the normal phenomenon of menopause. The menses terminate. The vaginal mucosa eventually becomes atrophic and does not lubricate. Estrogen replacement therapy reestablishes vaginal lubrication and allows normal sex life.

Hyposexual behavior related to neurogenic disorders

A blockage of the neurologic pathways anywhere between the brain and the genitopelvic area many induce a dysynchrony between genitopelvic and cerebrocognitional eroticism, in either males or females. In the male paraplegic patient, stimulation of pelvic erotic zones may produce erection by reflex action. Ejaculation is less likely, and sterility is the rule. The paraplegic man will be aware of erection only by palpation or visual observation. Sex fantasies and erotic dreams, including the mental experience of orgasm, occur independently of genital participation. In the female paraplegic patient, menstruation continues unchanged and sexual intercourse can be accomplished, but without the accompanying neural experience of erotic genital feeling and orgasm. Pregnancy is possible. Hormonal and drug therapy are not effective to relieve the sexual deficits of paraplegia. Counseling is helpful in social sexual rehabilitation.

In patients with temporal lobe epilepsy, associated hyposexual, hypersexual and paraphiliac sexual behavior have been reported. Hyposexuality, manifested as impotence in the male, and sexual inertia and/or difficulty in both sexes to reach orgasm, appears to be more common. In suppressing seizure activity, anticonvulsant drugs simultaneously increase sexual function in some, though not all cases.

Sexual hypofunction in the form of apathy and, in the male, impotence, are an early manifestation of psychotic depression. Treatment with antidepressive and/or anxiolytic drugs are often effective in correcting the depressive state and the sexual hypofunction.

Hyposexual behavior has been reported as a side effect of drug therapy, especially antihypertensive and psychotropic drug therapy, as a consequence of either a sympathetic or parasympathetic blockage or a central effect (Money and Yankowitz, 1967; Story, 1974). When the drug is discontinued, normal erotic behavior usually returns within a few days.

Hyposexual behavior related to pair-bonding relationship disorders

It is difficult to find a word that accurately conceptualizes this type of disorder, in which no endocrine, systemic or neurogenic disease can be diagnosed, and in which the pair-bonding between two partners is adversely affected.

In males, relationship disorders can result in sexual apathy and inertia, impotence and/or anorgasmia. Premature ejaculation is another such symptom. It is classed as a form of impotence because the erection is lost too soon; but it also is a form of hypersexuality in the sense of accelerated timing of ejaculation.

It is a common physician's practice to prescribe testosterone for the foregoing symptoms in the male. None, however, is responsive to sex-hormone therapy, except as a placebo effect, or except in cases of endogenous hormonal deficit. Thioridazine (Mallaril®), because of its sexually depressing effect, has been used to retard premature ejaculation. Other side-effects are too dangerous to permits its long-term use as a substitute for counseling therapy.

In females sexual apathy, anorgasmia, inability to lubricate and vaginal phobia are the symptoms of hyposexuality based on disorders of the relationship between erotic partners. Estrogen therapy is effective only if hypoestrogenism is present. A brief trial of local application of testosterone cream to the clitoris may be useful in some anorgasmic patients. The effect may be mostly that of a quasiplacebo. Scientific data are still lacking.

3. HYPERSEXUAL BEHAVIOR AND INHIBITORY THERAPY

Compulsive hypersexual behavior is conventionally labeled satyriasis in males and nymphomania in females. Hypersexual behavior is not correlated with an excess of endogenous sex hormones. In males, a course of treatment with antiandrogens may be helpful — medroxyprogesterone acetate (Depo-Provera®, Upjohn) or cyproterone acetate (Androcur®, Schering A.G.) — but needs to be combined with counseling therapy. There is no corresponding antihormone therapy for females.

Hypersexual behavior may be defined not only in terms of frequency, but also of precocious time of onset. In boys and girls with precocious onset of somatic puberty — which can occur even in the first year of life — there is no excessive frequency of sexual behavior. Such sexual behavior as does appear is in keeping with chronological and/or social age, rather than physique age.

Early appearance of secondary sexual characteristics does not produce promiscuous sexual behavior (Money and Alexander, 1969; Money and Walker, 1971). With effective sex education, there are no more sexual behavioral problems than in normal puberty. Therefore there is no special need for hormonal suppression treatment for the purpose of suppressing sexual behavior. In both boys and girls, hormonal suppression treatment — medroxyprogesterone acetate, or cyproterone acetate — is used in an attempt to retard the precocious appearance of secondary sexual characteristics. On the dosages currently used (in the case of medroxyprogesterone acetate, 200 mg every two to three weeks), there is no notable influence on behavior or on accelerated statural growth and bone fusion.

Hypersexuality, defined as an increased frequency effect, secondary to drug therapy, has been reported in the case of some patients treated with L-DOPA for Parkinson's disease. The evidence is still equivocal. The effect would presumably be mediated by way of brain indolamines. The function of indolamines and catecholamines in sexuality has yet to be elucidated in detail.

4. PARADOXICAL AND PARAPHILIAC SEXUAL FUNCTION

Related to endocrine disorders

In boys with masculine gender identity, breast growth, or gynecomastia, does not result in incongruent sexual object choice or sexual functioning. Surgery is the treatment of choice.

In girls with feminine gender identity, virilism does not automatically result in incongruent psychosexual functioning. In patients with congenital virilizing adrenal hyperplasia, cortisone replacement therapy prevents further virilization.

Homosexuality

Endocrine studies of homosexuality have produced contradictory results. The chief evidence, as of the present time, is that homosexual males and females as a group do not differ hormonally from matched controls. There is, however, a possibility that their prenatal hormonal history may have been atypical, at least in some cases.

Androgen given to male homosexuals has either no behavioral or psychic effect at all, or else induces an increased frequency of desire for homosexual activity. Given to female homosexuals, androgen virilizes the body and increases the frequency of sexual desire; estrogen and progestin do not change their sexual fantasies and behavior. Estrogen and progestin, if given to male homosexuals, have a functional castrating effect which is reversible. Estrogen also induces breast growth. In the typical homosexual, male or female, there is no indication for any form of hormonal treatment.

Transvestism

The syndrome of transvestism, which associates cross-dressing with erotic arousal, is reported only in men. It does not respond to treatment with androgen. Treatment with psychotropic drugs is hit-and-miss, and is without adequate rationale and effects. The use of antiandrogen when combined with counseling may be beneficial. When transvestism is on the borderline of transexualism, however, the antiandrogenic effect is subjectively experienced as a desirable shift towards femininity; then the ultimate goal is complete sex reassignment.

Transexualism

Hormonal therapy of transexualism is part of the process of sex reassignment. Sex reassignment is a form of rehabilitative therapy in the absence of any known curative therapy.

In male-to-female transexuals, the administration of estrogen and progestogen preparations induces partial demasculinization and feminization. Erection greatly diminishes and ejaculation disappears, both to the satisfaction of the transexual patient. Before treatment, male-to-female transexuals are typically hyposexual or erotically negative toward their genital function. Hormonal therapy and surgical construction of female genitalia allows pleasurable sexual intercourse.

In the female-to-male transexual, hormonal treatment consists of the administration of testosterone to induce defeminization and masculinization (for complete details see preceding chapter by Money and Walker). The clitoris enlarges and becomes more readily erectile. The orgasm is experienced as more intense, without loss of the female capacity for multiple orgasm. Surgical construction of male genitalia is unsatisfactory and never results in a functionally erectile penis.

Paraphilias

In recent years, the use of effective hormonal and drug therapy to treat noxious paraphiliac sexual function (Money, Ch. 72) has highlighted the ethical issue, still not resolved, of the right of a patient to elect or reject treatment.

Chemical aversion consists in the use of emetic drugs — apomorphine and emetine — along with behavioral modification, to produce nausea and vomiting in association with the unwanted sexual arousal.

Without any strong theoretical justification, phenothiazines, meprobamates and butyrophenones have been used in an attempt to reduce the paraphiliac sexual performance in some patients. A double-blind controlled study (Bancroft, 1974; Tennent et al., 1974) of the effects of a butyrophenone (Benperidol), a phenothiazine (Chlorpromazine) and a placebo on deviant sexual behavior does not support the superiority of one of these drugs, except a lower self-relating of frequency of sexual thoughts with Benperidol.

Antiandrogen has been used in the treatment of sex offenders since the mid-1960s. With cyproterone acetate (Laschet, 1967, 1973) at a daily dosage of 100—150 mg, erectile and ejaculatory capacity are reversibly reduced. There is a corresponding reduction of sexual behavior.

The antiandrogen or androgen-depleting hormone, medroxyprogesterone acetate, has been used in the treatment of sex offenders in association with counseling (Money, 1970; Money et al., 1975). The hormone is used intramuscularly with a dosage of Depo-Provera®, 200—400 mg weekly. Erectile potency and ejaculation are radically reduced. There is a beneficial elevation of the threshold for erotic imagery and sexual functioning, permitting increased self-regulation of behavior. The somatic effects are reversible upon discontinuance of treatment, and the reversal may be achieved in graduated phases by gradual reduction of dosage. With concurrent counseling, the patient may be able to achieve long-term freedom from his sexual compulsion.

5.SUMMARY

The expectancies of hormonal and drug therapy on sexual dysfunction are largely dependent on the etiology of the dysfunction. Hormonal replacement therapy can enhance hyposexual behavior only if hyposexuality is related to endocrine deficit. Antiandrogen can reduce unwanted paraphiliac sexual behavior in men. Associated with counseling and surgical sex ressignment, hormonal therapy can rehabilitate transexuals. Pharmacologic therapy can be effective in sexual behavioral problems associated with psychodynamic problems, either as an agent of behavior modification therapy, or by way of a placebo or partial placebo effect.

BIBLIOGRAPHY

Bancroft, J. (1974) *Deviant Sexual Behavior. Modification and Assessment.* (Clarendon Press, Oxford.)

Gardner, L.I. (1975) *Endocrine and Genetic Diseases of Childhood*, 2nd edn (W.B. Saunders, Philadelphia).

Laschet, U., Laschet, L., Fetzner, H.-R., Claesel, H.-U., Mall, G. and Naab, M. (1967) Results in the treatment of hyper- and abnormal sexuality of men with antiandrogens. *Acta Endrocrinol.*, suppl. 119: 54.

Laschet, U. (1973) A possibility of medical treatment of sexual deviations and perversions in men. *Med. News Schering.* (Berlin) 2: 11—18.

Money, J. (1968) *Sex Errors of the Body: Dilemmas, Education and Counseling.* (Johns Hopkins Press, Baltimore.)

Money, J. (1970) Use of an androgen-depleting hormone in the treatment of male sex offenders. *J. Sex Res.* 6: 165—172.

Money, J. and Alexander, D. (1967) Eroticism and sexual function in developmental anorchia and hyporchia with pubertal failure. *J. Sex Res.* 3: 31—47.

Money, J. and Alexander, D. (1969) Psychosexual development and absence of homosexuality in males with precocious puberty. *J. Nerv. Ment. Dis.* 148: 111—123.

1310

Money, J. and Clopper, R.R. (1975) Postpubertal psychosexual function in postsurgical male hypopituitarism. *J. Sex Res.* 11: 25—38.

Money, J. and Ehrhardt, A. (1972) *Man and Woman, Boy and Girl: The Differentiation and Dimorphism of Gender Identity.* (Johns Hopkins Press, Baltimore.)

Money, J. and Mittenthal, S. (1970) Lack of personality pathology in Turner's syndrome: relation to cytogenetics, hormones and physique. *Behav. Genet.* 1: 43—56.

Money, J. and Walker, P.A. (1971) Psychosexual development, maternalism, nonpromiscuity, and body image in 15 females with precocious puberty. *Arch. Sex. Behav.* 1: 45—60.

Money, J., Wiedeking, C., Walker, P., Migeon, C., Meyer, W. and Borgaonkar, D. (1975) 47,XYY and 46,XY males with antisocial and/or sex-offending behavior; antiandrogen therapy plus counseling. *Psychoneuroendocrinology* 1: 165—178.

Money, J. and Yankowitz, R. (1967) The sympathetic-inhibiting effects of the drug Ismelin on human male eroticism, with a note on Mellaril. *J. Sex Res.* 3: 69—82.

Story, N.L. (1974) Sexual dysfunction resulting from drug side effects. *J. Sex Res.* 10: 132—149.

Tennent, G., Bancroft, J. and Cass, J. (1974) The control of deviant sexual behavior by drugs: a double-blind controlled study of Benperidol, Chlorpromazine, and placebo. *Arch. Sex Behav.* 3: 261—271.

Wilkins, L. (1965) *The Diagnosis and Treatment of Endocrine Disorders in Childhood and Adolescence,* 3rd edn. (C.C. Thomas, Springfield, Ill.)

Williams, R.H. (1974) *Textbook of Endocrinology,* 5th edn. (W.B. Saunders, Philadelphia.)

SECTION XVII

Religion, ideology and sex

Section coordinator: Paul Sporken

CHAPTER 104

Introduction

PAUL SPORKEN

It would have left a gap, if, in a Handbook of Sexology, themes like religion, ideology and sex were not discussed. These three themes are closely connected with each other. Religion has in fact always greatly influenced official sexual ethics. Moreover, among many people and nations, sexual behavior is surrounded by religious rites. This actual connection of religion and sex has a very clear philosophical background, which I will only briefly mention here. Views on sexuality and the image of man are closely related, as being sexual is an aspect of being human. In turn, the image of man is the essence of every philosophy of life and of every culture and civilization.

Proclaiming a message on the meaning of human existence contains necessarily a message on the meaning of human sexuality. This has the very important consequence that the image of man and the view of human sexuality differs in accordance with the difference in philosophy of life, culture and religion. If, for instance, a certain philosophy of life is ruled by an extreme dualistic image of man, the soul being a prisoner in the dungeon of the body, this will easily lead to a depreciation of the body and of sexual enjoyment, and will therefore lead to more severe sexual norms. A second consequence is that the historical development of cultures and religions brings about at the same time a development of views on sexuality and on sexual ethics.

It would have been ideal to discuss in this section, all important religions of the world. The editors and the undersigned were forced to decide, however, in favor of the major Western religions. It was not possible to obtain manuscripts on sexuality from scholars in other religions. Therefore, we were obliged to confine ourselves to a reflection on the three great religions: Judaism, Protestant Christianity and Roman Catholic Christianity, completed with a contribution on the secular ideology of sex. These studies express how closely the philosophy of life and sex are related with one another, and what kinds of development come to pass in this field. These developments indeed contribute to a more open discussion on present-day problems.

Handbook of Sexology, edited by J. Money and H. Musaph
© *Elsevier/North-Holland Biomedical Press, 1977*

CHAPTER 105

Sexual attitudes and regulations in Judaism

ELIYAHU ROSENHEIM

Judaism's approach to human sexuality is a combination of unequivocal acceptance of this basic drive with well-defined regulation of its actual expression. The framework to be described in this chapter is that of the mainstream in Jewish tradition: the five books of Moses (the Pentateuch) and its Oral Law interpretations in the Talmud, as well as the subsequent rabbinical Codes and Responsa. These sources devoted much thought to the sexual matrix, especially in matrimony.

Jewish religion developed along two lines: meticulously formulated norms of conduct in the Halacha and more freely expressed ethical and experiential attitudes in the Agadah. The Halacha regulates sexual laws and practices, while the Agadah sheds light on the underlying perceptions of, and attitudes towards, the sexual need.

1. CONCEPTION OF SEXUALITY

While the body was never glorified as such, its functions were regarded as God's gift to His creatures. Thus, sexuality was not worshipped but was viewed as natural and, consequently, as a beneficial force when properly channeled. The overinclusive concept of 'Judeo-Christian tradition' is not really valid in this instance because of a fundamental dissonance of approach. The British scholar, Mace, points out in his book 'Hebrew Marriage' (1953): "I had always been struck by the unembarrassed plainess of speech with which they (the Hebrews) discussed sexual matters. But I had not fully realized that it had its roots in an essentially 'clean' conception of the essential goodness of the sexual function. This is something very difficult for us to grasp, reared as we have been in a tradition which has produced in many minds the rooted idea that sex is essentially sinful."

Handbook of Sexology, edited by J. Money and H. Musaph
© *Elsevier/North-Holland Biomedical Press, 1977*

The nature of the sexual drive

Man's sexual impulses are perceived in Judaism as both very central and powerful. It takes strong will power not to give in to each instinctual whim. With reference to King David's erotic desire it was written: "There is a small organ in man which satisfies him in his hunger and makes him hungry when satisfied." (Babylonian Talmud (BT), Sanhedrin, 107a). The temptation offered by sexual urges is keenly discussed by the Rabbis (Maimonides, Book V, Treatise Concerning Forbidden Intercourse, XXII). An illuminating example is the story about the prominent Talmudic scholar, Abaya, who was reported to have overheard a man say to a woman: "Let us rise early, and we will go on the road." He decided to follow them in order to "prevent them from a sin." After three miles he heard them say: "Our company has been very agreeable but our roads are separate." Abaya returned to town despondent because he doubted his own ability to contain himself. An old man approached him and reassured him: "The greater a man, the more he is tempted by his impulse" (BT, Sukkah, 52a).

Judaism maintains that wordly enjoyments were granted by God to be fully experienced unless specifically forbidden. However, moderation is called for. One's instincts should be " thrust aside with the left hand and drawn near with the right hand" (BT, Sotah, 47a). Judaism recommends the middle-of-the-road approach to gratification: neither avoidance nor overindulgence. The free man is portrayed as the one who is the master of his impulses, not their passive slave; Ben Zoma said: "Who is he who is mighty? He who subdues his inclination." (BT, Abboth, 4, 1);

Judaism firmly rejected sexual abstinence. Even the ascetically oriented sects of Jewish mystics "continued to regard marriage not as concession to the frailty of the flesh, but as one of the most sacred mysteries" (Scholem, 1971, p. 235). Not only is celibacy not valued as a virtue, but it is considered a sin for layman and priest alike.

The aims of sexuality

Man was endowed with sexual impulses as a divine device to guarantee mankind's self-propagation. "Be fruitful and multiply" (Genesis, I, 28) is the first command in the Bible. However, over and beyond this pragmatic motive, sexuality also draws people together: "It is not good that the man should be alone" (Genesis, II, 18).

The relational, affiliative dimension of sexual union is emphasized in Judaism apart from the biological value of this drive. The story of the creation of Eve from Adam's bone already represents the initial unity between male and female, which is to repeat itself with each act of marriage: "Therefore should a man leave his father and mother, and shall cleave unto his wife and they shall be one flesh" (Genesis, II, 24). A Talmudic scholar summarized the psychological needs of the male—female partnership from the point of view of the male: "Any man who has no wife lives without joy, without blessing and without goodness." Others added that a bachelor was also denied of peace and lives "without a (protective) wall" (BT, Yebamoth, 62a). There is no emphasis on sex as a medium for sensory pleasure per se, but the legitimacy of the joyfulness derived from sexual union is clearly established. For example, the term "to rejoice one's wife" is quite frequently employed in describing the husband's marital duties.

Sexual symbolism

The unique amalgamation in the sexual encounter was utilized to symbolize the closeness between God and the people of Israel. The mystical approach views the union of man and woman as re-enactment of the harmony between the diverse, even opposite attributes of God, specifically activity and passivity. More frequently the sexual analogy served to portray God as the lover and Israel as his beloved woman. The Song of Songs, with its elaborate sensual imagery, is interpreted as an allegory of this bond. The Talmud describes the cherubim in the Temple in Jerusalem as embracing each other to signify that God's affection to his people is equivalent to the attachment between the sexes.

Talmudic scholars were aware of the disguised sexual representation in apparently innocent dreams. Sexual interpretations are offered to a series of dreams, such as: a man who dreamt that he was pouring oil on olives was told by Rabbi Ishmael that the dream's meaning was intercourse with his mother. When told that the man saw in his dream that his eyes were kissing each other, Rabbi Ishmael interpreted it as incestual contact with his sister (BT, Berakoth, 56b).

While phallic vigor was not given special importance, one can hardly overlook the symbolic meaning of the ritual circumcision of every Jewish male on the eighth day of his birth as reaffirmation of the covenant with God as the Master of Israel.

2. REGULATION OF SEXUAL BEHAVIOR

The cardinal rule of sexual conduct is that sexual activity of any kind might take place solely in the heterosexual bond of legal marriage. The Jewish family is bestowed with supreme religious significance. Families are the nuclei of the nation and the carriers of its values. Meticulous legislative decrees and ethical teachings are all aimed at leading each Jew into marriage and keeping it as a viable and intact unit as long as possible. The legalities of divorce are beyond the scope of this chapter. Suffice to note that dissolution of wedlock is seen as a tragedy, but at times, an unavoidable one. A marriage can be terminated upon the valid request of one of the partners. In the extreme case of the wife's infidelity, the court is even obliged to enforce divorce whether the couple so wishes or not.

Sexual obligations and rights in marriage

The traditional sources urged early marriage: not later than 18—20 years for the male, but no formal age was set for the female. The male carries the religious obligation to secure reproduction and if he refrains from doing so, he is morally considered as having taken the lives of the children he was capable of giving life to.

Marriage being the only approved way to conduct sexual activity, both male and female are morally and emotionally better off the sooner they reach this avenue of sexual release, as indicated metaphorically by the saying: "You cannot compare one who has bread in his basket with one who has no bread in his basket" (BT, Yoma, 18a).

Virginity is highly valued. Its absence can be a cause for divorce, although it is no legal hinderance to marriage if the husband accepts this fact.

The Jewish ideal seems to have always been monogamy (Epstein, 1942; Mace, 1953), though the Bible and Talmud did not rule out polygamy. The de facto tendency to adhere to monogamy found its de jure formulation in Europe in the beginning of the 11th century in a ruling of Rabbenu Gershom and his colleagues. While oriental Jews were not bound by this decree, monogamy gradually became all but the rule among them as well.

Female and male have an equal right for sexual gratification by their partner and an equal obligation to be responsive to their partner's libidinal needs. A couple might abstain from intercourse only upon mutual consent, which is always reversible. However, such an agreement depends on the previous fulfillment of the minimal imperative of self-replacement by giving birth to one boy and one girl. This 'lower limit' is by no means the optimal norm. Judaism rejects birth control except in cases of real physical danger involved in pregnancy or extraordinary hardship, such as famine. Sheer economic considerations or other reasons of personal convenience are not acceptable for interfering with the natural course of fertilization established by divine design. There is a basic belief that He will provide for His creatures and, thus, the rabbis expressed no concern over the size of the family or population explosion in general. To the contrary, they cared about maintaining the ranks of the relatively small Jewish people, which were often depleted by external pressures and persecution. Out of deep regard even to potential life, therapeutic abortions will be permitted by rabbinical authorities only in individual cases of extreme danger to the mother's health (Jakobovits, 1962).

The husband's obligation to get together with his wife regularly ('Onah') is an integral part of the marriage contract. The frequency of this duty varies according to his physical capacity and his occupation. For example, the laborer's coital 'quota' is twice weekly and the scholar's once weekly. The woman is not perceived as a passive gratifier of masculine needs, but as a partaker in mutual gratification. If anything, the wife's 'claim' for coitus is mainly based on her physical and emotional pleasure, while in regard to the husband, the emphasis is put on his duty to secure reproduction. It is stated that women do not tend to accept material comfort as substitute for the joy of sex (BT, Sotah, 20a). If the husband is unwilling or unable (as in the case of impotence) to perform sexually, the wife is entitled to divorce. If she continuously, and out of ill will, refuses intercourse, the husband can sue for divorce without making the payments she would have otherwise received in case of divorce.

Modes of marital sexual behavior

The goal of propagation implies that the sexual act should lead to the emission of the male's semen in his wife's vagina. The emission of seed 'in vain' is sharply criticized, to the extent of comparing it to killing, since the potentially constructive fluid was destroyed. The famous Biblical example is that of Onan (Genesis, XXXVIII, 7) who "spilled his seed on the ground" (probably employing coitus interruptus). Any volitional ejaculation outside the coital state is forbidden. Moreover, it is advocated that men avoid physical stimuli and psychic arousal which could increase the probability of nocturnal emission. Masturbation is declared a grave sin whether the male is married or not. Conflicts over masturbatory activity frequently cause feelings of guilt, shame and depression among pious youngsters. Female autoeroticism has received little attention since there is no 'destruction of seed' involved, but is considered improper. However, conjugal activity which cannot lead to impregnation, as in the case of existing pregnancy or physical hinderance, is not objectionable (Feldman, 1968); sexual life should, nevertheless, continue as an expression of affinity and enjoyment.

Several religious authorities through the generations have disagreed with respect to the permissible sexual foreplay techniques and the employment of positions other than face-to-face intercourse, mainly anal intercourse, labeled as 'overturning the table'. As to the range of foreplay, the most extreme opinion advocated that a man should go through the sexual process "as though he were compelled by a demon" and that while with his wife he should "uncover a handbreadth and cover a handbreadth". However the prevailing view was that "a man might do whatever he pleases with his wife" (BT, Nedarim, 20b). The ultimate aim should remain to complete the act by internal ejaculation. The two approaches are drawn closer by the fact that even those who legally permit freedom of divergent erotic practices, including oral—genital contact, also praise pious self-restraint to preserve man's modesty and holiness. For example, even though there is no limitation on the frequency of marital coitus, one is called not to overdo it, lest he descends to becoming "like a cock is with a hen."

There seems to be a unanimous recommendation that the husband should arouse his wife and enhance her psychophysiological readiness for copulation by means of verbal or bodily arousal. It is stated that mutual willingness and emotional fitness are required. "Both of them should not be intoxicated, nor sluggish, nor in mourning ... nor when she be asleep, nor by the overpowering of her contrary mood, but with the consent and happy mood of both" (Maimonides, Book I, Treatise Concerning Ethics, V, 4). Angry feelings have to be resolved before the couple initiates erotic closeness. Furthermore, reciprocal feeling of belonging exclusively to each other is the necessary complement of the legal bond. In case of 'emotional divorce' that is, if a decision to separate was taken, the couple should refrain from sexual contact. The Talmud asks for affective fidelity as well as for physical fidelity in the following metaphor: "One may not drink out of one goblet and think of the other" (BT, Nedarim, 20b). It also points out, in the same vein, that the remarriage of two divorced persons entails the danger that there will be "four minds in the bed" (BT, Pesahim, 112a).

Menses (Nidah) imposes a considerable temporal limitation on conjugality. During menstruation the woman should not be approached sexually, as well as in any other manner of closeness, as a protection against temptation. The menstrual period is defined as including the actual days of menstruation (but encompassing not less than five days) plus seven days of purification. This period of impurity, lasting at least 12 days each month, ends with the ritual of immersion in a special pool (Mikvah), originating from a neutral source of water. Beyond the religious decree, based on the conception of 'uncleanness' of the menses, the Bible did not give further reasons for the nature of this prohibition. In the pursuit of explanations, later authorities postulated: repeated reinforcement of the capacity for instinctual mastery, especially in regard to a desire as intense as sex, allows one to achieve a higher level of religious commitment; and secondly, physical attraction between husband and wife is regularly renewed in the wake of forced periodic separation. Additionally, these Nidah regulations may enhance the possibility of conception, since the reunion of the couple will take place in the middle of the cycle, the most likely time of ovulation.

Modesty in the expression of sexuality is strongly urged. Conjugality should not be accompanied by boisterousness or profane language. Sexual intimacy should not take place in the presence of another person nor in a lighted room.

Trangressive behavior

Any sexual activity other than between a married couple is considered illicit in varying degrees of stringency and, accordingly, is punishable or, at least, morally reproachable. All premarital relations are discouraged. Much more gravely viewed is adultery, which is legally equated to incest. There is a sharp legal difference between adultery commited by a married woman or a married man. When committed by a married woman, both she and her lover (whether single or married) are condemned to death by the Biblical decree. Infidelity on the part of a husband is not a statutory crime in the Bible, but it was later censured as a deviation. While in the view of the Jewish law there is no such status as 'illegitimate child' even for children born out of wedlock, it created a special status of 'mamzer' for proven offspring of incestuous or adulterous relations which permits them to marry only their likes. It appears that the hope was that such severe sanction would deter this tabooed sexual activity.

Male homosexuality is declared by the Bible as an 'abomination' (Leviticus, XX, 13) and incurs capital punishment. Rabbinical sources make little reference to homosexuality. Pedophilia is also forbidden, but not treated with the same severity as homosexuality if one of the partners is less than nine years old. The Bible does not mention lesbianism, but rabbinical sources alerted against such practice. Bestiality (also punishable by death) and transvestism are two additional practices which were explicitly forbidden.

The probability of surrender to the temptation of illicit sexuality (designated 'the evil inclination') was repeatedly emphasized and strongly disapproved (Epstein, 1967). Numerous restrictive rules were established as protective 'fences' against such stimulation. To mention some: males and females should not mingle in public gatherings; women and a man who is not married to any of them are not to stay alone in a closed space; married women have to cover their hair (which, like the female voice, is defined as 'pudendum'); and men ought to avoid voyeuristic staring at other women or engaging in excessive talk with them.

The request for self-containment refers not only to overt and verbal behavior, but also to one's thoughts. One should contain his investment in instinctual cravings so he would not be engrossed in them. Rather, he should devote himself primarily to the spiritual domain and to his religious duties. Moreover, preoccupation in sexual desires which cannot be fulfilled legally might transcend thought and lead to action. Thus, abstinence is the only avenue approved for young people until they get married. Also, for the married male whose heart desires prohibited sexuality, the advice offered is to immerse himself in the study of Scripture in order to conquer his unacceptable desires.

If temptation prevails, the last resort is prescribed in the Talmud: "let him go to a place where he is not known, and put on black garments ... and let him do what his heart wishes; but let him not profane the Name of Heaven publicly" (BT, Hagiga, 16b). Such a 'safety valve' can prevent a momentary transgression from causing lasting alienation from the normative standard.

A note is in order regarding the relation between doctrine and actual behavior. This chapter's aim is to describe sexuality in Judaism as a normative system. The historical commitment to this legacy was considerably lessened among many Jews who had gradually internalized the secular values prevalent in their social surroundings. The factual details of sexual behavior and feelings of observant Jewry can, of course, be appropriately established only through future in-depth study encompassing the different groups of orthodoxy. However, it seems that among devout Jews, existing deviations from the norms portrayed in this chapter are more often those of omission than of commission. In other words, there is probably quite a low incidence of major transgressions (adultery, homosexuality or even premarital sex), but on the other hand, there are recognizable tendencies in segments of observant Jewry to develop a rather anxious, overly inhibitory approach to sexual expression and orientation. Thus, the balance between restriction and spontaneity, prescribed by major traditional authorities, is not infrequently tipped in the direction of the former.

3. SUMMARY

"Enjoy life with the wife you love" (Ecclesiastes, IX, 9). This biblical verse is essentially a succinct compendium of 'sexual ideology' in Judaism. The sexual drive, like other physiological and psychological needs, is conceived of in Judaism as divine endowment and this, in itself, defines it as being potentially of positive value. Judaism teaches that human needs are constructive if expressed within controlled boundaries and hazardous if one is passively dominated by them and acts impulsively upon them. In the same vein, human sexuality should be fully experienced and appreciated, provided that it is guided by normative guidelines.

Sexuality is viewed as beneficial both biosocially, as a 'trigger' for engagement in procreation, which is a formal religious duty, and psychologically as a medium for male—female affiliation and closeness. The libidinal impulses are directed towards the establishment of a family. Judaism zealously guards the exclusiveness of matrimony against alternative, competitive forms of sexual outlet. Any other erotic activity, premarital or extramarital, autoerotic or homosexual, is considered illicit with varying degrees of sternness. Since sexual urges are perceived as very intense, rabbinical authorities throughout the generations established detailed, precautionary measures to reinforce successful resistance to morally and religiously unwarranted sexual behavior.

Both husband and wife are entitled to sexual responsiveness by their partner, to the extent that if one of them is unwilling, or unable to have regular relations, the other has a legally valid claim for divorce. Rabbinical authorities had differences of opinion in regard to the permissible range of sexual practices within the marriage, some expressly consenting to every technique of foreplay, and others restricting such behavior to a minimum. However, they are in agreement that steps should always be taken to ensure that the sexual act will not be isolated from genuine, effective commitment between husband and wife; closeness of body should take place only if it is accompanied by intimacy of feeling.

BIBLIOGRAPHY

Babylonian Talmud, English translation (The Soncino Press, London).
Epstein, L.M. (1942) *Marriage Laws in the Bible and Talmud.* (Harvard University Press, Cambridge, Mass.)

Epstein, L.M. (1967) *Sex Laws and Customs in Judaism.* (Ktav Publishing House, Inc., New York.)

Feldman, D.M. (1968) *Birth Control in Jewish Law.* (New York University Press, New York.)

Jakobovits, I. (1962) *Jewish Medical Ethics.* Chs. 13 and 14 (Bloch Publishing Co., New York.)

Mace, D.R. (1953) *Hebrew Marriage. A Sociological Study.* (Philosophical Library, New York.)

Maimonides, Mishneh Torah, Book I. English translation by S. Glaser, 1927(Maimonides Publishing Co., New York.)

Maimonides, Mishneh Torah, Book V. English translation by L.I. Rabinowitz and P Grossman, 1965 (Yale University Press, New Haven).

Scholem, G.G. (1971) *Major Trends in Jewish Mysticism.* (Schocken Books, New York.)

CHAPTER 106

Marriage and sexual ethics in the Catholic church

PAUL SPORKEN

1. INTRODUCTION

Views on marriage and on sexual ethics of the Catholic Church certainly have developed in the course of centuries although they still are balancing between Biblical thinking on the one hand, and the influences from several (especially western) cultures on the other. This is easy to understand; religion can only find its concrete form in human thinking, feeling and behavior that reign in a culture. For a good understanding of current thinking about marriage and sexual ethics, the following should be remembered:

First: norms for sexual ethics, originating from reciprocal Biblical and cultural elements, were often sanctioned by Popes and the Holy Officium, so that correction almost looked like a violation of Biblical tradition.

Further: until recently, a uniformity of thinking about sexual ethics could be noticed, which was mostly due to the binding character of statements from the Church (roma locuta, causa finita).

Nowadays, people are again actively aware of the fact that statements of the Church on ethical norms are mostly not guaranteed by the infallible authority of the Church. Consequently, personal conscience can be shown to full advantage, as in this light, statements of the Church are only one, though an important, element in the entirety of factors defining a personal decision.

The following may assist a fuller understanding of today's views on ethics within the Christian-Catholic Church. It is obvious, however, that for that purpose a short survey on historical development is required.

2. THE NEW TESTAMENT

Dr. Rosenheim has already given a clear exposition on marriage and sexuality, based on the Old Testament view. This exposition has pointed out that the nuptial tie between husband and wife was a symbol for the relation between Yahweh and the people of Israel.

Handbook of Sexology, edited by J. Money and H. Musaph
© *Elsevier/North-Holland Biomedical Press, 1977*

The New Testament view is based on this starting point, subsequently developed by St. Paul, but makes an addition on two points: Jesus re-establishes the indissolubility of marriage, which had already been given in Genesis; and a voluntarily chosen celibacy is recommended as a typical Christian service to the Kingdom of God.

Little further direction with regard to sexual behavior can be found in the Gospels.

3. ST. PAUL AND THE YOUNG CHURCH

St. Paul elaborated several aspects of the husband—wife relation and sexual ethics. The union between husband and wife is a symbol and a realization of the love between Jesus and his Church. A later theological view on marriage as a sacrament was based on this theory (Schillebeeckx, 1963). Concerning the norms regarding the husband—wife relation in general, it can be said that neither with St. Paul, nor in the young Church is there question of 'typical' Christian ethics in this regard. In principle, St. Paul adopted the ethical norms from the Jewish and the Hellenian way of life. However, starting from the Gospel, St. Paul, and later several more great Christian authors from the young Church, tried to give these national ethics a deeper inspiration, and, if necessary, a correction. In Ef. V we can clearly read that this was a gradual process. On the one hand, we can see both an accent on Biblical thinking about the religious meaning of love in marriage as a symbol of the love between Jesus and his church and the equality of both partners, while on the other hand, there still is the influence from Hellenistic culture, where a husband demands full submission. With St. Paul and the young Church we can mostly find the same ideas about specific sexual norms, as they are found in Jewish thinking, for instance: the rejection of illicit sexuality (other than between a married couple), adultery and homosexuality. It is remarkable that in contrast with the Jewish thinking (see preceding chapter by Rosenheim), a positive appreciation of sexuality is not explicitly given.

4. FURTHER DEVELOPMENTS

In later developments, until the Middle Ages, Greek philosophy, especially Neo-Platonism, strongly influenced Christian views on sexuality. This led to under-appreciation and even rejection of physical pleasure. Sexual ethics became increasingly conditioned by the starting point that the matrimonial act is only permitted within marriage and as such, solely for procreative purposes. It was considered sinful to desire the matrimonial act only for physical pleasure.

Although leading theologians like Albert the Great and Thomas of Aquinas tried to give sensual and physical pleasure a positive appreciation (Sporken,

1963), later manuals on moral theology increasingly separated the unity of matrimonial love and the pleasure of its expression. Church lawyers dealt almost exclusively with concepts of sexuality in marriage. With the exclusion of a more positive view during the Renaissance, sexuality became increasingly taboo. Moreover, equality and real partnership of the women regarding sexuality in Western culture declined (Van Ussel, 1970).

The culture-defined view influenced the manuals of moral theology. The acceptance of matrimony was juridically interpreted as 'being entitled to each other's body'; especially the wife had to permit her husband the 'debitum conjungale' (the matrimonial duty).

The leading thread through the history of sexual ethics is that the worth of a human being is to be considered as a basic rule. The 'translation' of this basic rule in concrete regulations shall always be determined by a number of factors connected to a culture. For instance, during the 3rd and 4th century, surrender to the sexual pleasure of the orgasm was regarded sinful, as under the Stoic influence, 'obnibulatio mentis' (mistiness of the mind) induced by orgasm was considered unworthy of a human being. In the past also the use of mechanical and chemical contraceptives was considered sinful, and a violation of 'human nature' and as such a violation of the sexual act unworthy of a human being.

In the present day, however, conviction gains strength that the value of the human being demands that sexuality be primarily ruled by love. Consequently, norms for procreation stipulate a loving and responsible parenthood, and it is in this perspective that the worthiness of a human being is judged.

5. THE BEGINNING OF THE 20th CENTURY

Views on sexuality and sexual ethics, as they were generally proclaimed within Catholicism during the first half of this century, can be summarized as follows. Procreation was considered the first aim of marriage; mutual love and its sexual expression were of secondary importance. Coitus was reserved for marriage and was further ruled by its aim to procreate. The matrimonial act and procreation were absolutely related, from which all the other sexual norms were derived. Except for total or periodical continence, all contraceptive methods were forbidden, as they violated 'the nature' of the act by preventing procreation; artificial insemination was also forbidden, because it also detached the sexual act from procreation. By 'natural law', not the demands of man's nature in its totality were meant, but the laws of biological and physiological processes. Sexual pleasure (varying from rather simple pleasures to orgasm) were ethically acceptable only in connection with the matrimonial act within a valid marriage. For this reason premarital or extramarital sexual intercourse, masturbation, and homosexuality were considered sinful. Expression of affection, even bearing only slight resemblance to eroticism, was not regarded as a positive manifestation of a human relationship and the development of personal emotional life, but as a temptation to unchastity.

6. RECENT DEVELOPMENTS

After the World War II, a fundamental reorientation entered Catholic ethical thinking. Many factors figured there in. Owing to reliable contraceptives, the relation between sexual intercourse and pregnancy could, de facto, be split, which led to profound reflection on the typical human meaning of love and sexuality. For an ever increasing number of married couples, effective birth control became a necessity. Many married couples got into a serious conflict of conscience as periodic continence dictated by illness of the partner or for psychological reasons, proved unfeasible.

Pastoral solution

As the normative system did not seem to permit any further developments, Catholic pastors searched for a solution to conflicts of conscience in pastoral practice, though not in changing Catholic moral theology. Many pastors came to the practical rule: one should maintain strict principles, but be mild in practice. Others indeed considered breaking the norms set by Rome — an 'objectively' mortal sin — but they thought that in many cases 'subjectively' there could be no question of grievous guilt. As Gospel became more integrated in moral theology, other pastors came to the conclusion that the ideal of ethical norms should be respected, but at the same time one should dare to accept that this ideal is, for the time being, not yet realizable.

There were other pastors who called on the old pastoral adage of St. Thomas: one is sometimes forced, and so justified, to choose the lesser of two evils, which means concerning matrimonial ethics that one is sometimes forced to give the value of continued matrimonial love priority over regulations prohibiting birth control.

Development of moral theory

Attempts of Catholic married couples to solve sexual conflicts of conscience ended in fact in an undesirable rupture between what moral theology taught and what was done in the practice of pastoral care. This could not leave moral theology undisturbed. The development of anthropology and behavioral sciences as well as the gravity of the religious problem, caused an evolution within moral theology itself. The most important point of this evolution is the integration of the image of man with natural law, which was formerly interpreted solely in a biological way. This led to correction of the ethical norms regarding birth control by 'personification' of these norms. In other words emotional, psychological and social aspects and so human love, came to the fore in delineating the norms. This development was confirmed by statements of the second Vatican Council.

The 2nd Vatican Council

In the pastoral letter 'Gaudium ed Spes' (1924) Christian marriage was described primarily as a community of love. There was no longer any question of the traditional order of the aims of marriage; the traditional priority of procreation in marriage, was no longer upheld. In 'Gaudium ed Spes', disparity between matrimonial love and its sexual expression was abandoned, as fertility was looked upon as human fertility and as a task for marriage in its totality, including responsible parenthood. The Council did not promulgate an ethical judgement regarding birth-control methods: it said only that a decision is not solely dependent on good intentions and motives but is also determined by the individual and the objective consequences resulting from it. In later years the Pope would enlarge upon this matter.

The encyclical letter: 'Humanae Vitae'

The encyclical letter 'Humanae Vitae' of 1968 can be seen as a defense of the worth of human life and as an appeal for responsibility in sexuality and marriage. The strong negative criticism of this encyclical letter from inside and outside the Catholic Church, was mainly addressed to the ethical judgement on methods of birth-control (Böckle, 1968). With the exception of periodic continence all other methods were rejected. This was disenchanting for many Catholic married couples and pastors, and caused many a conflict of conscience, because they believed that the encyclical letter demanded absolute obedience. This, however, was not the case, for no encyclical letters are supported by the infallibility ascribed to the Church and the Pope. The Pope himself stated about the encyclical letter 'Humanae Vitae' that he did not want to make a statement 'ex cathedra' on methods of birth-control. The significance of this encyclical letter for Catholic married couples is that it leaves room for the personal decision of Catholics, but at the same time should be taken into account as one of the many factors influencing a decision. This basic right of personal decision was acknowledged by statements of several conferences of bishops.

Diverting the focus of attention from biological processing of the sexual act to its truly human aspects indeed gives an increased breadth of decision. The choice of the method, for example, should always be made by the married couple in mutual consent. Modified circumstances could compel change to another method. In short: breadth of decision means at the same time continuous appeal to personal responsibility in matrimonial love.

7. OTHER MODES OF SEXUAL BEHAVIOR

It goes without saying that fundamental reorientation on marital ethics influenced sexual ethics in other fields. The decrease of the sexual taboo, the revaluation of human emotional and physical life, the great value of an inter-human relation that gives warmth and security, and the general personalization of norms on sexual ethics influences ethical decisions on premarital and extramarital behavior.

Understanding improved regarding the acceptability of masturbation as a manifestation of growth in young people, and as an act of an adult in an isolated situation. In the opinion of many faithful people, including pastors and a number of moral theologists, premarital and extramarital sexual intercourse seemed more and more acceptable and could no longer be absolutely denounced (Gross, 1973). Especially here, the predominant idea is that human sexuality means in the first place a possibility to reach someone, to communicate, to love. When considering this, one should not only think of genital sexuality, but all expressions of affection and eroticism, in short, of all expressions of being a man and a woman. Although hesitantly, several moral theologists have begun to look at homosexuality from a more positive angle (Beemer, 1968).

Looking at sexual ethics in general, one can say that their present development is not characterized by stress on the sexual rule, but by a more profound appeal to personal responsibility in human love. This means that educating to mature sexual behavior does not consist of indoctrinating sexual norms, but of assistance in unfolding as a man or a woman. Judging ethical aspects of abortion is not directly a part of sexual ethics. However, it deals with sexual ethics in so far as responsible sexual behavior and good use of contraceptives are the best means to prevent undesired pregnancy. An absolute condemnation of almost all contraception as well as abortion seems contradictory.

8. CONCLUSION

Development of sexual ethics, as it is now proceeding in the Catholic religious community, has not yet come to an end. Undoubtedly, characteristic of this development are the efforts to personalize ethical norms on sexuality, against the background of the Biblical image of man. Another feature is the tension between statements of Rome on the one hand, and the feeling of the faithful, the pastors and the moral theologists on the other. If polarization can be avoided and if traditional thinking can function as a positive criterion to apply to more modern thinking, the tension will be reduced in the entirety of ethical development.

BIBLIOGRAPHY

Beemer, Th. (1969) Kan het evangelie een bijdrage vormen tot een nieuwe visie op sexualiteit? *Metamedica* 48 (4) 124.

Böckle, Fr. (1968) *Die Enzyklika in der Diskussion,* (Zürich).

Gross, A. and Pfürtner, St.H. (1973) *Sexualität und Gewissen,* (Mainz).

Gaudium et Spes (1964) *Constitutio pastoralis de Ecelesia in Mundohuius Temporis* Pars II, Caput I, Concilium Vaticanum II.

Humanae Vitae, Encyclical of Pope Paul VI (1968).

Schillebeeckx, E. (1963) *Het huwelijh. Aardse werhelijhheid en Heilsmysterie.* (Bilthoven).

Sporken, P. (1963) *Gemoedsleven en deugd. Thomas contra Suarez?* (Nijmegen, Netherlands).

Sporken, P. (1973) *Darf die Medizin was sie kann?* (Düsseldorf, G.F.R.).

Sporken, P. (1974) *Geistig Behinderte, Erotik und Sexualität,* (Düsseldorf, G.F.R.).

Ussel, J.M.W. van (1970) *Geschiedenis van het sexuele probleem,* (Meppel, Netherlands).

CHAPTER 107

Sexual ethics in Protestant churches

F.O. VAN GENNEP

1. AN HISTORICAL OUTLINE STARTING AT THE REFORMATION

In the course of cultural developments between the 16th and the 19th century, Protestantism went along with changing sexual ethics rather than initiating anything new. More and more restrictions with respect to sexuality were adopted, reaching a climax in 19th century Victorianism. In practice, this meant an excessive emphasis on sexual prohibitions, not only concerning premarital or extramarital sex, but concerning every aspect of sexuality such as masturbation and nudity in bathhouses and bedrooms. The churches acted here as mediators between man and his sexuality (Van Ussel, 1968). In no way did either the Roman Catholic or the Protestant Churches express themselves independently on the sexual aspects of the existing cultural development.

For the reformed churches this development is remarkable in that both Luther and Calvin after some hesitations got married as a conscious act of protest against the Roman Catholic position on celibacy. Especially Luther is known to have repeatedly expressed himself very freely on the subject of marriage, possibly showing himself to have been in this respect a man from the late middle ages rather than a reformation man. The 'waning of the middle ages' was, from our point of view, a time of rather free sexual morals. Tolerance was the accepted practice and relations between men and women were easy and relaxed. Erasmus, for instance, in his Colloquia (1522) still considered sexuality meaningful not only for reproduction but also for pleasure. The marriage between Luther, a monk, and Katharina von Bora, a nun, in 1525 certainly was a revolutionary act. It was not, however, meant to be a reformation of sexual ethics, but of the Church. Besides warmly approving of marriage, a school for character he called it, Luther had rather a patriarchal attitude. He saw the role of husband and father in terms of the role of monarch of the realm. He ascribed to it sovereign powers. He did, however, more than other reformers, show a realistic attitude, being able to

Handbook of Sexology, edited by J. Money and H. Musaph
© *Elsevier/North-Holland Biomedical Press, 1977*

speak freely about such things as libido, impotence and unfaithfulness.

Calvinists have generally had an ascetic point of view. Calvin felt that celibacy, which emphasizes the exceptional position of priests, should be abolished, but his point of view was characterized by an emphasis on duty and hard work. Strict Sunday-observance came to symbolize this way of life.

With respect to sexual ethics, this did not lead to essential differences with the Lutheran tradition, except that it made the general atmosphere more serious, and obligations more strict. Nor was there later any difference to speak of between Lutheran pietists and the Calvinist-related puritans, even though originally the Lutheran 17th and 18th century pietists had a warmer attitude towards sexuality. They were not afraid even to describe their relationship with God in erotic terms and images.

Great changes took place in the 18th and 19th century, in the wake of industrialization. The patriarchal extended family which Luther had in mind, was gradually dissolved. Farmworkers moved to the big cities in large numbers and had to make a new life for themselves there in tenement houses, under conditions resembling slavery. Prostitution of women and children increased as never before. Protestantism gave birth to a movement called Réveil which was very active in ethical matters. Many countries started help-centers for young prostitutes and unmarried mothers. There was concern for the victims of this absurd society, but few signs of a critical attitude towards that society itself.

Protestant leaders mostly followed a strategy of trying to strengthen the nuclear family. This was considered the focal point for a Christian society, which would be able to combat the disorientation of the workers displaced from their former rural lives (Wichern, 1848). The movement for women's liberation arising towards the end of the 19th century and the pleas for birth-control were generally sharply rejected in Protestant circles. Our children are a gift of God and the idea of oneself being able to decide whether to have any children and how many, seemed simply blasphemous. The patriarchal structure was deemed ideal for the family.

In the 20th century, new ideas did find their way into the protestant churches, especially after World War I. This first happened in liberal and religious-socialist circles which had always had a more receptive attitude towards what was going on in the surrounding culture. But also in authoritative ethical writings stemming from more right-wing Protestant circles (Brunner, 1932), one finds moderate arguments in favor of sexual education, birth control, a positive appreciation of sex and the social emancipation of women. There has been quite a large difference between the various protestant denominations *, since the growth of liberalism in the 19th century. Especi-

---

* Sociologically but not theologically the American Mormons may be considered a protestant denomination. Their founder Joseph Smith introduced polygamy or "the patriarchal marriage" in 1836. This had less to do with changed sexual ethics, than with the need for women and children in the far west of the U.S. and no doubt also with the needs of Joseph Smith. Polygamy was officially abolished in 1890.

ally in right-wing Calvinist or fundamentalist * groups and churches, there was a dominant and deep-seated tendency to resist influences from the non-religious culture, particularly on sexual matters.

2. SOME HIGHLIGHTS OF DEVELOPMENT SINCE 1945

The writer is most familiar with the situation in the Netherlands. He therefore mainly describes developments in Dutch churches. The Netherlands do have a reputation for being very tolerant in sexual matters, but the churches' point of view is surely not radically different from that of churches in other parts of the world. The difficulty is rather that the various Protestant churches differ so much, particularly in the field of sexual ethics.

The stormy development of sexual morals since 1945 has forced many Protestant churches to formulate in writing their position in these matters. By doing this the churches did not mean to criticize the authorities or to attempt to create a completely new sexual ethic, but to help their own confused members in forming an opinion and making up their minds. No prescriptions for dictated behavior, but guidelines were laid down to help church members in forming an opinion, collectively or individually. Some things the churches said did indeed cause violent discussion.

As an example one may take the question of women in office in the church. In the smaller liberal churches this question had already been dealt with in the beginning of this century. Women could be ordained as clergymen, elders and deacons. Several Calvinist and Lutheran churches followed hesitatingly in the 1950s. Generally, however, an official declaration that an office is open to women has not meant that in actual fact women fill those offices. There is in fact still quite a lot of resistance. In this respect the Protestant churches prove to be no different than other, nonreligious institutions or the business world. Since 1948 the ecumenical movement has been doing a great deal for the legal and actual emancipation of women in its member churches.

Protestantism is still much concerned with marriage and the family. More than formerly, great emphasis is put on the personal love between two people. This growth in the emphasis on personal relationships means that there is more room for a recognition of so-called 'mixed marriages'. Fifteen or twenty years ago a marriage between a Roman Catholic and a Protestant almost invariably was a great tragedy for religiously minded families, whereas nowadays one finds, except of course in strictly orthodox circles, a tolerant

---

* Fundamentalism is defined as that movement in Protestantism in which one attempts to live literally according to the Bible. This fundamentalism is found in many Protestant churches and sects.

attitude. This tolerance is partly the result of the greatly increased incidence of these marriages and the growing lack of interest in the church.

Sporadically (Ringeling, 1968), one finds in Protestant thinking about ethics, traces of Marxist and especially neo-Marxist criticism of marriage and the family. Politicalization of sexuality signifies that one has understood that sexuality is an aspect of an unconscious social system of repression of which women and children are the victims. Society is reflected in the family. The father is a sergeant-major ('Feldwebel') as Wilhelm Reich has it, and acts out at home the frustrations suffered in his job. These criticisms of marriage and the family have thus far had little attention in official Protestant circles.

Although there has always been some room in Protestantism for the possibility of divorce, in practice it has proved almost impossible. After the two world wars, divorce started to increase in the entire western world. In several Protestant churches the conclusion was reached that dissolving a marriage legally when it is broken already, is preferable to letting husband, wife and children live on in an atmosphere of constant conflict. Some churches expressed the opinion that a second marriage in church should be allowed. At first only the innocent party was given this opportunity, but eventually it became clear that it is usually almost impossible to determine where the guilt lies. Thereby the position was taken that the laws of the land should not indicate adultery as the only legal ground for divorce. Adultery certainly is an important factor, but generally rather the effect of a broken marriage than the cause.

Since the 1960s, birth control generally has been considered a liberation for the sexual life of man and wife. Not every church may have publicly said as much, but nevertheless birth control is widely practised. However, there are minorities whose emotional resistance has not yet been conquered.

With respect to artificial insemination, some Protestant churches are of the opinion that homologous insemination where the husband's own sperm is used, is not only acceptable, but may even be desirable. Heterologous insemination, however, is less acceptable, not only because it may emphasize the husband's sterility and may worsen marital problems if they already exist, but because it could cause identity problems for the child thus conceived. Only one or two Protestant churches are known to have expressed themselves on the matter.

In Protestantism, one generally considers sexuality to be an expression of the total personality, and based therefore on a relationship between two people who want to know and love each other. This position leads many churches to sharply reject a consumer mentality which would allow an unrestricted acting out of sexual passion. Unintentionally people are pushed back into an upsidedown Victorianism, again leading to a separation of body and soul, the physical need this time repressing the desire for social contact and relationship.

The main point in the discussion of sexuality is whether premarital and extramarital relationships should be allowed. As to the latter, Protestants are agreed that marriage is an indivisible unity of man and wife which excludes sexual relationships with others. Sporadically, one finds nevertheless a tolerant attitude. The well-known paper *Sex and Morality* (1966), rejected by the English council of churches, refused at the time to condemn in any way exceptional cases such as married people excluded from sex because of impotence or homosexuality of their partner.

One is even more careful in judging premarital sex. In the Netherlands the biggest Calvinist church, the 'Nederlands Hervormde Kerk', accepted a paper in 1972 (Roscam Abbing, 1972), which said among other things that it may be cruel and unrealistic in a sexually overstimulated society like ours to demand chastity from people not yet married, even though this does remain the ideal.

A paper which went further, proposing to make sexual monogamy obligatory for married couples, but to leave the matter open for unmarried and not yet married people was rejected by that same church (Van Gennep, 1972). There are some Protestant ethical thinkers who do not entirely reject premarital sex, especially in the case of engaged couples (Barczay, 1967; Cox, 1965/6; Robinson, 1963, 1964; Trillhaas, 1969).

In quite a few Protestant churches there is a serious discussion going on concerning abortion. A paper was published in the Netherlands in 1974 which deemed it necessary to make a call for saving and conserving human life, including that as yet unborn (Van Boven et al., 1974). This paper was strongly opposed however by those who feel that expectant mothers should have more say in the matter. The paper did concede that medical and psychosocial considerations may lead to the decision to interrupt an unwanted pregnancy. The tolerant abortion laws in the Netherlands were a factor in the discussion around this paper. The problem of abortion and the related question of the definition of 'life' will keep us all busy for quite a while yet. The problem is to find a clear anthropological—social formulation which can help both doctors and theologians. There is a great deal of uncertainty concerning this point particularly in progressive Protestantism.

In quite a few Protestant churches there has lately been a growing concern for homosexuals. Groups of workers in the field of spiritual care in various countries have greatly contributed to an improvement of the situation for homosexuals, even though simultaneously there has been growing resistance from the orthodox side. The Bible certainly in general questions homosexual behavior, but for some Protestant philosophers it does not follow that one may not admit that for quite a lot of people a homosexual relationship is the way to achieve human sexual contact (for example, Bailey, 1955). Allowing for the difference in their situation, the same rules of faithfulness and care are valid for these people as for heterosexuals. In 1972, a paper was accepted in one of the smaller, definitely orthodox Calvinist churches in the Netherlands which pleaded for the acceptance of homosexual behavior (Van der Meulen et al., 1971/72).

3. CONCLUSION

The sexual ethics of most of the Protestant churches are in process of change and generally striving to formulate the basic values of human existence in a way which is valid for our age. Tradition is regarded critically and one tries to emphasize that the essence of ethics and therefore of sexual ethics, lies in knowing and loving the other. Specifically, in sexual ethics Protestanism retains its personalistic structure. Protestant ethics thus mainly concentrates on determining the value of human relationships.

BIBLIOGRAPHY

Bailey, D.S. (1955) *Homosexuality and the Western Christian Tradition.* (London-New York-Toronto).

Bailey, D.S. (1959) *The Man-Woman Relation in Christian Thought.* (London).

Barczay, G. (1967) *Revolution der Moral.* Die Wandlung der Sexualnormen als Frage an die Evangelische Ethik. (Zürich-Stuttgart).

Barth, K. (1951) *Die Lehre von der Schöpfung. Die Kirchliche Dogmatik III/4.* (Zollikon Verlag, Zürich) pp. 127—269.

Brunner, E. (1932) *Das Gebot und die Ordnungen.* Entwurf einer protestantisch theologischen Ethik. (Zwingli Verlag, Zürich) pp. 324—365.

Cox, H. (1965/6). *The Secular City.* (Macmillan, New York) Ch. IX.

Fletcher, J. (1966) *Situation Ethics. The New Morality.* (Westminster Press, Philadelphia).

Lehmann, P. (1963) *Ethics in a Christian Context.* (SCM Press, London) pp. 134—139.

Ringeling, H. (1968) *Theologie und Sexualität.* Das private Verhalten als Thema der Sozialethik. (Gerd Mohn Verlag, Gütersloh).

Robinson, J.A.T. (1963) *Honest to God.* (SCM Press, London) Ch. 6.

Robinson, J.A.T. (1964) *Christian Morals Today.* (SCM Press, London).

Roscam Abbing, P.J. (1972) *Liefde en Sexualiteit.* (Boekencentrum, 's-Gravenhage).

Sex and Morality (1966) Report to the British Council of Churches. (SCM Press, London).

Strunk, G., Wagner, F. and Von Stern, P. (1971) *Liebe, Ehe und Sexualität.* (Gerd Mohn Verlag, Gütersloh).

Thielicke, H. (1964) *Ethik der Sexualität. Theologische Ethik III.* (J.C.B. Mohr Verlag, Tubingen) pp. 507—810.

Trillhaas, W. (1969) *Sexualethik.* (Göttingen).

Van Boven, J.A., Diemer-Lindeboom, F.T., Kremer, J., Mante, A.W., Plomp-Van Harmelen, M.M. and Schroten, E. (1974) *Leven en laten leven.* Paper presented to the General Synod of the "Nederlands Hervormde Kerk". (Not for sale.)

Van der Meulen, J., Polman, S.W.R., Rothuizen, G.Th., Vlaardingerbroek, J., Zeegers, M. and Zijlstra, H.R. (1971/72) *Over mensen die homofiel zijn.* Paper presented to the General Synod of the "Gereformeerde Kerken" in the Netherlands. Published by Kerkinformatie, Wilhelminapark 2, Utrecht, Holland. The "Gereformeerde Kerken", seceded from the "Nederlands Hervormde Kerk", are considered more orthodox.

Van Gennep, F.O. (1972) *Mensen hebben mensen nodig.* Een studie over seksualiteit en nieuwe moraal. Oecumene-reeks. (Baarn).

Van Ussel, J.M.W. (1968) *De geschiedenis van het seksuele probleem.* (Meppel) pp. 61—82.

Wichern, J.H. (1848) *Die innere Mission der Deutschen Evangelische Kirche,* published 1849.

CHAPTER 108

Secular ideology of sex and gender roles

ALICE S. ROSSI

1. THE CHANGED MEANING OF 'SECULAR'

It is difficult in 1976 to get a firm fix on the meaning of 'secular' because the concept has changed so markedly during the course of this century. In the past, 'secular' was opposed to 'sacred', suggesting that one was secular with respect to religious belief system alone, by rejecting the other-worldly assumptions underlying institutionalized religion, in preference for an enlightenment—rationalist ethos (Brinton, 1959). A secular ideology in any substantive area — politics, family, sexuality — was formulated in opposition to the theological views on such matters held by the various Judeo-Christian faiths. A secular ideology, then, was almost by definition not a positive affirmation of a set of values, but a reactive opposition to values espoused by the defenders of the sacred. Agnostics and atheists do not affirm, they reject.

Secularization of religious institutions

Over the past half-century, new elements have emerged in western societies which complicate the use of the concept of 'secular'. For one, religious institutions have themselves undergone a process of secularization: like other components of a society, belief systems themselves change over time. A practice that might have precipitated excommunication for a Catholic in the past may be tolerated today, and fully accepted in the future. Religious institutions which were opposed to legal access to abortion, premarital sex or divorce in the past, have been under pressure in more recent years to change their doctrinal stand, if only because so large a proportion of their members engage in the disapproved social acts. In 1976, American Catholics differ very little from Protestants in their approval of and resort to contraception, abortion or divorce. Organized churches in a post-Christian era are faced with the difficult choice of retaining their doctrinal purity, and thereby

Handbook of Sexology, edited by J. Money and H. Musaph
© *Elsevier/North-Holland Biomedical Press, 1977*

losing significant numbers of their members, or secularizing their doctrine in order to retain their members. In the long run, most have opted for secularization. The 'situational ethic' espoused by many Protestant denominations today would shock their Calvinist predecessors, acknowledging as it does the privatization of moral judgments. If morals shift from the sacred to the secular realm, established religions have a shrunken sphere of authority indeed.

A second new element, partially the result of social science investigations of religious institutions, is the realization that religion is often subtly intertwined with politics and the economy, lending an aura of prestige to the maintenance of the status quo. Indeed, established religions have contributed to the support of established nation-states and established corporate power, sharing in the latter's commitment to elitist authority structures and political conservatism. The Protestant ethic fired the entrepreneurial split that built the mighty industrial machine and together forged the powerful nation-states of the western world, and contributed to the subjugation of the far-flung colonial empires of the west. The secular underside of sacred institutions has thus further blurred the old meaning of 'secular'.

The new quality of secular ideologies in our time is that they are not merely negative, reactive, or focussed on opposition to religious belief systems. Nor are they any longer narrowly based on rationality and logic. There is emotional fervor, positive affirmation, and intense political commitment to ideological movements seeking new relationships between the human animal and the natural habitat, between men and women, and among the diverse races and cultures of the world, as observers of the conservation, zero population, civil rights or feminist movements in the U.S. can testify. Science is no substitute God to the new secularists, for a pervasive note in many secular ideologies is a fundamental skepticism toward all formal institutions in western societies, not merely religion, but public and private bureaucracies, established marriage and family forms, and the very structure of the nation-state itself.

2. YOUTH AS A NEW DEVELOPMENTAL MATRIX

The sharpened critique of all formal institutions which provides an altered sense to the concept of 'secular' is rooted in one fundamental change in advanced industrial societies that has occurred during the 20th century: the emergence of a new, prolonged phase of the life cycle between childhood and full adulthood, the years stretching roughly from the mid-teens to the early twenties (Keniston, 1970). A technological society presses for ever more training in order to do the complex work of a modern economy, thus keeping ever larger proportions of young people in educational institutions for longer periods of their youth. It is ironic that this same technology also provided the altered conditions of improved nutrition, along perhaps, with increased lighting that has lowered the age of sexual maturation. In the past, young people were out of school and at work before they were fully mature sexually. As a result they moved directly from the authority of parents and teachers to the discipline imposed by adult economic responsibility. Today, sexual maturation peaks in early adolescence, but it is followed by many years of schooling, including the critical years of age-segregation in residential colleges and universities, away from parental authority and subject only to peer social pressure. The combination of earlier maturation and a lengthened period of schooling provides a prolonged moratorium for today's youth, during which attitudes, values and behavior may change markedly from those taught by the family, church, and community in which young men and women spent their childhood years.

In the absence of the discipline of economic responsibility, young people have the time and the opportunity to re-evaluate the structure of their society and their own future position in that society. This prolonged moratorium represents a new historical phenomenon, what Keniston (1971) calls a 'changed developmental matrix' that has triggered the unprecedented scale of restiveness and skepticism among the young of western societies since World War II, promoting among other things, a sharp increase in the individualization of moral judgments, the acceptance of the relativity of truth, and greatly increased explorations of sexuality outside the family.

3. YOUTH AND THE MEANING OF CONTEMPORARY SECULARISM

What is important about this new life stage is the altered meaning of 'secular' and 'sacred' that is involved. Today's youth does not accept on faith moral evaluations hallowed by tradition and espoused by religious institutions. They reject parental values concerning sex and marriage, or traditional prescriptions for the goals of life style they should aspire to. They are not simply skeptical of religious belief systems, but of any belief system translated into a formal, structured social institution. They are not agnostics or atheists in the old sense any longer, for their battle is not with parental authority, a particular church, or a specific political party, but with all formal institutions. They may in fact have deeply religious experiences, but such experiences do not lead them into western churches, any more than their serious heterosexual experiences necessarily lead them to the altar and the formal institution of marriage. They are a generation on a quest, insisting on the primacy of personal relationships and resistant to the institutions in which these relationships were once expressed.

Educated youth: the future in our midst

It is of course the case that this perspective is not shared by all young people in all western societies. At any one point in time, societies or belief systems are best seen as layers or strata, some of which have more in common with a previous century than the present one, while other beliefs may be closer to what will be typical in the next century.

A second component of the framework that informs this chapter is the view that ideas and beliefs of the upper educated strata of a society, and in particular the young in these strata, trickle down to the lower strata, in a process Young and Willmott (1973) call the 'principle of stratified diffusion'. In this view a cross-sectional slice of contemporary society may reveal patterns of belief and behavior that were typical of an earlier century, and others so new they may characterize no more than a small minority until the next century. Thus, a contemporary potter selling his wares at a county fair may be more like an 18th century handicraft worker than his neighbor who works at an assembly line in a modern factory, while a contemporary computer specialist interpreting data fed back to earth by lunar astronauts may share more with some future generation than his neighbors in a Texas town. This theory also suggests that the important cues to the shape of the future are to be found among the educated youth of today. The present, in this view, is not disjunctive from the past and the future: the present contains both past and future.

Since contraceptive technology is more advanced and more widely utilized in the U.S. than any other western society, and the ferment on the issue of gender roles triggered by the feminist movement is most pronounced in the U.S., an examination of recent American data on attitudes and behavior among young men and women concerning sex experience, marriage, and the position of women, will provide us with some sense of the direction of change we may anticipate in the future in western societies.

4. THE AMERICAN FEMINIST MOVEMENT: 1966—1975

A brief sketch of the emergence of the feminist movement in the U.S. during the past decade will provide the necessary historical context within which to examine some recent evidence of youthful attitudes.

The first formal sign of political action on behalf of women was the formation of the National Organization for Women (NOW) in 1966. A major precipitant to the emergence of NOW was the post-Sputnik national concern for increasing American professional and technical manpower. That need sparked the formation of the Kennedy Commission on the Status of Women. When women found a great deal of foot-dragging in the implementation of the recommendations of the Kennedy Commission, they moved to found an independent organization of their own, hoping thereby to organize women to exert political pressure for change in the status of women in employment, politics, and civil rights. NOW has been joined by dozens of similar organizations in the ensuing years, all pressing for reform in law, regulations and practices that would expand the options available to women. These groups constitute the 'women's rights' sector of the feminist movement.

At about the time of NOW's founding, quite a different cluster of women began to organize. Younger, more radical, experienced in new left and civil rights politics, these women pressed for a more searching examination of how and why social and economic patterns oppressed women. Where the women's rights groups concentrated on sex discrimination, widening options and opportunities for women, and worked through legislative and organizational channels, the women's liberation groups used the concepts of patriarchy, sexism, oppression and exploitation of women to suggest the depth of radical change needed to liberate women. This has been a teaching movement, working through small networks of 'consciousness-raising' groups, many of which went on to found numerous independent ventures in publishing, health care, and film, art and music groups (Rossi, 1973; Carden, 1974).

In 1976, the reformism vs. revolution polarity is still visible in the feminist movement, but it has been largely superceded by a willingness of the reformists to adopt more radical politics when liberal tactics fail, and of the radical feminists to develop short-run tactics to redress grievances of women in the here-and-now and to build separatist centers and programs within or outside of existing institutions. It is probably the case that every segment of American society has been scrutinized through and been found wanting by the feminist lens.

Feminist impact on contemporary attitudes

Since 1970, there has been a sharp and lively debate in America on all aspects of sexuality, marriage, maternity, and relations between the sexes. While much of this dialogue was stimulated by feminist activists and writers, and clearly has been most salient to educated middle class youth, by 1976 discussion of gender roles extends far beyond feminist circles: it is a theme in comic books, TV shows, novels, union contracts, political campaigns. In the feminist movement, there is a growing consensus on one fundamental norm pertinent to the present analysis: that women must have full and exclusive rights over their own bodies, including sexual access and use, contraception, legal abortion. Criticism of the medical establishment for its unsympathetic and hostile treatment of women has triggered the development of independent women's health collectives, rape crisis centers, and the publication of self-help manuals, covering everything from auto-mechanics and household repair to gynecological advice.

There has also been considerable heat generated on the topic of sexuality, as increasing numbers of women broke the barrier of silence imposed by cultural taboos to share and analyze their personal sexual experiences. The publications which resulted from their analysis (Sherfey, 1972) have probably been more effective than any publishers' ads or professional reviews, in spreading the word from Masters and Johnson's (1965, 1970) research on the nature of female sexuality, in particular their refutation of the lingering view that a 'mature' female orgasm was a vaginal orgasm. The airing of sexual experiences, the realization that many women faked orgasm to please their partners, and the general hostility often shown by men to the feminists' efforts at self-analysis and social reform, have all had serious effects. Sexual separatism in the form of a rejection of marriage or choice of homosexuality; the growth of women's programs and centers at colleges and universities; women's collectives in private residence; and women-owned and operated businesses, have all clearly increased in recent years, particularly among unmarried and older separated and divorced American women.

Though not a primary cause, the feminist movement has probably contributed to the sharp continuation of several significant demographic trends in the U.S.: marriage and birth rates are down, divorce rates are up, sharply so since 1970. National vital statistics released in late 1974 showed the birth rate has reached its lowest point in American history — for the first ten months of 1974, the birth rate was 14.9 and the fertility rate 68.4 (National Center for Health Statistics, 1974). At least some part of these low rates is attributable to the undercurrent of ambivalence concerning marriage and maternity among young women today.

Attitudes toward marriage and women's roles

Informal surveys of undergraduate college women show sharp increases in the proportion who expect to postpone marriage for at least several years, to remain childless, to combine nondomestic careers with family responsibilities (Angrist, 1972; Meier, 1972). An unpublished 1974 study at a midwestern unversity showed a large majority of the women seniors consider early marriage 'stifling'; report strong pressure from peers against getting married; and give overwhelming endorsement to the expectation of meaningful employment for most of their adult lives. At prestigious Radcliffe College, David Riesman (1974) reports numerous women students consider marriage so antithetic to their goal of getting established as professional women that they talk about marriage 'after thirty'. The profile of recent survey results strongly suggests young American women in the mid-1970s have rejected the 'altruistic wife syndrome' that was so prevalent in the 1950s (Cox, 1968).

A note of caution is called for in these low expectations of youthful marriage. There may be few 'unexpected' pregnancies in an educated contracepting generation, but quite a few 'unexpected' marriages: national college freshmen surveys have shown fewer than 10% of the women students expect to marry while they are in college, but when re-interviewed four years later, 38% had married since they entered college (Bayer et al., 1973).

These same national freshmen surveys provide us with interesting examples of the rapidity with which attitudes have been changing among American youth during the 1970s. Table I illustrates three typical trends found in recent survey research. In the course of just four years (1970 to 1974), there

Table I

Attitudes toward women and family salience among university freshmen, by sex and cohort.

Attitude item		1970	1972	1974
Attitude toward women: Percent agree strongly or somewhat that 'the activities of married women are best confined to the home and family.'				
	Women	28.2	18.4	14.5
	Men	50.4	38.9	33.8
Family salience: Percent consider 'raising a family' to be an essential or very important objective in their life.				
	Women	70.7	63.7	53.4
	Men	61.7	60.3	51.0

Source: American Council on Education (1970) pp. 26–27, 34–35; (1972) pp. 23, 31; Astin (1974) pp. 24, 36.

has been a marked decline in the endorsement among women of the view that married women's activities ought to be confined to home and family. Men also show attitudinal change, though not as strongly as do the women. Thirdly, there is still a marked tendency for men to be more conservative on the position of women than women themselves are. In the most recent survey, in the fall of 1974, a third of the men but only 14% of the women took the conservative view of women's role.

This is consistent with Komarovsky's research on college men (1973) which showed that while the men sought intellectual companionship with women as friends and future wives, they also held the view that as mothers of young children, their wives should work "only if they can manage" both responsibilities. Sharing in marriage does not seem to carry over to parenthood sharing in the men's anticipation of their future family life.

That these changing views toward the position of women may reflect a general lowering of the salience of family commitments is suggested by the further finding that the cohorts of freshmen between 1970 and 1974 show a steady decline in the expectation that "raising a family" will be an essential part of their future life: there was a decline from 70 to 53% among the women and from 62 to 51% among the men during these four years. Other evidence, not reproduced here, shows that the four years of college itself contributes a liberalizing effect, for college seniors in 1971 showed markedly more liberal attitudes toward the position of women than the entering freshmen did that same year.

5. SEXUAL ATTITUDES AND BEHAVIOR: 1900—1970

It has been an expected and actual pattern throughout this century for American men to enter marriage with some premarital sexual experience behind them. But there have been two decades in American history when women showed significant changes in their premarital sexual behavior — the 1910s and the 1970s. Kinsey (1953) established the fact that the 1910s were a transitional decade in female sexual behavior: of women born before 1900 less than half as many had premarital coitus as women born in any subsequent decade from 1900 to the late 1940s, when Kinsey concluded his research. Thus it was the generation of American women who came to adolescence and early adulthood between World War I and the depression in the 1930s who broke the pattern of premarital chastity for women. Subsequent studies have shown a retention of this pattern from the 1930s through the 1960s, although a majority of the premarital coitus experienced by women was with a partner who subsequently became the husband.

There was much regional and religious group variation in the extent of premarital coitus in the studies conducted with college samples during the 1960s, ranging from a low of 9.5% among Mormon women (Christensen and Carpenter, 1962) to more typical levels of about 45% (Luckey and Nass, 1969). Several researchers attempted careful replications to trace the amount of change in sex behavior in the course of a decade from 1958 to 1968. Thus Bell and Chaskes (1970) showed a steady increase in the frequency of coitus from a dating relationship (11%) to going steady (15%) to engagement (31%) in their sample of college women in 1958. A replication in 1968, matching students from the same university and with similar characteristics (age, religion, parental occupation), showed somewhat elevated levels of sex experience (23% in dating or going-steady relationships, to 39% among engaged women).

More dramatic than the actual coital frequency figures was the sharp drop over the decade in guilt (as measured by the proportion of the sexually active who said they felt they "had gone too far") — from 65 to 36% among the dating women and from 41 to 20% among the engaged women. Table II

Table II
Premarital coital experience (%) of American and Scandinavian college women: 1958—1968.

Sample	1958	1968
American:		
Intermountain (Mormon)	9.5	32.4
Midwestern	20.7	34.3
Danish:	59.8	96.6

Source: Adapted from Christensen and Gregg (1970) in Broderick (1972).

is of special interest in showing not only regional and decade changes among American women, but with a matched sample of Danish women, the markedly higher European coital rate compared to the American (Christensen and Gregg, 1970). The Scandinavian pattern is not of recent origin, for acceptance of premarital coitus for women as well as men in northern Europe has been noted by many late 19th and early 20th century researchers.

C. SEX AND MARRIAGE IN THE 1970s

There are growing indications that the 1970s will show a second major shift in female sexual behavior, as more young women embark on their sexual lives at earlier ages, when full adulthood is so far in the future that there is little expectation of marriage with the first sex partner. Indeed, when Sorensen (1973) pretested several attitude items about premarital sex for a national study of 13—19 year old adolescents, he was greeted with the query "What marriage?" He found that 59% of the boys and 45% of the girls in this sample of adolescents had had coital experience. From acceptance of coitus without guilt with a future spouse, behavior shifted during the 1960s to acceptance of coitus if 'you were in love'. In the 1970s the norms may shift still further to embrace a more casual attitude toward sex and its further differentiation from marriage. Several recent studies show some empirical evidence of such a trend. In the young adolescents Sorensen studied, a majority of the males to a third of the females considered sex "a good way for two people to get acquainted", and felt it was "better over a period of time to have sex with several different people than with just one person". Two-thirds of the boys and a fifth of the girls thought sex was "all right with someone known only for a few hours."

An item similar to the latter in tapping attitudes toward casual sex was included for the first time in the 1974 national college freshman survey, with results quite similar to Sorensen's and with an example of the extent to which sexual attitudes are no longer governed by religious affiliation but by a privatized morality. Table III shows the responses by sex and institutional type on the issue of casual sex and cohabitation before marriage. Students attending church-affiliated colleges are only slightly less apt than those attending public or private nonsectarian institutions to take a permissive view toward either issue. And if anything, Catholics seem slightly more permissive than those attending Protestant denominational colleges. By far the strongest relationship is that of sex: young men are far more likely than young women to take a casual view of sex.

It is this difference between the sexes which puts some question on the assumption that an open sexuality is now an easy and accepted part of the liberation of women. At least some feminists have argued that the 'sexual revolution', far from liberating women, has led to their further sexual exploitation (Bengis, 1972). It seems from the evidence, that despite lesser fears of

Table III
Attitudes toward cohabitation and casual sex among college freshmen, by sex and institutional type: 1974 (per cent agree strongly or somewhat).

Institutional type	Cohabitation *		Casual sex **	
	Men	Women	Men	Women
All institutions	51.2	38.9	60.9	29.8
Four-year colleges				
Protestant	38.3	23.9	46.6	17.7
Catholic	47.1	30.5	54.6	20.5
Public	47.8	37.6	59.9	29.0
Private nonsectarian	52.6	48.4	61.3	38.6
Universities				
Public	50.9	40.2	60.6	29.8
Private	50.6	38.4	59.1	29.8

* Cohabitation item read: "A couple should live together for some time before deciding to get married."
** Casual sex item read: "If two people really like each other, it's alright for them to have sex even if they've known each other for a very short time."
Source: Astin (1974) pp. 24, 36.

pregnancy as a consequence of more effective contraceptives, women still bring rather different expectations to their sexual encounters than men do. The idea proposed by Gagnon and Simon (1973) that the sex developmental sequence for women is from sociosexuality to sexuality, while that for men is from sexuality to sociosexuality, still appears to hold among the younger generation in the 1970s. Virginity may be seen increasingly as a social stigma among college-aged women, but they are still searching for meaningful relationships within which to express their sexual natures.

The irony is that control by the woman of her own body, facilitated by modern contraceptives which place that control in her hands (IUD, pill, diaphragm, foam) rather than in her partner's (condom, coitus interruptus) may involve a loss rather than a gain of social control over sex for the woman. Women nowadays are expected to be the contraceptors, and therefore to be available sexually when males assert their sexual overtures. Bardwick's research (1973) suggests that many young women are conflicted about using the pill after a love affair is terminated because it defines them as sexually available, with the unhappy possibility that unwanted pregnancies in this generation may be more apt to occur in casual than in intimate relationships. It also seems to be the case that contraceptive responsibility leads to abortion responsibility. When the condom was widely used, unmarried men shared financial and emotional responsibility with women facing an unwanted pregnancy. Today, unmarried women in these circumstances are increasingly assuming the full and lonely responsibility by themselves (Luker, 1974).

The Sorensen study found a firm barrier to communications between adolescents and their parents: the young people believed their parents thought it immoral to have sex outside marriage, and told their parents only what they thought their mothers and fathers wanted to hear. Their own views are clear departures from the perceived values of the parents: 90% of the adolescents believed "people should decide for themselves what is moral or immoral", and a majority subscribed to the view that they do "what I want to do regardless of what society thinks." This means that in the new and prolonged, age-segregated youth stage of life, young people rely heavily on their peers rather than trusted adults, to cope with the choices they make about sexual matters. This may mean a good deal of independence and sexual experience for young men, but an increased vulnerability to male pressure for young women.

An indirect sign of what is involved can be seen in the sex and marriage manuals that have flourished in the past twenty years. They have perpetuated the traditional image of women: they grant the women's right to experience sexual desire and to have this desire satisfied, but always with the man calling the tune (Gordon and Shankweiler, 1971). Since the manuals read like engineering guides that project a mechanistic view of sexuality, the skills acquired by young men who read them may only further the separation of the sex act from the feelings and emotions of desire and love, which will leave countless women starved for something emotionally nourishing that their 'skillful' lovers can not provide.

7. A SUMMARY PROFILE

From the bits of evidence on young men and women in the 1970s, a profile emerges that looks something like the following. Both sexes share some degree of disenchantment with the formal institutions of society, but they are embarked on a search for meaning in personal relationships with little to guide them except their own experiences within their own age-segregated world. The institutions subjected to the most critical examination are those that have been most pressing in the past, so that young men have become more critical about the economy and their place in it, and young women have become more critical about the family and their place in the home. It seems quite likely that in the coming years, more women will reject marriage unless men are willing to adopt more of a partnership concept of both marriage and parenthood; more women will reject heterosexuality if men do not move toward a more meaningful intimacy in sexual relationships; and more women will reject male-dominant institutions unless they see some hope that they can be changed to more humane ones.

In arguing that there has been a blurring between the reformist and the revolutionary sectors of the contemporary feminist movement, it should not be thought that such blurring takes the sting from women's motivation to secure significant change in their society. Though a small note as yet in 1976, there is evidence of growing confidence among women as they think about industrial society and the options possible for women within it. As that confidence grows, so too will the assertion of values counter to that society. One hears such conviction in the feminist poetry of Adrienne Rich (1973):

A man's world. But finished.
They themselves have sold it to the machines.

The feminist insight has built upon the anti-institutional perspective of the generation that came to maturity in the 1960s. As Daly (1975) has succinctly explained the central meaning of the concept of sexism, a theology that proclaimed God is male reflects a society that says the male is God. In 1975, we may be at a negative Lysistrata stage of feminist consciousness, negative in its definition of power as the withholding of sexual favors from men. Beyond this stage is a different kind of power, an affirmative power that if restrained, will move on to build alternative institutions of its own. Thanks to the combined effect of increased education, economic independence, and the feminist movement, the restraints that held women in competition with each other have broken. Women are acquiring a new set of criteria for personal relationships and for systems of thought and belief against which to assess those espoused by men. As they look around at the world men have made, women find it warped and wanting indeed. The author would hazard the prediction and the hope that a *Handbook of Sexology* in the 21st century will begin where this one ends.

BIBLIOGRAPHY

American Council on Education (1970) *National Norms for Entering College Freshmen —
   Fall 1970.* Washington, ACE Research Reports 5, 6.
American Council on Education (1972) *The American Freshman: National Norms for
   Fall 1972.* Washington, ACE Research Reports, 7, 5.
Angrist, S. (1972) Variations in women's adult aspirations during college. *J. Marr. Fam.*
   34(3) 465—468.
Astin, A.W., King, M., Light, J.M. and Richardson, G.T. (1974) *The American Freshman:
   National Norms for Fall 1974.* (Cooperative Institutional Research Program, American
   Council on Education, Los Angeles.)
Bardwick, J. (1973) Psychological factors in the acceptance and use of oral contracep-
   tives. In: (J.T. Fawcett, Ed.) *Psychological Perspectives on Population.* (Basic Books,
   New York.)
Bayer, A., Royer, J. and Webb, R. (1973) *Four Years after College Entry.* Washington,
   ACE Research Reports 8, 1.
Bell, R.R. and Chaskes, J.B. (1970) Premarital sexual experience among coeds, 1958 and
   1968. *J. Marr. Fam.* 32: 81—84.
Bengis, I. (1972) *Combat in the Erogenous Zone.* (Alfred A. Knopf, New York.)

Brinton, C. (1959) *History of Western Morals*, (Hartcourt Brace, New York.)

Broderick, C. (Ed.) (1972) *A Decade of Family Research and Action*. (National Council on Family Relations, Minneapolis.)

Cannon, K.L. and Long, R. (1972) Premarital sexual behavior in the sixties. In: (C. Broderick, Ed.) *A Decade of Family Research and Action*. (National Council on Family Relations, Minneapolis) pp. 25—38.

Carden, M.L. (1974) *The New Feminist Movement*. (Russell Sage Foundation, New York.)

Christensen, H.T. and Carpenter, G.R. (1962) Value-behavior discrepancies regarding premarital coitus in three western cultures. *Am. Sociol. Rev.* 27: 66—74.

Christensen, H.T. and Grogg, C.F. (1070) Changing sex norms in America and Scandinavia. *J. Marr. Fam.* 32: 616—627.

Cox, F. (1968) *Youth, Marriage and the Seductive Society*. (William C. Brown, Dubuque, Iowa.)

Daly, M. (1975) Feminist Postchristian introduction. In: *The Church and the Second Sex*, 2nd edn, (Harper Colophon, New York.)

Gagnon, J.H. and Simon, W. (1973) *Sexual Conduct: the Social Sources of Human Sexuality*. (Aldine, Chicago.)

Gordon, M. and Shankweiler, P.J. (1971) Different equals less: female sexuality in recent marriage manuals. *J. Marr. Fam.* 33(3) 459—465.

Keniston, K. (1970) Youth: a "new" stage of life. *Am. Schol.* 39(4) 631—653.

Keniston, K. (1971) Psychological development and historical change. *J. Interdisc. His.* 2(2) 329—345.

Kinsey, A.C., Pomeroy, W.B., Martin, C.E. and Gebhard, P.H. (1953) *Sexual Behavior in the Human Female*. (W.B. Saunders, Philadelphia.)

Komarovsky, M. (1973) Cultural contradictions and sex roles. the masculine case. In: (J. Huber, Ed.) *Changing Women in a Changing Society*. (University of Chicago Press, Chicago) pp. 111—122.

Luckey, E.B., and Nass, C.D. (1969) A comparison of sexual attitudes and behavior in an international sample. *J. Marr. Fam.* 31: 364—369.

Luker, K.C. (1974) *Patterns of Pregnancy: Towards a Theory of Contraceptive Risk-Taking*. Unpublished Ph.D. dissertation. (Yale University, New Haven.)

Masters, W.H. and Johnson, V. (1966) *Human Sexual Response*. (Little, Brown and Co., Boston.)

Masters, W.H. and Johnson, V. (1970) *Human Sexual Inadequacy*. (Little, Brown and Co., Boston.)

Meier, C. (1972) Mother-centeredness and college youth's attitudes toward social equality for women: some empirical findings. *J. Marr. Fam.* 34(1) 121—151.

National Center for Health Statistics (1974) Births. Marriages, Divorces, and Deaths for October 1974. *Monthly Vital Statistics Report* 23(10) 1—8 (U.S. Department of Health, Education and Welfare, Washington, D.C.).

Rich, A. (1973) Waking in the dark. *Diving into the Wreck*. (W.W. Norton, New York.)

Riesman, D. (1974) Quoted in *Harvard Today Newsletter*. (Cambridge) p. 8.

Rossi, A.S. (1973) *Academic Women on the Move*. (Russell Sage Foundation, New York.)

Sherfey, M.J. (1972) *The Nature and Evolution of Female Sexuality*. (Random House, New York.)

Sorensen, P. (1973) *Adolescent Sexuality in Contemporary America*. (World, New York.)

Young, M. and Willmott, P. (1973) *The Symmetrical Family*. (Pantheon, New York.)

Acronyms and abbreviations

ACTH	adrenocorticotropic hormone
bpm	beats per minute
CNS	central nervous system
CS	conditioned stimulus
DHT	dihydrotestosterone
DOC	11-deoxycortisol
FSH	follicle-stimulating hormone
g, gm	gram(s)
GIF	growth hormone inhibiting factor
h, hr	hour(s)
5-HT	5-hydroxytryptamine
5HTP	5-hydroxytryptophan
K_a	association constant
K_d	dissociation constant
LH	luteinizing hormone
LH-RF	luteinizing hormone releasing factor
M	molar concentration
MAO	monoamine oxidase
MAOI	monoamine oxidase inhibitor
MER-25	ethamoxytriphetol
mg	milligram(s)
min	minute(s)
ml	milliliter(s)
mU	milliunit(s)
pg	picogram(s)
pM	picomole(s)
S	sedimentation constant
sec	second
UCS	unconditioned stimulus
μg	microgram(s)
μl	microliter(s)

Author index

Subject index

Prepared by Russell Jobaris

973; effeminate boys, 1062—3; sex laws, 1129—30; therapeutic approaches, 1202, 1204, 1246, 1307—8.

Trichomonas vaginalis: discussed, 1030.

Troilism: Polynesian culture, 512; mentioned, 926, 1081; described, 883, 1075. *See also* Paraphilias.

TSH (thyroid stimulating hormone): mentioned, 742.

Turner's syndrome: *See* 45,X syndrome.

20α-hydroxylase: deficiency and hermaphroditism, 164.

20,22-desmolase: deficiency and hermaphroditism, 263.

21-hydroxylase: deficiency and hermaphroditism, 169, 171.

Urophilia: mentioned, 19, 32, 925—6. *See also* Paraphilias.

Vagina: female to male transexualism, 72, 1296; atresia mentioned, 77, 596; contraction measurement, 330, 454; infections of, 697, 1034. *See also* Erotic arousal; Lubrication; Sex and aging, females; Syndromes.

Vaginal orgasm: *See* Orgasm.

Vaginismus: mentioned, 861, 921; psychoanalytic theory of, 880—1, 904; unconsummated marriage, 895—6; therapy for, 896—9, 1207, 1220—1, 1229, 1242.

Vasectomy: *See* Sterilization.

Venereal disease: *See* Sexually transmitted diseases.

Vertebrates, sex reversal: *See* Sex reversal.

Vestigation hypothesis: fetal differentiation and, 61.

Victorianism: *See* Moral standards.

Virginity: trend data, 319—320, 842; Polynesian culture, 514—5; imposed on mentally handicapped, 934; medical school students, 1111. *See also* Double standards; Moral standards; Premarital sex.

Visual arousal: woman's versus man's arousal, 64, 67—8, 319, 338—9, 571, 927; excessive Victorianism, 273, 275; cortex and neocortex, 319, 332, 457; exposure to erotica, 327—32, 336—9, 341—3, 346—8; human capacity for, 332—3; primate arousal, 457; paraphilias, 925—8; skin appearance, 1158—9. *See also* Erotic arousal; Sex (erotic) imagery.

Vocalizations: primate copulation, 463; nonprimate mother-infant, 737—40, 746; primates during delivery, 752; primate mother-infant, 753; human neonate and maternal behavior, 764, 794.

Voyeurism: mentioned, 70, 83, 300, 342—3, 925—6, 1074, 1081, 1088, 1090, 1092, 1122—4. *See also* Paraphilias.

Wet dreams: *See* Dreams.

Witchcraft: mentioned, 501.

Wolffian ducts: fetal differentiation, 59, 60, 158; birds, 127; experimental hermaphroditism, 140.

Women's liberation: marriage and divorce, 32, 312, 553—4, 556, 559, 565, 1334; mentioned, 76, 301—2, 313, 547—8, 564—6; industrial era, 275, 278, 281; female participation and enjoyment of sex, 571—3, 577, 861—2, 876—7, 1230—1; contraception, 580, 656—72; pregnancy and childbirth, 705—6, 715—6; sex laws, 1126; historical and future perspectives, 1342—5.

XXY and XYY: *See* 47,XXY (Klinefelter's) syndrome; 47,XYY syndrome.

Yohimbine: mentioned, 430, 434, 1097.

Zoophilia: mentioned, 926, 1089, 1321. *See also* Paraphilias.